Thermophysical Properties of High Temperature Solid Materials

CONTRIBUTORS

G. C. Y. Wang, PROJECT COORDINATOR

E. H. Buyco	*Specific Heat*
R. S. Hernicz and R. L. Feng	*Thermal Linear Expansion*
J. J. G. Hsia and G. C. Y. Wang	*Thermal Conductivity*
C. K. Hsieh, I. M. Yeyinmen, J. J. G. Hsia, and I. Keskin	*Thermal Radiative Properties*
I. Keskin and C. Y. Lee	*Melting Point*
C. Y. Lee	*Vapor Pressure, Density, and Heats of Transformation*
G. C. Y. Wang	*Thermal Diffusivity*
G. C. Y. Wang and C. Y. Lee	*Electrical Resistivity*

Purdue University, Lafayette, Ind. Thermophysical Properties Research Center

Thermophysical Properties of High Temperature Solid Materials

VOLUME 6: INTERMETALLICS, CERMETS, POLYMERS, AND COMPOSITE SYSTEMS

Part II: Cermets, Polymers, Composite Systems

Thermophysical Properties Research Center
PURDUE UNIVERSITY

Y. S. Touloukian, EDITOR

Distribution of This Document Is Unlimited

SPONSORED BY
Air Force Materials Laboratory
Research and Technology Division
Air Force Systems Command
Wright-Patterson Air Force Base, Ohio

THE MACMILLAN COMPANY, NEW YORK
COLLIER-MACMILLAN LIMITED, LONDON

First Printing

Library of Congress catalog card number: 67-15295

THE MACMILLAN COMPANY, NEW YORK
COLLIER-MACMILLAN CANADA, LTD., TORONTO, ONTARIO

Printed in the United States of America

PREFACE

The phenomenal growth of science and technology since the early forties has brought about a universal appreciation of the fact that present limitations in many technical developments are often a direct result of the paucity of knowledge on the properties of materials. Engineering developments in the years ahead will be closely linked to the research that is done today to contribute to a better understanding of the properties of matter, of which thermophysical properties constitute a major segment.

With a realization of the seriousness of this situation, a great deal of research effort has been made in recent years on the thermophysical properties of materials with the result that the volume of research literature has increased many fold. In spite of this fact, it is generally agreed that the present level of research on thermophysical properties still falls substantially short of existing needs and anticipated future demands. However, what is even more disturbing is the fact that engineering groups across the nation are using no more than a fraction of the information already available, either because it is in a form not directly useful to them or, often, because its existence is not generally known.

To partially remedy this situation concerning the thermophysical properties of high temperature materials, the Materials Laboratory of the U.S. Air Force at Wright-Patterson Air Force Base sponsored a project in 1957 to bring together a large portion of the then available data in a single work for easy reference. From this compilation, performed by the Armour Research Foundation, a four-volume work entitled *Handbook of Thermophysical Properties of Solid Materials* emerged. It was first published in 1960 as WADC TR58-476; in 1961 it was issued as a hard-bound set by The Macmillan Company.

Because of the favorable reception given to this original work, the Materials Laboratory of the U.S. Air Force requested the Thermophysical Properties Research Center (TPRC), in 1964, to update and revise this reference work in order to increase its usefulness and to put it on a more current basis. The present six-volume work, entitled *Thermophysical Properties of High Temperature Solid Materials*, consists of nine books totaling more than 8,500 pages. It is the result of a two-year project by TPRC. This new encyclopedic reference work cannot be called a revised edition of the earlier publication since nearly every page has been changed through major additions, corrections, and re-evaluation. An effort was made to adhere to the basic format of the earlier work. However, the organization of the material and the index to materials have been completely redesigned for greater ease in locating the information desired.

Inevitably, not all of the properties covered have received the same degree of attention. The material on thermal radiative properties, thermal diffusivity, and specific heat has been totally revised and rewritten. Materials on the coefficient of thermal expansion and thermal conductivity have received major revisions, and those on electrical resistivity, density, and melting point have had moderate revisions. Finally, lesser revisions were made to data concerning vapor pressure and heats of transformation. The new information incorporated into the work covered research conducted primarily during the years 1957 to 1964, although some major references are included from 1965 and some from as far back as 1910.

In processing the large amount of new and old data incorporated in these volumes, it was necessary that some degree of selectivity be exercised both from the standpoint of the references cited and the data extracted from them. It is hoped, however, that no major source of information has been omitted. Whenever possible, an effort was made to suggest recommended values of the properties. In the plots, recommended values are indicated by curves. It should be clear, however, that the designation of "recommended values" in no way implies that a critical analysis has been performed in all cases, nor does it suggest that they represent definitive values. Because most of the materials covered are not well-defined engineering materials, and because there is often a great paucity of information, any critical evaluation of these data is most difficult—if not impossible.

With a full appreciation of these inherent difficulties it is nevertheless hoped that the present compendia will prove to be of great usefulness to engineers seeking information on thermophysical properties. In spite of the extreme care exercised in processing the data and proofing the manuscript, it is possible that some errors might have been inadvertently overlooked. Should any instance of such oversight be uncovered, the Editor would be most indebted if it is brought to his attention.

The fact that such an enormous undertaking could be accomplished in such a short time is attributable primarily to TPRC's unique resources in the area of thermophysical properties information. Grateful acknowledgment is made to the Electronic Properties Information Center for assistance in providing bibliographic searches on electrical resistivity and to the Air Force Materials Laboratory for general assistance in bibliographic information. Extensive personal inquiries were made to the authors of research papers and reports requesting clarification and original data. The enthusiastic response to these inquiries (in the majority of the cases) is also gratefully acknowledged. The Editor and the contributing staff wish to give a special note of thanks in acknowledging the valuable assistance and cooperation they received individually and collectively from TPRC's Scientific Documentation Division personnel and the supporting staff of graphics and technical typists without whose painstaking and skillful contributions this work would not have been possible.

This work was performed under Contract No. AF33(615)1642, sponsored by the Air Force Materials Laboratory, Research and Technology Division, Air Force Systems Command, Wright-Patterson Air Force Base, Ohio. The personnel directly affiliated with this program were Mr. D. A. Shinn, Chief, Materials Information Branch; Mr. E. Dugger, Technical Manager, Information Processing; and Mr. J. H. Charlesworth, engineer in charge of this project. Their understanding cooperation has contributed much to the success of the program.

It is sincerely hoped that *Thermophysical Properties of High Temperature Solid Materials* will constitute an even more valuable contribution to technology than its predecessor. This work should prove to be an invaluable source of information on an important group of properties of materials to every engineer, providing him with reliable information of a scope that would be impossible for any one individual to master. If we have been able to approach these goals, the results will be highly gratifying.

June 1966

Y. S. Touloukian, Director
Thermophysical Properties Research Center
Purdue University
2595 Yeager Road
West Lafayette, Indiana 47906

TABLE OF CONTENTS

VOLUME 1 – ELEMENTS

VOLUME 2 – NONFERROUS ALLOYS

VOLUME 3 – FERROUS ALLOYS

VOLUME 4 – OXIDES AND THEIR SOLUTIONS AND MIXTURES

VOLUME 5 – NONOXIDES AND THEIR SOLUTIONS AND MIXTURES, INCLUDING MISCELLANEOUS CERAMIC MATERIALS

VOLUME 6 – INTERMETALLICS, CERMETS, POLYMERS, AND COMPOSITE SYSTEMS

EXPLANATORY TEXT

I. SCOPE OF COVERAGE

Thermophysical Properties of High Temperature Solid Materials comprises six volumes. Volumes 2, 4, and 6 each consist of two parts because of the large amount of material covered. The general contents of the respective volumes are as follows:

Volume 1—Elements
Volume 2—Nonferrous Alloys
  PART I—Nonferrous Binary Alloys
  PART II—Nonferrous Multiple Alloys
Volume 3—Ferrous Alloys
Volume 4—Oxides and Their Solutions and Mixtures
  PART I—Simple Oxygen Compounds and Their Mixtures
  PART II—Solutions and Their Mixtures of Simple Oxygen Compounds, Including Glasses and Ceramic Materials
Volume 5—Nonoxides and Their Solutions and Mixtures, Including Miscellaneous Ceramic Materials
Volume 6—Intermetallics, Cermets, Polymers, and Composite Systems
  PART I—Intermetallics
  PART II—Cermets, Polymers, and Composite Systems

The specific properties covered in each volume are:

1. Density (ρ)
2. Melting Point (M. P.)
3. Heat of Fusion (Δh_f)
4. Heat of Vaporization (Δh_v)
5. Heat of Sublimation (Δh_s)
6. Electrical Resistivity (r)
7. Specific Heat at Constant Pressure (c_p)
8. Thermal Conductivity (k)
9. Thermal Diffusivity (α)
10. Thermal Linear Expansion ($\Delta L/L$)
11. Thermal Radiative Properties:
    Absorptance (α), Emittance (ϵ), Reflectance (ρ), and Transmittance (τ)
12. Vapor Pressure (p)

Generally, only materials with melting points above 800°K (approximately 1000°F) are included, except for materials within the categories of polymers, plastics, and composites. A detailed discussion of the material classification procedure is presented in the following sections. A Material Index for the entire work is included at the end of each volume.

II. TPRC CLASSIFICATION OF MATERIALS

Materials are classified into the eight categories listed below. Whenever applicable, the compositions are reported in weight percent of the constitutents. For purposes of material classification TPRC considers the following elements as nonmetallic: H, He, C, N, O, F, Ne, P, S, Cl, A, Br, Kr, I, Xe, At, and Rn.

1. *Elements*: For the purpose of classification an element is specified as follows:
   A. For metallic elements, the limit of impurities is <0.20 percent for each foreign constituent and <0.50 percent total impurities.
   B. For nonmetallic elements (i.e., carbon including graphite and diamond), the limit of impurities is ≤ 2.0 percent for each foreign constituent and ≤ 5.0 percent total impurities.
2. *Nonferrous Alloys*: This category is for alloys in which the major constituent is other than iron. For the purpose of classification, nonferrous alloys are specified as follows:
   A. Nonferrous Binary Alloys: The sum of the binary constituents is ≥ 99.50 percent and other constituents ≤ 0.20 percent each.
   B. Nonferrous Multiple Alloys: The sum of the first two constituents is <99.50 percent and/or any other constituent >0.20 percent. Alternatively, the major constituent is ≤ 99.50 percent and each of the other constituents <0.20 percent (or not given).
3. *Ferrous Alloys*: This category is for alloys in which iron is greater than or equal to any other constituent. For the purpose of classification, ferrous alloys are specified as follows:
   A. Carbon Steels: Carbon ≤ 2.0 percent and carbon $\geq$ any other alloying constituent.
      a. Group I: Every other alloying constituent is ≤ 0.20 percent except for Mn, P, S, Si, which may be ≤ 0.60 percent each.
      b. Group II: At least one other alloying constituent >0.20 percent and/or any of Mn, P, S, Si >0.60 percent.
   B. Cast Irons: Carbon >2.0 percent and carbon $\geq$ any other alloying constituent.
      a. Group I: Every other alloying constituent ≤ 0.20 percent except for Mn, P, S, Si, which may be ≤ 0.60 percent each.
      b. Group II: At least one other alloying constituent >0.20 percent and/or any of Mn, P, S, Si >0.60 percent.
   C. Alloy Steels (including alloy cast iron): The major alloying constituent is other than carbon.
      a. Group I: Every other alloying constituent ≤ 0.20 percent except for Mn, P, S, Si, which may be ≤ 0.60 percent each, and C ≤ 2.0 percent.*
      b. Group II: At least one other alloying constituent >0.20 percent and/or any of Mn, P, S, Si >0.60 percent.*
4. *Nonmetallic Compounds and Their Mixtures and Solutions*: Ceramic materials such as oxides, bromides, carbides, carbonates, nitrides, silicates, etc., are included in this category. For the purpose of classification, they are specified as follows:
   A. For simple compounds and their solutions, the limit of impurities is ≤ 2.0 percent for each foreign constituent and ≤ 5.0 percent total impurities.

---

* Exception is made when Mn, P, S, or Si is the major alloying constituent. For instance, in the case of Fe + Mn + ΣX_i alloys the specifications corresponding to Groups I and II would be as follows:

a. Group I: Every other alloying constituent ≤ 0.20 percent except for P, S, Si, which may be ≤ 0.60 percent each, and C ≤ 2.0 percent.

b. Group II: At least one other alloying constituent >0.20 percent and/ any of P, S, Si >0.60 percent.

In the above example, Mn has a higher weight percentage than any of P, S, or Si but does not necessarily have a weight percentage higher than 0.60 percent. Thus, the limits of Mn percentage may be written:

$$\text{Fe} \geq \text{Mn} > \text{P, S, Si and any other alloying constituent and Mn} \geq 0.20.$$

The same guideline is applied to ferrous alloys containing P, S, or Si as major alloying constituents.

B. For mixtures of simple compounds and their solutions, the major constituent is <95.0 percent, or any other constituent is >2.0 percent.

5. *Intermetallics*: An intermetallic is a metal-metal compound formed by metallic elements in a fixed simple atomic ratio. For the purpose of classification, specifications are the same as those for Class 4.
6. *Cermets*: Cermets are ceramic materials such as carbides, oxides, etc., fused with or bonded by one or more pure metals. However, there are also metal-metal cermets, metal-intermetallic cermets, etc., which are also included in this category.
7. *Polymers*: Polymers are chemical compounds or mixtures of compounds formed by polymerization and consisting essentially of repeating molecular structural units.
8. *Composite Systems*: A composite system may consist of materials in combination, with clearly defined boundaries existing between components of the system, or a homogeneous material having a distinct configuration.

For the reader's convenience, the classification scheme for Classes 1 through 4, described above, is summarized in the following table.

SUMMARY TABLE OF TPRC CLASSIFICATION OF MATERIALS

Classification			Limits of Composition (weight percent)			
			X_1	$X_1 + X_2$	X_2	X_3
1. ELEMENTS	A. METALLIC		>99.50	--	<0.20	<0.20
	B. NONMETALLIC		≥ 95.0	--	≤ 2.0	≤ 2.0
2. NONFERROUS ALLOYS ($X_1 > Fe$)	A. BINARY ALLOYS		--	≥ 99.50	≥ 0.20	≤ 0.20
	B. MULTIPLE ALLOYS		--	≥ 99.50	>0.20	>0.20
			--	<99.50	≥ 0.20	≤ 0.20
			--	<99.50	>0.20	>0.20
			≤ 99.50	--	<0.20	<0.20

Classification			X_1	X_2	X_3	Mn, P S or Si
3. FERROUS ALLOYS ($X_1 = Fe \geq X_2$)	A. CARBON STEELS	GROUP I	Fe	C ≤ 2.0	≤ 0.20	≤ 0.60
		GROUP II	Fe	C ≤ 2.0	≤ 0.20	>0.60
			Fe	C ≤ 2.0	>0.20	≤ 0.60
			Fe	C ≤ 2.0	>0.20	>0.60
	B. CAST IRONS	GROUP I	Fe	C >2.0	≤ 0.20	≤ 0.60
		GROUP II	Fe	C >2.0	≤ 0.20	>0.60
			Fe	C >2.0	>0.20	≤ 0.60
			Fe	C >2.0	>0.20	>0.60
	C. ALLOYS* STEELS	GROUP I	Fe	$\neq$ C	≤ 0.20 and C ≤ 2.0	≤ 0.60
		GROUP II	Fe	$\neq$ C	≤ 0.20	>0.60
			Fe	$\neq$ C	>0.20	≤ 0.60
			Fe	$\neq$ C	>0.20	>0.60

4. NONMETALLIC COMPOUNDS AND THEIR MIXTURES AND SOLUTIONS

Classification	X_1	X_2
A. SIMPLE COMPOUNDS AND THEIR SOLUTIONS	≥ 95.0	≤ 2.0
B. MIXTURES OF SIMPLE COMPOUNDS AND THEIR SOLUTIONS	<95.0	≤ 2.0
	≥ 95.0	>2.0
	<95.0	>2.0

NOMENCLATURE:

X_1 = Major Constituent

X_2 = Second Highest Constituent

X_3 = Third Highest Constituent

Where: $X_1 \geq X_2 \geq X_3 \geq X_4 \geq \cdots\cdots$

---

*In case Mn, P, S, or Si represents X_2 this particular element is dropped from the last column.

III. PRESENTATION OF DATA

Each of the six volumes consists of seven sections arranged in the following order:

1. Preface
2. Table of Contents
3. Explanatory Text
4. Conversion Factors
5. Body of Data
6. References
7. Material Index.

In the following paragraphs a detailed description of Sections 5, 6, and 7 is given. The contents of the first four sections are self-explanatory.

BODY OF DATA

Data on each material are presented in graphical or tabular form for selected sets of measurements, and are accompanied by a Reference Information Table with corresponding specifications and remarks. The first five properties listed in Section I of this Explanatory Text are considered as *point values* and are grouped together in a single table in the same manner as the graphs for the other remaining properties. Furthermore, for a given material group, where several properties are reported, data are arranged in accordance with the order of the property list given in Section I of this text.

Graphic Presentation

Data extracted from various references on a given material and property are shown on a single graph by means of distinct plotting symbols, which are identified in the Reference Information Table on the page following the graph. Each set of symbols indicates the data of a given investigator, but does not necessarily imply actual measured points. In numerous instances authors present only smoothed values, either in graphical or tabular form, and it is frequently impossible to distinguish interpolated or smoothed values from actual observed data.

In reporting data on thermal linear expansion, investigators sometimes give a single average value of this property for a considerable temperature range. In such instances it is assumed that a linear relationship is implied. All data on thermal linear expansion were reduced to a datum of 293°K (20°C); i.e., $(\Delta L/L) = 0$ at 293°K (20°C). This point is identified by a cross (+) on each graph.

The definition of $(\Delta L/L)$ used in this work is

$$(\Delta L/L) = \frac{L_T - L_{293}}{L_{293}} \times 100$$

where L_T = length of specimen at temperature T.

L_{293} = length of specimen at 293°K (20°C).

To compute the "coefficient" of thermal linear expansion β from 293°K to any temperature T, the following relation may be used.*

$$\beta = \frac{1}{100\,(T - 293)}\,\frac{\Delta L}{L}\text{, in } K^{-1}$$

* It is necessary to divide the right-hand side of this equation by 100 because the graphical presentation of $(\Delta L/L)$ is in percent expansion from 293°K.

In some instances the coefficient of thermal linear expansion is reported in tabular form.

Curves drawn through the plotted points are the "most probable" curves based on the data shown. As additional information becomes available in the future, these recommendations may well be modified.

Point Value Table

Data extracted from various references are identified by distinct symbols in the same manner as data points on a graph. "Most probable" values are given either at the top of the table or are indicated in a footnote. These selections are usually made solely on the basis of the data presented. Sometimes these point values are also reported as a function of temperature or composition, in which case they are shown in graphical form and placed immediately following the tabular values.

Reference Information Table

A table giving the reference information associated with each set of data obtained in the graph immediately follows the graph. The table contains the following information:

1. Symbol. The plotting symbols are identical with and correspond to those used in the graph.
2. Reference. References are identified by hyphenated numbers which serve to locate the bibliographic citation in the section of References at the end of each volume. The initial two digits indicate the year of publication and the last digits identify the specific reference within the given year. In those instances where a reference does not carry a date, the letter symbol ND is used in place of the year of publication. Undated references are listed at the end of the list of References.
3. Temperature Range. Range covered by the data in a given paper or report.
4. Reported Error. The author's estimated accuracy (or precision).
5. Sample Specification. This column contains all pertinent available information about the test sample. This information consists of the following:
   a. Commercial trade name, chemical formula, etc., followed by manufacturer's name, if it is necessary for correct identification.
   b. Composition of the sample, expressed in weight percent. Unless otherwise stated, the percent sign is omitted.
   c. Physical characteristics of the material, such as a single crystal, polycrystalline, density, crystal structures, etc.
   d. Specimen designation by the author is given in brackets at the end of the citation.
6. Remarks. This column contains information on:
   a. Special process used in fabrication of the sample, such as being sintered, chill-cast, etc.
   b. Sample history, such as cold-worked, hot-pressed, annealed, etc.
   c. Conditions under which the specimen was investigated, environment, etc.
   d. Other pertinent remarks.

REFERENCES

The section on Reference gives complete bibliographic citations for all the references from which data were extracted. They are arranged chronologically by year of publication, and in arbitary sequence within any given year.

For the preparation of the references, the following order and convention is used.

Periodicals

1. Author(s) name: Last name first, followed by initials.
2. Journal name: Standard TPRC journal name abbreviations are used.
3. Series, volume, and number.

a. If the series is represented by a letter, it is underlined together with the volume number.
b. If the series is represented by a number, then only the numeral representing the volume is underlined.
c. The numeral for the issue number is shown in parentheses.

4. Pages: Indicate the beginning and ending pages.

Reports

1. Author(s) name is given in the same form as for periodicals.
2. The name of the responsible organization, if any.
3. The name of sponsor.
4. Report, bulletin, or circular designation.
5. Number.
6. Part.
7. Pages (same as for periodicals).
8. AD and PB numbers or equivalents.

Books

The bibliographic citation for books lists: author(s), title, volume, edition, publisher, and page(s).

In general, private communications are not listed as references. However, if TPRC did obtain additional substantive information from an author through private communication, and if this information was used, the remark "additional data obtained from author(s)" is added at the end of the reference citation.

MATERIAL INDEX

The Material Index lists all the materials included in this work by their proper trade or commercial names arranged in alphabetical order and, for materials designated by number codes, the listing is in increasing numerical order. Location of information on a particular property for a particular material is specified by the volume number and page numbers indicated within the appropriate property column of the index. The page number always indicates the starting page of the graphs or point value tables. Chemical formulas are given in parentheses following the proper names of materials which can be chemically identified. However, for materials within a general group, e.g., different oxides of cerium, the entries are only by chemical formulas listed under the material group designation, such as "cerium oxides." Whenever applicable, an effort is made to list commercial materials under their several accepted names. In the case of broad classes of materials, such as steels, glasses, etc., the materials are listed under their common names as well as under the heading of their general class when the designation is merely a letter and number code.

Simpler inorganic compounds (e.g., aluminum oxide, tantalum boride) are named according to the convention given in the *Handbook of Chemistry and Physics* (The Chemical Rubber Co., 45th edition, 1964, and—if not available there—the 43rd edition, 1962). Other inorganic compounds are generally named in accordance with the convention given in the *Chemical Abstracts* by giving the more electropositive part of the name first and the more electronegative part second. For nonferrous and ferrous alloys, only the first two components are listed and ΣX_i is added to designate multiple alloys. An exception is made, however, for chromium-nickel and nickel-chromium ferrous alloys, in which cases, all three major constituents are listed. For other inorganic compounds and their mixtures and solutions, all components with weight percent greater than 2 percent are listed. Finally, for cermets, the name of the ceramic part is given first and the metal part second, each in their respective alphabetical order regardless of their weight percentages, with the exception of beryllium cermet (e.g., Beryllium YB-9052), in which case the name of the metal part is given first.

CONVERSION FACTORS

NOTE: In preparing the conversion factors, the following basic definitions were used:

$$1 \text{ in.} = 2.54 \text{ cm}^*$$

$$1 \text{ lb.} = 453.59237 \text{ g}^*$$

$$1 \text{ cal}_{\text{Th}} = 4.184 \text{ (exactly) Joule}^*$$

$$1 \text{ cal}_{\text{IT}} = 4.1868 \text{ (exactly) Joule}^*$$

$$1 \text{ Btu}_{\text{IT}}\text{lb}^{-1}\text{F}^{-1} = 1 \text{ cal}_{\text{IT}}\text{g}^{-1}\text{C}^{-1}\ddagger$$

The subscripts "Th" and "IT" denote "Thermochemical" and "International Steam Table" units, respectively.

---

* *NBS Technical News Bulletin*, **47**(10), 1963.

‡ Mueller, E. F., and Rossini, F. D., *Am. J. Physics*, **12**(1), 4, 1944.

CONVERSION FACTORS FOR UNITS OF DENSITY

MULTIPLY ↓ by appropriate factor to OBTAIN →	$g\ cm^{-3}$	$g\ in.^{-3}$	$kg\ m^{-3}$	$kg\ ft^{-3}$	$lb\ in.^{-3}$	$lb\ ft^{-3}$
$g\ cm^{-3}$	1	1.63872×10	1.0×10^{3}	2.83170×10	3.61275×10^{-2}	6.24283×10
$g\ in.^{-3}$	6.10234×10^{-2}	1	6.10234×10	1.72800	2.20462×10^{-3}	3.80959
$kg\ m^{-3}$	1.0×10^{3}	1.63872×10^{-2}	1	2.83170×10^{-2}	3.61275×10^{-5}	6.24283×10^{-2}
$kg\ ft^{-3}$	3.51446×10^{-2}	5.78704×10^{-1}	3.53145×10	1	1.27582×10^{-3}	2.20462
$lb\ in.^{-3}$	2.76797×10	4.53592×10^{2}	2.76797×10^{4}	7.83808×10^{2}	1	1.72800×10^{3}
$lb\ ft^{-3}$	1.60184×10^{-2}	2.62496×10^{-1}	1.60184×10	4.53592×10^{-1}	5.78704×10^{-4}	1

CONVERSION FACTORS FOR UNITS OF LATENT HEAT

MULTIPLY ↓ by appropriate factor to OBTAIN →	$cal_{Th}g^{-1}$	$cal_{IT}g^{-1}$	$W\ sec\ g^{-1}$	$J_{Int}g^{-1}$	$Btu_{Th}lb^{-1}$	$Btu_{IT}lb^{-1}$
$cal_{Th}g^{-1}$	1	9.99331×10^{-1}	4.184	4.18331	1.8	1.79880
$cal_{IT}g^{-1}$	1.00067	1	4.1868	4.18611	1.80120	1.8
$W\ sec\ g^{-1}$	2.39006×10^{-1}	2.38846×10^{-1}	1	9.99835×10^{-1}	4.30210×10^{-1}	4.29923×10^{-1}
$J_{Int}g^{-1}$	2.39045×10^{-1}	2.38885×10^{-1}	1.00017	1	4.30281×10^{-1}	4.29994×10^{-1}
$Btu_{Th}lb^{-1}$	5.55556×10^{-1}	5.55184×10^{-1}	2.32444	2.32406	1	9.99331×10^{-1}
$Btu_{IT}lb^{-1}$	5.55927×10^{-1}	5.55556×10^{-1}	2.326	2.32562	1.00067	1

CONVERSION FACTORS FOR UNITS OF SPECIFIC HEAT

MULTIPLY ↓ by appropriate factor to OBTAIN →	$cal_{Th}g^{-1}C^{-1}$	$cal_{IT}g^{-1}C^{-1}$	$W\ sec\ g^{-1}K^{-1}$	$J_{Int}g^{-1}K^{-1}$	$Btu_{Th}lb^{-1}F^{-1}$	$Btu_{IT}lb^{-1}F^{-1}$
$cal_{Th}g^{-1}C^{-1}$	1	9.99331×10^{-1}	4.184	4.18331	1	9.99331×10^{-1}
$cal_{IT}g^{-1}C^{-1}$	1.00067	1	4.1868	4.18611	1.00067	1
$W\ sec\ g^{-1}K^{-1}$	2.390006×10^{-1}	2.38846×10^{-1}	1	9.99835×10^{-1}	2.39006×10^{-1}	2.38846×10^{-1}
$J_{Int}g^{-1}K^{-1}$	2.39045×10^{-1}	2.38885×10^{-1}	1.00017	1	2.39045×10^{-1}	2.38885×10^{-1}
$Btu_{Th}lb^{-1}F^{-1}$	1	9.99331×10^{-1}	4.184	4.18331	1	9.99331×10^{-1}
$Btu_{IT}lb^{-1}F^{-1}$	1.00067	1	4.1868	4.18611	1.00067	1

Note: To convert quantities per "gram" to "mol" basis multiply conversion factor by the molecular weight M.

CONVERSION FACTORS FOR UNITS OF THERMAL CONDUCTIVITY

MULTIPLY ↓ by appropriate factor to OBTAIN →	$Btu_{IT} hr^{-1} ft^{-1} F^{-1}$	$Btu_{IT} in. hr^{-1} ft^{-2} F^{-1}$	$cal_{IT} sec^{-1} cm^{-1} C^{-1}$	$cal_{Th} sec^{-1} cm^{-1} C^{-1}$	$kcal_{Th} hr^{-1} m^{-1} C^{-1}$	$W cm^{-1} K^{-1}$
$Btu_{IT} hr^{-1} ft^{-1} F^{-1}$	1	1.2 x 10	4.13379×10^{-3}	4.13656×10^{-3}	1.48916	1.73073×10^{-2}
$Btu_{IT} in. hr^{-1} ft^{-2} F^{-1}$	8.33333×10^{-2}	1	3.44482×10^{-4}	3.44713×10^{-4}	1.24097×10^{-1}	1.44228×10^{-3}
$cal_{IT} sec^{-1} cm^{-1} C^{-1}$	2.41909×10^{2}	2.90291×10^{3}	1	1.00067	3.60241×10^{2}	4.1868
$cal_{Th} sec^{-1} cm^{-1} C^{-1}$	2.41747×10^{2}	2.90096×10^{3}	9.99331×10^{-1}	1	3.6×10^{2}	4.184
$kcal_{Th} hr^{-1} m^{-1} C^{-1}$	6.71520×10^{-1}	8.05824	2.77592×10^{-3}	2.77778×10^{-3}	1	1.16222×10^{-2}
$W cm^{-1} K^{-1}$	5.77789 x 10	6.93347×10^{2}	2.38846×10^{-1}	2.39006×10^{-1}	8.60421 x 10	1

CONVERSION FACTORS FOR UNITS OF THERMAL DIFFUSIVITY

MULTIPLY ↓ by appropriate factor to OBTAIN →	cm^2sec^{-1}	cm^2hr^{-1}	m^2hr^{-1}	$in.^2sec^{-1}$	ft^2sec^{-1}	ft^2hr^{-1}
cm^2sec^{-1}	1	3.60×10^3	3.60×10^{-1}	1.550×10^{-1}	1.07639×10^{-3}	3.87501
cm^2hr^{-1}	2.77778×10^{-4}	1	1.0×10^{-4}	4.30556×10^{-5}	2.98998×10^{-7}	1.07639×10^{-3}
m^2hr^{-1}	2.77778	1.0×10^4	1	4.30556	2.98998×10^{-3}	1.07639×10
$in.^2sec^{-1}$	6.45160	2.32258×10^4	2.32258	1	6.94444×10^{-3}	2.50×10
ft^2sec^{-1}	9.29030×10^2	3.34451×10^6	3.34451×10^2	1.440×10^2	1	3.60×10^3
ft^2hr^{-1}	2.58064×10^{-1}	9.29030×10^2	9.29030×10^{-2}	4.0×10^{-2}	2.77778×10^{-4}	1

CONVERSION FACTORS FOR UNITS OF VAPOR PRESSURE

MULTIPLY ↓ by appropriate factor to OBTAIN →	dyne cm^{-2}	atm	kg cm^{-2}	mm Hg	in. Hg	lb in.$^{-2}$
dyne cm^{-2}	1	9.8690×10^{-7}	1.01970×10^{-6}	7.5010×10^{-4}	2.9530×10^{-5}	1.45040×10^{-5}
atm	1.01330×10^{6}	1	1.03320	7.60×10^{2}	2.9920×10	1.46960×10
kg cm^{-2}	9.8070×10^{5}	9.6780×10^{-1}	1	7.3560×10^{2}	2.8960×10	1.42230×10
mm Hg	1.33320×10^{3}	1.31580×10^{-3}	1.35950×10^{-3}	1	3.9370×10^{-2}	1.93370×10^{-2}
in. Hg	3.3860×10^{4}	3.3420×10^{-2}	3.4530×10^{-2}	2.540×10	1	4.9120×10^{-1}
lb in.$^{-2}$	6.89470×10^{4}	6.80460×10^{-2}	7.0310×10^{-2}	5.1710×10	2.0360	1

INTERMETALLICS, CERMETS, POLYMERS, AND COMPOSITE SYSTEMS

PART II

CERMETS

(Ceramic materials such as carbides, oxides, etc., fused with or bonded by one or more pure metals.)

Thermal Linear Expansion, percent

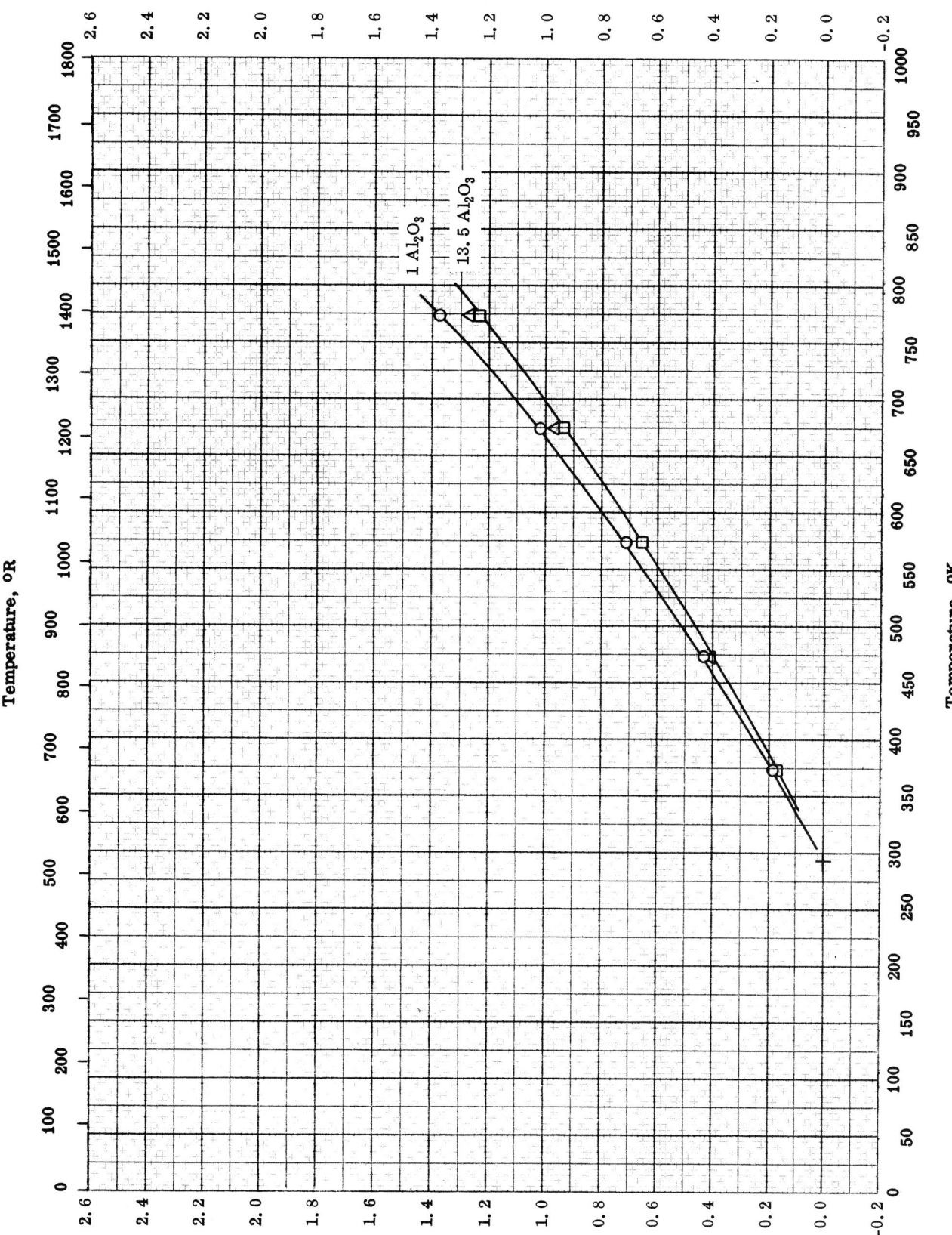

THERMAL LINEAR EXPANSION -- [ALUMINUM OXIDE + ALUMINUM] CERMET

Thermal Linear Expansion, percent

THERMAL LINEAR EXPANSION -- [ALUMINUM OXIDE + ALUMINUM] CERMET

REFERENCE INFORMATION

Symbol	Ref.	Temp. Range °K	Rept. Error %	Sample Specifications	Remarks
○	63-32	293-773		1 Al_2O_3; density 2.65 - 2.7 g cm^{-3}.	Pressed rod made of sintered aluminum powder.
△	63-32	293-773		10 Al_2O_3; density 2.70 - 2.71 g cm^{-3}.	Pressed rod made of sintered aluminum powder.
□	63-32	293-773		13.5 Al_2O_3; density 2.72 - 2.73 g cm^{-3}.	Pressed rod made of sintered aluminum powder.

PROPERTIES OF [ALUMINUM OXIDE + CHROMIUM] CERMET

REPORTED VALUES

Density		g cm^{-3}	lb ft^{-3}
○	71.4 Cr	5.92	370
□	63.3 Cr	5.66	353
△	70 Cr	5.91	369
▽	77 Cr	5.9	368
◇	30 Cr	4.7	293

PROPERTIES OF [ALUMINUM OXIDE + CHROMIUM] CERMET

REFERENCE INFORMATION

Symbol	Ref.	Temp. Range °K	Rept. Error %	Sample Specifications	Remarks
○	52-17	298		Nominal: 71.4 Cr and 28.6 Al_2O_3; prepared from electrolytic 99^+ Cr and 99.5^+ corundum; author suspects 2-3 W.	Milled with WC slugs in alcohol, dried, screened 65 mesh, vacuum pressed at 35,000 psi, fired at 3050-3100 F in H; theoretical density 5.85 g cm^{-3}.
□	52-17	298		Nominal: 63.3 Cr and 36.7 Al_2O_3; same as above.	Same as above; theoretical density 5.6 g cm^{-3}.
△	52-20	298		Metamic LT-1; nominal 70 Cr and 30 Al_2O_3.	Average density of 5 sample by weight and volume from measured dimensions.
▽	60-31	298		77 Cr and 23 Al_2O_3.	
◇	60-31	298		30 Cr and 70 Al_2O_3.	

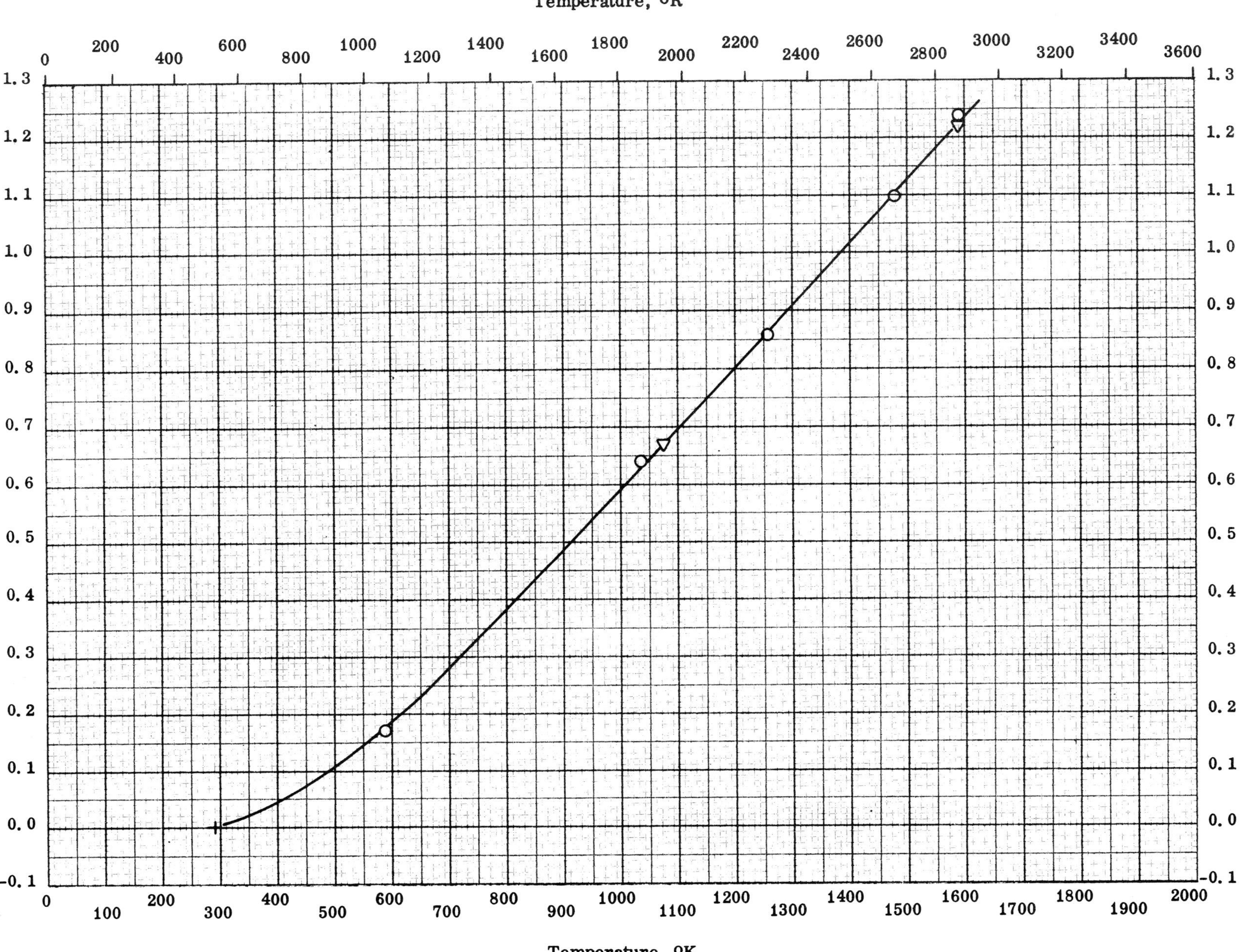

THERMAL LINEAR EXPANSION -- [ALUMINUM OXIDE + CHROMIUM] CERMET

THERMAL LINEAR EXPANSION -- [ALUMINUM OXIDE + CHROMIUM] CERMET

REFERENCE INFORMATION

Symbol	Ref.	Temp. Range °K	Rept. Error %	Sample Specifications	Remarks
○	52-17	367-1589		70 Al_2O_3 and 30 Cr.	
▽	51-2	296-1589		70 Al_2O_3 and 30 Cr; impurities picked up in grinding: 3 - 5 Fe, 2 - 3 WC, 0.75 Co, traces of Si, Mn; density 287 - 290 lb ft^{-3}.	Prepared from: 1) Corundum 99.5 Al_2O_3 and 0.02 Na_2O 2) Al hydrate 99^+ pure and 34.7 combined water 3) Electrolytic Cr 99^+ pure; pressed at 5500 psi and sintered at 3100 F.

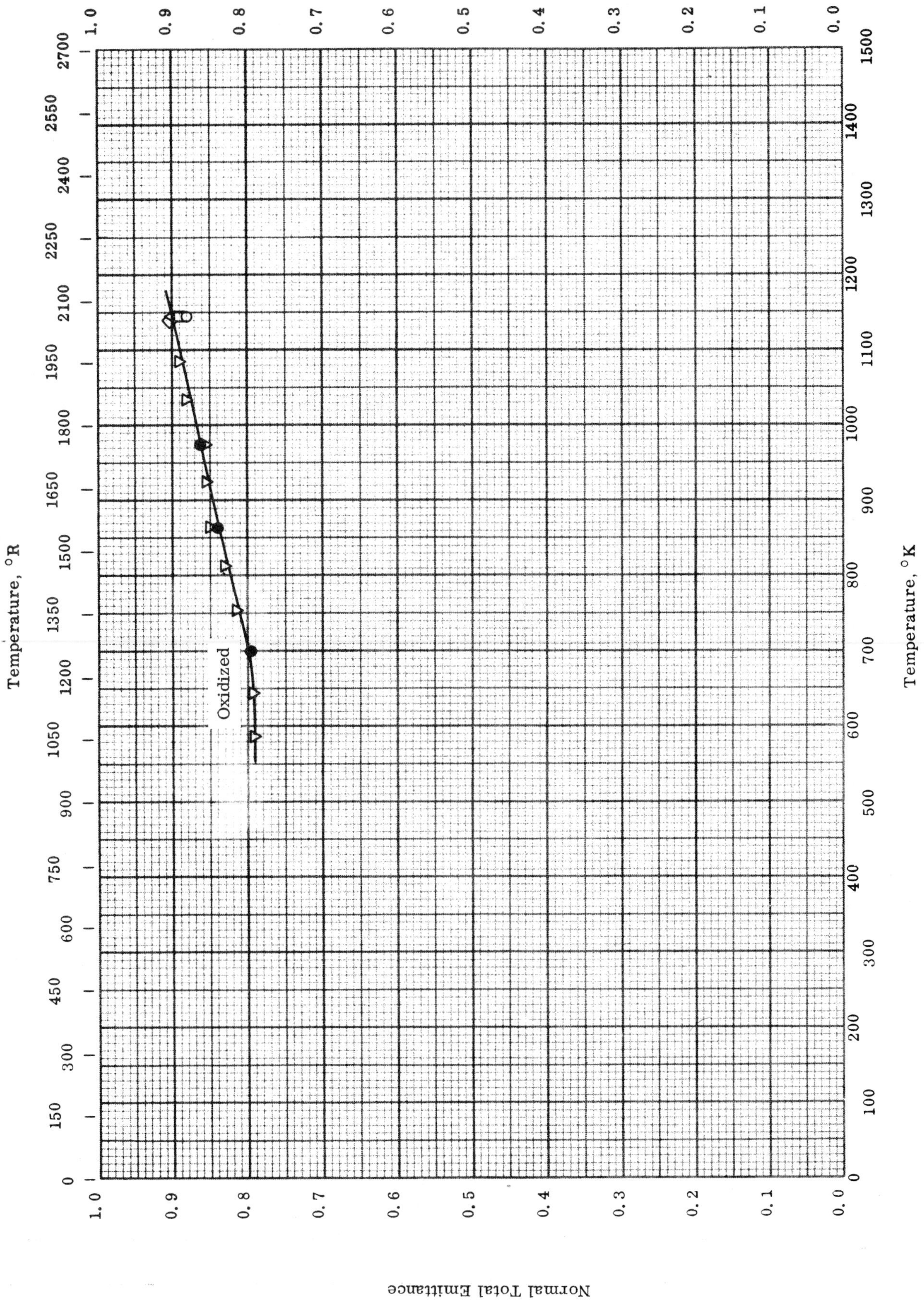

NORMAL TOTAL EMITTANCE -- [ALUMINUM OXIDE + CHROMIUM] CERMET

NORMAL TOTAL EMITTANCE -- [ALUMINUM OXIDE + CHROMIUM] CERMET

REFERENCE INFORMATION

Symbol	Ref.	Temp. Range °K	Rept. Error %	Sample Specifications	Remarks
○	62-31	1144		Haynes LT - 1 cermet; 77 Cr and 23 Al_2O_3.	Ground and polished; cleansing with alcohol and distilled water.
□	62-31	1144		Same as above.	Same as above; after heating in air at 1144 K for 5 min.
△	62-31	1144		Same as above.	Same as above; after heating in air at 1144 K for 10 min.
◇	62-31	1144		Same as above.	Same as above; after heating in air at 1144 K for 20 min.
▽	62-31	589-1144		Same as above.	Same as above; after oxidized in air at 1144 K for 20 min.
●	62-31	589-1144		Same as above.	Same as above; another sample.

PROPERTIES OF [ALUMINUM OXIDE + CHROMIUM + MOLYBDENUM] CERMET

REPORTED VALUES

Density	$g\ cm^{-3}$	$lb\ ft^{-3}$
O 60 Cr and 19 Mo	6.0	374.4

PROPERTIES OF [ALUMINUM OXIDE + CHROMIUM + MOLYBDENUM] CERMET

REFERENCE INFORMATION

Symbol	Ref.	Temp. Range °K	Rept. Error %	Sample Specifications	Remarks
○	60-31	298		60 Cr, 19 Al_2O_3, 19 Mo, and 2 TiO_2.	

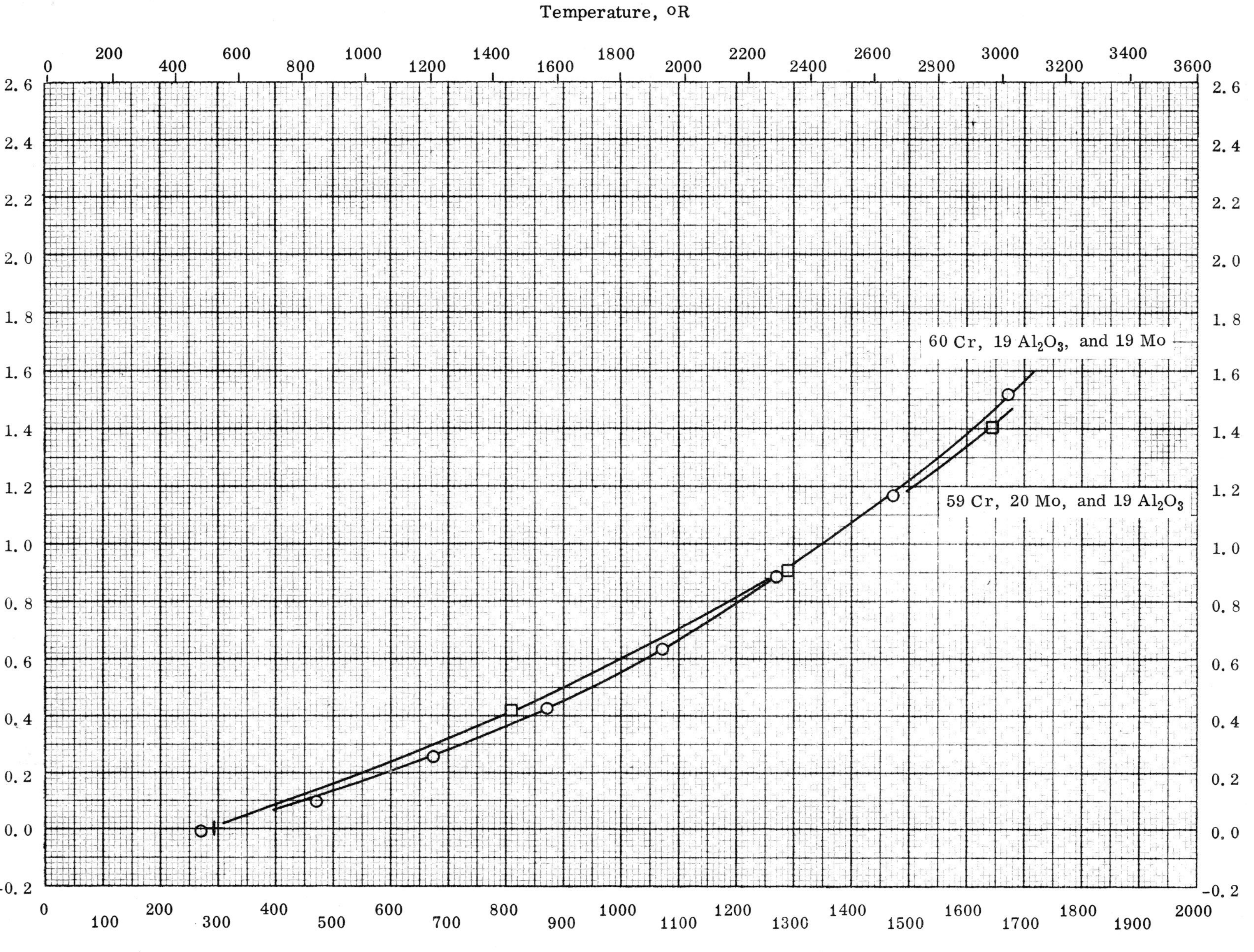

THERMAL LINEAR EXPANSION -- [ALUMINUM OXIDE + CHROMIUM + MOLYBDENUM] CERMET

THERMAL LINEAR EXPANSION -- [ALUMINUM OXIDE + CHROMIUM + MOLYBDENUM] CERMET

REFERENCE INFORMATION

Symbol	Ref.	Temp. Range °K	Rept. Error %	Sample Specifications	Remarks
○	60-31	273-1673		19 Al_2O_3, 60 Cr, 19 Mo, 2 TiO_2; dense polycrystalline specimen; density 6.0 g cm^{-3}.	
□	60-23	299-1641	<5	LT-1B; 59 Cr, 20 Mo, 19 Al_2O_3, and 2 TiO_2; specimen 3/8 in. diameter by 3 in. long. [Author's design.: E-24]	Sintered at about 2900 F in hydrogen-argon atmosphere.

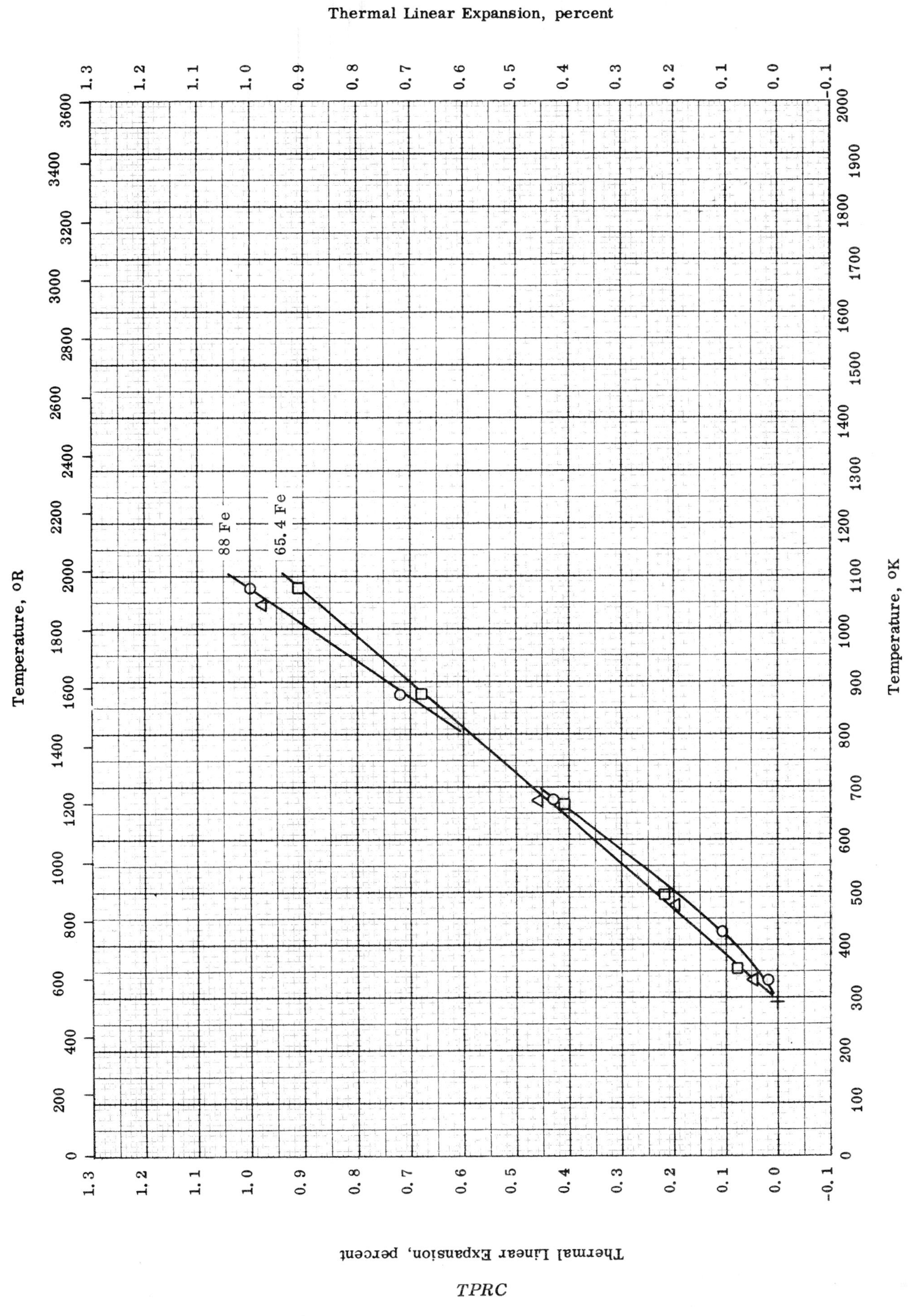

Thermal Linear Expansion, percent
Temperature, °R
Temperature, °K
88 Fe
65.4 Fe
Thermal Linear Expansion, percent

THERMAL LINEAR EXPANSION -- [ALUMINUM OXIDE + IRON] CERMET

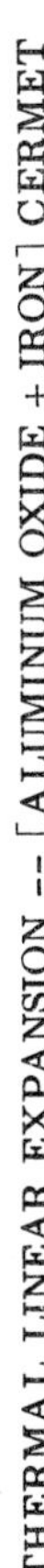

THERMAL LINEAR EXPANSION -- [ALUMINUM OXIDE + IRON] CERMET

REFERENCE INFORMATION

Symbol	Ref.	Temp. Range °K	Rept. Error %	Sample Specifications	Remarks
○	58-14	293-1073		88. 0 Fe, 10. 8 Al_2O_3, and 1. 2 Cr_2O_3.	Al_2O_3 in the form of corundum; milled 50 hrs, dried, dry pressed at 35000 psi, dried, fired, soaked 4 hrs, and furnace cooled.
△	58-14	293-1073		78. 6 Fe, 19. 3 Al_2O_3, and 2. 1 Cr_2O_3.	Same as above.
□	58-14	293-1073		65. 4 Fe, 31. 1 Al_2O_3, and 3. 5 Cr_2O_3.	Same as above.

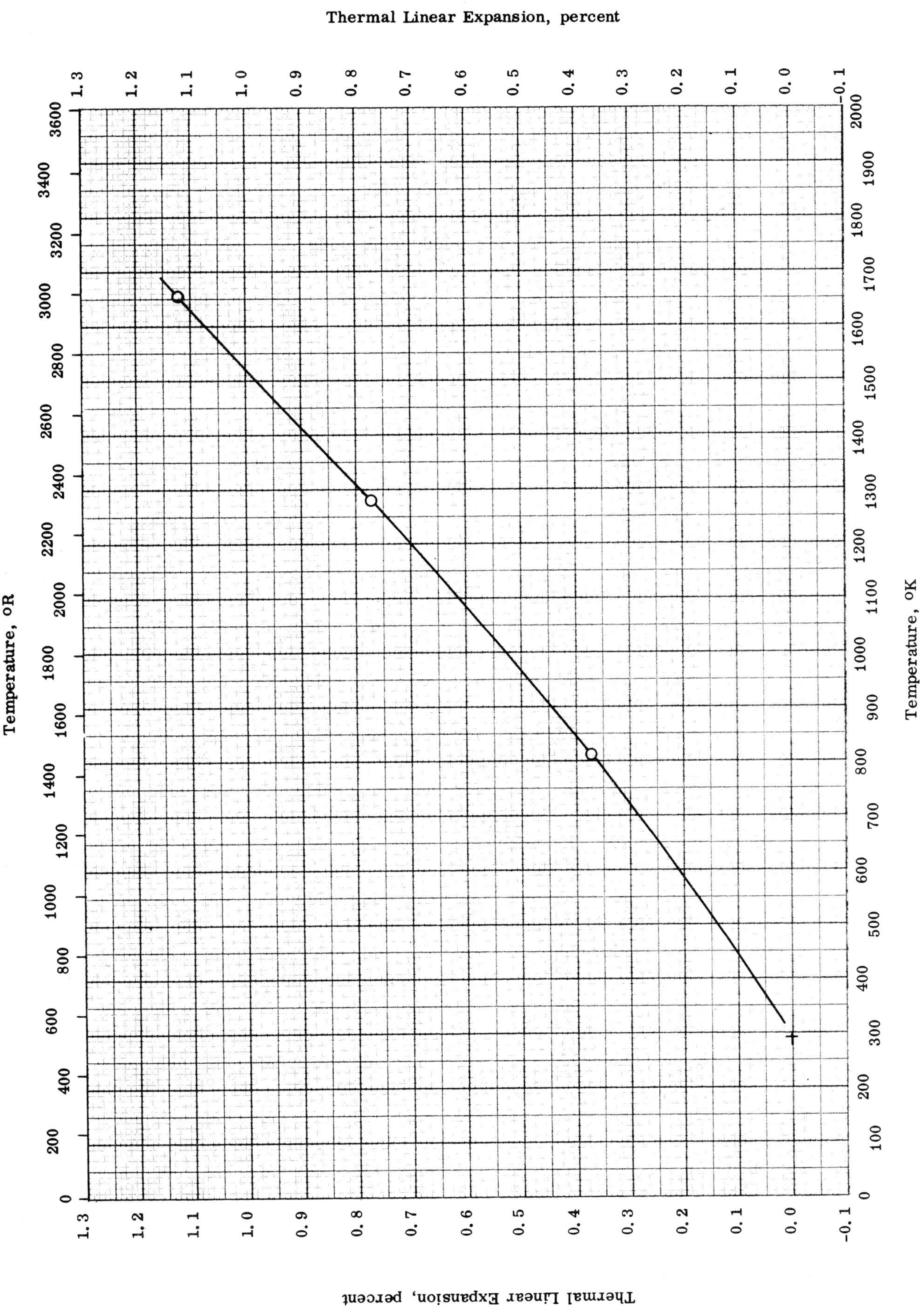

Temperature, °R

Temperature, °K

Thermal Linear Expansion, percent

THERMAL LINEAR EXPANSION -- [ALUMINUM OXIDE + TUNGSTEN + CHROMIUM] CERMET

THERMAL LINEAR EXPANSION -- [ALUMINUM OXIDE + TUNGSTEN + CHROMIUM] CERMET

REFERENCE INFORMATION

Symbol	Ref.	Temp. Range °K	Rept. Error %	Sample Specifications	Remarks
○	60-23	300-1655	< 5	LT-2; 15 Al_2O_3, 60 W, and 25 Cr; dimension: 3/8 in. diameter by 3 in. long.	Sintered at 3050 F.

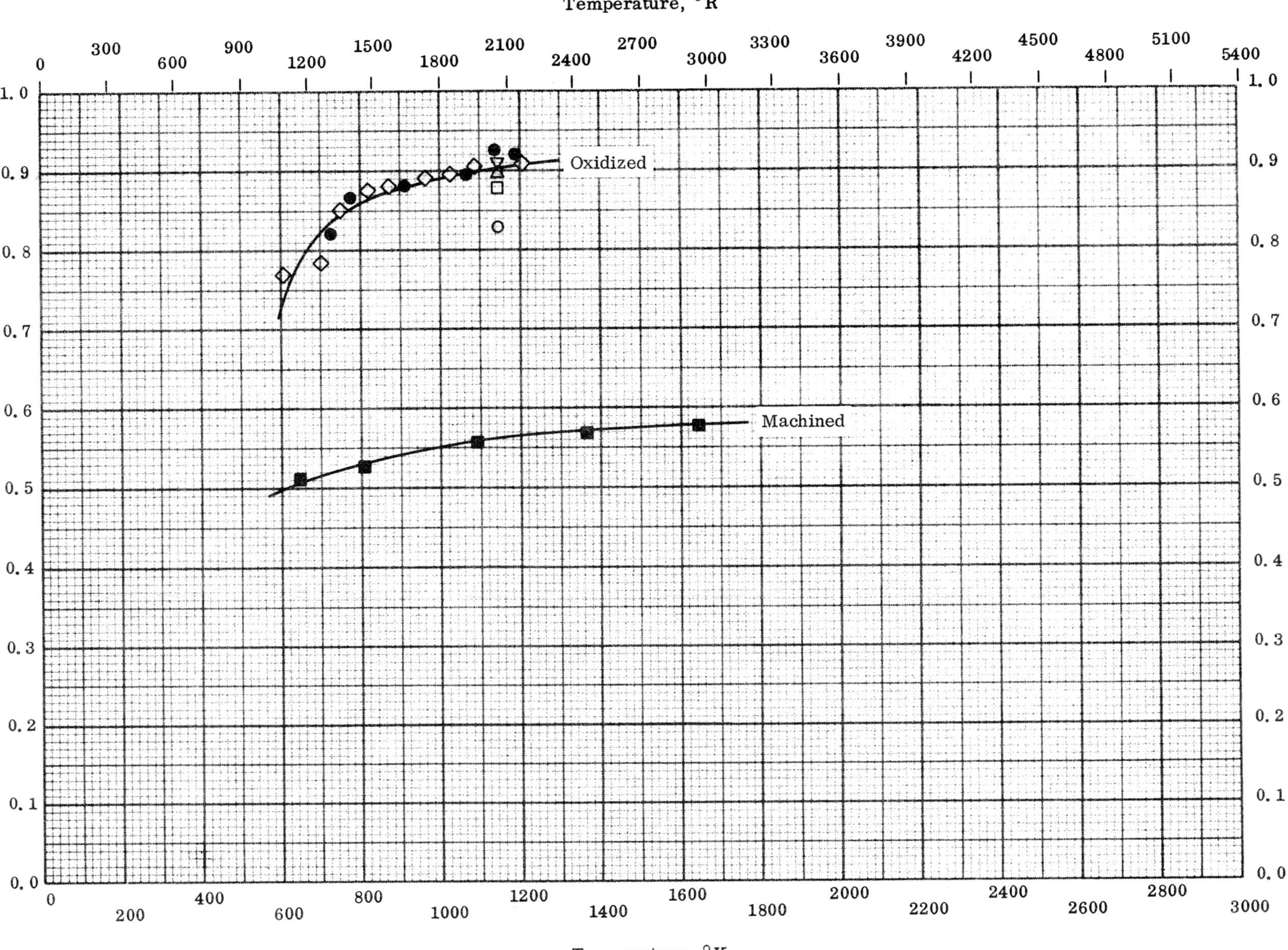

NORMAL TOTAL EMITTANCE -- [ALUMINUM OXIDE + TUNGSTEN + CHROMIUM] CERMET

NORMAL TOTAL EMITTANCE -- [ALUMINUM OXIDE + TUNGSTEN + CHROMIUM] CERMET

REFERENCE INFORMATION

Symbol	Ref.	Temp. Range °K	Rept. Error %	Sample Specifications	Remarks
○	62-31	1144		Haynes LT-2 cermet; 60 W, 25 Cr, and 15 Al_2O_3.	Ground and polished, cleansing with alcohol and distilled water; after heating in air at 1144 K for approximately 1 min.
□	62-31	1144		Same as above.	Same as above; after heating in air at 1144 K for for 6 min.
△	62-31	1144		Same as above.	Same as above; after heating in air at 1144 K for 10 min.
▽	62-31	1144		Same as above.	Same as above; after heating in air at 1144 K for 20 min.
◇	62-31	605-1202		Same as above.	Same as above; after oxidized in air at 1144 K for 20 min.
●	62-31	722-1194		Same as above.	Same as above.
■	60-23	644-1644		Haynes LT-2 cermet; 60 W, 25 Cr, and 15 Al_2O_3.	Sintered in a hydrogen-argon atmosphere at 1950 K; machined; measured in dry helium atm.

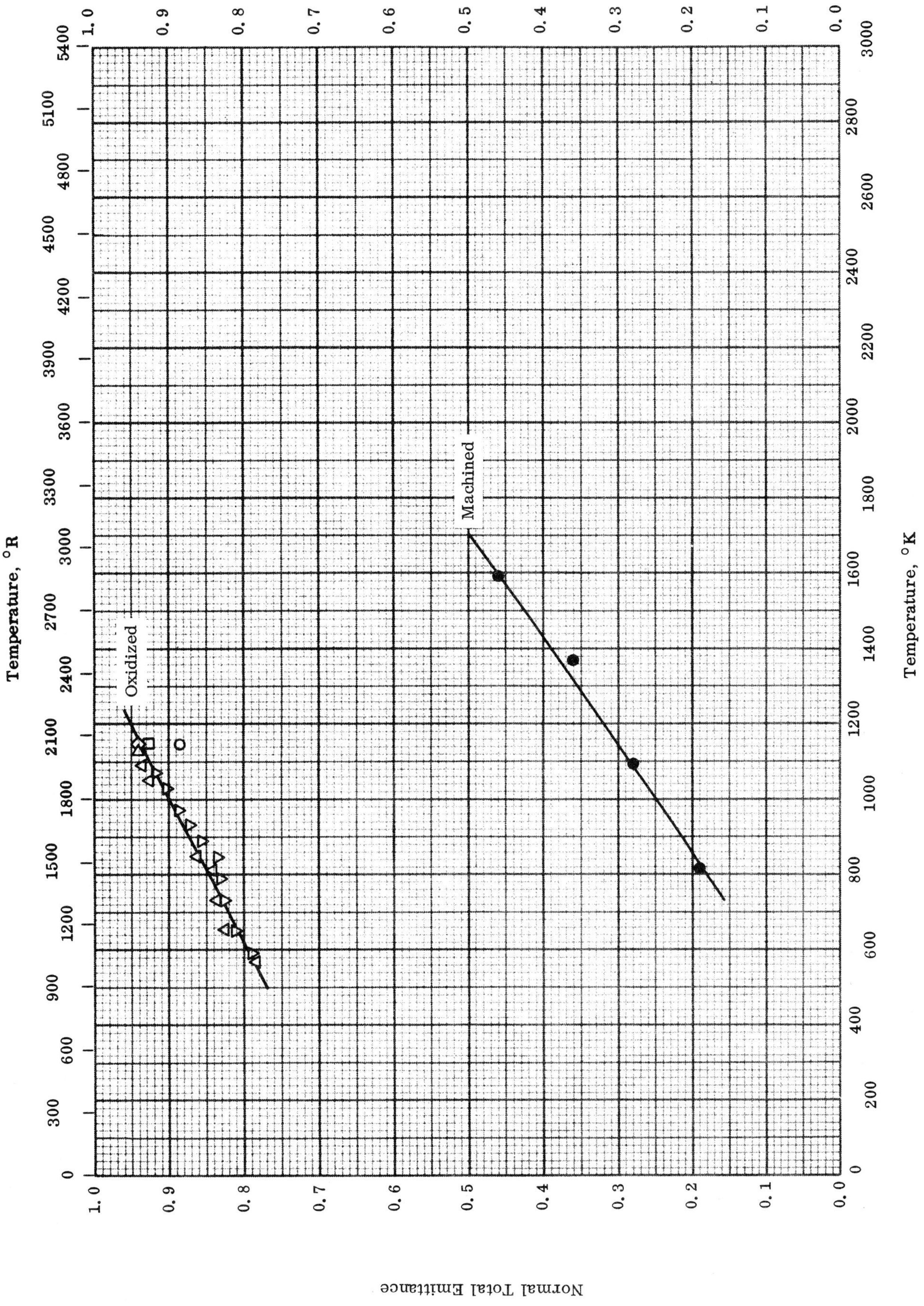

NORMAL TOTAL EMITTANCE -- [ALUMINUM OXIDE + TITANIUM DIOXIDE + CHROMIUM + MOLYBDENUM] CERMET

NORMAL TOTAL EMITTANCE -- [ALUMINUM OXIDE + TITANIUM DIOXIDE + CHROMIUM + MOLYBDENUM] CERMET

REFERENCE INFORMATION

Symbol	Ref.	Temp. Range °K	Rept. Error %	Sample Specifications	Remarks
○	62-31	1144		Haynes LT - 1 B cermet, 60 Cr, 19 Mo, 19 Al_2O_3, and 2 TiO_2.	Ground and polished; cleansing with alcohol and distilled water; after heating in air at 1144 K for approximately 1 min.
□	62-31	1144		Same as above.	Same as above; after heating in air at 1144 K for 5 min.
◇	62-31	1144		Same as above.	Same as above; after heating in air at 1144 K for 10 min.
▷	62-31	1144		Same as above.	Same as above; after heating in air at 1144 K for 20 min.
▽	62-31	589-1144		Same as above.	Same as above; after oxidized in air at 1144 K for 20 min.
△	62-31	566-1144		Same as above.	Same as above; another sample.
●	60-23	811-1589	±20	Haynes LT - 1 B cermet, 59 Cr, 20 Mo, 19 Al_2O_3, and 2 TiO_2.	Sintered in a hydrogen-argon atmosphere at 1867 K; machined; measured in dry helium atmosphere.

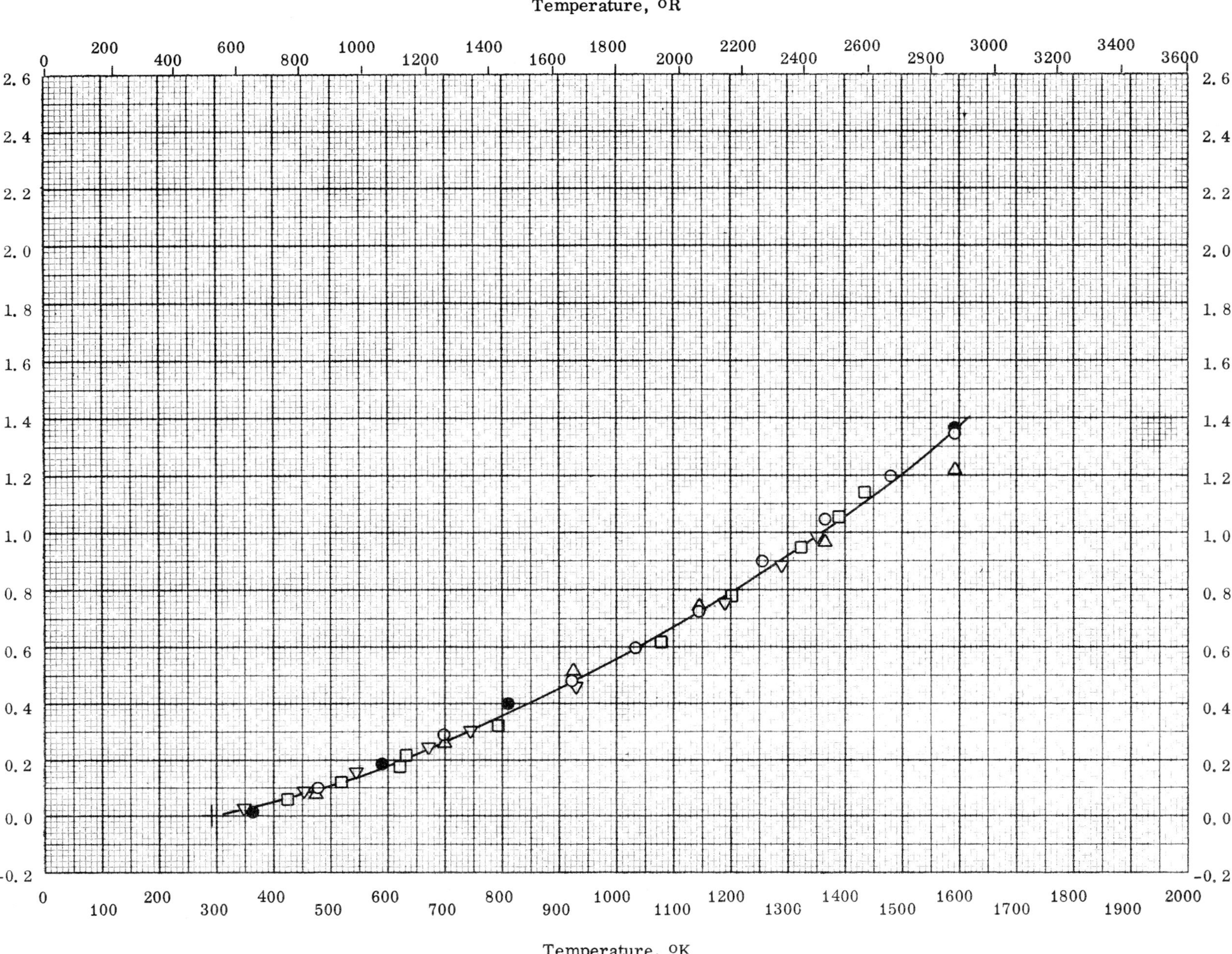

THERMAL LINEAR EXPANSION -- OTHER ALUMINUM OXIDE CERMETS

THERMAL LINEAR EXPANSION -- OTHER ALUMINUM OXIDE CERMETS

REFERENCE INFORMATION

Symbol	Ref.	Temp. Range °K	Rept. Error %	Sample Specifications	Remarks
○	54-19	293-1589		26 Al_2O_3, 69 Cr, 3 Fe, and 2 W; prepared from electrolytic Cr and α-Al_2O_3 in corundum form (Alcoa grade T-61); density 369.4 lb ft^{-3}.	Fe and W impurities picked up in preparing sample; possibly same work as following entry.
●	52-17	367-1589		28.6 Al_2O_3 and 71.4 Cr; Al_2O_3 in corundum form with 99.5$^+$ pure and electrolytic Cr with 99$^+$ pure; density 370 lb ft^{-3}.	Milled and granulated material pressed at 35000 psi in vacuum of 1 mmHg and fired at 3050 - 3100 F in H_2 atm.
△	52-17	367-1589		36.7 Al_2O_3 and 63.3 Cr; raw materials same as above.	Same as above.
□	54-18 also 55-19	293-1433		34.4 Al_2O_3 and 65.6 binder of 80 Cr - 20 Mo alloy; density 363 lb ft^{-3}.	Fired at 3150 F; heating.
▽	54-18 also 55-19	293-1433		Same as above.	Cooling curve of above sample.

PROPERTIES OF [BERYLLIUM OXIDE + BERYLLIUM] CERMET

REPORTED VALUES

Density	g cm^{-3}	lb ft^{-3}
○ 1.19 - 1.34 BeO	1.848 ± 0.001	115.4 ± 0.1
Heat of Sublimation	**cal g^{-1}**	**Btu lb^{-1}**
□ 1.34 BeO	$8,538_{0K}$ ± 24	$15,370_{0R}$ ± 43

PROPERTIES OF [BERYLLIUM OXIDE + BERYLLIUM] CERMET

REFERENCE INFORMATION

Symbol	Ref.	Temp. Range °K	Rept. Error %	Sample Specifications	Remarks
○	50-5	298		1.19-1.34 BeO, 0.025-0.35 Al, 0.013-0.021 Fe, 0.012-0.021 Cu, 0.015 Ni, 0.006-0.0085 Si, 0.01 Cr, 0.005 Ca, 0.003-0.0035 Mn, and 0.002-0.003 Mg.	Two samples of cold compacted flake, heated to 1850 F and hot compacted at 128,000 psi; reheated to 1850 F and extruded.
□	50-2	0		98.85 Be, 1.34 BeO, 0.10 slag, 0.114 Fe, 0.11 Al, 0.048 Mg, 0.017 Cu, 0.012 Mn, 0.0094 Ni, 0.006 Zn, 0.005 Ag, 0.001 each Co and Sn, 0.00003 Li, and 0.00002 Cd.	Δhs from vapor pressure data.

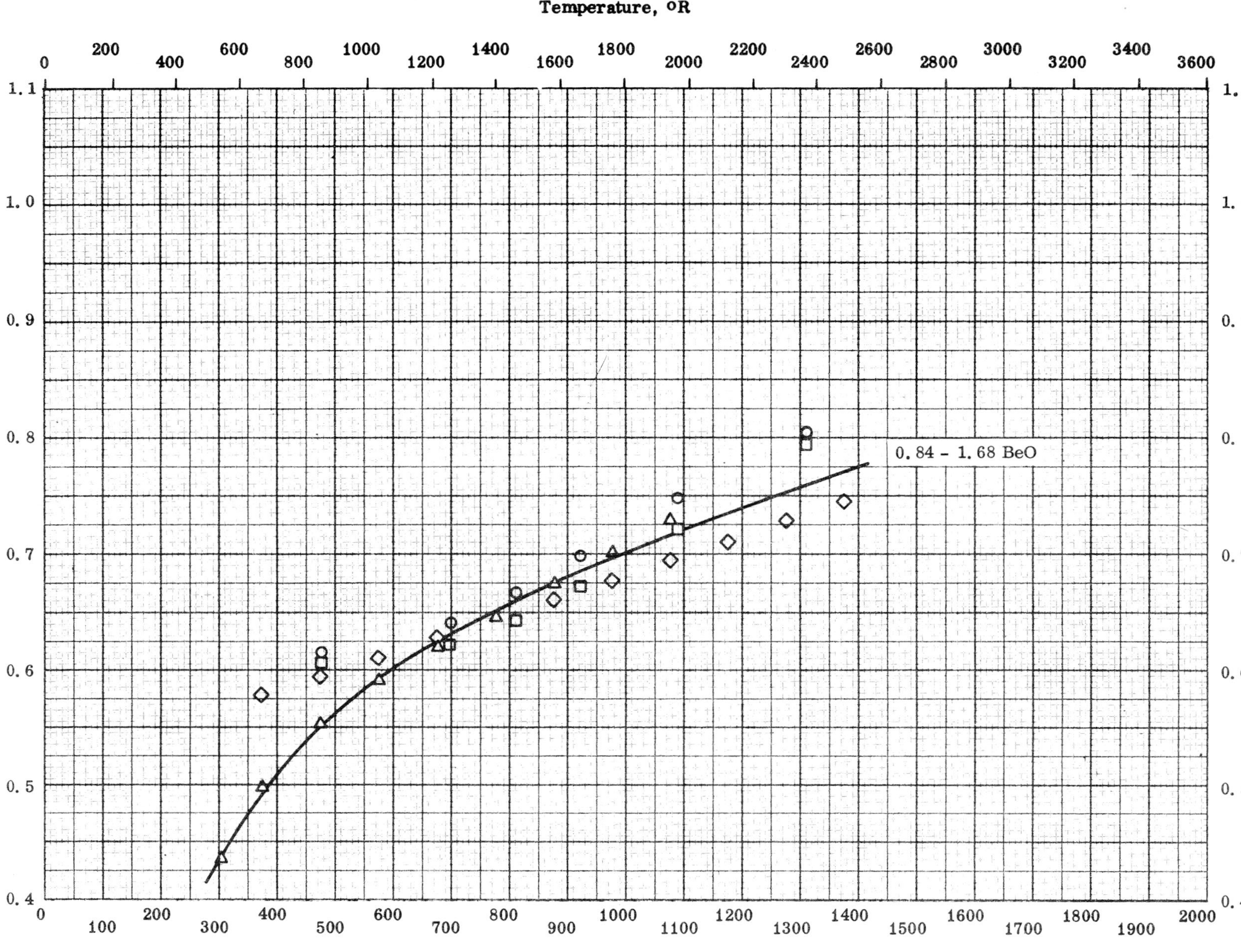

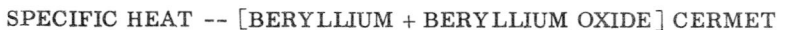

SPECIFIC HEAT -- [BERYLLIUM + BERYLLIUM OXIDE] CERMET

SPECIFIC HEAT -- [BERYLLIUM + BERYLLIUM OXIDE] CERMET

REFERENCE INFORMATION

Symbol	Ref.	Temp. Range °K	Rept. Error %	Sample Specifications	Remarks
○	58-9	478-1310	3	YB9052; 99.16 Be and 0.84 BeO.	
□	58-9	478-1310	3	YB9054; 98.32 Be and 1.68 BeO.	
△	62-27	303-1075	<3.0	99.3 Be, 0.9 BeO, 0.1 Fe and 0.1 various metals.	
◇	60-22	373-1373	≤ 2.7	1.16 BeO, 0.15 Al, 0.10 Fe, 0.013 Mg and 0.01 others. [Author's design.: QMV Beryllium].	

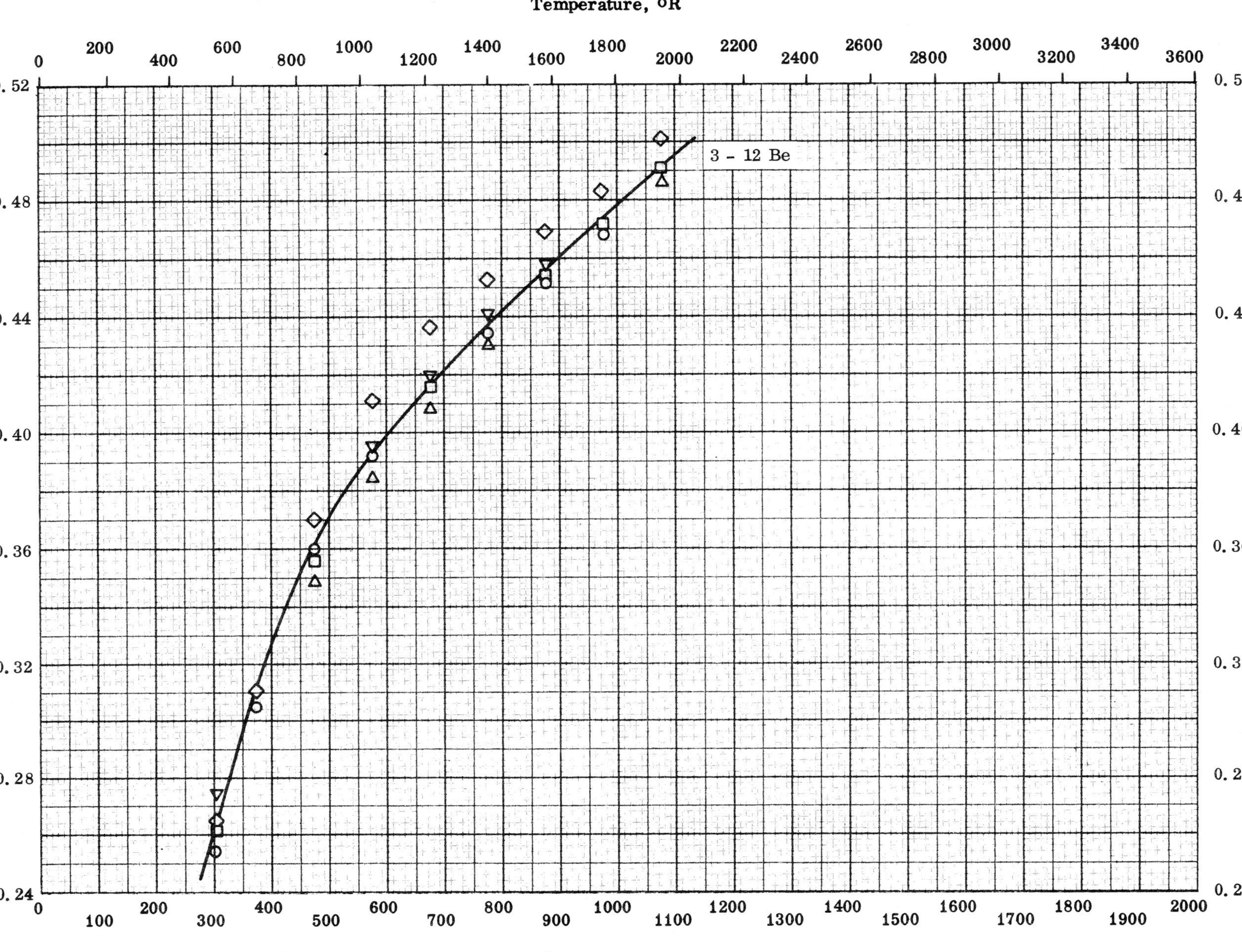

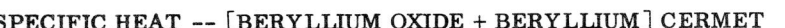

SPECIFIC HEAT -- [BERYLLIUM OXIDE + BERYLLIUM] CERMET

SPECIFIC HEAT -- [BERYLLIUM OXIDE + BERYLLIUM] CERMET

REFERENCE INFORMATION

Symbol	Ref.	Temp. Range °K	Rept. Error %	Sample Specifications	Remarks
○	62-27	303-1073	<3	97 BeO and 3 Be.	
□	62-27	303-1073	<3	94 BeO and 6 Be.	
△	62-27	303-1073	<3	93 BeO and 7 Be.	
▽	62-27	303-1073	<3	91 BeO and 9 Be.	
◇	62-27	303-1073	<3	88 BeO and 12 Be.	

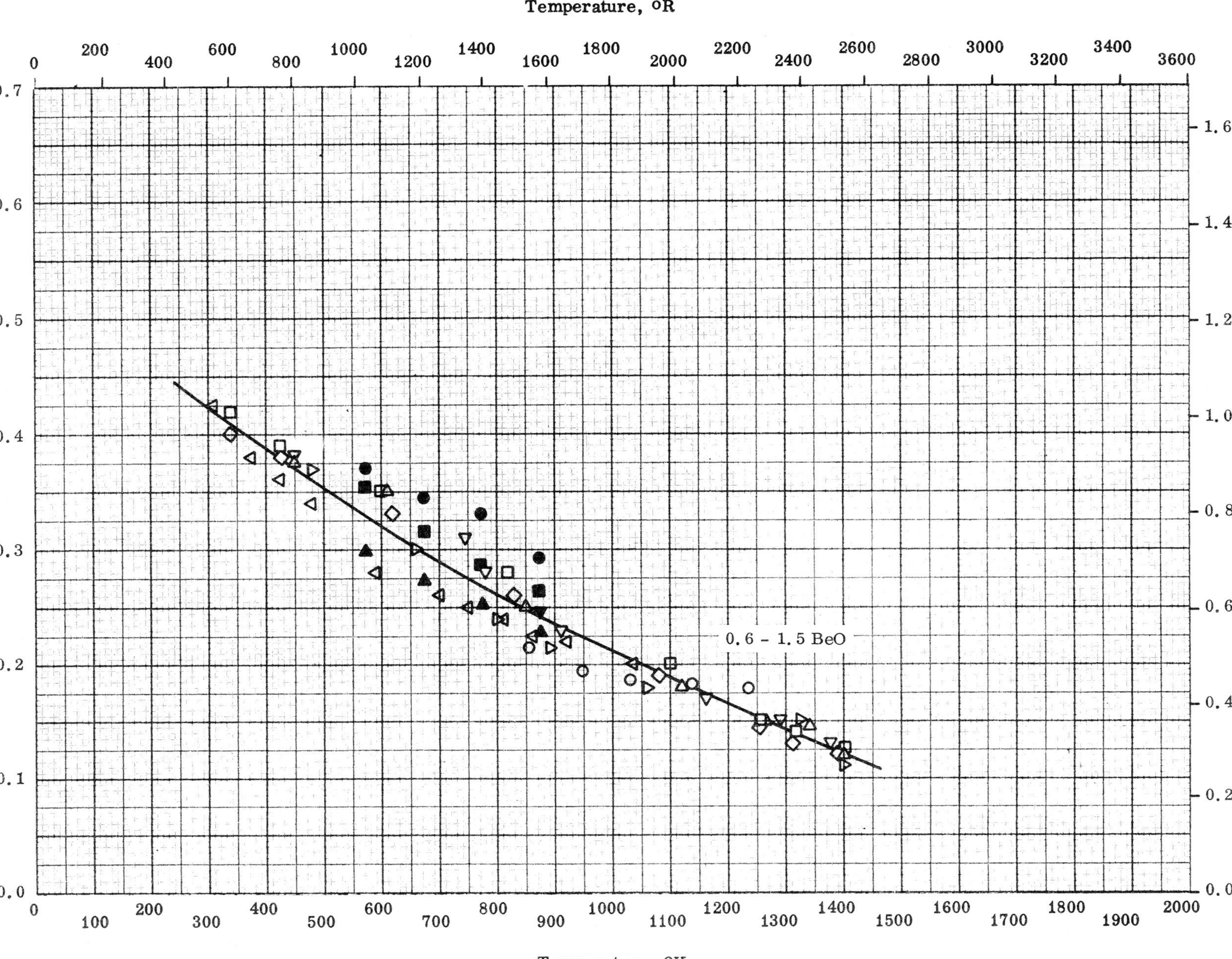

THERMAL CONDUCTIVITY -- [BERYLLIUM + BERYLLIUM OXIDE] CERMET

THERMAL CONDUCTIVITY -- [BERYLLIUM + BERYLLIUM OXIDE] CERMET

REFERENCE INFORMATION

Symbol	Ref.	Temp. Range °K	Rept. Error %	Sample Specifications	Remarks
○	58-9	850-1238		YB-9052; 0.84 BeO.	
□	60-16	340-1400		Y6825; 1.48 BeO, 0.15 Fe, 0.015 Al, 0.01 Si, 0.008 Cr, 0.005 Mn, 0.004 Cu, 0.003 Mg, 0.002 Ti, 0.001 CaO.	
△	60-16	450-1400		Y9384; 0.845 BeO, 0.15 Fe, 0.05 Al, 0.015 Ni, 0.01 Cr, 0.01 Cu, 0.008 Mn, 0.008 Si, 0.006 Mg, 0.004 Ti, and 0.002 Ca.	
▽	60-16	450-1375		Y6826; 1.292 BeO, 0.15 Fe, 0.03 Al, 0.02 Si, 0.015 Ni, 0.01 Cr, 0.01 Cu, 0.01 Mg, 0.006 Mn, 0.002 Ca, and 0.002 Ti.	
◇	60-16	340-1390		YB1000; 1.229 BeO, 0.15 Fe, 0.03 Al, 0.02 Ni, 0.015 Cu, 0.015 Mg, 0.01 Cr, 0.01 Mn, 0.008 Si, 0.002 Ca, and 0.002 Ti.	
▷	60-16	480-1400		LYB1102; 0.992 BeO, 0.20 Fe, 0.04 Al, 0.04 Si, 0.02 Cr, 0.02 Mg, 0.02 Ni, 0.01 Cu, 0.008 Mn, 0.0040 Ti, and 0.002 Ca.	
◁	60-16	310-1035		BM15; 0.609 BeO, 0.20 Fe, 0.03 Al, 0.015 Cu, 0.015 Cr, 0.015 Mg, 0.015 Ni, 0.01 Si, 0.008 Mn, 0.003 Ti, and 0.001 Ca.	
●	62-8	573-873		99.0 Be, 0.85 BeO, 0.11 Fe, and 0.02 Al; density 1.845 g cm^{-3} (99^{+}% theoretical).	

(Continued onto next page)

REFERENCE INFORMATION

Symbol	Ref.	Temp. Range °K	Rept. Error %	Sample Specifications	Remarks
■	62-8	573-873		99.0 Be, 0.83 BeO, 0.16 Fe, and 0.10 Al; density 1.835 g cm^{-3} (99% theoretical).	
▲	62-8	573-873		98.6 Be, 1.43 BeO, 0.17 Fe, and 0.04 Al; density 1.851 g cm^{-3} (99^{+}% theoretical).	
▼	62-8	573-873		98.9 Be, 1.20 BeO, 0.13 Fe, and 0.05 Al; density 1.851 g cm^{-3} (99^{+}% theoretical).	

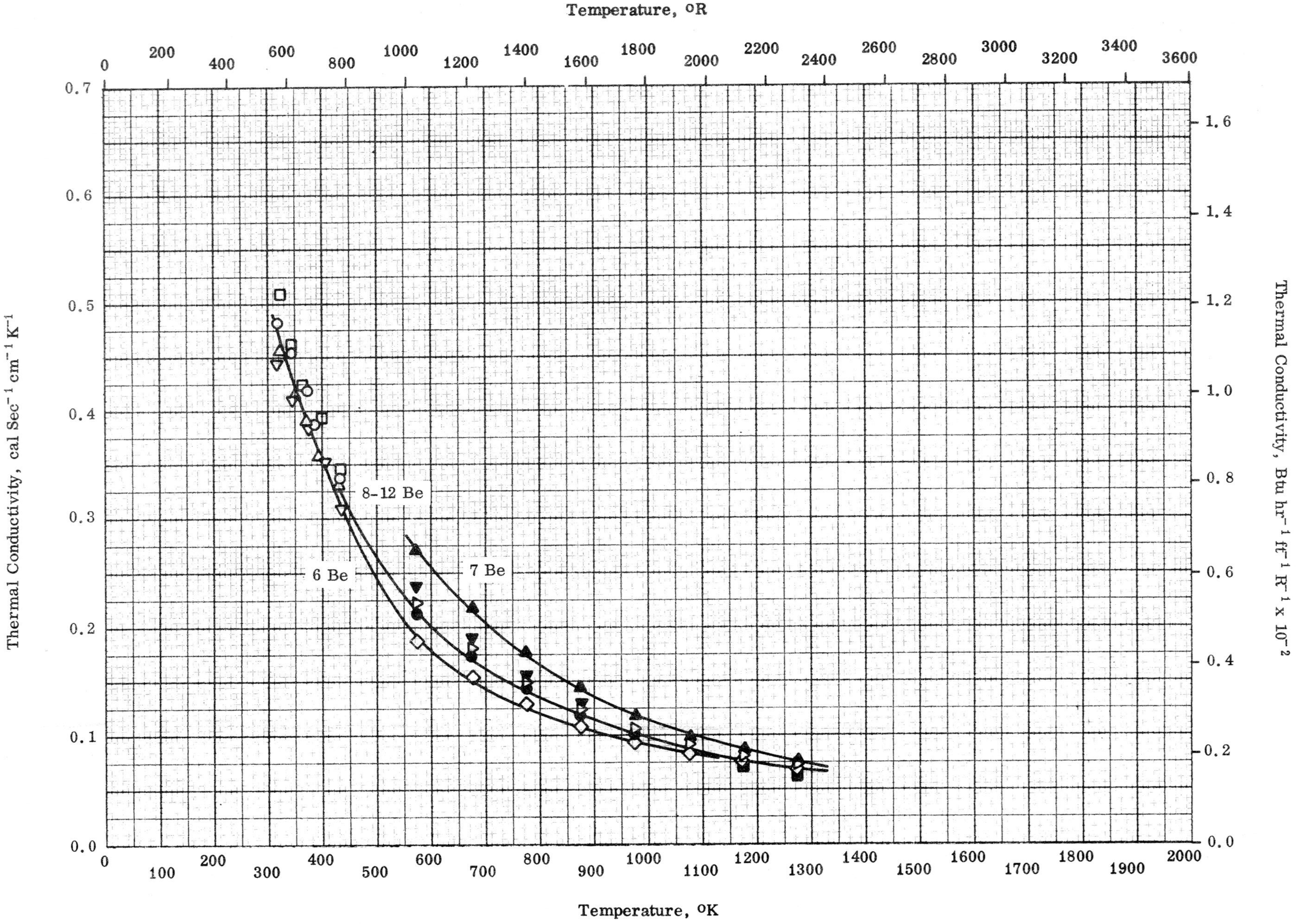

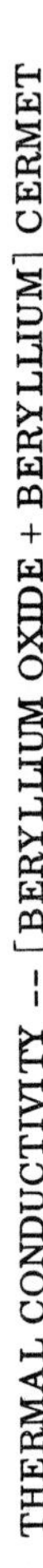

THERMAL CONDUCTIVITY -- [BERYLLIUM OXIDE + BERYLLIUM] CERMET

REFERENCE INFORMATION

Symbol	Ref.	Temp. Range °K	Rept. Error %	Sample Specifications	Remarks
○	53-8	320-432		6.06 Be (computed); metal particle size 15 to 25 μ; zero apparent porosity and density 179 lb ft^{-3}.	
△	53-8	323-430		Same as above (Sample 2).	
□	53-8	325-434		5.65 Be (computed); metal particle size 2 to 5 μ; zero apparent porosity and density 179 lb ft^{-3}.	
▽	53-8	320-436		8.24 Be (computed); metal particle size 2 to 5 μ; zero apparent porosity and density 175 lb ft^{-3}.	
▷	62-8	573-1273	±2-±4	3 Be; density 2.945 g cm^{-3} (99^{+}% theoretical).	
◇	62-8	573-1273	±2-±4	6 Be; density 2.905 g cm^{-3} (99^{+}% theoretical).	
●	62-8	573-1273	±2-±4	9 Be; density 2.834 g cm^{-3} (99^{+}% theoretical).	
■	62-8	573-1273	±2-±4	12 Be; density 2.787 g cm^{-3} (99^{+}% theoretical).	
▲	62-8	573-1273	±2-±4	7 Be; density 2.842 g cm^{-3} (98^{+}% theoretical).	
▼	62-8	573-1273	±2-±4	7 Be; density 2.917 g cm^{-3} (100% theoretical).	

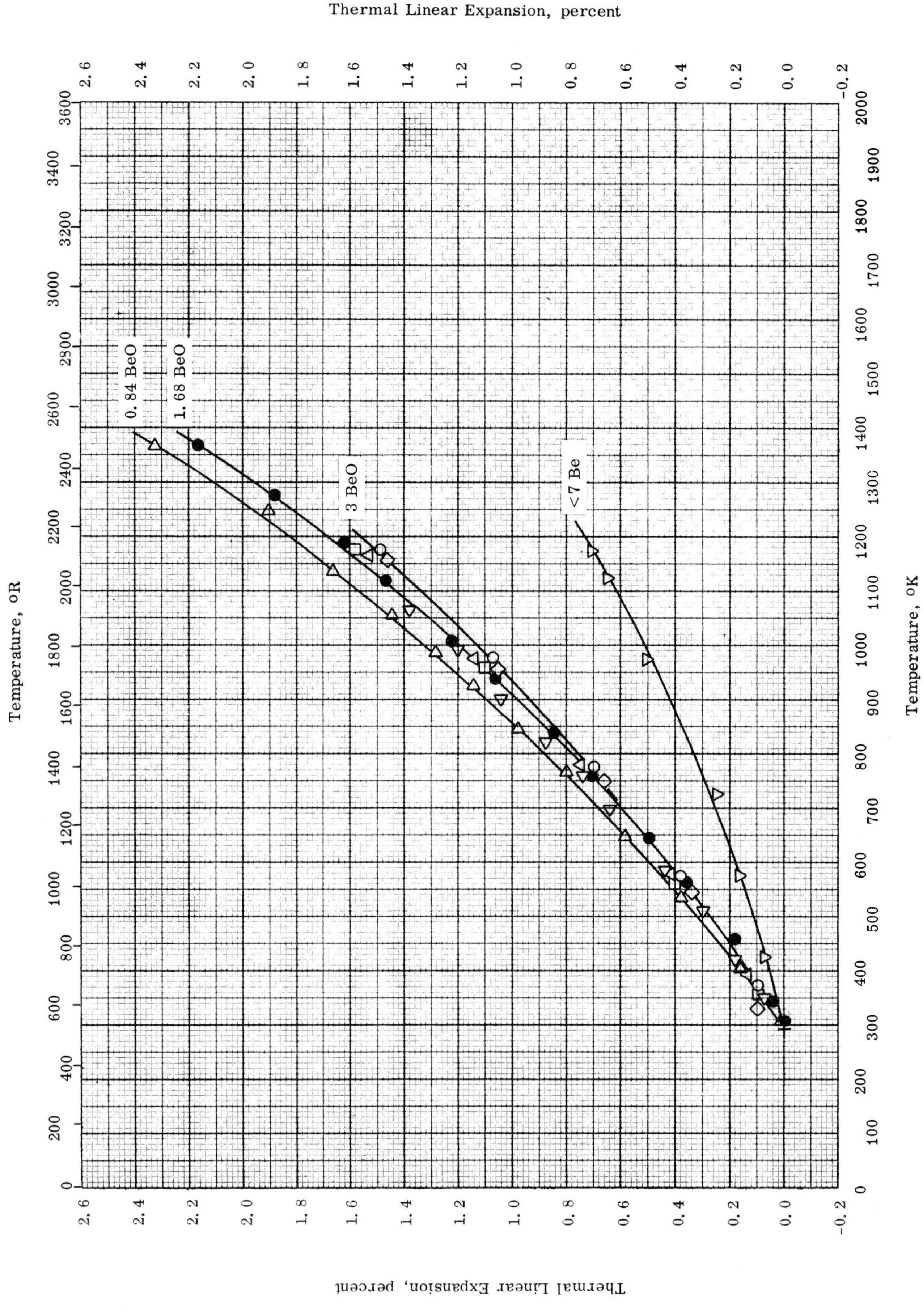

Thermal Linear Expansion, percent
Temperature, °R
Temperature, °K
0.84 BeO
1.68 BeO
3 BeO
<7 Be
Thermal Linear Expansion, percent

THERMAL LINEAR EXPANSION -- [BERYLLIUM OXIDE + BERYLLIUM] CERMET

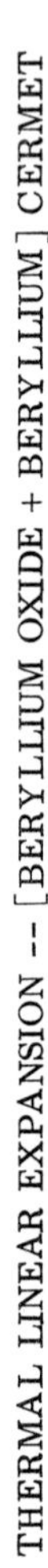

REFERENCE INFORMATION

Symbol	Ref.	Temp. Range °K	Rept. Error %	Sample Specifications	Remarks
○	56-17	293-1173		1 BeO.	Hot pressed.
□	56-17	293-1173		1. 5 BeO.	Same as above.
△	56-17	293-1173		2 BeO.	Same as above.
◇	56-17	293-1173		3 BeO.	Same as above.
▽	53-14	293-1173		<7 Be; specimen 1/2 in. diameter by 1 in. long.	Hot pressed the mixture of Be and BeO at the temperature between 1700 and 1800 C at 2000 psi in vacuum.
▷	58-9	300-1363		Beryllium YB 9052; 0. 84 BeO.	
◁	58-9	296-1065		Beryllium YB 9053; 1. 49 BeO.	Blend.
●	58-9	300-1367		Beryllium YB 9054; 1. 68 BeO.	100% recycle.

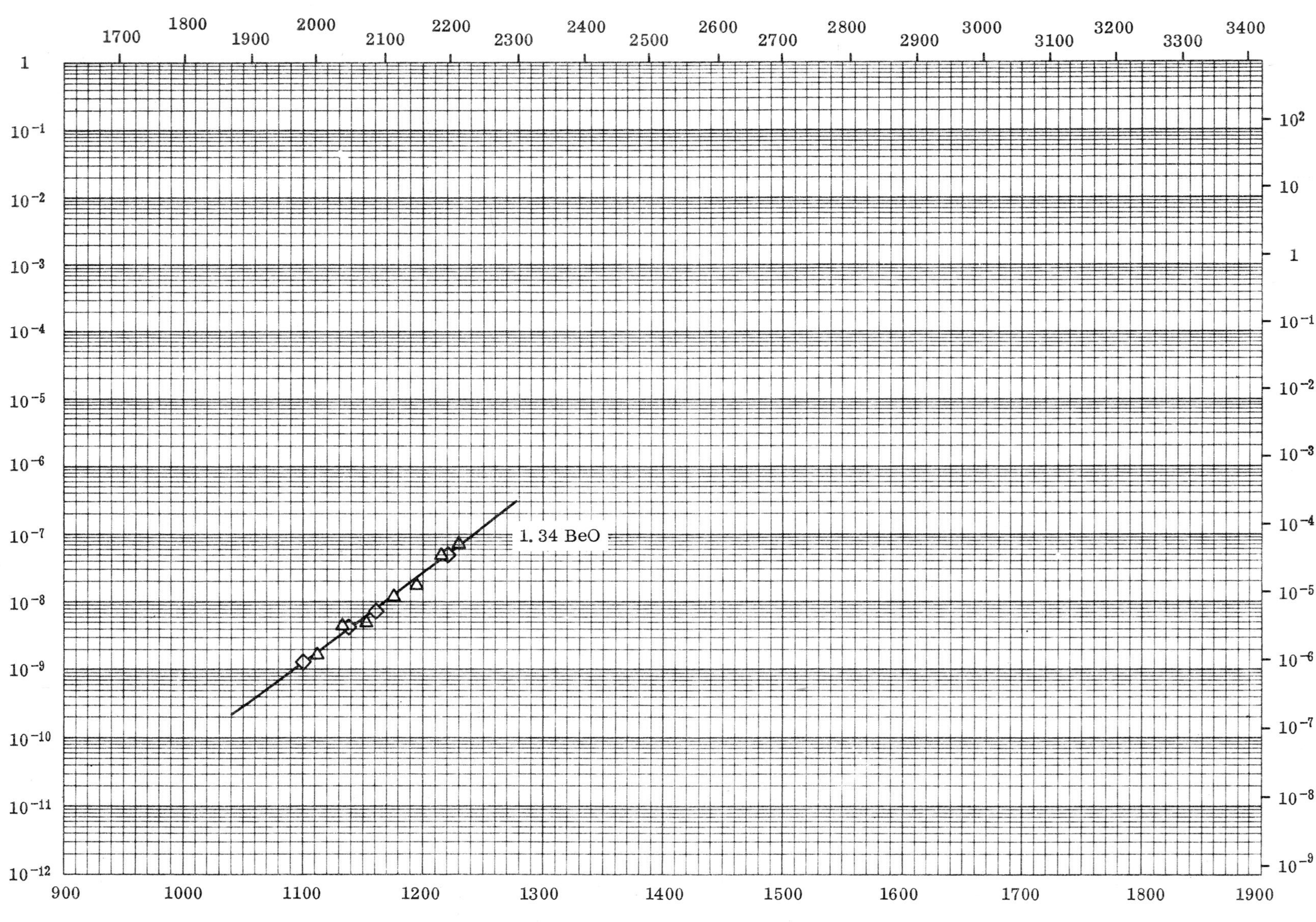

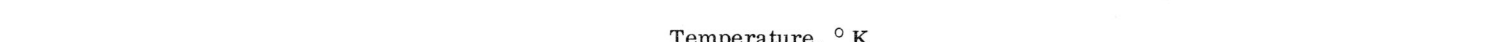

VAPOR PRESSURE -- [BERYLLIUM + BERYLLIUM OXIDE] CERMET

VAPOR PRESSURE -- [BERYLLIUM + BERYLLIUM OXIDE] CERMET

REFERENCE INFORMATION

Symbol	Ref.	Temp. Range °K	Rept. Error %	Sample Specifications	Remarks
△	50-2	1103-1229		98.85 Be, 1.34 BeO, 0.114 Fe, 0.11 Al, 0.10 slag, 0.048 Mg, 0.0170 Cu, 0.0120 Mn, 0.0094 Ni, 0.0060 Zn, 0.0005 Ag, 0.0001 ea. Sn, Co, and 0.00002 Cd.	Abraded; as received.
◇	50-2	1103-1229		Same as above.	Abraded; vacuum treated 1 hr at 900 C.

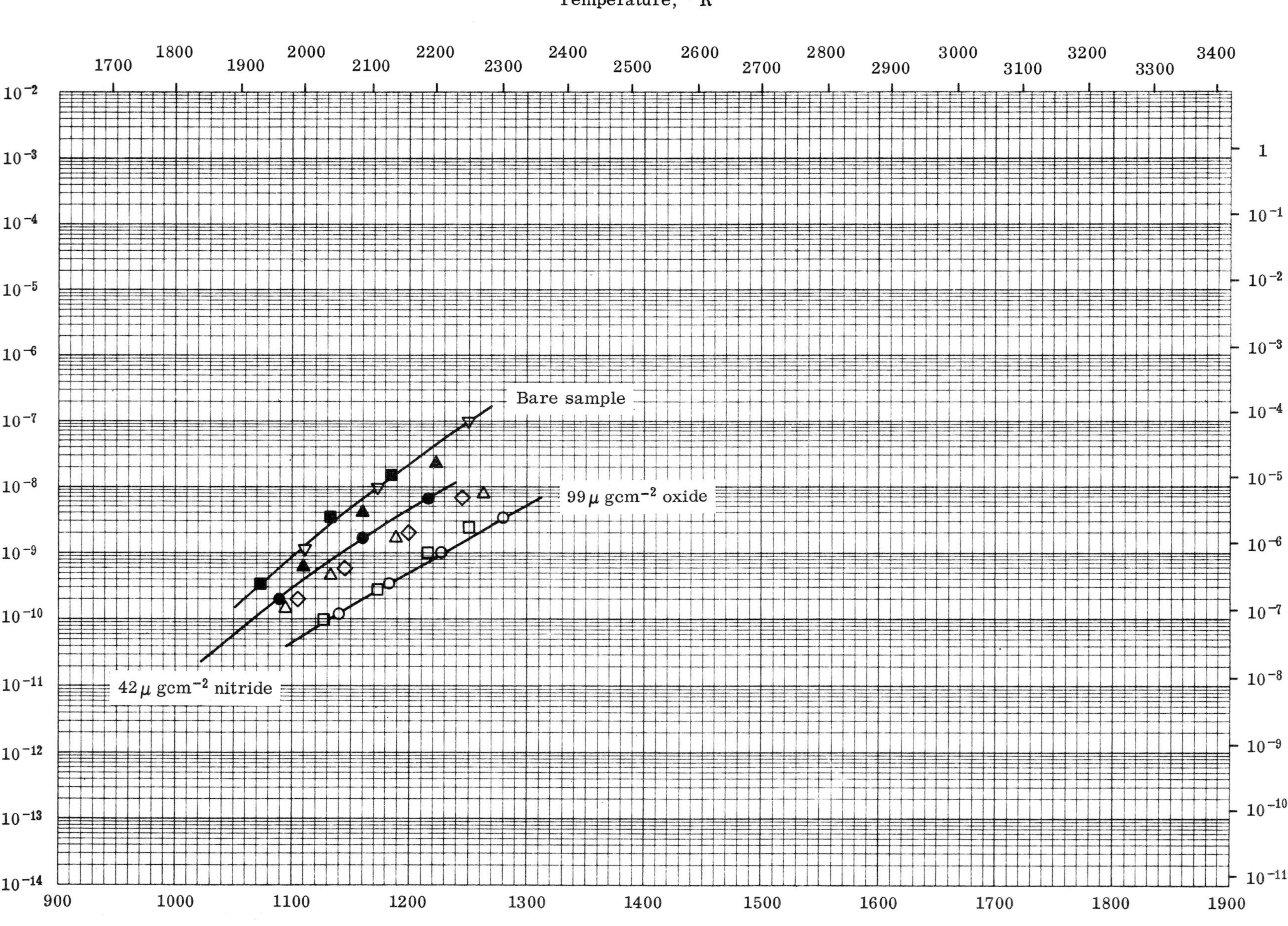

VAPOR PRESSURE -- [BERYLLIUM + BERYLLIUM OXIDE] CERMET WITH OXIDE OR NITRIDE FILM

VAPOR PRESSURE -- [BERYLLIUM + BERYLLIUM OXIDE] CERMET WITH OXIDE OR NITRIDE FILM

REFERENCE INFORMATION

Symbol	Ref.	Temp. Range °K	Rept. Error %	Sample Specifications	Remarks
○	50-2	1149-1282		Be base with oxide film; composition of base material: 98.35 pure Be, 1.34 BeO, 0.114 Fe, 0.11 Al, 0.0480 Mg, 0.170 Cu, 0.120 Mn, 0.0094 Ni, 0.0060 Zn, 0.0005 Ag, 0.0001 Co, 0.0001 Sn, 0.00003 Li, and 0.00002 Cd.	Oxide film 99 μ g cm^{-2}.
□	50-2	1127-1250		Same as above.	57 μ g cm^{-2} oxide film.
△	50-2	1099-1266		Same as above.	29 μ g cm^{-2} oxide film.
◇	50-2	1099-1247		Same as above.	11 μ g cm^{-2} oxide film.
▽	50-2	1111-1235		Base materials same as above.	No film.
●	50-2	1089-1217		Be base with nitride film; base material same as above.	42 μ g cm^{-2} nitride film.
▲	50-2	1111-1224		Same as above.	21 μ g cm^{-2} nitride film.
■	50-2	1075-1185		Same as above.	7.35 μ g cm^{-2} nitride film.

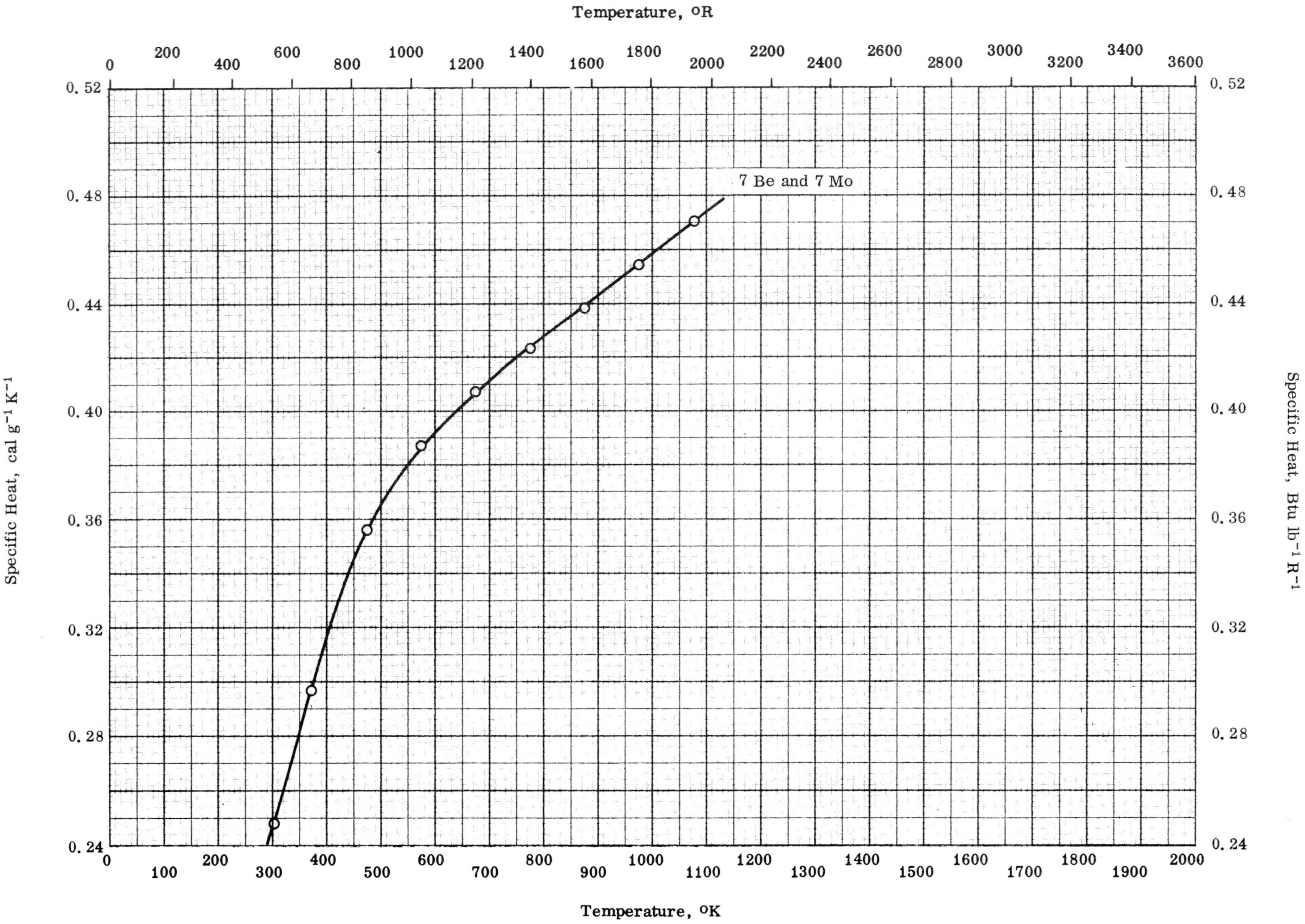

Specific Heat, Btu lb^{-1} R^{-1}

0.52 0.48 0.44 0.40 0.36 0.32 0.28 0.24

Temperature, °R

0 200 400 600 800 1000 1200 1400 1600 1800 2000 2200 2400 2600 2800 3000 3200 3400 3600

7 Be and 7 Mo

Temperature, °K

0 100 200 300 400 500 600 700 800 900 1000 1100 1200 1300 1400 1500 1600 1700 1800 1900 2000

0.52 0.48 0.44 0.40 0.36 0.32 0.28 0.24

Specific Heat, cal g^{-1} K^{-1}

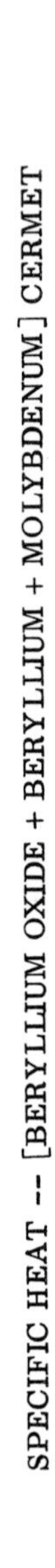

SPECIFIC HEAT -- [BERYLLIUM OXIDE + BERYLLIUM + MOLYBDENUM] CERMET

SPECIFIC HEAT -- [BERYLLIUM OXIDE + BERYLLIUM + MOLYBDENUM] CERMET

REFERENCE INFORMATION

Symbol	Ref.	Temp. Range °K	Rept. Error %	Sample Specifications	Remarks
○	62-27	302-1073	<3	88 BeO, 7 Be, and 7 Mo.	

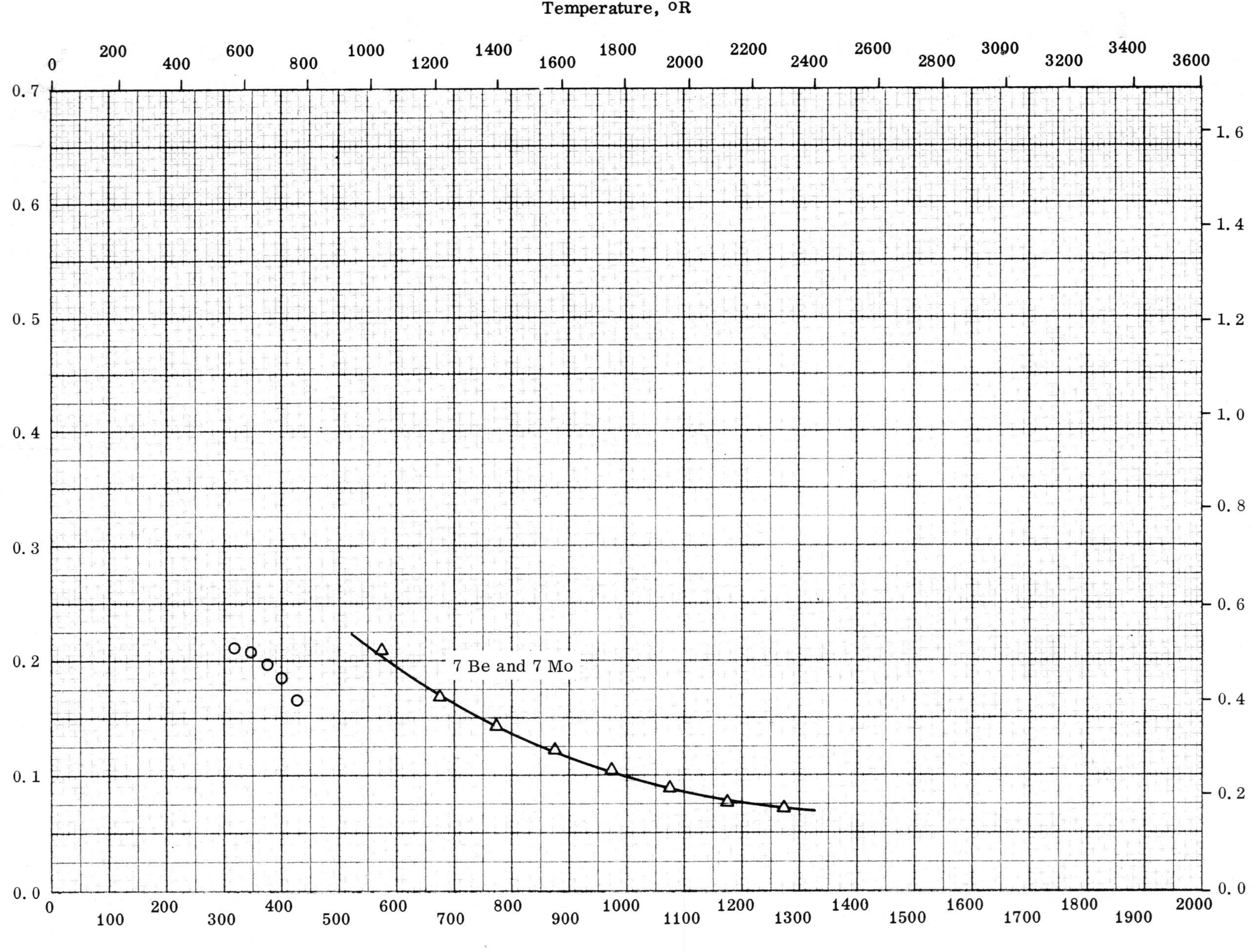

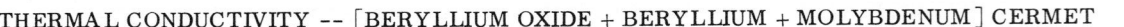

THERMAL CONDUCTIVITY -- [BERYLLIUM OXIDE + BERYLLIUM + MOLYBDENUM] CERMET

THERMAL CONDUCTIVITY -- [BERYLLIUM OXIDE + BERYLLIUM + MOLYBDENUM] CERMET

REFERENCE INFORMATION

Symbol	Ref.	Temp. Range °K	Rept. Error %	Sample Specifications	Remarks
○	53-8	292-427		6.2% apparent porosity and density 171 lb ft^{-3}.	
△	62-8	573-1273		86 BeO, 7 Be, and 7 Mo; density 2.975 g cm^{-3} (98% of theoretical).	

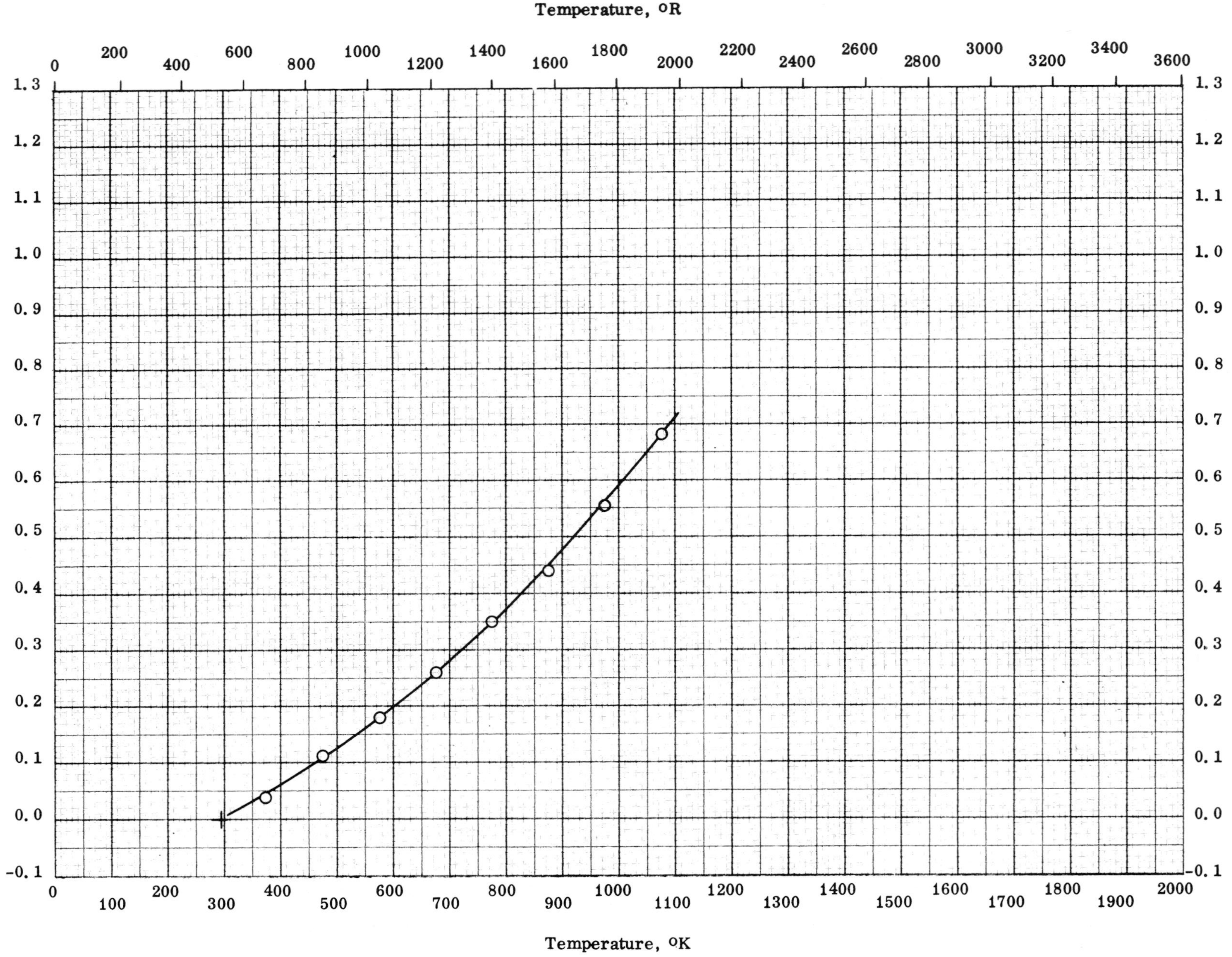

THERMAL LINEAR EXPANSION -- [BERYLLIUM OXIDE + BERYLLIUM + MOLYBDENUM] CERMET

THERMAL LINEAR EXPANSION -- [BERYLLIUM OXIDE + BERYLLIUM + MOLYBDENUM] CERMET

REFERENCE INFORMATION

Symbol	Ref.	Temp. Range °K	Rept. Error %	Sample Specifications	Remarks
○	53-14	293-1073		Not given.	Hot pressed -60 mesh high-fired BeO, 15 - 25 μ Be, and Mo (reduced on BeO from molybdenum trioxide in hydrogen atm. at 1100 C) at 2000 psi at the temperature between 1700 and 1800 C in vacuum.

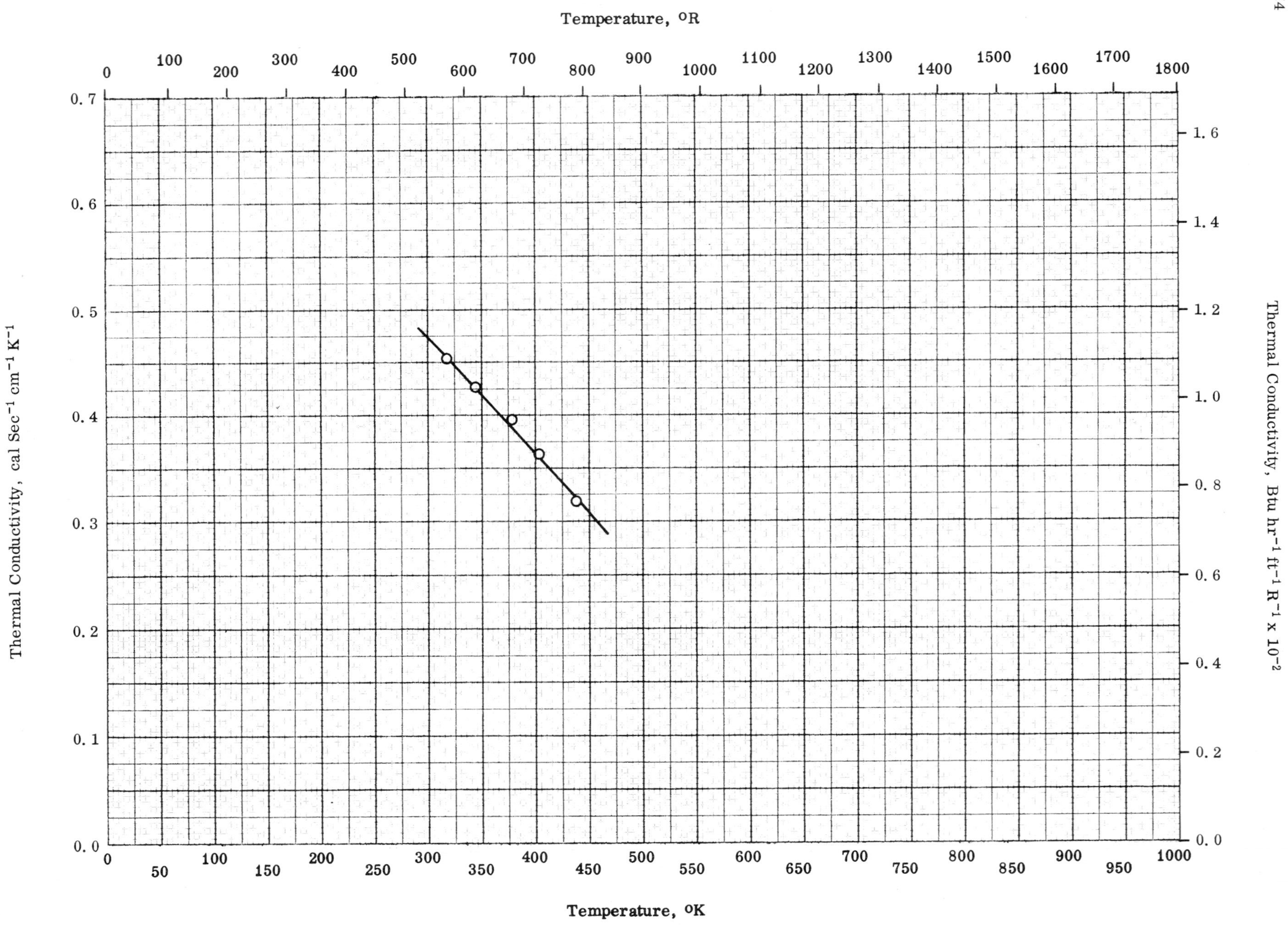

Thermal Conductivity, Btu hr^{-1} ft^{-1} R^{-1} x 10^{-2}

Temperature, °R

Temperature, °K

Thermal Conductivity, cal Sec^{-1} cm^{-1} K^{-1}

THERMAL CONDUCTIVITY -- [BERYLLIUM OXIDE + BERYLLIUM + SILICON] CERMET

THERMAL CONDUCTIVITY -- [BERYLLIUM OXIDE + BERYLLIUM + SILICON] CERMET

REFERENCE INFORMATION

Symbol	Ref.	Temp. Range °K	Rept. Error %	Sample Specifications	Remarks
○	53-8	317-437		Zero apparent porosity; density 181 lb ft^{-3}.	

Thermal Linear Expansion, percent

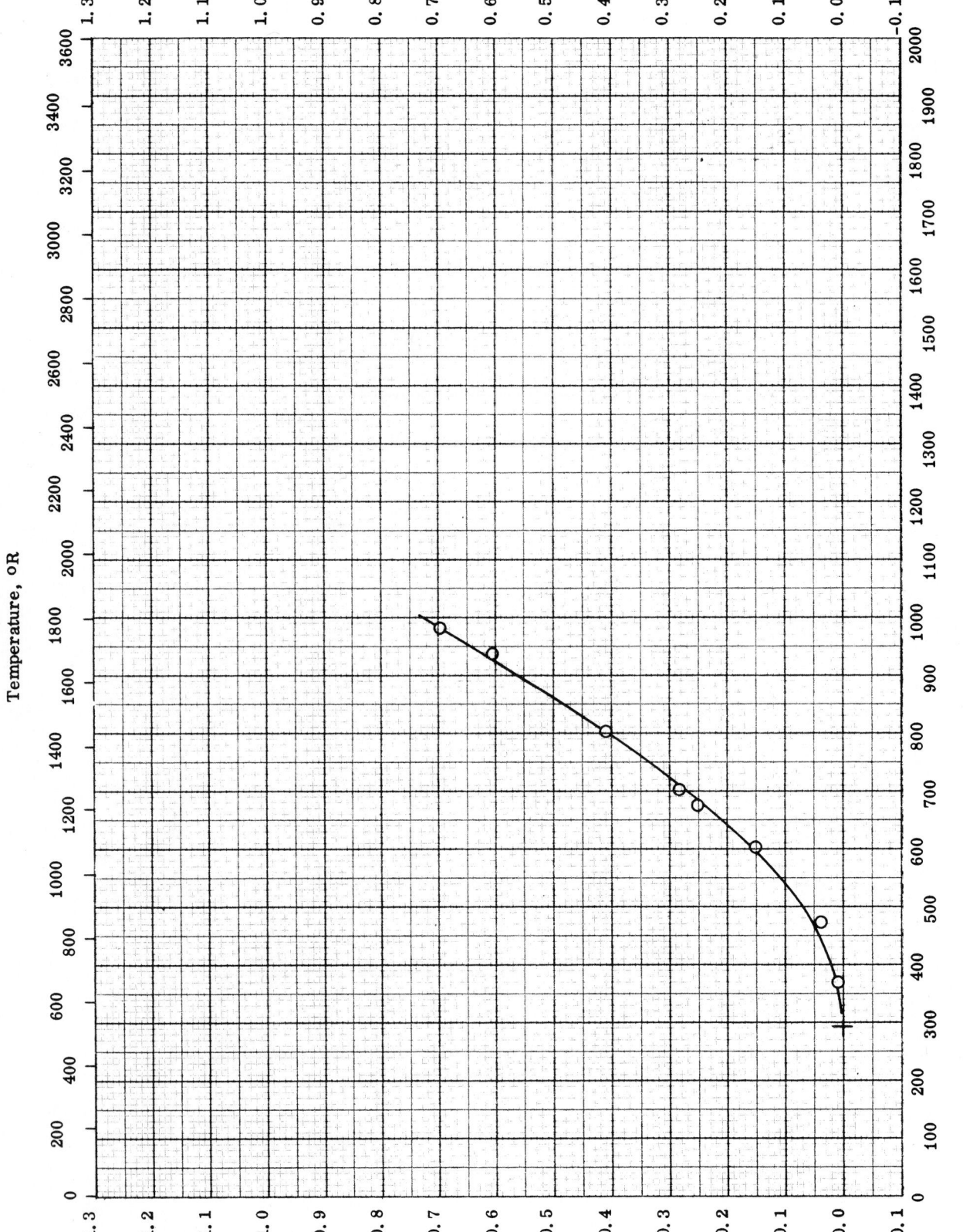

Temperature, °R

Temperature, °K

Thermal Linear Expansion, percent

THERMAL LINEAR EXPANSION -- [BERYLLIUM OXIDE + BERYLLIUM + SILICON] CERMET

REFERENCE INFORMATION

Symbol	Ref.	Temp. Range °K	Rept. Error %	Sample Specifications	Remarks
○	53-14	293-978		Not given.	Hot pressed -60 mesh high-fired BeO, 15 - 25μ Be, and -43μ 97 Si at 2000 psi at the temperature between 1700 and 1800 C in vacuum.

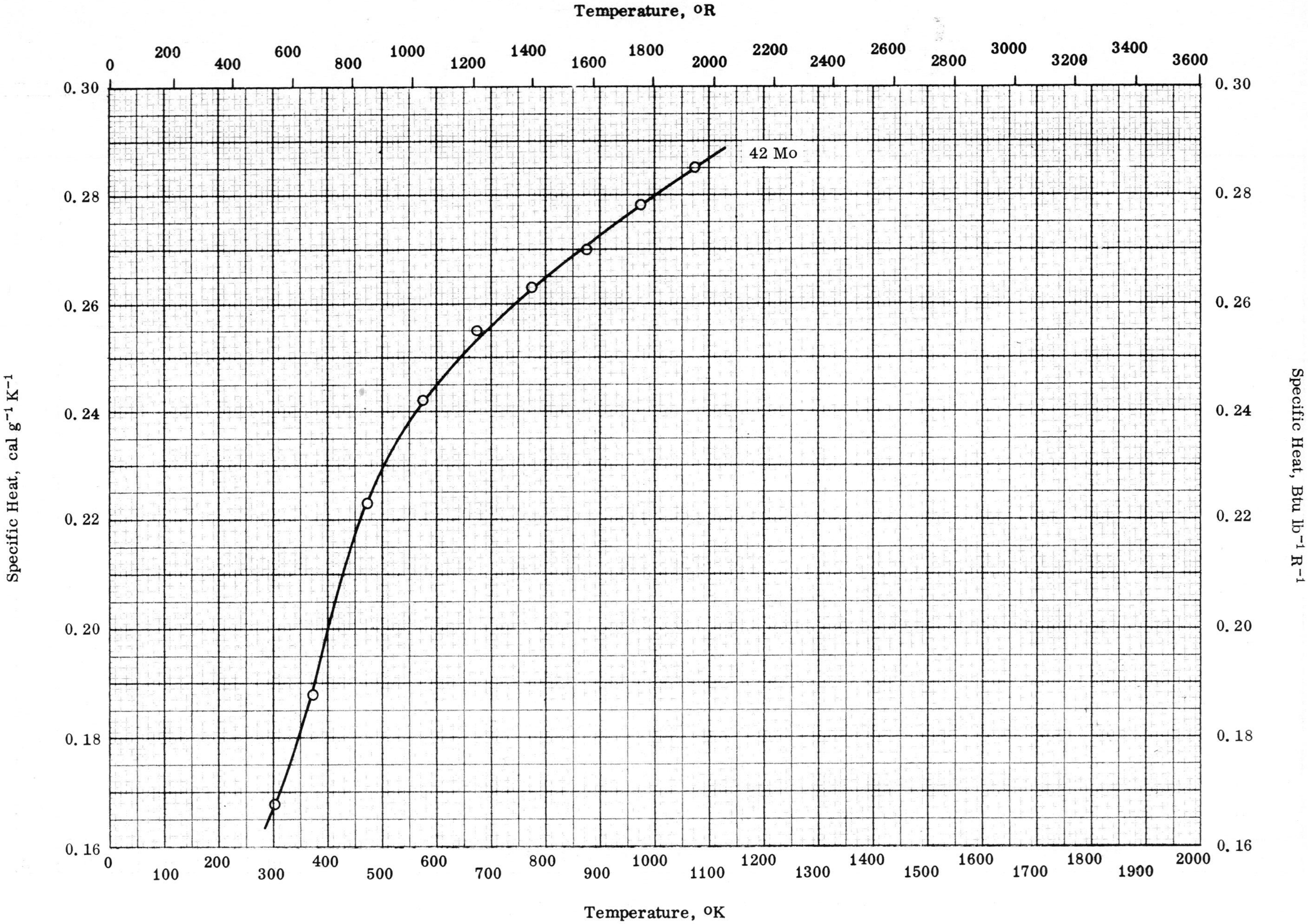

Specific Heat, Btu lb^{-1} R^{-1}

SPECIFIC HEAT -- [BERYLLIUM OXIDE + MOLYBDENUM] CERMET

SPECIFIC HEAT -- [BERYLLIUM OXIDE + MOLYBDENUM] CERMET

REFERENCE INFORMATION

Symbol	Ref.	Temp. Range °K	Rept. Error %	Sample Specifications	Remarks
○	62-27	303-1073	<3	57.6 BeO and 42.4 Mo.	

PROPERTIES OF [BERYLLIUM OXIDE + NIOBIUM] CERMET

REPORTED VALUES

Density		$g\ cm^{-3}$	$lb\ ft^{-3}$
○	2.0 Nb	3.06	190.7
□	5.0 Nb	3.11	193.8
△	8.0 Nb	3.15	196.3
▽	10.0 Nb	3.24	202.1
◁	12.0 Nb	3.27	204.2
▷	15.0 Nb	3.30	205.7

REFERENCE INFORMATION

Symbol	Ref.	Temp. Range °K	Rept. Error %	Sample Specifications	Remarks
○	51-5	293		2.0 Nb.	
□	51-5	293		5.0 Nb.	
△	51-5	293		8.0 Nb.	
▽	51-5	293		10.0 Nb.	
◁	51-5	293		12.0 Nb.	
▷	51-5	293		15.0 Nb.	

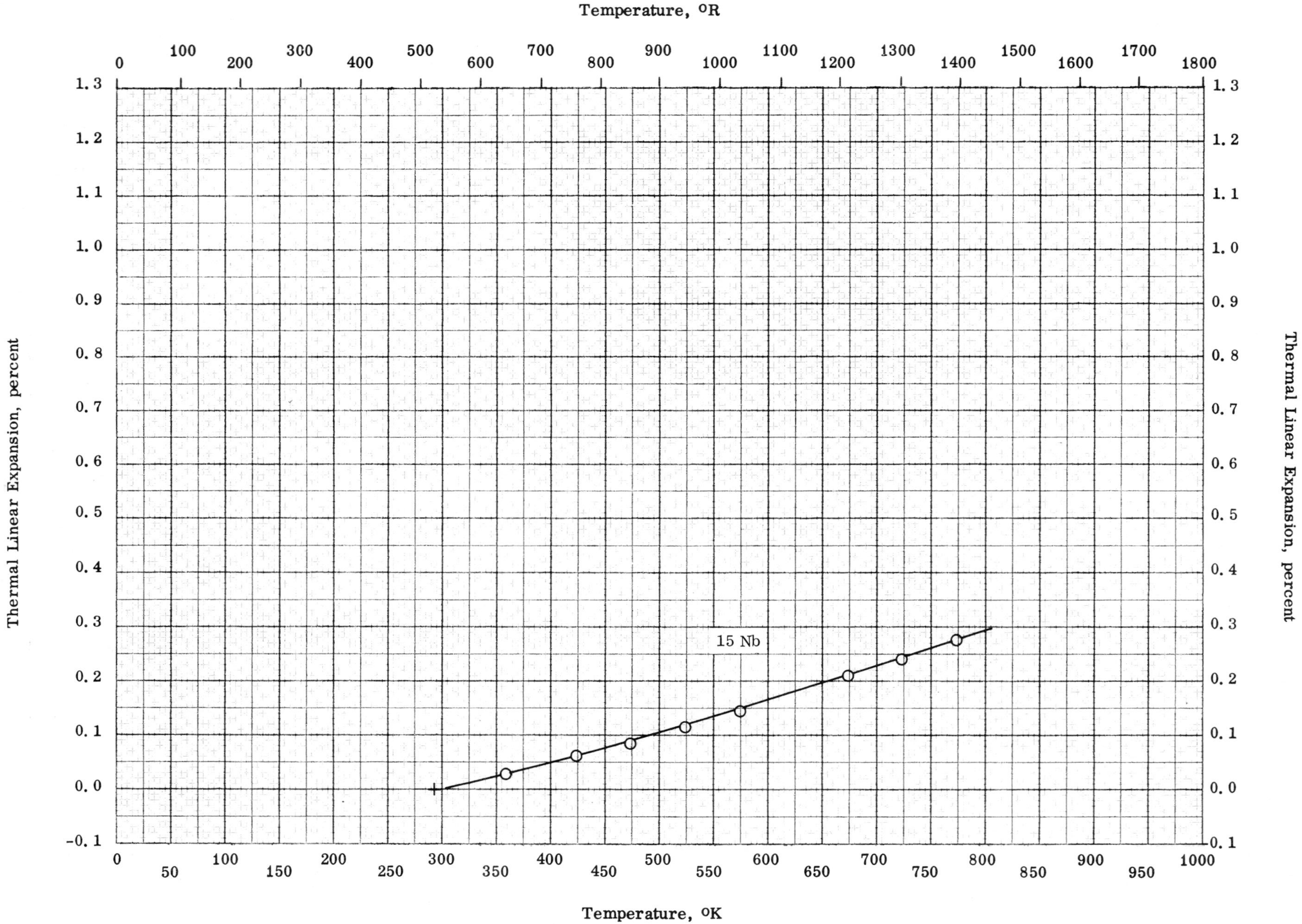

Thermal Linear Expansion, percent

Thermal Linear Expansion, percent

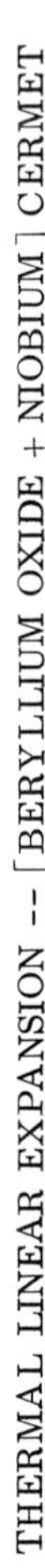
THERMAL LINEAR EXPANSION -- [BERYLLIUM OXIDE + NIOBIUM] CERMET

THERMAL LINEAR EXPANSION -- [BERYLLIUM OXIDE + NIOBIUM] CERMET

REFERENCE INFORMATION

Symbol	Ref.	Temp. Range °K	Rept. Error %	Sample Specifications	Remarks
○	51-5	293-773		85 BeO and 15 Nb.	

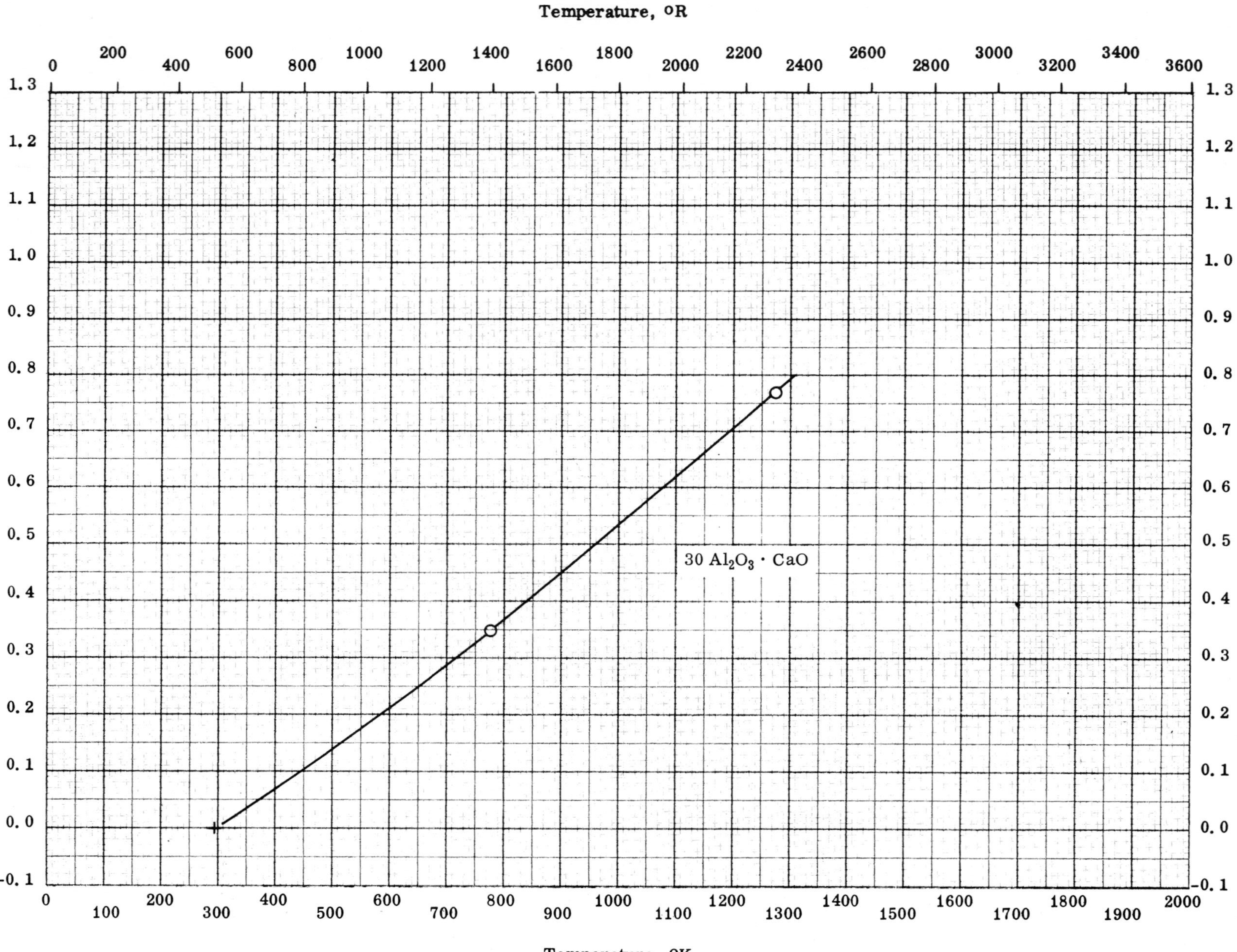

THERMAL LINEAR EXPANSION -- [CALCIUM ALUMINATE + MOLYBDENUM DISILICIDE] CERMET

THERMAL LINEAR EXPANSION -- [CALCIUM ALUMINATE + MOLYBDENUM DISILICIDE] CERMET

REFERENCE INFORMATION

Symbol	Ref.	Temp. Range °K	Rept. Error %	Sample Specifications	Remarks
○	52-16	293-1273		70 $MoSi_2$ and 30 $Al_2O_3 \cdot CaO$.	Fine powders mixed, pressed at 15 - 60 tsi, presintered at 900 - 1200 C and fired approx 45 min at 1500 C in cracked ammonia.

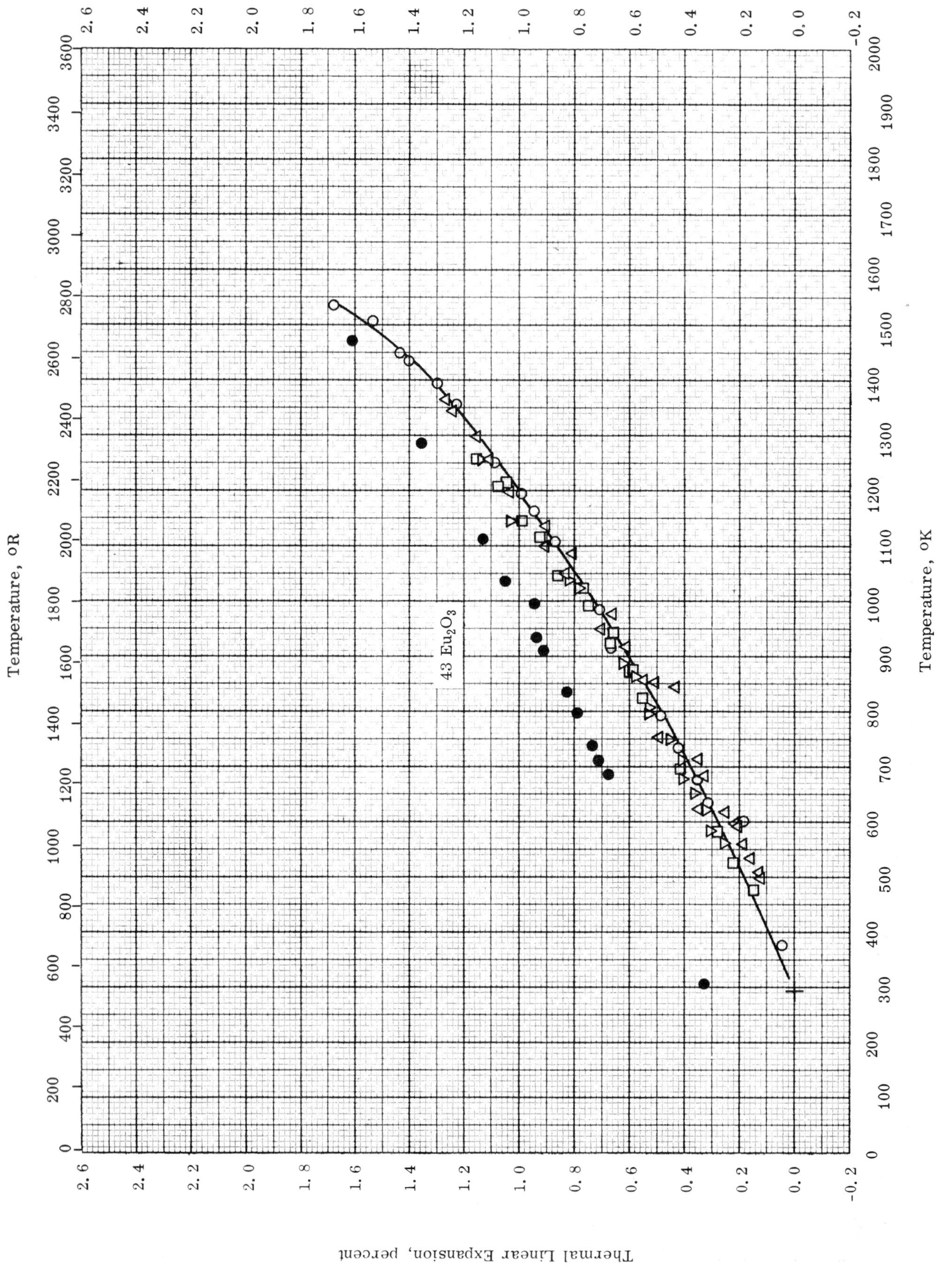

Temperature, °R

Temperature, °K

43 Eu_2O_3

Thermal Linear Expansion, percent

THERMAL LINEAR EXPANSION -- [EUROPIUM OXIDE + IRON-CHROMIUM ALLOY] CERMET

REFERENCE INFORMATION

Symbol	Ref.	Temp. Range °K	Rept. Error %	Sample Specifications	Remarks
○	61-27	293-1533		57 (Fe · 30Cr · 1Y) and 43 Eu_2O_3 ; specimen 1/4 in. diameter by 2 in. long.	Specimen prepared from 92. 8 dense Fe · 30Cr · 1Y - 43 Eu_2O_3 extruded material; heated slowly in argon.
●	61-27	307-1533		Same as above.	Cooling curve of above specimen; about 0. 3% permanent increase in length observed.
□	61-28	293-1258		Same as above.	Specimen prepared from 92. 8 dense Fe · 30Cr · 1Y - 43 Cr_2O_3 extruded material; heated slowly in vacuum.
△	61-28	293-1365		Same as above.	2nd run of above specimen; 0. 015% increase in length observed.
▽	61-28	293-1258		Same as above.	3rd run.

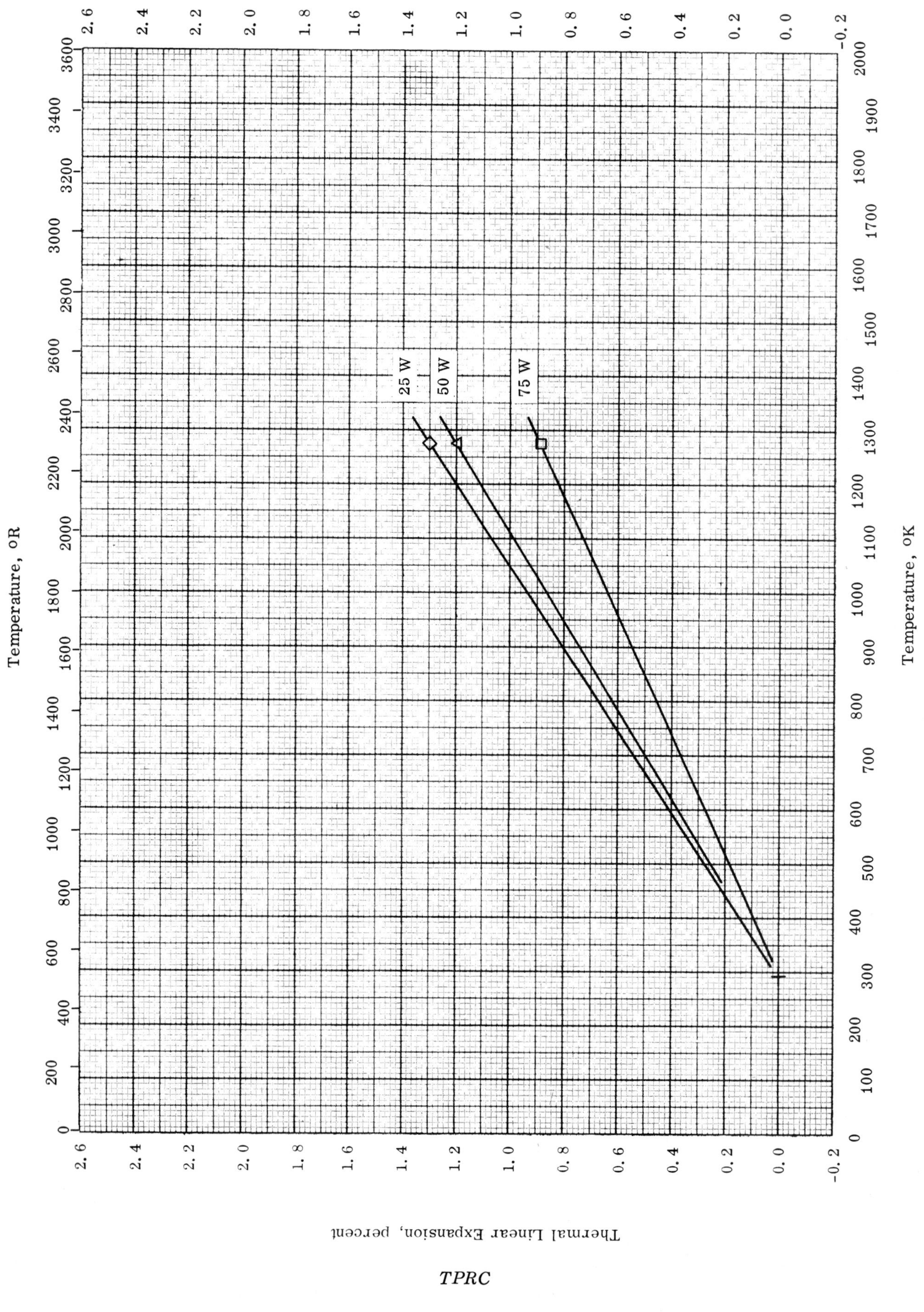

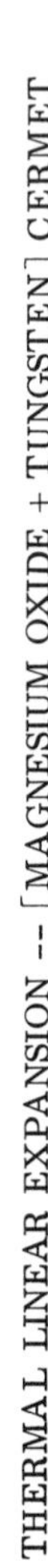

Temperature, °R
Temperature, °K
Thermal Linear Expansion, percent
25 W
50 W
75 W

THERMAL LINEAR EXPANSION -- [MAGNESIUM OXIDE + TUNGSTEN] CERMET

THERMAL LINEAR EXPANSION -- [MAGNESIUM OXIDE + TUNGSTEN] CERMET

REFERENCE INFORMATION

Symbol	Ref.	Temp. Range °K	Rept. Error %	Sample Specifications	Remarks
□	57-27	293-1273		75 W and 25 MgO.	Prepared by mixing powders, pressing, and sintering at 1750 C.
△	57-27	293-1273		50 W and 50 MgO.	Same as above.
◇	57-27	293-1273		25 W and 75 MgO.	Same as above.

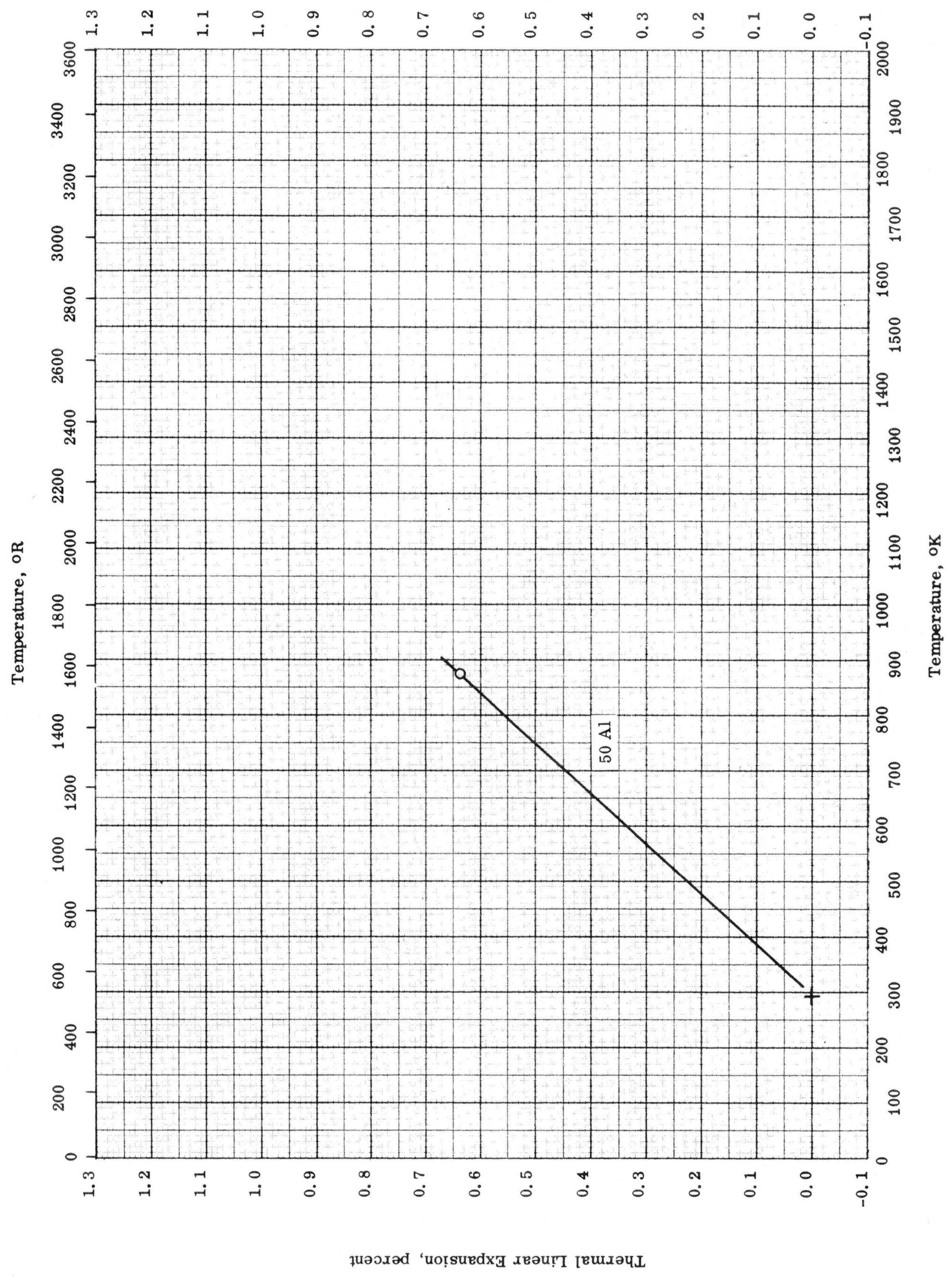

Temperature, °R

50 Al

Temperature, °K

Thermal Linear Expansion, percent

THERMAL LINEAR EXPANSION -- [SILICON DIOXIDE + ALUMINUM] CERMET

THERMAL LINEAR EXPANSION -- [SILICON DIOXIDE + ALUMINUM] CERMET

REFERENCE INFORMATION

Symbol	Ref.	Temp. Range °K	Rept. Error %	Sample Specifications	Remarks
○	57-27	293-873		50 SiO_2 and 50 Al.	Prepared by mixing powders, pressing and sintering at 650 C.

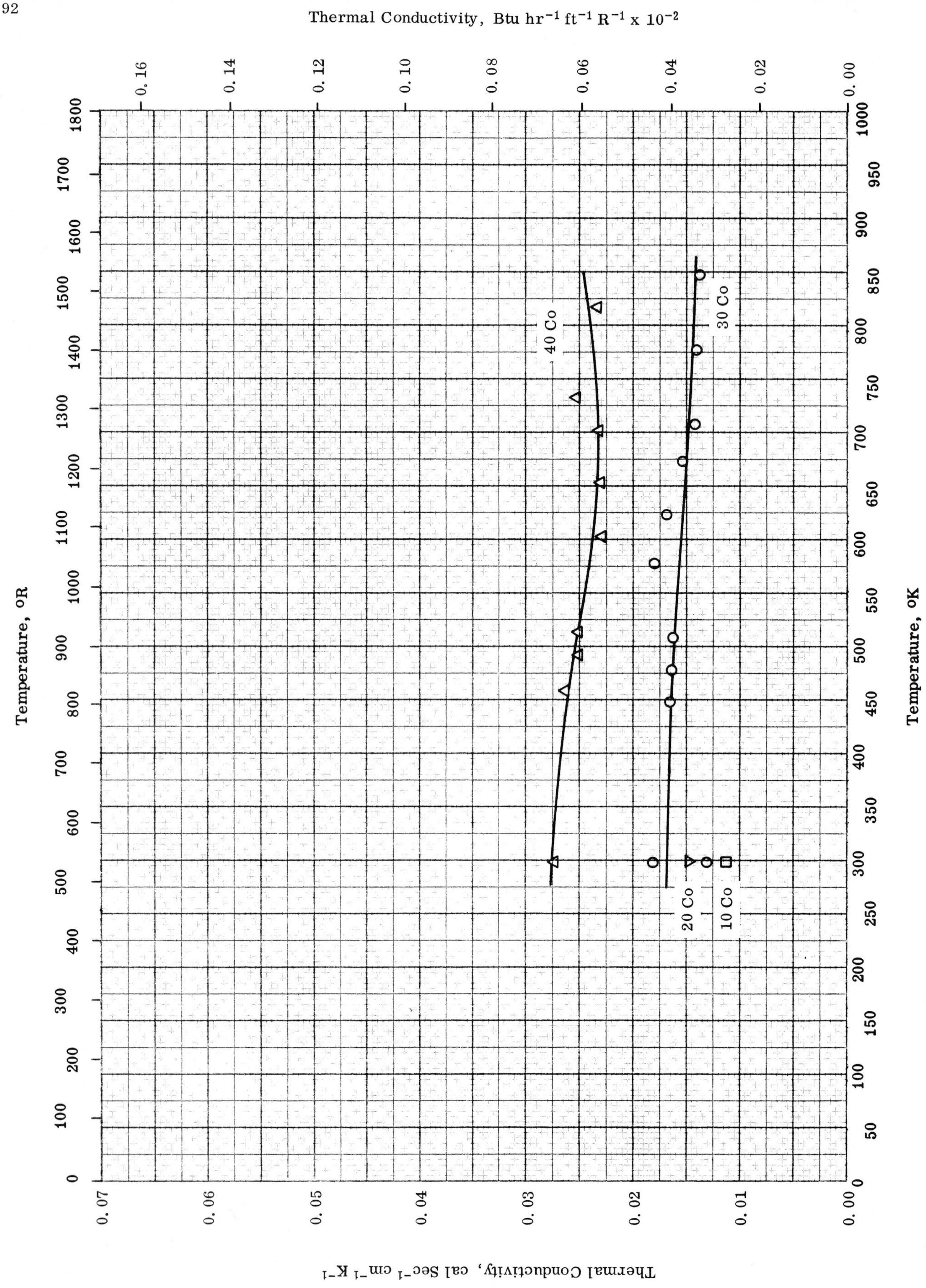

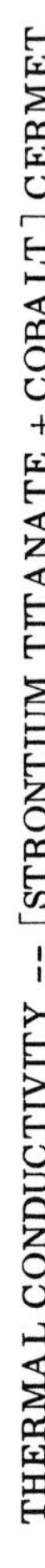

THERMAL CONDUCTIVITY -- [STRONTIUM TITANATE + COBALT] CERMET

Thermal Conductivity, Btu hr^{-1} ft^{-1} R^{-1} x 10^{-2}

0.16 0.14 0.12 0.10 0.08 0.06 0.04 0.02 0.00

Temperature, °R

0 100 200 300 400 500 600 700 800 900 1000 1100 1200 1300 1400 1500 1600 1700 1800

Temperature, °K

0 50 100 150 200 250 300 350 400 450 500 550 600 650 700 750 800 850 900 950 1000

Thermal Conductivity, cal Sec^{-1} cm^{-1} K^{-1}

0.07 0.06 0.05 0.04 0.03 0.02 0.01 0.00

40 Co

30 Co

20 Co

10 Co

THERMAL CONDUCTIVITY -- [STRONTIUM TITANATE + COBALT] CERMET

REFERENCE INFORMATION

Symbol	Ref.	Temp. Range °K	Rept. Error %	Sample Specifications	Remarks
□	59-9	298		10 Co.	
▽	59-9	298		20 Co.	
○	59-9	298-848		30 Co.	
△	59-9	298-818		40 Co.	

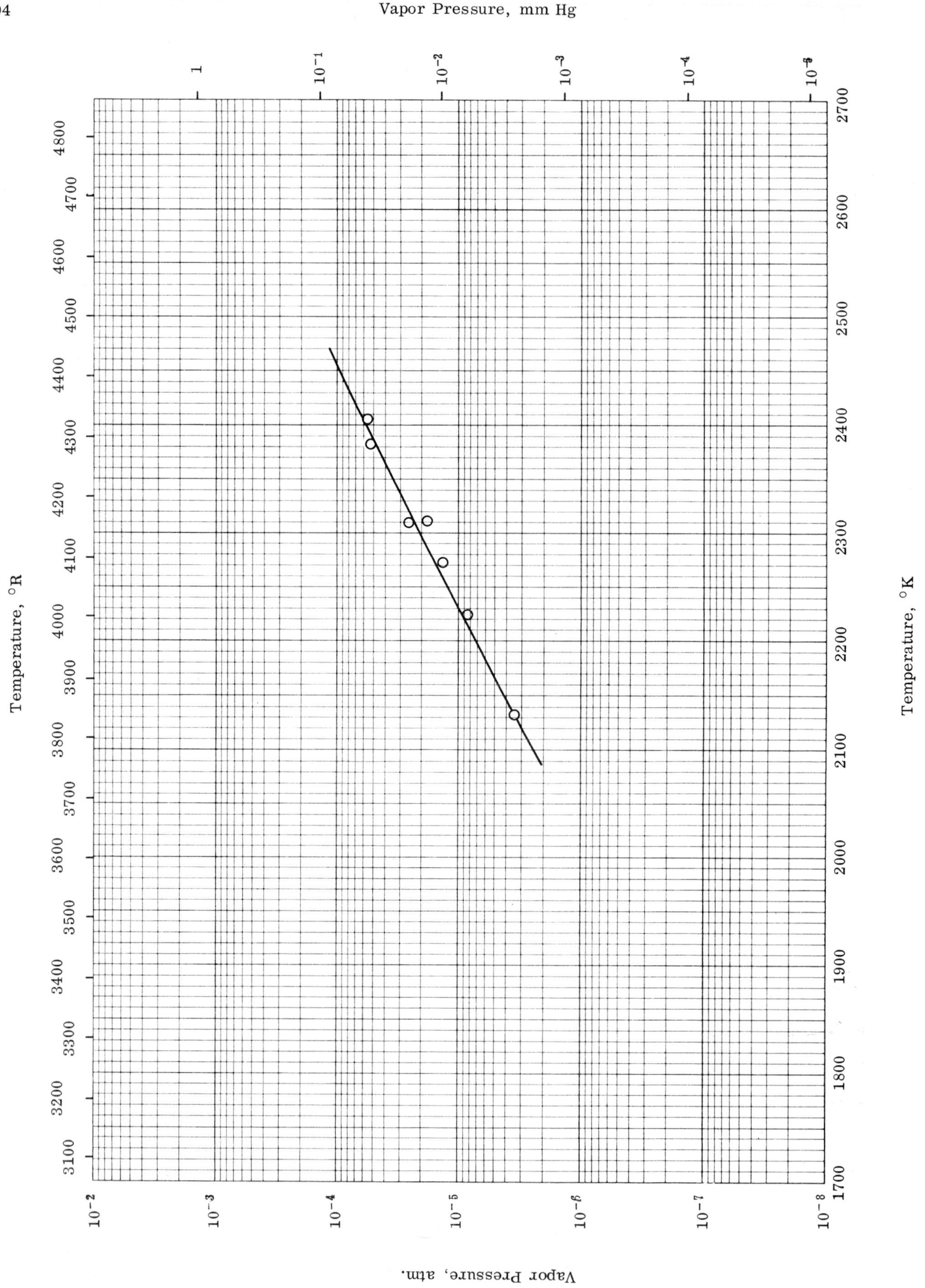

Vapor Pressure, mm Hg

1 — 10^{-1} — 10^{-2} — 10^{-3} — 10^{-4} — 10^{-5}

Temperature, °R

3100 3200 3300 3400 3500 3600 3700 3800 3900 4000 4100 4200 4300 4400 4500 4600 4700 4800

Temperature, °K

1700 1800 1900 2000 2100 2200 2300 2400 2500 2600 2700

10^{-2} 10^{-3} 10^{-4} 10^{-5} 10^{-6} 10^{-7} 10^{-8}

Vapor Pressure, atm.

VAPOR PRESSURE -- [THORIUM DIOXIDE + TUNGSTEN] CERMET

VAPOR PRESSURE -- [THORIUM DIOXIDE + TUNGSTEN] CERMET

REFERENCE INFORMATION

Symbol	Ref.	Temp. Range °K	Rept. Error %	Sample Specifications	Remarks
○	54-4	2389-2661		ThO_2 and W equimolecular mixture; 58.95 ThO_2 and 41.05 W.	

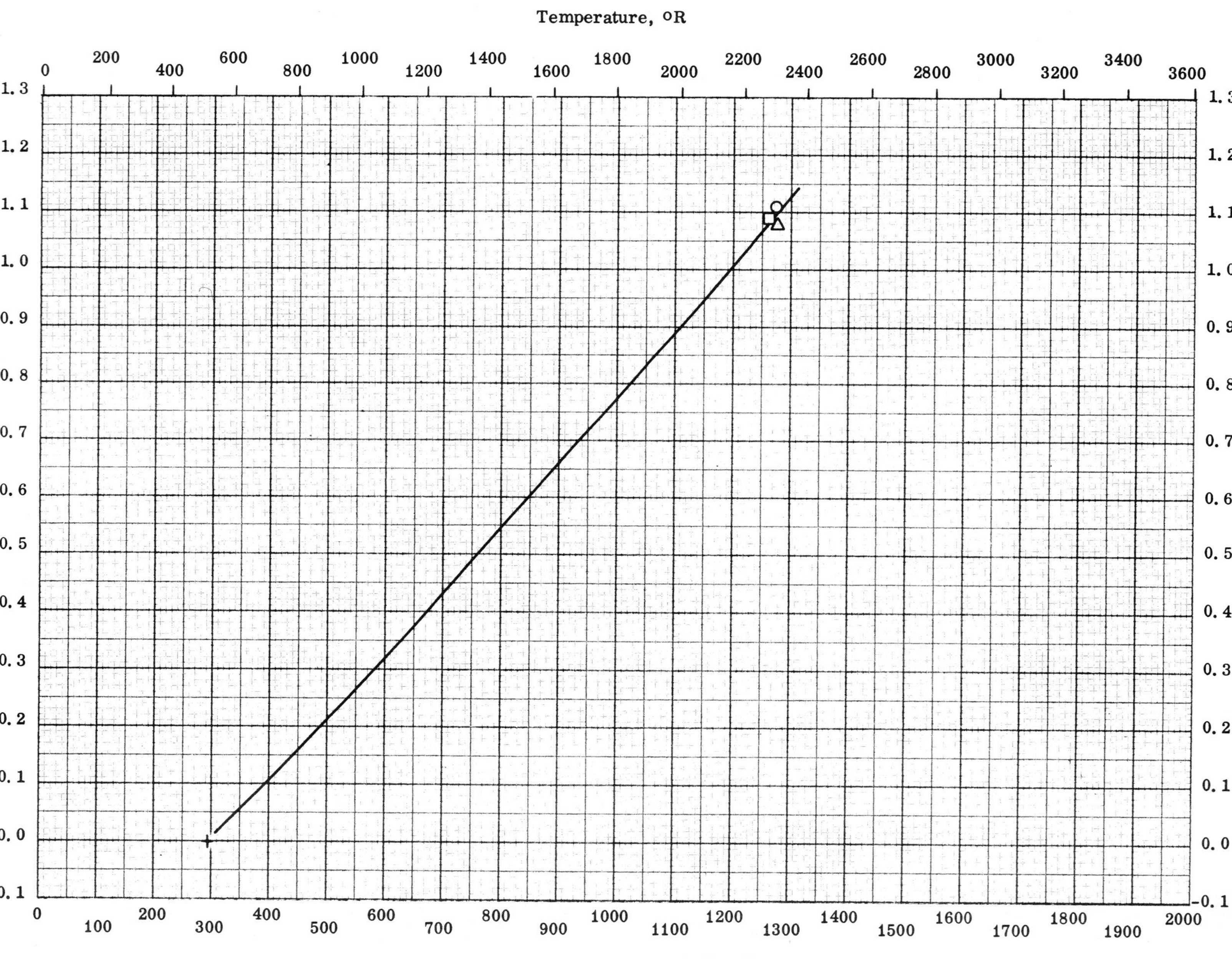

THERMAL LINEAR EXPANSION -- [TITANIUM MONOXIDE + CHROMIUM - TITANIUM ALLOYS] CERMET

THERMAL LINEAR EXPANSION -- [TITANIUM MONOXIDE + CHROMIUM - TITANIUM ALLOYS] CERMET

REFERENCE INFORMATION

Symbol	Ref.	Temp. Range °K	Rept. Error %	Sample Specifications	Remarks
○	54-14	293-1273		Phases present: TiO + chromium rich Cr - Ti solid solution; 65 Cr, 29.9 Ti, 1.81 O, 1.24 N, 0.57 Fe, and 0.005 C.	Hot pressed to 100% theoretical density.
□	54-14	293-1273		Phases present: TiO + chromium rich Cr - Ti solid solution; 58.9 Cr, 34.6 Ti, 4.78 O, 0.36 N, 0.72 Fe, and 0.026 C.	Hot pressed to 99.7% theoretical density.
△	54-14	293-1273		TiO cermet; Cr rich binder of Cr - Ti solid solution; 57.4 Cr, 31.4 Ti, 3.51 O, 1.69 N, 3.03 Fe, and 0.57 C.	Hot pressed to 99.3% theoretical density.

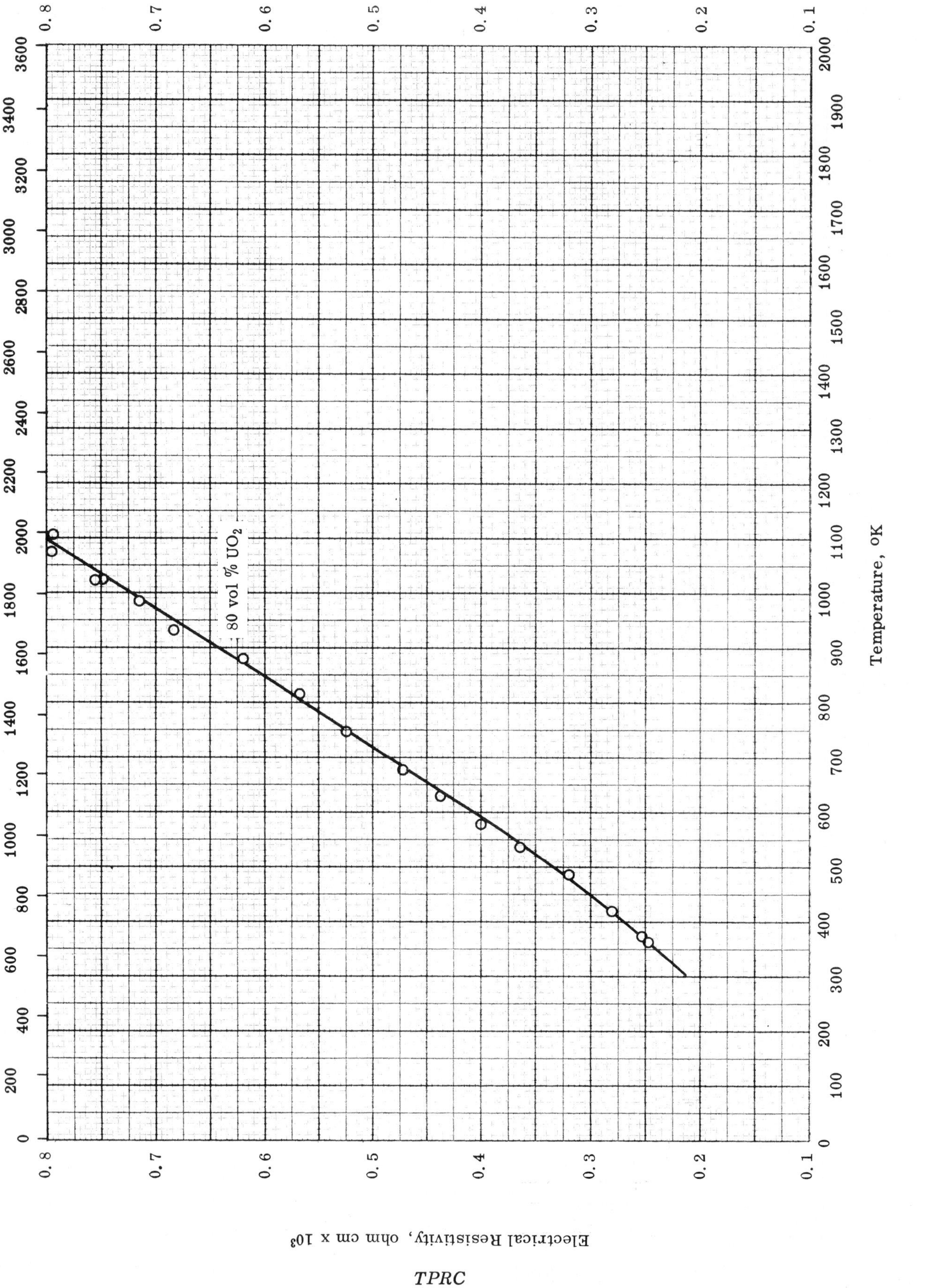

Temperature, °R

80 vol % UO_2

Electrical Resistivity, ohm cm x 10^3

Temperature, °K

ELECTRICAL RESISTIVITY -- [URANIUM DIOXIDE + CHROMIUM] CERMET

ELECTRICAL RESISTIVITY -- [URANIUM DIOXIDE + CHROMIUM] CERMET

REFERENCE INFORMATION

Symbol	Ref.	Temp. Range °K	Rept. Error %	Sample Specifications	Remarks
○	61-14	363-1104		80 vol % spherical type UO_2 particles of size -100 + 140 mesh; green and fabricated densities 74. 0% and 97. 1% of theoretical values; sample design. as TC-104.	Pressured bonded at 2300 F.

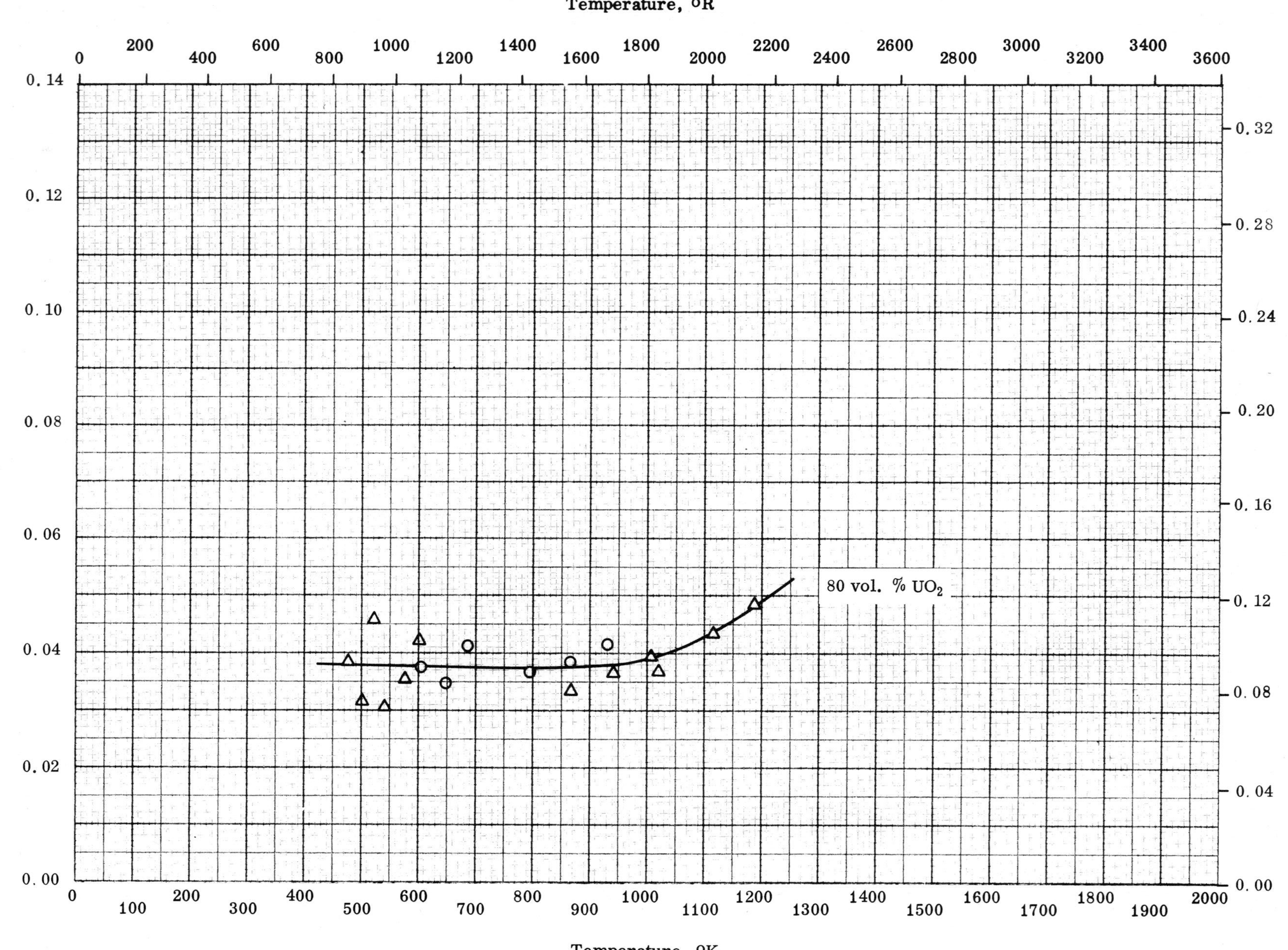

THERMAL CONDUCTIVITY -- [URANIUM DIOXIDE + CHROMIUM] CERMET

THERMAL CONDUCTIVITY -- [URANIUM DIOXIDE + CHROMIUM] CERMET

REFERENCE INFORMATION

Symbol	Ref.	Temp. Range °K	Rept. Error %	Sample Specifications	Remarks
○	61-14	602-927	<± 5	80 vol. % - 100 + 140 mesh spherical UO_2; 97. 1% of theoretical density.	Gas-pressure bonded for 3 hrs at 2300 F and 10, 000 psi of helium gas pressure.
△	61-14	474-1188	<± 5	Same as above.	Second run of the above sample.

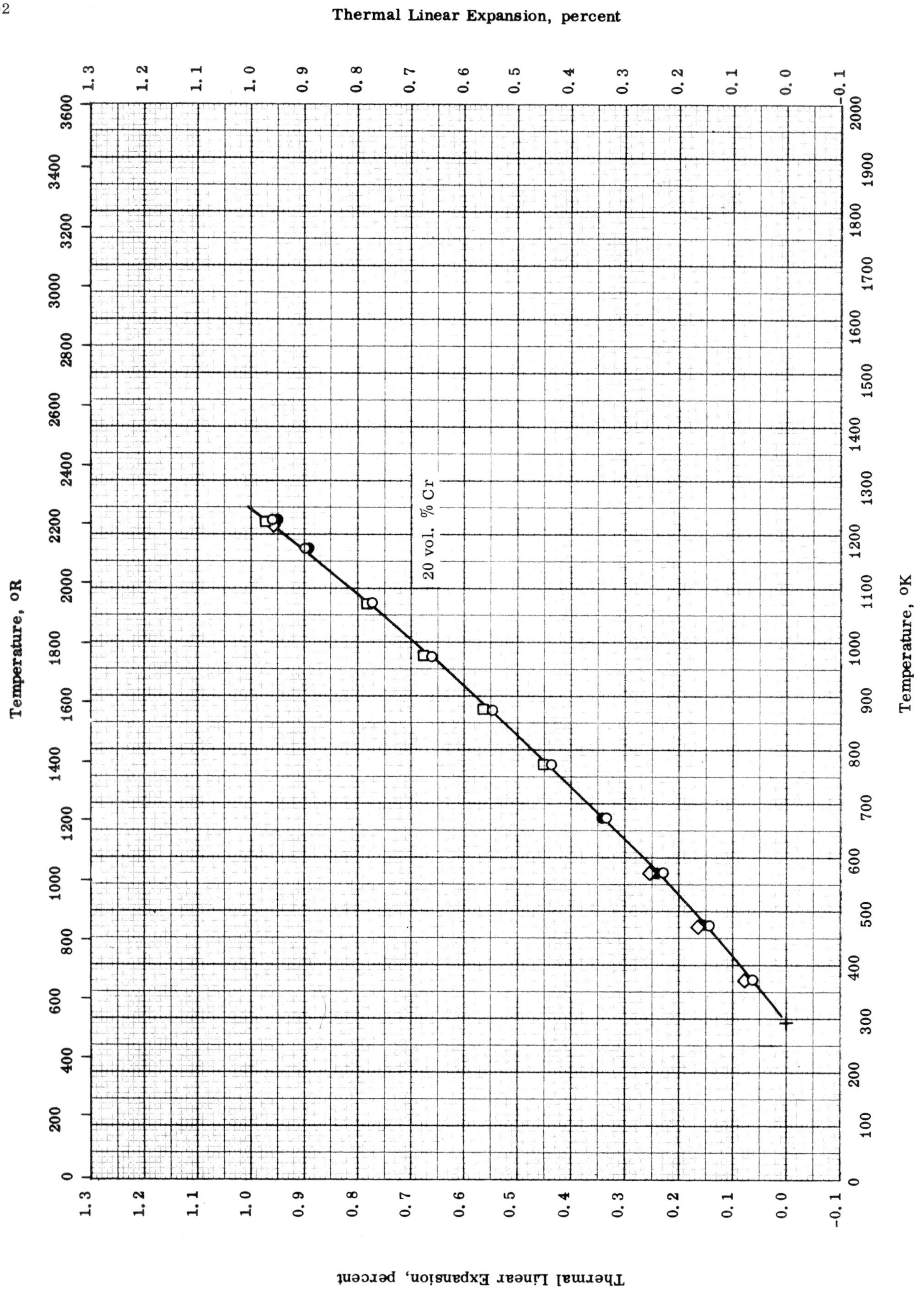

THERMAL LINEAR EXPANSION -- [URANIUM DIOXIDE + CHROMIUM] CERMET

Thermal Linear Expansion, percent

1.3 1.2 1.1 1.0 0.9 0.8 0.7 0.6 0.5 0.4 0.3 0.2 0.1 0.0 -0.1

Temperature, °R

0 200 400 600 800 1000 1200 1400 1600 1800 2000 2200 2400 2600 2800 3000 3200 3400 3600

Temperature, °K

0 100 200 300 400 500 600 700 800 900 1000 1100 1200 1300 1400 1500 1600 1700 1800 1900 2000

20 vol. % Cr

Thermal Linear Expansion, percent

THERMAL LINEAR EXPANSION -- [URANIUM DIOXIDE + CHROMIUM] CERMET

REFERENCE INFORMATION

Symbol	Ref.	Temp. Range °K	Rept. Error %	Sample Specifications	Remarks
○	60-33	293-1223	<2	UO_2 and 20 vol % Cr; 97.1% theoretical density. [Author's design.: TC-104]	Gas pressure bonded 80 vol% -100 + 140 mesh spherical UO_2 particles and -325 mesh Cr at 2300 F and at 10000 psi of helium gas pressure for 3 hrs; max heating rate 3 F per min; measured in a vac of approx 5 x 10^{-5} mm Hg; 1st thermal cycle.
●	60-33	293-1223	<2	Same as above.	Cooling data of above specimen.
□	60-33	293-1223	<2	Same as above.	2nd thermal cycle of TC-104; heating.
◇	60-33	293-1223	<2	Same as above.	Cooling data of above specimen.

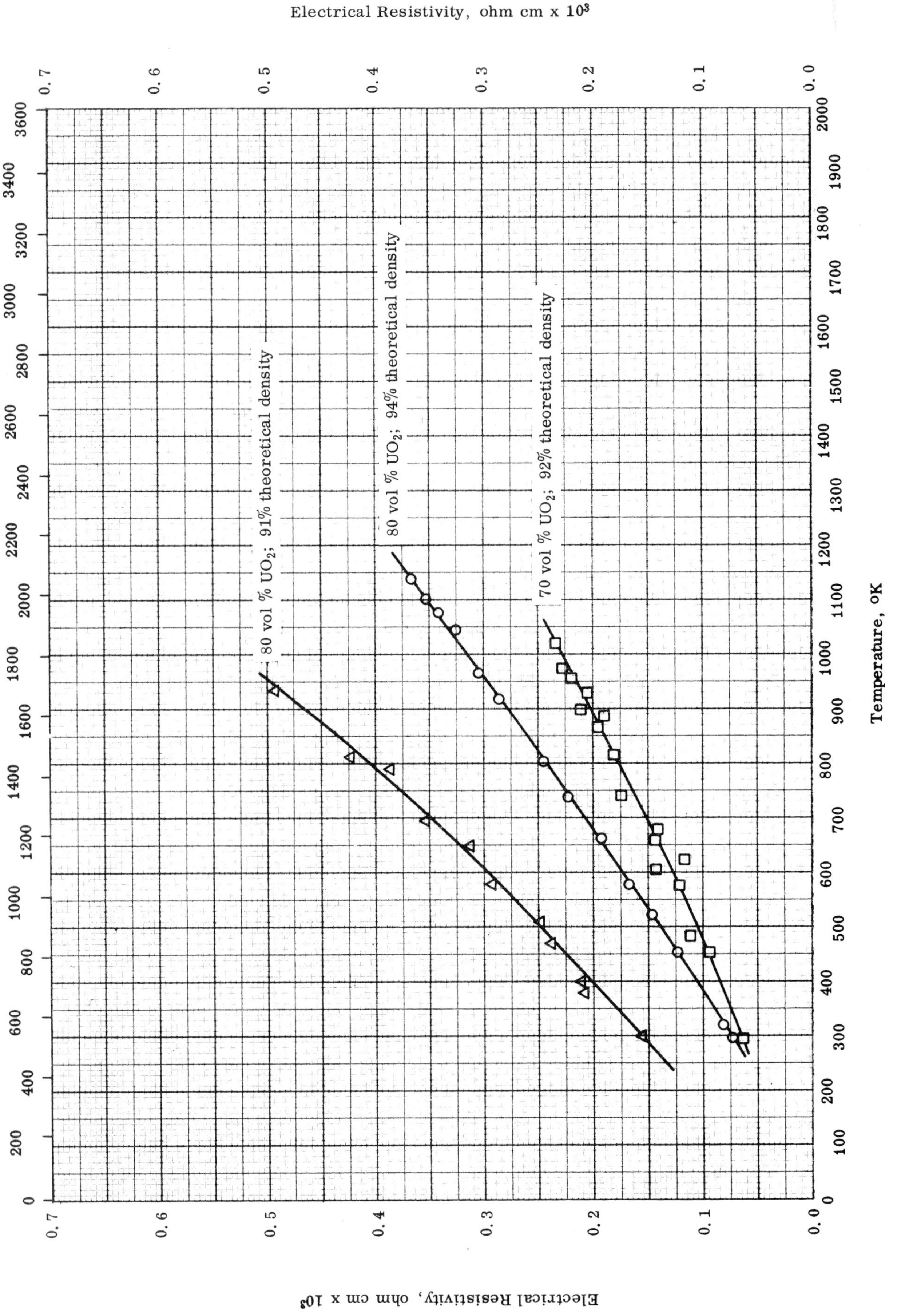

Electrical Resistivity, ohm cm x 10³
Temperature, °R
Temperature, °K
80 vol % UO₂; 91% theoretical density
80 vol % UO₂; 94% theoretical density
70 vol % UO₂; 92% theoretical density
Electrical Resistivity, ohm cm x 10³

ELECTRICAL RESISTIVITY -- [URANIUM DIOXIDE + MOLYBDENUM] CERMET

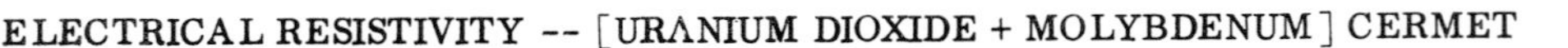

REFERENCE INFORMATION

Symbol	Ref.	Temp. Range °K	Rept. Error %	Sample Specifications	Remarks
○	61-14	299-1137		80 vol % spherical type UO_2 particles of size -100 + 140 mesh; green and fabricated densities 72% and 94.4% of theoretical respectively; sampe design. as TC-105.	Pressure bonded at 2350 F.
□	61-14	296-1020		70 vol % hydrothermal type UO_2 particles of size -100 + 140 mesh; fabricated density 91.7% of theoretical value; sample design. as TC-82.	Pressure bonded at 2300 F.
△	61-14	300-932		80 vol % of same type and size UO_2 of the above sample; fabricated density 91.1% of theoretical value; sample design. as TC-90.	Pressure bonded at 2400 F.

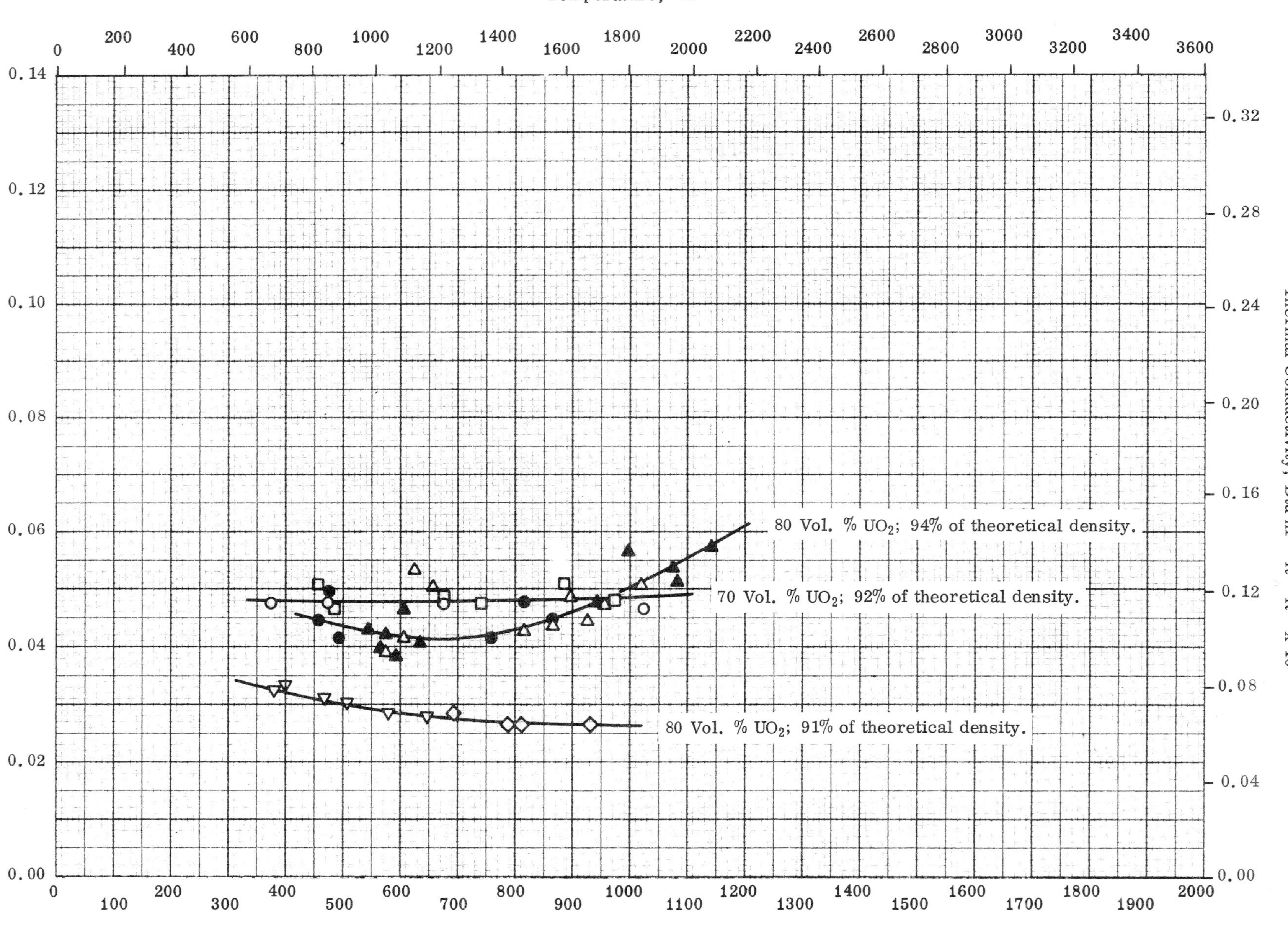

THERMAL CONDUCTIVITY -- [URANIUM DIOXIDE + MOLYBDENUM] CERMET

REFERENCE INFORMATION

Symbol	Ref.	Temp. Range °K	Rept. Error %	Sample Specifications	Remarks
○	59-11	373-1023		70 vol. % UO_2; 91.7% theoretical density.	
□	61-14	456-972	<± 5	70 vol. % - 100 + 140 mesh hydrothermal UO_2; 91.7% theoretical density.	Gas-pressure bonded for 3 hrs at 2300 F and 10,000 psi of helium gas pressure.
△	61-14	575-1020	<± 5	Same as above.	Second run of above sample.
▽	61-14	379-647	<± 5	80 vol. % of same UO_2 as the above sample; 91.1% theoretical density.	Same as above except bonded at 2400 F.
◇	61-14	692-932	<± 5	Same as above.	Second run of above sample.
●	61-14	458-866	<± 5	80 vol. % - 100 + 140 mesh spherical UO_2; 94.4% theoretical density.	Same as above except bonded at 2350 F.
▲	61-14	544-1143	<± 5	Same as above.	Second run of above sample.

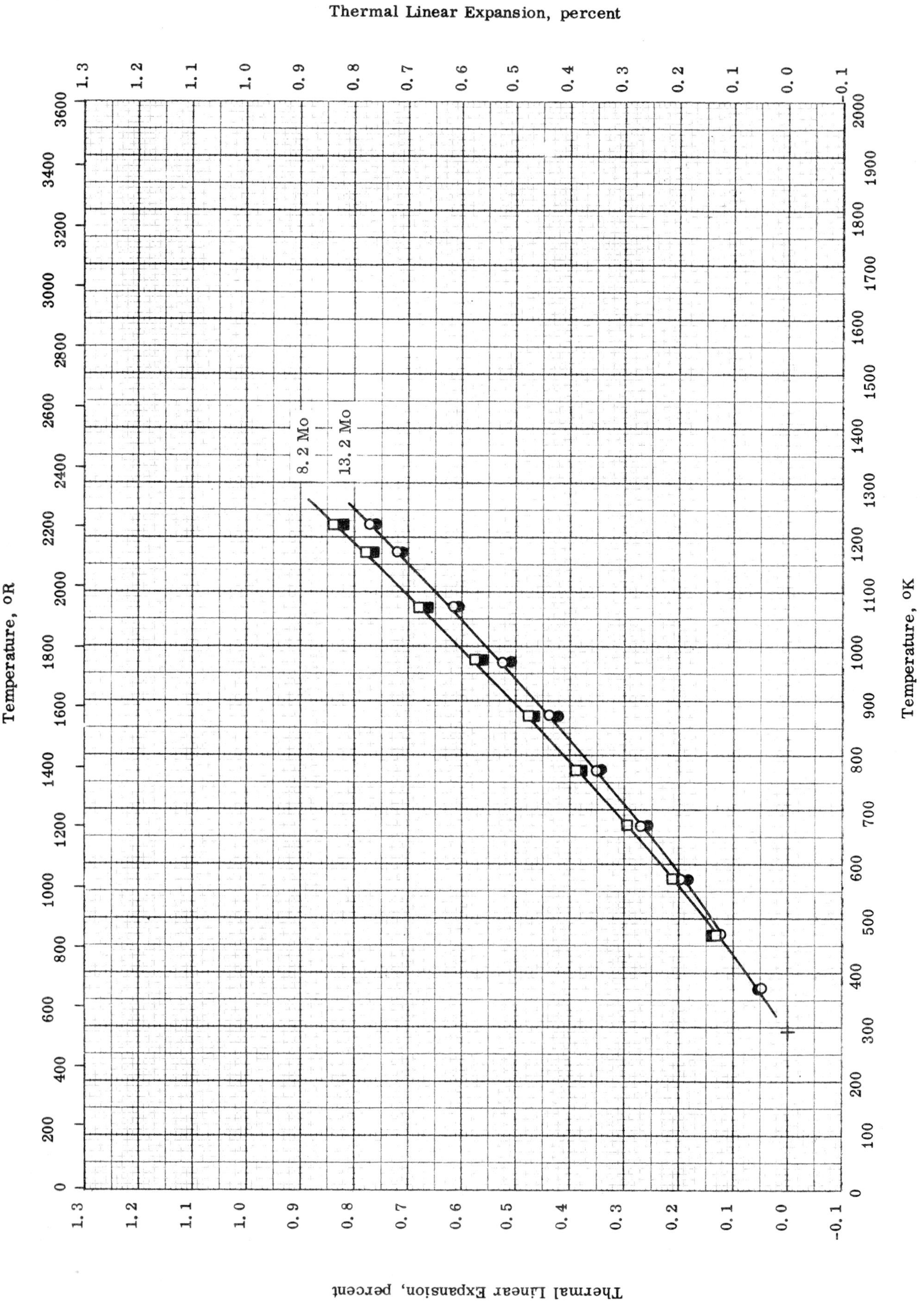

Thermal Linear Expansion, percent

THERMAL LINEAR EXPANSION -- [URANIUM DIOXIDE + MOLYBDENUM] CERMET

8.2 Mo

13.2 Mo

Temperature, °R

Temperature, °K

Thermal Linear Expansion, percent

THERMAL LINEAR EXPANSION -- [URANIUM DIOXIDE +MOLYBDENUM] CERMET

REFERENCE INFORMATION

Symbol	Ref.	Temp. Range °K	Rept. Error %	Sample Specifications	Remarks
○	60-33	293-1223	<2	86.70 UO_2 and 13.21 Mo; 91.7% theoretical density. [Author's design. TC-82]	Gas pressure bonded 70 vol % -100 + 140 mesh hydrothermal UO_2 particles and -325 mesh Mo at 2300 F and at 10000 psi of helium gas pressure for 3 hrs; max heating rate 3 C per min; measured in vac of approx 5 x 10^{-5} mm Hg; heating.
●	60-33	293-1223	<2	Same as above.	Cooling data of above specimen.
□	60-33	293-1223	<2	91.88 UO_2 and 8.22 Mo; 94.9% theoretical density. [Author's design. TC-105]	Same as TC-82 except 80 vol % spherical UO_2 particles and pressure bonded at 2350 F; heating.
■	60-33	293-1223	<2	Same as above.	Cooling data of above specimen.

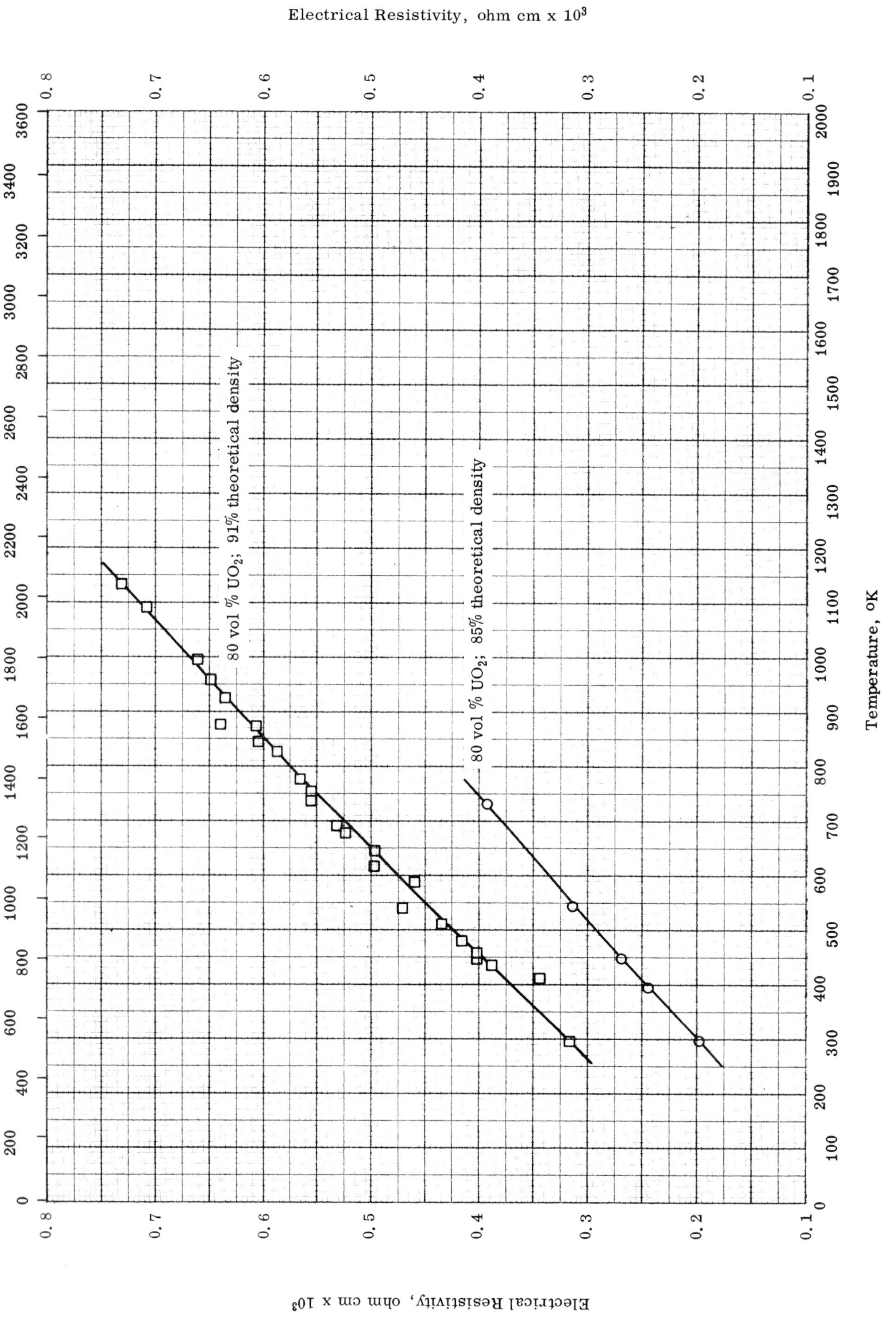

ELECTRICAL RESISTIVITY -- [URANIUM DIOXIDE + NIOBIUM] CERMET

80 vol % UO_2; 91% theoretical density

80 vol % UO_2; 85% theoretical density

Temperature, °R

Temperature, °K

Electrical Resistivity, ohm cm x 10^3

REFERENCE INFORMATION

Symbol	Ref.	Temp. Range °K	Rept. Error %	Sample Specifications	Remarks
○	61-14	299-730		80 vol % vapor-deposit niobium-coated spherical type UO_2 particles of size -100 + 140 mesh; green and fabricated densities 76.4% and 85.3% of theoretical values respectively; sample design. as TC-115.	Pressure bonded at 2100 F.
□	61-14	297-1131		80 vol % vapor-deposit niobium-coated hydrothermal type UO_2 particles of size -140 + 200 mesh; green and fabricated densities 73.0% and 93.5% of theroetical values respectively; sample design. as TC-130.	Pressure bonded at 2350 F.

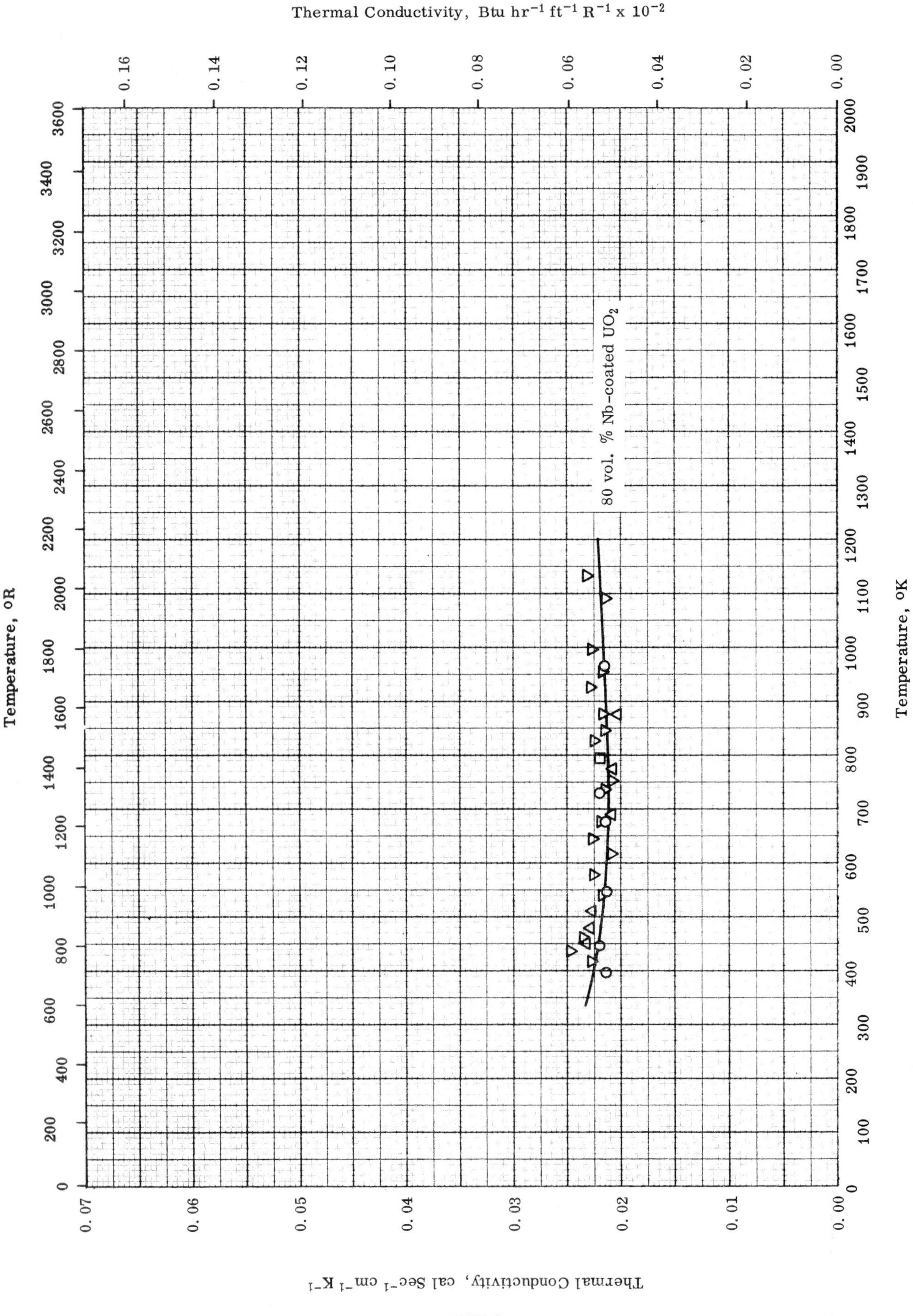

Thermal Conductivity, Btu hr^{-1} ft^{-1} R^{-1} x 10^{-2}

0.16 0.14 0.12 0.10 0.08 0.06 0.04 0.02 0.00

Temperature, °R

0 200 400 600 800 1000 1200 1400 1600 1800 2000 2200 2400 2600 2800 3000 3200 3400 3600

80 vol. % Nb-coated UO_2

Temperature, °K

0 100 200 300 400 500 600 700 800 900 1000 1100 1200 1300 1400 1500 1600 1700 1800 1900 2000

0.07 0.06 0.05 0.04 0.03 0.02 0.01 0.00

Thermal Conductivity, cal Sec^{-1} cm^{-1} K^{-1}

THERMAL CONDUCTIVITY -- [URANIUM DIOXIDE + NIOBIUM] CERMET

REFERENCE INFORMATION

Symbol	Ref.	Temp. Range °K	Rept. Error %	Sample Specifications	Remarks
○	61-14	397-966	<± 5	80 vol. % Nb-coated -100 + 140 mesh spherical UO_2; 85% theoretical density.	Gas-pressure bonded for 3 hrs at 2100 F and 10, 000 psi of helium gas pressure.
□	61-14	795	<± 5	Same as above.	Second run of above sample.
△	61-14	450-872	<± 5	80 vol. % Nb-coated -140 + 200 mesh hydrothermal UO_2; 93. 5% theoretical density.	Same as above except bonded at 2350 F.
▽	61-14	413-1131	<± 5	Same as above.	Second run of above sample.

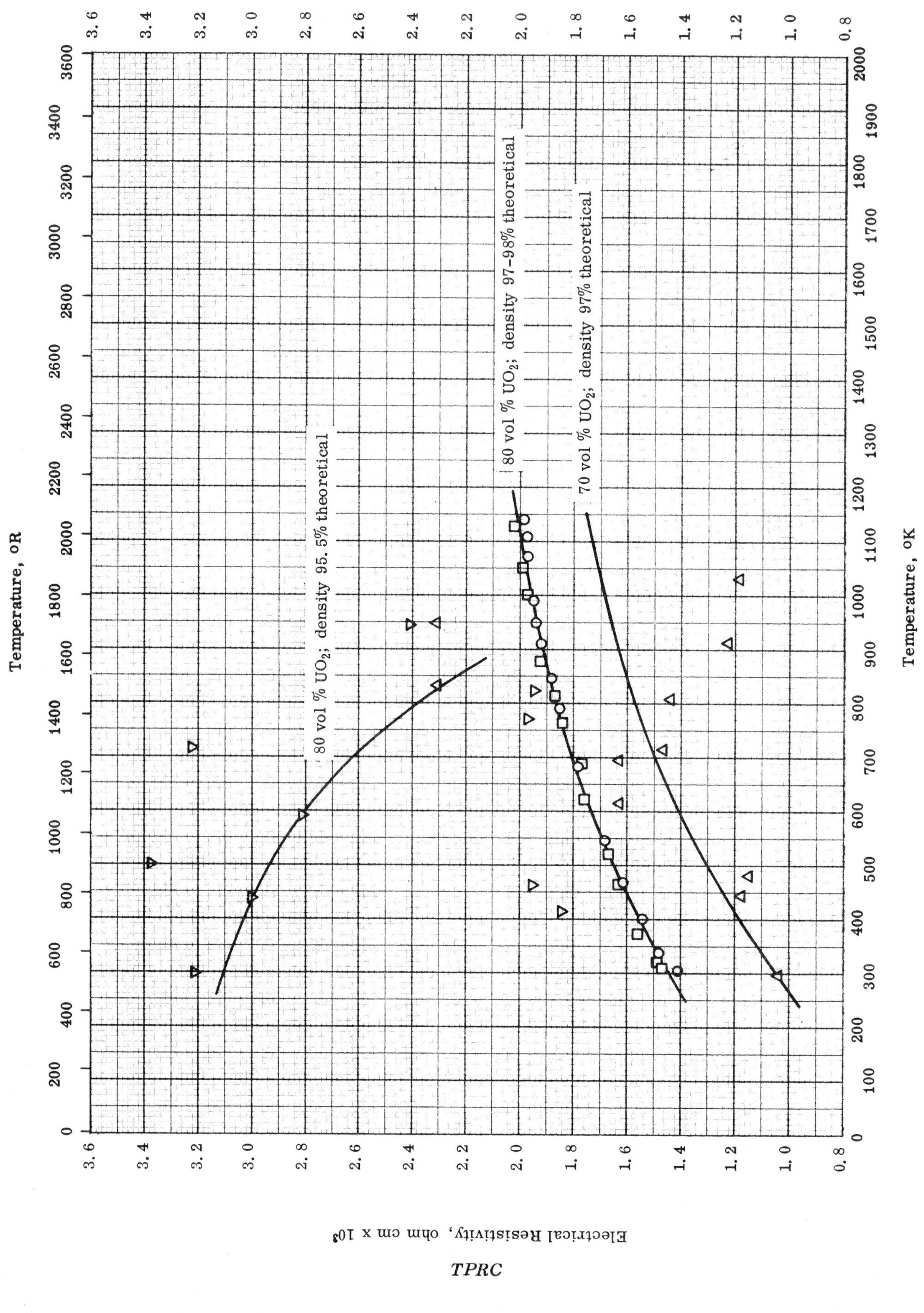

Electrical Resistivity, ohm cm x 10^3

Temperature, °R

Temperature, °K

80 vol % UO_2; density 95.5% theoretical

80 vol % UO_2; density 97–98% theoretical

70 vol % UO_2; density 97% theoretical

Electrical Resistivity, ohm cm x 10^3

ELECTRICAL RESISTIVITY -- [URANIUM DIOXIDE + STAINLESS STEEL] CERMET

ELECTRICAL RESISTIVITY -- [URANIUM DIOXIDE + STAINLESS STEEL] CERMET

REFERENCE INFORMATION

Symbol	Ref.	Temp. Range °K	Rept. Error %	Sample Specifications	Remarks
○	61-14	304-1141		80 vol % hydrothermal type UO_2 particles of size -100 + 140 mesh; green and fabricated densities 75.0% and 98.4% of theoretical value; sample design. as TC-102.	Pressure bonded at 2300 F.
□	61-14	311-1127		Same as above except spherical type UO_2 particles; green and fabricated densities 72.0% and 97.2% of theoretical values; sample design. TC-103.	Same as above.
△	61-14	298-1031		70 vol % of hydrothermal type of UO_2 with particle size -100 + 140 mesh; fabricated density 97.0% of theoretical; sample design. as TC-81.	Same as above.
▽	61-14	298-945		80 vol % of sampe type and size UO_2 particles; green and fabricated densities 67.8% and 95.5% theoretical values; sample design. as TC-80.	Same as above.

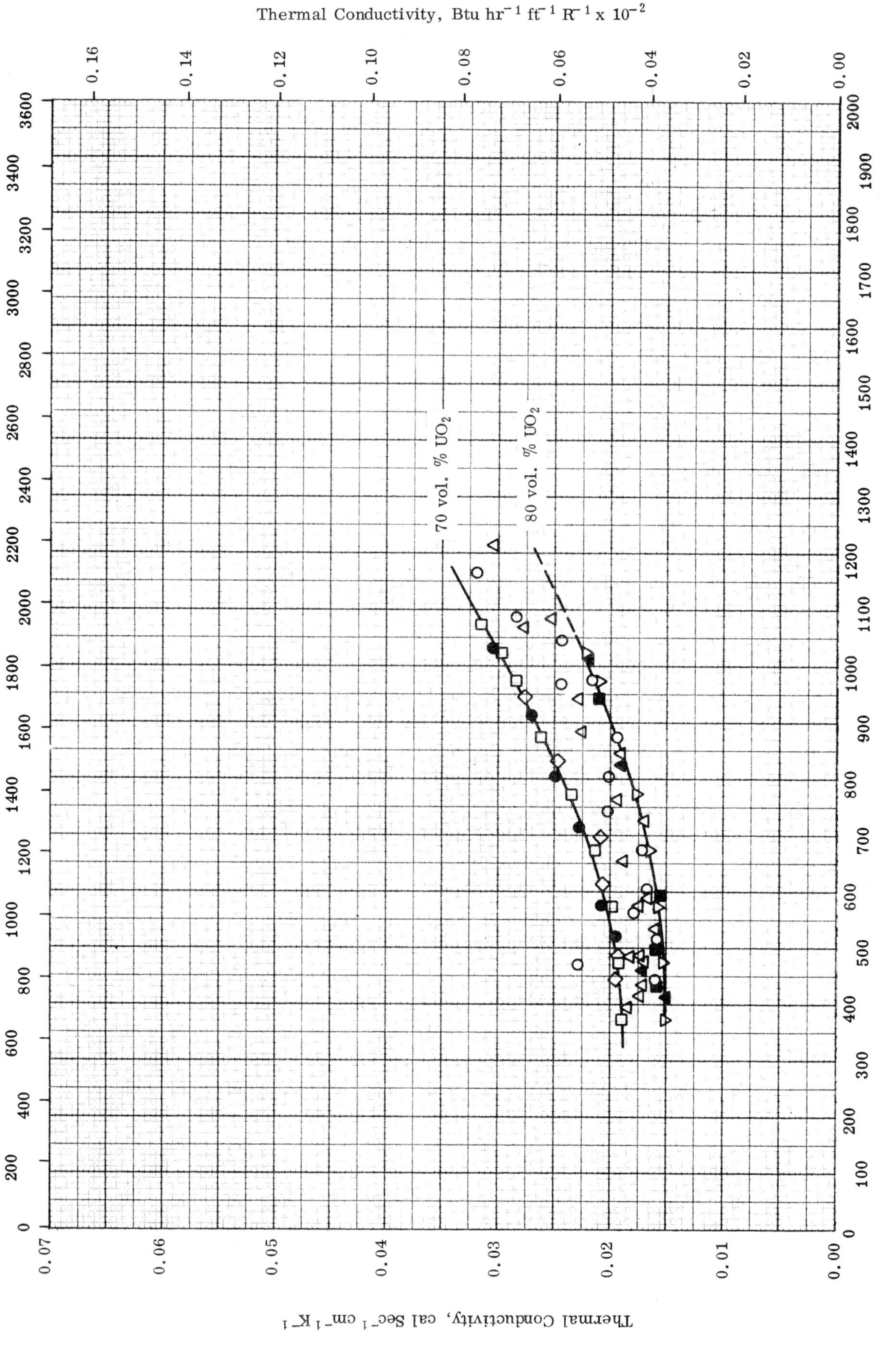

THERMAL CONDUCTIVITY -- [URANIUM DIOXIDE + STAINLESS STEEL] CERMET

REFERENCE INFORMATION

Symbol	Ref.	Temp. Range °K	Rept. Error %	Sample Specifications	Remarks
○	60-15	395-1213		80 vol. % UO_2.	Pressure - bonded for 3 hrs at 2300 F and 10, 000 psi.
□	60-15	442-1169		Same as above.	Same as above.
△	59-11	373-1073		70 vol. % UO_2; 97% theoretical density.	
▽	59-11	373-1023		80 vol. % UO_2; 95. 5% theoretical density.	
◇	61-14	446-947	<± 5	70 vol. % -100 + 140 mesh hydrothermal UO_2 and 302 B stainless steel.	Gass-pressure bonded for 3 hrs at 2300 F and 10, 000 psi of helium gas pressure.
●	61-14	521-1031	<± 5	Same as above.	Second run of above sample.
■	61-14	437-945	<± 5	80 vol. % -100 + 140 mesh hydrothermal UO_2 and 302 B stainless steel.	Same as above.
▲	61-14	415-1012	<± 5	Same as above.	Second run of above sample.

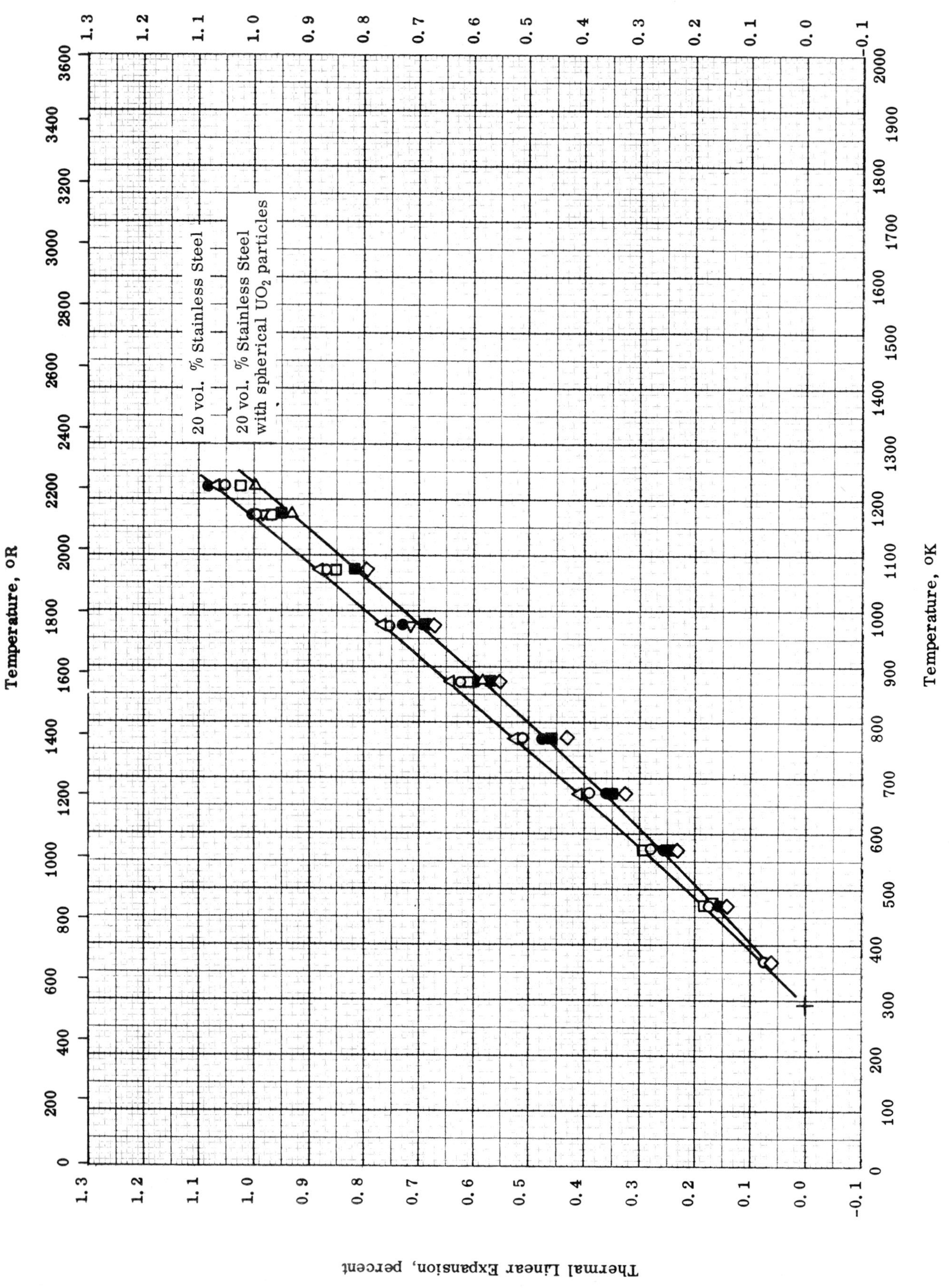

Thermal Linear Expansion, percent

20 vol. % Stainless Steel

20 vol. % Stainless Steel with spherical UO_2 particles

Temperature, °R

Temperature, °K

Thermal Linear Expansion, percent

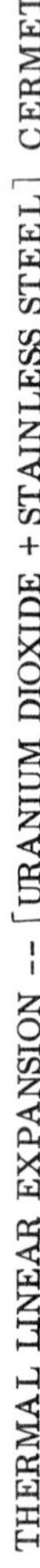
THERMAL LINEAR EXPANSION -- [URANIUM DIOXIDE + STAINLESS STEEL] CERMET

REFERENCE INFORMATION

Symbol	Ref.	Temp. Range °K	Rept. Error %	Sample Specifications	Remarks
○	60-33	293-1223	<2	UO_2 and 30 vol % S. S. ; 97% theoretical density. [Author's design. TC-81]	Gas pressure bonded 70 vol % -100 + 140 mesh hydrothermal UO_2 particles and -325 mesh 302 B stainless steel at 2300 F and at 10000 psi of helium gas pressure for 3 hrs; max heating rate 3 C per min; measured in a vac of approx 5 x 10^{-5} mm Hg; 2nd thermal cycle.
●	60-33	293-1223	<2	Same as above.	Cooling data of above sample with cooling rate of 3 C per min.
□	60-33	293-1223	<2	UO_2 and 20 vol % S. S. ; 95. 5% theoretical density. [Author's design. TC-80]	Same as that of TC-81 except 80 vol % hydrothermal UO_2 particles and 1st thermal cycle; heating.
■	60-33	293-1223	<2	Same as above.	Cooling data of above sample.
△	60-33	293-1223	<2	UO_2 and 20 vol % S. S. ; 98. 4% theoretical density. [Author's design. TC-102]	Same as that of TC-80; heating.
◁	60-33	293-1223	<2	Same as above.	Cooling data of above sample.
▷	60-33	293-1223	<2	UO_2 and 20 vol % S. S. ; 97. 2% theoretical density. [Author's design. TC-103]	Same as that of TC-80 except spherical UO_2 particles; heating.
◇	60-33	293-1223	<2	Same as above.	Coolint data of above sample.

PROPERTIES OF [URANIUM DIOXIDE + ZIRCONIUM] CERMET

REPORTED VALUES

Density	g cm^{-3}	lb ft^{-3}
○ 20 Zr	8.71	544

PROPERTIES OF [URANIUM DIOXIDE + ZIRCONIUM] CERMET

REFERENCE INFORMATION

Symbol	Ref.	Temp. Range °K	Rept. Error %	Sample Specifications	Remarks
○	54-7	298		80 UO_2 and 20 Zr.	

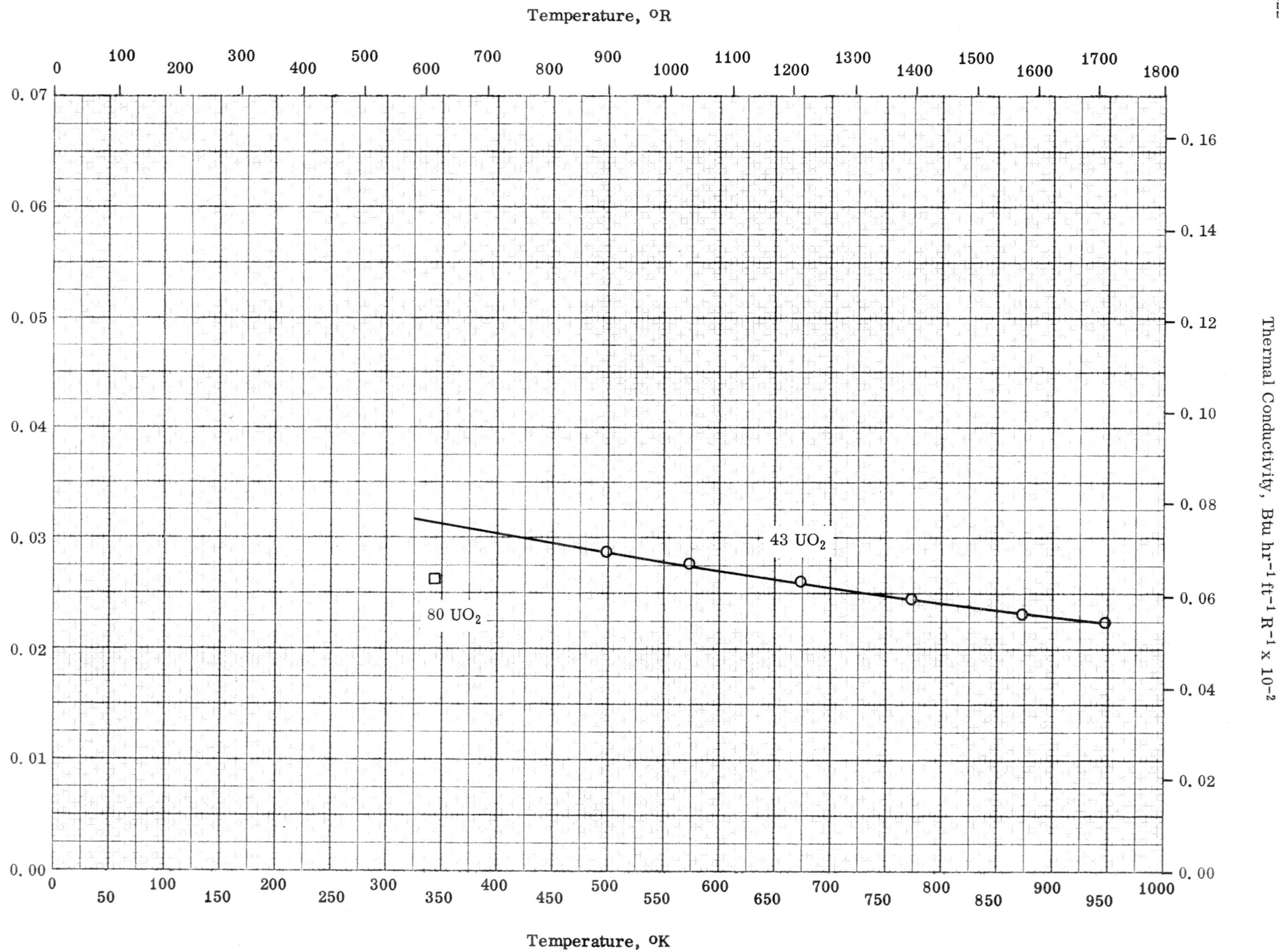

Thermal Conductivity, Btu hr^{-1} ft^{-1} R^{-1} x 10^{-2}

Temperature, °R

43 UO_2

80 UO_2

Temperature, °K

Thermal Conductivity, cal Sec^{-1} cm^{-1} K^{-1}

REFERENCE INFORMATION

Symbol	Ref.	Temp. Range °K	Rept. Error %	Sample Specifications	Remarks
○	57-10	498-948		43 UO_2 and 57 Zr; 59% porous.	
□	54-7	343		80 UO_2 and 20 Zr; density 544 lb ft^{-3}.	

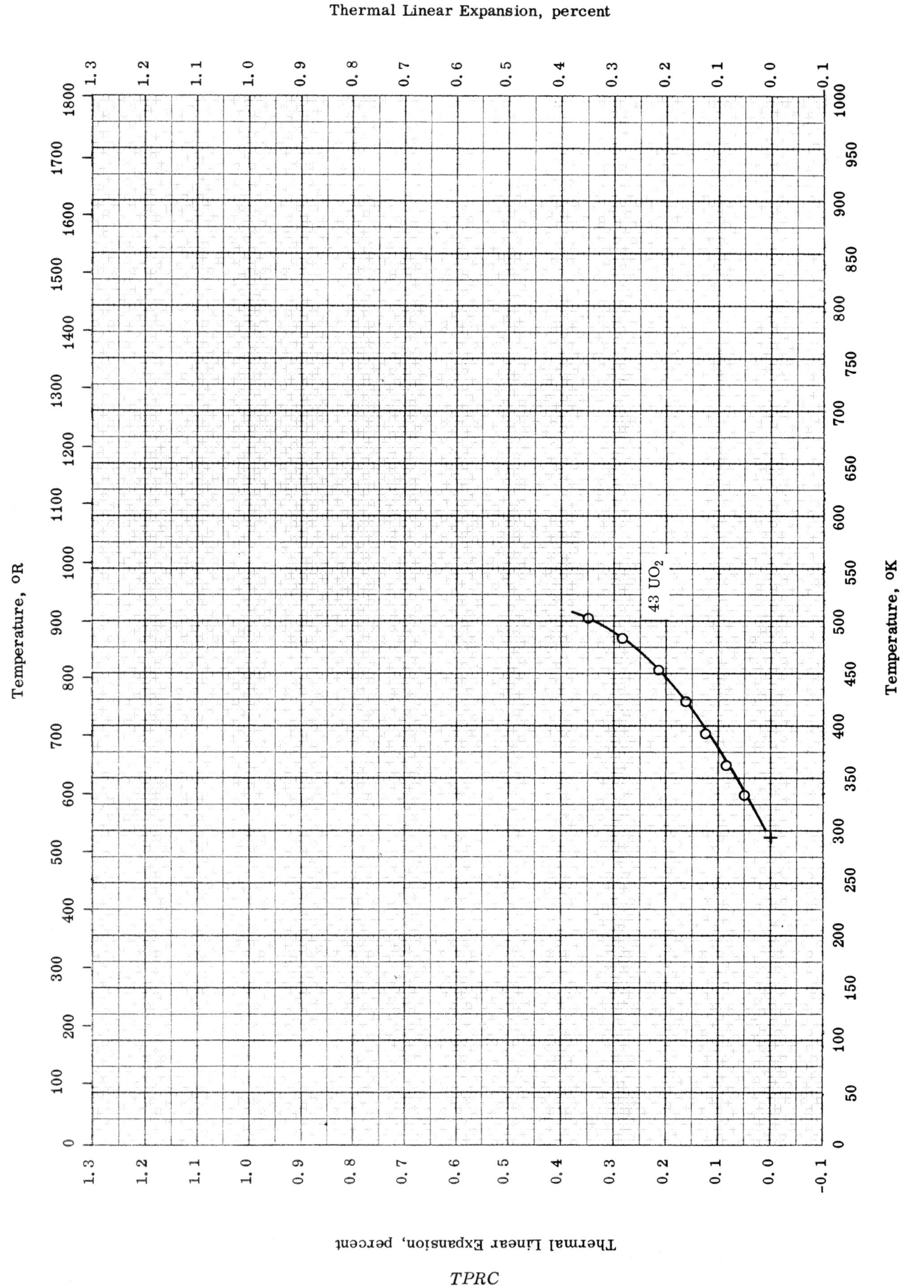

Thermal Linear Expansion, percent

Temperature, °R

Temperature, °K

$43\ UO_2$

Thermal Linear Expansion, percent

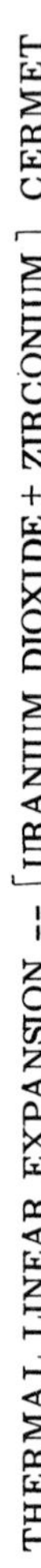

THERMAL LINEAR EXPANSION -- [URANIUM DIOXIDE + ZIRCONIUM] CERMET

THERMAL LINEAR EXPANSION -- [URANIUM DIOXIDE + ZIRCONIUM] CERMET

REFERENCE INFORMATION

Symbol	Ref.	Temp. Range °K	Rept. Error %	Sample Specifications	Remarks
o	52-18	293-503		57 Zr and 43 UO_2; density 80% of theoretical.	Prepared from ZrH_2 and UO_2, pressed, heated in vacuum to 1300 C; measured in argon atmosphere.

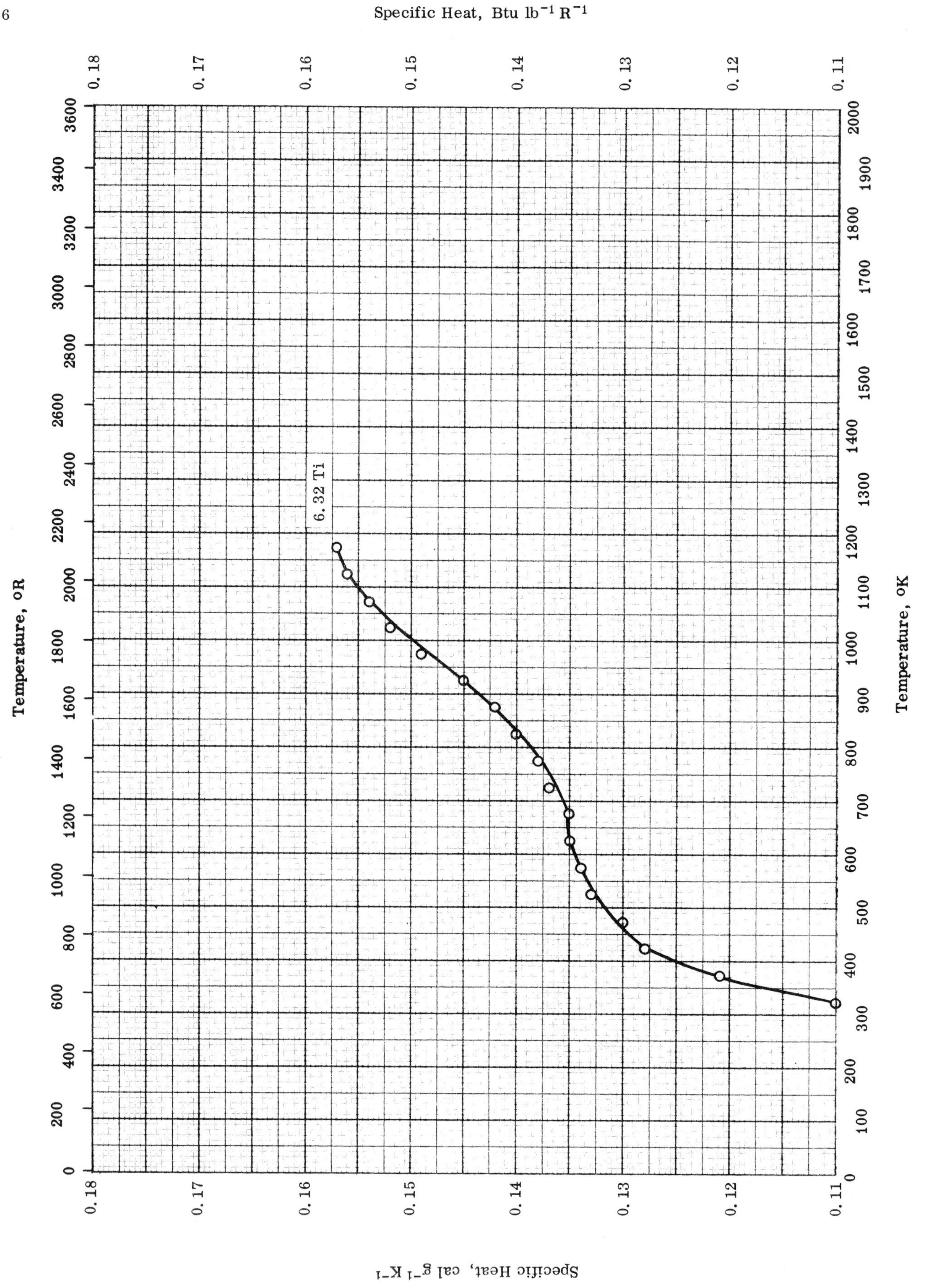

Specific Heat, Btu lb^{-1} R^{-1}

Temperature, °R

Temperature, °K

6.32 Ti

Specific Heat, cal g^{-1} K^{-1}

SPECIFIC HEAT -- [ZIRCONIUM DIOXIDE + TITANIUM] CERMET

SPECIFIC HEAT -- [ZIRCONIUM DIOXIDE + TITANIUM] CERMET

REFERENCE INFORMATION

Symbol	Ref.	Temp. Range °K	Rept. Error %	Sample Specifications	Remarks
○	64-1	323-1173	5	ZT-15-M; 93.68 ZrO_2 and 6.32 Ti.	

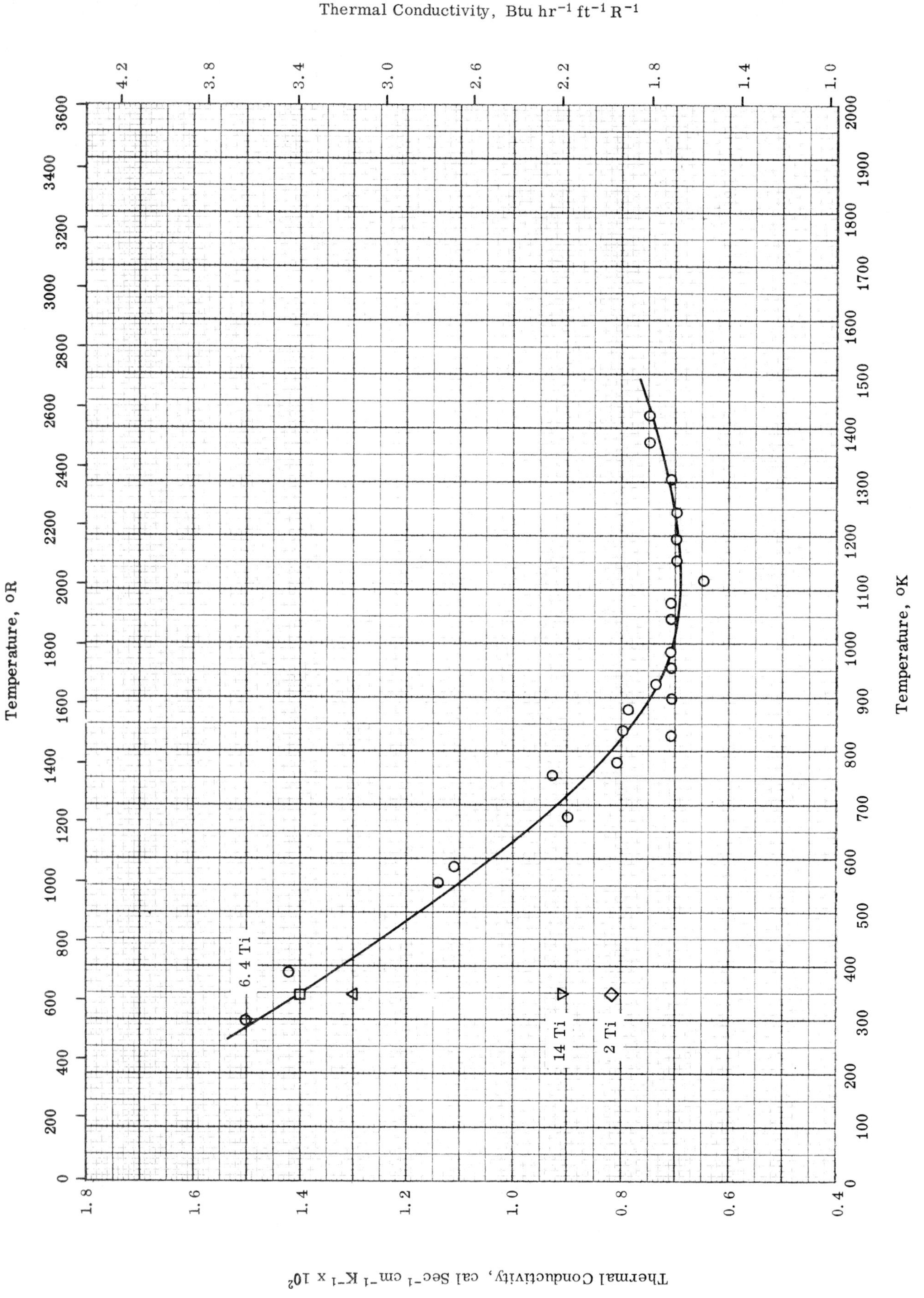

THERMAL CONDUCTIVITY -- [ZIRCONIUM DIOXIDE + TITANIUM] CERMET

REFERENCE INFORMATION

Symbol	Ref.	Temp. Range °K	Rept. Error %	Sample Specifications	Remarks
○	64-1	298-1423		93.58 monoclinic ZrO_2 (98.8 ZrO_2 + HfO_2, 0.33 Si, 0.10 TiO_2, and 0.10 CaO; original particle size 0.26 μ) and 6.42 Ti (98 Ti and 1.1 N; original particle size -325 mesh); density 5.65 - 5.75 g cm^{-3}.	Milled, cold-pressed, and vacuum sintered at 1870 C for 1 hr.
◇	63-6	348		98 ZrO_2 (99.87 pure including 2 HfO_2) and 2 Ti (99.5 pure with 2-3 H_2; obtained from TiH by thermal decomposition in vacuum at 810 C).	Prepared by mixing raw materials in methyl alcohol and pressing into wafer-type sample after dried and pelletized; fired at 1800 C for 2 hrs and cooled at a rate of approx. 60 C per min.
□	63-6	348		Same as above except 6.4 Ti.	Same as above.
△	63-6	348		Same as above.	Same as above except fired at 2000 C.
▽	63-6	348		Same as above except 14.3 Ti.	Same as above except fired at 1800 C.

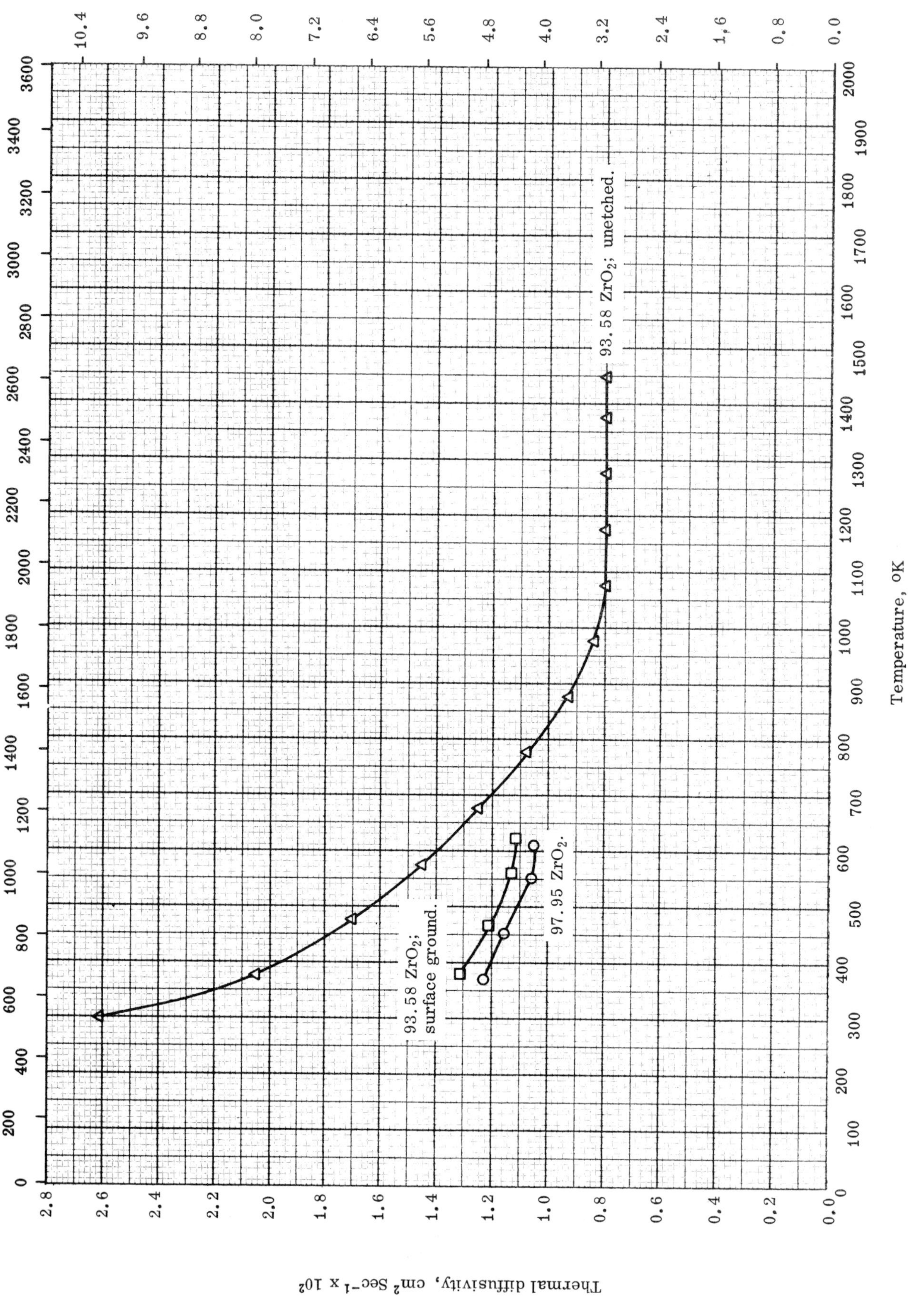

Temperature, °R

93.58 ZrO_2; surface ground.

97.95 ZrO_2.

93.58 ZrO_2; unetched.

Thermal diffusivity, $cm^2\ Sec^{-1} \times 10^2$

Thermal diffusivity, $ft^2\ hr^{-1} \times 10^2$

Temperature, °K

THERMAL DIFFUSIVITY -- [ZIRCONIUM DIOXIDE + TITANIUM] CERMET

REFERENCE INFORMATION

Symbol	Ref.	Temp. Range °K	Rept. Error %	Sample Specifications	Remarks
○	63-1	368-608		97.95 ZrO_2 and 2.05 Ti (corresponding to 5.0 mole %).	Zirconia stabilized; sintered at 2000 C in a vacuum furnace and cooled to room temperature in 1 hr; all surface ground
□	63-1	378-620		93.58 ZrO_2 and 6.42 Ti (corresponding to 15.0 mole %).	Same as the above sample.
△	64-1	298-1448		ZT - 15 - M; 93.58 ZrO_2 and 6.42 Ti (corresponding to 15.0 mole %)	Milled, cold-pressed, and then sintered in vacuum at 1870 C for 1 hr; unetched.

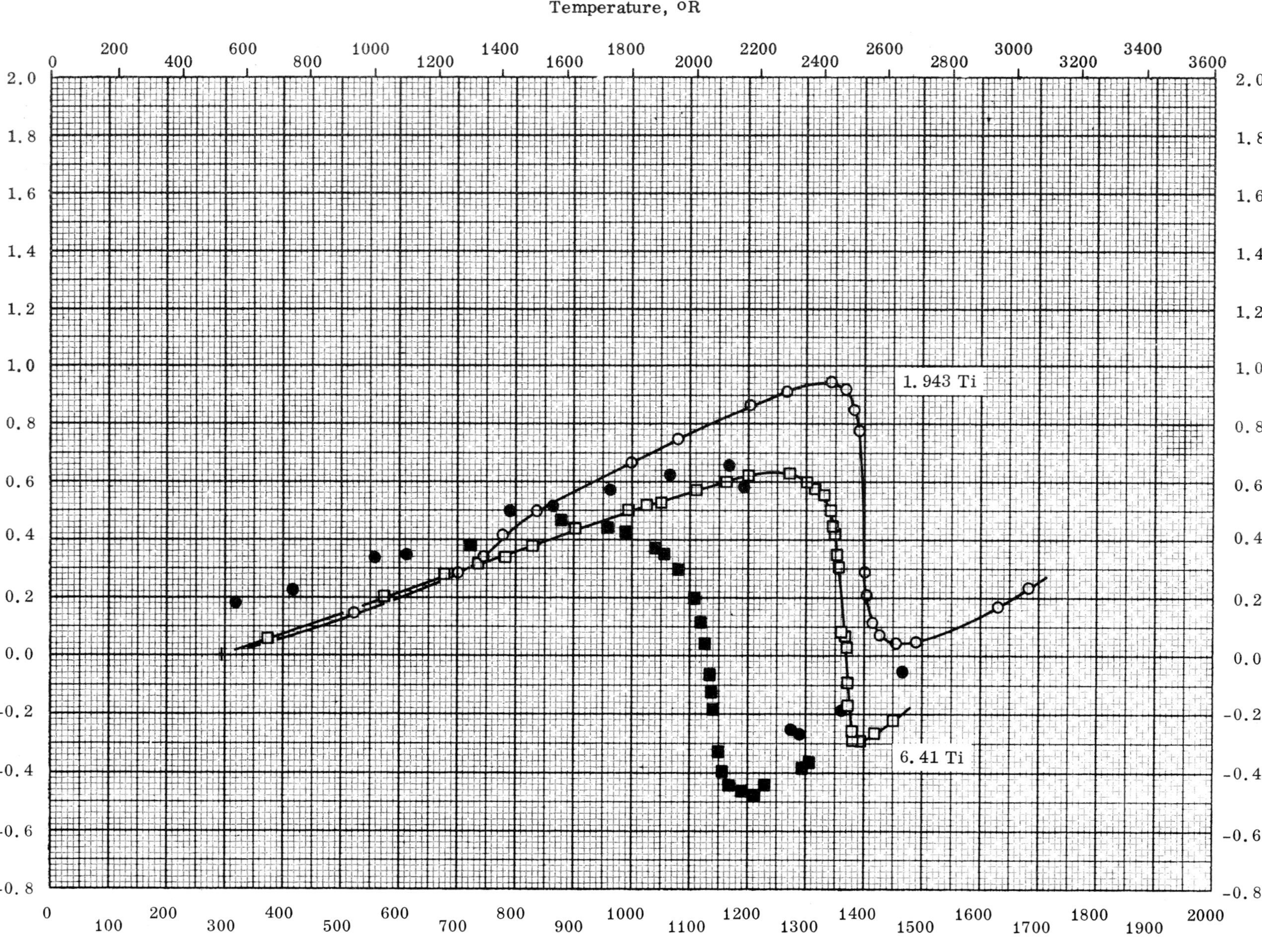

THERMAL LINEAR EXPANSION -- [ZIRCONIUM DIOXIDE + TITANIUM] CERMET

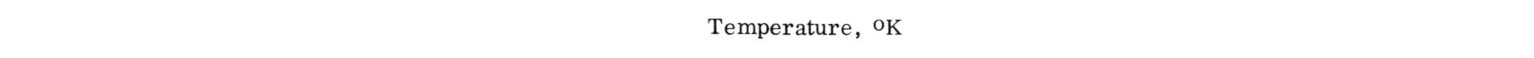

REFERENCE INFORMATION

Symbol	Ref.	Temp. Range °K	Rept. Error %	Sample Specifications	Remarks
○	63-1	293-1681		98.057 ZrO_2 and 1.943 Ti; dimension: 3/4 in. long by 3/8 in. square cross-section. [Author's design.: ZrO_2 + 5 m/o Ti]	Cold pressed, and sintered at 2000 C in a vac furnace, and cooled to room temp in 1 hr; measured with increasing temp with a rate at about 2.5 C per min; purified argon used as the inert gas.
●	63-1	320-1681		Same as above.	Cooling data of above specimen; permanent expansion of 0.19 %; weight gain of 0.2 %; the edges of specimen were light-colored indicating slight oxidation.
□	64-1	298-1450		6.41 Ti, max 0.37 W, Co, C each; dimension: 3 in. long by 0.4 in. square cross-section; density 5.65 - 5.75 g cm^{-3}. [Author's design. ZT - 15-M]	Milled, cold pressed, vac sintered at 1870 C for 1 hr, and then ground; measured in vac of less than 0.5×10^{-6} mm Hg with a heating rate of less than 0.1 C per min.
■	64-1	723-1303		Same as above.	Cooling data of above specimen with a cooling rate of less than 0.1 C per min.

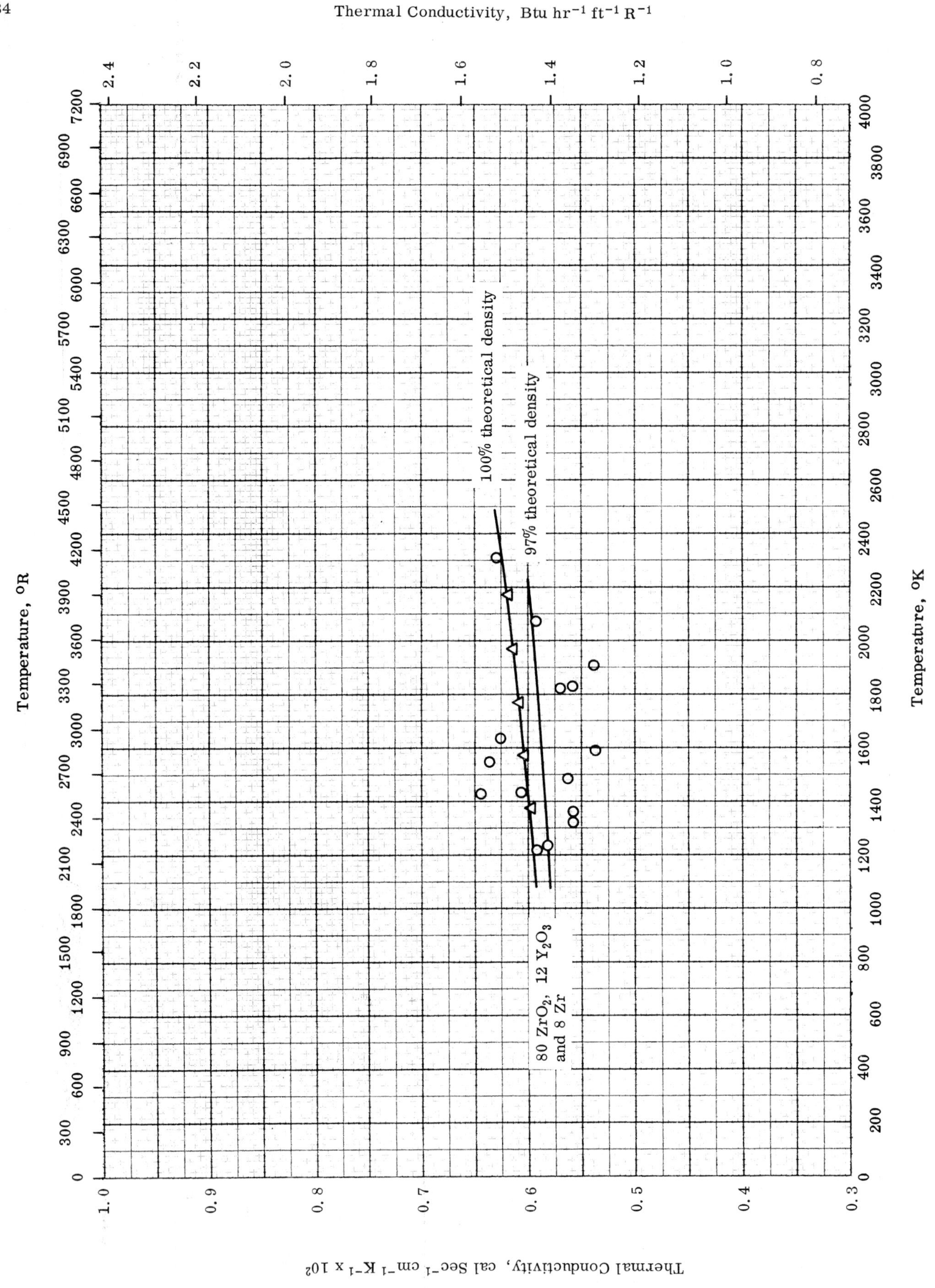

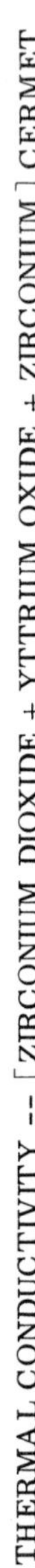

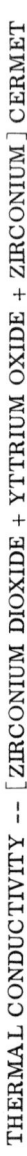

Thermal Conductivity, Btu hr^{-1} ft^{-1} R^{-1}
Temperature, °R
Temperature, °K
Thermal Conductivity, cal Sec^{-1} cm^{-1} K^{-1} x 10^2
100% theoretical density
97% theoretical density
80 ZrO_2, 12 Y_2O_3 and 8 Zr

THERMAL CONDUCTIVITY -- [ZIRCONIUM DIOXIDE + YTTRIUM OXIDE + ZIRCONIUM] CERMET

THERMAL CONDUCTIVITY -- [ZIRCONIUM DIOXIDE + YTTRIUM OXIDE + ZIRCONIUM] CERMET

REFERENCE INFORMATION

Symbol	Ref.	Temp. Range °K	Rept. Error %	Sample Specifications	Remarks
○	64-2	1213-2308		80 ZrO_2, 12 Y_2O_3, and 8 Zr; raw materials in powder form; 97% theoretical density; black color.	ZrO_2 stabilized; prepared by hot-pressing the mixed powders at 1900 C and then machined; particles of Zr distributed uniformly in sample.
△	64-2	1373-2173		Same as above.	Data corrected to 100% theoretical density.

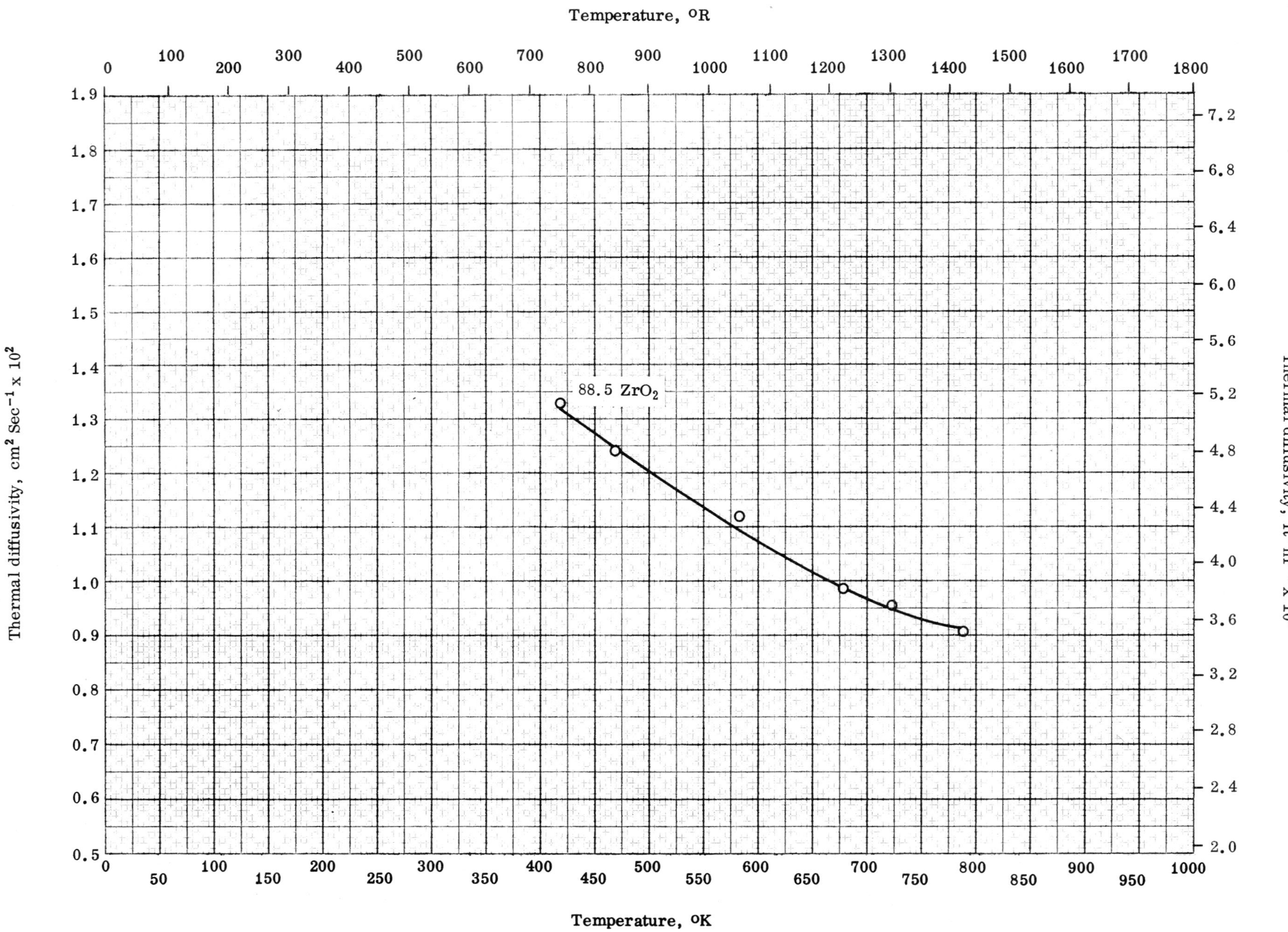

Thermal diffusivity, $ft^2\ hr^{-1} \times 10^2$

Temperature, °R

88.5 ZrO_2

Temperature, °K

Thermal diffusivity, $cm^2\ Sec^{-1} \times 10^2$

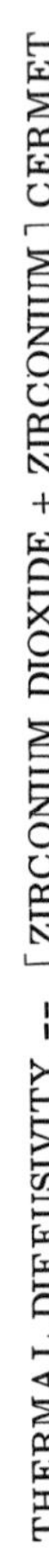

THERMAL DIFFUSIVITY -- [ZIRCONIUM DIOXIDE + ZIRCONIUM] CERMET

THERMAL DIFFUSIVITY -- [ZIRCONIUM DIOXIDE + ZIRCONIUM] CERMET

REFERENCE INFORMATION

Symbol	Ref.	Temp. Range °K	Rept. Error %	Sample Specifications	Remarks
○	63-1	418-788		88.5 ZrO_2 and 11.5 Zr (corresponding to 15.0 mole %)	Zirconia stabilized; sintered 2 hrs at 2000 C in a a vacuum furnace and cooled to room temperature in 1 hr; all surfaces ground.

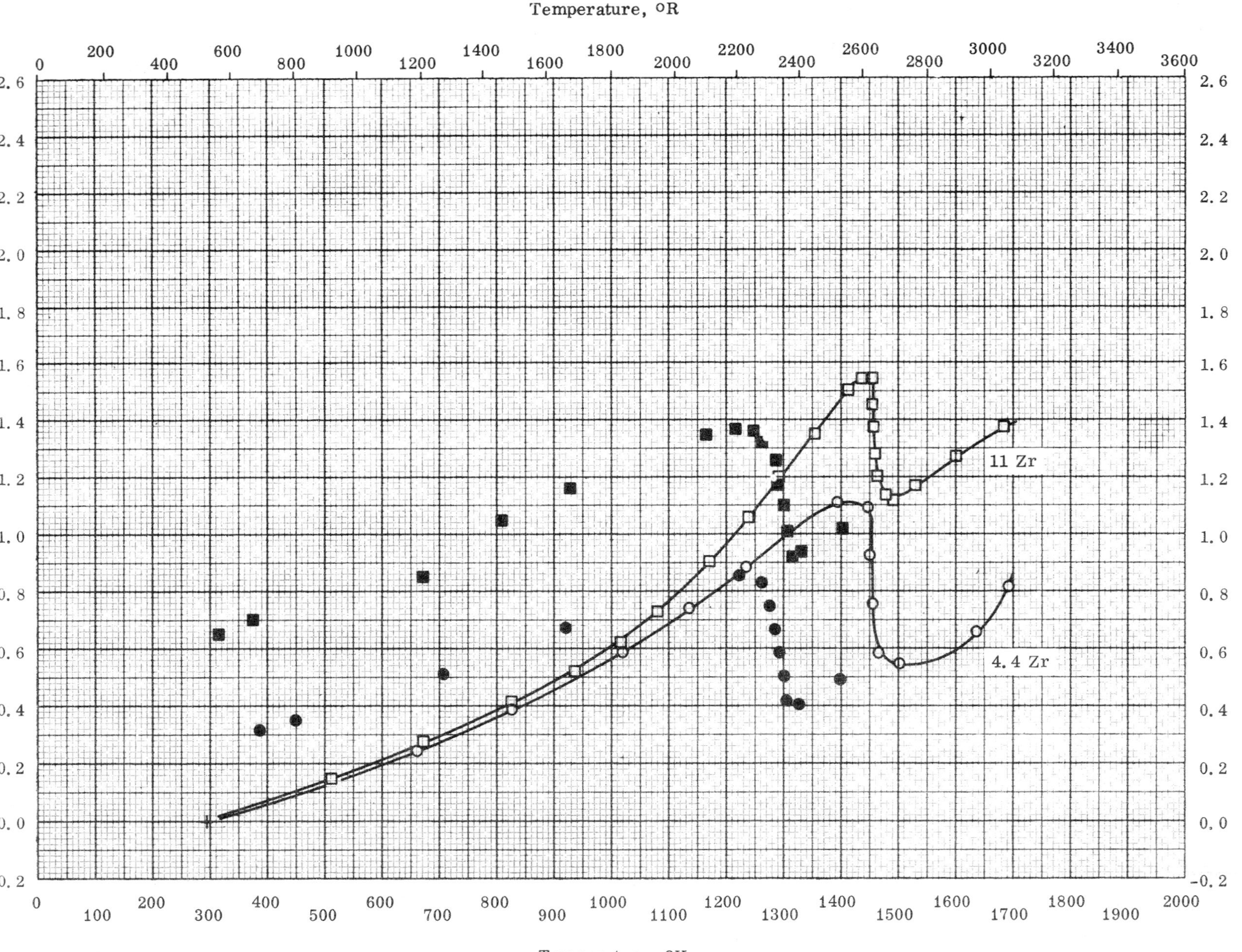

THERMAL LINEAR EXPANSION -- [ZIRCONIUM DIOXIDE + ZIRCONIUM] CERMET

REFERENCE INFORMATION

Symbol	Ref.	Temp. Range °K	Rept. Error %	Sample Specifications	Remarks
○	63-1	293-1691		95.623 ZrO_2, 4.376 Zr; dimension: 3/4 in. long by 3/8 in. square cross-section. [Author's design. ZrO_2 + 6 $m/_o$ Zr]	Cold pressed and sintered at 2000 C in a vac furnace, and cooled to room temperature in 1 hr; measured with a heating rate at about 2.5 C per min; either argon or helium used as protective atmosphere.
●	63-1	377-1691		Same as above.	Cooling data of above specimen; length increased 0.4%, weight gained 0.936%.
□	63-1	293-1683		88.768 ZrO_2, 11.232 Zr; same dimension as above. [Author's design. ZrO_2 + 15 $m/_o$ Zr]	Same as that of ZrO_2 + 6 $m/_o$ Zr; heating.
■	63-1	317-1683		Same as above.	Cooling data of above specimen; length increased 0.73%, weight gained 1.07%.

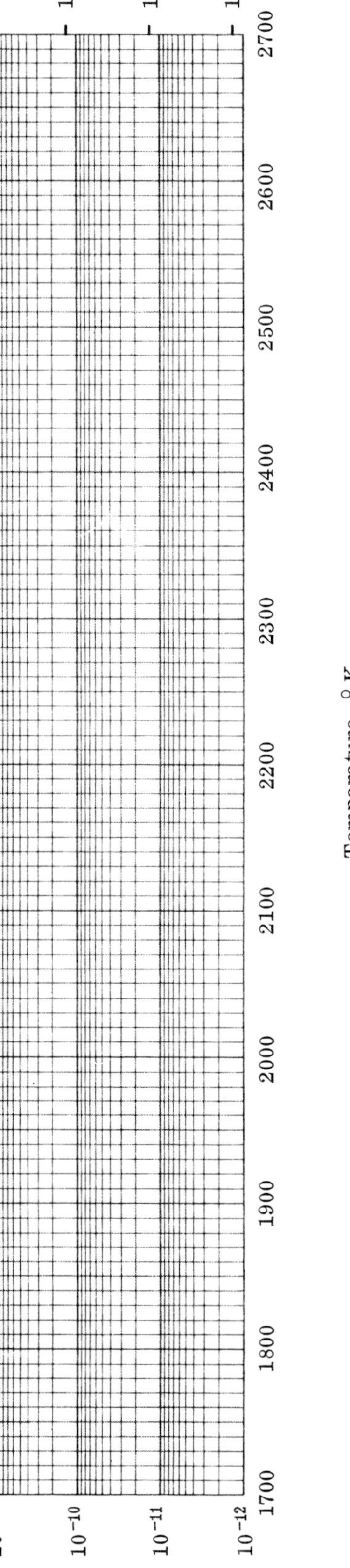

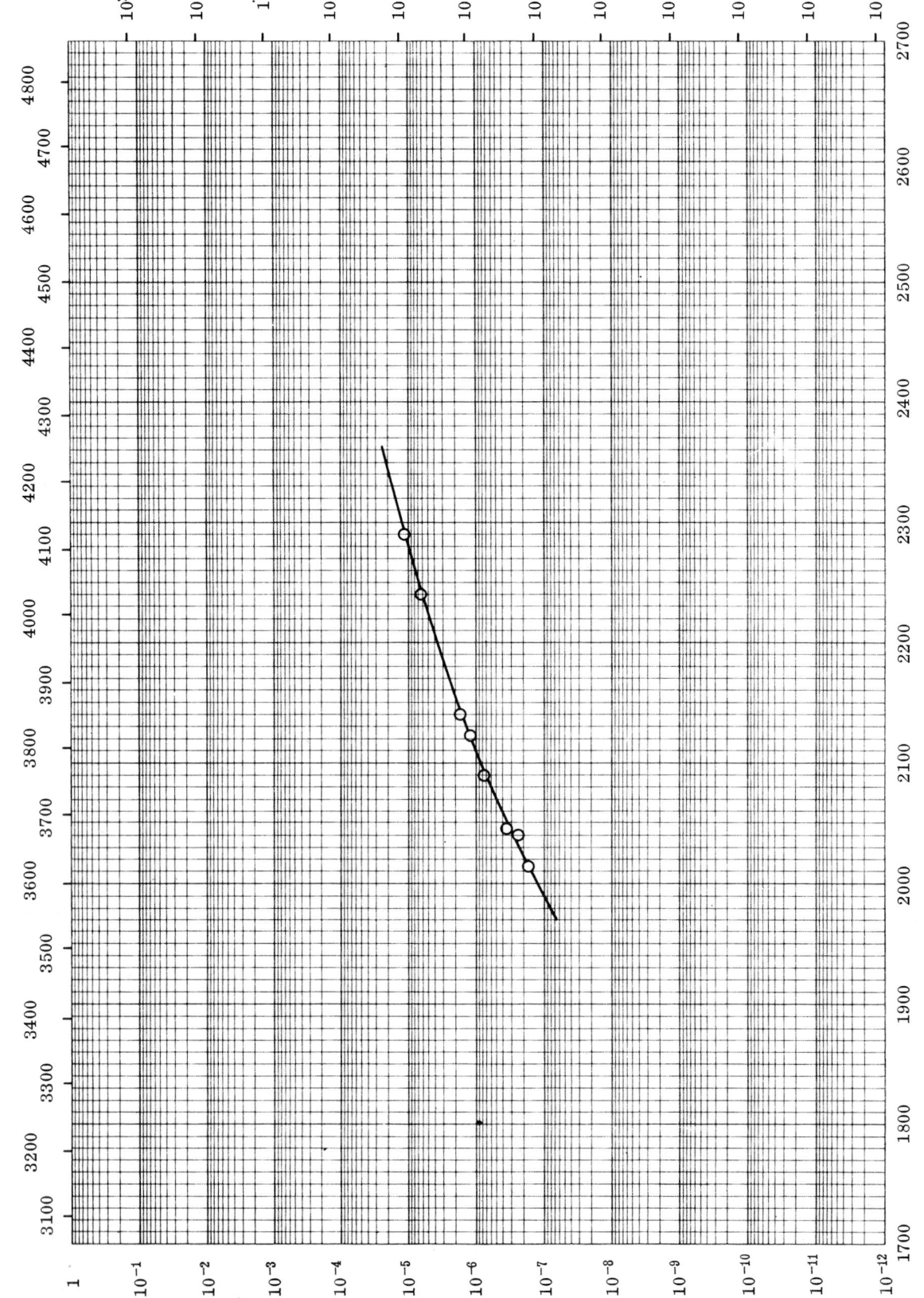

VAPOR PRESSURE -- [ZIRCONIUM DIOXIDE + ZIRCONIUM] CERMET

VAPOR PRESSURE -- [ZIRCONIUM DIOXIDE + ZIRCONIUM] CERMET

REFERENCE INFORMATION

Symbol	Ref.	Temp. Range °K	Rept. Error %	Sample Specifications	Remarks
○	53-3	2014-2290		ZrO_2 + Zr cermet.	

PROPERTIES OF ZIRCONIUM DIBORIDE CERMET

MOST PROBABLE VALUES

Property	C.G.S. Units	Brit. Eng. Units
Density	5.09	318

REPORTED VALUES

Density	$g\ cm^{-3}$	$lb\ ft^{-3}$
O 90 ZrB_2	5.09	318

PROPERTIES OF ZIRCONIUM DIBORIDE CERMET

REFERENCE INFORMATION

Symbol	Ref.	Temp. Range °K	Rept. Error %	Sample Specifications	Remarks
○	52-20	298		Borolite; nominal 90^{+} ZrB_2.	Average of 3 samples.

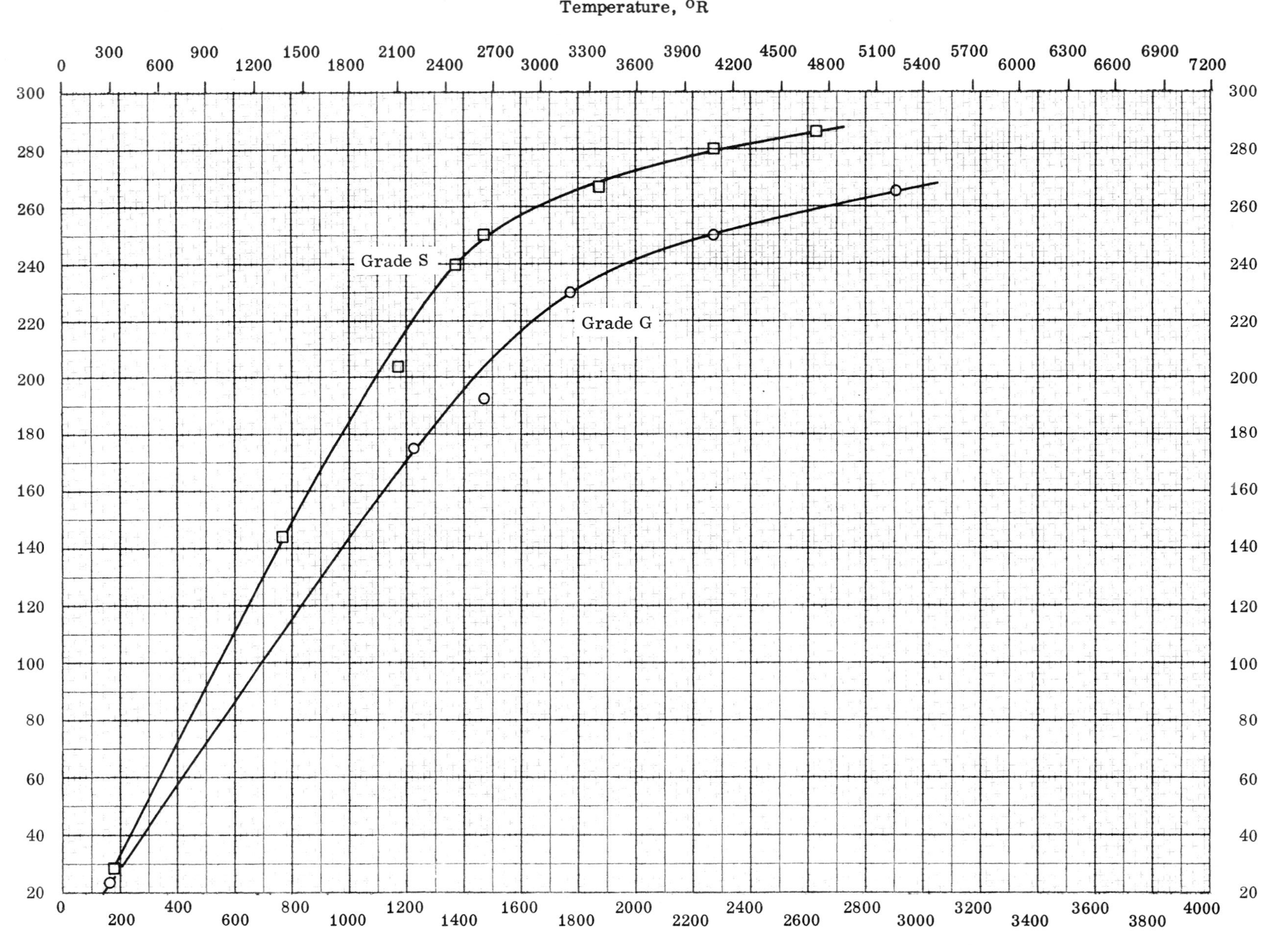

ELECTRICAL RESISTIVITY -- ZIRCONIUM DIBORIDE CERMET

ELECTRICAL RESISTIVITY -- ZIRCONIUM DIBORIDE CERMET

REFERENCE INFORMATION

Symbol	Ref.	Temp. Range °K	Rept. Error %	Sample Specifications	Remarks
○	52-6	273-2773		ZrB_2; borolite I, Grade G; 4.5% binder.	
□	52-6	273-2773		ZrB_2; borolite I, Grade S; 5.7% binder.	

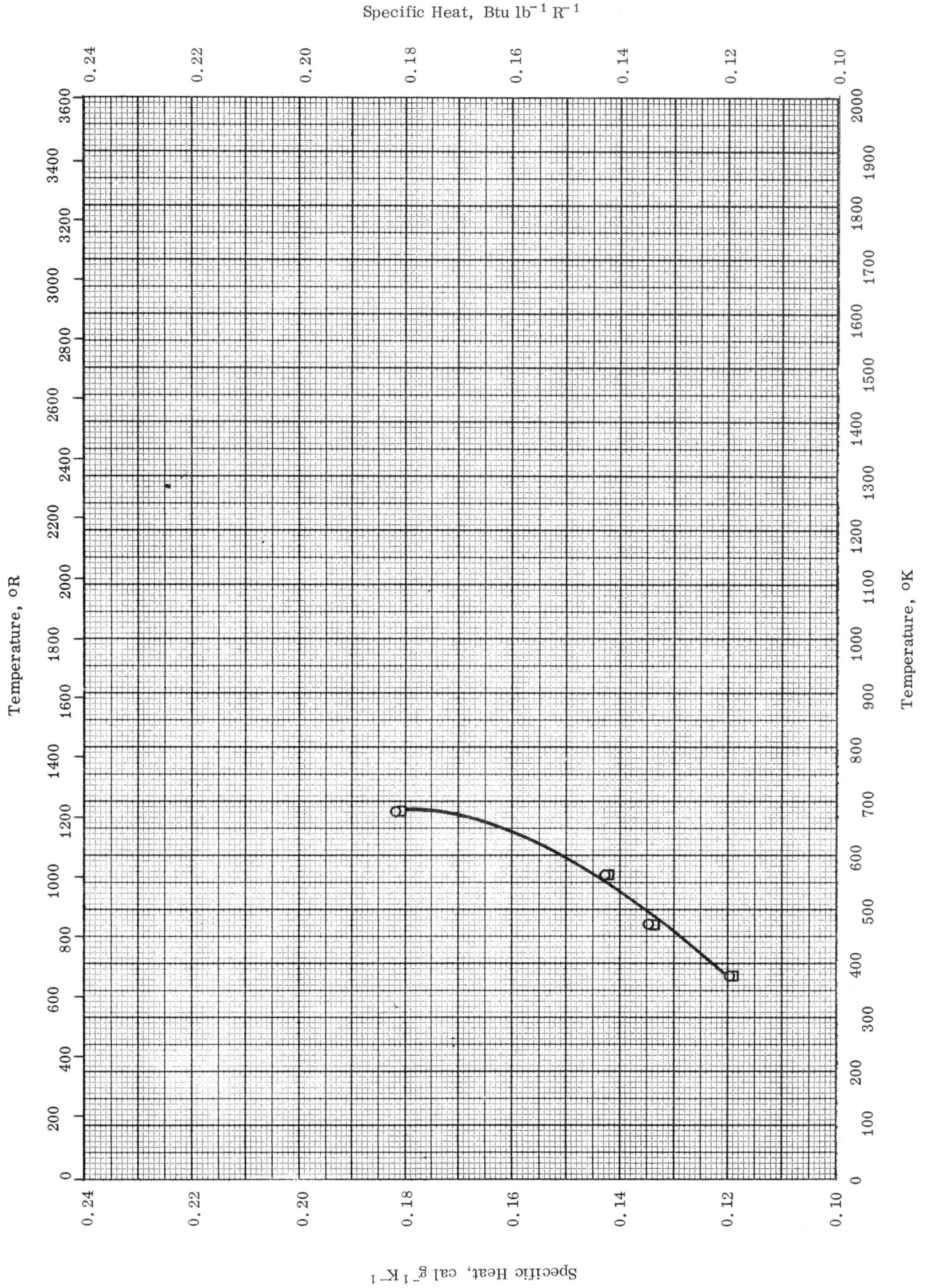

SPECIFIC HEAT -- ZIRCONIUM DIBORIDE CERMET

REFERENCE INFORMATION

Symbol	Ref.	Temp. Range °K	Rept. Error %	Sample Specifications	Remarks
○	52-6	373-673		Borolite I, Grade S; 7.5 binder.	
□	52-6	373-673		Borolite I, Grade F; binder not given.	

Thermal Conductivity, Btu $hr^{-1} ft^{-1} R^{-1} \times 10^{-2}$

0.20 0.18 0.16 0.14 0.12 0.10 0.08 0.06

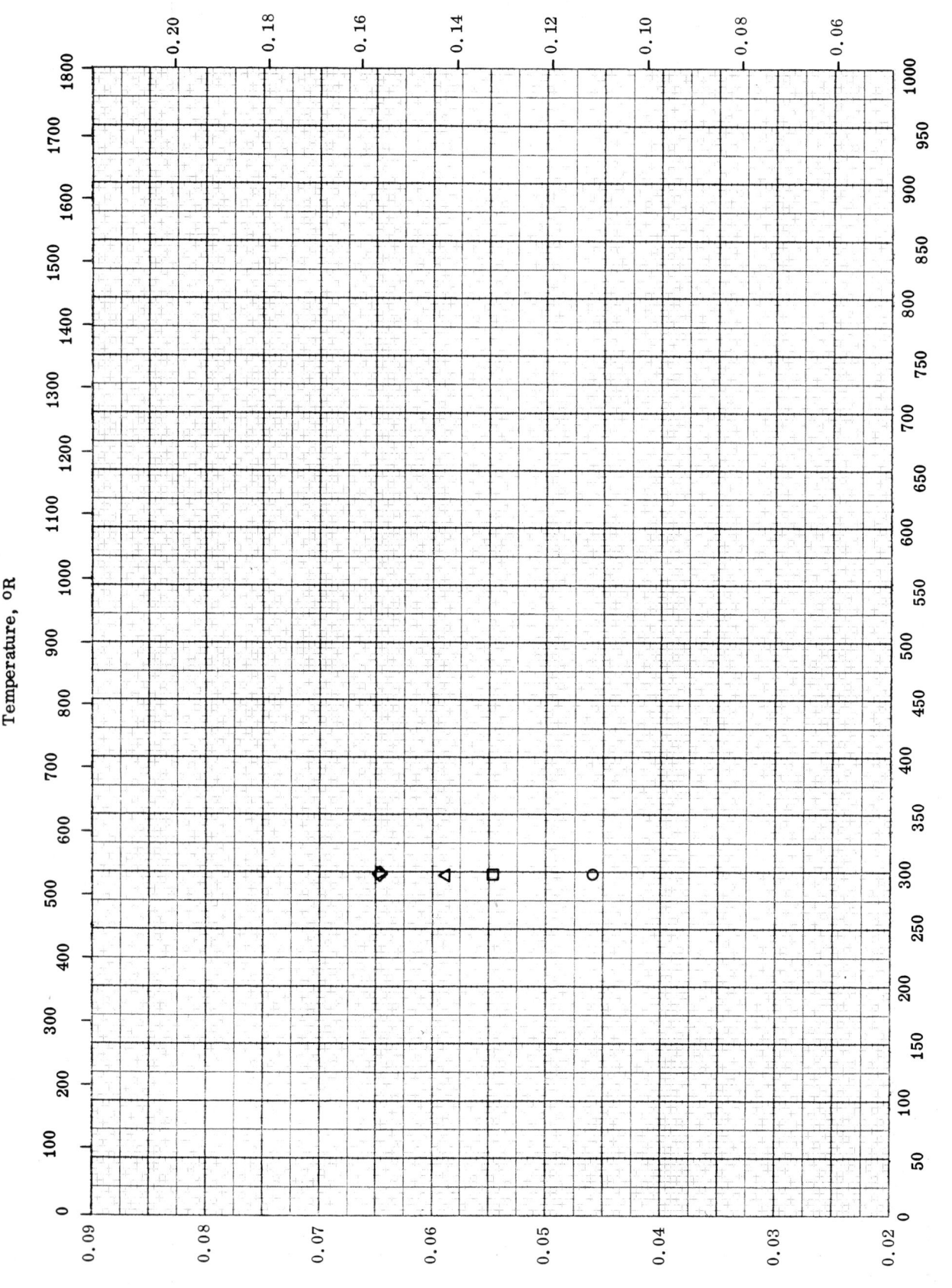

Temperature, °R

0 100 200 300 400 500 600 700 800 900 1000 1100 1200 1300 1400 1500 1600 1700 1800

Temperature, °K

0 50 100 150 200 250 300 350 400 450 500 550 600 650 700 750 800 850 900 950 1000

Thermal Conductivity, cal $Sec^{-1} cm^{-1} K^{-1}$

0.09 0.08 0.07 0.06 0.05 0.04 0.03 0.02

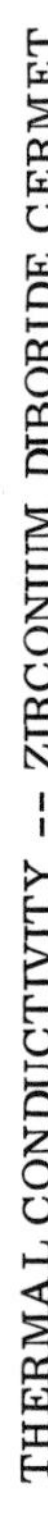

THERMAL CONDUCTIVITY -- ZIRCONIUM DIBORIDE CERMET

REFERENCE INFORMATION

Symbol	Ref.	Temp. Range °K	Rept. Error %	Sample Specifications	Remarks
○	52-1	298		99.5 ZrB_2 and 0.5 binder.	Binder not stated.
□	52-1	298		96 ZrB_2 and 4 binder.	Same as above.
△	52-1	298		95 ZrB_2 and 5 binder.	Same as above.
◇	52-1	298		92.5 ZrB_2 and 7.5 binder.	Same as above.
▽	52-1	298		85 ZrB_2 and 15 binder.	Same as above.

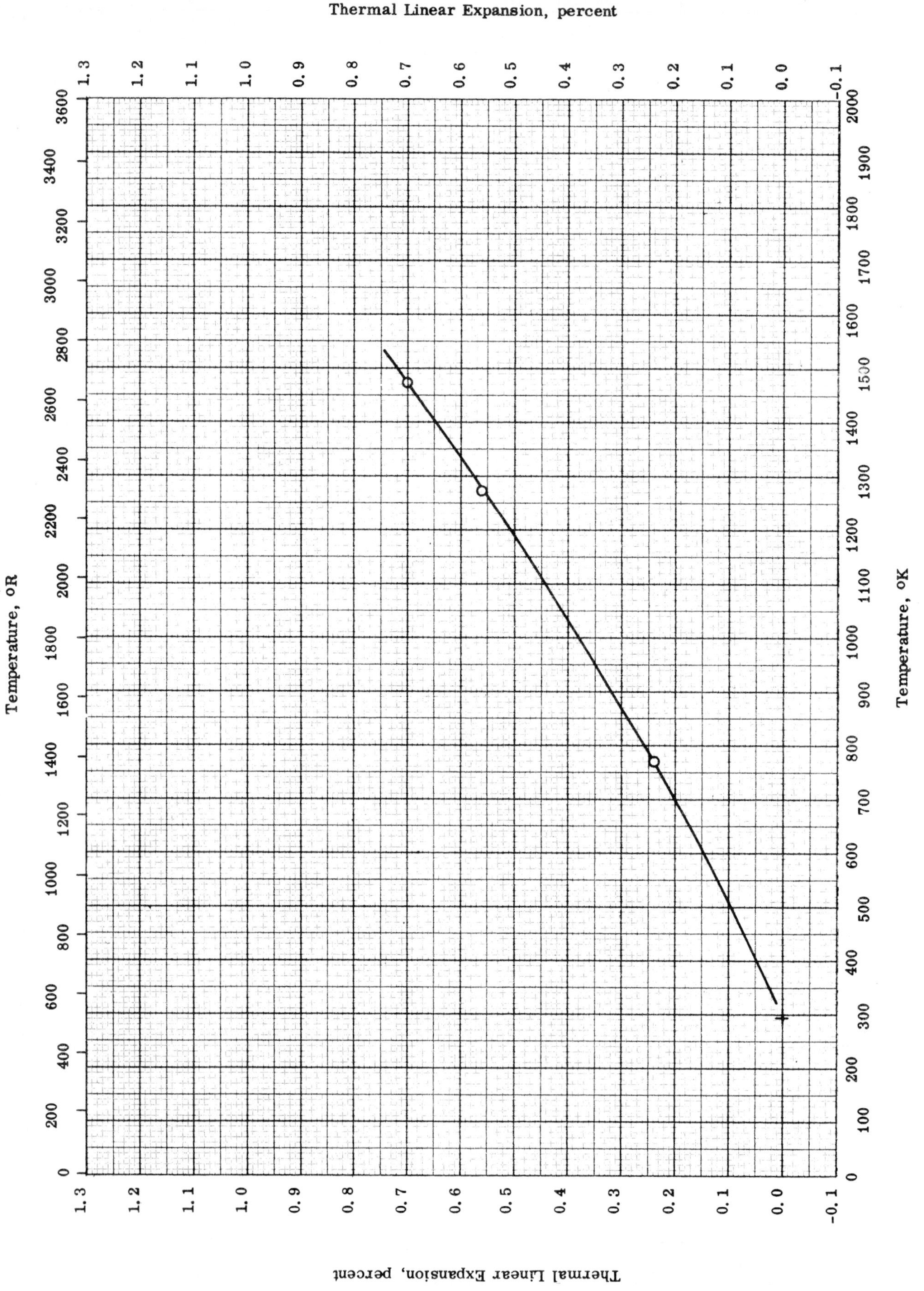

Temperature, °R

Temperature, °K

Thermal Linear Expansion, percent

THERMAL LINEAR EXPANSION -- ZIRCONIUM DIBORIDE CERMET

REFERENCE INFORMATION

Symbol	Ref.	Temp. Range °K	Rept. Error %	Sample Specifications	Remarks
o	52-6	293-1473		Borolite 1, Grade G; 4.5 binder and 95.5 ZrB_2.	Type of binder not given.

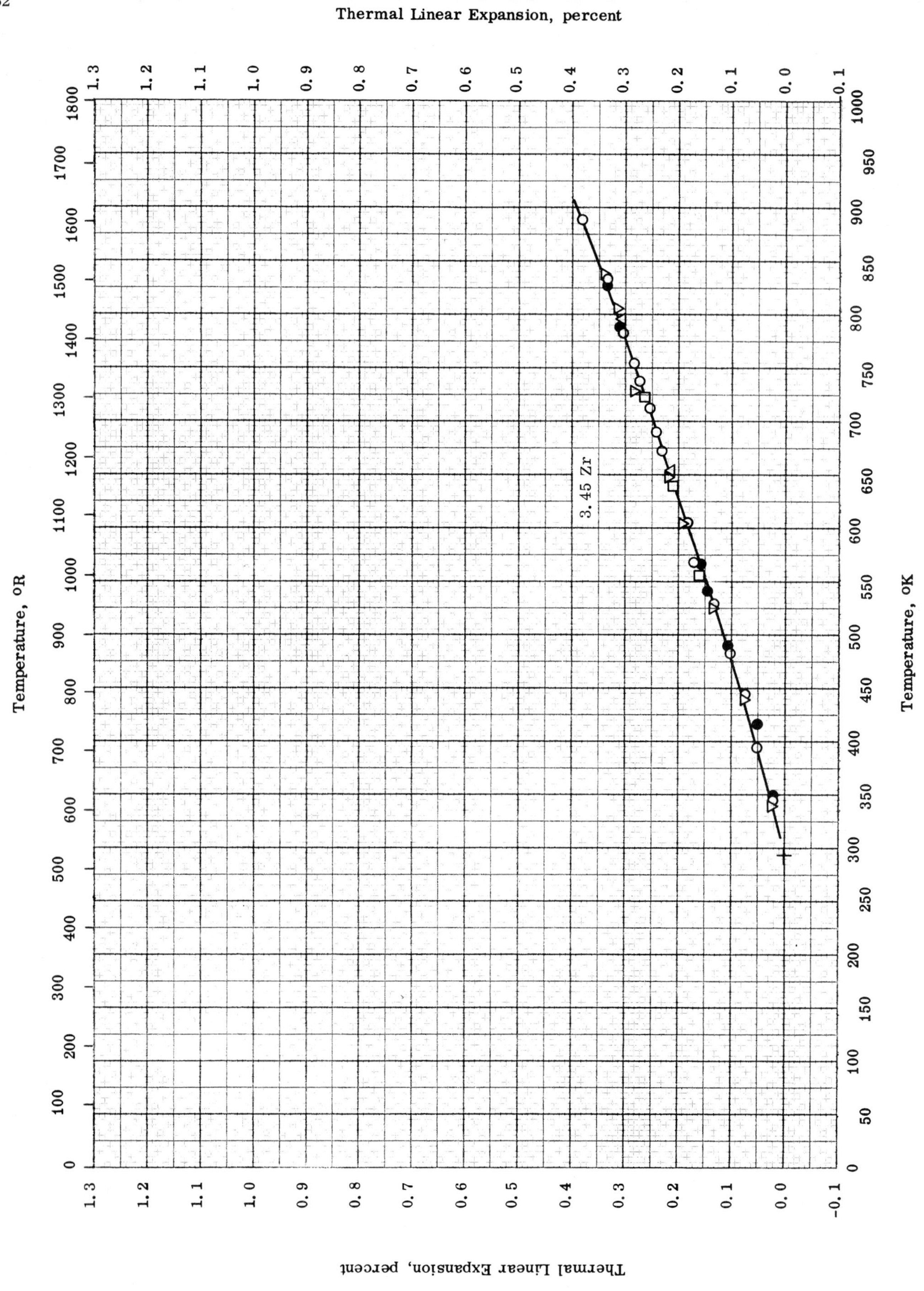

Thermal Linear Expansion, percent

1.3 1.2 1.1 1.0 0.9 0.8 0.7 0.6 0.5 0.4 0.3 0.2 0.1 0.0 -0.1

Temperature, °R

0 100 200 300 400 500 600 700 800 900 1000 1100 1200 1300 1400 1500 1600 1700 1800

3.45 Zr

Temperature, °K

0 50 100 150 200 250 300 350 400 450 500 550 600 650 700 750 800 850 900 950 1000

1.3 1.2 1.1 1.0 0.9 0.8 0.7 0.6 0.5 0.4 0.3 0.2 0.1 0.0 -0.1

Thermal Linear Expansion, percent

THERMAL LINEAR EXPANSION -- [HAFNIUM CARBIDE + ZIRCONIUM] CERMET

REFERENCE INFORMATION

Symbol	Ref.	Temp. Range °K	Rept. Error %	Sample Specifications	Remarks
○	60-30	298-889		89.36 Hf, 6.06 C, 3.45 Zr, 0.72 B, 0.39 Ti, 0.03 free C, total other metal impurities 0.05; 97.5% theoretical density.	Prepared by hot-pressing -325 mesh HfC powder into pellets and then diamond ground into cones; heating rate 8 F per min.
●	60-30	298-828		Same as above except 99.2% theoretical density.	Same as above; heating.
△	60-30	653-828		Same as above.	Cooling data of above specimen.
▽	60-30	298-839		Same as above except 96.2% theoretical density.	Same as above; heating.
□	60-30	555-839		Same as above.	Cooling data of above specimen.

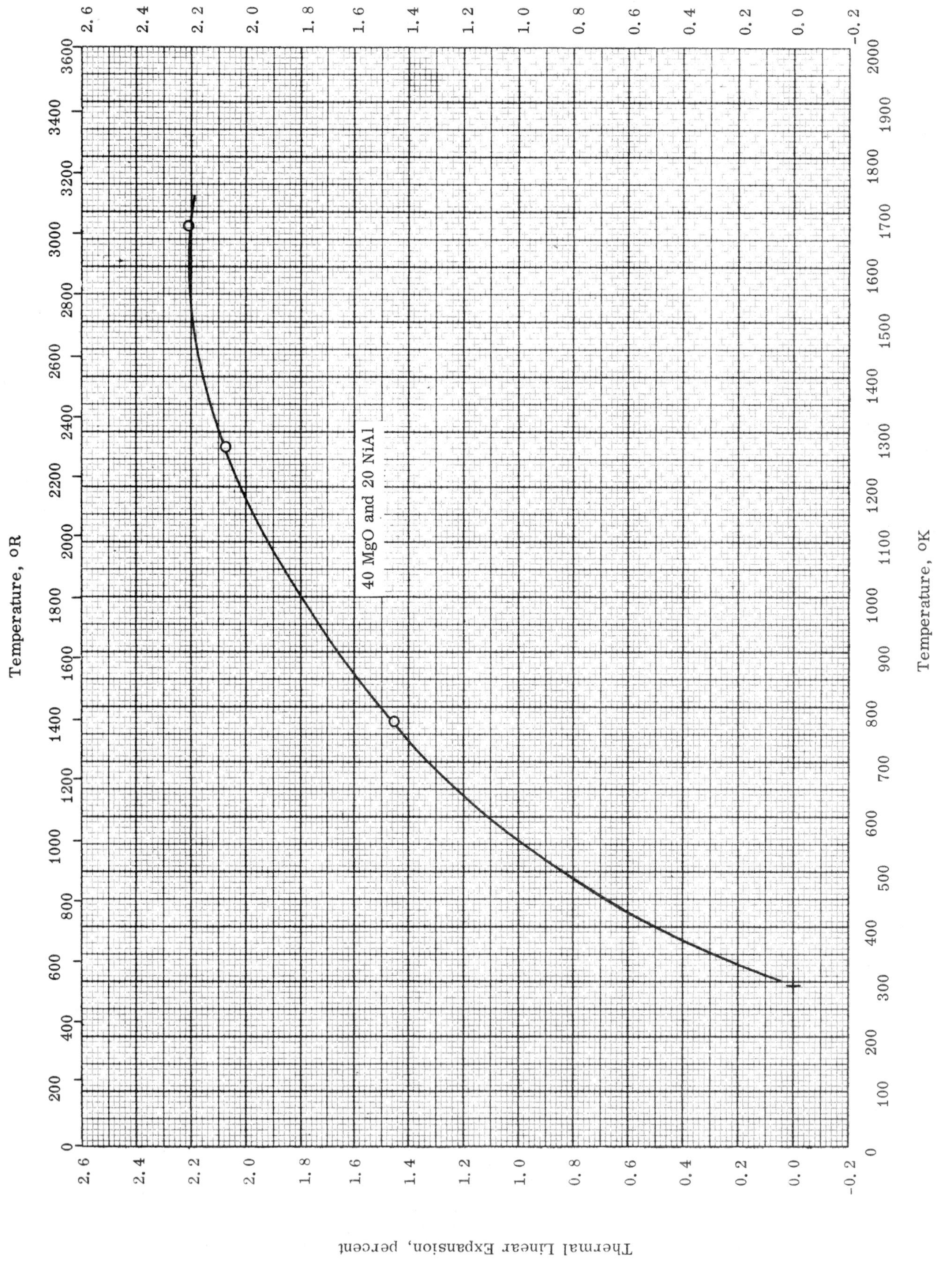

Temperature, °R

0 200 400 600 800 1000 1200 1400 1600 1800 2000 2200 2400 2600 2800 3000 3200 3400 3600

Thermal Linear Expansion, percent

2.6 2.4 2.2 2.0 1.8 1.6 1.4 1.2 1.0 0.8 0.6 0.4 0.2 0.0 -0.2

40 MgO and 20 NiAl

Temperature, °K

0 100 200 300 400 500 600 700 800 900 1000 1100 1200 1300 1400 1500 1600 1700 1800 1900 2000

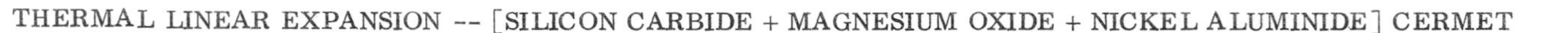

THERMAL LINEAR EXPANSION -- [SILICON CARBIDE + MAGNESIUM OXIDE + NICKEL ALUMINIDE] CERMET

REFERENCE INFORMATION

Symbol	Ref.	Temp. Range °K	Rept. Error %	Sample Specifications	Remarks
○	51-3	293-1673		40 SiC, 40 MgO, and 20 NiAl.	Hot pressed.

Temperature, °R

Thermal Conductivity, cal $Sec^{-1} cm^{-1} K^{-1}$

Thermal Conductivity, Btu $hr^{-1} ft^{-1} R^{-1} \times 10^{-2}$

2.5 Si

23.7 Si

Temperature, °K

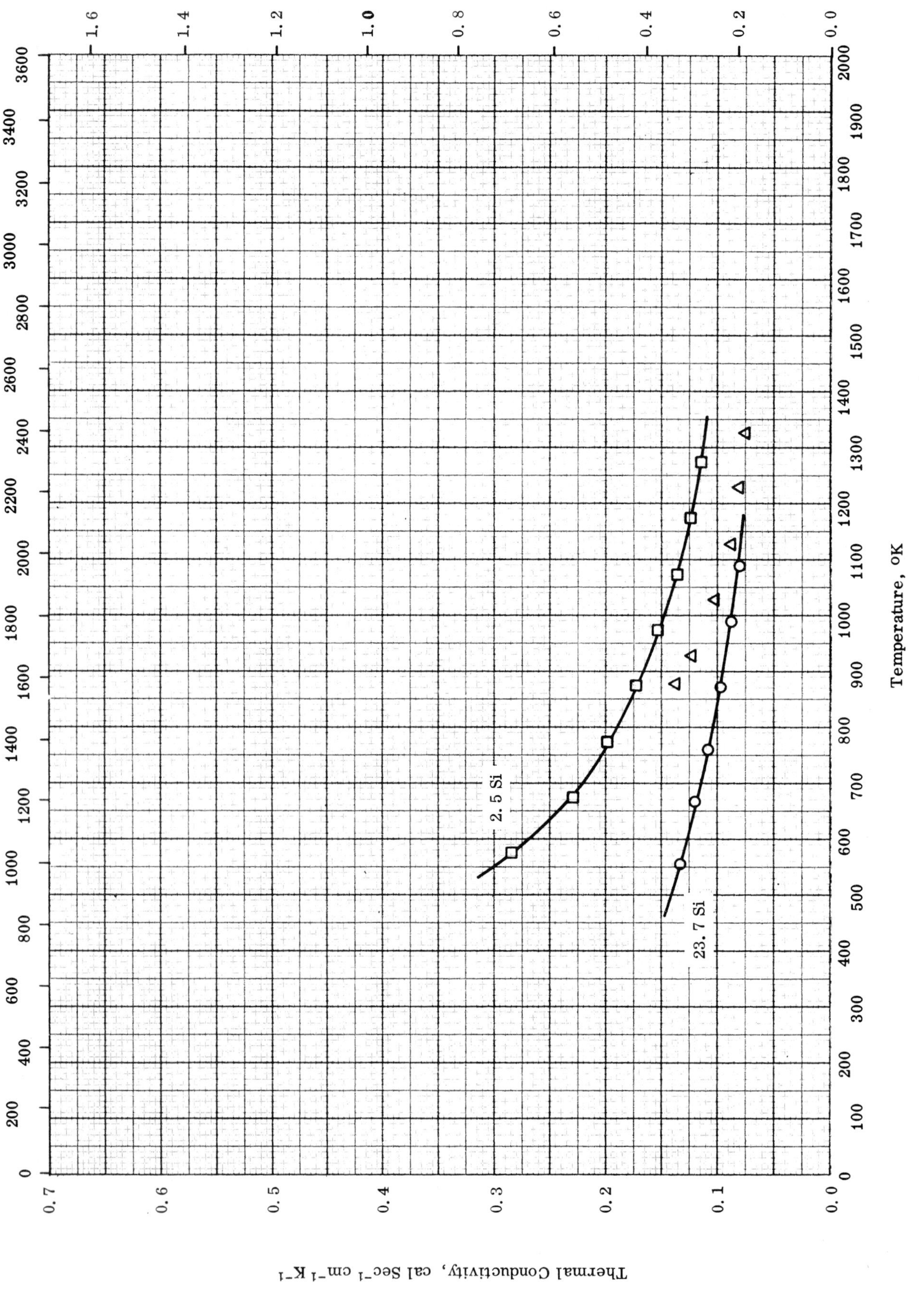

THERMAL CONDUCTIVITY -- [SILICON CARBIDE + SILICON] CERMET

THERMAL CONDUCTIVITY -- [SILICON CARBIDE + SILICON] CERMET

REFERENCE INFORMATION

Symbol	Ref.	Temp. Range °K	Rept. Error %	Sample Specifications	Remarks
○	59-10	556-1089	±4	Beta silicon carbide with 23.7 silicon.	Corresponding to 30 vol. % Si; weight percent calculated by assuming theoretical density.
□	62-8	573-1273	±4-±6	96.5 SiC, 2.5 Si, 0.4 Al, 0.4 C, and 0.2 Fe; density 3.01 g cm^{-3} (95% theoretical).	Measured parallel to the direction of the pressing pressure.
△	55-7	623-1073		Consisted of continuous Si phase and cubic SiC.	

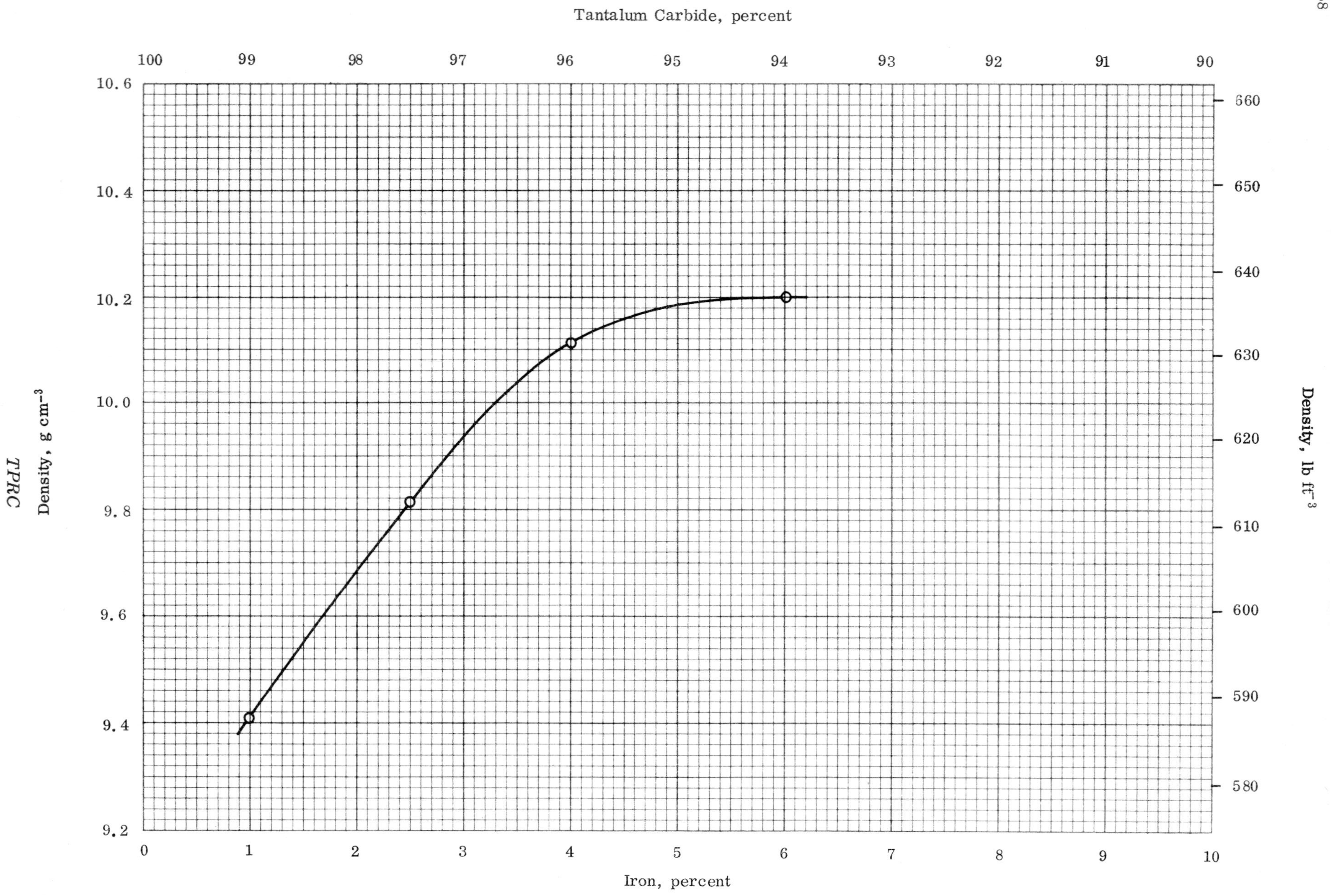

Tantalum Carbide, percent

100 99 98 97 96 95 94 93 92 91 90

Density, g cm^{-3}

10.6 10.4 10.2 10.0 9.8 9.6 9.4 9.2

Density, lb ft^{-3}

660 650 640 630 620 610 600 590 580

0 1 2 3 4 5 6 7 8 9 10

Iron, percent

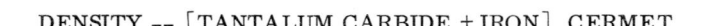

DENSITY -- [TANTALUM CARBIDE + IRON] CERMET

TPRC

DENSITY -- [TANTALUM CARBIDE + IRON] CERMET

REFERENCE INFORMATION

Symbol	Ref.	Temp. Range °K	Rept. Error %	Sample Specifications	Remarks
○	50-10	298		1 - 6 Fe.	Fired to 2750 C.

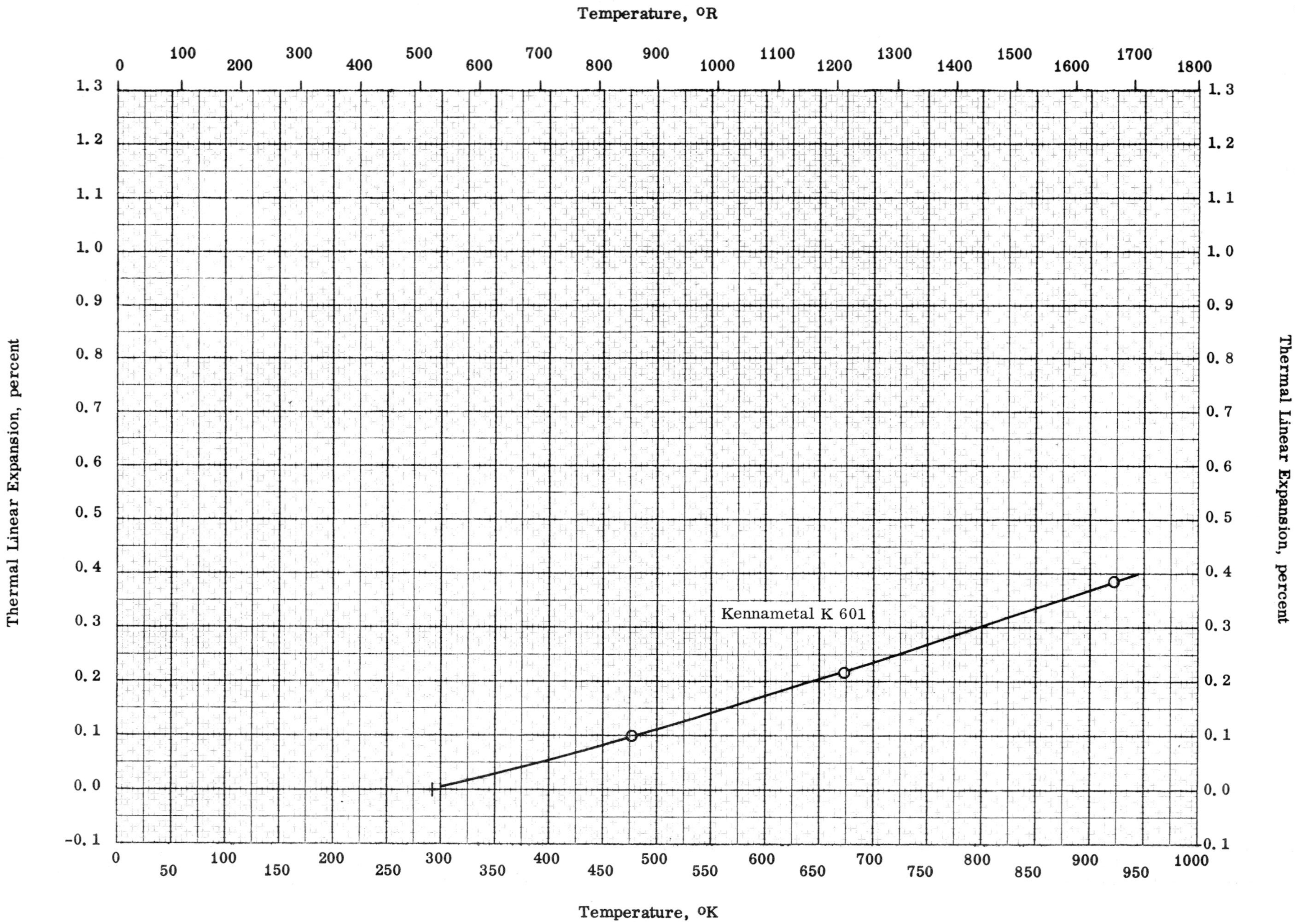

Thermal Linear Expansion, percent

THERMAL LINEAR EXPANSION -- [TANTALUM CARBIDE + TUNGSTEN] CERMET

THERMAL LINEAR EXPANSION -- [TANTALUM CARBIDE + TUNGSTEN] CERMET

REFERENCE INFORMATION

Symbol	Ref.	Temp. Range °K	Rept. Error %	Sample Specifications	Remarks
○	64-20	293-922	2	Kennametal K 601; binder free carbide of tantalum and tungsten.	

PROPERTIES OF [TITANIUM CARBIDES + COBALT] CERMET

REPORTED VALUES

Density		$g\ cm^{-3}$	$lb\ ft^{-3}$
○	80 TiC and 20 Co.	5.54 ± 0.004	346 ± 0.3
□	65 TiC, 20 Co, and 15 other carbides.	5.79 ± 0.006	361 ± 0.4

REFERENCE INFORMATION

Symbol	Ref.	Temp. Range °K	Rept. Error %	Sample Specifications	Remarks
○	55-20	298		K 138: nominal 80 TiC, 20 Co.	
□	55-20	298		K 138A: nominal 65 TiC, 20 Co, 15 solid solution of Nb, Ta, Ti carbides.	

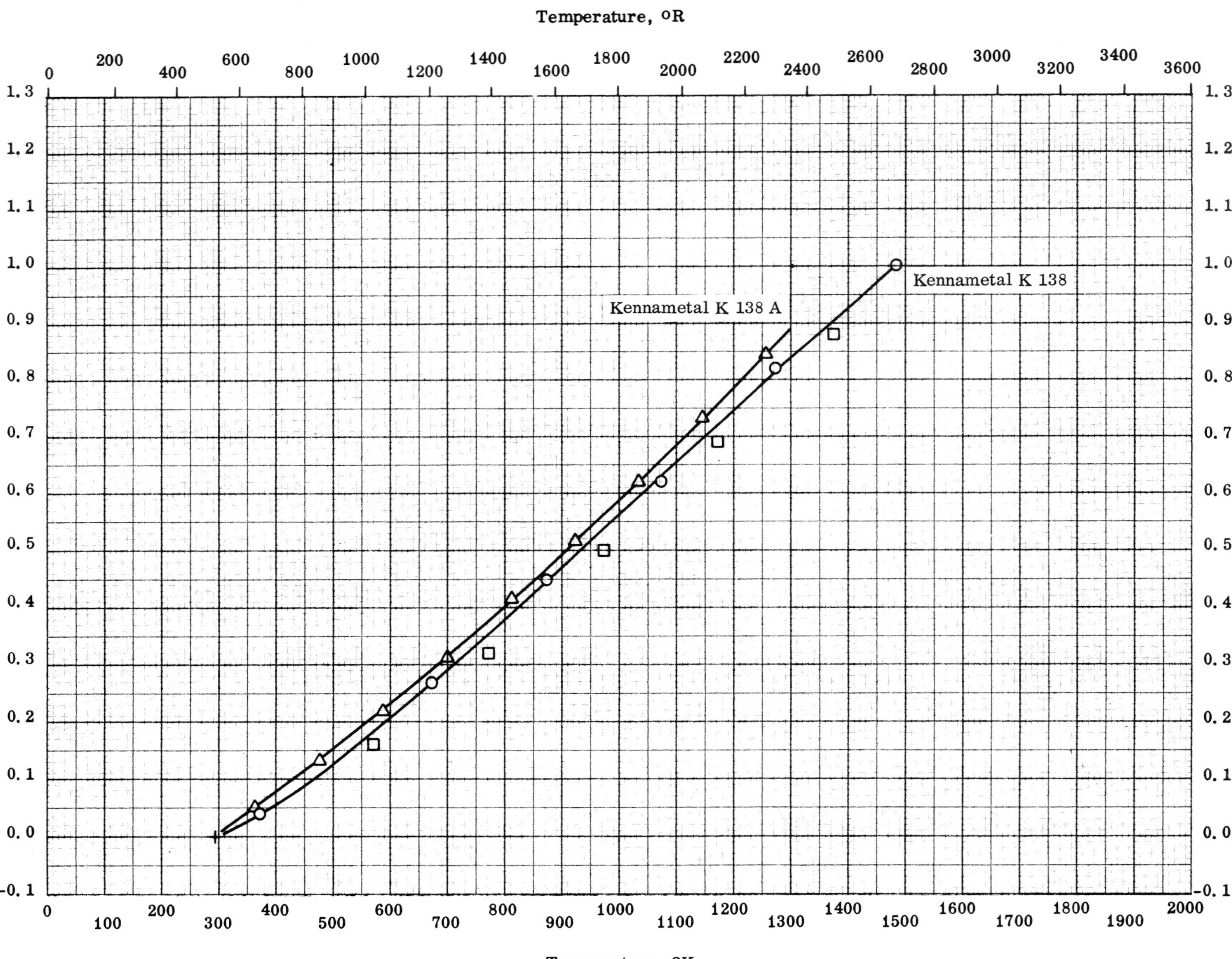

THERMAL LINEAR EXPANSION -- [TITANIUM CARBIDE + COBALT] CERMET
[0 ≤ Nb (TaTi)C ≤ 10]

THERMAL LINEAR EXPANSION -- [TITANIUM CARBIDE + COBALT] CERMET
[$0 \le$ Nb (TaTi)C ≤ 10]

REFERENCE INFORMATION

Symbol	Ref.	Temp. Range °K	Rept. Error %	Sample Specifications	Remarks
○	55-20	299-1482		Kennametal K 138; 80 TiC and 20 Co binder.	Measured with a heating rate of 3 C per min. in vacuum.
□	55-20	573-1482		Same as above.	Cooling data of above specimen with cooling rate 3 C per min.
△	63-30	293-1255	3	Kennametal K 138 A; 70 TiC, 20 Co, and 10 Nb (TaTi)C; dimension: 4 mm diameter by 50 mm long; density 5.75 g cm^{-3}.	Nb (TaTi)C added as a solid solution containing about 90 NbC; heating rate at about 3 F per min gradually increased to 5 F per min in vacuum; no permanent change in length.

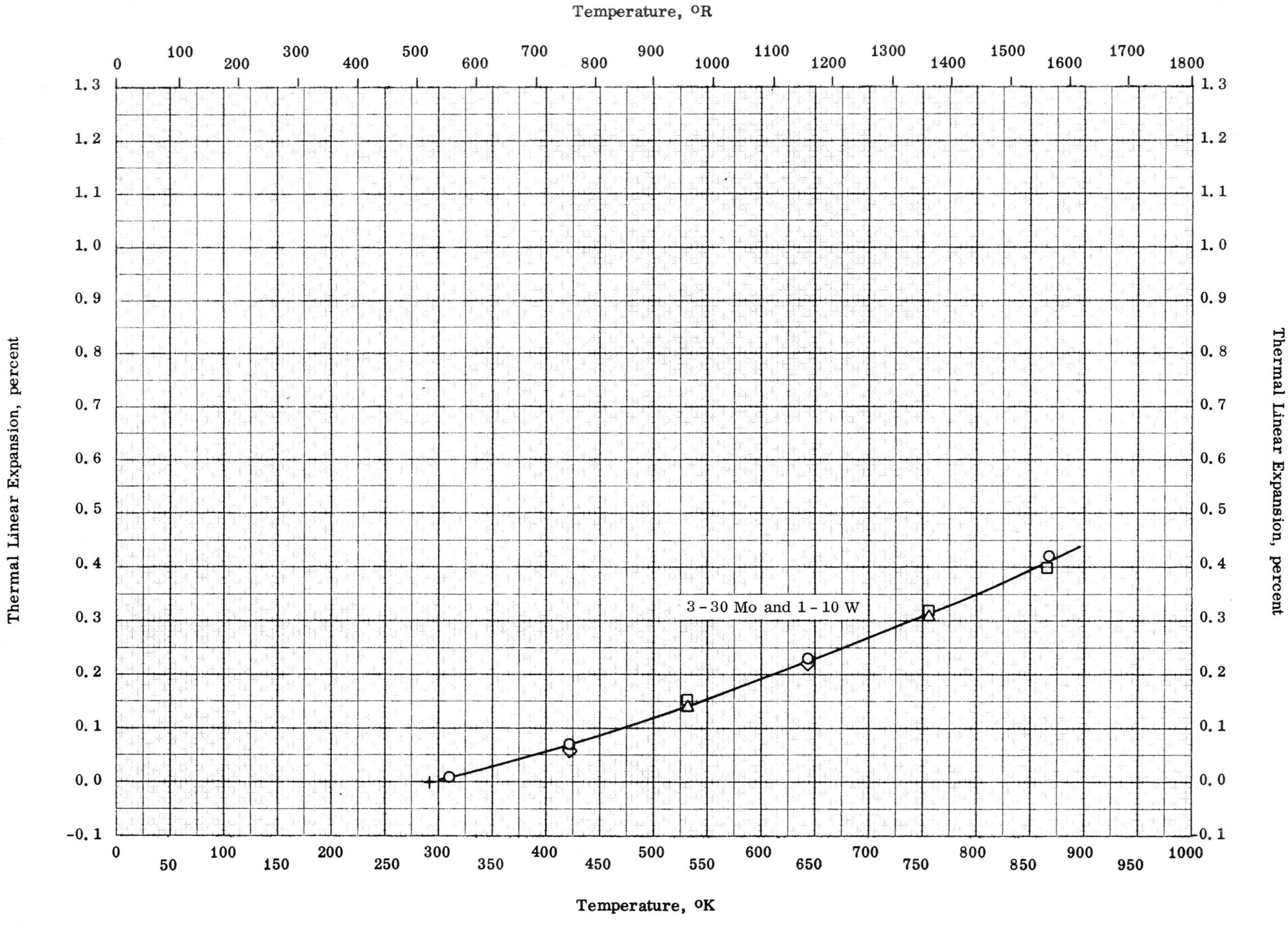

Temperature, °R

Thermal Linear Expansion, percent

3 - 30 Mo and 1 - 10 W

Temperature, °K

Thermal Linear Expansion, percent

THERMAL LINEAR EXPANSION -- [TITANIUM CARBIDE + MOLYBDENUM + TUNGSTEN] CERMET

REFERENCE INFORMATION

Symbol	Ref.	Temp. Range °K	Rept. Error %	Sample Specifications	Remarks
○	49-4	311-867		Two samples; 72.38 - 72.99 Ti, 17.05 - 17.36 total C, 5.56 - 6.04 W, 3.92 - 4.04 Mo, and trace -0.01 free C.	
□	49-4	311-867		Three samples; 67.45 - 68.10 Ti, 16.55 - 16.73 total C, 8.44 - 10.43 Mo, 5.84 - 6.62 W, and < 0.01 free C.	
△	49-4	311-867		Three samples; 57.76 - 66.03 Ti, 16.81 - 18.13 Mo, 15.20 - 15.40 total C, 1.59 - 9.36 W, and < 0.01 free C.	
◇	49-4	311-867		Four samples; 48.75 - 57.61 Ti, 24.54 - 28.96 Mo, 13.41 - 13.62 C total, 4.56 - 7.17 W, and < 0.07 free C.	

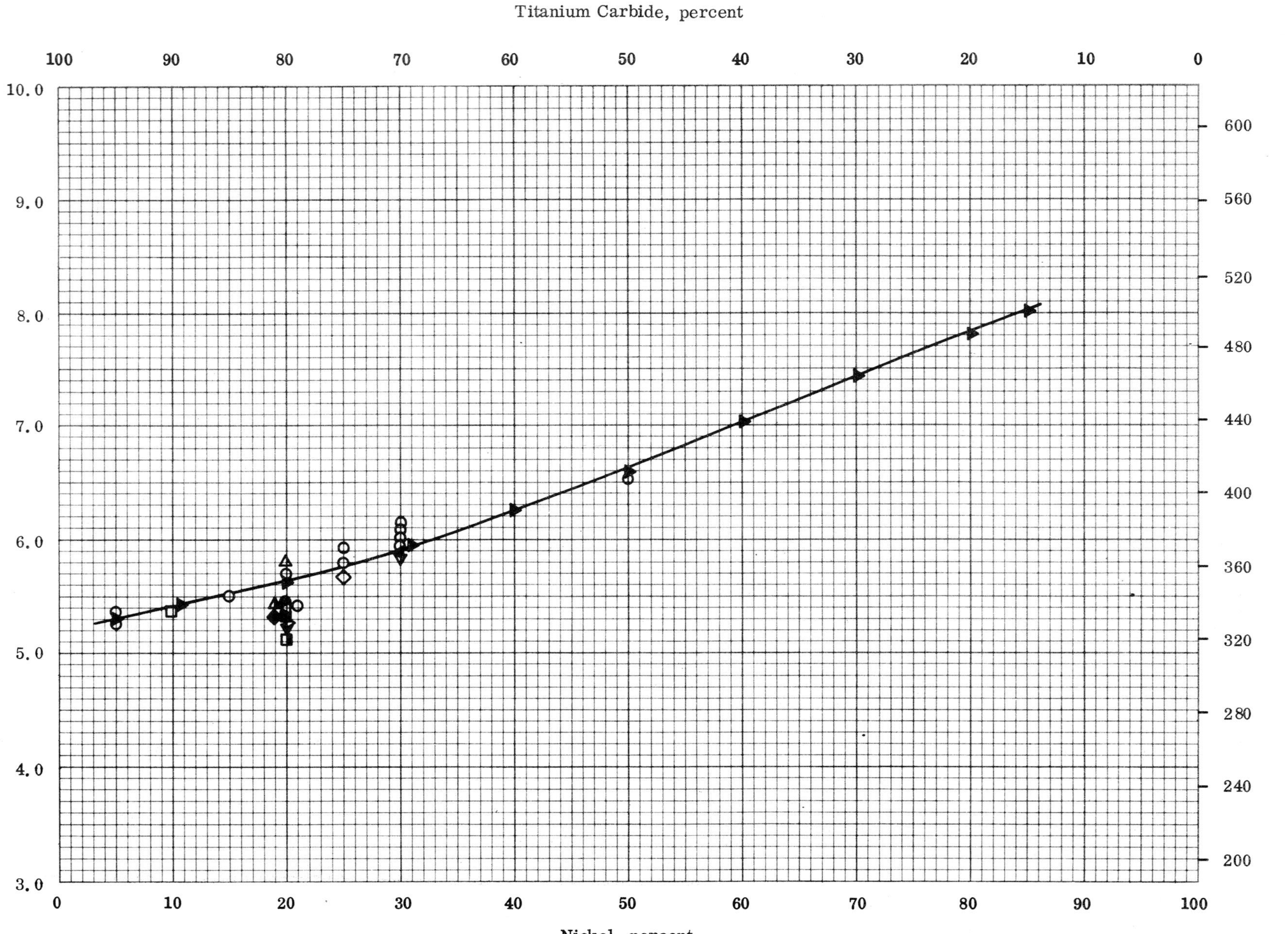

DENSITY -- [TITANIUM CARBIDE + NICKEL] CERMET

REFERENCE INFORMATION

Symbol	Ref.	Temp. Range °K	Rept. Error %	Sample Specifications	Remarks
○	55-20	298		TiC Cermet - Ni bonded, series from 5 - 50 Ni; samples contained small percentages of TaC and NbC.	Samples as received.
□	52-19	298		10 Ni.	Probably included in above work.
△	52-19	298		20 Ni.	Same as above.
◇	52-19	298		25 Ni.	Same as above.
▽	52-19	298		30 Ni.	Same as above.
◀	52-20	298		K152B; nominal: 70 T_2C and 30 Ni.	Averace of 5 samples.
▶	52-24	298		TiC Cermet - Ni bonded, series from 5 to 85% Ni; TiC analysis: 79.22 Ti, 19.66 total C, 0.60 free C, 0.01 - 0.5 Cr, Va, Fe, and traces of others.	Ball milled with CCl_4 as vehicle; pressed wet at 10,000 - 30,000 psi; sintered at pressure of 10^{-4} mm and temp. of 1310 - 1400 C for 0.25 - 4 hrs.
●	54-25 also 54-26	298		20 Ni bonded; TiC sample K-4.	Prepared by mixing TiC with 20 nickel in a carbon tet. medium and pressed hot or cold as shown below; sintered in vacuum for 2 hours at 1350 C; author gives same density for hot or cold pressed.
■	54-25 also 54-26	298		20 Ni bonded; TiC sample R-1.	Same as above; hot pressed.
◁	54-25 also 54-26	298		Same as above.	Same as above; cold pressed.
				(Continued onto next page)	

DENSITY -- [TITANIUM CARBIDE + NICKEL] CERMET (Continued)

REFERENCE INFORMATION

Symbol	Ref.	Temp. Range °K	Rept. Error %	Sample Specifications	Remarks
▼	54-25 also 54-26	298		20 Ni bonded; TiC sample MC-1; analysis: 79.0 Ti, 19.0 combined C, 0.54 free C, 0.67 N_2, 0.16 O_2, and 0.11 Fe.	Same as above; hot pressed.
▷	54-25 also 54-26	298		Same as above.	Same as above; cold pressed.
▲	54-25 also 54-26	298		20 Ni bonded; TiC sample N-3; analysis: 78.0 Ti, 16.8 combined C, 1.93 O_2, 1.54 Fe, 0.86 N_2, 0.45 free C, 0.1 each Ac, Si, and 0.03 others.	Same as above; hot pressed and flotation purified.
◆	54-25 also 54-26	298		Same as above.	Same as above; cold pressed and flotation purified.
◑	54-25 also 54-26	298		20 Ni bonded; TiC sample T-3; analysis: 79.1 Ti, 19.1 combined C, 0.57 O_2, 0.45 N_2, 0.22 Fe, 0.20 free C, and <0.01 others.	Same as above; hot pressed.
◨	54-25 also 54-26	298		Same as above.	Same as above; cold pressed.

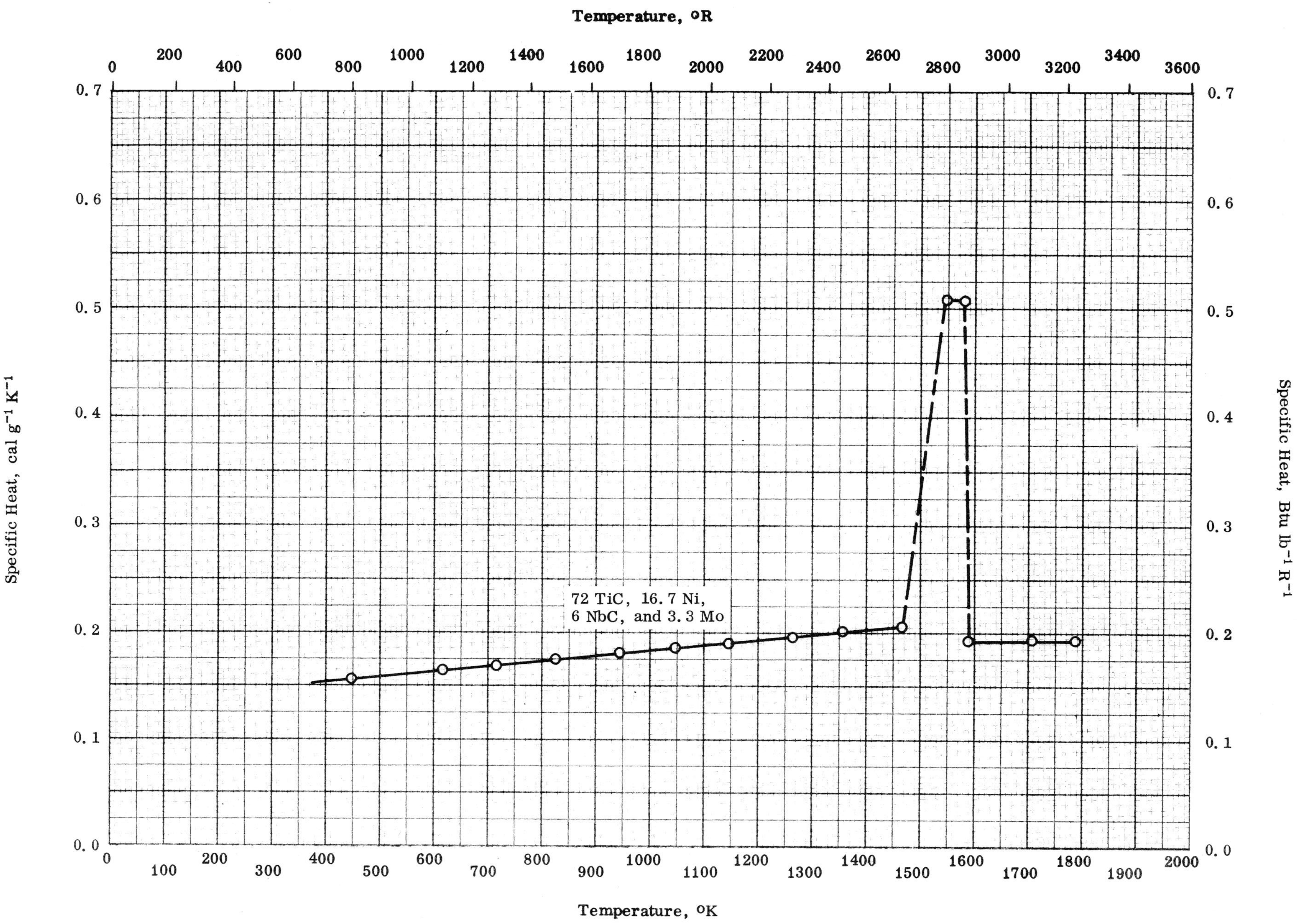

SPECIFIC HEAT -- [TITANIUM CARBIDE + NICKEL] CERMET

SPECIFIC HEAT -- [TITANIUM CARBIDE + NICKEL] CERMET

REFERENCE INFORMATION

Symbol	Ref.	Temp. Range °K	Rept. Error %	Sample Specifications	Remarks
○	61-7	448-1785	3.0	K 161B; 72 TiC, 16.7 Ni, 6 NbC, 3.3 Mo and 2 TaC; density 353 lb ft^{-3}.	Under helium atmosphere.

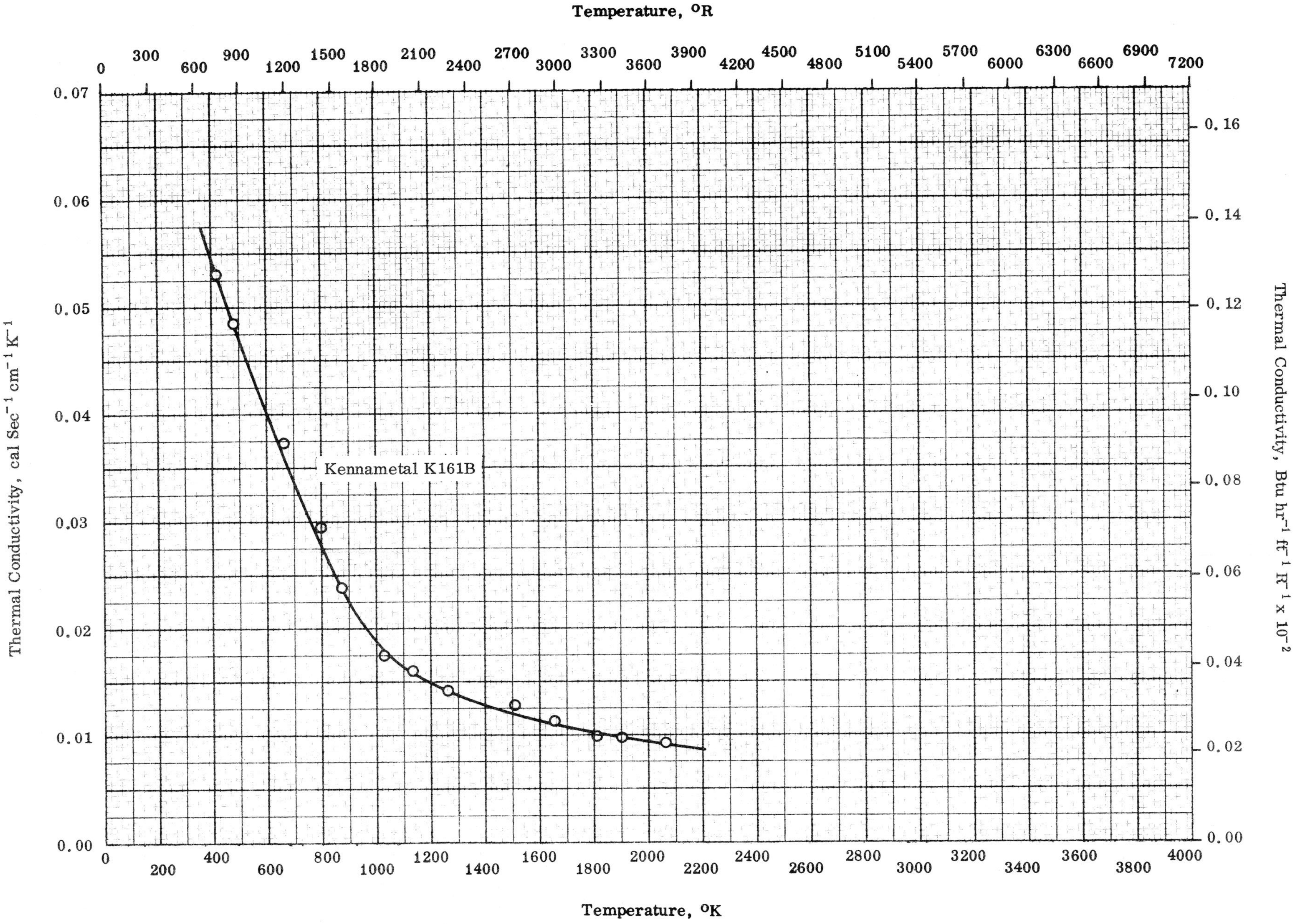
Temperature, °R
0
300
600
900
1200
1500
1800
2100
2400
2700
3000
3300
3600
3900
4200
4500
4800
5100
5400
5700
6000
6300
6600
6900
7200
Thermal Conductivity, cal Sec⁻¹ cm⁻¹ K⁻¹
0.07
0.06
0.05
0.04
0.03
0.02
0.01
0.00
Kennametal K161B
Thermal Conductivity, Btu hr⁻¹ ft⁻¹ R⁻¹ x 10⁻²
0.16
0.14
0.12
0.10
0.08
0.06
0.04
0.02
0.00
0
200
400
600
800
1000
1200
1400
1600
1800
2000
2200
2400
2600
2800
3000
3200
3400
3600
3800
4000
Temperature, °K

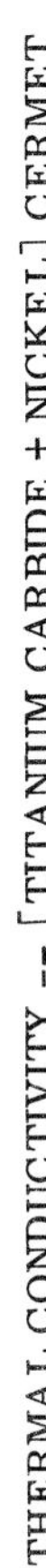

THERMAL CONDUCTIVITY -- [TITANIUM CARBIDE + NICKEL] CERMET

THERMAL CONDUCTIVITY -- [TITANIUM CARBIDE + NICKEL] CERMET

REFERENCE INFORMATION

Symbol	Ref.	Temp. Range °K	Rept. Error %	Sample Specifications	Remarks
○	61-7	420-2062	< 5	Kennametals K161B; 72 TiC, 16.7 Ni, 6 NbC, and 3.3 Mo.	Sample contained 5 one-inch discs.

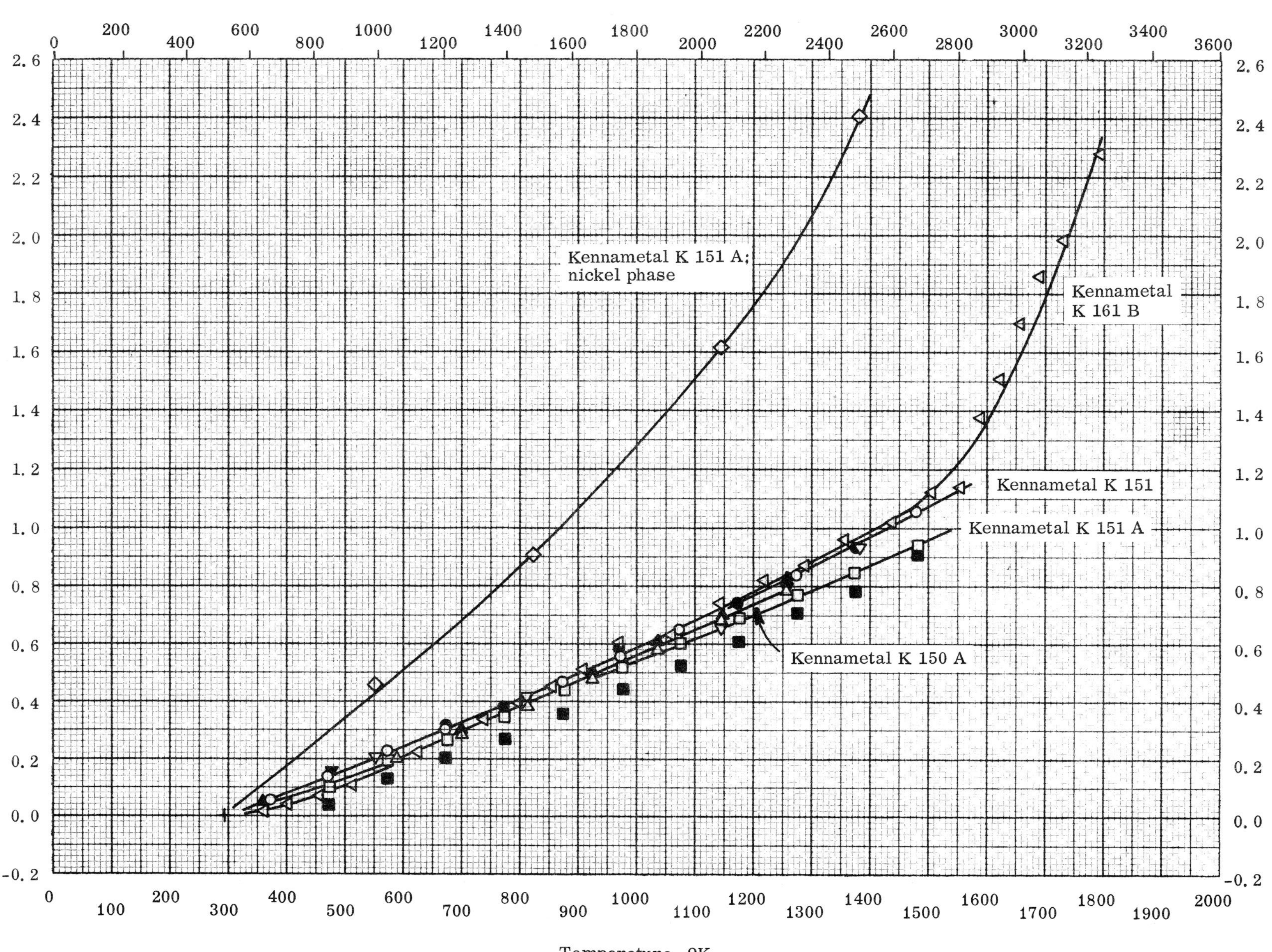

THERMAL LINEAR EXPANSION -- [TITANIUM CARBIDE + NICKEL] CERMET
[10 - 20 Ni and 0 - 15 Nb(TaTi) C]

THERMAL LINEAR EXPANSION -- [TITANIUM CARBIDE + NICKEL] CERMET
[10 - 20 Ni and 0 - 15 Nb(TaTi) C]

REFERENCE INFORMATION

Symbol	Ref.	Temp. Range °K	Rept. Error %	Sample Specifications	Remarks
○	55-20	299-1478		Kennametal K-151; 80 TiC and 20 Ni; density 361 lb ft^{-3}.	Measured in vacuum with a heating rate of 3 C per min.
●	55-20	299-1478		Same as above.	Cooling rate 3 C per min.
□	54-20	299-1478		Kennametal K-151A; 67 TiC, 18 Ni, and 15 Nb(TaTi)C.	Same as K-151.
■	54-20	299-1478		Same as above.	Cooling rate 3 C per min.
△	63-30	293-1255	3	Kennametal K-150A; 80 TiC, 10 Ni, and 10 Nb(TaTi)C; dimension: 4 mm diameter by 50 mm long; density 5.82 g cm^{-3}.	Nb(TaTi)C added as a solid solution containing 90 NbC; measured in vacuum with heating rate at 3 F per min gradually increased to 5 F per min; no permanent change in length.
▲	63-30	293-1255	3	Kennametal K-151A; 70 TiC, 20 Ni, and 10 Nb(TaTi)C; same dimension as above; density 5.64 g cm^{-3}.	Same as above.
▽	58-15	296-1380	1	Kennametal K-151A; nominal batch composition: 65 TiC, 20 Ni, and 15 Nb(TaTi)C, spectrographic analysis revealed the presence of Ti, Ta, Nb, Ni as major elements, W, Cu, Cr, Co, Fe, Si as minor elements, trace Mo, V, and Al. [Author's design.: Carbide phase K-151A]	X-ray method.
◇	58-15	296-1380	1	Same as above except nickel phase K-151A.	X-ray method.
▼	64-20	293-922	2	Kennametal K-151A; 70 TiC, 20 Ni, and 10 Nb(TaTi)C; density 5.8 g cm^{-3}.	
◁	61-7	300-1790		Kennametal K-161B; 72 TiC, 16.7 Ni, 6 Nb(TaTi)C, and 3.3 Mo; density 5.66 g cm^{-3}.	

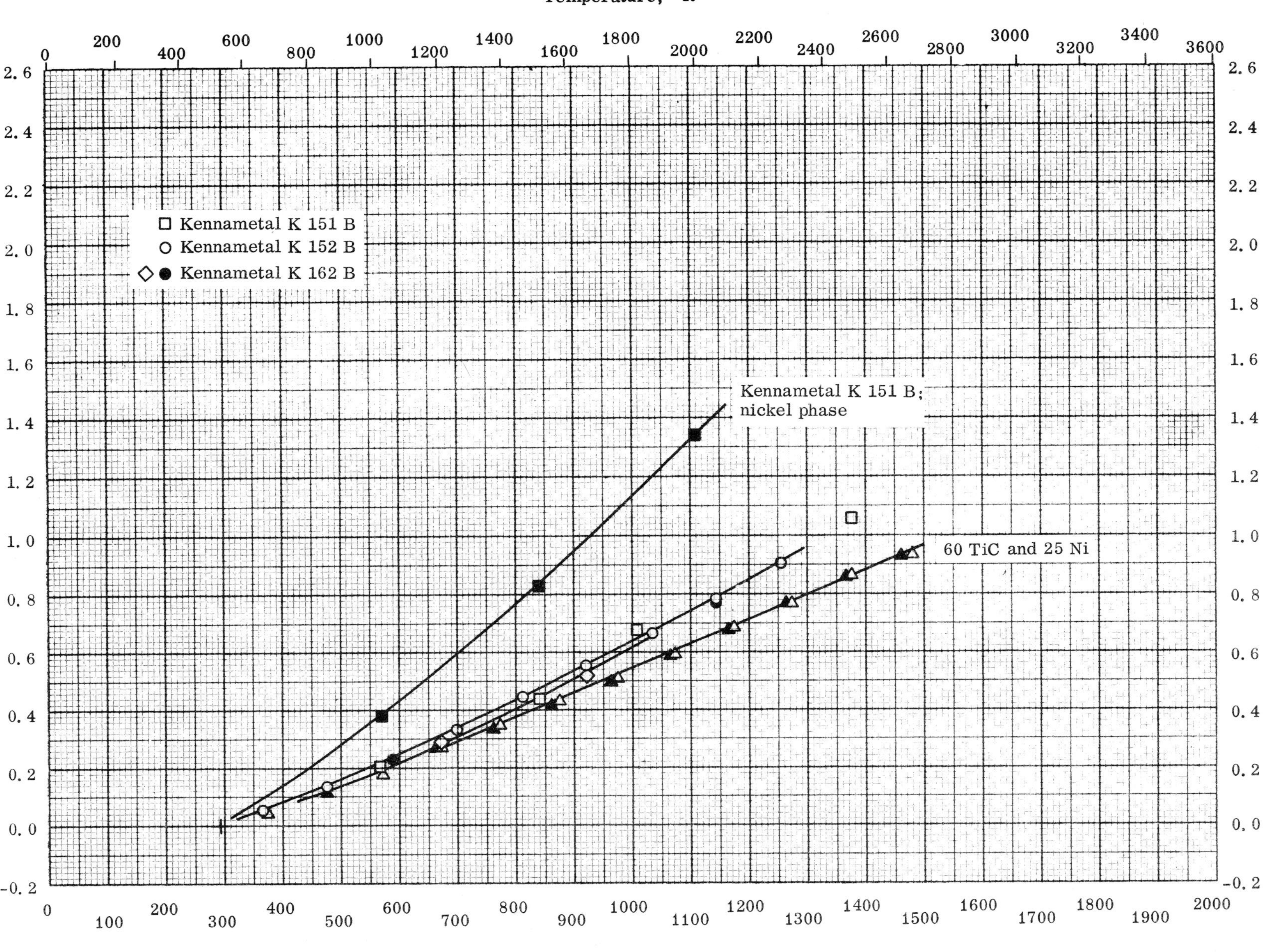

THERMAL LINEAR EXPANSION -- [TITANIUM CARBIDE + NICKEL] CERMET
[25 - 30 Ni and 6 - 15 Nb(TaTi) C]

THERMAL LINEAR EXPANSION -- [TITANIUM CARBIDE + NICKEL] CERMET
[25 - 30 Ni and 6 - 15 Nb(TaTi) C]

REFERENCE INFORMATION

Symbol	Ref.	Temp. Range °K	Rept. Error %	Sample Specifications	Remarks
○	63-30	293-1255	3	Kennametal K 152B; 64 TiC, 30 Ni, and 6 Nb(TaTi)C; dimension: 4 mm diameter by 50 mm long; density 5.93 g cm^{-3}.	Nb(TaTi)C added as a solid solution containing 90 NbC; heating rate at about 3 F per min gradually increased to 5 F per min; measured in vacuum; no permanent change in length.
●	63-30	293-1255	3	Kennametal K 162B; 64 TiC, 25 Ni, 6 Nb(TaTi)C, and 5 Mo; same dimension as above; density 6.07 g cm^{-3}.	Same as above.
□	58-15	296-1374	1	Kennametal 151B; nominal batch composition: 62 TiC, 30 Ni, and 8 Nb(TaTi)C; spectrographic analysis revealed the presence of Ti, Ta, Nb as major elements, W, Cu, Cr, Co, Fe, Si as minor elements, trace Mo, V, and Al. [Author's design.: Carbide phase K-151-B]	X-ray method.
■	58-15	296-1374	1	Same as above except nickel phase K-151-B.	X-ray method.
△	55-20	300-1478		60 TiC, 25 Ni, and 15 Nb(TaTi)C.	Measured in vacuum with a heating rate at 3 C per min.
▲	55-20	300-1478		Same as above.	Cooling data of above specimen with cooling rate 3 C per min.
◇	64-20	293-922	2	Kennametal K 162B; 62 TiC, 25 Ni, 8 Nb(TaTi)C, and 5 Mo; density 6.0 g cm^{-3}.	

Temperature, °R

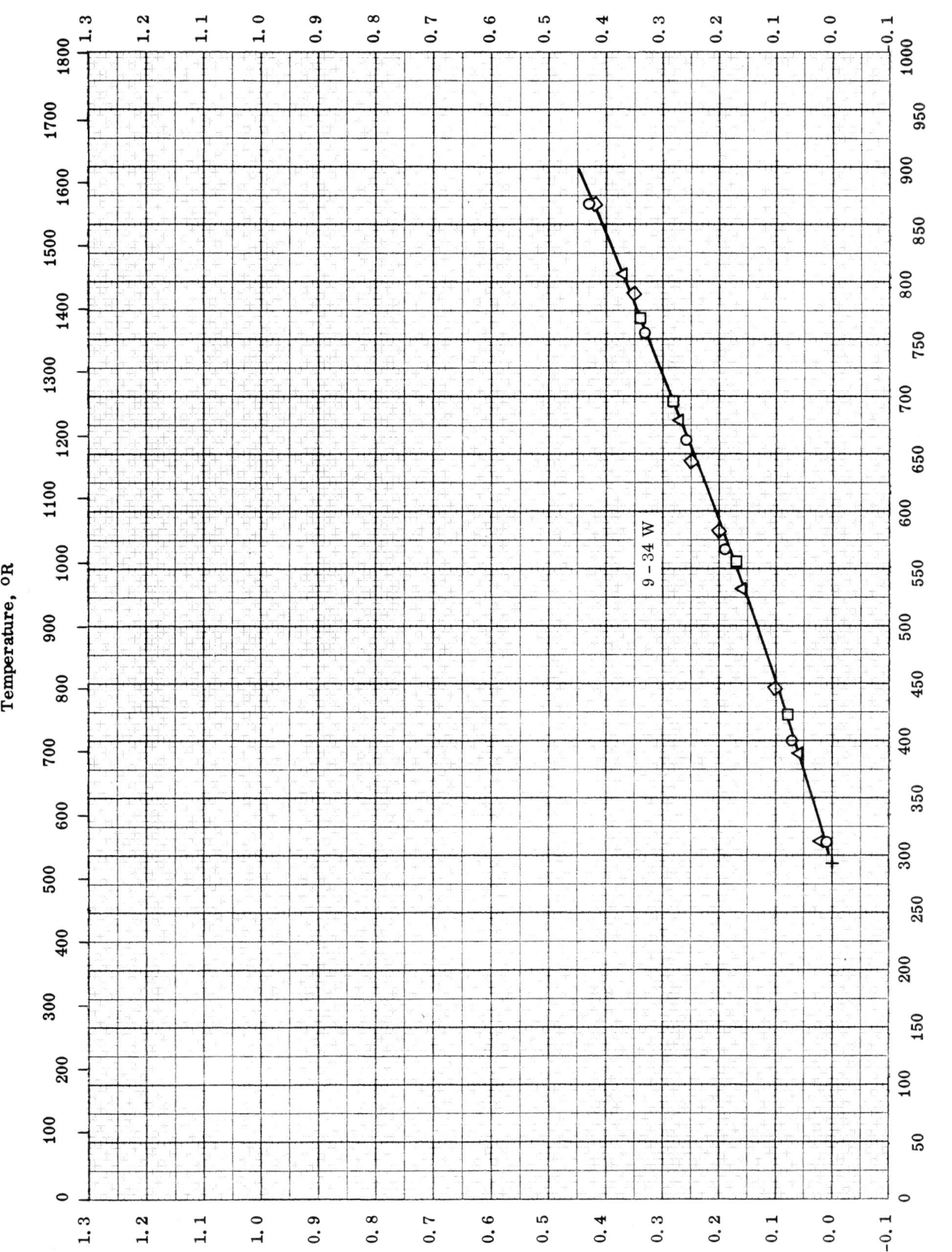

Thermal Linear Expansion, percent

9 - 34 W

Thermal Linear Expansion, percent

Temperature, °K

THERMAL LINEAR EXPANSION -- [TITANIUM CARBIDE + TUNGSTEN] CERMET

THERMAL LINEAR EXPANSION -- [TITANIUM CARBIDE + TUNGSTEN] CERMET

REFERENCE INFORMATION

Symbol	Ref.	Temp. Range °K	Rept. Error %	Sample Specifications	Remarks
○	49-4	311-867		Three samples; 67. 50 - 71. 99 Ti, 15. 56 - 17. 52 total C, 9. 33 - 10. 15 W, and 0. 01 - 0. 05 free C.	
□	49-4	311-867		Three samples; 64. 56 - 68. 07 Ti, 15. 68 - 16. 41 total C, 15. 16 - 15. 69 W, and trace -0. 04 free C.	
△	49-4	311-867		Three samples; 58. 48 - 61. 43 Ti, 20. 02 - 24. 27 W, 14. 40 - 14. 96 total C, and 0. 01 - 0. 040 free C.	
◇	49-4	311-867		50. 17 - 53. 50 Ti, 32. 14 - 34. 08 W, 12. 77 - 13. 47 total C, and < 0. 05 free C.	

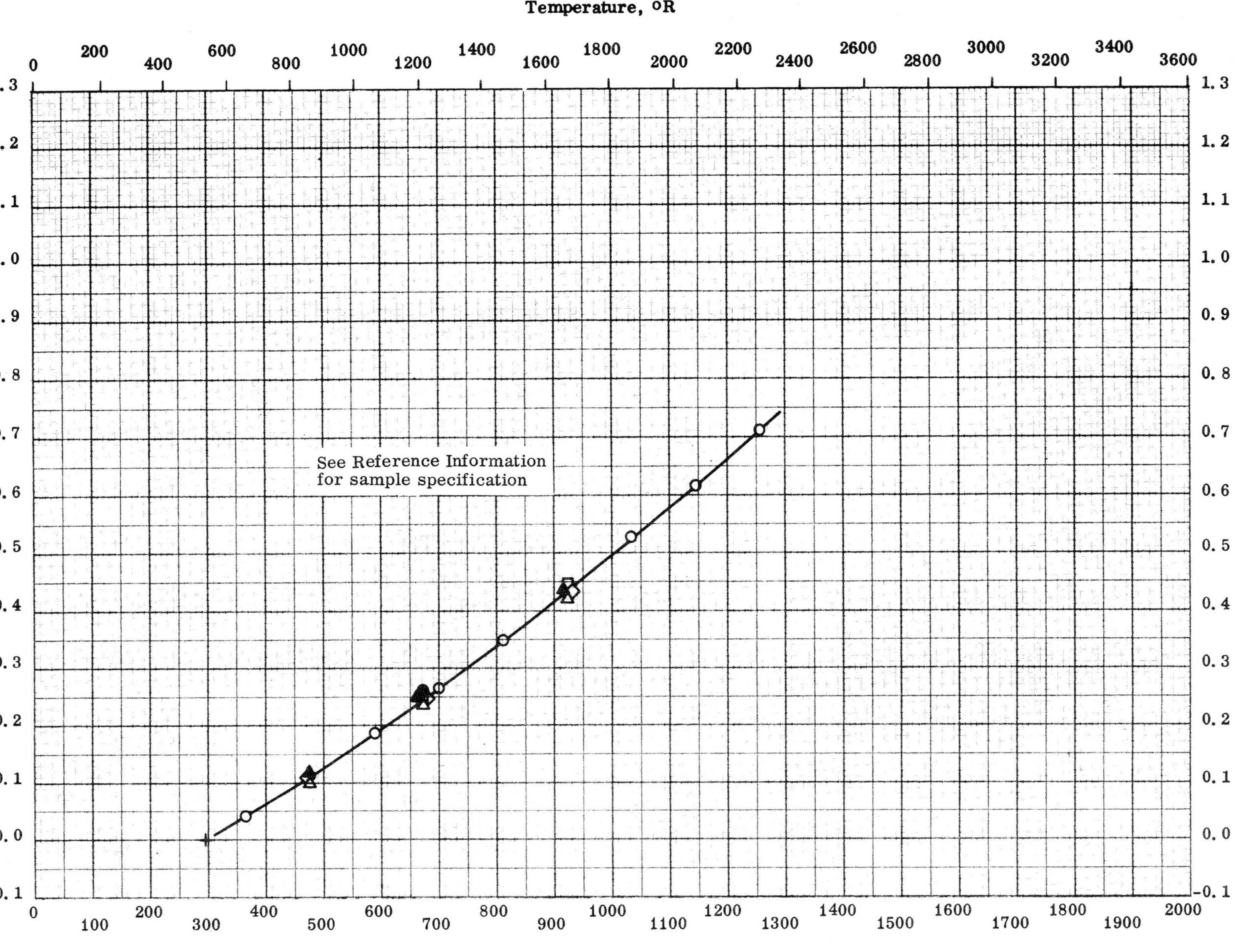

THERMAL LINEAR EXPANSION -- [TITANIUM TUNGSTEN DICARBIDE + COBALT] CERMET

THERMAL LINEAR EXPANSION -- [TITANIUM TUNGSTEN DICARBIDE + COBALT] CERMET

REFERENCE INFORMATION

Symbol	Ref.	Temp. Range °K	Rept. Error %	Sample Specifications	Remarks
○	63-31	293-1255		Kennametal K 3 H, $WTiC_2$ and cobalt cermet; nominal composition: 65 W, 11.0 Ti, 8.75 Co, 7.6 C, 5.8 T, 1.8 Nb; dimension: 4 mm dia by 50 mm long; density 10.84 g cm^{-3}.	Measured in vac with a heating rate of 3 F per min gradually increased to 5 F per min at the end of heating; no significant permanent change in length observed after test.
□	64-20	293-922	2	Kennametal K 86, W TiC_2 and cobalt cermet; density 11.1 g cm^{-3}.	
△	64-20	293-922	2	Kennametal K 84, W TiC_2 and cobalt cermet; density 11.9 g cm^{-3}.	
●	64-20	293-922	2	Kennametal K 82, W TiC_2 and cobalt cermet; densit 11.8 g cm^{-3}.	
▲	64-20	293-922	2	Kennametal K 81, W TiC_2 and cobalt cermet; density 11.6 g cm^{-3}.	
◇	64-20	293-922	2	Kennametal K 3H, W Ti_2C and cobalt cermet; density 11.1 g cm^{-3}.	

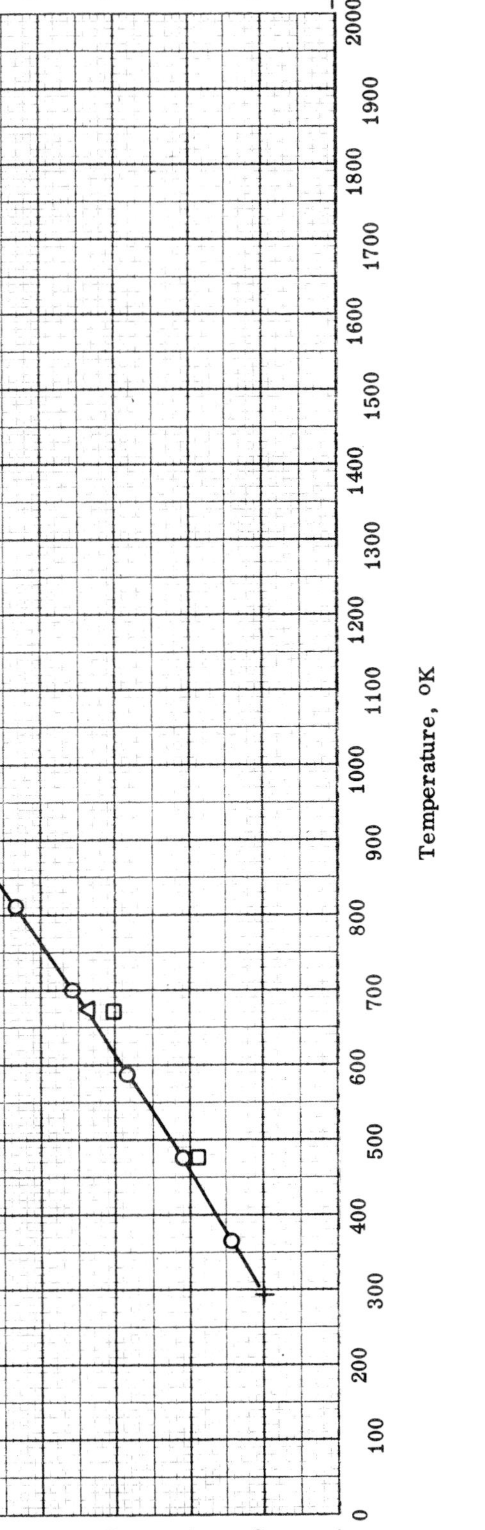

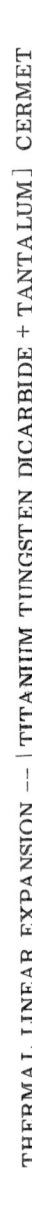

THERMAL LINEAR EXPANSION -- [TITANIUM TUNGSTEN DICARBIDE + TANTALUM] CERMET

THERMAL LINEAR EXPANSION -- ⌊TITANIUM TUNGSTEN DICARBIDE + TANTALUM⌋ CERMET

REFERENCE INFORMATION

Symbol	Ref.	Temp. Range °K	Rept. Error %	Sample Specifications	Remarks
○	63-31	293-1255		Kennametal K 21; W TiC_2 and tantalum; nominal composition: 65. 8 W, 10. 8 Ta, 10 Co, 6. 7 C, 6. 0 Ti, 0. 6 Nb; dimension: 4 mm dia by 50 mm long; density 12. 40 g cm^{-3}.	Measured in vac with a heating rate of 3 F per min gradually increased to 5 F per min at the end of heating; no significant permanent change in length observed after test.
□	64-20	293-922	2	Kennametal K 21; W TiC_2 and tantalum; density 12. 3 g cm^{-3}.	
△	64-20	293-922	2	Kennametal KM; 55. 5 W, 13. 6 TaC, 10. 7 Co, 10. 2 TiC; density 12. 9 g cm^{-3}.	

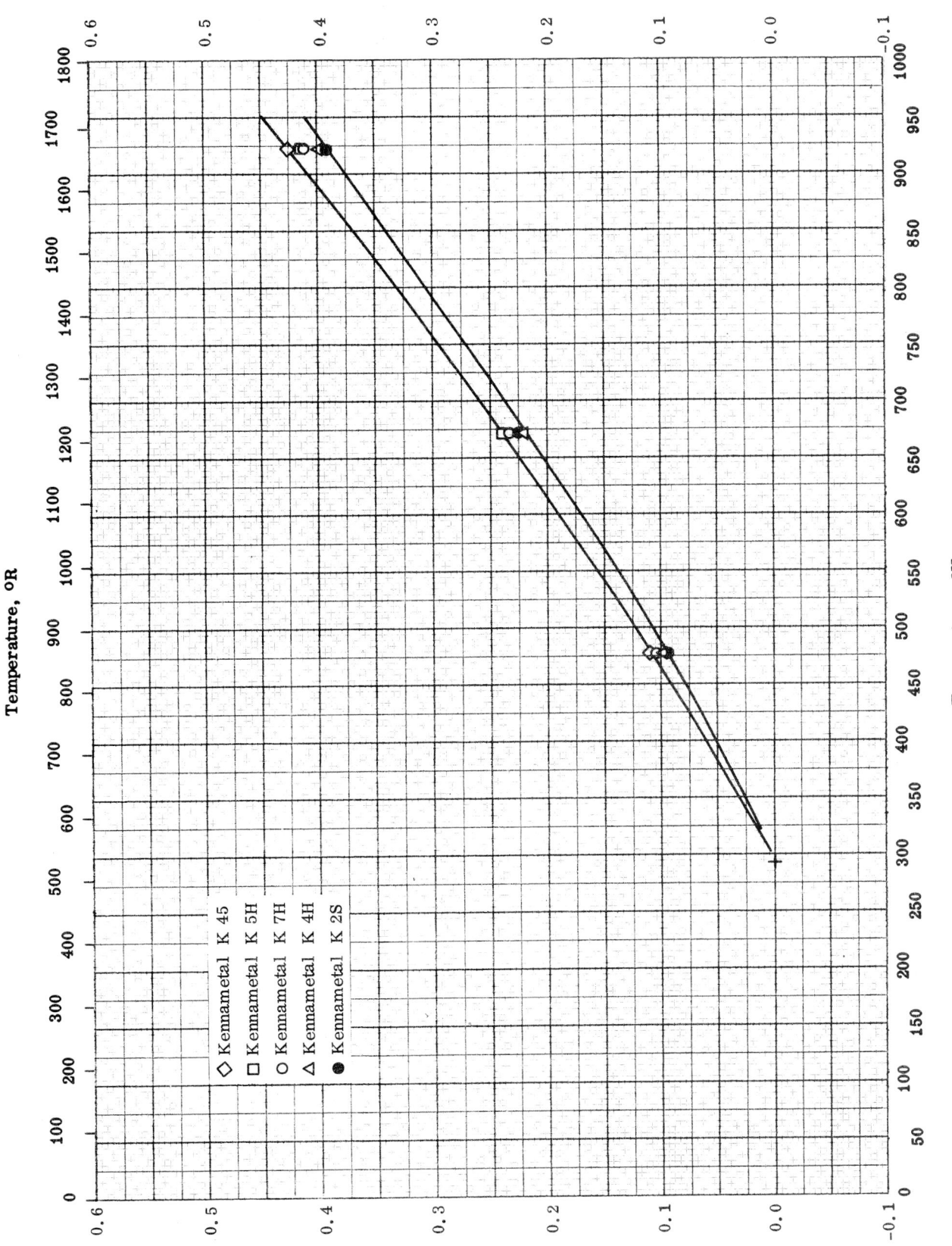

THERMAL LINEAR EXPANSION -- OTHER TITANIUM TUNGSTEN CARBIDE CERMETS

THERMAL LINEAR EXPANSION -- OTHER TITANIUM TUNGSTEN CARBIDE CERMETS

REFERENCE INFORMATION

Symbol	Ref.	Temp. Range °K	Rept. Error %	Sample Specifications	Remarks
○	64-20	293-922	2	Kennametal K7H; density 11.1 g cm^{-3}.	
□	64-20	293-922	2	Kennametal K5H; density 11.5 g cm^{-3}.	
△	64-20	293-922	2	Kennametal K4H; density 12.5 g cm^{-3}.	
◇	64-20	293-922	2	Kennametal K45; density 12.2 g cm^{-3}.	
●	64-20	293-922	2	Kennametal K2S; density 12.9 g cm^{-3}.	

PROPERTIES OF [TUNGSTEN CARBIDE + COBALT] CERMET

REPORTED VALUES

Density	g cm^{-3}	lb ft^{-3}
○ 94 WC and 6 Co	14.86	927.7
□ 87 WC and 13 Co	14.09	879.6

PROPERTIES OF [TUNGSTEN CARBIDE + COBALT] CERMET

REFERENCE INFORMATION

Symbol	Ref.	Temp. Range °K	Rept. Error %	Sample Specifications	Remarks
○	52-20	298		Carboloy 44A; nominal 94 WC and 6 Co.	Average for 5 samples by weight and volume from measured dimensions.
□	52-20	298		Carboloy 55A; nominal 87 WC and 13 Co.	Same as above.

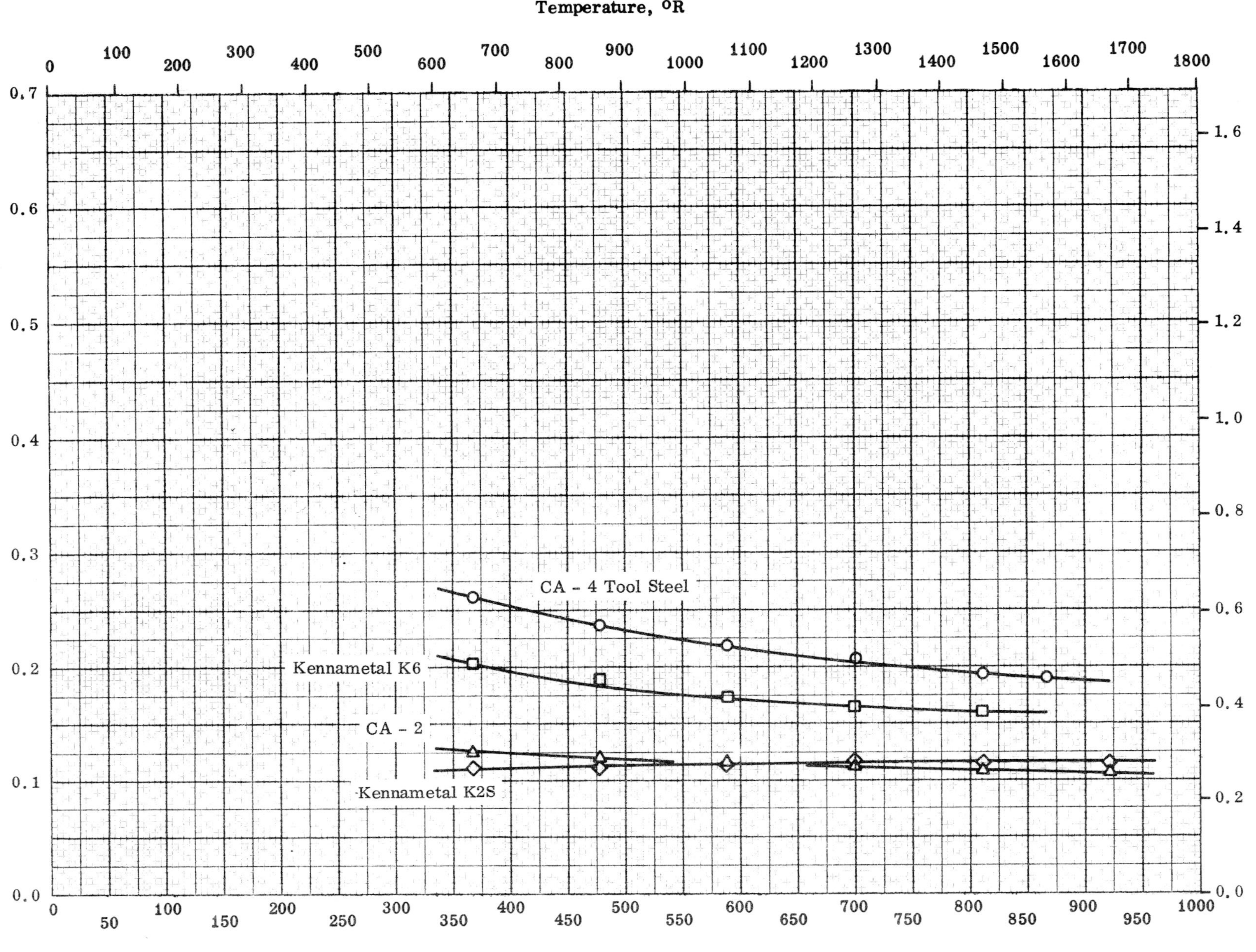

THERMAL CONDUCTIVITY -- [TUNGSTEN CARBIDE + COBALT] CERMET

THERMAL CONDUCTIVITY -- [TUNGSTEN CARBIDE + COBALT] CERMET

REFERENCE INFORMATION

Symbol	Ref.	Temp. Range °K	Rept. Error %	Sample Specifications	Remarks
○	56-6	367-867	<7	Carbide Tool Steel CA-4 (Allegheny Ludlum Steel Co.)	
□	56-6	367-811	<7	Carbide Tool Steel Kennametal K6.	
△	56-6	367-922	<7	Carbide Tool Steel CA-2 (Allegheny Ludlum Steel Co.)	
◇	56-6	367-922	<7	Carbide Tool Steel Kennametal K2S.	

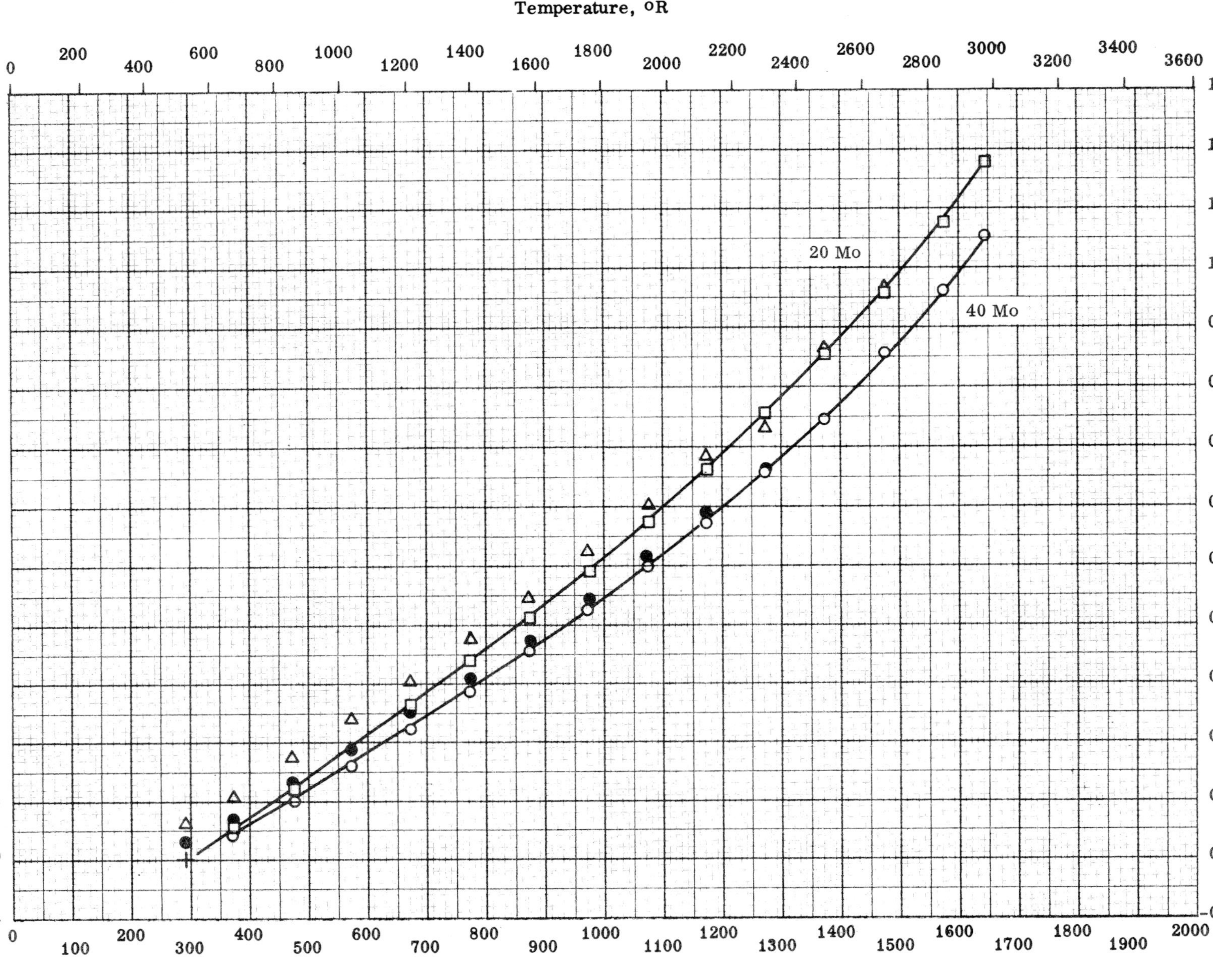

THERMAL LINEAR EXPANSION -- [URANIUM MONOCARBIDE + MOLYBDENUM] CERMET

THERMAL LINEAR EXPANSION -- [URANIUM MONOCARBIDE + MOLYBDENUM] CERMET

REFERENCE INFORMATION

Symbol	Ref.	Temp. Range °K	Rept. Error %	Sample Specifications	Remarks
○	62-40	293-1643	±2	60 vol % UC and 40 vol% Mo; 95% ≤ theoretical density.	Heating.
●	62-40	293-1643	±2	Same as above.	Cooling.
□	62-40	293-1643	±2	80 vol% UC and 20 vol% Mo; 95% ≤ theoretical density.	Heating.
△	62-40	293-1643	±2	Same as above.	Cooling.

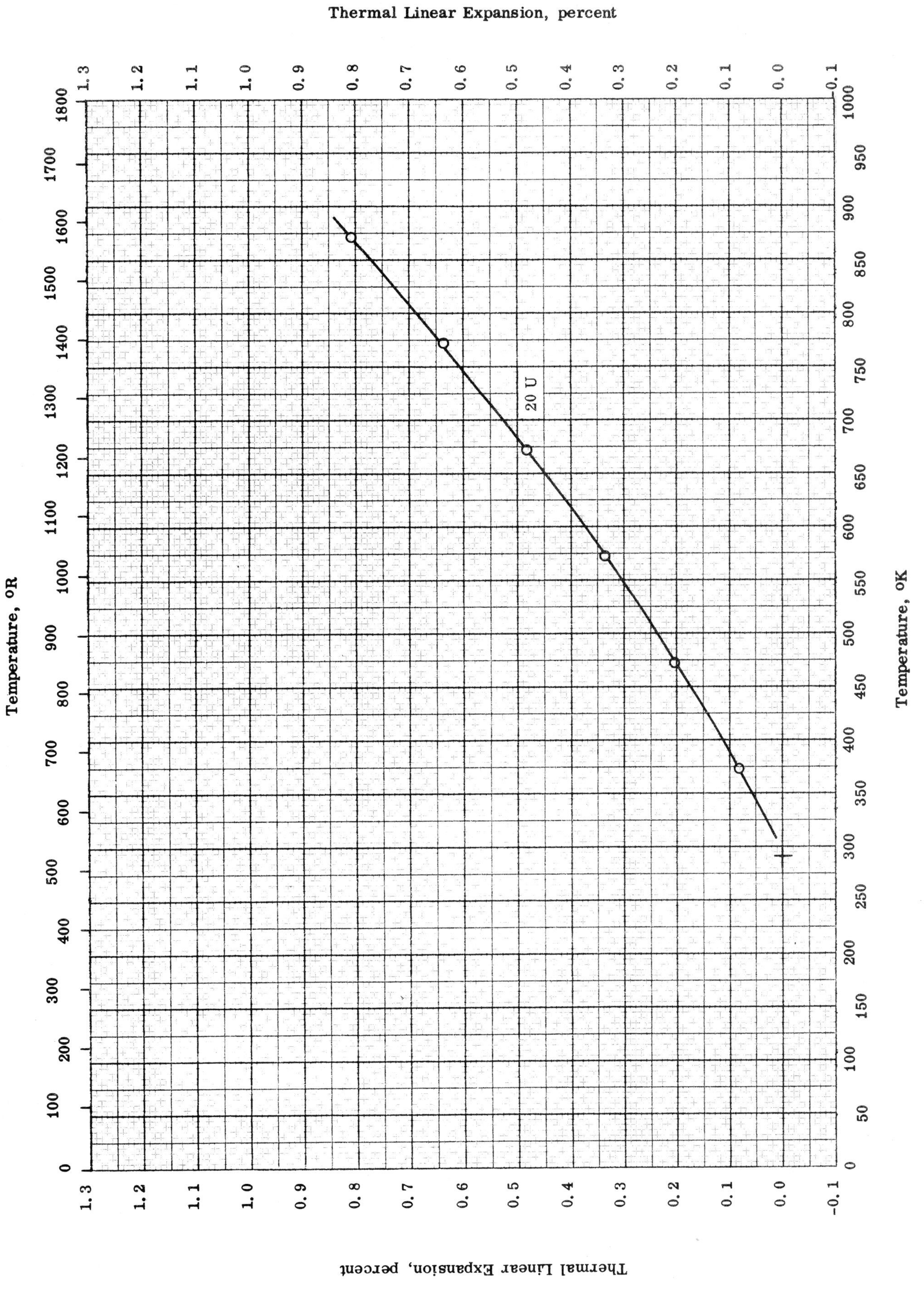

Temperature, °R

Thermal Linear Expansion, percent

20 U

Temperature, °K

THERMAL LINEAR EXPANSION -- [URANIUM MONOCARBIDE + URANIUM] CERMET

THERMAL LINEAR EXPANSION -- [URANIUM MONOCARBIDE + URANIUM] CERMET

REFERENCE INFORMATION

Symbol	Ref.	Temp. Range °K	Rept. Error %	Sample Specifications	Remarks
○	60-32	293-873		UC and 20 U.	Pressed from a mixture UC + 20 U and sintered in a vacuum furnace.

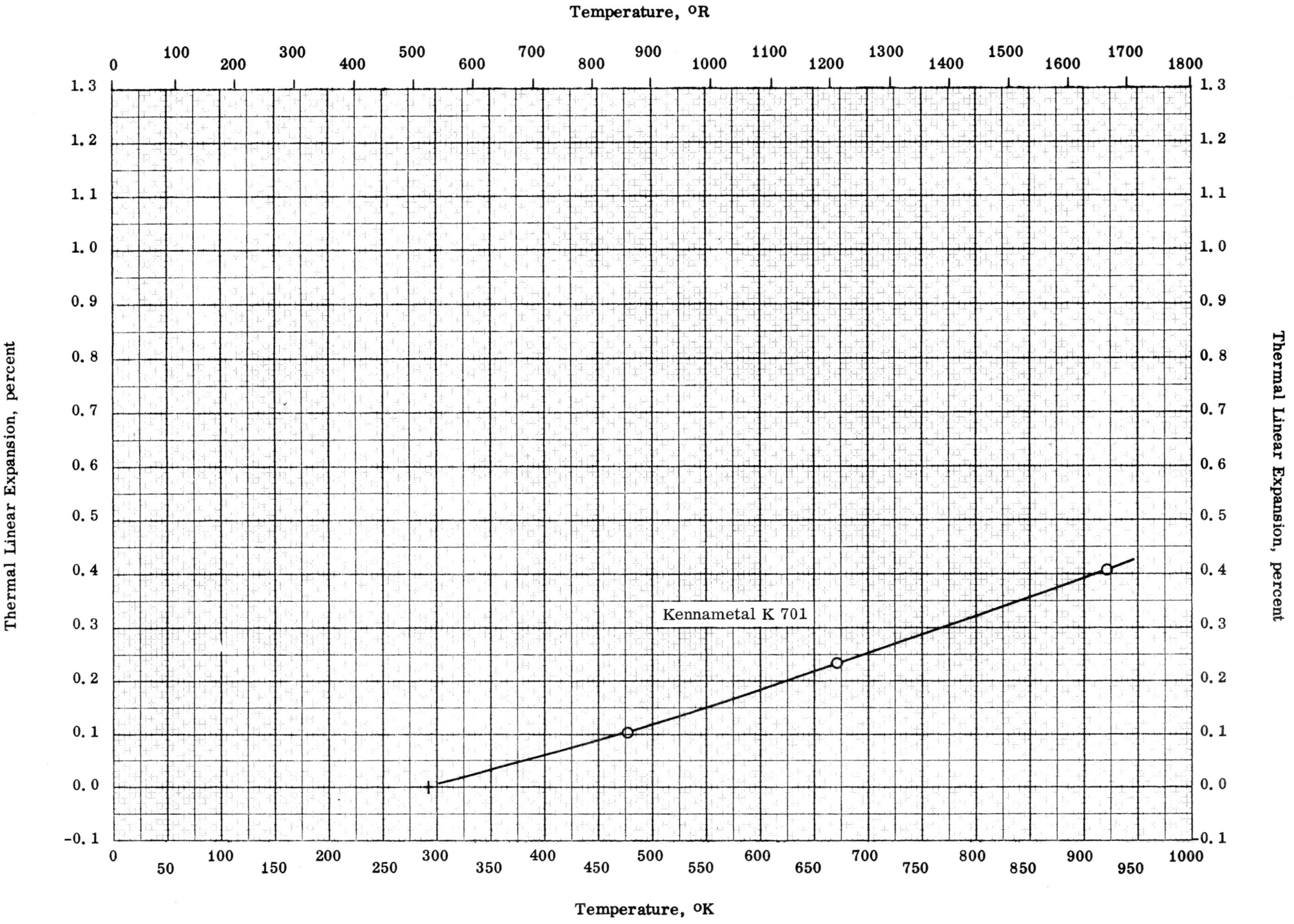

Thermal Linear Expansion, percent

Kennametal K 701

Temperature, °R

Temperature, °K

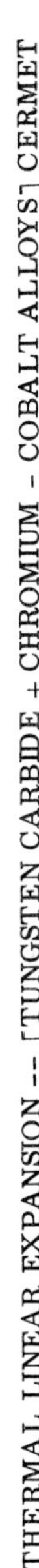

THERMAL LINEAR EXPANSION -- [TUNGSTEN CARBIDE + CHROMIUM - COBALT ALLOYS] CERMET

REFERENCE INFORMATION

Symbol	Ref.	Temp. Range °K	Rept. Error %	Sample Specifications	Remarks
○	64-20	293-922	2	Kennametal K 701; density 14.0 g cm^{-3}.	

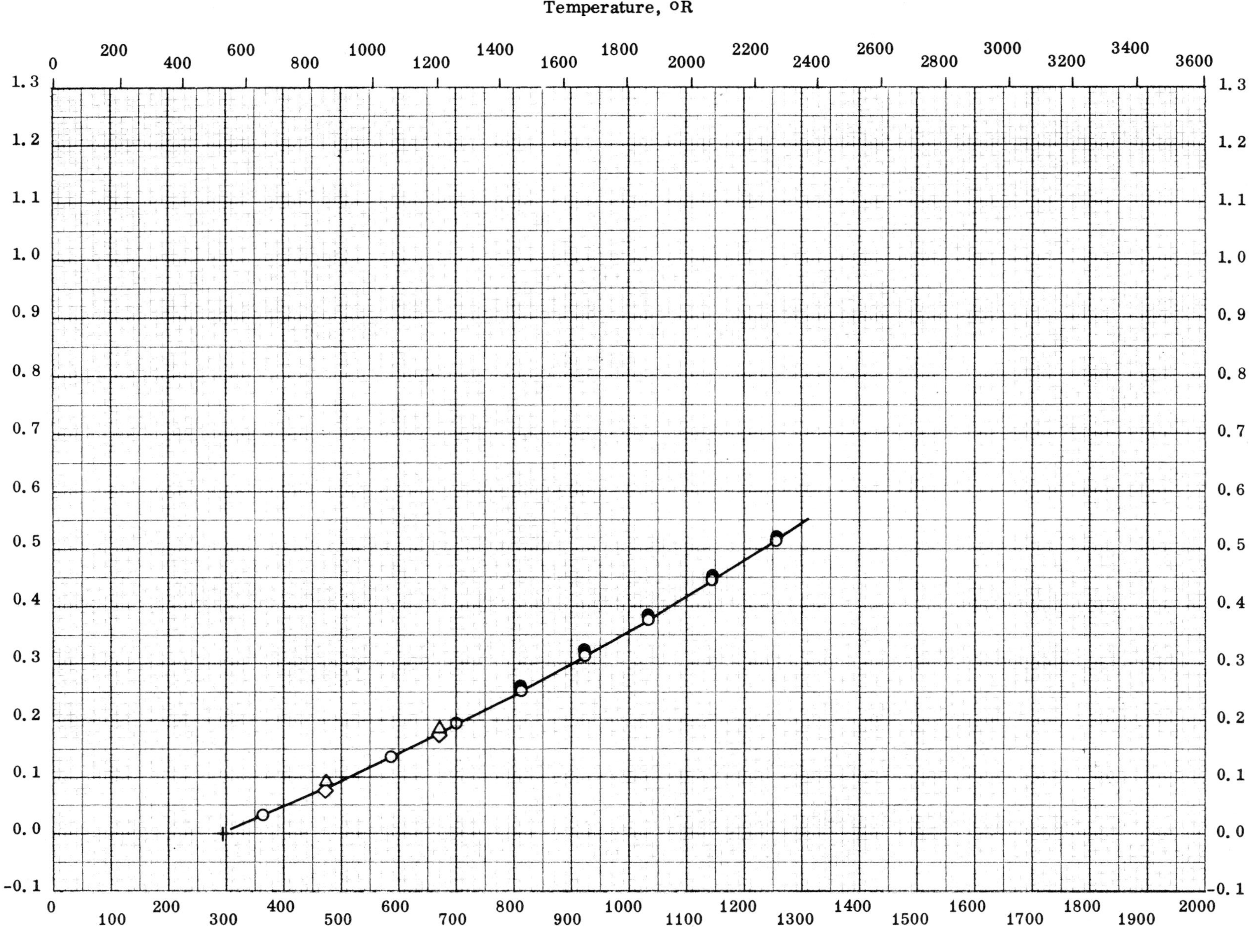

THERMAL LINEAR EXPANSION -- [TUNGSTEN CARBIDE + COBALT] CERMET
(2 < Co < 4)

THERMAL LINEAR EXPANSION -- [TUNGSTEN CARBIDE + COBALT] CERMET
($2 < Co < 4$)

REFERENCE INFORMATION

Symbol	Ref.	Temp. Range °K	Rept. Error %	Sample Specifications	Remarks
○	63-31	293-1225		Kennametal K 11; nominal: 92.5 W, 6.0 C, and 2.5 Co; dimension: 4 mm dia by 5 mm long; density 15.2 g cm^{-3}.	Heated in vacuum at a rate about 3 F per min and increased to 5 F per min at the end of heating; no significant permanent change in length observed after test.
●	63-31	293-1225		Kennametal K 8; nominal: 90.3 W, 5.9 C, 3.5 Co, and 0.3 Ta; dimension: 4 mm dia by 50 mm long; density 15.10 g cm^{-3}.	Same as above specimen.
△	64-20	293-922	2	Kennametal K 11; density 15.2 g cm^{-3}.	
◇	64-20	293-922	2	Kennametal K 8; density 15.1 g cm^{-3}.	

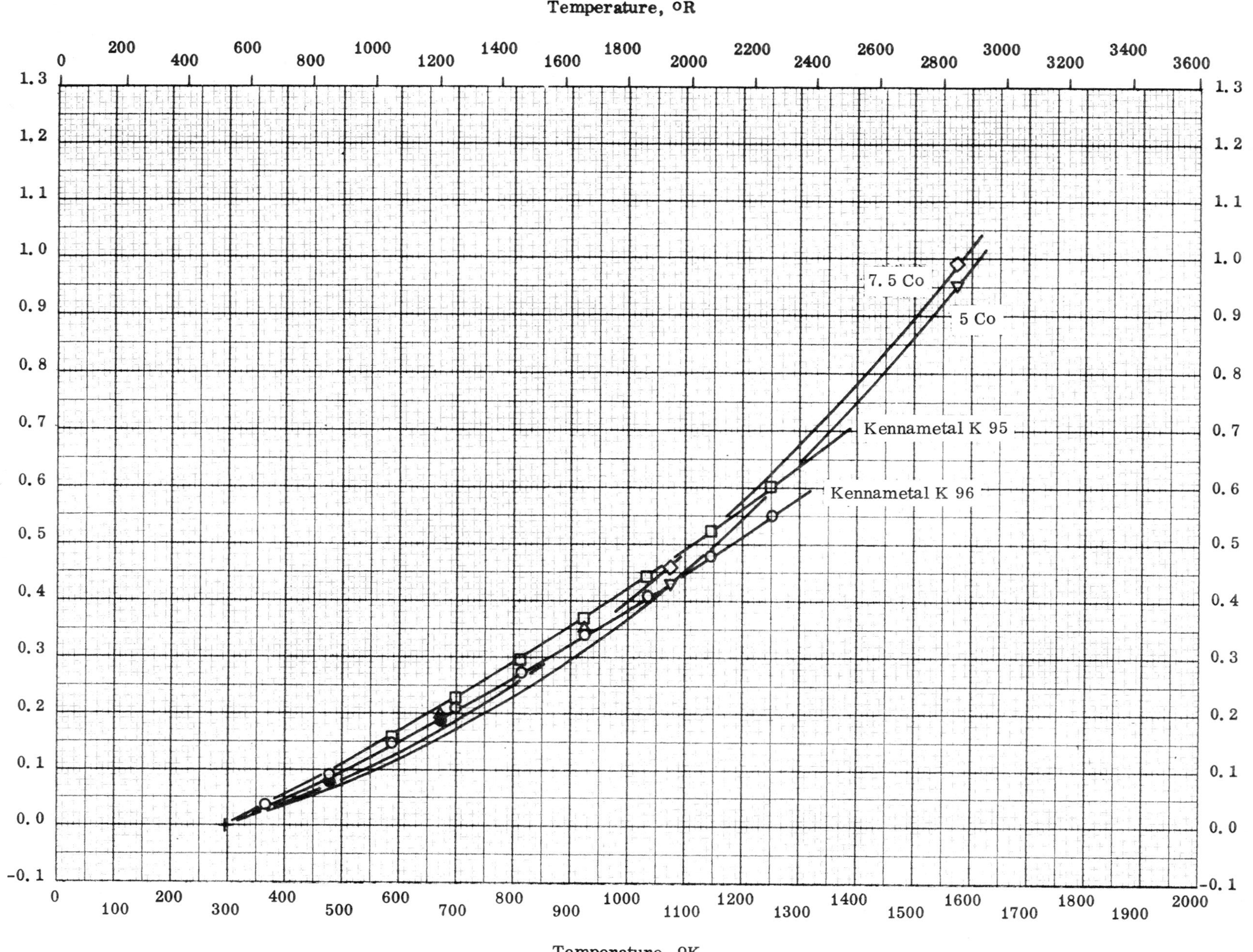

THERMAL LINEAR EXPANSION -- [TUNGSTEN CARBIDE + COBALT] CERMET
(5 ≤ Co < 9)

THERMAL LINEAR EXPANSION -- [TUNGSTEN CARBIDE + COBALT] CERMET
($5 \leq Co < 9$)

REFERENCE INFORMATION

Symbol	Ref.	Temp. Range °K	Rept. Error %	Sample Specifications	Remarks
○	63-31	293-1250		Kennametal K 96; nominal: 86.3 W, 5.8 C, 5.75 Co, 1.8 Ta, and 0.3 Nb; dimension: 4 mm dia by 50 mm long; density 14.93 g cm^{-3}.	Heated in vac at a rate about 3 F min^{-1} and increated to 5 F min^{-1} at the end of heating; no significant permanent change in length observed after test.
□	63-31	293-1247		Kennametal K 95; nominal: 85.6 W, 8.75 Co, 5.6 C, 0.6 Ta, and 0.3 Nb; dimension as above; density 14.49 g cm^{-3}.	Same as above specimen.
●	64-20	293-922	2	Kennametal K 96; density 14.9 g cm^{-3}.	
△	64-20	293-922	2	Kennametal K 95; density 14.6 g cm^{-3}.	
▽	52-15	293-1573		95 WC and 5 Co.	
◇	52-15	293-1573		92.5 WC and 7.5 Co.	

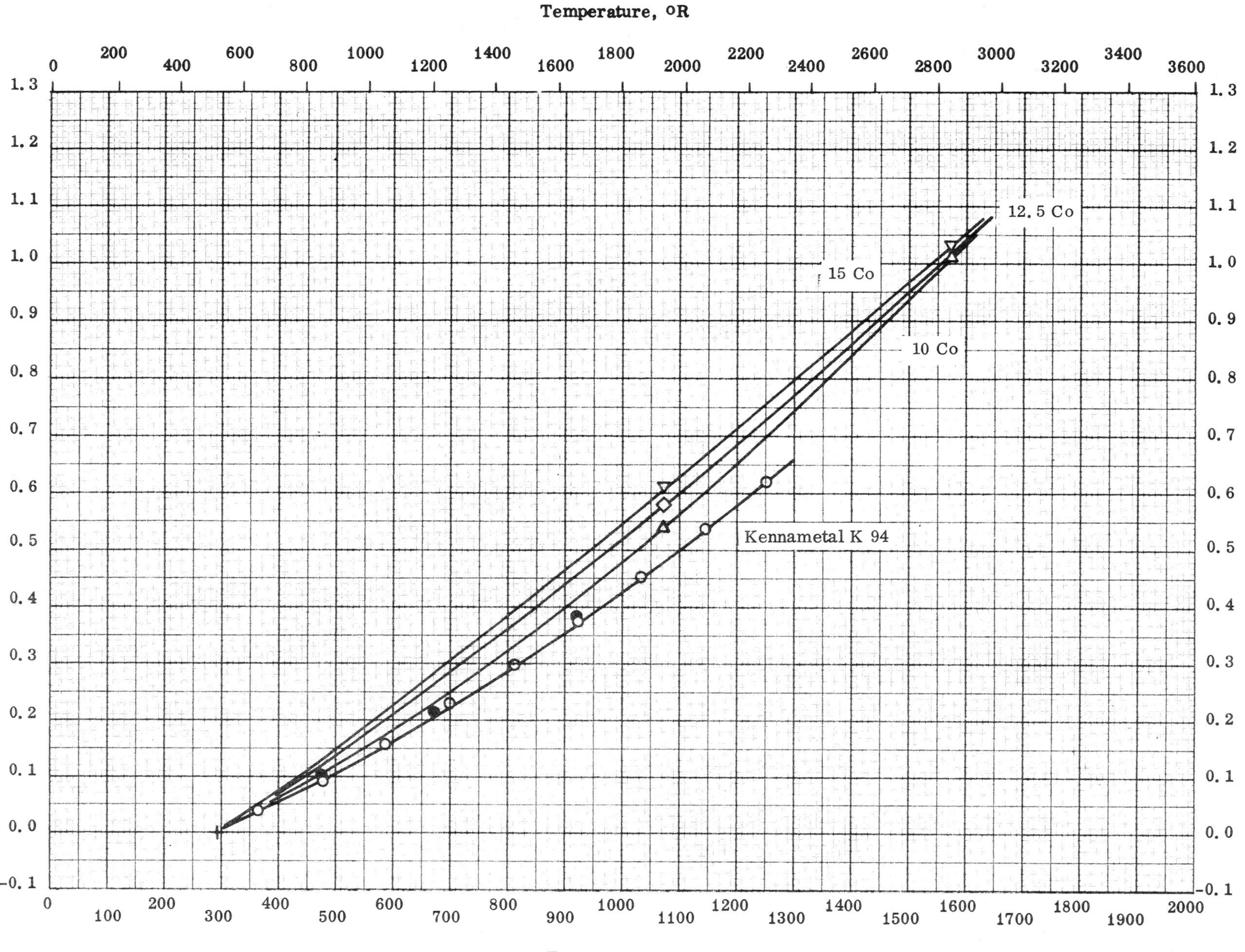

THERMAL LINEAR EXPANSION -- [TUNGSTEN CARBIDE + COBALT] CERMET
($10 \le Co \le 15$)

THERMAL LINEAR EXPANSION -- [TUNGSTEN CARBIDE + COBALT] CERMET ($10 \leq Co \leq 15$)

REFERENCE INFORMATION

Symbol	Ref.	Temp. Range °K	Rept. Error %	Sample Specifications	Remarks
○	63-31	293-1250		Kennametal K 94; nominal: 80.6 W, 11.75 Co, 5.4 C, 1.4 Ta, and 0.3 Nb; dimension: 4 mm dia by 50 mm long; density 14.29 g cm^{-3}.	Heated in vac at a rate about 3 F min^{-1} and increased to 5 F min^{-1} at the end of heating; no signficant permanent change in length observed after test.
●	64-20	293-922	2	Kennametal K 94; density 14.1 g cm^{-3}.	
△	52-15	293-1573		90 WC and 10 Co.	
◇	52-15	293-1573		87.5 WC and 12.5 Co.	
▽	52-15	293-1573		85 WC and 15 Co.	

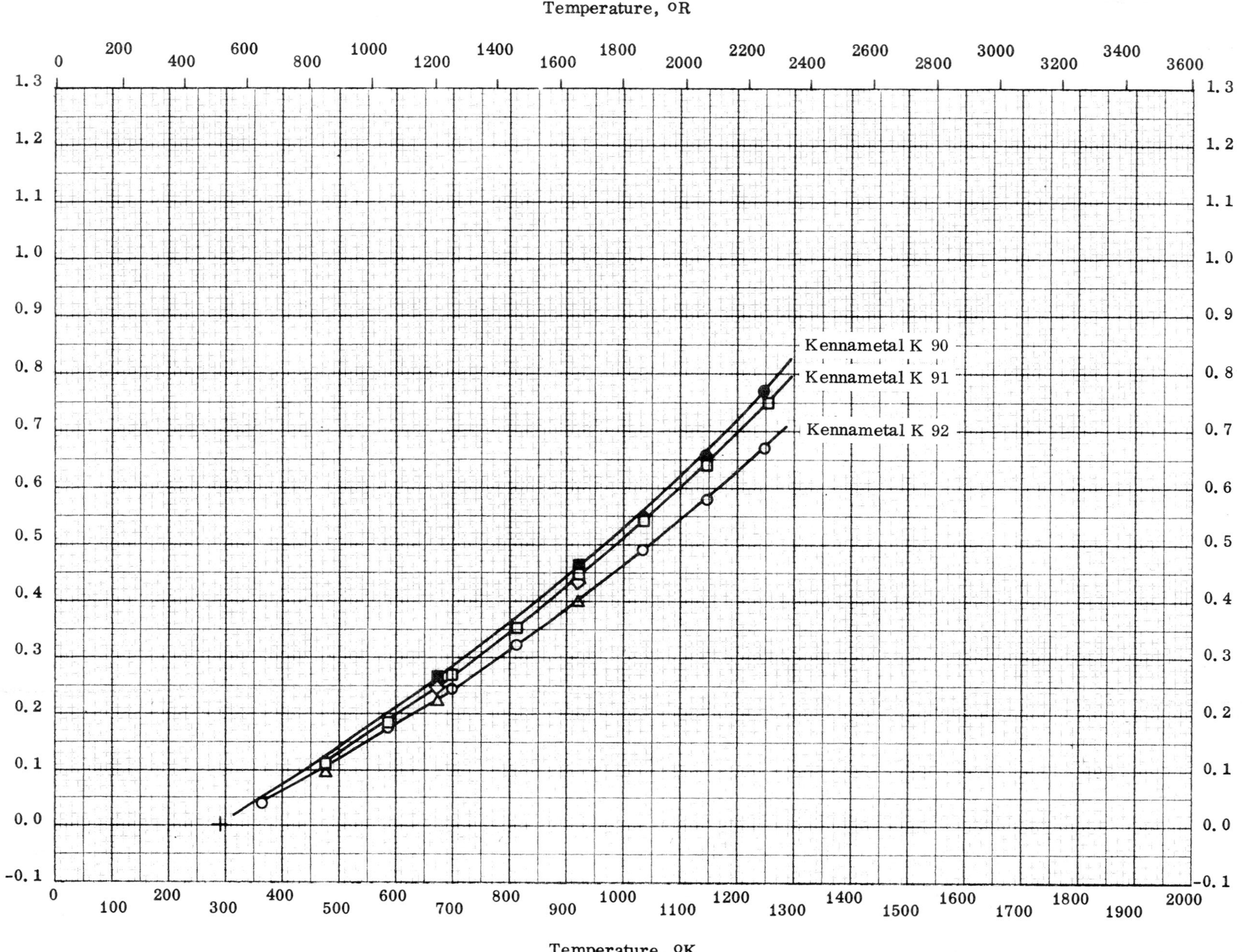

THERMAL LINEAR EXPANSION -- [TUNGSTEN CARBIDE + COBALT] CERMET
($16 \leq Co \leq 25$)

THERMAL LINEAR EXPANSION -- [TUNGSTEN CARBIDE + COBALT] CERMET
($16 \leq Co \leq 25$)

REFERENCE INFORMATION

Symbol	Ref.	Temp. Range °K	Rept. Error %	Sample Specifications	Remarks
○	63-31	293-1244		Kennametal K 92; nominal: 77 W, 16 Co, 5.1 C, 1.6 Ta, and 0.3 Nb; dimension: 4 mm diameter by 50 mm long; density 13.86 g cm^{-3}.	Heated in vacuum at a rate about 3 F min^{-1} and increased to 5 F min^{-1} at the end of heating; no significant permanent change in length observed after test.
□	63-31	293-1253		Kennametal K 91; nominal: 71.7 W, 20 Co, 4.7 C, 2.7 Ta, and 0.9 Nb; dimension: 4 mm diameter by 50 mm long; density 13.34 g cm^{-3}.	Same as above.
●	63-31	293-1244		Kennametal K 90; nominal: 65.6 W, 25 Co, 4.4 C, 3.0 Ta, and 1.6 Nb; dimension: 4 mm diameter by 50 mm long; density 13.04 g cm^{-3}.	Same as above.
△	64-20	293-922	2	Kennametal K 92; density 13.8 g cm^{-3}.	
◇	64-20	293-922	2	Kennametal K 91; density 13.4 g cm^{-3}.	
■	64-20	293-922	2	Kennametal K 90; density 12.9 g cm^{-3}.	

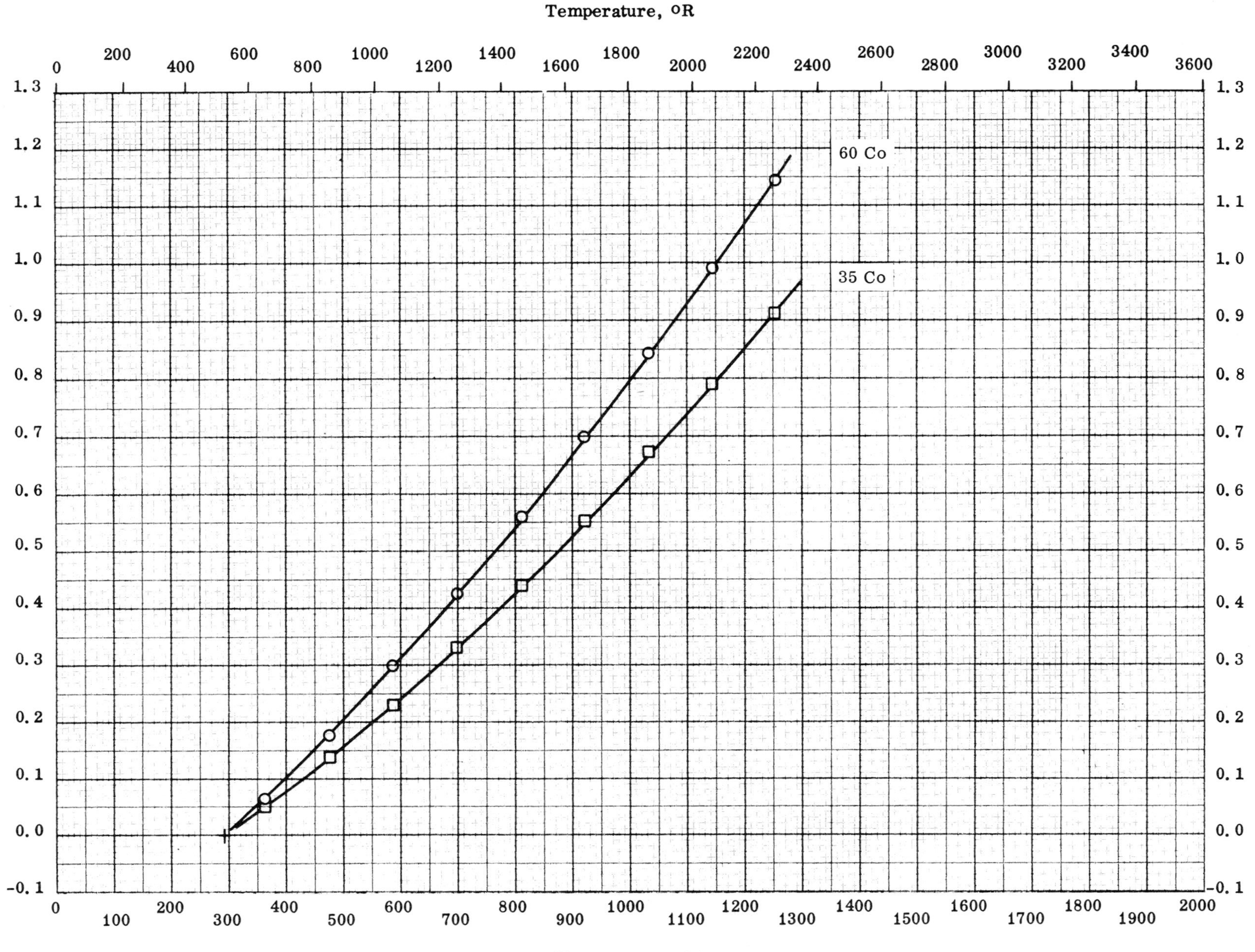

THERMAL LINEAR EXPANSION -- [TUNGSTEN CARBIDE + COBALT] CERMET
(35 ≤ Co ≤60)

THERMAL LINEAR EXPANSION -- [TUNGSTEN CARBIDE + COBALT] CERMET ($35 \leq Co \leq 60$)

REFERENCE INFORMATION

Symbol	Ref.	Temp. Range °K	Rept. Error %	Sample Specifications	Remarks
○	63-31	293-1225		Nominal: 40 WC and 60 Co; dimension: 4 mm dia by 50 mm long; density 10.67 g cm^{-3}.	Heated in vac at a rate 3 F min^{-1} and increased to 5 F min^{-1} at the end of heating; no significant permanent change in length observed after test.
□	63-31	293-1225		Nominal: 65 WC and 35 Co; same dimension as above; density 12.22 g cm^{-3}.	Same as above.

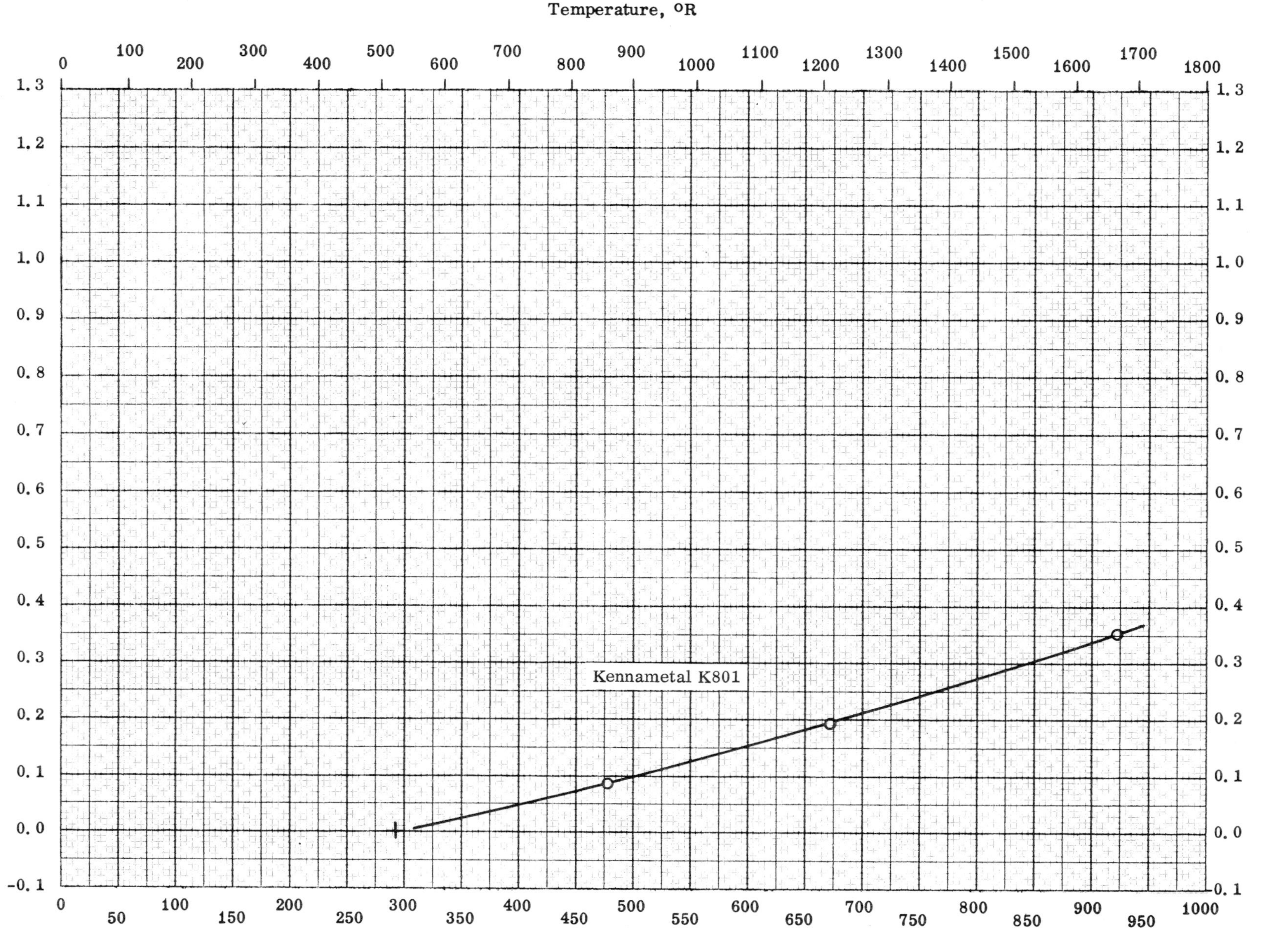

THERMAL LINEAR EXPANSION -- [TUNGSTEN CARBIDE + NICKEL] CERMET

THERMAL LINEAR EXPANSION -- [TUNGSTEN CARBIDE + NICKEL] CERMET

REFERENCE INFORMATION

Symbol	Ref.	Temp. Range °K	Rept. Error %	Sample Specifications	Remarks
○	64-20	293-922	2	Kennametal K 801; density 14.8 g cm^{-3}.	

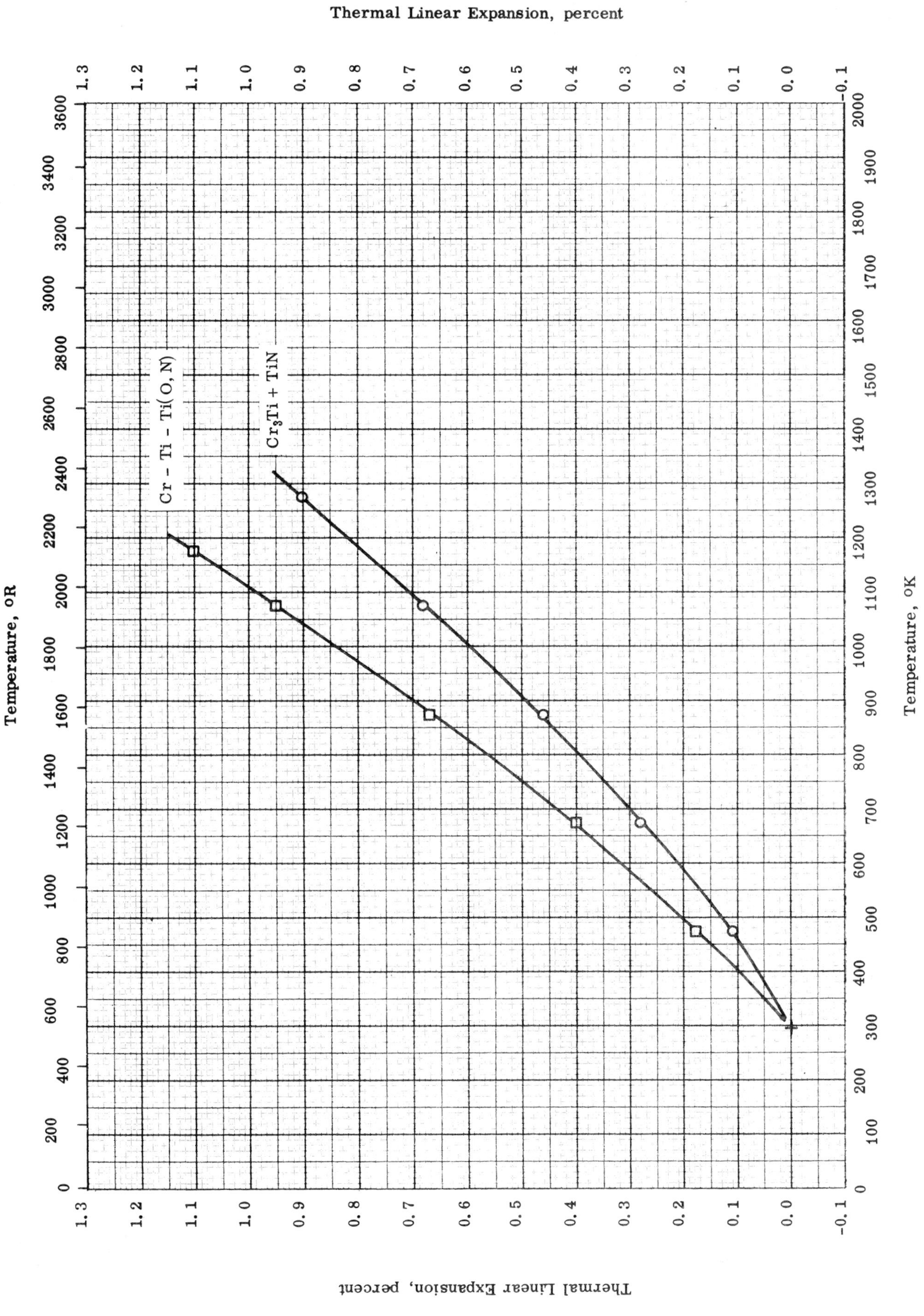

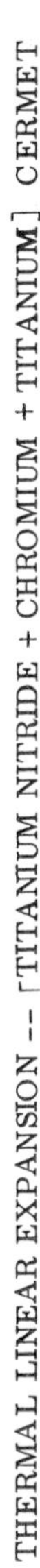

Thermal Linear Expansion, percent
Temperature, °R
Temperature, °K
Cr – Ti – Ti(O, N)
Cr_3Ti + TiN
Thermal Linear Expansion, percent

THERMAL LINEAR EXPANSION -- [TITANIUM NITRIDE + CHROMIUM + TITANIUM] CERMET

THERMAL LINEAR EXPANSION -- [TITANIUM NITRIDE + CHROMIUM + TITANIUM] CERMET

REFERENCE INFORMATION

Symbol	Ref.	Temp. Range °K	Rept. Error %	Sample Specifications	Remarks
○	53-13	293-1273		58.8 Cr, 32.1 Ti, 2.1 N, phases present: $Cr_3Ti + TiN$.	Prepared by sintering 1 hr at 1400 C in H_2 atmosphere; author states curves ○ and □ indicate range of therm. exp. coef. for the various Cr - Ti composite materials.
□	51-13	293-1173		Phases present: Cr, Ti, Ti (O, N).	See last comment above.

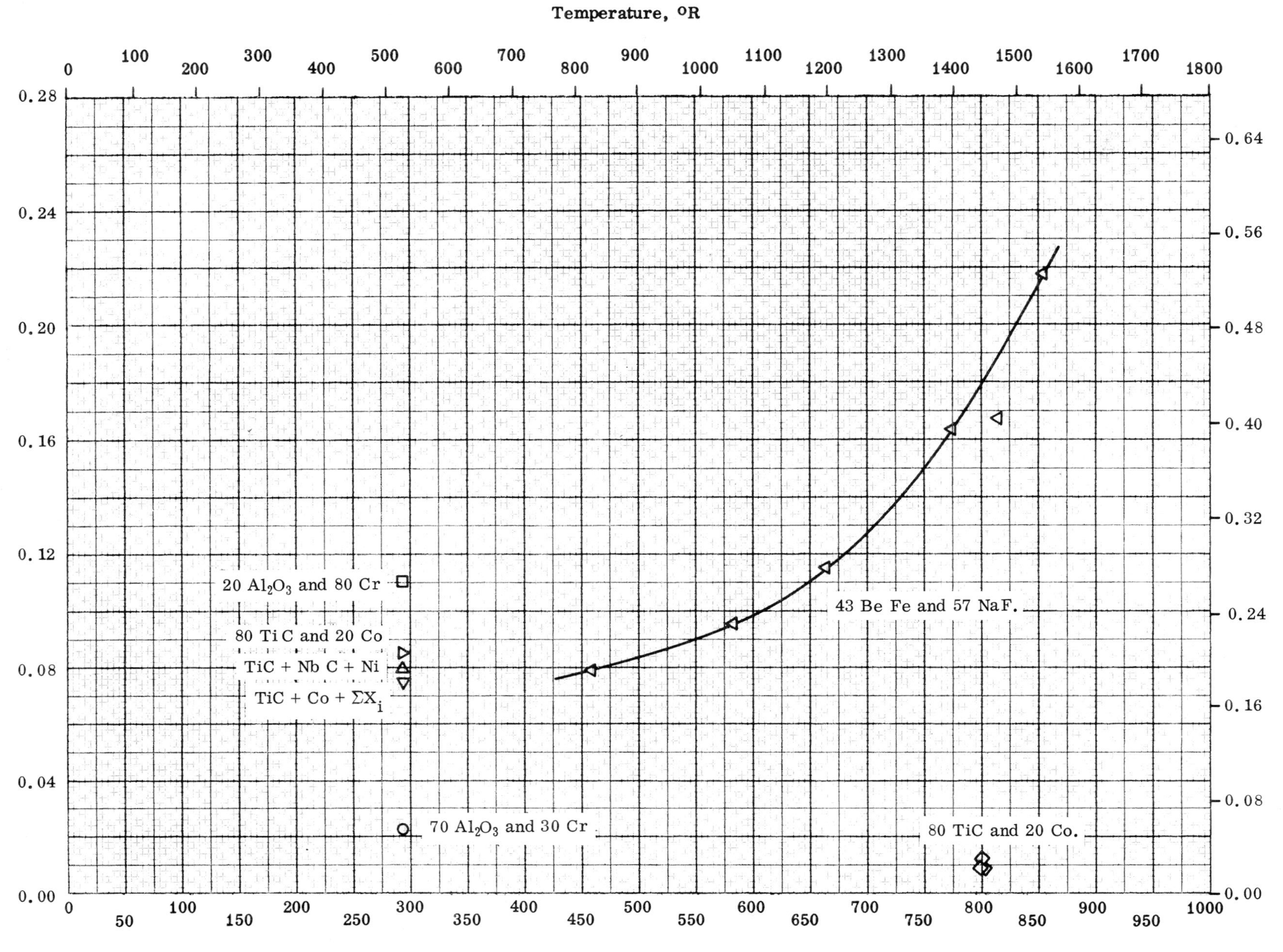

THERMAL CONDUCTIVITY -- MISCELLANEOUS CERMETS

THERMAL CONDUCTIVITY -- MISCELLANEOUS CERMETS

REFERENCE INFORMATION

Symbol	Ref.	Temp. Range °K	Rept. Error %	Sample Specifications	Remarks
○	51-2	298		70 Al_2O_3, 30 Cr, 3-5 Fe, 2-3 WC, 0.75 Co, and traces Si, Mn; raw materials: a. corundum 99.5 Al_2O_3, 0.02 Na_2O; b. 99^+ pure aluminum hydrate, 34.7 combined water; c. 99^+ pure electroytic Cr pressed at 55,000 lb in^2, then sintered at 3100 F; impurities picked up while components were being ground.	
□	58-10	293		20 Al_2O_3 and 80 Cr.	
△	58-10	293		TiC + NbC + Ni.	
▽	49-1	298		66.3 TiC, 18.7 Co, and 15.0 NbC, TaC, and TiC.	
▷	49-1	298		80 TiC and 20 Co; density 5.42 g cm^{-3}.	
◇	52-5	799-801		43 BeFe and 57 NaF.	
◁	55-6	458-853		An equimolecular mixture of polycrystalline BaO and SrO with 5.0 Zr added.	

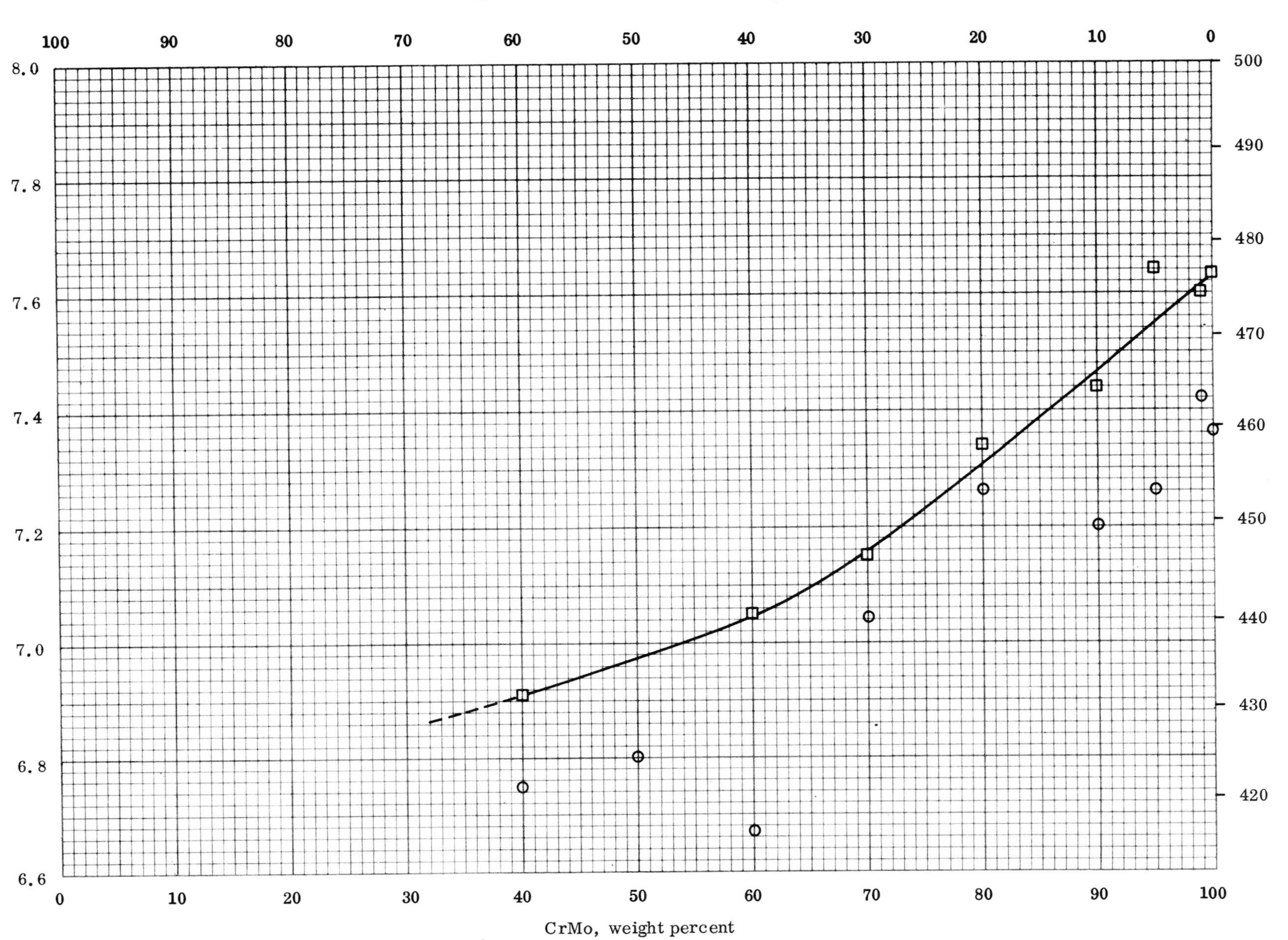

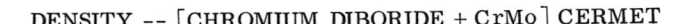

DENSITY -- [CHROMIUM DIBORIDE + CrMo] CERMET

DENSITY -- [CHROMIUM DIBORIDE + CrMo] CERMET

REFERENCE INFORMATION

Symbol	Ref.	Temp. Range °K	Rept. Error %	Sample Specifications	Remarks
□	55-21	298		Borolite IV cermet series, ranging from 0-60 Cr_2B and 40-100 CrMo; Cr_2B: 87.2 Cr, 8.96 B, 1.03 O_2, 0.36 Fe, 0.31 N_2, and 0.04 C; CrM_O: 79 Cr, 19.8 M_O, 0.31 O_2, 0.11 Fe, 0.08 Ni, and 0.01 > C.	Sintered; sintered impurities 0.21 O; 0.06 N; 0.01 C; theoretical density 7.68 g cm^{-3} by x-ray.
○	55-21	298		Same as above.	Hot pressed.

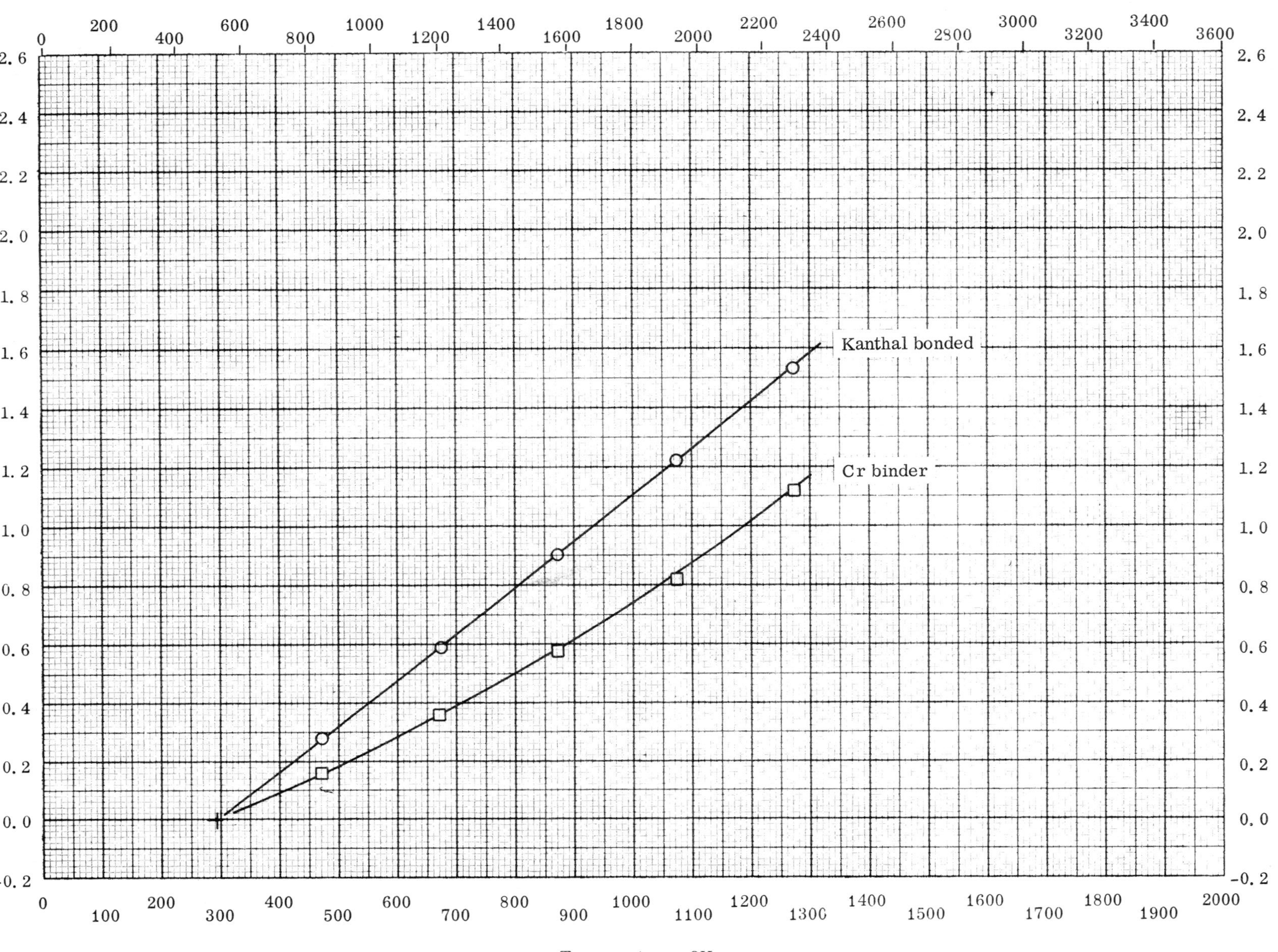

THERMAL LINEAR EXPANSION -- CHROMIUM SILICIDE CERMET

THERMAL LINEAR EXPANSION -- CHROMIUM SILICIDE CERMET

REFERENCE INFORMATION

Symbol	Ref.	Temp. Range °K	Rept. Error %	Sample Specifications	Remarks
○	54-14	293-1273		Cr_3Si and Kanthal: 55.8 Cr, 29.1 Fe, 7.29 Si, 2.41 Al, and 0.67 Co; Kanthal: 69 Fe, 23 Cr, 6 Al, and 2 Co; 97% theoretical density.	Hot pressed.
□	53-13	298-1273		Nominal: 60 Cr_3Si; 40 Cr.	

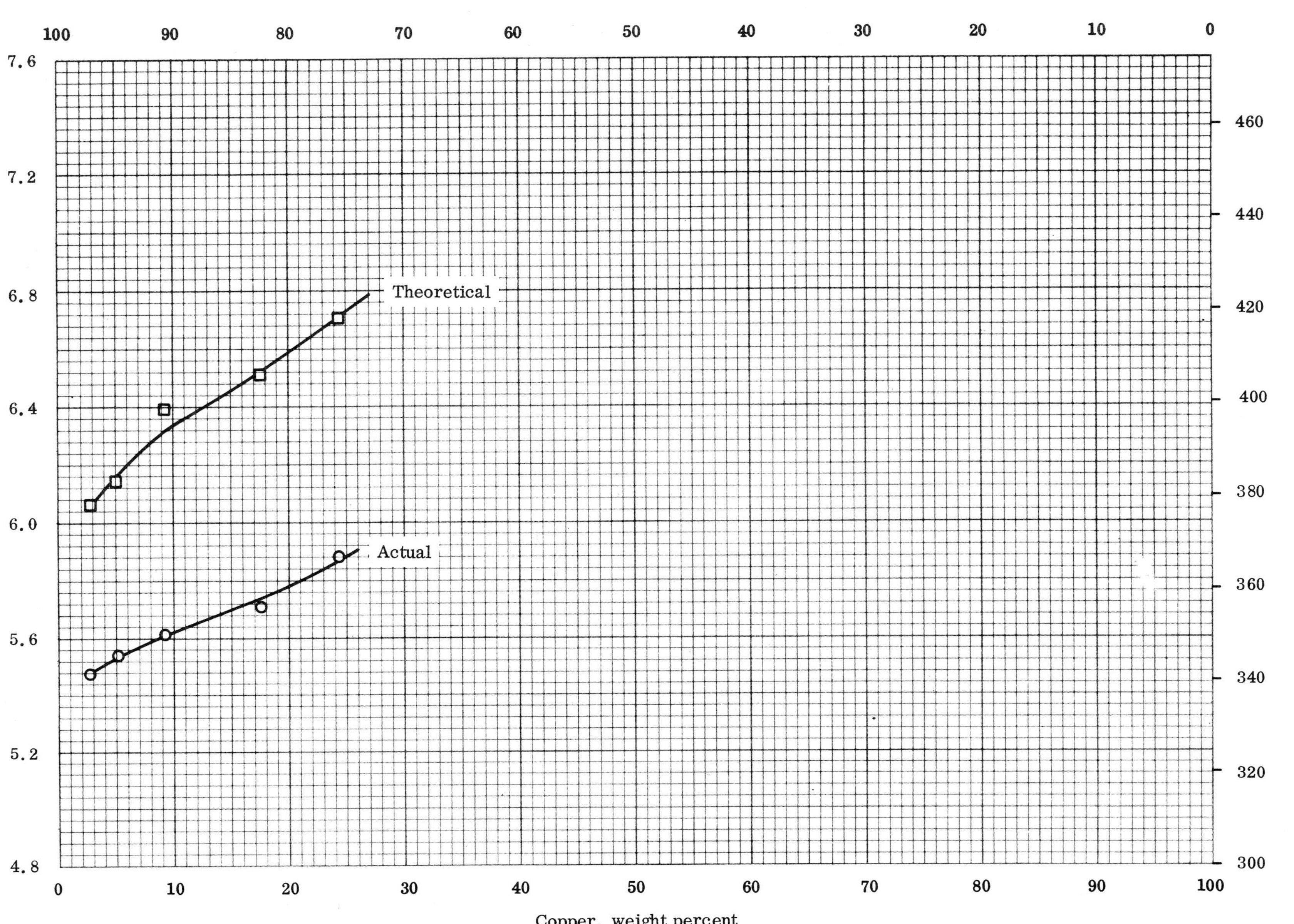

DENSITY -- [CHROMIUM-TITANIUM INTERMETALLICS + COPPER] CERMETS

DENSITY -- [CHROMIUM-TITANIUM INTERMETALLICS + COPPER] CERMETS

REFERENCE INFORMATION

Symbol	Ref.	Temp. Range °K	Rept. Error %	Sample Specifications	Remarks
○	56-24	298		2.8 - 24.3 Cu.	Actual.
□	56-24	298		2.8 - 24.3 Cu.	Theoretical.

DENSITY -- [CHROMIUM-TITANIUM INTERMETALLICS + MOLYBDENUM] CERMETS

Symbol	Major Components Cr	Ti	Mo	Density $g\ cm^{-3}$	$lb\ ft^{-3}$
○	63.5	29.2	7.3	6.34	396
□	54.3	25.8	15.5	6.78	423
△	54.3	25.8	15.5	6.90	431
◇	54.3	25.8	15.5	6.30	393
▽	54.3	25.8	15.5	6.32	395
◁	40.4	19.5	36.4	7.36	460
▷	40.4	19.5	36.4	7.52	470
●	40.4	19.5	36.4	6.60	412
■	40.4	19.5	36.4	6.59	411
▲	28.9	14.8	52.8	7.40	462
◆	28.9	14.8	52.8	8.05	503
▼	28.9	14.8	52.8	6.50	406
◀	28.9	14.8	52.8	6.41	400
▶	20.1	9.3	66.0	8.60	537
◑	12.6	5.8	81.6	9.15	571
◐	63.4	29.3	7.3	6.34	396
◓	63.4	29.3	7.3	6.29	393
◒	56.5	26.1	17.4	6.78	423
◨	56.5	26.1	17.4	6.72	420
◧	41.9	19.3	38.8	7.36	459
⬓	41.9	19.3	38.8	7.26	453

DENSITY -- [CHROMIUM-TITANIUM INTERMETALLICS + MOLYBDENUM] CERMETS

REFERENCE INFORMATION

Symbol	Ref.	Temp. Range °K	Rept. Error %	Sample Specifications	Remarks
○	57-31	298		Intended phases: 93 Cr_2Ti and 7 Mo; intended composition: 63.5 Cr, 29.2 Ti, and 7.3 Mo.	Mixed, compacted, reacted 16 hrs at 1300 C in H_2, crushed, milled, compacted, and sintered at 1500-1620 C, cooled rapidly; weight and volume by displacement in liquid.
□	57-31	298		Intended phases: 83 Cr_2Ti and 17 Mo; actual composition: 54.3 Cr, 25.8 Ti, 15.5 Mo, 0.76 Fe, and 0.74 N.	Same as above; computed from x-ray measurements of lattice.
△	57-31	298		Same as above.	Same as above; weight and volume by displacement in liquid.
◇	57-31	298		Same as above.	Same as above, then held 16 hrs at 2832 R and cooled rapidly.
▽	57-31	298		Same as above.	Same as above, then held 8 hrs at 1932 R and cooled rapidly.
◁	57-31	298		Intended phases: 62 Cr_2Ti and 38 Mo; actual composition: 40.4 Cr, 36.4 Mo, 19.5 Ti, 0.59 Fe, and 0.45 N.	Mixed, compacted, reacted 16 hrs at 1300 C in H_2, crushed, milled, compacted, and sintered at 1500-1620 C, cooled rapidly; same as above.
▷	57-31	298		Same as above.	Same as above; computed from x-ray measurements of lattice.
●	57-31	298		Same as above.	Same as above, then held 16 hrs at 2832 R and cooled rapidly; weight and volume by displacement in liquid.
■	57-31	298		Same as above. (Continued onto next page)	Same as above, then held 8 hrs at 1932 R and cooled rapidly.

REFERENCE INFORMATION

Symbol	Ref.	Temp. Range °K	Rept. Error %	Sample Specifications	Remarks
▲	57-31	298		Intended phases: 44 Cr_2Ti and 56 Mo; actual composition: 52.8 Mo, 28.9 Cr, 14.8 Ti, 0.69 Fe, and 0.44 N.	Mixed, compacted, reacted 16 hrs at 1300 C in H_2 atm., crushed, milled, compacted, and sintered at 1500-1620 C, cooled rapidly; same as above.
◆	57-31	298		Same as above.	Same as above; computed from x-ray measurements of lattice.
▼	57-31	298		Same as above.	Same as above, then held 16 hrs at 2832 R and cooled rapidly; weight and volume by displacement in liquid.
◀	57-31	298		Same as above.	Same as above, then held 8 hrs at 1932 R and cooled rapidly.
▶	57-31	298		Intended phases: 30 Cr_2Ti and 70 Mo; actual composition: 66.0 Mo, 20.1 Cr, 9.3 Ti, 0.74 Fe, and 0.59 N.	Mixed, compacted, reacted 16 hrs at 1300 C in H_2 atm., crushed, milled, compacted, and sintered at 1500-1620 C, cooled rapidly; computed from x-ray measurements of lattice.
◑	57-31	298		Intended phases: 19 Cr_2Ti and 81 Mo. Intended composition: 81.6 Mo, 12.6 Cr, and 5.8 Ti.	Same as above.
◐	57-28	298		Cr_2Ti + Mo: 63.4 Cr, 29.3 Ti, and 7.3 Mo.	Cold pressed from prereacted powder, sintered in H_2, and held 1 hr at 1500 C.
◓	57-28	298		Same as above.	Same as above, then held 1 week at 600 C.
◒	57-28	298		Cr_2Ti + Mo: 56.5 Cr, 26.1 Ti, and 17.4 Mo.	Cold pressed from prereacted powder, sintered in H_2, and held 1 hr at 1500 C.
				(Continued onto next page)	

DENSITY -- [CHROMIUM-TITANIUM INTERMETALLICS + MOLYBDENUM] CERMETS (Continued)

REFERENCE INFORMATION

Symbol	Ref.	Temp. Range °K	Rept. Error %	Sample Specifications	Remarks
◨	57-28	298		Same as above.	Same as above, then held 1 week at 600 C.
◧	57-28	298		Cr_2Ti + Mo: 41.9 Cr, 38.8 Mo, and 19.3 Ti.	Cold pressed from prereacted powder, sintered in H_2, and held 1 hr at 1500 C.
⬓	57-28	298		Same as above.	Same as above, then held 1 week at 600 C.

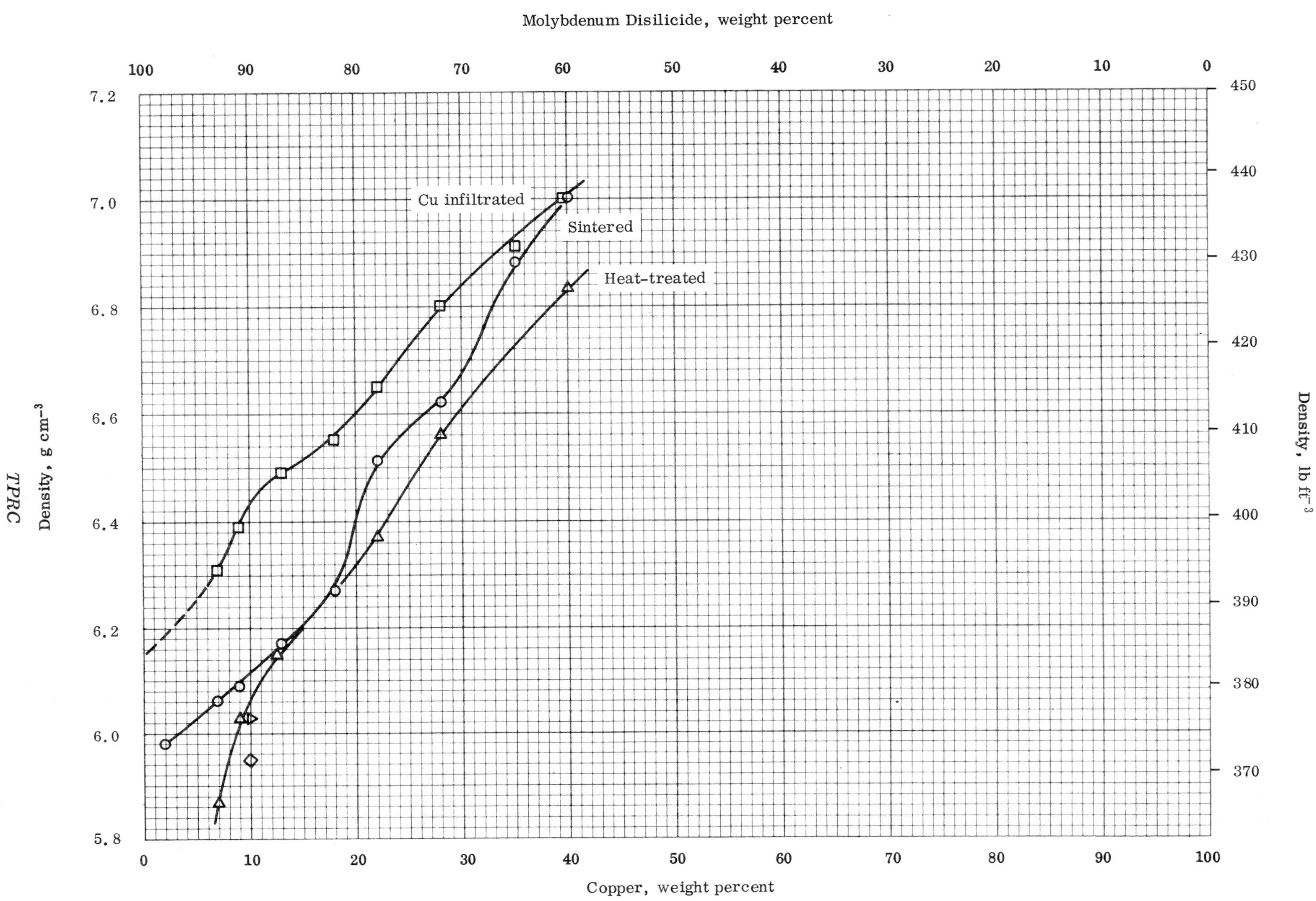

Molybdenum Disilicide, weight percent

100 90 80 70 60 50 40 30 20 10 0

450 440 430 420 410 400 390 380 370

7.2 7.0 6.8 6.6 6.4 6.2 6.0 5.8

Density, g cm^{-3}

Cu infiltrated

Sintered

Heat-treated

0 10 20 30 40 50 60 70 80 90 100

Copper, weight percent

DENSITY -- [MOLYBDENUM DISILICIDE + COPPER] CERMET

TPRC

DENSITY -- [MOLYBDENUM DISILICIDE + COPPER] CERMET

REFERENCE INFORMATION

Symbol	Ref.	Temp. Range °K	Rept. Error %	Sample Specifications	Remarks
○	55-29	298		2.0 - 40.0 Cu.	Mixed and compressed Mo and Si; heated to 1050 C, 30 min at 1100 C in A atm., milled 24 hrs, mixed with Cu, compacted, sintered 1 hr at 1400 C in H_2 atm., sintered with a liquid phase present.
□	55-29	298		7 - 39.5 Cu.	Same preparation as above except Cu infiltrated.
△	55-29	298		7.0 - 40.0 Cu.	Same preparation as above but also heat treated 4 hrs at 1600 F.
◇	55-29	298		10 Cu.	Same preparation as above avg. of 2 samples.
▷	55-29	298		90 $MoSi_2$ and 10 Cu.	Reheated 1600 F 4 hrs after sintering; avg. of two samples.

DENSITY -- MISCELLANEOUS CERMETS
(Metals bonded by metals)

Symbol	Material Composition	Density g cm^{-3}	Density lb ft^{-3}
○	49.2 Mo, 37.1 Si, and 10.2 Cr.	5.78	361
	42.4 Si, 28.8 Mo, and 24.2 Cr.	5.34	333
	47.2 Si, 40.6 Cr, and 8.6 Mo.	5.02	313
	58.0 Mo, 32.5 Si, and 5.7 Cr.	6.18	386
	45.6 Mo, 26.8 Si, and 23.2 Cr.	6.36	397
	70.3 Cr, 19.1 Mo, and 10.1 Si.	6.54	408
	61.8 Mo, 32.5 Cr, and 3.9 Si.	8.18	511
	56.8 Cr, 38.0 Mo, and 4.5 Si.	7.94	496
	46.3 Cr, 35.5 Mo, and 17.2 Si.	6.21	388
	70.3 Cr, 19.1 Mo, and 10.1 Si.	6.54	408
●	49.2 Mo, 37.1 Si, and 10.2 Cr.	5.96	372
	42.4 Si, 28.8 Mo, and 24.2 Cr.	5.49	343
	47.2 Si, 40.6 Cr, and 8.6 Mo.	5.12	320
	58.0 Mo, 32.5 Si, and 5.7 Cr.	6.24	389
	70.3 Cr, 19.1 Mo, and 10.1 Si.	6.70	418
□	75.9 Cr, 12.3 Si, and 11.8 Ti.	5.46	341
	75 Cr, 18.6 Si, and 6.1 Ti.	5.93	370
	46.6 Cr, 44.7 Si, and 9.2 Ti.	5.08	317

(Continued onto next page)

DENSITY -- MISCELLANEOUS CERMETS (Continued)
(Metals bonded by metals)

Symbol	Material Composition	Density $g\ cm^{-3}$	Density $lb\ ft^{-3}$
□	53.6 Si, 24.9 Ti, and 22.0 Cr.	4.15	259
△	54.2 Ti, 31.6 Al, and 14.4 Ni.	4.33	270
▽	54.2 Ti, 31.6 Al, and 14.4 Ni.	3.92	245
◇	53.7 Ti, 30.2 Al, and 14.5 Ni.	4.29	268
◁	55.0 Ti, 27.4 Al, and 16.7 Ni.	4.16	260
▷	45.7 Ti, 29.2 Ni, and 28.7 Al.	4.68	292
■	39.9 Ni, 37.9 Ti, and 22.8 Al.	4.91	306
▲	55.1 Ni, 31.0 Al, and 11.2 Ti.	5.03	314
▼	47.2 Ti, 27.8 Al, and 20.3 Ni.	3.90	243

DENSITY -- MISCELLANEOUS CERMETS
(Metals bonded by metals)

REFERENCE INFORMATION

Symbol	Ref.	Temp. Range °K	Rept. Error %	Sample Specifications	Remarks
○	56-24	298		Cr-Mo-Si series.	Mixed elemental powders, compacted, heated in argon without melting, crushed, ball-milled, compacted with 2 camphor, and sintered in H_2 to max density; density measured.
●	56-24	298		Cr-Mo-Si series.	Same as above except density computed from x-ray measurements of lattice.
□	56-24	298		Cr-Si-Ti series.	Same as above.
◇	56-24	298		53.7 Ti, 30.2 Al, 14.5 Ni, and 0.54 C.	Melted in H_2, crushed, milled, and hot-pressed in graphite dies.
■	56-24	298		39.9 Ni, 37.9 Ti, 22.8 Al, and 0.14 O_2.	Same as above.
△	56-24	298		54.2 Ti, 31.6 Al, 14.4 Ni, and 0.83 O_2.	Same as above.
▽	56-24	298		Same as above.	Same as above except cold-pressed and sintered.
▷	56-24	298		45.7 Ti, 29.2 Ni, 28.7 Al, and 0.34 O_2.	Same as above.
▲	56-24	298		55.1 Ni, 31.0 Al, 11.2 Ti, 0.13 O_2, 0.11 N_2, and 0.01 H_2.	Same as above except high frequency melted in fireclay crucible in H_2.
◁	56-24	298		55.0 Ti, 27.4 Al, 16.7 Ni, 0.15 N_2, and 0.03 H_2.	Same as above except crushed, milled, and hot-pressed in graphite dies.
▼	56-24	298		47.2 Ti, 27.8 Al, 20.3 Ni, and 1.92 N_2.	High frequency melted in fireclay crucible.

DENSITY -- MISCELLANEOUS CERMETS
(Ceramics bonded by metals or alloys)

Symbol	Material Composition	Density g cm^{-3}	Density lb ft^{-3}
○	64 TiC and 25 Ni	6.0	374.4
□	54 TiC and 33 Ni	6.3	393.1
△	Stainless steel and 9 SiO_2	6.0	374.4
▽	B_4C with 36.4 Fe	3.24	202
◇	9 Fiberfrax fine grade fiber	6.31	394
●	9 Fiberfrax coarse grade fiber	6.3	393
■	35 vol.% Cr-Mo alloy	3.38	211
▲	35 vol.% Cr-Mo alloy	3.46	216
▼	35 vol. % vitallium	3.13	195

DENSITY -- MISCELLANEOUS CERMETS
(Ceramics bonded by metals or alloys)

REFERENCE INFORMATION

Symbol	Ref.	Temp. Range °K	Rept. Error %	Sample Specifications	Remarks
○	60-31	298		64 TiC, 25 Ni, 6 NbC (90 NbC + TaC + TiC), and 5.0 Mo.	
□	60-31	298		54 TiC, 33 Ni, 7 Mo, and 6.0 NbC (90 NbC + TaC + TiC).	
△	55-22	298		Fiber cermet; 91.0 - 325 mesh No. 302B stainless steel powder and 9.0 Refrasil fiber, containing 96 SiO_2.	Crushed from woven cloth; ground 72-130 hrs mixed in methanol, air-dried, and hot-pressed as dry mixture, at 2560 R under 3170 psi.
▽	52-21	298		Boron carbide, iron-bonded; 48.9 B, 36.4 Fe, and 13.75 C.	Auth. remark that microstructure indicates much higher Fe content, perhaps due to reaction of Fe with B_4C.
◇	55-22	298		Fiber cermet with 91-325 mesh No. 302 stainless steel powder and 9 Fiberfrax grade 212 3 μ dia fibers; fiber containing 50 SiO_2 and 50 Al_2O_3.	Ground the powder and fiber mixture 72-130 hrs in methanol, air-dried, hot-pressed as dry mixtures at 2660 R under 2110 psi.
●	55-22	298		Same as above except coarse grade Fiberfrax fibers average 20 μ dia by several hundred dia long.	Same as above except hot-pressed under 3170 psi.
■	53-15	298		Nominal 65 vol. % SiC, 35 vol. % of Cr-Mo alloys (50 Cr and 50 Mo); porosity 12.5 %.	Mixed 24 hrs, dried, hot-pressed under 5000 psi at 3400 F.
▲	53-15	298		Same as above; sample picked up <1.0 Fe in mill; porosity 10%.	Mixed in steel ball mill, dried, hot-pressed under 5000 psi at 3650 F.
▼	53-15	298		65 vol. % SiC, and 35 vol.% vitallium; nominal composition of vitallium: 62 Co, 30 Cr, 5.5 Mo, 2.5 Ni, 27 Fe, and 0.25 C; density 8.3 g $c.c.^{-3}$; porosity 13.6%.	Mixed in steel ball mill with CCl_4, dried, hot-pressed under 5000 psi to 2640 F.

DENSITY -- MISCELLANEOUS CERMETS
(Intermetallics bonded by metals)

Symbol	Material Composition	Density g cm^{-3}	Density lb ft^{-3}
○	49.4 Mo, 33.7 Si, and 16.8 Ti.	5.49	343
□	44.7 Mo, 30.5 Si, and 24.8 Ti.	5.30	331
△	Not given.	4.97	320
◇	Not given.	5.48	352
▽	Not given.	5.31	341
●	TiB_2 and 5 Al.	4.2	262
	TiB_2 and 10 Al.	3.93	245
	TiB_2 and 25 Al.	3.25	203
■	90 X-40 and 10 TiB_2 .	5.2 ± 0.3	325 ± 19
▲	Same as above.	7.92	494
▼	64.4 Ni, 24.6 Al, and 6.0 Cr.	6.07	379
◑	64.5 Ni, 29.5 Al, and 6.0 Cr.	5.87	366
◆	60.4 Ni, 27.7 Al, and 11.9 Cr.	6.14	383
◐	60.3 Ni, 27.8 Al, and 11.4 Cr.	6.02	376
◁	52.5 Ni, 24.2 Al, and 23.3 Cr.	6.28	392
◨	52.6 Ni, 24.2 Al, and 23.2 Cr.	6.14	383
▷	45.1 Ni, 34.2 Cr, and 20.7 Al.	6.41	400
◧	45.1 Ni, 34.2 Cr, and 20.7 Al.	6.29	393
◀	44.7 Cr, 37.9 Ni, and 17.4 Al.	6.54	408
◭	44.8 Cr, 37.8 Ni, and 17.4 Al.	6.50	406
▶	54.8 Cr, 31.0 Ni, and 14.2 Al.	6.66	416
◮	54.9 Cr, 30.9 Ni, and 14.2 Al.	6.54	408

DENSITY -- MISCELLANEOUS CERMETS
(Intermetallics bonded by metals)

REFERENCE INFORMATION

Symbol	Ref.	Temp. Range °K	Rept. Error %	Sample Specifications	Remarks
○	56-24	298		49.4 Mo, 33.7 Si, and 16.8 Ti; phase present: $(Ti,Mo)_5Si_3$ and unknown.	Mixed elemental powders, compacted and heated in argon without intentional melting, crushed, ball-milled, and hot-pressed at 1550-1650 C.
□	56-24	298		44.7 Mo, 30.5 Si, and 24.8 Ti; phase present: $(Ti,Mo)_5Si_3$ and (Mo, Ti).	Same as above.
△	56-24	298		Composition unknown; phases present: Ti Mo Si_4 and unknown.	Same as above.
◇	56-24	298		Composition unknown; phases present: $(Ti\ Mo)_5Si_3$ and (Mo, Ti).	Same as above.
▽	56-24	298		Composition unknown; phase present: $(Ti,Mo)_5Si_3$ and Ti.	Same as above.
●	56-25	298		TiB_2 and 5-25 Al.	Produced by carbon reduction of Ti oxide and B_2O_3 at 2000 C, crushed, milled 24 hrs, mixed, held 1 hr at 1800 C, again crushed, and hot-pressed.
■	55-27	298		90 X-40 (Haynes Stellite 31) and 10 TiB_2; composition of TiB_2: 68.08 Ti, 30.70 B, 1.19 C, trace of Fe, and 0.03 others.	Mixed and pressed at various pressure: 30,000-90,000 psi with wax, heated 6 hrs at 575 F in argon, and fired at 2250-2400 F for 30 min in argon; bulk density.
▲	55-27	298		Same as above.	Same as above; density computed from x-ray measurements of lattice.
▼	57-31	298		64.4 Ni, 24.6 Al, and 6.0 Cr; intended phases 94 Ni Al and 6 Cr.	Mixed, compacted, reacted at 1000-1500 C in H_2, crushed, heated in vacuo at 1440 C, crushed, and milled; computed from x-ray measurements of lattice.

(Continued onto next page)

DENSITY -- MISCELLANEOUS CERMETS (Continued)
(Intermetallics bonded by metals)

REFERENCE INFORMATION

Symbol	Ref.	Temp. Range °K	Rept. Error %	Sample Specifications	Remarks
◆	57-31	298		60.4 Ni, 27.7 Al, and 11.9 Cr; intended phases 88 Ni Al and 12 Cr.	Same as above.
◁	57-31	298		52.5 Ni, 24.2 Al, and 23.3 Cr; intended phases: 77 Ni Al and 23 Cr.	Same as above.
▷	57-31	298		45.1 Ni, 34.2 Cr, and 20.7 Al; intended phases: 66 Ni Al and 34 Cr.	Same as above.
◀	57-31	298		44.7 Cr, 37.9 Ni, and 17.4 Al; intended phases: 55 Ni Al and 45 Cr.	Same as above.
▶	57-31	298		54.8 Cr, 31.0 Ni, and 14.2 Al; intended phases: 45 Ni Al and 55 Cr.	Same as above.
◑	57-28	298		64.5 Ni, 29.5 Al, and 6.0 Cr; intended phases: 94 Ni Al and 6 Cr.	Same as above.
◐	57-28	298		60.3 Ni, 27.8 Al, and 11.4 Cr; intended phases: 88 Ni Al and 12 Cr.	Same as above.
◨	57-28	298		52.6 Ni, 24.2 Al, and 23.2 Cr; intended phases: 77 Ni Al and 23 Cr.	Same as above.
◧	57-28	298		45.1 Ni, 34.2 Cr, and 20.7 Al; intended phases: 66 Ni Al and 34 Cr.	Same as above.
▲	57-28	298		44.8 Cr, 37.8 Ni, and 17.4 Al; intended phases: 55 Ni Al and 45 Ti.	Same as above.

DENSITY -- MISCELLANEOUS CERMETS (Continued)
(Intermetallics bonded by metals)

REFERENCE INFORMATION

Symbol	Ref.	Temp. Range °K	Rept. Error %	Sample Specifications	Remarks
▲	57-28	298		54.9 Cr, 30.9 Ni, and 14.2 Al; intended phases: 45 Ni Al and 55 Cr.	Same as above.

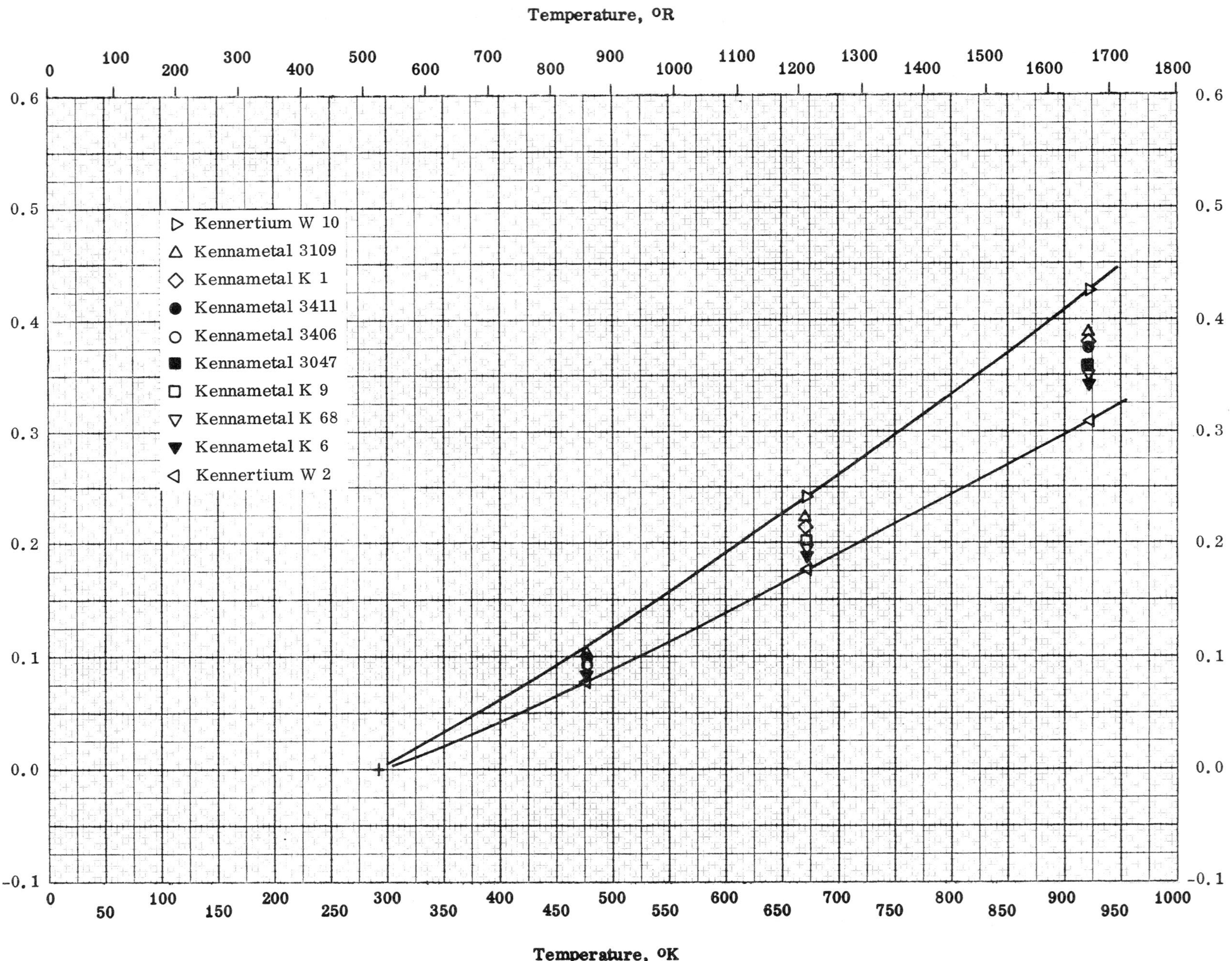

THERMAL LINEAR EXPANSION -- OTHER KENNAMETAL CERMETS WITH UNSPECIFIED COMPOSITION

REFERENCE INFORMATION

Symbol	Ref.	Temp. Range °K	Rept. Error %	Sample Specifications	Remarks
○	64-20	293-922	2	Kennametal 3406; density 14.7 g cm^{-3}.	
●	64-20	293-922	2	Kennametal 3411; density 14.5 g cm^{-3}.	
■	64-20	293-922	2	Kennametal 3047; density 14.5 g cm^{-3}.	
△	64-20	293-922	2	Kennametal 3109; density 14.2 g cm^{-3}.	
□	64-20	293-922	2	Kennametal K9; density 14.6 g cm^{-3}.	
▽	64-20	293-922	2	Kennametal K68; density 14.9 g cm^{-3}.	
▼	64-20	293-922	2	Kennametal K6; density 14.9 g cm^{-3}.	
◇	64-20	293-922	2	Kennametal K1; density 14.1 g cm^{-3}.	
◁	64-20	293-922	2	Kennertium W-2; density 18.5 g cm^{-3}.	
▷	64-20	293-922	2	Kennertium W-10; density 17.0 g cm^{-3}.	

POLYMERS

(A chemical compound or a mixture of compounds formed by polymerization and consisting essentially of repeating molecular structural units.)

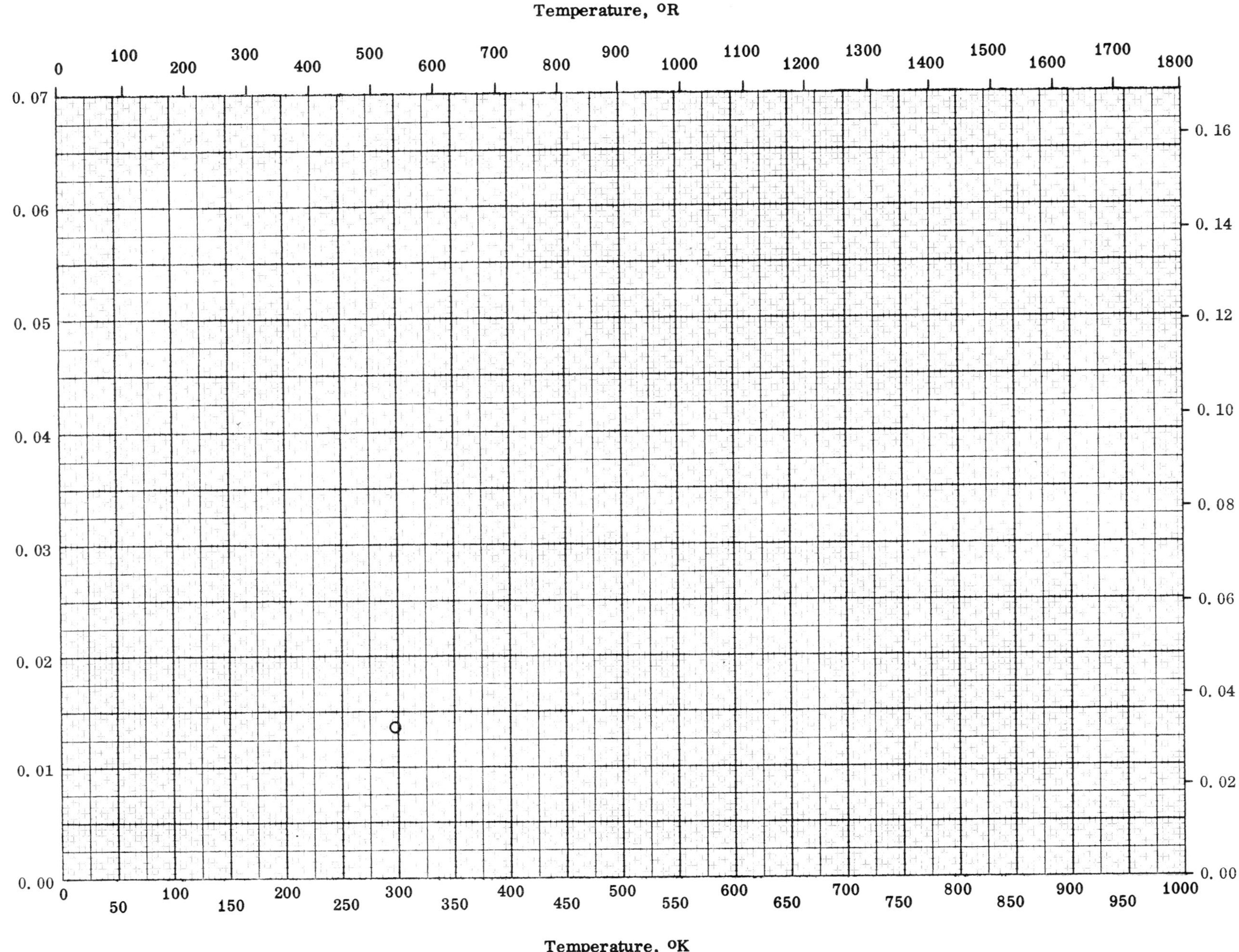

THERMAL CONDUCTIVITY -- EXPANDED CELLULOSE ACETATE

THERMAL CONDUCTIVITY -- EXPANDED CELLULOSE ACETATE

REFERENCE INFORMATION

Symbol	Ref.	Temp. Range °K	Rept. Error %	Sample Specifications	Remarks
○	45-2	297		Expanded cellulose acetate from DuPont; density 5.3 lb ft^{-3}.	Oven dried 16 hrs at 140-150 F; 0.5 in. thick, with cylindrical cells perpendicular to plane of the sheet.

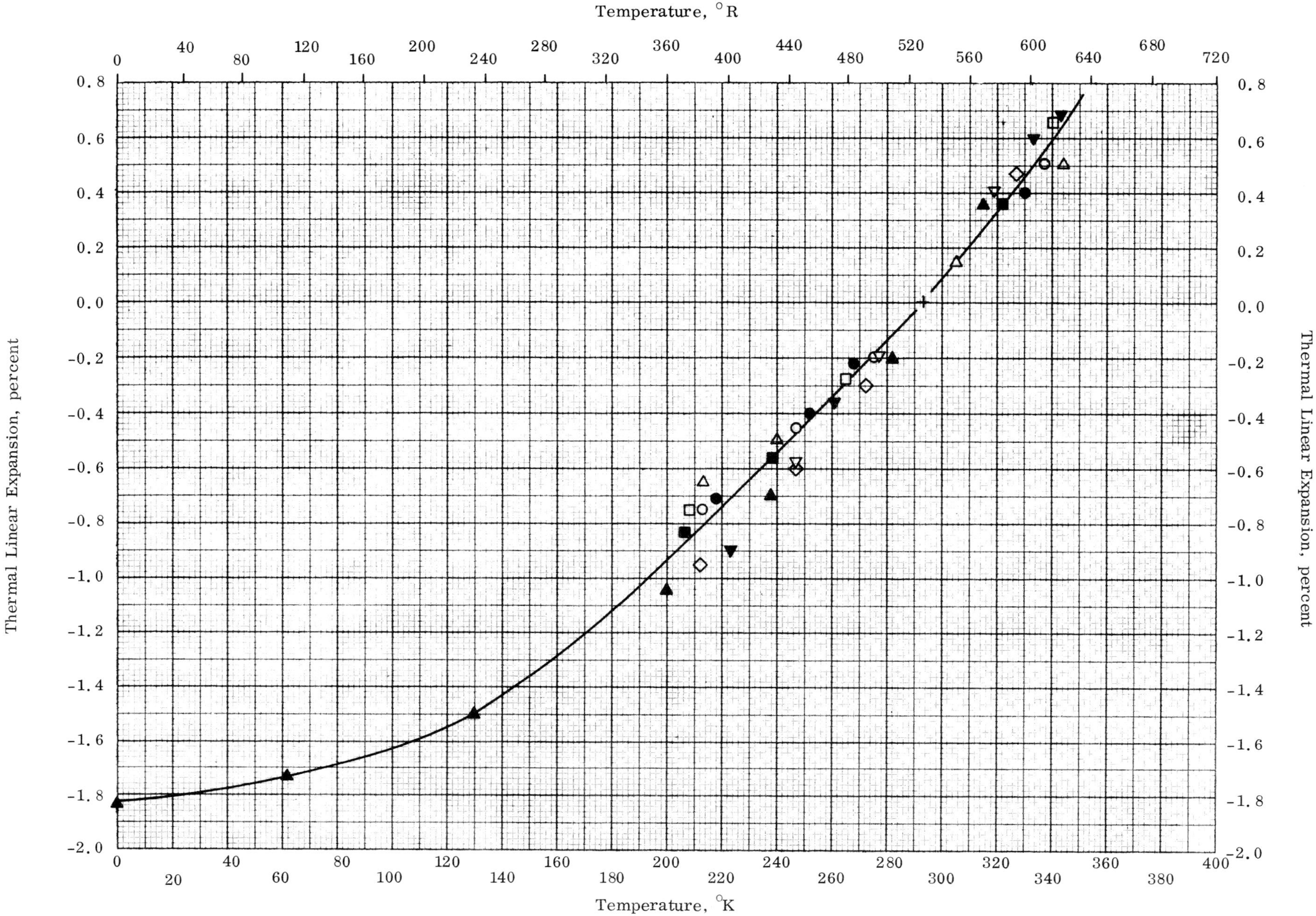

Temperature, °R

Temperature, °K

Thermal Linear Expansion, percent

THERMAL LINEAR EXPANSION -- CELLULOSE ACETATE

REFERENCE INFORMATION

Symbol	Ref.	Temp. Range °K	Rept. Error %	Sample Specifications	Remarks
○	54-16	211-339		Chemaco SPZ 326 made by Chemaco Corp.; cellulose acetate molding composition with normal acetyl formulation; 67.5 cellulose acetate, 22.75 diethyl phthalate, and 9.75 dimethyl phthalate.	Held at 77 F and 50% relative humidity for 24 to 48 hrs; general purpose material; flow is MS.
□	54-16	211-339		Chemaco SPZ 325 from Chemaco Corp.; cellulose Acetate molding composition with normal acetyl formulation; 74 cellu lose acetate, 18 diethyl phthalate, and 8 dimethyl phthalate.	Same as above, except the flow is H_2.
△	54-16	211-339		Chemaco SPZ 329 from Chemaco Corp.; cellulose acetate molding composition with high acetyl formulation; 74 cellulose acetate, 18 diethyl phthalate, and 8 dimethyl phthalate.	Same as above.
◇	54-16	211-328		Chemaco SPZ 330, from Chemaco Corp.; cellulose acetate molding composition with high acetyl formulation; 67.5 cellulose acetate, 22.5 diethyl phthalate, and 9.75 dimethyl phthalate.	Same as above, except the flow is MS.
▽	54-16	211-339		Chemaco SPZ-332 made by Chemaco Corp.; cellulose acetate molding composition with high acetyl formulation; 62.5 cellulose acetate, 18.75 diethyl phthalate, 12.5 triphenyl phosphate, and 6.25 dimethyl phthalate.	Held at 77 F and 50% relative humidity for 24 to 48 hrs; max moisture resistance; min plasticizer volatility; flow MS.
●	54-16	211-328		Chemaco SPZ-331, from Chemaco Corp.; cellulose acetate molding composition with high acetyl formulation; 68.75 cellulose acetate, 15.5 diethyl phthalate, 10.5 triphenyl phosphate, and 5.25 dimethyl phthalate. (Continued onto next page)	Same as above except the flow is H_2.

THERMAL LINEAR EXPANSION -- CELLULOSE ACETATE (Continued)

REFERENCE INFORMATION

Symbol	Ref.	Temp. Range °K	Rept. Error %	Sample Specifications	Remarks
▼	54-16	211-339		Chemaco SPZ-327 from Chemaco Corp.; cellulose acetate molding composition with normal acetyl formulation; 68.75 cellulose acetate, 15.5 diethyl phthalate, 10.5 triphenyl phosphate, and 5.25 dimethyl phthalate.	Same as above.
■	54-16	211-328		Chemaco SPZ-327-MS, from Chemaco Corp.; cellulose acetate molding composition with normal acetyl formulation; 62.5 cellulose acetate, 18.75 diethyl phthalate, 12.5 triphenyl phosphate, and 6.25 dimethyl phthalate.	Same as above except the flow is MS.
▲	52-13	0-320		Tenite I, formula 0072-MS cellulose acetate by Tenn. Eastman Corp.	Molded for 20 min at 5000 psi and 150 C; values avg. for 2 or more cycles, measured parallel to axis of cylinder.

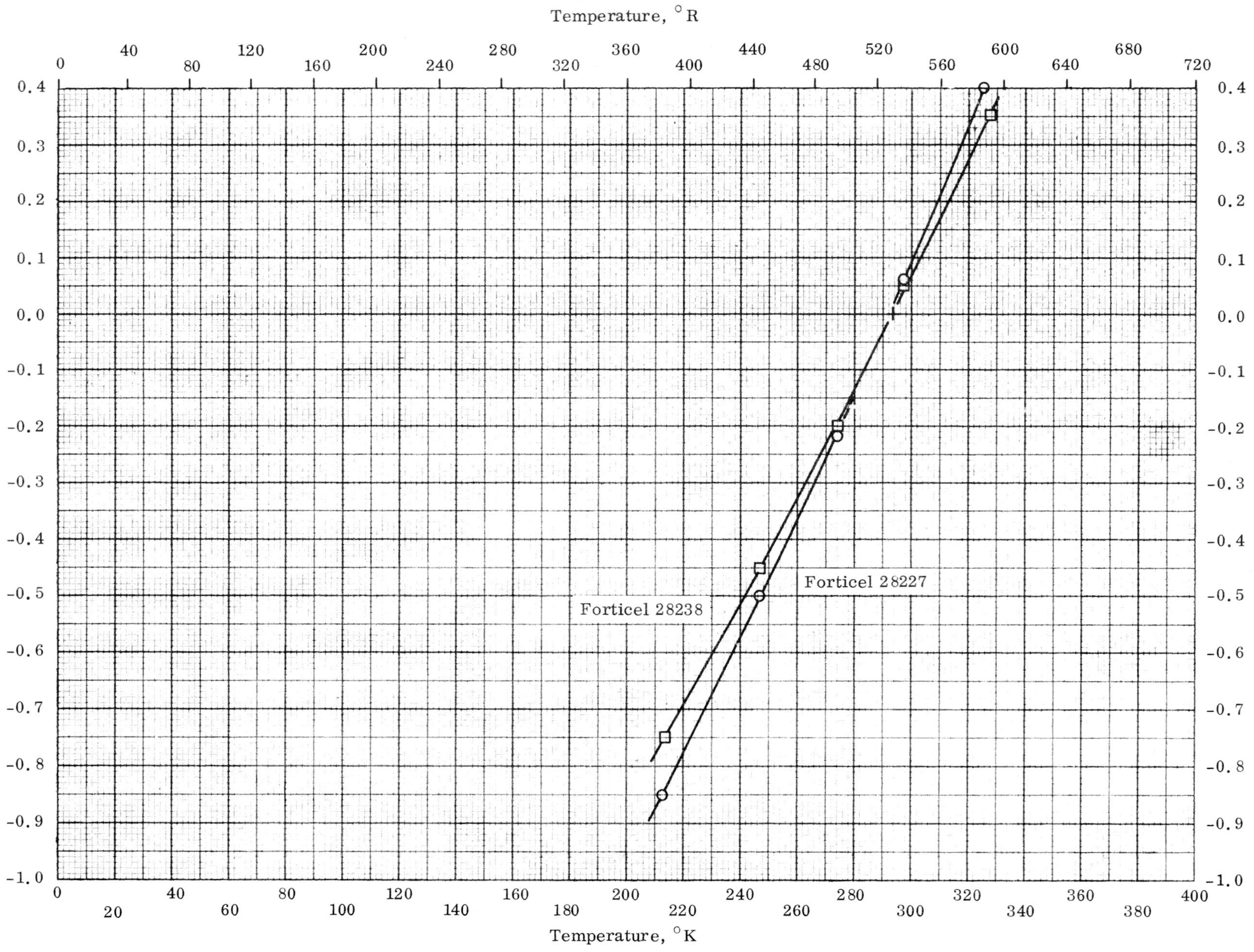

THERMAL LINEAR EXPANSION -- CELLULOSE PROPIONATE

THERMAL LINEAR EXPANSION -- CELLULOSE PROPIONATE

REFERENCE INFORMATION

Symbol	Ref.	Temp. Range °K	Rept. Error %	Sample Specifications	Remarks
○	54-16	213-326		Fortical 28227 from Celanese Corp.	Held at 77 F and 50% humidity for 24-48 hrs before test "Mat'l no longer manufactured"; general purpose material; flow MS.
□	54-16	215-327		Forticel 28238.	Same as above except flow H_2.

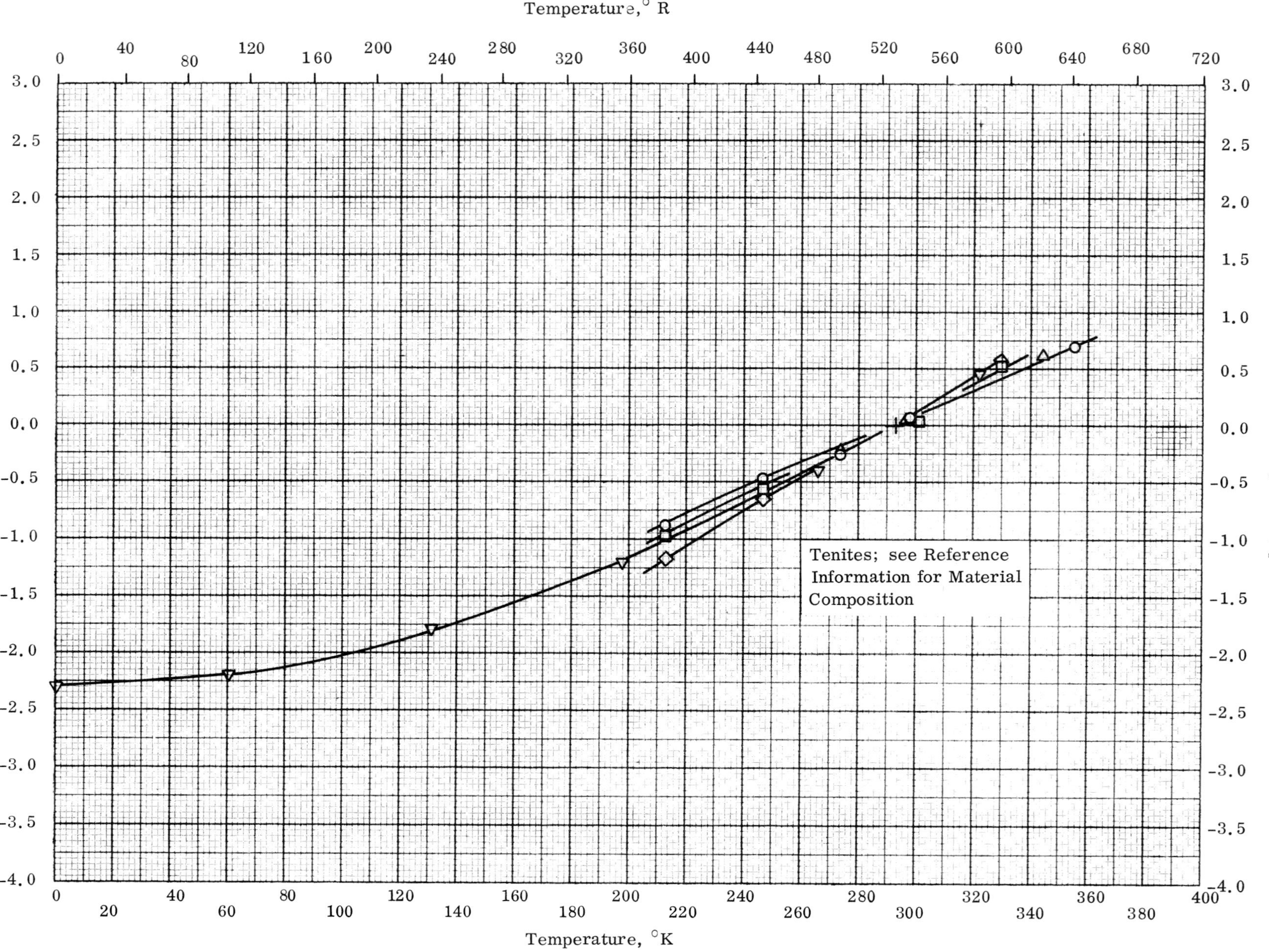

THERMAL LINEAR EXPANSION -- CELLULOSE ACETATE BUTYRATE

REFERENCE INFORMATION

Symbol	Ref.	Temp. Range °K	Rept. Error %	Sample Specifications	Remarks
○	54-16	213-356		Tenite G 204-H2 from Tennessee Eastman Corp.; 100 parts C.A.B., 6 parts Triphenyl phosphate; resin type AB 381; max water resistance; min plasticizer volatility; flow H_2.	Held at 77 F and 50% humidity for 24-48 hrs before test.
□	54-16	213-331		Tenite I 204-MS; as above except 14 parts Triphenyl phosphate; flow MS.	Same as above.
△	54-16	213-345		Tenite Q 264-H 2; as above except 5 parts Dibutyl sebacate; general purpose material; flow H2.	Same as above.
◇	54-16	213-330		Tenite S 264-MS; as above except 14.5 parts Dibutyl sebacate; flow MS.	Same as above.
▽	52-13	0-320		Tenite II, formula 205A-MS, by Tenn. Eastman Corp.	Molded for 20 min at 5000 psi and 150 C; values average for 2 or more cycles; measured parallel to axis of cylinder.

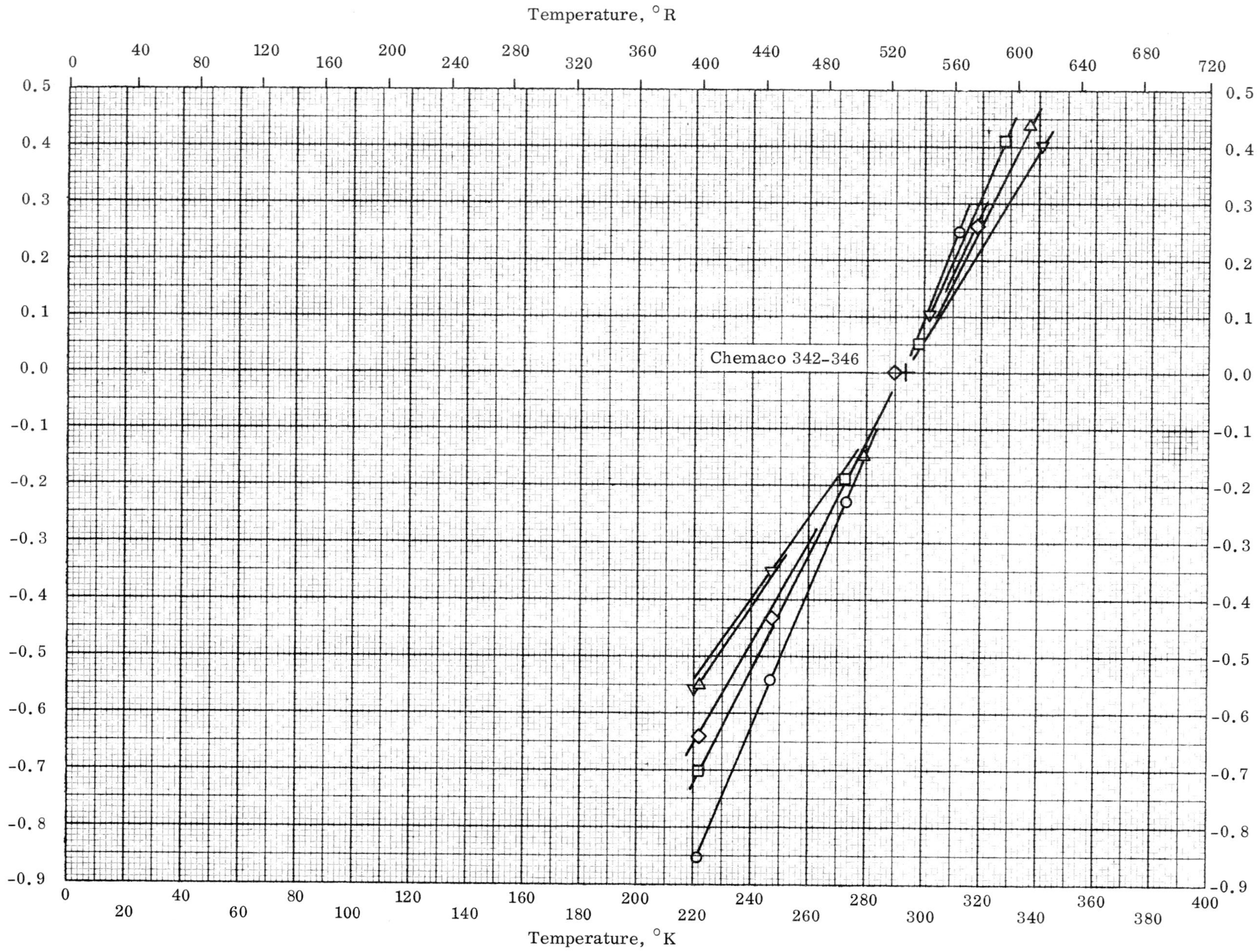

THERMAL LINEAR EXPANSION -- ETHYL CELLULOSE

REFERENCE INFORMATION

Symbol	Ref.	Temp. Range °K	Rept. Error %	Sample Specifications	Remarks
○	54-16	222-312		Chemaco 346 from Chemaco Corp.; 77 parts EC-N-100, 23 parts mineral oil, 2 parts di (diisobutyl) phenol; Nitroglycerin resistant; min solvent resistance; max impact strength at low temp ; medium soft flow.	Held at 77 F and 50% humidity for 24-48 hrs before test.
□	54-16	213-329		Chemaco 345; 80 parts EC-K100B, 14 parts DOW 276-V2, 6 parts Tricresyl phosphate, and 2 parts di (diisobutyl) phenol; general purpose; improved low temp properties; medium soft flow.	Same as above.
△	54-16	215-338		Chemaco 344; 90 parts, 7 parts, 3 parts, and 2 parts, respectively of above; general purpose; improved low temp properties; hard flow.	Same as above.
◇	54-16	213-319		Chemaco 343; same as 345 except Triphenyl phosphate substituted for Tricresyl phosphate; general purpose; medium soft flow.	Same as above.
▽	54-16	222-342		Chemaco 342; same as 344 except Triphenyl phosphate substituted for Tricresyl phosphate; general purpose; hard flow.	Same as above.

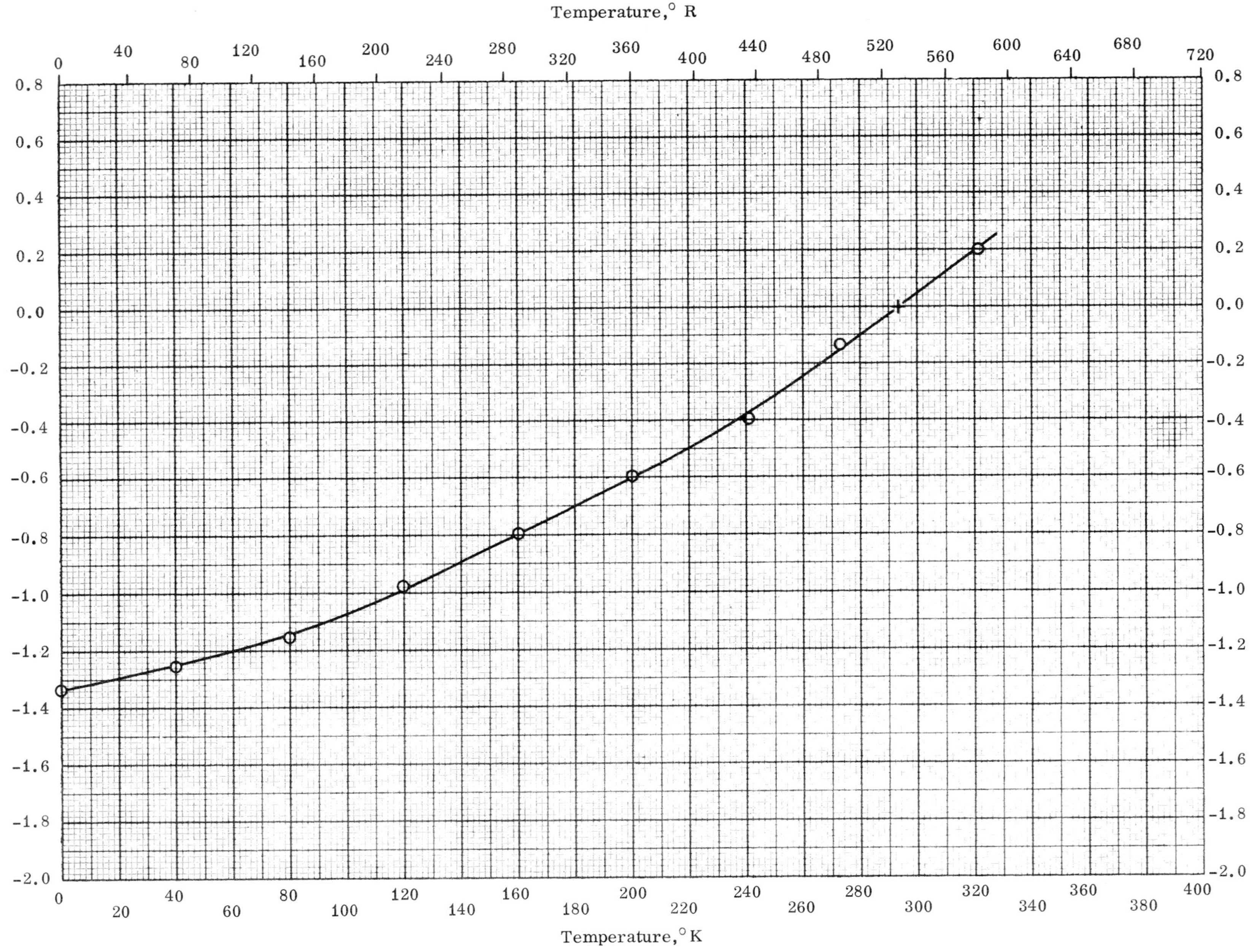

THERMAL LINEAR EXPANSION -- COPOLYVINYL CHLORIDE + ACETATE

REFERENCE INFORMATION

Symbol	Ref.	Temp. Range °K	Rept. Error %	Sample Specifications	Remarks
○	52-13	0-320		2 samples: 1. Vinylite VMCH (86 vinyl chloride, 13 vinyl acetate, 0.7-0.8 dicarboxylic acid) 2. Vinylite VYDR (95 vinyl chloride, 5 vinyl acetate) from Union Carbide and Carbon Co.; stabilized with 5% dibutyl tin maleate.	Measured parallel to axis of 1 in. dia cylinders, 1. - Molded at 5,000 psi and 130 C for 30 min 2. - Molded at 6,5000 psi and 150 C for 5 min ; data reported average for the two samples over 2 or more cycles.

PROPERTIES OF ALKYD-ISOCYANATE FOAM

MOST PROBABLE VALUES

Property	C.G.S. Units	Brit. Eng. Units
Density	0.16	10.0

REPORTED VALUES

Density		$g\ cm^{-3}$	$lb\ ft^{-3}$
	○	0.16	10.0
	□	0.16	10.0
	△	0.16	10.0

REFERENCE INFORMATION

Symbol	Ref.	Temp. Range °K	Rept. Error %	Sample Specifications	Remarks
○	55-3	298		Conforms to MIL-C-8087; by Zenith.	
□	55-3	298		Same as above; by Goodyear.	
△	55-3	298		Same as above.	

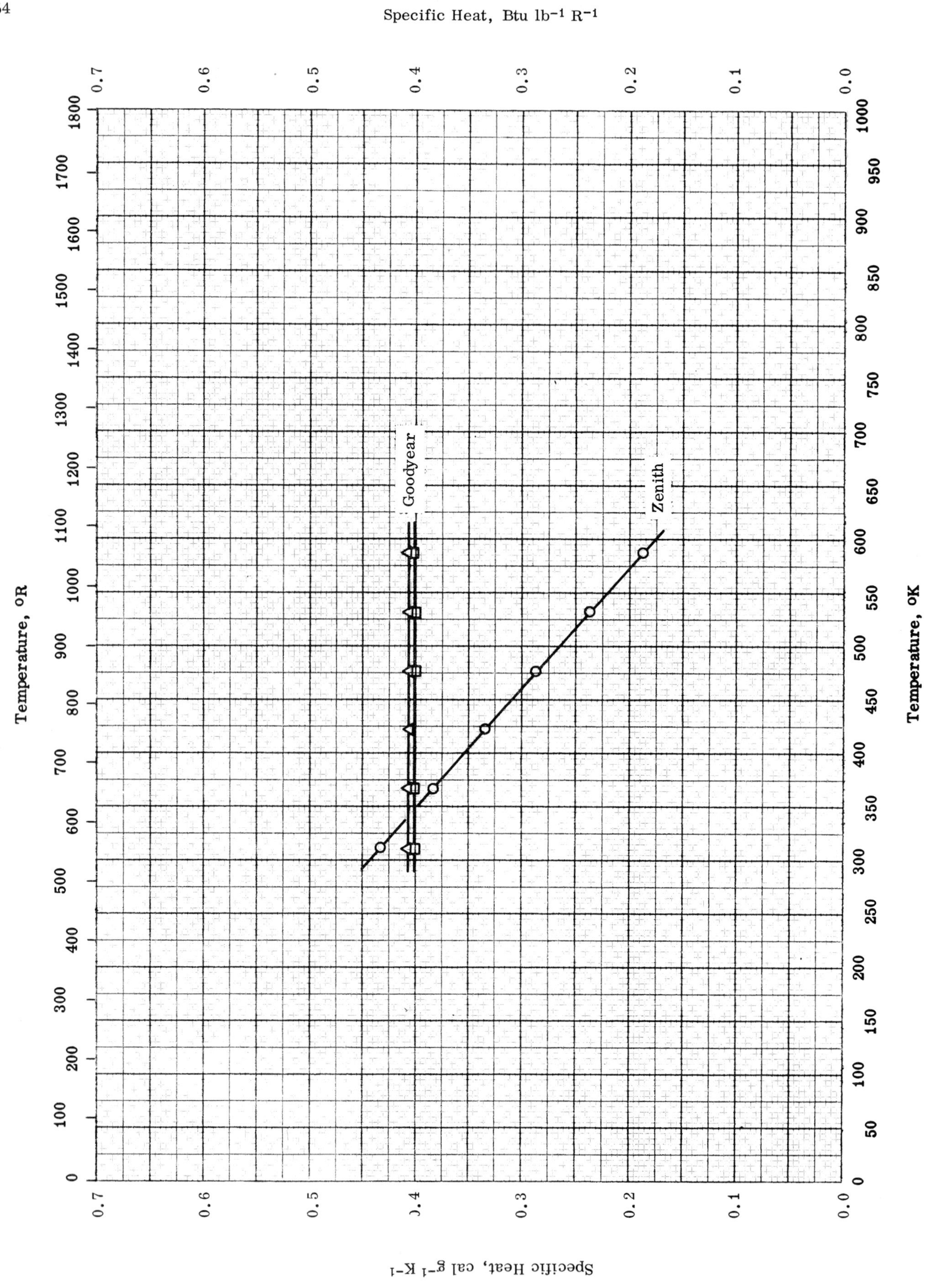

Temperature, °R

Specific Heat, cal g^{-1} K^{-1}

Goodyear

Zenith

Specific Heat, Btu lb^{-1} R^{-1}

Temperature, °K

SPECIFIC HEAT -- ALKYD ISOCYANATE FOAM

REFERENCE INFORMATION

Symbol	Ref.	Temp. Range °K	Rept. Error %	Sample Specifications	Remarks
○	55-3	311-478		By Zenith (MIL-C-8087); density 10 lb ft^{-3}.	Thermal conductivity data indicated change in material above 250 F; author did not take this into account in fitting enthalpy data.
□	55-3	311-495		By Goodyear (MIL-C-8087); density 10 lb ft^{-3}.	Same as above for temperature greater than 300 F.
△	55-3	311-478		By Goodyear (MIL-C-8087); density 18 lb ft^{-3}.	Same as above.

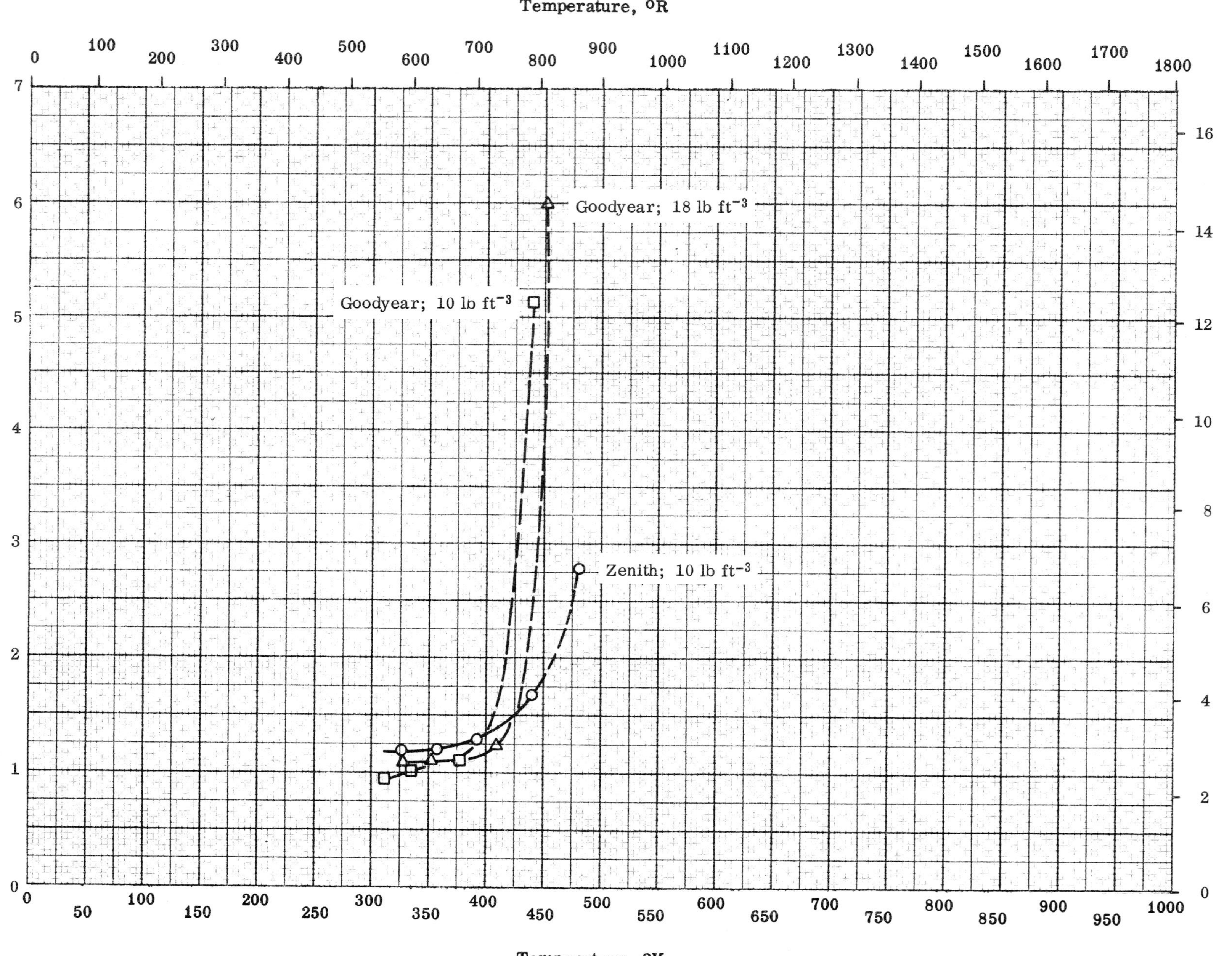

THERMAL CONDUCTIVITY -- ALKYD - ISOCYANATE FOAM

REFERENCE INFORMATION

Symbol	Ref.	Temp. Range °K	Rept. Error %	Sample Specifications	Remarks
○	55-3	326-481		MIL-C-8087 manufactured by Zenith; density 10 lb ft^{-3}.	Decompose at 250 F.
□	55-3	312-440		MIL-C-8087 manufactured by Goodyear; density 10 lb ft^{-3}.	Decompose rapidly above 220 F.
△	55-3	323-452		MIL-C-8087 manufactured by Goodyear; density 18 lb ft^{-3}.	Decompose rapidly above 280 F.

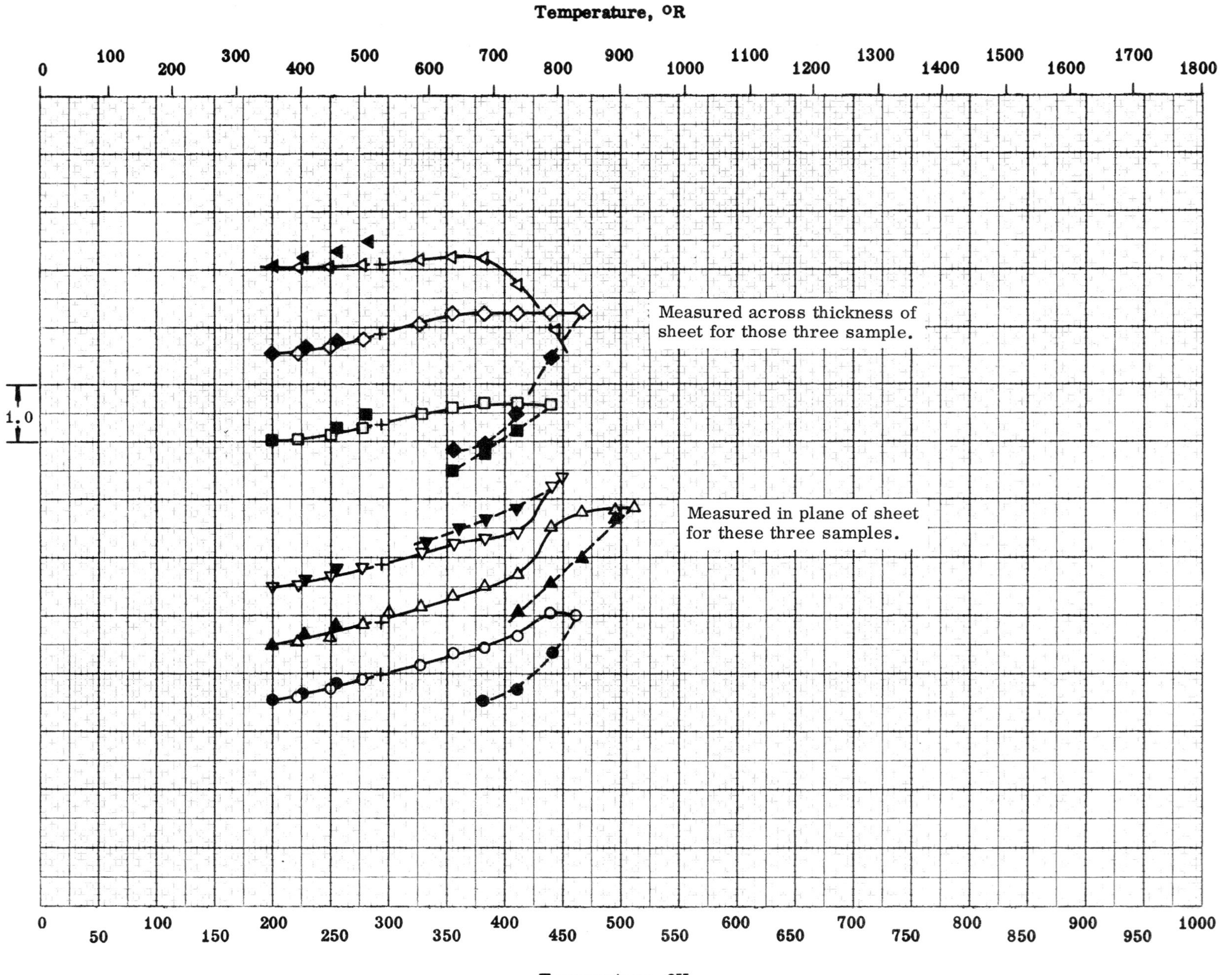

THERMAL LINEAR EXPANSION -- ALKYD ISOCYANATE FOAM

REFERENCE INFORMATION

Symbol	Ref.	Temp. Range °K	Rept. Error %	Sample Specifications	Remarks
○	55-3	200-461		Alkyd Isocyanate Foam, conforms to MIL-C-8087; density 10 lb ft^{-3}; from Goodyear.	Average of 5 tests; measured in plane of sample sheet; heating.
●	55-3	200-439		Same as above.	Cooling.
□	55-3	200-439		Same as above.	Same as above except measured across thickness of sample; heating.
■	55-3	200-439		Same as above.	Cooling.
△	55-3	200-511		Alkyd Isocyanate Foam, conforms to MIL-C-8087; density 18 lb ft^{-3}; made by Goodyear.	Average of 5 tests; measured in plane of sample sheet; heating
▲	55-3	200-511		Same as above.	Cooling.
◇	55-3	200-467		Same as above.	Same as above except measured across thickness of sample; heating.
◆	55-3	200-467		Same as above.	Cooling.
▽	55-3	200-450		Alkyd Isocyanate Foam, conforms to MIL-C-8087; density 10 lb ft^{-3}; made by Zenith.	Measured in plane of sample sheet; heating.
▼	55-3	200-450		Same as above.	Cooling.
◁	55-3	200-450		Same as above.	Same as above except measured across thickness of sample; heating.
◀	55-3	200-450		Same as above.	Cooling.

PROPERTIES OF ISOCYANATE POLYESTER ELASTOMER

MOST PROBABLE VALUES

Property	C.G.S. Units	Brit. Eng. Units
Density	1.25	78

REPORTED VALUES

Density		$g\ cm^{-3}$	$lb\ ft^{-3}$
	○	1.245	77.72
	□	1.252	78.16

REFERENCE INFORMATION

Symbol	Ref.	Temp. Range °K	Rept. Error %	Sample Specifications	Remarks
○	57-29	298		Di-isocyanate polyester elastomer.	Large gasket.
□	57-29	298		Same as above.	Small gasket.

PROPERTIES OF POLYURETHANE FOAM

REPORTED VALUES

Density		$g\ cm^{-3}$	$lb\ ft^{-3}$
○	Lockfoam	0.179	11.2
□	Goodyear	0.227	14.2
△	Isofoam	0.263	16.4
◇	Armofoam	0.160	10.0
▽	Hamilton standard	0.173	10.8

REFERENCE INFORMATION

Symbol	Ref.	Temp. Range °K	Rept. Error %	Sample Specifications	Remarks
○	55-25	298		Lock foam, foam in place plastic.	
□	55-25	298		Goodyear, foam in place plastic.	
△	55-25	298		Isofoam, foam in place plastic.	
◇	55-25	298		Armofoam, foam in place plastic.	
▽	55-25	298		Hamilton standard, foam in place plastic.	

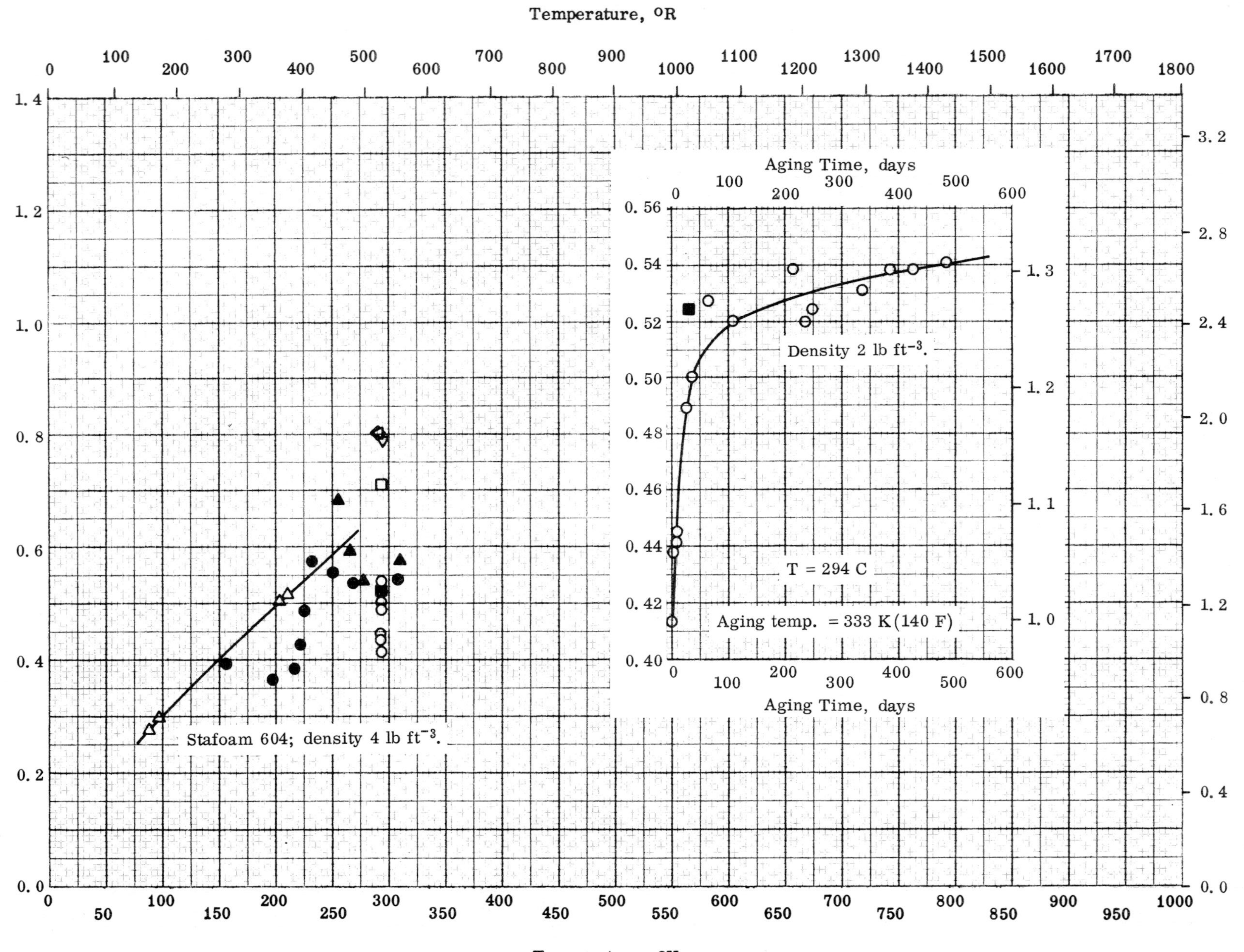

THERMAL CONDUCTIVITY -- POLYURETHANE FOAM

REFERENCE INFORMATION

Symbol	Ref.	Temp. Range °K	Rept. Error %	Sample Specifications	Remarks
△	62-11	89-209		Stafoam 604; density 4 lb ft^{-3}.	Measured in CO_2.
□	62-12	294		Density 2.1 lb ft^{-3}; expanded with CCl_3F; 13% open cells.	Crushed and re-expanded in air; aged 28 days at 140 F.
▽	62-12	294		Same as above.	The above sample crushed and re-expanded second time; aged 2 more days.
◆	62-12	294		Same as above.	The above sample crushed and re-expanded for the third time; aged 3 more days.
◁	62-12	294		Same as above; 99^+ % open cells after treatment.	The above sample crushed and re-expanded for the fourth time; aged 3 more days.
■	62-12	294		Same as above; 13% open cells.	Crushed, re-expanded, and aged at 140 F continuously for 35 days and measurements taken periodically during aging.
○	62-12	294		Rigid foam with cell size 0.4 - 0.5 mm; density 2 lb ft^{-3} and expanded with CCl_3F.	Aged at 140 F; measurements made against aging time.
▲	62-12	255-310		Rigid foam expanded with CCl_3F.	
●	62-12	157-309		Same as above.	

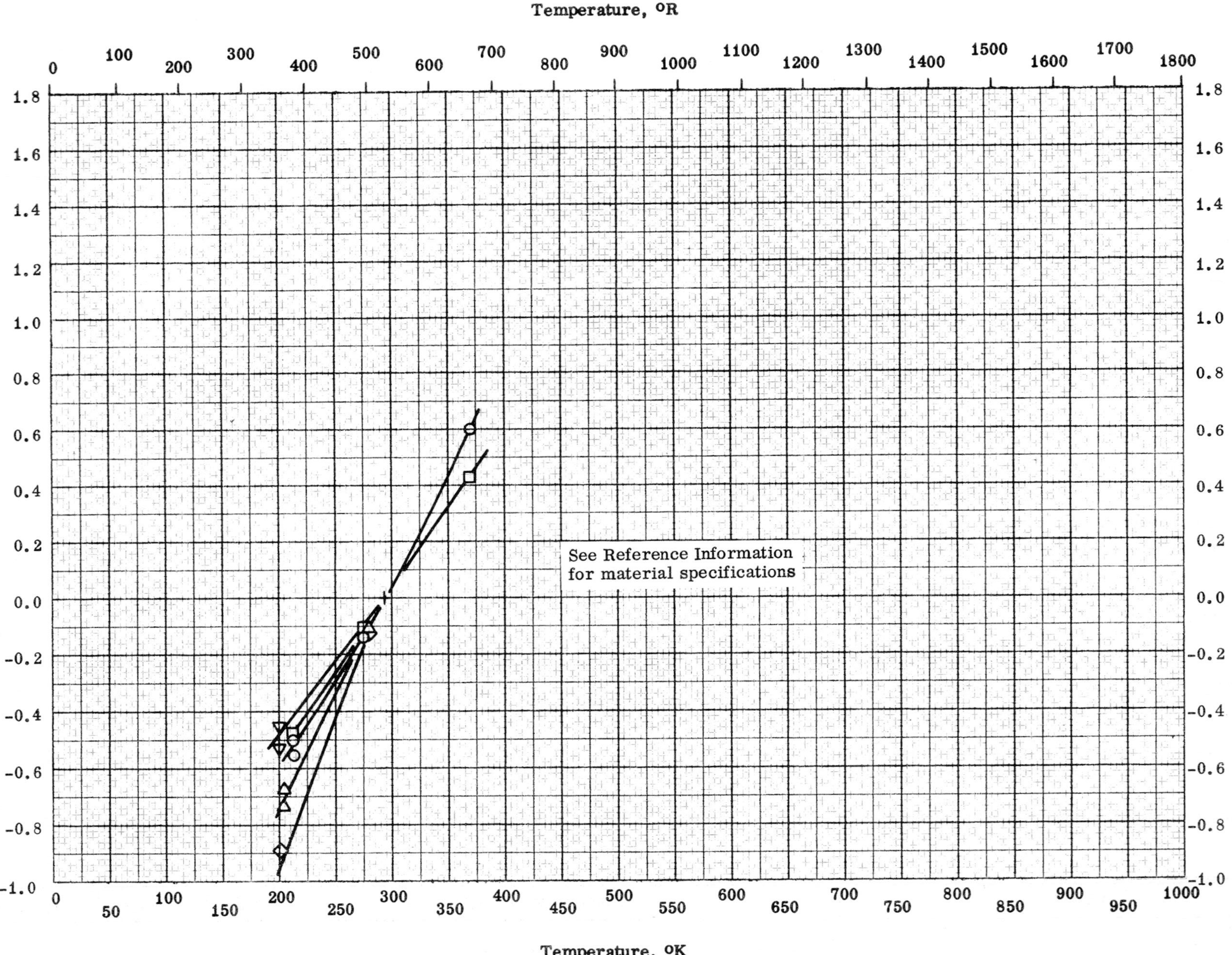

THERMAL LINEAR EXPANSION -- POLYURETHANE FOAM (FOAM IN PLACE)

REFERENCE INFORMATION

Symbol	Ref.	Temp. Range °K	Rept. Error %	Sample Specifications	Remarks
○	55-16	215-371		Lockfoam; density 11.2 lb ft^{-3}.	Measured parallel to foam rise; auth. est. precision ± 10% between samples.
□	55-16	216-371		Goodyear; density 14.2 lb ft^{-3}.	Same as above.
△	55-16	206-278		Isofoam; density 16.4 lb ft^{-3}.	Same as above.
◇	55-16	202-278		Armofoam; density 10.0 lb ft^{-3}.	Same as above.
▽	55-16	204-277		Hamilton Standard; density 10.8 lb ft^{-3}.	Same as above.

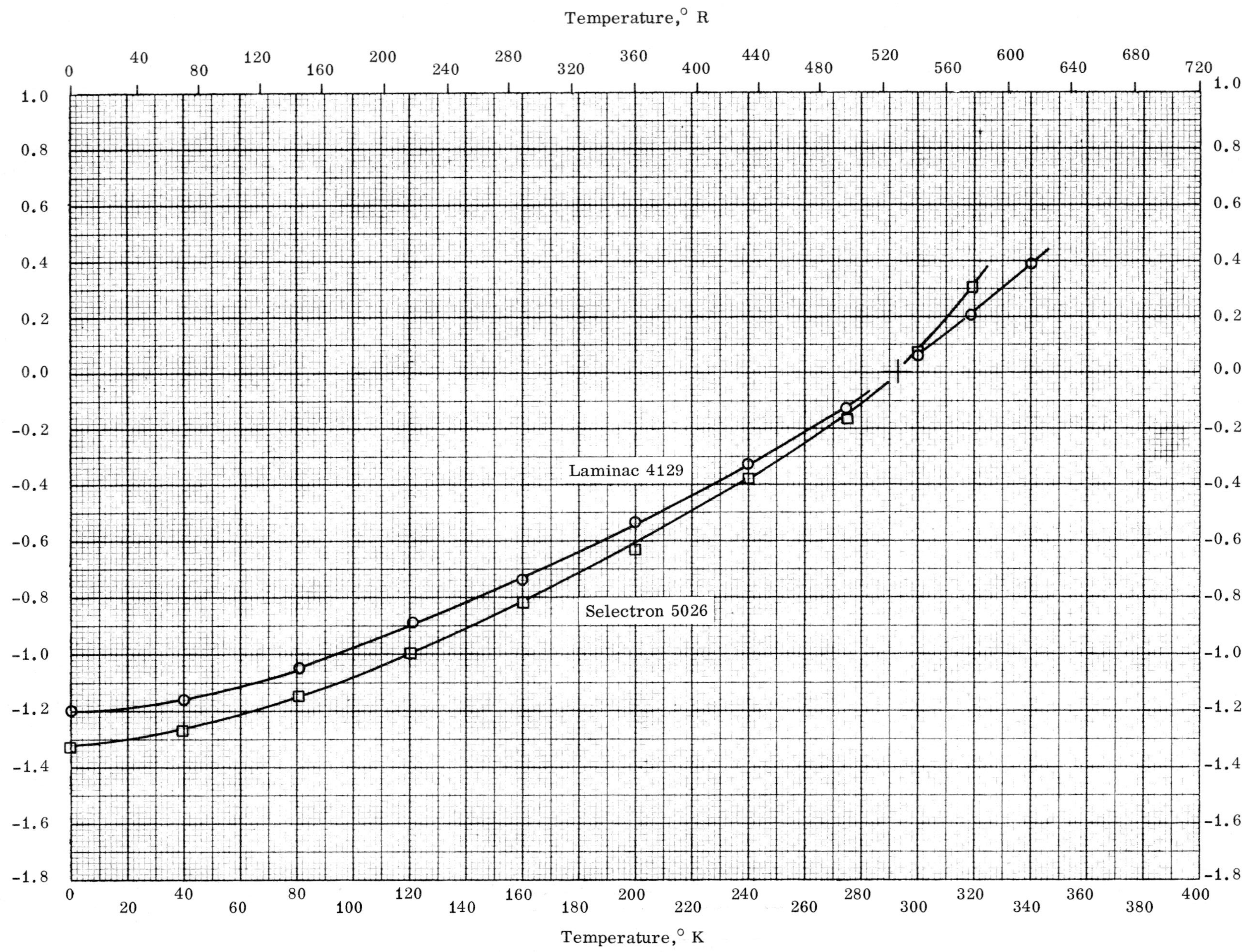

THERMAL LINEAR EXPANSION -- UNSATURATED POLYESTER

REFERENCE INFORMATION

Symbol	Ref.	Temp. Range °K	Rept. Error %	Sample Specifications	Remarks
○	52-13	0-340		Laminac 4129 from American Cyanamid Co.; 0.5 tert. butyl hydroperoxide catalyst.	Cured 48 hrs at room temperature and 1 hr at 100 C; auth. est. accuracy ± 1% at 0 R, ± 4% at 612 R.
□	52-13	0-320		Selectron 5026 from Pittsburgh Plate Glass Co.; 0.5 tert. butyl hydroperoxide catalyst.	Cured as above; auth. est. accuracy ± 1% at 0 R.

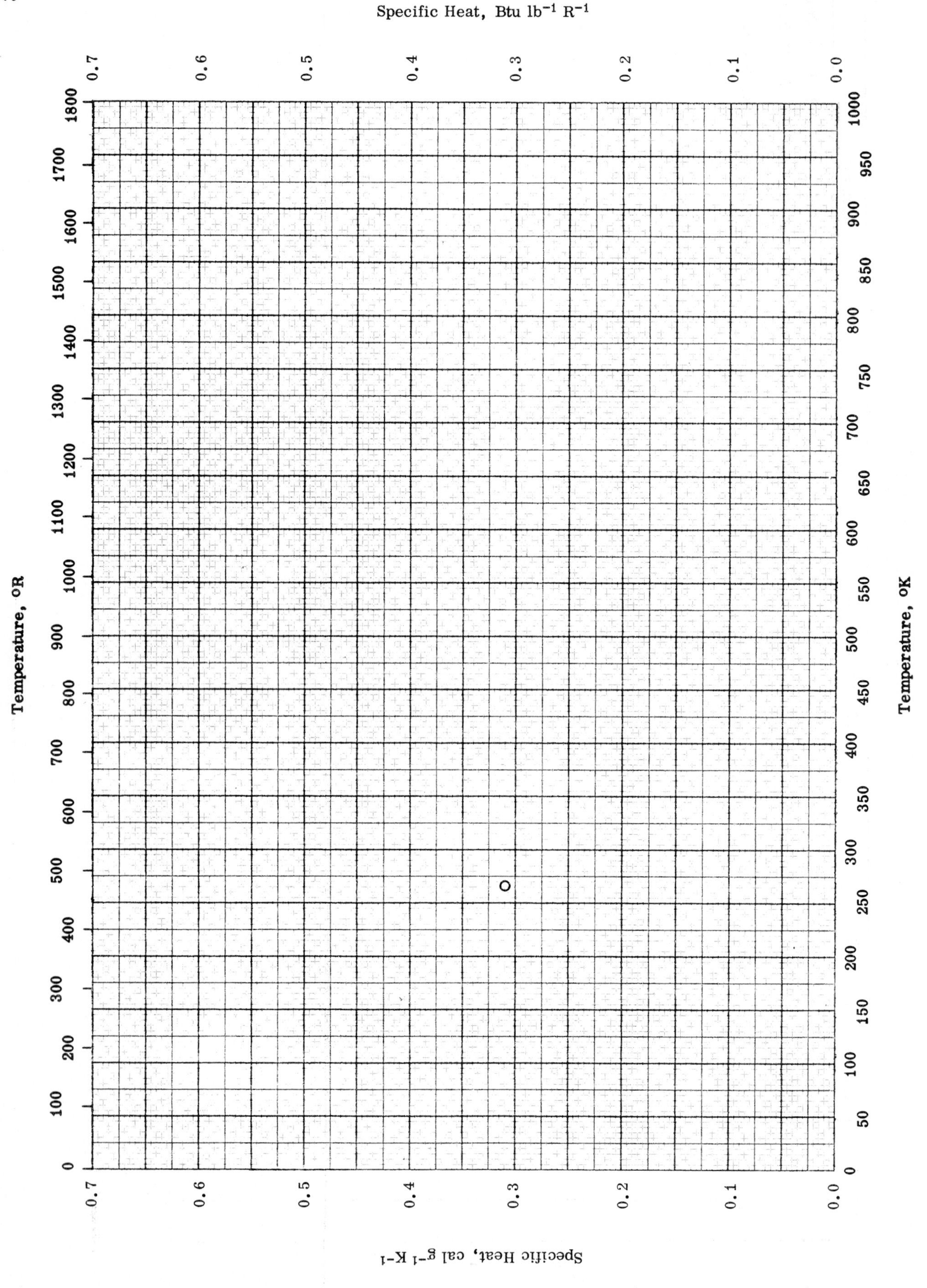

Specific Heat, Btu lb^{-1} R^{-1}

0.7 0.6 0.5 0.4 0.3 0.2 0.1 0.0

Temperature, °R

0 100 200 300 400 500 600 700 800 900 1000 1100 1200 1300 1400 1500 1600 1700 1800

Temperature, °K

0 50 100 150 200 250 300 350 400 450 500 550 600 650 700 750 800 850 900 950 1000

Specific Heat, cal g^{-1} K^{-1}

0.7 0.6 0.5 0.4 0.3 0.2 0.1 0.0

SPECIFIC HEAT -- POLYVINYL CARBAZOLE

SPECIFIC HEAT -- POLYVINYL CARBAZOLE

REFERENCE INFORMATION

Symbol	Ref.	Temp. Range °K	Rept. Error %	Sample Specifications	Remarks
○	40-1	333		Trolitul Luvican Luv - M150 polyvinyl carbazole.	Author report avg. specific heat from 20 to 1000 C.

Temperature, °R

Thermal Conductivity, cal Sec^{-1} cm^{-1} K^{-1} x 10^2

Thermal Conductivity, Btu hr^{-1} ft^{-1} R^{-1}

Temperature, °K

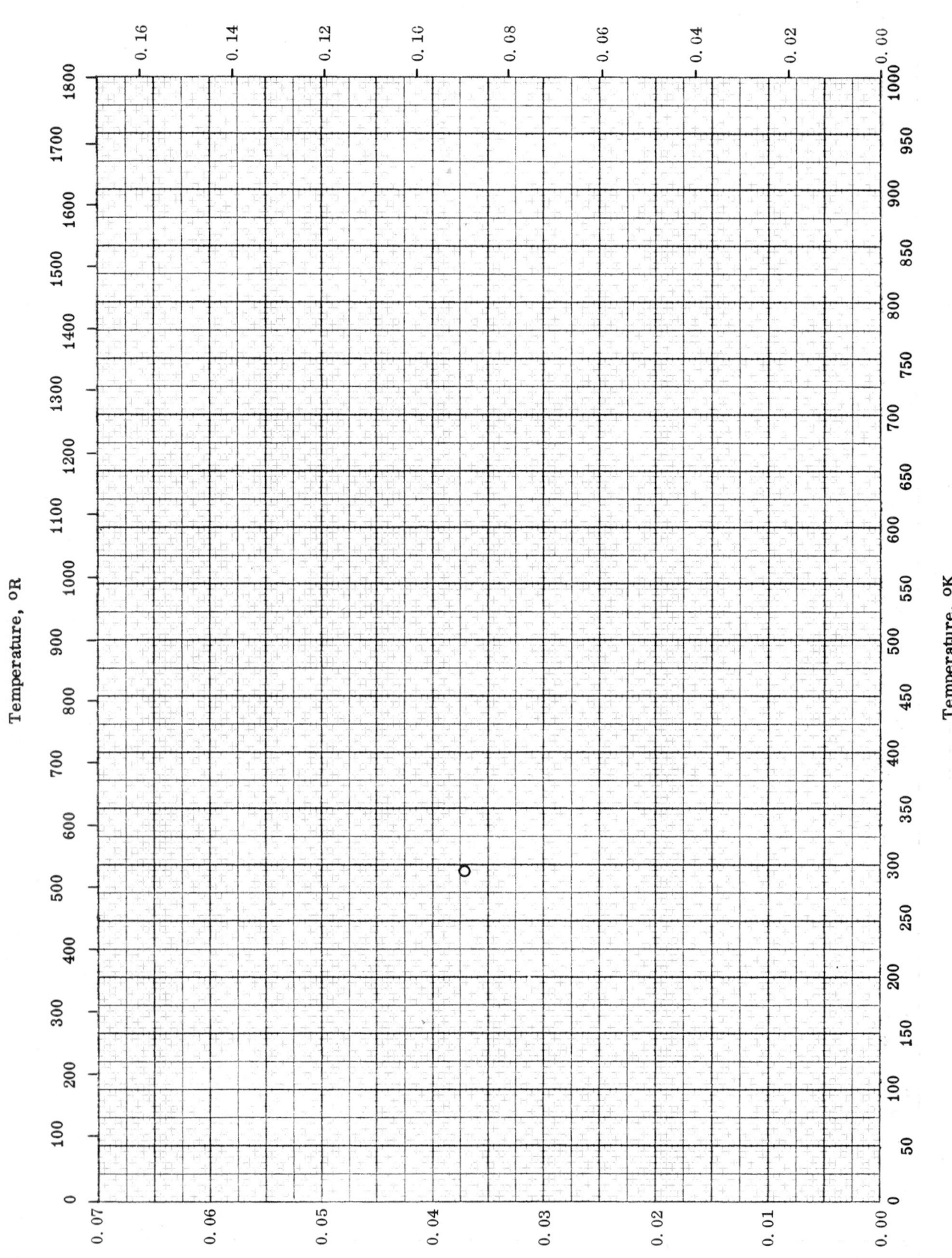

THERMAL CONDUCTIVITY -- POLYVINYL CARBAZOLE

REFERENCE INFORMATION

Symbol	Ref.	Temp. Range °K	Rept. Error %	Sample Specifications	Remarks
○	40-1	293		Trolitul Luv-M150 (German desig.); polyvinyl Carbazole Luvican; density 74 lb ft^{-1}.	

PROPERTIES OF TAC POLYESTER

MOST PROBABLE VALUES

Property	C.G.S. Units	Brit. Eng. Units
Density, Castolite	1.23	76.7

REPORTED VALUES

Density	$g\ cm^{-3}$	$lb\ ft^{-3}$
	O 1.23	76.7

REFERENCE INFORMATION

Symbol	Ref.	Temp. Range °K	Rept. Error %	Sample Specifications	Remarks
○	57-1	267		Castolite polyester resin.	

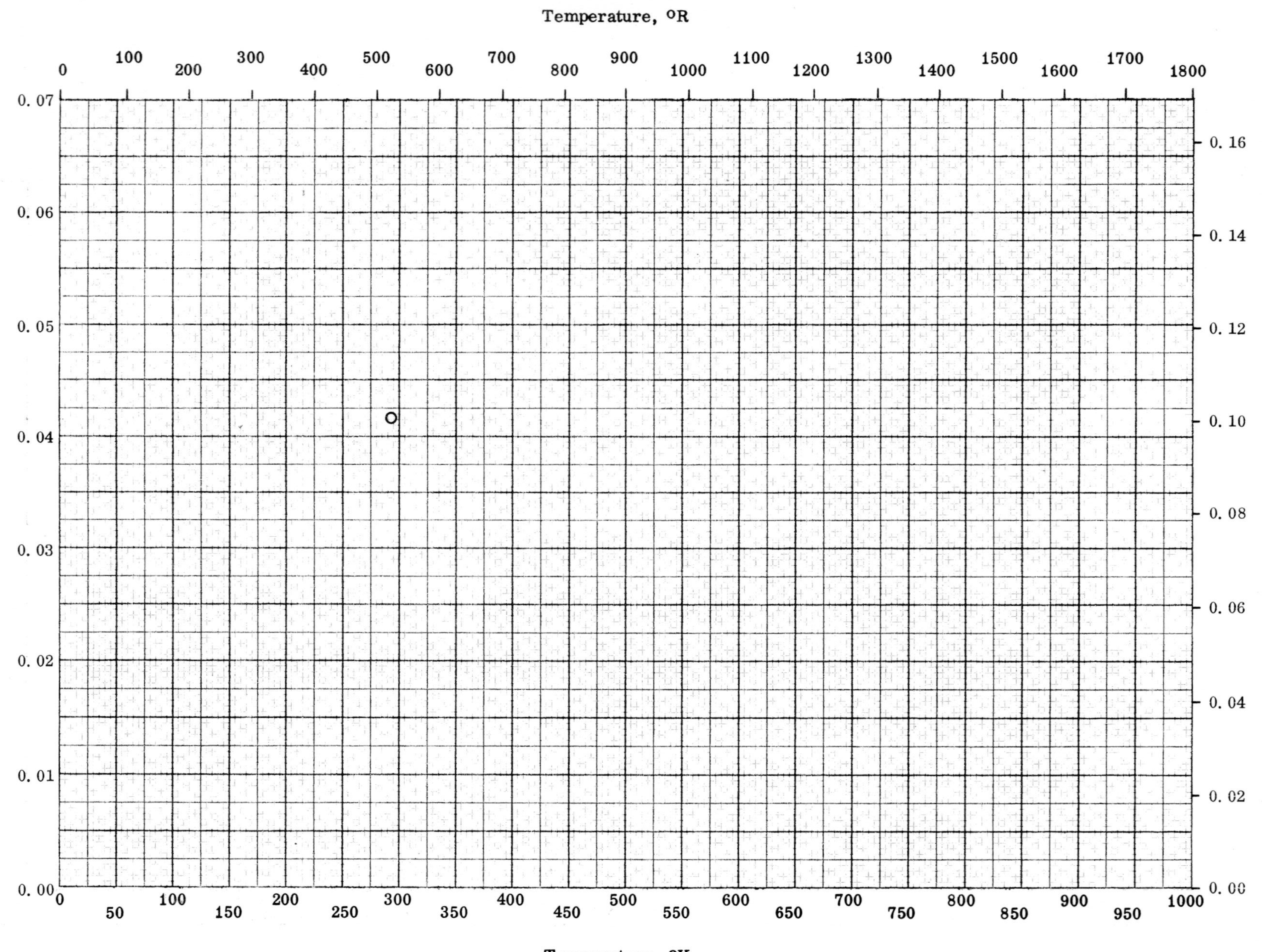

THERMAL CONDUCTIVITY -- TAC POLYESTER

REFERENCE INFORMATION

Symbol	Ref.	Temp. Range °K	Rept. Error %	Sample Specifications	Remarks
○	57-8	267		Castolite; density 77 lb ft^{-3}.	

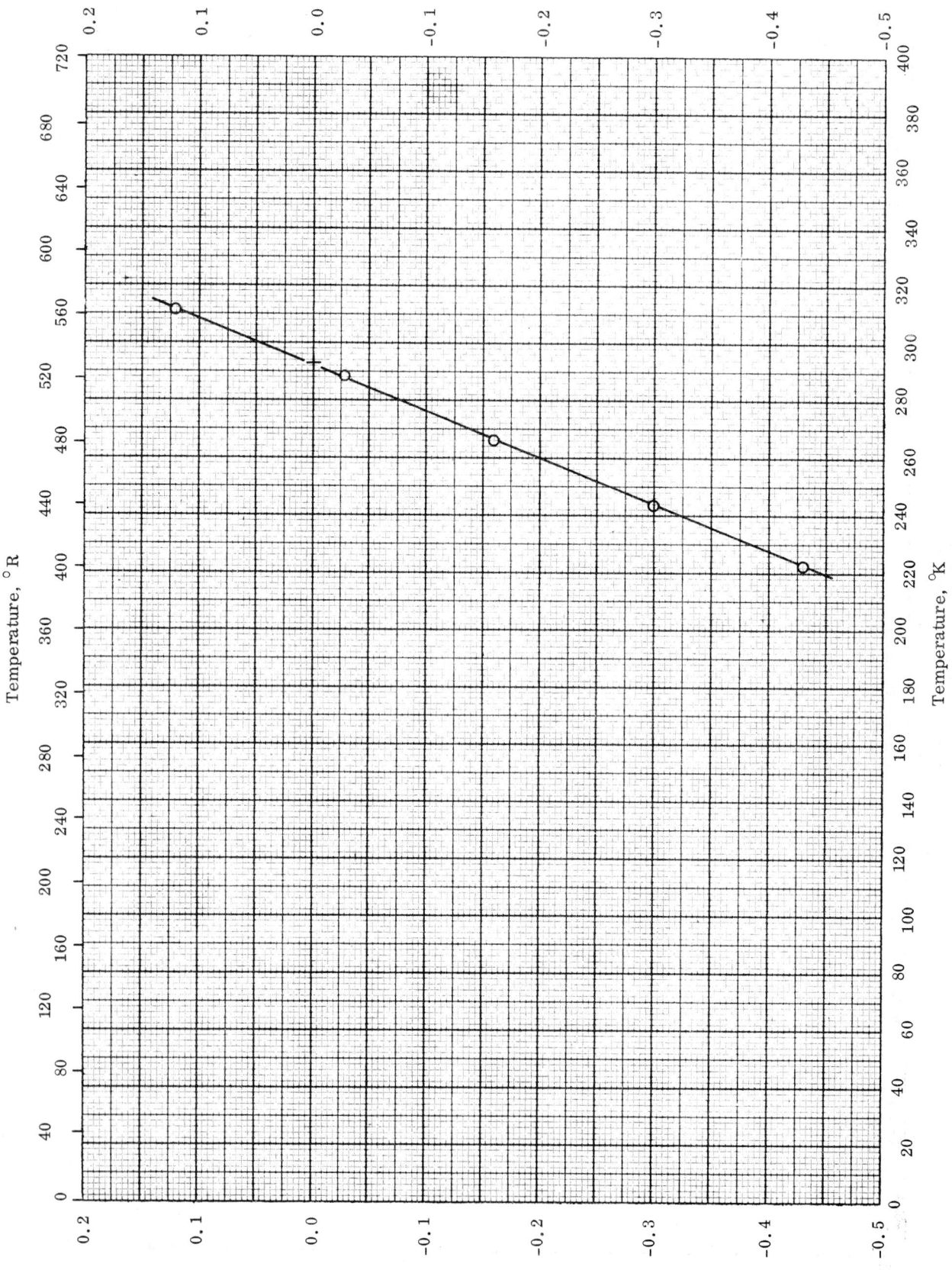

Temperature, °R
0 40 80 120 160 200 240 280 320 360 400 440 480 520 560 600 640 680 720
Thermal Linear Expansion, percent
0.2 0.1 0.0 -0.1 -0.2 -0.3 -0.4 -0.5
Temperature, °K
0 20 40 60 80 100 120 140 160 180 200 220 240 260 280 300 320 340 360 380 400

THERMAL LINEAR EXPANSION -- TAC POLYESTER

THERMAL LINEAR EXPANSION -- TAC POLYESTER

REFERENCE INFORMATION

Symbol	Ref.	Temp. Range °K	Rept. Error %	Sample Specifications	Remarks
○	57-1	223-311		Two samples: (a) Paraplex P43 (b) Castolite	Identical data for both samples.

PROPERTIES OF PHENOLIC RESIN

MOST PROBABLE VALUES

Property	C.G.S. Units	Brit. Eng. Units
Density	1.3*	80*

*Approximate value for engineering purposes.

REPORTED VALUES

Density		g cm⁻³	lb ft⁻³
	○	1.27	79.2
	□	1.37	85.5
	△	1.40	87.4

REFERENCE INFORMATION

Symbol	Ref.	Temp. Range °K	Rept. Error %	Sample Specifications	Remarks
○	40-1	298		Phenolic resin.	Pressed.
□	40-1	298		50 resin, type S.	
△	40-1	298		40 resin, type S.	

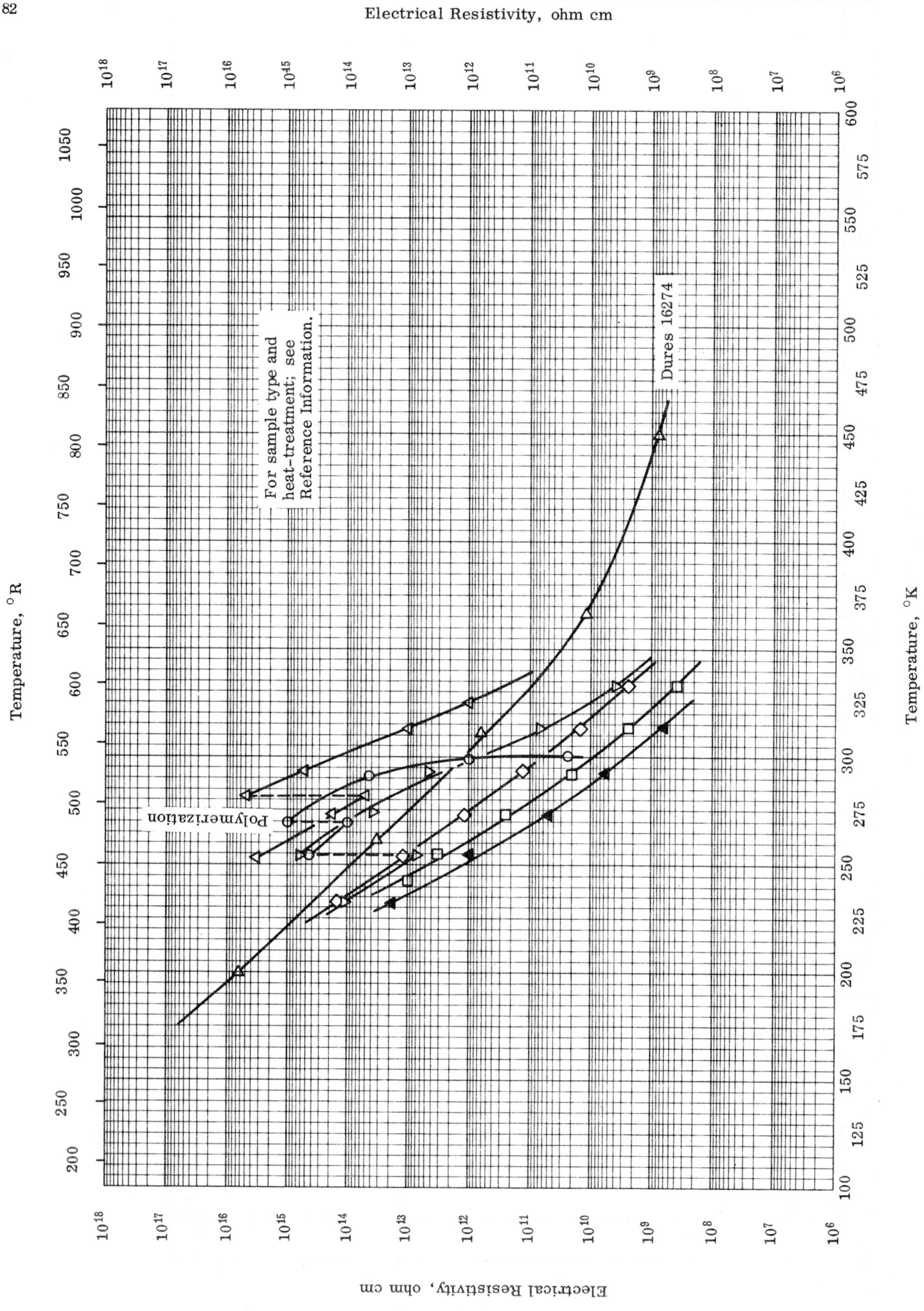

Electrical Resistivity, ohm cm

Temperature, °R

Temperature, °K

For sample type and heat-treatment; see Reference Information.

Dures 16274

Polymerization

Electrical Resistivity, ohm cm

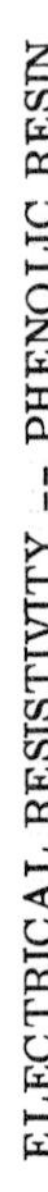

REFERENCE INFORMATION

Symbol	Ref.	Temp. Range °K	Rept. Error %	Sample Specifications	Remarks
○	57-15	243-333		Alberit 1005; directly polymerizing phenolic resin without filler.	Finely pulverized mixture pressed in hot forms; aged one week at 50% relative humidity.
□	57-15	243-333		Same as above.	Same as above; hardened 16 min. at 160 C.
△	57-15	233-333		Alberit 8291 - SO for high frequencies; with mineral filler.	Hot pressed and aged as above; not hardened.
◇	57-15	233-333		Same as above.	Hot pressed and aged as above; hardened 16 min. at 160 C.
▽	57-15	233-333		Type 31 mixture of phenolic novolak with hexamethylentetramin and 40-60 wood flour.	Hot pressed and aged as above; not hardened.
▲	57-15	233-333		Same as above.	Hot pressed and aged as above; hardened 16 min. at 160 C.
▷	57-18	200-450		Dures 16274, mineral filled phenolic; made by Dures Plastic Div. of Hooker Electromechanical Co.	Conditioned 48 hrs at 120 F at 90% humidity, then 7 cycles, each of which consists of 12 hr at 100 F and 100% humidity, plus 12 hr at 120 F and 95% humidity.

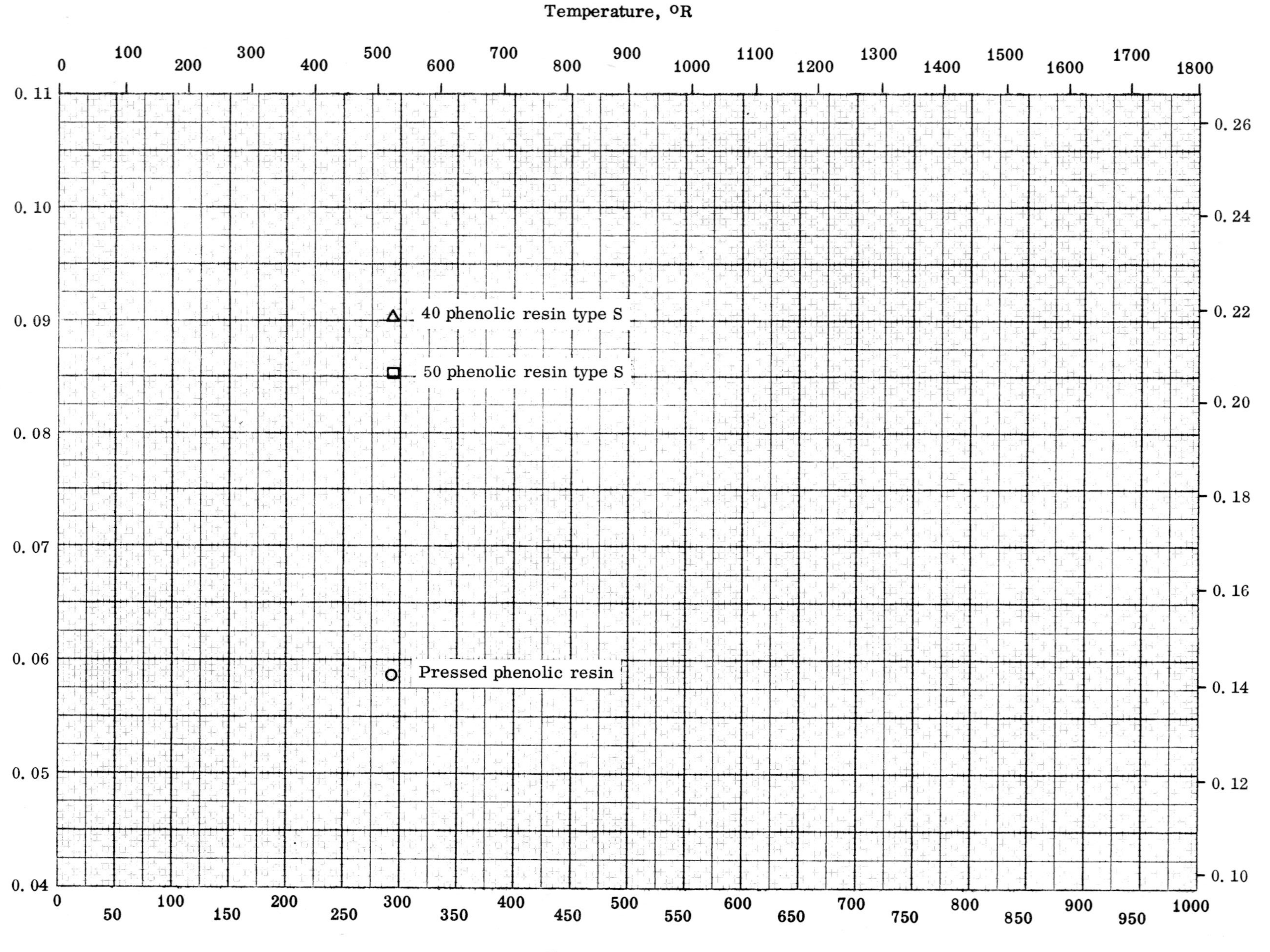

THERMAL CONDUCTIVITY -- PHENOLIC RESIN

REFERENCE INFORMATION

Symbol	Ref.	Temp. Range °K	Rept. Error %	Sample Specifications	Remarks
○	40-1	293		Phenolic resin; pressed; density 79.2 lb ft^{-3}.	
□	40-1	293		50% Phenolic resin type S; density 85.5 lb ft^{-3}.	
△	40-1	293		40% Phenolic resin type S; density 87.4 lb ft^{-3}.	

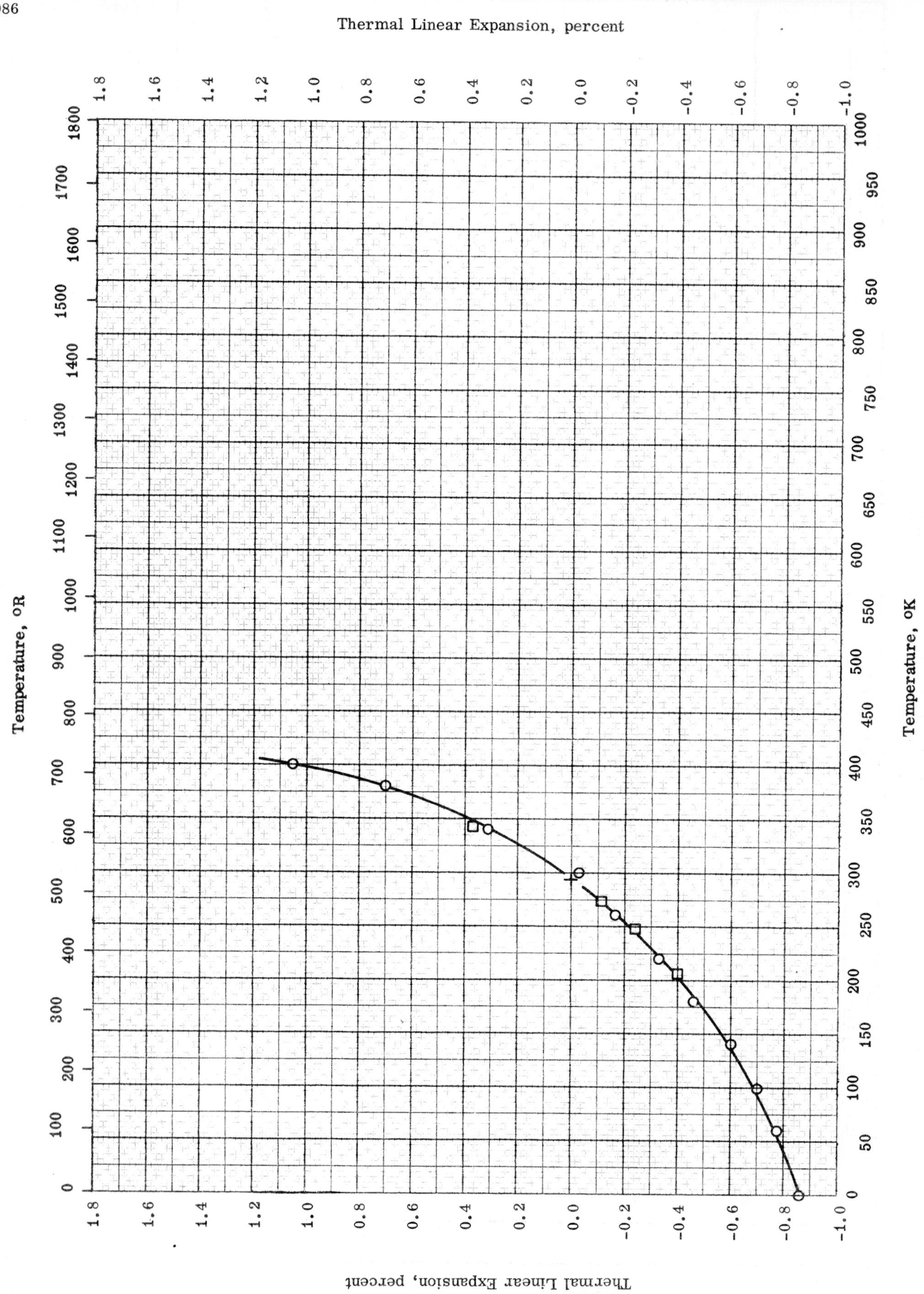

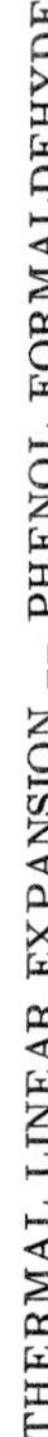
THERMAL LINEAR EXPANSION -- PHENOL FORMALDEHYDE

REFERENCE INFORMATION

Symbol	Ref.	Temp. Range °K	Rept. Error %	Sample Specifications	Remarks
○	52-13	0-400		"Catalin" from Catalin Corp. of America.	Auth. est. accuracy: ± 1% at 0 R, ± 2% at 685 R, and ± 3% at 720 R.
□	54-16	215-342		Catalin; mechanical grade unplasticized.	Held at 77 F and 50% humidity for 24-48 hrs before test.

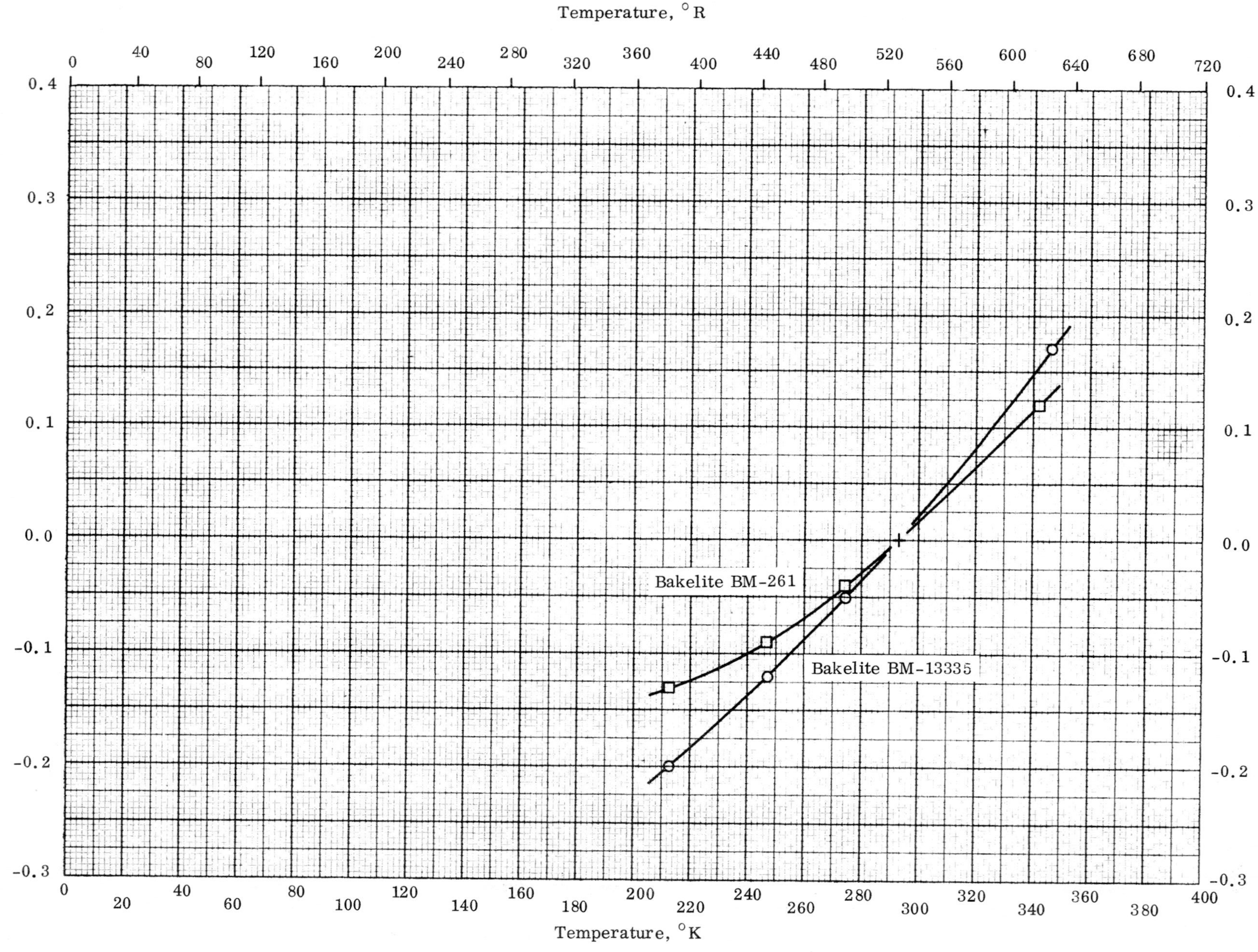

THERMAL LINEAR EXPANSION -- PHENOL FORMALDEHYDE, ASBESTOS FILLED

THERMAL LINEAR EXPANSION -- PHENOL FORMALDEHYDE, ASBESTOS FILLED

REFERENCE INFORMATION

Symbol	Ref.	Temp. Range °K	Rept. Error %	Sample Specifications	Remarks
○	54-16	213-346		Bakelite BM-13335 from Union Carbide and Carbon Co.; black; molding resin; max heat and water resistance.	Held at 77 F and 50% humidity for 24-48 hrs before test.
□	54-16	213-342		Bakelite BM-261; black; 2-step molding resin; max moisture resistance.	Same as above.

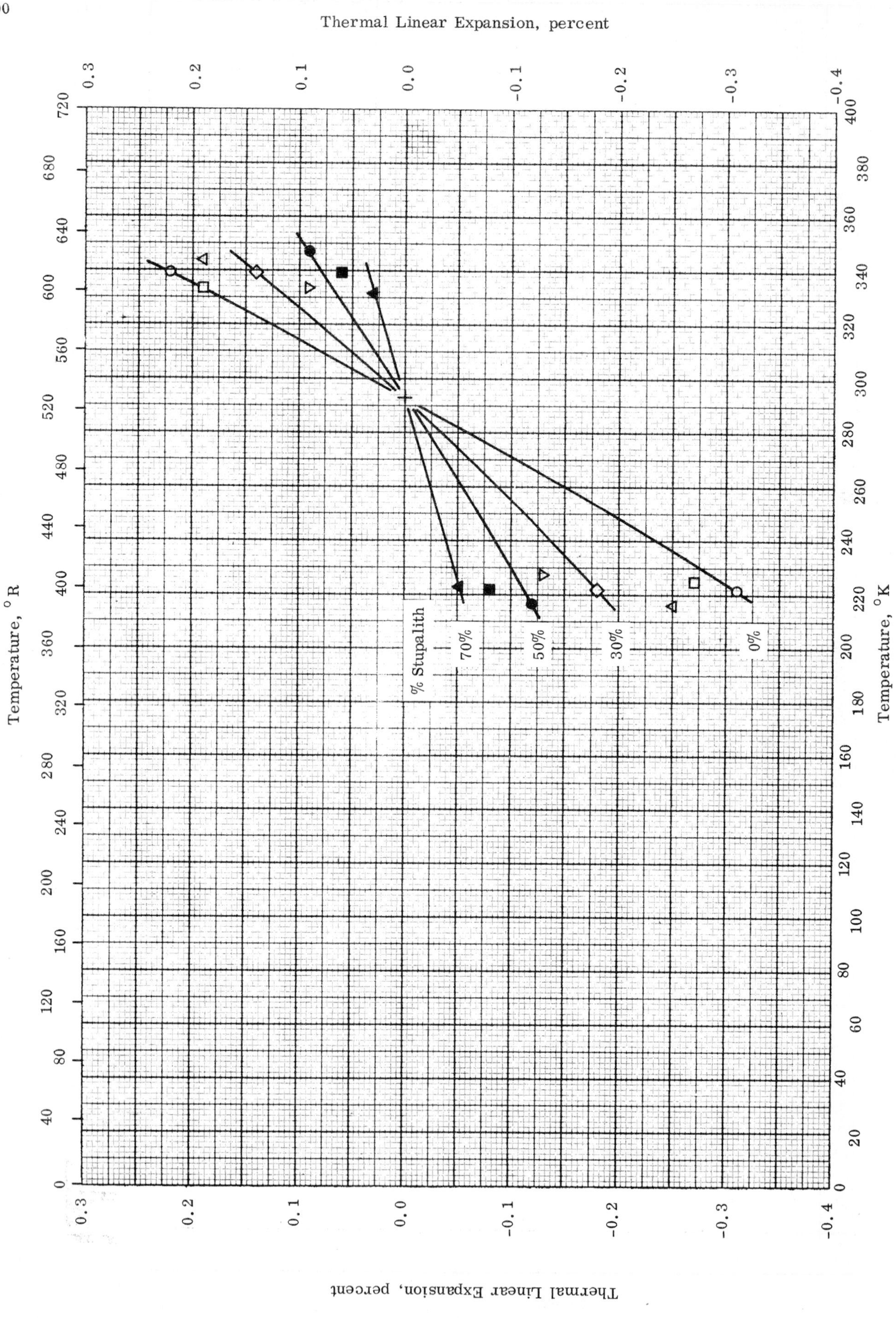

THERMAL LINEAR EXPANSION -- PHENOL FORMALDEHYDE, CERAMIC FILLED

THERMAL LINEAR EXPANSION -- PHENOL FORMALDEHYDE, CERAMIC FILLED

REFERENCE INFORMATION

Symbol	Ref.	Temp. Range °K	Rept. Error %	Sample Specifications	Remarks
○	56-16	222-345		Unfilled phenolic resin.	Samples conditioned at 543 R and 50% relative humidity; molded 10 min at 320 F under 1900 psi.
□	56-16	222-345		10 Stupalith A-2412 filler.	Same as above.
△	56-16	222-345		20 Stupalith A-2412 filler.	Same as above.
◇	56-16	222-345		30 Stupalith A-2412 filler.	Same as above.
▽	56-16	222-345		40 Stupalith A-2412 filler.	Same as above.
●	56-16	222-345		50 Stupalith A-2412 filler.	Same as above.
■	56-16	222-345		60 Stupalith A-2412 filler.	Same as above.
▲	56-16	222-345		70 Stupalith A-2412 filler.	Same as above.

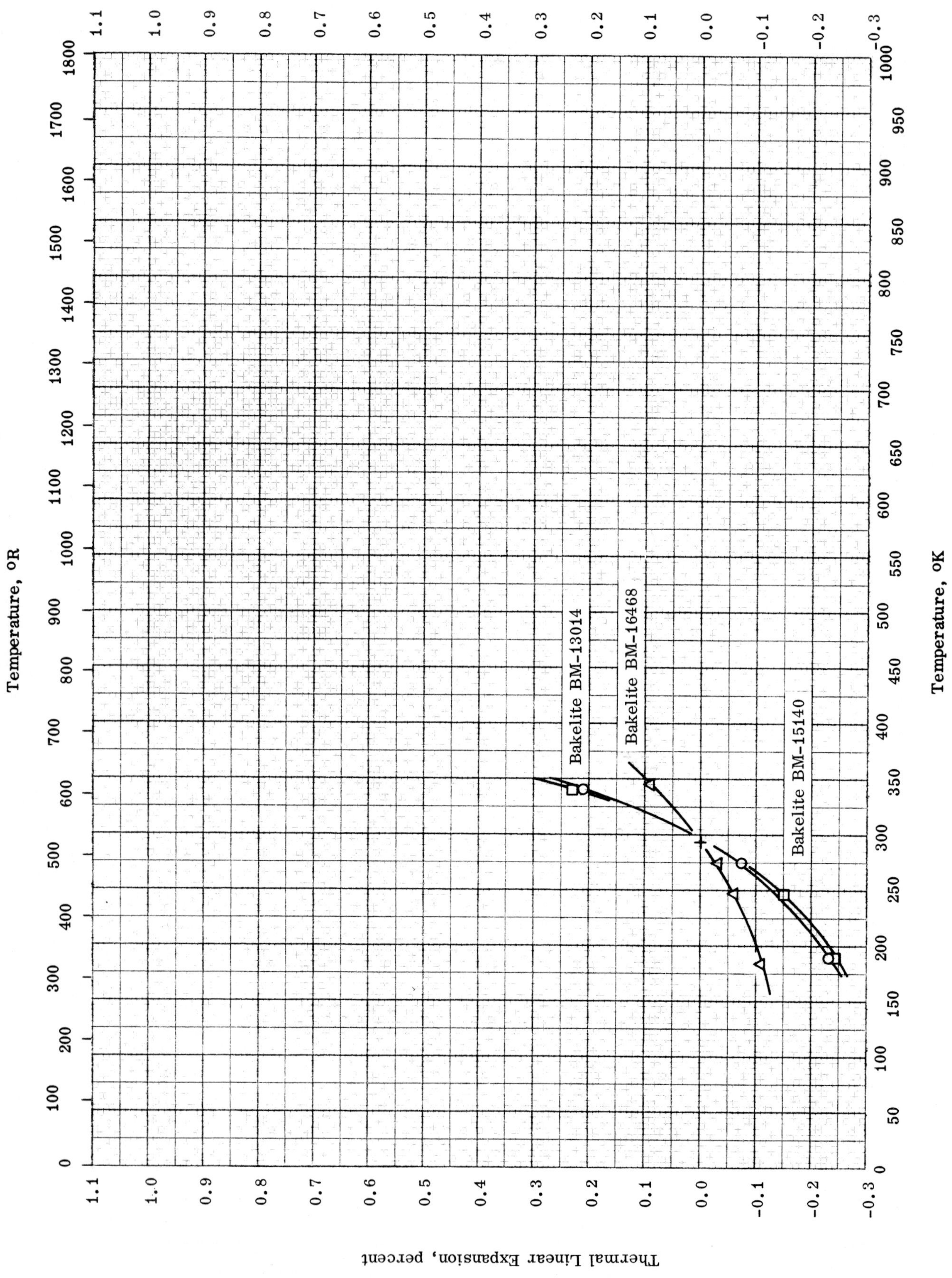

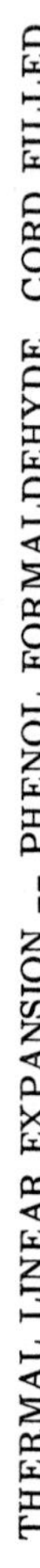

Thermal Linear Expansion, percent

Temperature, °R

Temperature, °K

Bakelite BM-13014

Bakelite BM-16468

Bakelite BM-15140

Thermal Linear Expansion, percent

REFERENCE INFORMATION

Symbol	Ref.	Temp. Range °K	Rept. Error %	Sample Specifications	Remarks
○	54-16	219-341		Bakelite BM - 13014 from Union Carbide and Carbon Co.;2-step molding resin; nigrosine dye coloring; max impact strength.	Held at 70 F and 50%humidity for 24-48 hrs before test.
□	54-16	219-341		Bakelite BM - 15140; 2-step molding resin; carbon black coloring; max impact strength;fast curing; low density.	Same as above.
△	54-16	215-346		Bakelite BM - 16468; 2-step molding resin; max impact strength.	Same as above.

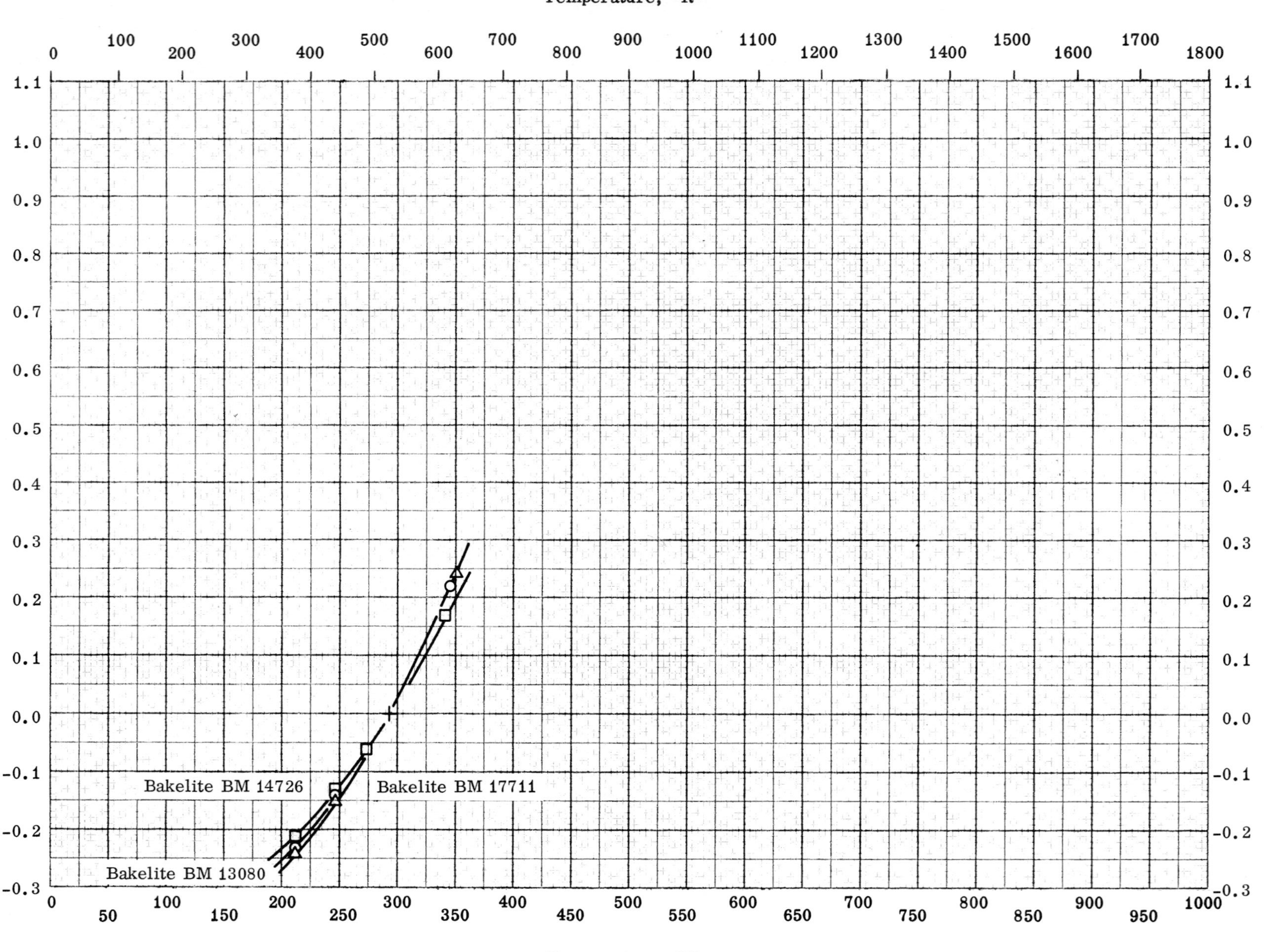

THERMAL LINEAR EXPANSION -- PHENOL FORMALDEHYDE, COTTON FLOCK FILLED

REFERENCE INFORMATION

Symbol	Ref.	Temp. Range °K	Rept. Error %	Sample Specifications	Remarks
○	54-16	213-346		Bakelite BM-13080 from Union Carbide and Carbon Co.; 1-step molding resin; transfer molding material with improved flow.	Held at 77 F and 50% humidity for 24-48 hrs before test.
□	54-16	213-342		Bakelite BM-14726; 2-step molding resin; max impact strength without hand preforming.	Same as above.
△	54-16	213-351		Bakelite BM-17711; 2-step molding resin; high filler to resin ratio; high impact and flexural strength; moisture resistance.	Same as above.

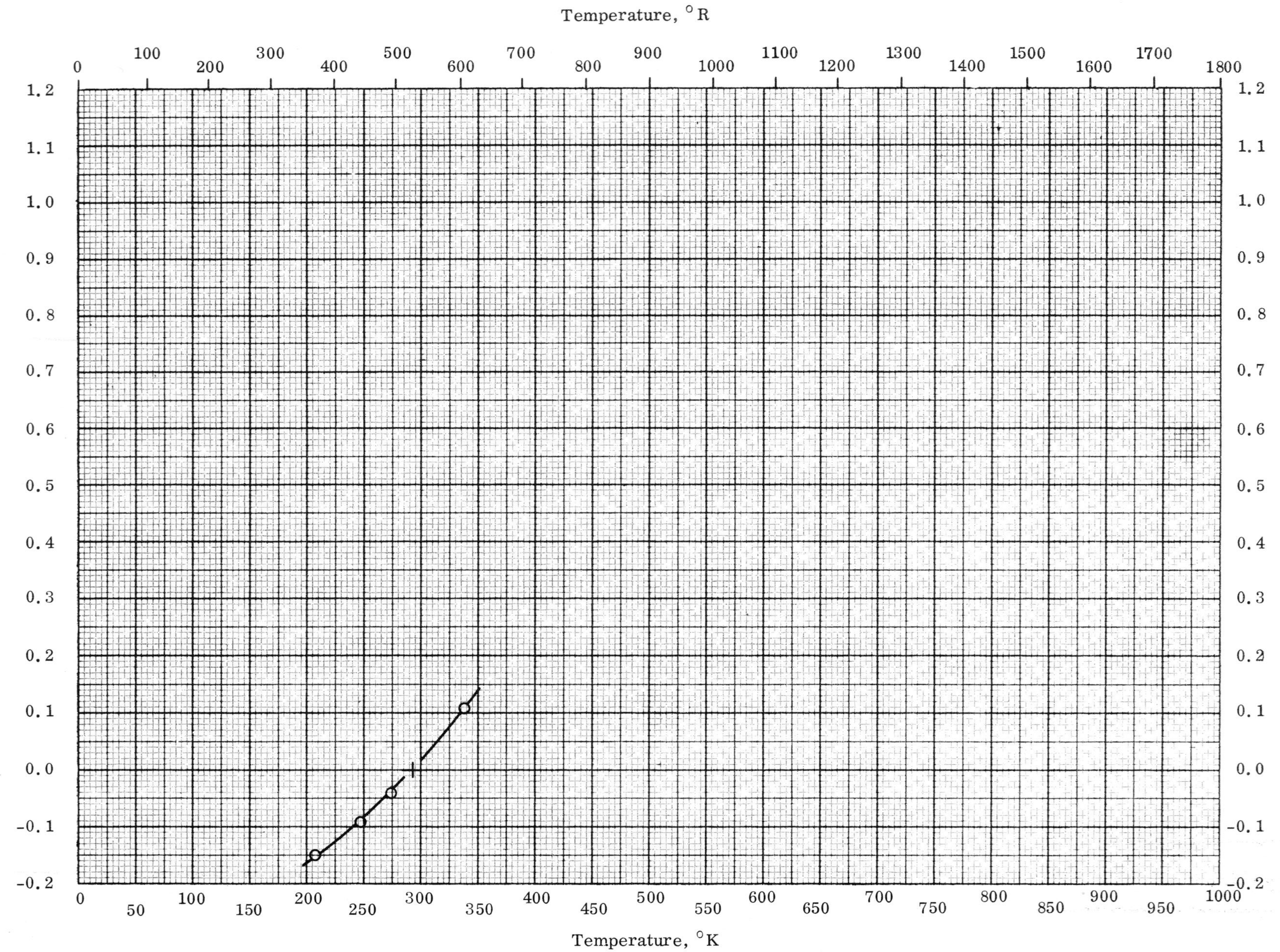

THERMAL LINEAR EXPANSION -- PHENOL FORMALDEHYDE, FABRIC FILLED

REFERENCE INFORMATION

Symbol	Ref.	Temp. Range °K	Rept. Error %	Sample Specifications	Remarks
○	54-16	213-339		Bakelite BM-3510 from Union Carbide and Carbon Co.; 2-step molding resin; high impact strength.	Held at 77 F and 502 humidity for 24-48 hrs before test.

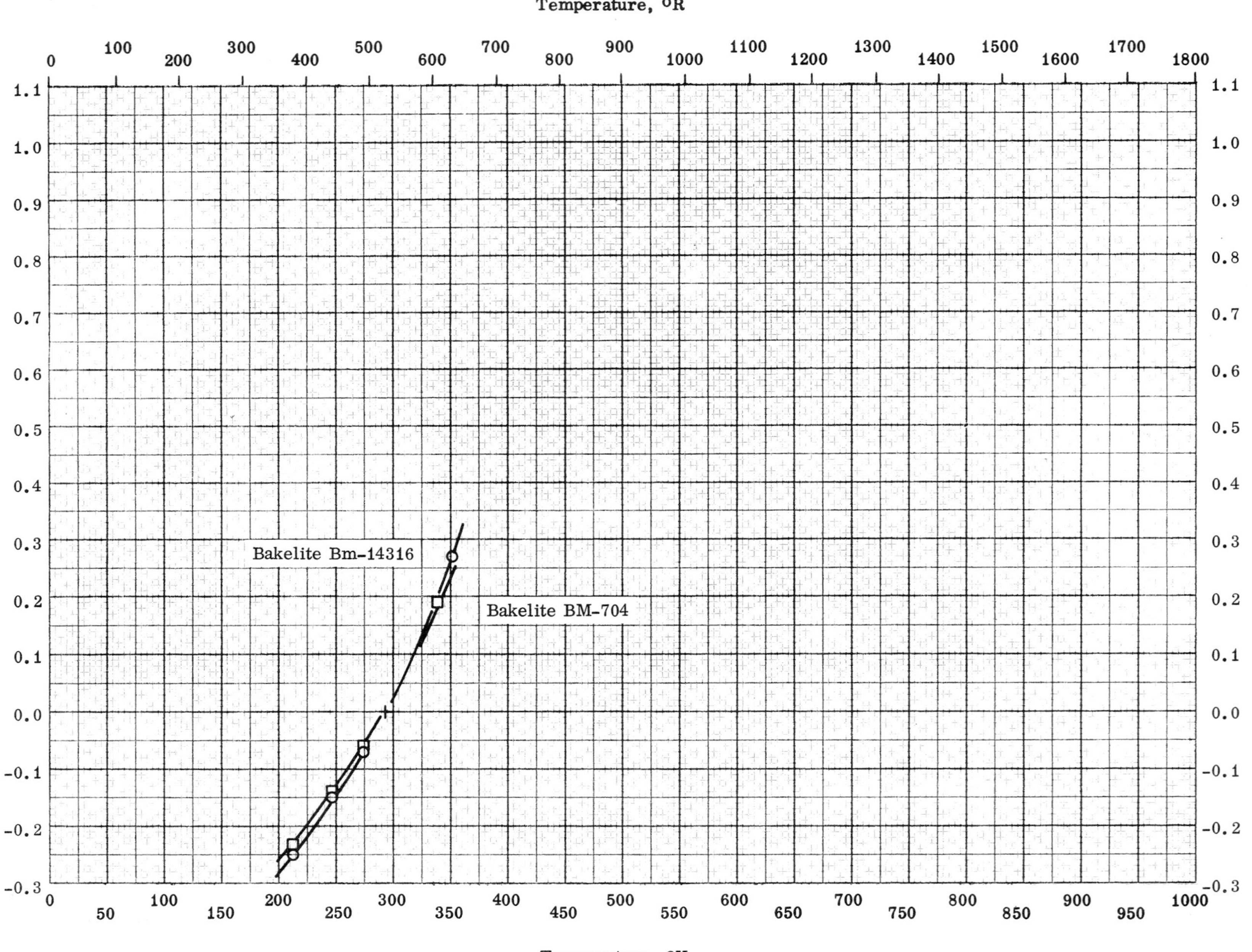

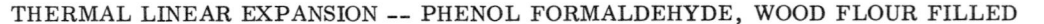

THERMAL LINEAR EXPANSION -- PHENOL FORMALDEHYDE, WOOD FLOUR FILLED

REFERENCE INFORMATION

Symbol	Ref.	Temp. Range °K	Rept. Error %	Sample Specifications	Remarks
○	54-16	215-351		Bakelite BM-14316 from Union Carbide and Carbon Co.; 2-step molding resin; long flow, easy mold release.	Held at 77 F and 50% humidity for 24-48 hrs before test.
□	54-16	215-339		Bakelite BM-704; 2-step molding resin; general purpose.	Same as above.

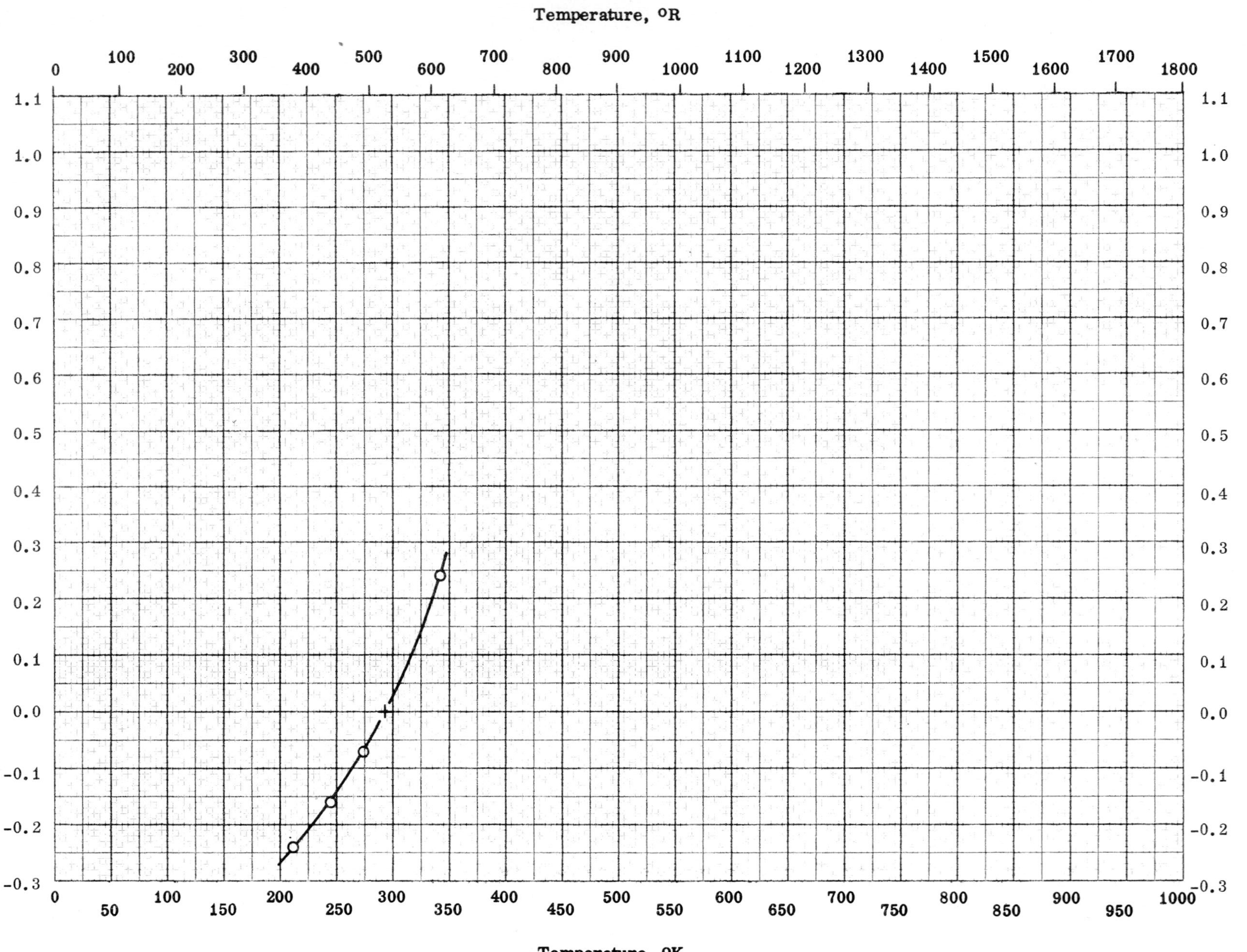

THERMAL LINEAR EXPANSION -- FURFURAL FORMALDEHYDE, WOOD FLOUR FILLED

REFERENCE INFORMATION

Symbol	Ref.	Temp. Range °K	Rept. Error %	Sample Specifications	Remarks
O	54-16	219-342		"Bakelite BM-17849" from Union Carbide and Carbon Co.; 2-step modified molding resin, wood-flour filled.	Held at 77 F and 50% humidity for 24-48 hrs before test.

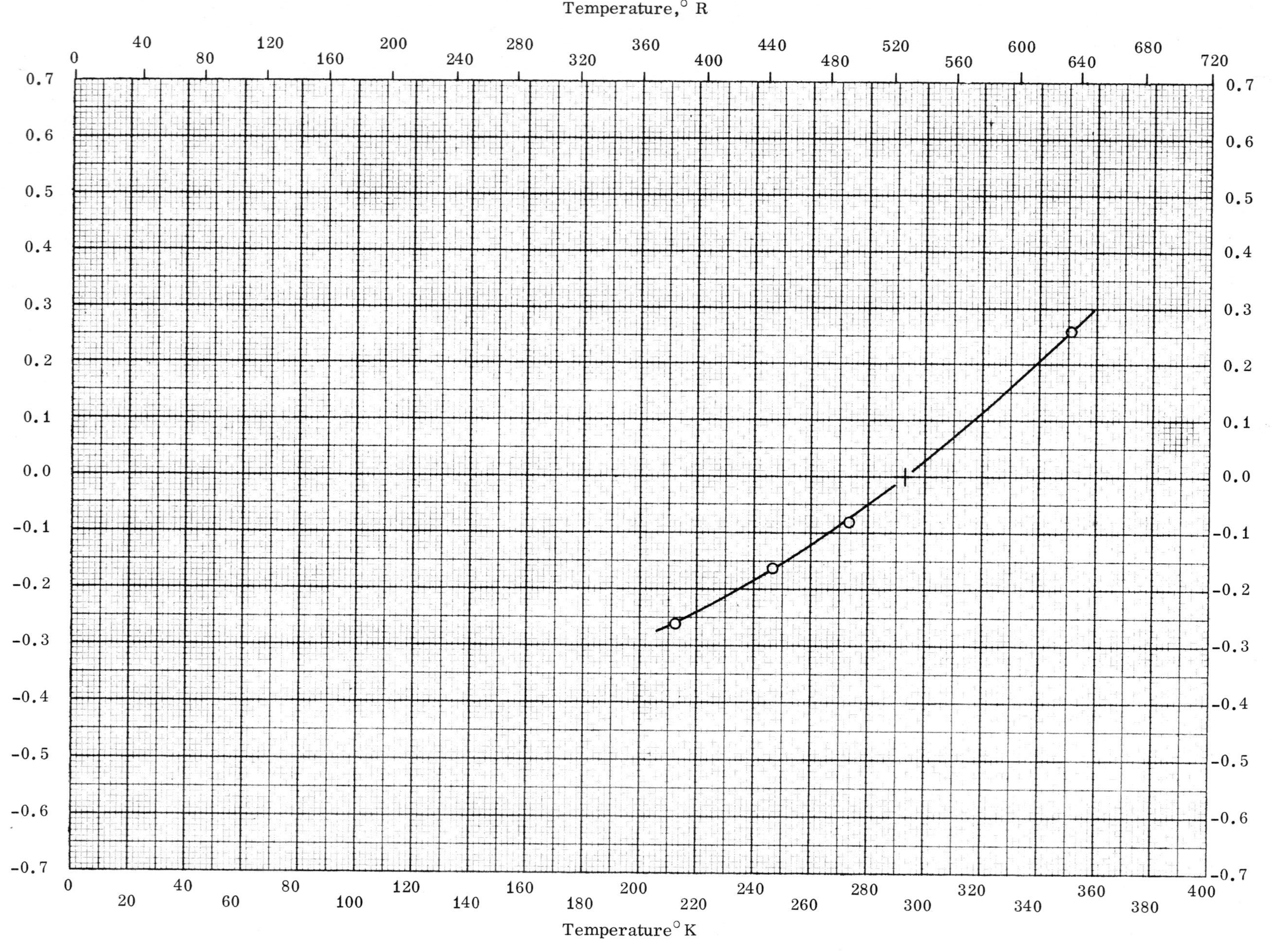

THERMAL LINEAR EXPANSION -- UREA FORMALDEHYDE, ALPHA CELLULOSE FILLED

THERMAL LINEAR EXPANSION -- UREA FORMALDEHYDE, ALPHA CELLULOSE FILLED

REFERENCE INFORMATION

Symbol	Ref.	Temp. Range °K	Rept. Error %	Sample Specifications	Remarks
o	54-16	213-351		"Beetle" from American Cyanamid Co.; molding material, colorless, translucent.	Held at 77 F and 50% humidity for 24-48 hrs before test.

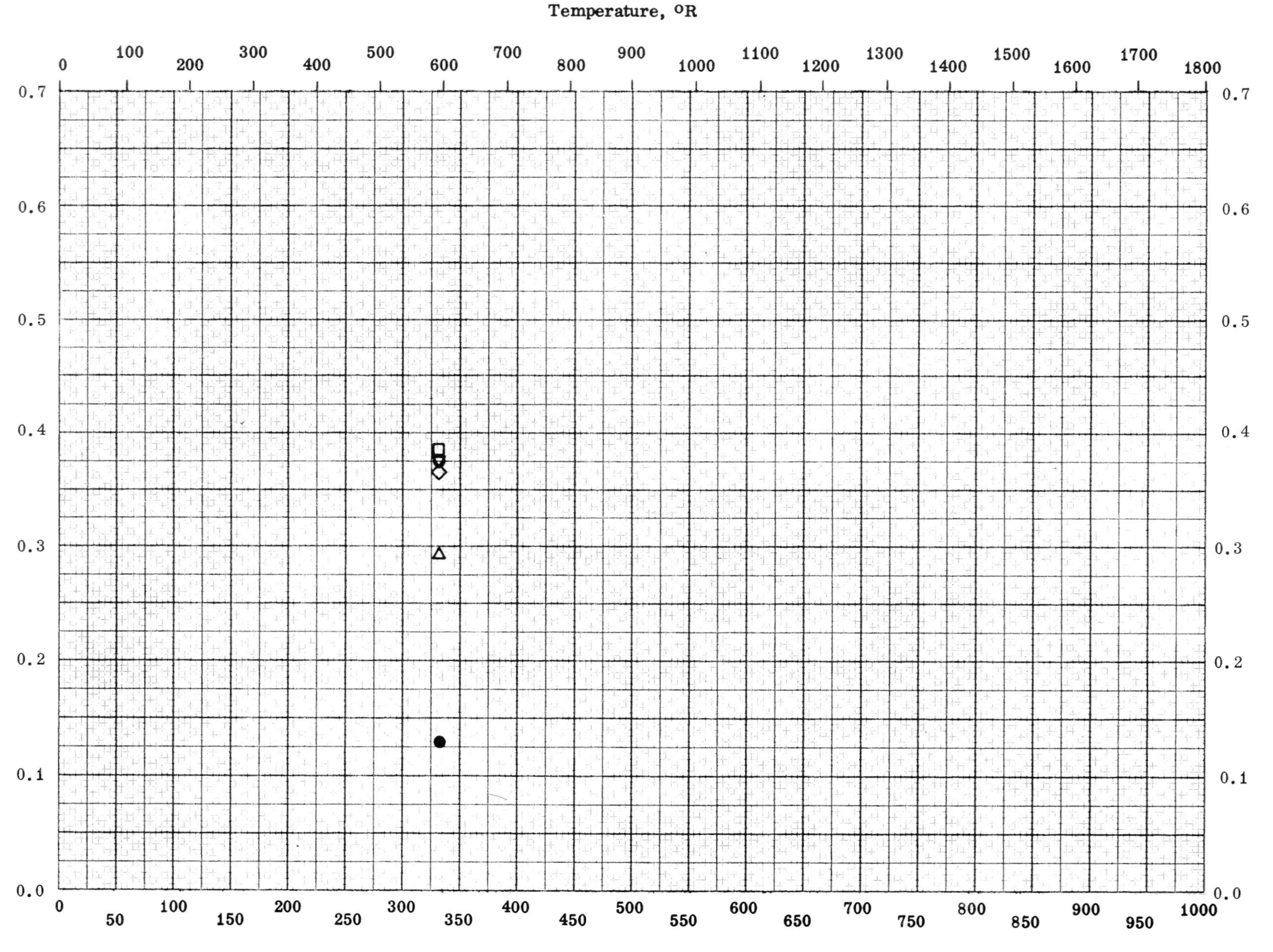

SPECIFIC HEAT -- CRESOL RESIN

SPECIFIC HEAT -- CRESOL RESIN

REFERENCE INFORMATION

Symbol	Ref.	Temp. Range °K	Rept. Error %	Sample Specifications	Remarks
○	40-1	333		50 cresol resin and 50 resin type S.	Report average C_p between 20 - 100 C.
□	40-1	333		60 cresol resin and 40 resin type S.	Same as above.
△	40-1	333		67 cresol resin and 33 resin type 11.	Same as above.
◇	40-1	333		67 cresol resin and 33 resin type T2.	Same as above.
▽	40-1	333		67 cresol resin and 33 resin type Z2.	Same as above.
●	40-1	333		67 cresol resin and 33 resin type Y.	Same as above.

PROPERTIES OF EPOXIDE

MOST PROBABLE VALUES

Property	C.G.S. Units	Brit. Eng. Units
Density	1.21	75.3

REPORTED VALUES

Density		g cm^{-3}	lb ft^{-3}
	O	1.21	75.3

REFERENCE INFORMATION

Symbol	Ref.	Temp. Range °K	Rept. Error %	Sample Specifications	Remarks
○	57-1	267		Hysol 6000 - OP Epoxide.	

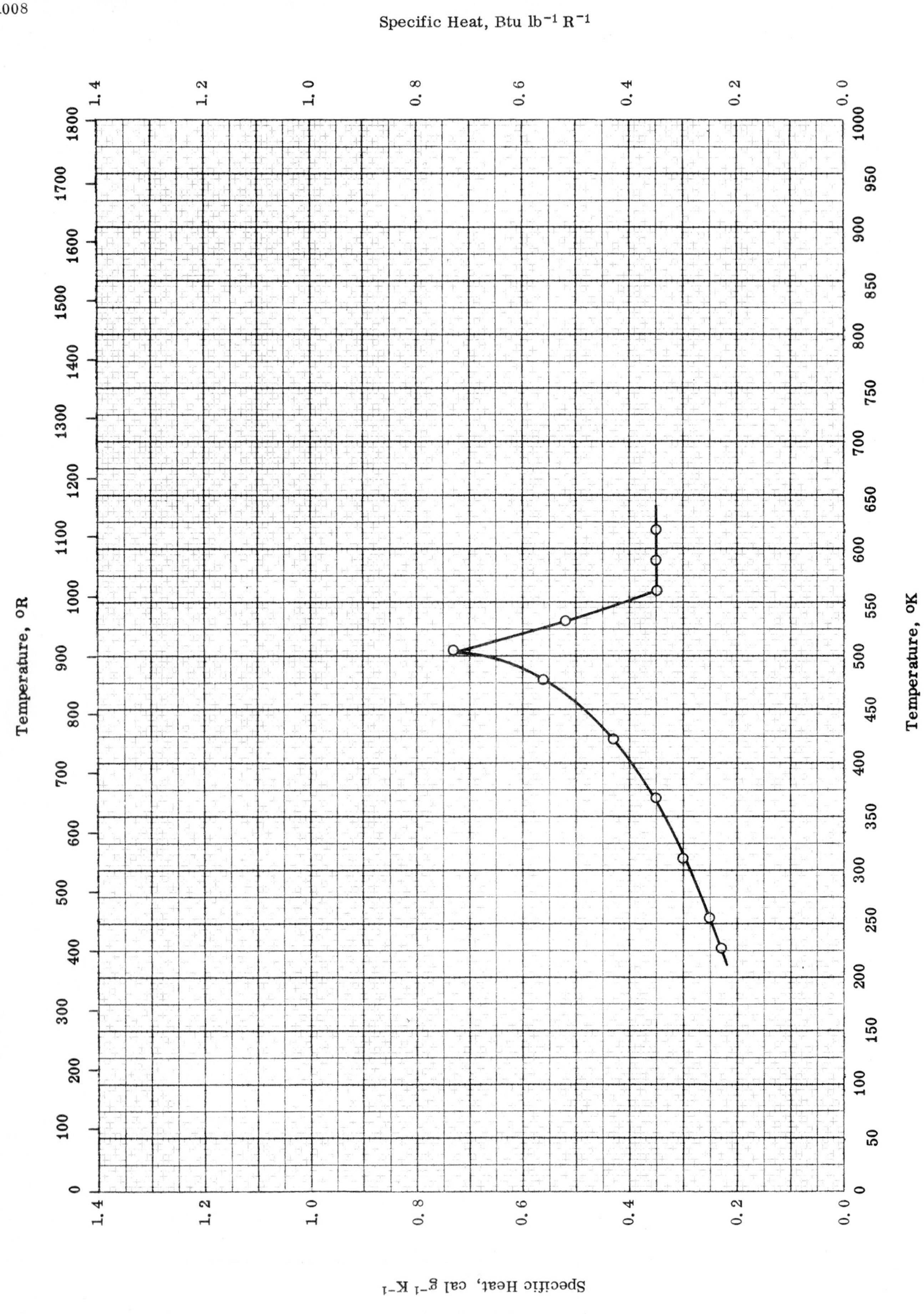

Specific Heat, Btu lb^{-1} R^{-1}

Temperature, °R

Temperature, °K

Specific Heat, cal g^{-1} K^{-1}

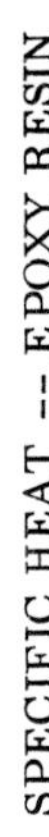

SPECIFIC HEAT -- EPOXY RESIN

REFERENCE INFORMATION

Symbol	Ref.	Temp. Range °K	Rept. Error %	Sample Specifications	Remarks
○	63-18	228-616		100 resin; DER 332 epoxy with curing agents DMP 30, 2%. [Author's design.: f-3].	Cured for 1 hr at 250 F; post cured 2 hrs at 300 F.

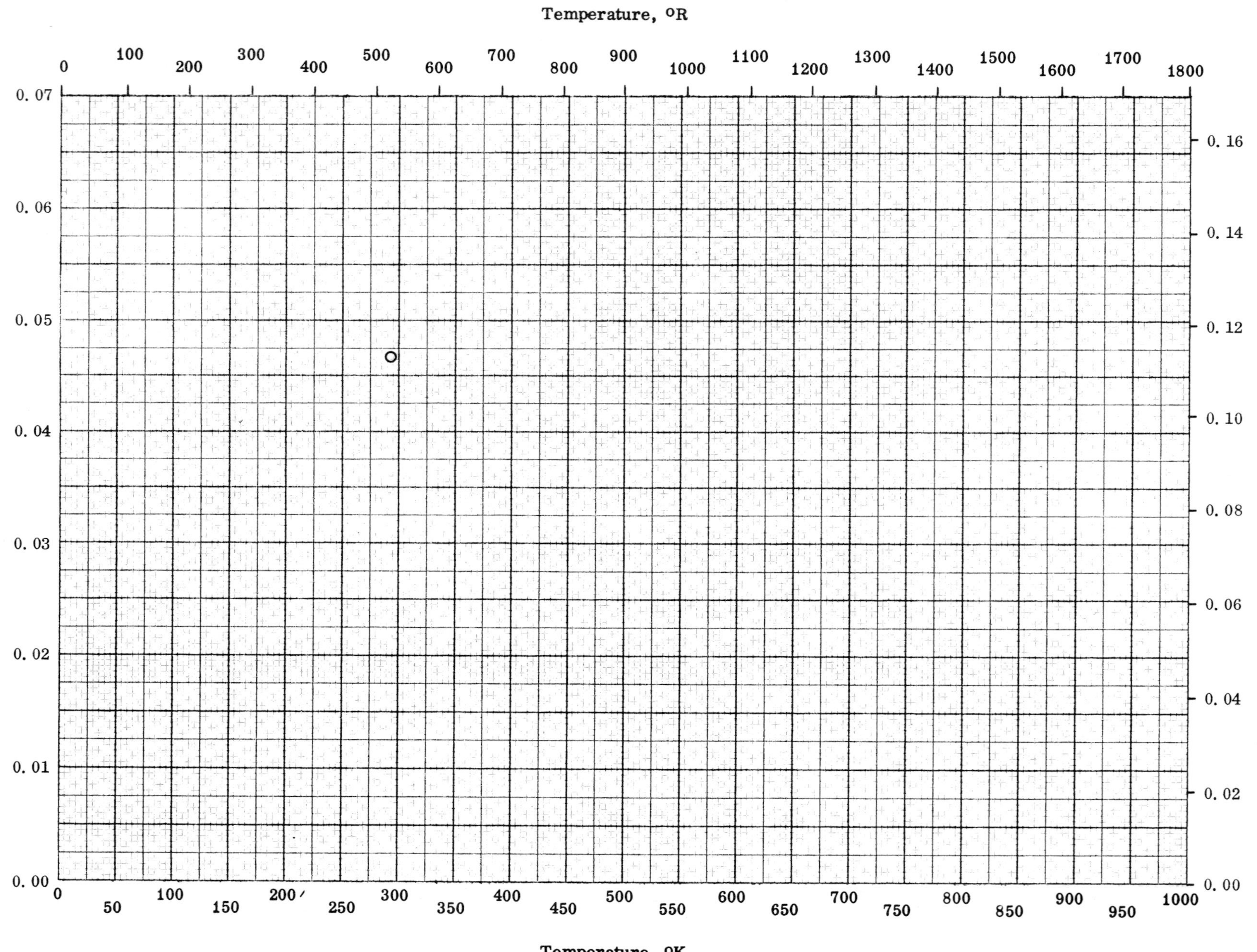

THERMAL CONDUCTIVITY -- EPOXIDE

REFERENCE INFORMATION

Symbol	Ref.	Temp. Range °K	Rept. Error %	Sample Specifications	Remarks
○	57-1	293		Hysol 6000-OP; density 75.3 lb ft^{-3}.	Calculated from ρ, α and c_p.

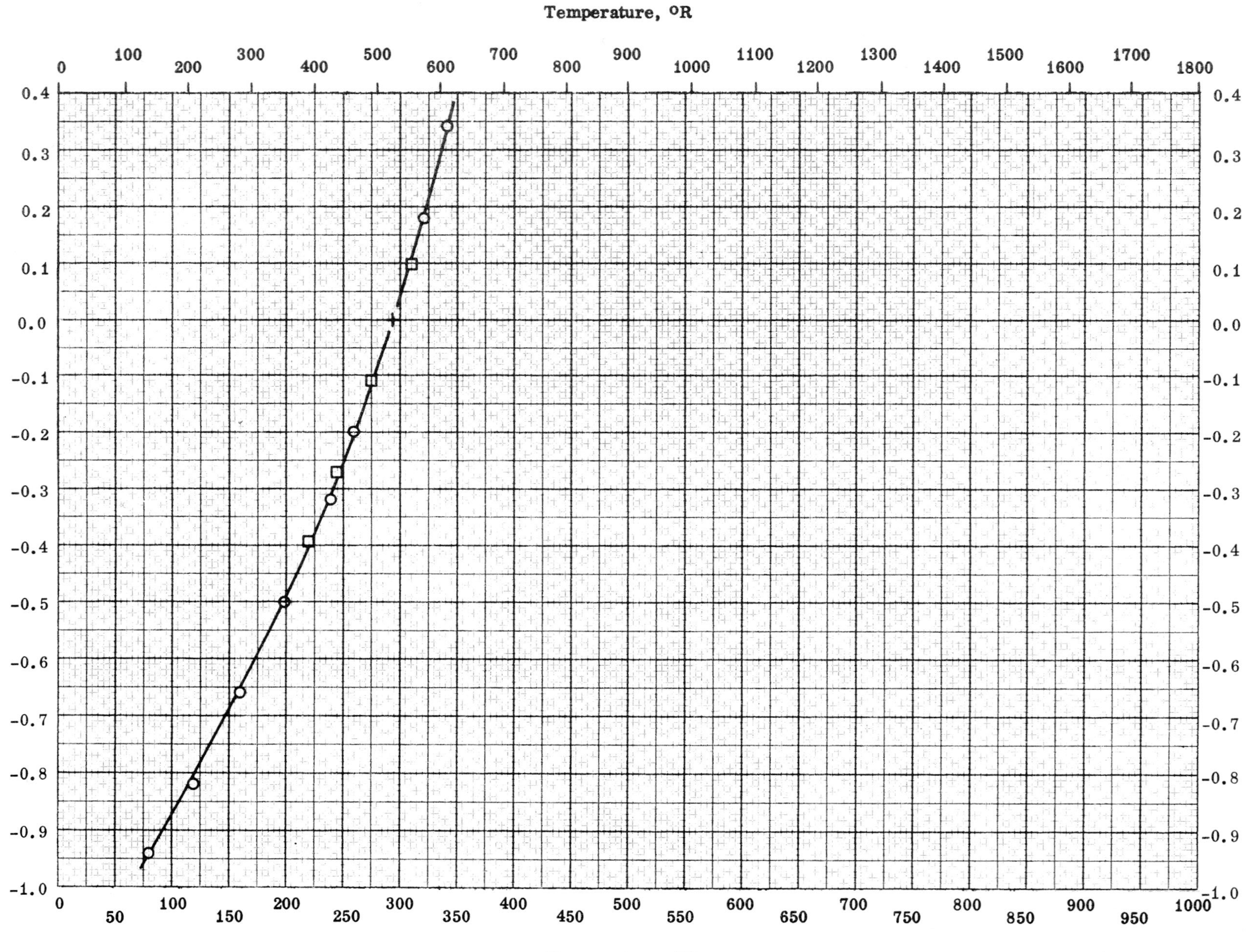

THERMAL LINEAR EXPANSION -- EPOXIDE

REFERENCE INFORMATION

Symbol	Ref.	Temp. Range °K	Rept. Error %	Sample Specifications	Remarks
○	52-13	0-340		Araldite Casting Resin 501 from Ciba Co.; 2cc triethanolamine catalyst/40g material.	Cured 8 hrs at 120 C, 24 hrs at 180 C; measured perpendicular to axis of 2 in. dia; casting.
□	57-1	222-311		Hysol 6000-OP.	

PROPERTIES OF MELAMINE FORMALDEHYDE

MOST PROBABLE VALUES

Property	C.G.S. Units	Brit. Eng. Units
Softening Point	363	654

REPORTED VALUES

Softening Point	K	R
	O 363	654

REFERENCE INFORMATION

Symbol	Ref.	Temp. Range °K	Rept. Error %	Sample Specifications	Remarks
○	56-26	363-393		Melamine Formaldehyde (Monsanto Resimene 814 resin).	Fused at 708 R.

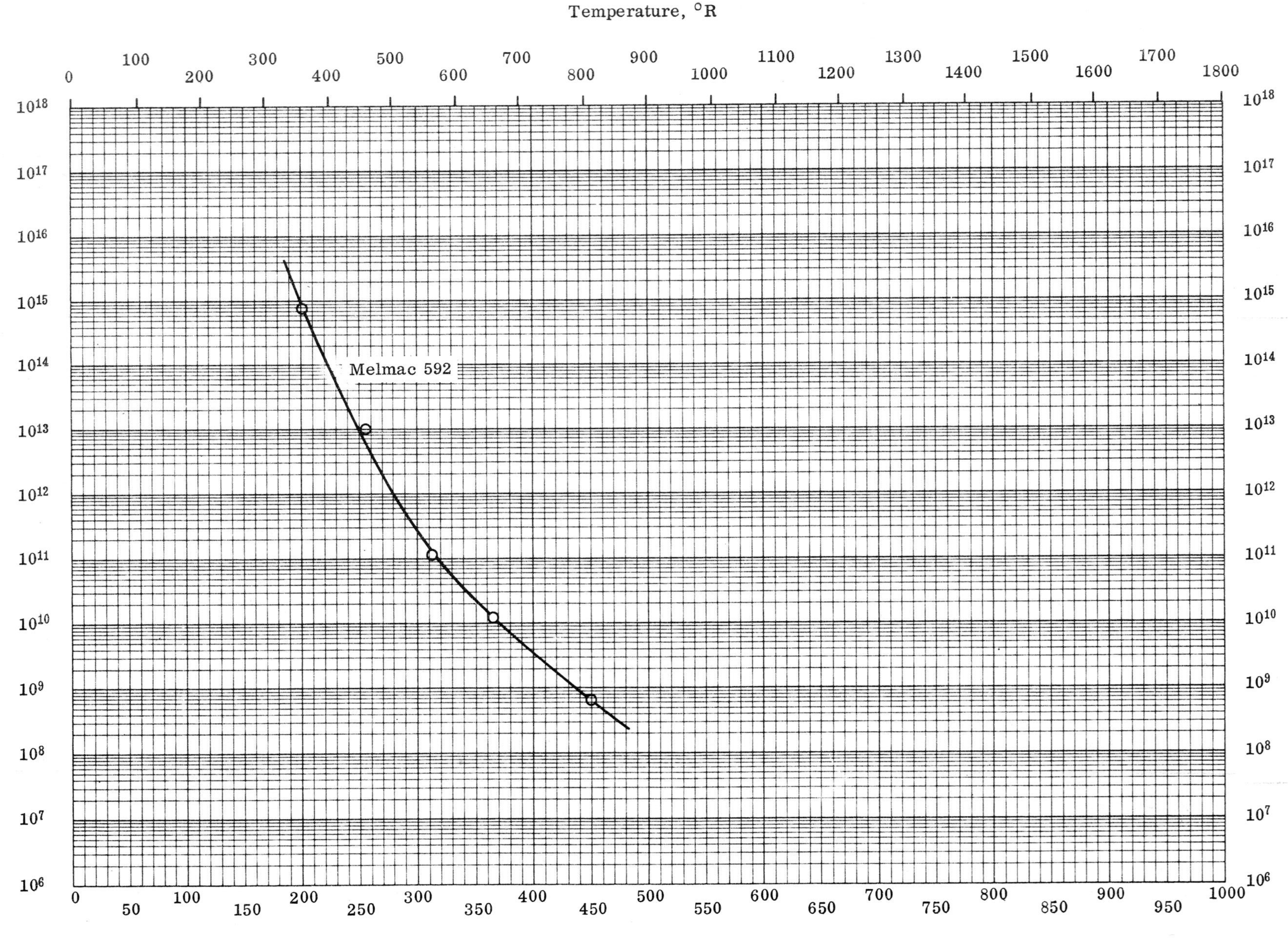

ELECTRICAL RESISTIVITY -- MINERAL FILLED MELAMINE FORMALDEHYDE

ELECTRICAL RESISTIVITY -- MINERAL FILLED MELAMINE FORMALDEHYDE

REFERENCE INFORMATION

Symbol	Ref.	Temp. Range °K	Rept. Error %	Sample Specifications	Remarks
○	57-18	200-450		Melmac 592, mineral filled melamine; made by American Cyanamid Co.	Conditioned 48 hrs at 120 F at 90% humidity, then 7 cycles, ea. of which consists of 12 hrs at 100 F and 100% humidity plus 12 hrs at 120 F and 95% humidity.

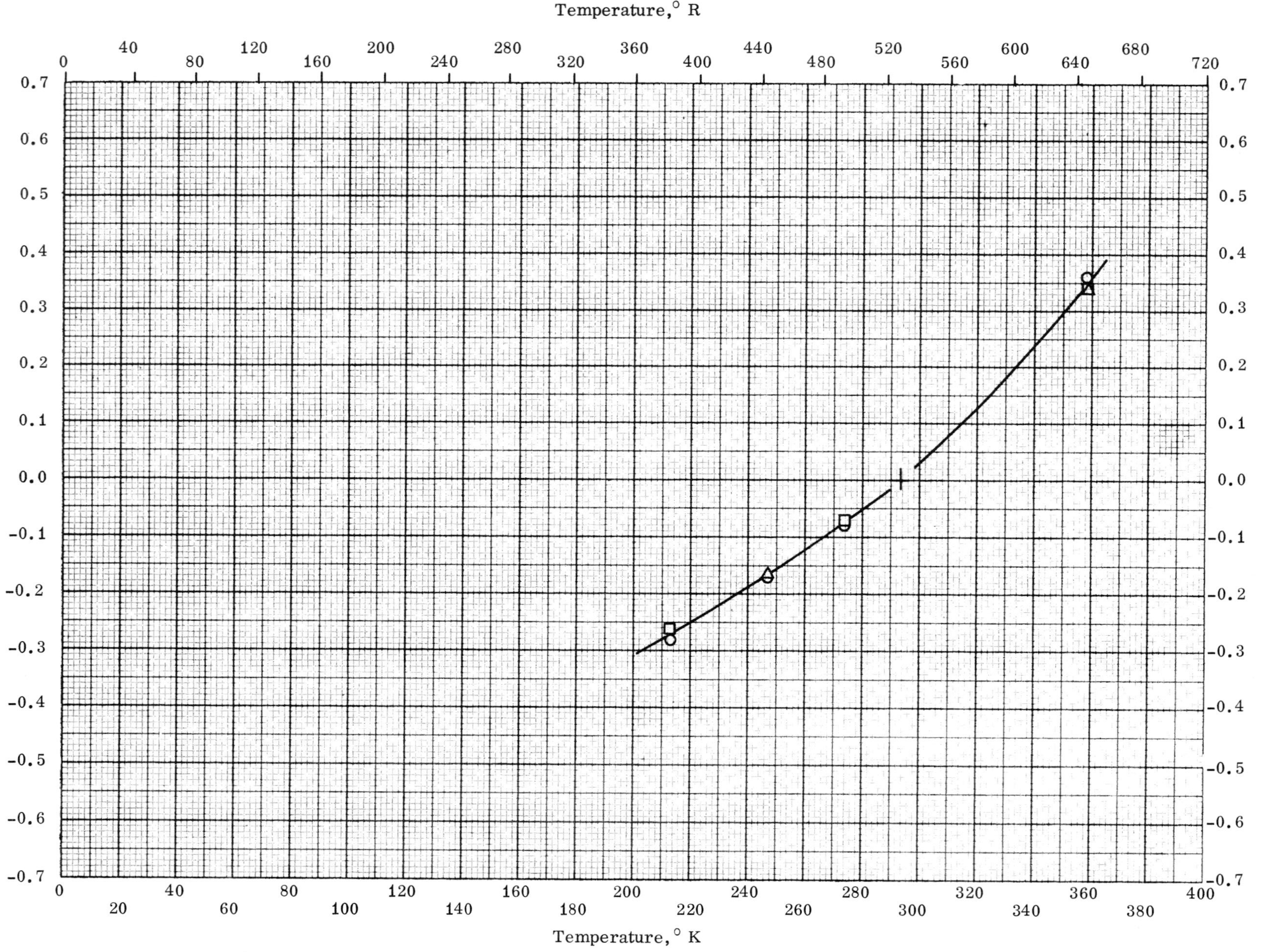

THERMAL LINEAR EXPANSION -- MELAMINE FORMALDEHYDE, ALPHA CELLULOSE FILLED

THERMAL LINEAR EXPANSION -- MELAMINE FORMALDEHYDE, ALPHA CELLULOSE FILLED

REFERENCE INFORMATION

Symbol	Ref.	Temp. Range °K	Rept. Error %	Sample Specifications	Remarks
○	54-16	213-359		Melmac 1077, natural, from American Cyanamid Co; max water resistance.	Held at 77 F and 50% humidity for 24-48 hrs before test.
□	54-16	213-359		Melmac 1079, natural; general purpose.	Same as above.
△	54-16	213-359		Melmac 1502, natural; arc resistant.	Same as above.

PROPERTIES OF ACRYLICS

REPORTED VALUES

Density	$g\ cm^{-3}$	$lb\ ft^{-3}$
○ Selectron 400	1.24	77
□ Plexiglas	1.184	73.88
△ Lucite	1.19	74

Softening Point	K	R
▽ Plexiglas	353	636

REFERENCE INFORMATION

Symbol	Ref.	Temp. Range °K	Rept. Error %	Sample Specifications	Remarks
○	57-24	296		Selectron 400 acrylic resin by Pittsburgh Plate Glass Co.; thermoplastic as received and becomes thermosetting after curing.	Cured 2 hrs at 160 C; conditioned 72 hrs at 72 F and 50% relative humidity.
□	51-6 also 52-4	293		Plexiglas AN-P-44A made by Rohm and Haas Chem. Co.; aircraft quality.	Density by weight in air and in water.
▽	51-6 also 52-4	353		Same as above.	
△	55-4	298		Lucite.	

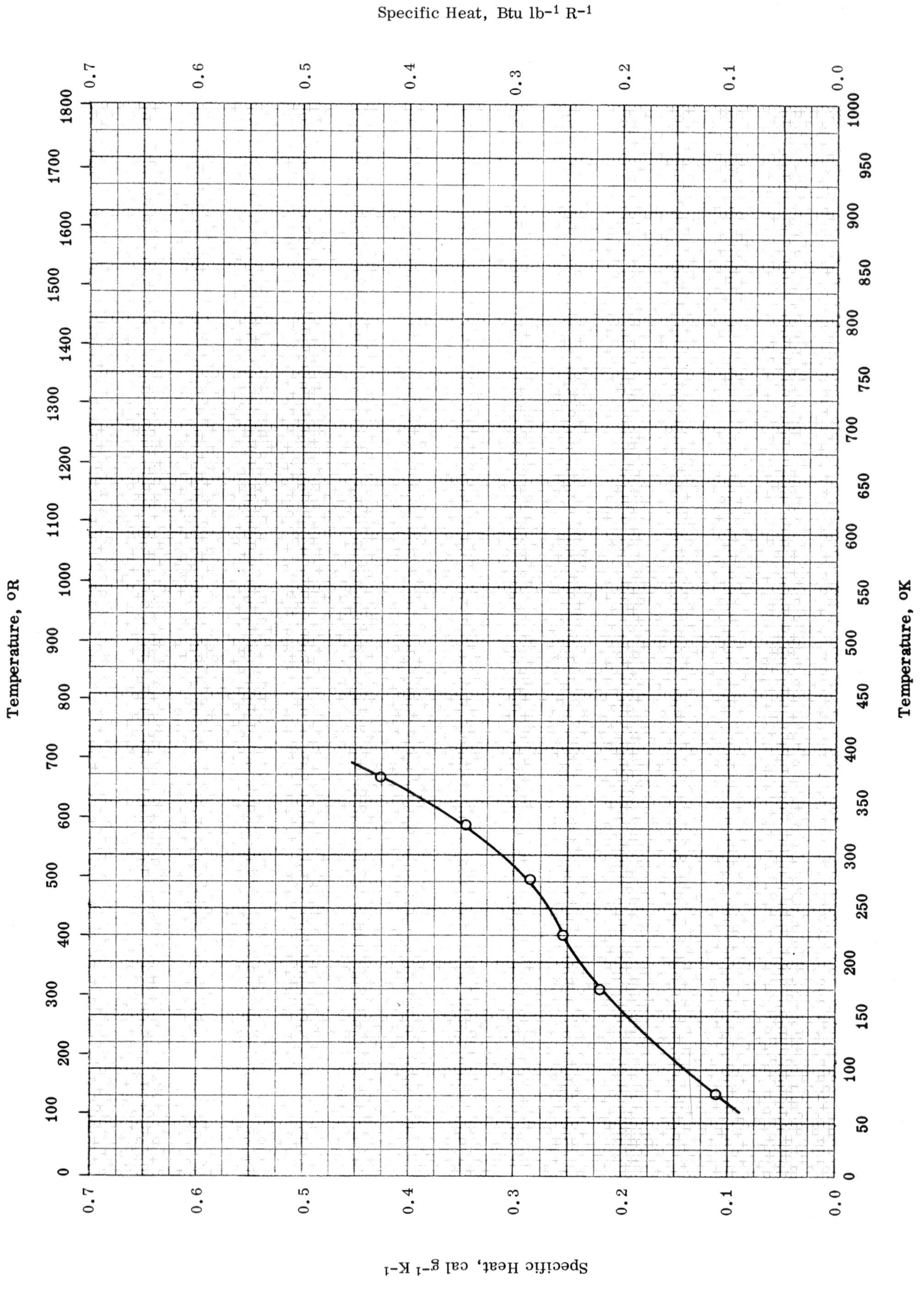

Specific Heat, Btu lb^{-1} R^{-1}

Temperature, °R

Temperature, °K

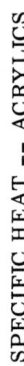

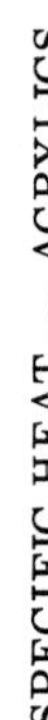

Specific Heat, cal g^{-1} K^{-1}

REFERENCE INFORMATION

Symbol	Ref.	Temp. Range °K	Rept. Error %	Sample Specifications	Remarks
○	54-11	78-373		Plexiglass type AN-P-44A.	

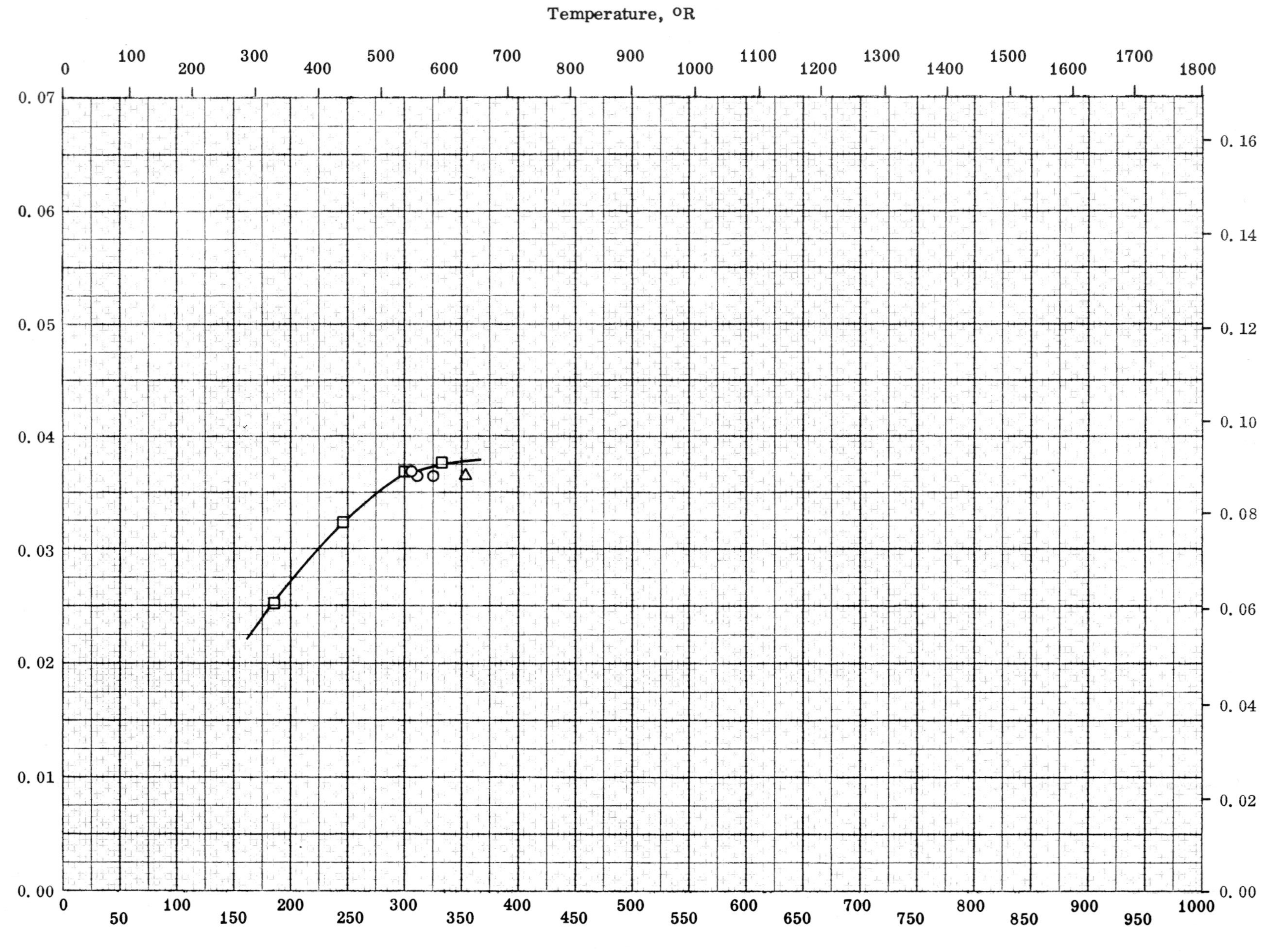

THERMAL CONDUCTIVITY -- ACRYLICS

REFERENCE INFORMATION

Symbol	Ref.	Temp. Range °K	Rept. Error %	Sample Specifications	Remarks
○	52-4	306-325		Plexiglass (AN-P-44A aircraft quality) by Rohm and Haas Chem. Co.	
□	52-4	183-332		Same as above.	
△	55-4	353.4		Lucite; density 74 lb ft^{-3}.	Conflicting data given in same report; results of doubtful accuracy.

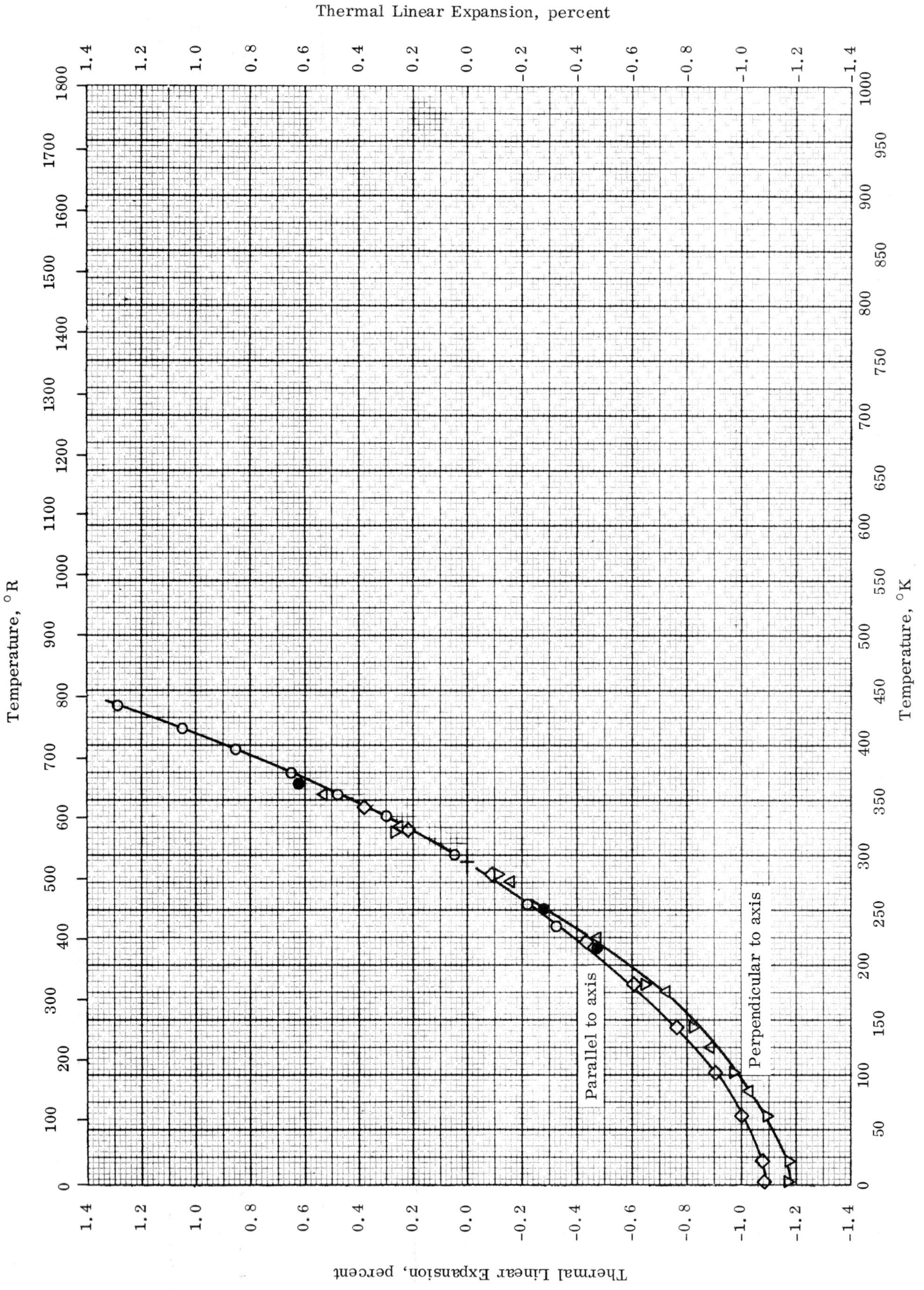

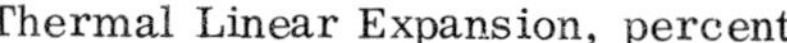

THERMAL LINEAR EXPANSION -- ACRYLICS

REFERENCE INFORMATION

Symbol	Ref.	Temp. Range °K	Rept. Error %	Sample Specifications	Remarks
○	57-24	233-433		Selectron 400 by Pittsburgh Plate Glass; thermoplastic as received, becomes thermosetting after cure at 160-180 C.	Cured at 160 C for 2 hrs; conditioned at 75 F and 50% humidity for > 72 hrs before test.
◇	52-13	0-340		Polymethylmethacrylate rod probably from Du Pont Lucite by Plax. Corp.	Measured parallel to axis of rod; auth. est. accuracy ± 1% at 0 R and ± 2% at 612 R; values given are average for 2 or more cycles.
▽	52-13	0-340		Same as above.	Measured perpendicular to axis of rod; values given are average for 2 or more cycles.
△	52-4	83-353		Plexiglas AN-P-44A aircraft quality by Rohm and Haas Chem. Co. (polymethylmethacrylate).	Softens at 80 C.
●	54-16	213-361		Plexiglas 11 by Rohm and Haas; max heat resistance (polymethylmethacrylate).	Held at 77 F and 50% humidity for 24-48 hrs before test.

THERMAL LINEAR EXPANSION -- FILLED POLYMETHYL METHACRYLATE

Symbol	Type of Filler	Filler	Average coefficient of linear expansion x 10^5	
			273-298 K	492-537 R
o	No Filler	0	6.90	3.83
	Zinc Oxide	10	6.87	3.82
	Zinc Oxide	20	6.80	3.78
	Zinc Oxide	30	6.43	3.57
	Zinc Oxide	40	6.13	3.41
	Zinc Oxide	50	5.17	2.87
	Silica	10	6.77	3.76
	Silica	20	6.23	3.46
	Silica	30	5.53	3.07
	Silica	40	5.07	2.82
	Silica	50	4.20	2.33
	Alumina	10	6.73	3.74
	Alumina	20	6.40	3.56
	Alumina	30	5.97	3.32
	Alumina	40	5.63	3.13
	Alumina	50	4.63	2.57
	Calcium Carbonate	10	6.43	3.57
	Calcium Carbonate	20	6.03	3.35
	Calcium Carbonate	30	5.43	3.02
	Calcium Carbonate	40	4.61	2.59
	Calcium Carbonate	50	4.33	2.41
	Boron Phosphate	10	6.33	3.52
	Boron Phosphate	20	5.87	3.26
	Boron Phosphate	30	5.33	2.96
	Boron Phosphate	40	4.57	2.54
	Boron Phosphate	50	3.47	1.93

THERMAL LINEAR EXPANSION -- FILLED POLYMETHYL METHACRYLATE

REFERENCE INFORMATION

Symbol	Ref.	Temp. Range °K	Rept. Error %	Sample Specifications	Remarks
○	54-15	273-298		Various filler materials; see data sheet.	Fine ground fillers and polymers mixed, then ball-milled for 16 hrs, and polymerized under pressure.

PROPERTIES OF POLYETHYLENE AND HALOGENATED POLYETHYLENE

REPORTED VALUES

Density		$g\ cm^{-3}$	$lb\ ft^{-3}$
□	Alathon-10	0.923	57.6
△	Super Dylon	0.958	59.8
◇	Fluorothene	2.1115	131.82
▽	Kel-F	2.16	135
◁	Teflon	2.18	136
▷	Teflon, TF-1	2.14	134

Softening Point		K	R
○	Polyethylene	373	672

REFERENCE INFORMATION

Symbol	Ref.	Temp. Range °K	Rept. Error %	Sample Specifications	Remarks
○	56-26	373-383		Polyethylene (Monsanto PE575).	Flowed at 686 R.
□	57-29	298		Alathon-10 (polyethylene-low density); by DuPont.	
△	57-29	298		Super Dylon (polyethylene-high density); by Koppers.	
◇	47-2	298		Fluorothene (chlorotrifluoro-ethylene).	
▽	58-6	298		Kel-F, commercial grade.	Annealed 24 hrs at 390 F.
◁	58-6	298		Teflon, commercial grade.	Annealed 4 hrs at 590 F.
▷	54-17	298		Teflon type TF-1.	Teflon molding powder was mixed in micropulverizer using liquid N_2 as coolant. Molding pressure was 4000 psi.

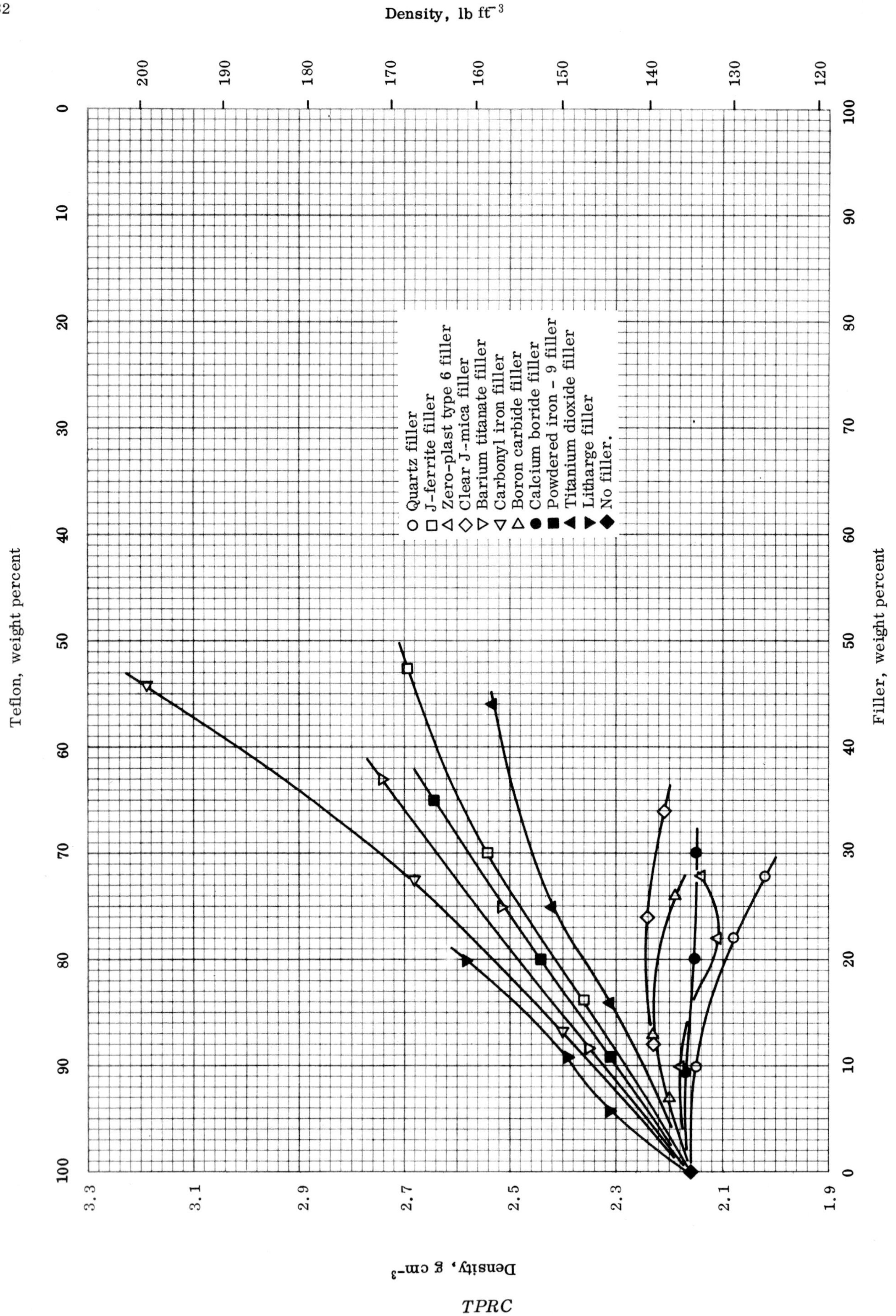

Density, lb ft^{-3}
200
190
180
170
160
150
140
130
120
Teflon, weight percent
0
10
20
30
40
50
60
70
80
90
100
Filler, weight percent
100
90
80
70
60
50
40
30
20
10
0
Density, g cm^{-3}
3.3
3.1
2.9
2.7
2.5
2.3
2.1
1.9
○ Quartz filler
□ J-ferrite filler
△ Zero-plast type 6 filler
◇ Clear J-mica filler
▽ Barium titanate filler
◁ Carbonyl iron filler
△ Boron carbide filler
● Calcium boride filler
■ Powdered iron - 9 filler
▲ Titanium dioxide filler
▶ Litharge filler
◆ No filler.

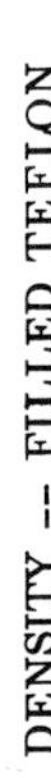

DENSITY -- FILLED TEFLON

REFERENCE INFORMATION

Symbol	Ref.	Temp. Range °K	Rept. Error %	Sample Specifications	Remarks
○	54-17	298		Quartz No. 7900 filled.	Molding powder mixed with fillers in micro-pulverizer with liquid N_2 cooler; molded under pressure of 2 tons in^{-2} density of filler 135 lb ft^{-3}.
□	54-17	298		J-ferrite filled.	Same preparation as above; density of filler 280 lb ft^{-3}.
△	54-17	298		Zero-plast type 6 filled.	Same preparation as above; density of filler 142 lb ft^{-3}.
◇	54-17	298		Clear J-mica filled.	Same preparation as above; density of filler 154 lb ft^{-3}.
▽	54-17	298		Barium titanate filled.	Same preparation as above; density of filler 321 lb ft^{-3}.
◁	54-17	298		Carbonyl iron grade HP filled.	Same preparation as above; density of filler 445 lb ft^{-3}.
▷	54-17	298		Boron carbide (B_4C) filler.	Same preparation as above; density of filler 147 lb ft^{-3}.
●	54-17	298		Calcium boride (CaB_6) filler.	Same preparation as above; density of filler 127 lb ft^{-3}.
■	54-17	298		Powdered iron - 9 filler.	Same preparation as above; density of filler 297 lb ft^{-3}.
▲	54-17	298		Titanium dioxide (TiO_2) filler.	Same preparation as above; density of filler 242 lb ft^{-3}.

(Continued onto next page)

DENSITY -- FILLED TEFLON (Continued)

REFERENCE INFORMATION

Symbol	Ref.	Temp. Range °K	Rept. Error %	Sample Specifications	Remarks
▼	54-17	298		Litharge filler.	Same preparation as above; density of filler 522 lb ft^{-3}.
◆	54-17	298		No filler.	Same preparation as above.

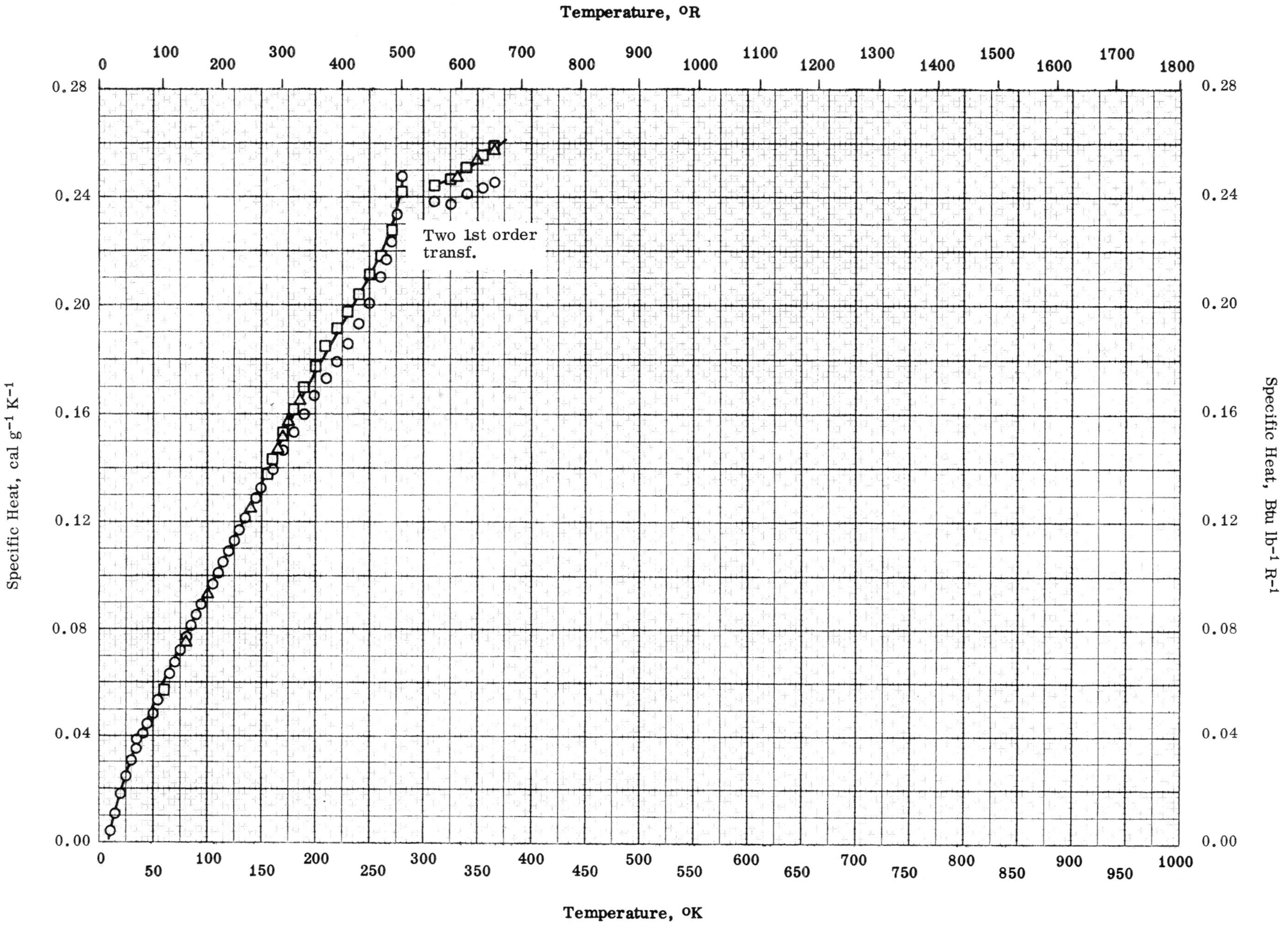

Specific Heat, Btu lb^{-1} R^{-1}

0.28 0.24 0.20 0.16 0.12 0.08 0.04 0.00

Temperature, °R

0 100 200 300 400 500 600 700 800 900 1000 1100 1200 1300 1400 1500 1600 1700 1800

Two 1st order transf.

Temperature, °K

0 50 100 150 200 250 300 350 400 450 500 550 600 650 700 750 800 850 900 950 1000

SPECIFIC HEAT -- POLYTETRAFLUOROETHYLENE

0.28 0.24 0.20 0.16 0.12 0.08 0.04 0.00

Specific Heat, cal g^{-1} K^{-1}

SPECIFIC HEAT -- POLYTETRAFLUOROETHYLENE

REFERENCE INFORMATION

Symbol	Ref.	Temp. Range °K	Rept. Error %	Sample Specifications	Remarks
○	52-8	0-365		Teflon.	Molded under vacuum (10^{-4} mm Hg); heated 4 hrs at 350 C in vacuum and cooled slowly to room temperature.
□	52-8	0-365		Teflon.	Molded under vacuum (10^{-4} mm Hg); no further treatment.
△	53-12	0-365		Teflon.	

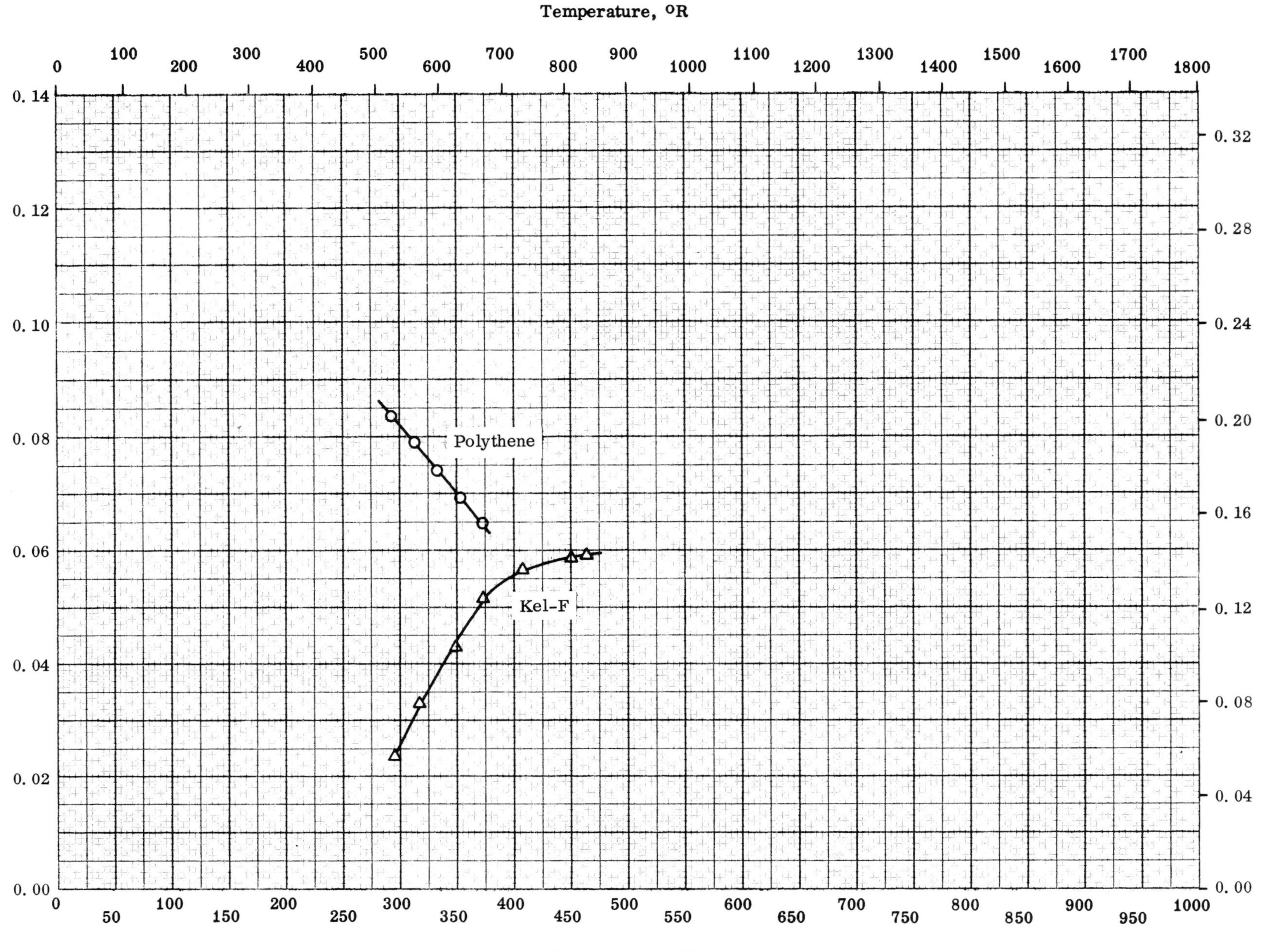

THERMAL CONDUCTIVITY -- POLYETHYLENE AND POLYCHLOROTRIFLUOROETHYLENE

THERMAL CONDUCTIVITY -- POLYETHYLENE AND POLYCHLOROTRIFLUOROETHYLENE

REFERENCE INFORMATION

Symbol	Ref.	Temp. Range °K	Rept. Error %	Sample Specifications	Remarks
○	53-4	293-373		Polythene (polyethylene).	
△	58-6	295-467		Kel-F (Polylchlorotrifluoroethylene); commercial grade; density 135 lb ft^{-3}.	Annealed 24 hrs at 390 F.

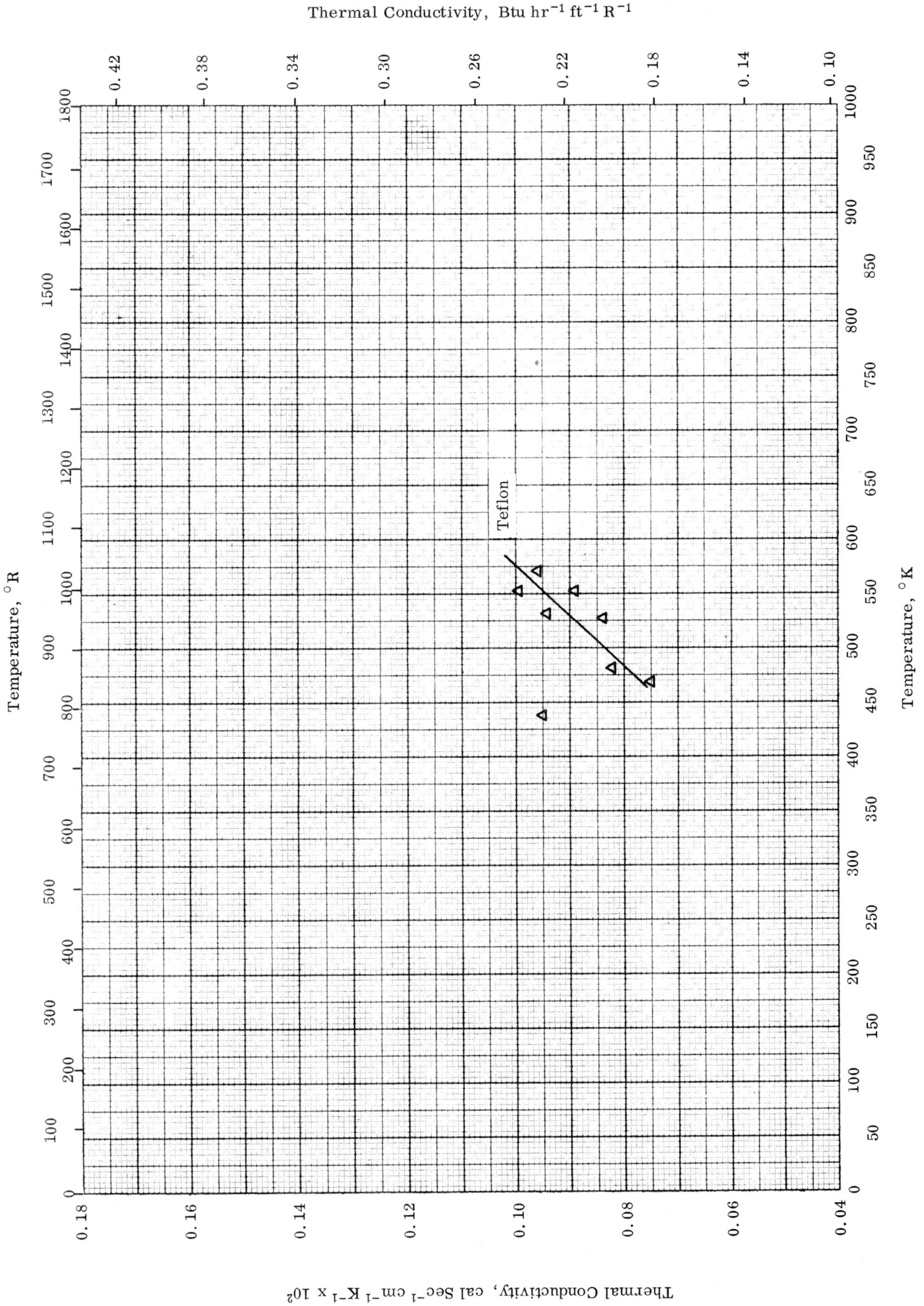

Thermal Conductivity, Btu hr^{-1} ft^{-1} R^{-1}

Teflon

Temperature, °R

Temperature, °K

Thermal Conductivity, cal Sec^{-1} cm^{-1} K^{-1} x 10^2

THERMAL CONDUCTIVITY -- POLYTETRAFLUOROETHYLENE

REFERENCE INFORMATION

Symbol	Ref.	Temp. Range °K	Rept. Error %	Sample Specifications	Remarks
△	58-6	439-572		Teflon; crystalline with density 2.17 g cm^{-3}.	Annealed 4 hrs at 590 F and cooled in furnace.

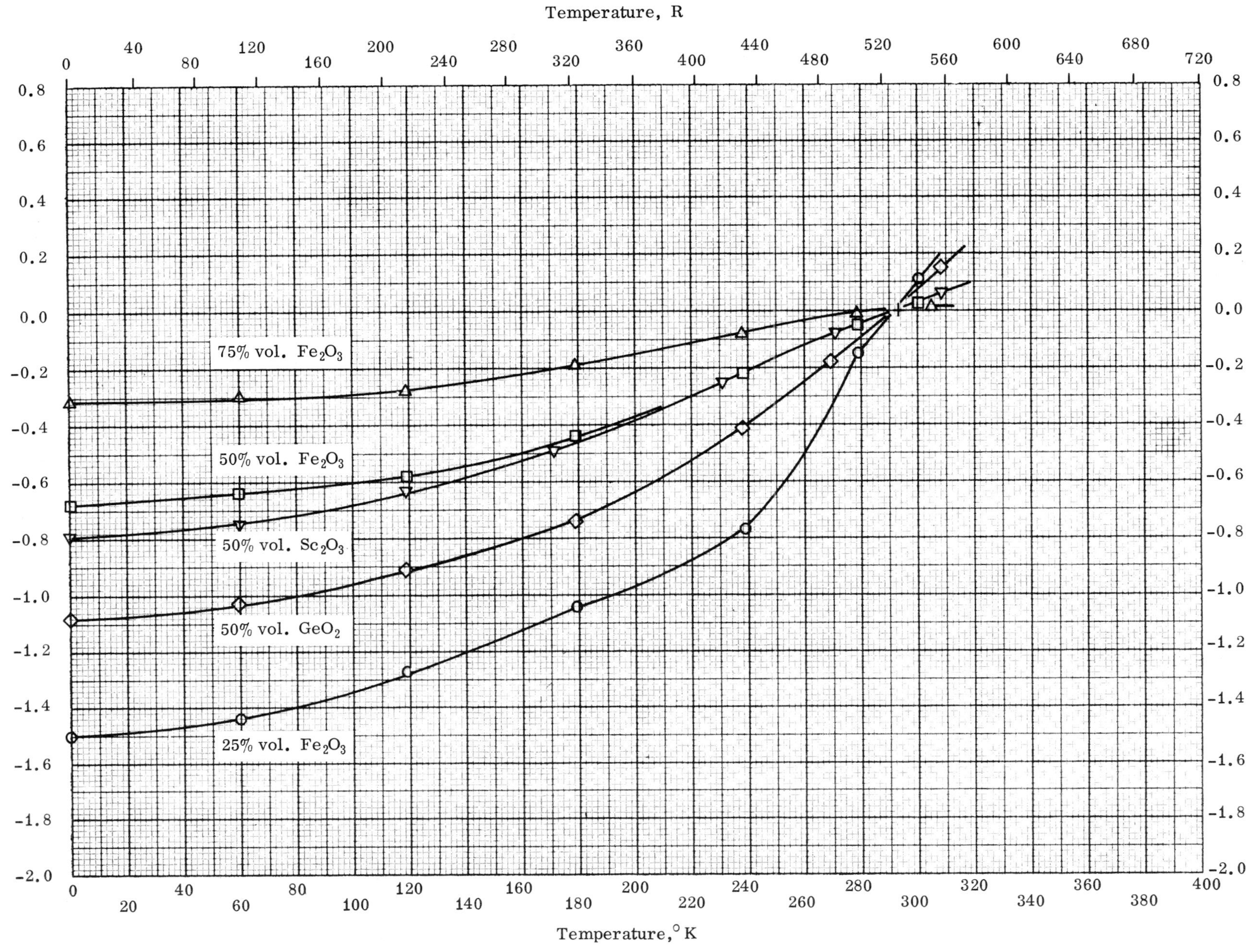

THERMAL LINEAR EXPANSION -- POLYTHENE WITH OXIDE FILLER

THERMAL LINEAR EXPANSION -- POLYTHENE WITH OXIDE FILLER

REFERENCE INFORMATION

Symbol	Ref.	Temp. Range °K	Rept. Error %	Sample Specifications	Remarks
○	52-12	0-300	±1	25% by vol. Fe_2O_3; density 123 lb ft^{-3}.	Molded 10 min at 2000 psi and 150-165 C; cooled in mold under pressure; author uncertain of final composition.
□	52-12	0-300	±2	50% by vol. Fe_2O_3; density 182 lb ft^{-3}.	Same as above.
△	52-12	0-300	±5	75% by vol. Fe_2O_3; density 177 lb ft^{-3}.	Same as above.
◇	52-12	0-300	±2	50% by vol. GeO_2; density 155 lb ft^{-3}.	Same as above.
▽	52-12	0-300	±3	50% by vol. Sc_2O_3; density 124 lb ft^{-3}.	Same as above.

THERMAL LINEAR EXPANSION -- FILLED TEFLON

Symbol	Type of Filler	Filler	Average coefficient of linear expansion x 10^4 293-478 K	528-860 R
○	No filler	0. 0	1. 31	0. 728
	Boron Carbide	7. 0	1. 39	0. 772
	Boron Carbide	13. 0	1. 30	0. 722
	Boron Carbide	26. 0	1. 02	0. 567
	Calcium Boride	10. 2	1. 20	0. 667
	Calcium Boride	20. 0	1. 09	0. 606
	Calcium Boride	30. 4	1. 08	0. 600
	Powdered Iron-9	10. 7	1. 27	0. 706
	Powdered Iron-9	20. 0	1. 31	0. 728
	Powdered Iron-9	35. 0	1. 14	0. 633
	Titanium Dioxide	16. 0	1. 32	0. 733
	Titanium Dioxide	25. 0	1. 32	0. 733
	Titanium Dioxide	44. 0	1. 16	0. 644
	Litharge	5. 6	1. 20	0. 667
	Litharge	10. 6	1. 31	0. 728
	Litharge	20. 0	1. 25	0. 694
	Quartz No. 7900	10. 0	1. 32	0. 733
	Quartz No. 7900	22. 0	1. 34	0. 744
	Quartz No. 7900	27. 7	1. 08	0. 600
	J-Ferrite	16. 2	1. 29	0. 717
	J-Ferrite	30. 0	1. 29	0. 717
	J-Ferrite	47. 5	1. 00	0. 556
	Zero-Plast Type 6	10. 0	1. 34	0. 744
	Zero-Plast Type 6	22. 0	1. 10	0. 611
	Zero-Plast Type 6	27. 8	1. 10	0. 611
	Clear J-Mica	12. 0	1. 52	0. 844
	Clear J-Mica	24. 0	1. 48	0. 822
	Clear J-Mica	34. 1	1. 44	0. 800
	Barium Titanate	11. 7	1. 30	0. 722
	Barium Titanate	25. 0	1. 39	0. 772
	Barium Titanate	38. 0	1. 37	0. 761
	Carbonyl Iron Grade HP	13. 4	1. 30	0. 722
	Carbonyl Iron Grade HP	27. 5	1. 33	0. 739
	Carbonyl Iron Grade HP	46. 0	1. 27	0. 706

THERMAL LINEAR EXPANSION -- FILLED TEFLON

REFERENCE INFORMATION

Symbol	Ref.	Temp. Range °K	Rept. Error %	Sample Specifications	Remarks
○	54-17	293-478		Various filler materials; see data sheet.	Molding powder mixed with fillers in micro-pulverizer with liquid N_2 cooler; molded under pressure of 2 tons in.$^{-2}$.

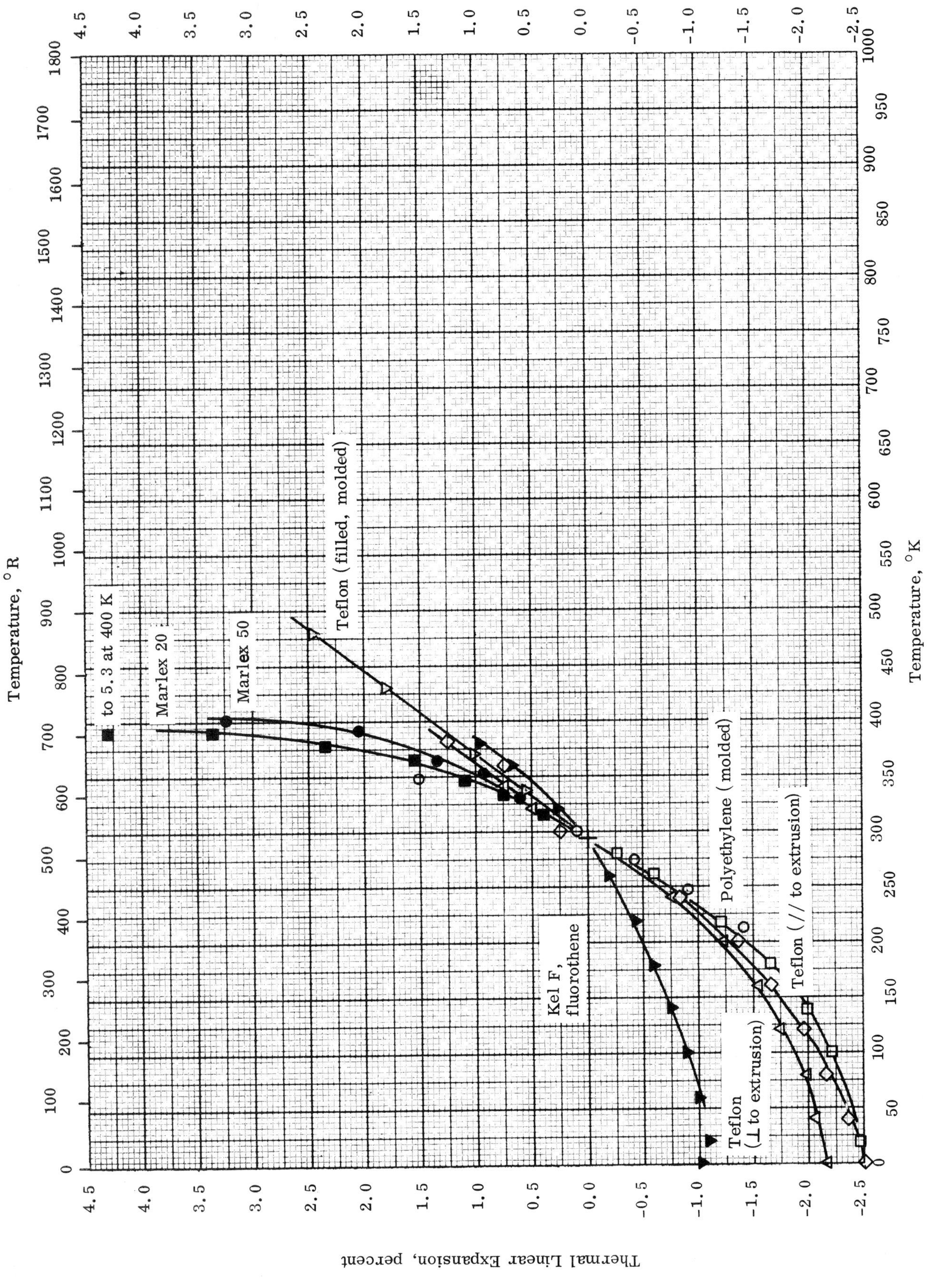

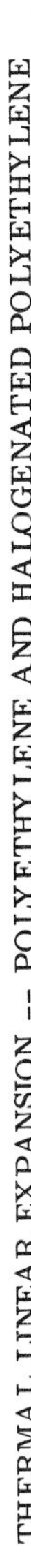

THERMAL LINEAR EXPANSION -- POLYETHYLENE AND HALOGENATED POLYETHYLENE

THERMAL LINEAR EXPANSION -- POLYETHYLENE AND HALOGENATED POLYETHYLENE

REFERENCE INFORMATION

Symbol	Ref.	Temp. Range °K	Rept. Error %	Sample Specifications	Remarks
○	54-16	213-348		Bakelite DYNH (polyethylene) from Union Carbide and Carbon Corp.	Held at 77 F and 50% humidity for 24-48 hrs before test.
△	52-13	0-340		Teflon (Du Pont polytetrafluorethylene).	Extruded by U.S. Gasket Co.; meas perpendicular to axis of extrusion; auth. est. accuracy ± 2% at 0 R and ± 5% at 576 R.
◇	52-13	0-380		Same as above.	Extruded by Graef Eng. Co.; meas parallel to axis of extrusion; auth. est. accuracy ± 2% at 0 R.
▽	54-17	293-478		Teflon Type TF-1 (filled); density 134 lb ft^{-3}.	Molded at 2 tons $in.^{-2}$
▼	52-13	0-280		2 samples: fluorothene rod and Kel-F sheet (polychlorotrifluoroethylene).	Fluorothene molded by Union Carbon (probably annealed), Kel-F by M.W. Kellogg Co. (probably quenched); data are average for 2 samples for 2 or more cycles; auth. est. accuracy ± 3% at 0 R and ± 4% at 648 R.
●	57-26	298-401		Marlex 50 (Linear polyethylene by Phillips Petroleum Co.).	
□	52-13	0-300		Polythene PM-1 (Du Pont polyethylene).	Molded at 2000 psi and 150 C for 10 min; data average of 2 samples to 2 or more cycles; ± 5% estimated accuracy at 0 R.
■	57-26	298-400		Marlex 20.	

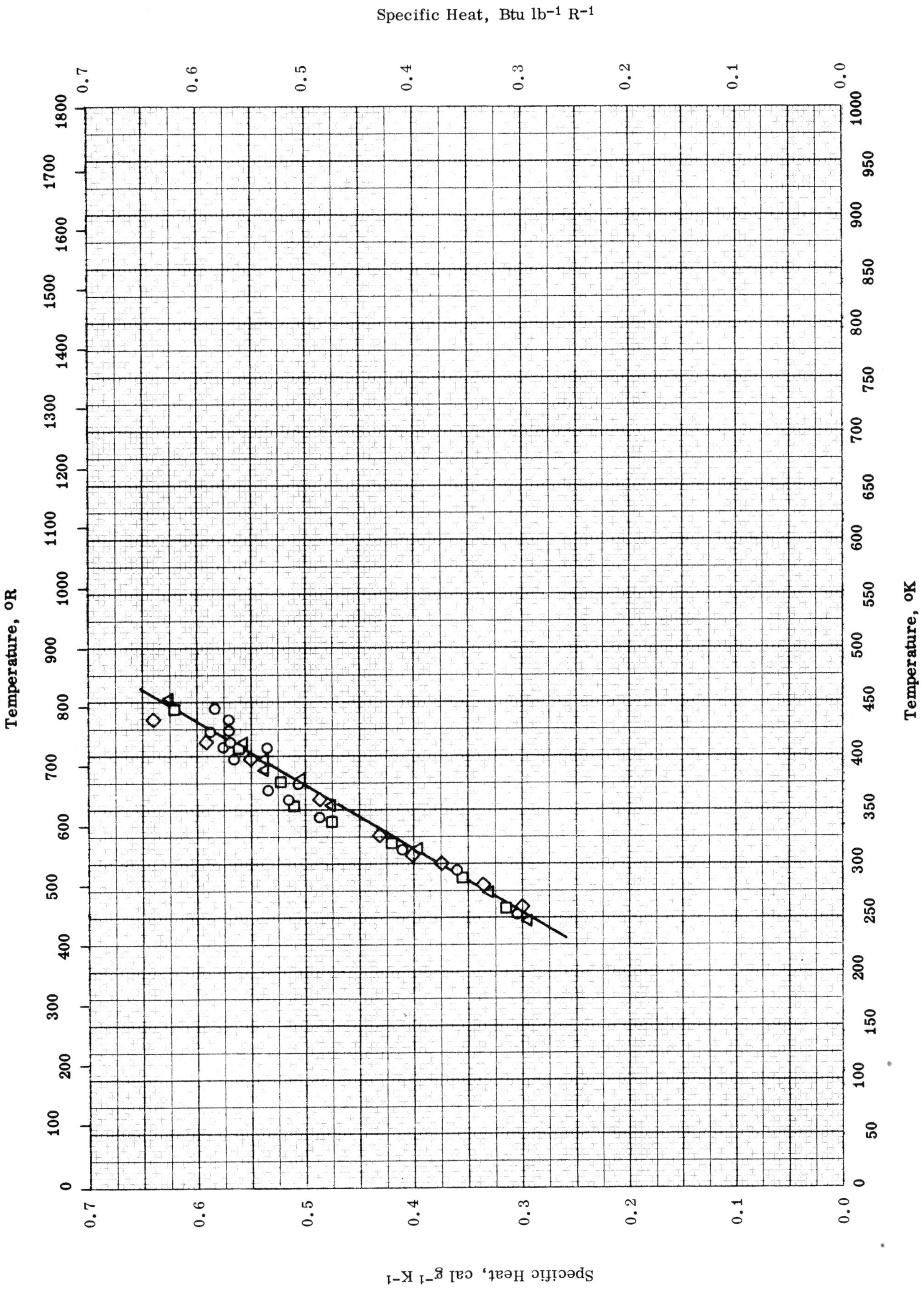

Specific Heat, Btu lb^{-1} R^{-1}

Temperature, °R

Temperature, °K

Specific Heat, cal g^{-1} K^{-1}

SPECIFIC HEAT -- NYLON

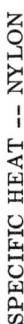

SPECIFIC HEAT -- NYLON

REFERENCE INFORMATION

Symbol	Ref.	Temp. Range °K	Rept. Error %	Sample Specifications	Remarks
○	55-14	253-443	±0.5	6-nylon (polycaprolactam) undrawn yarn (1050 denier, 34 filaments); 18,500 average mol. weight; 4% water extractables.	As received, dried to constant weight by evacuation.
□	55-14	253-443	±0.5	6-nylon (polycaprolactam) undrawn flakes; 20,000 average mol. weight; 1.7% water extractables.	Same as above.
△	55-14	253-453	±0.5	6-nylon (polycaprolactam) drawn yarn (210 denier, 34 filaments); 18,500 average mol. weight; 4% water extractables.	Same as above.
◇	55-14	253-453	±0.5	6-nylon (polycaprolactam) "melt-annealed".	Prepared by slow cooling after heating above M. P; glass transition 15 - 20 C.

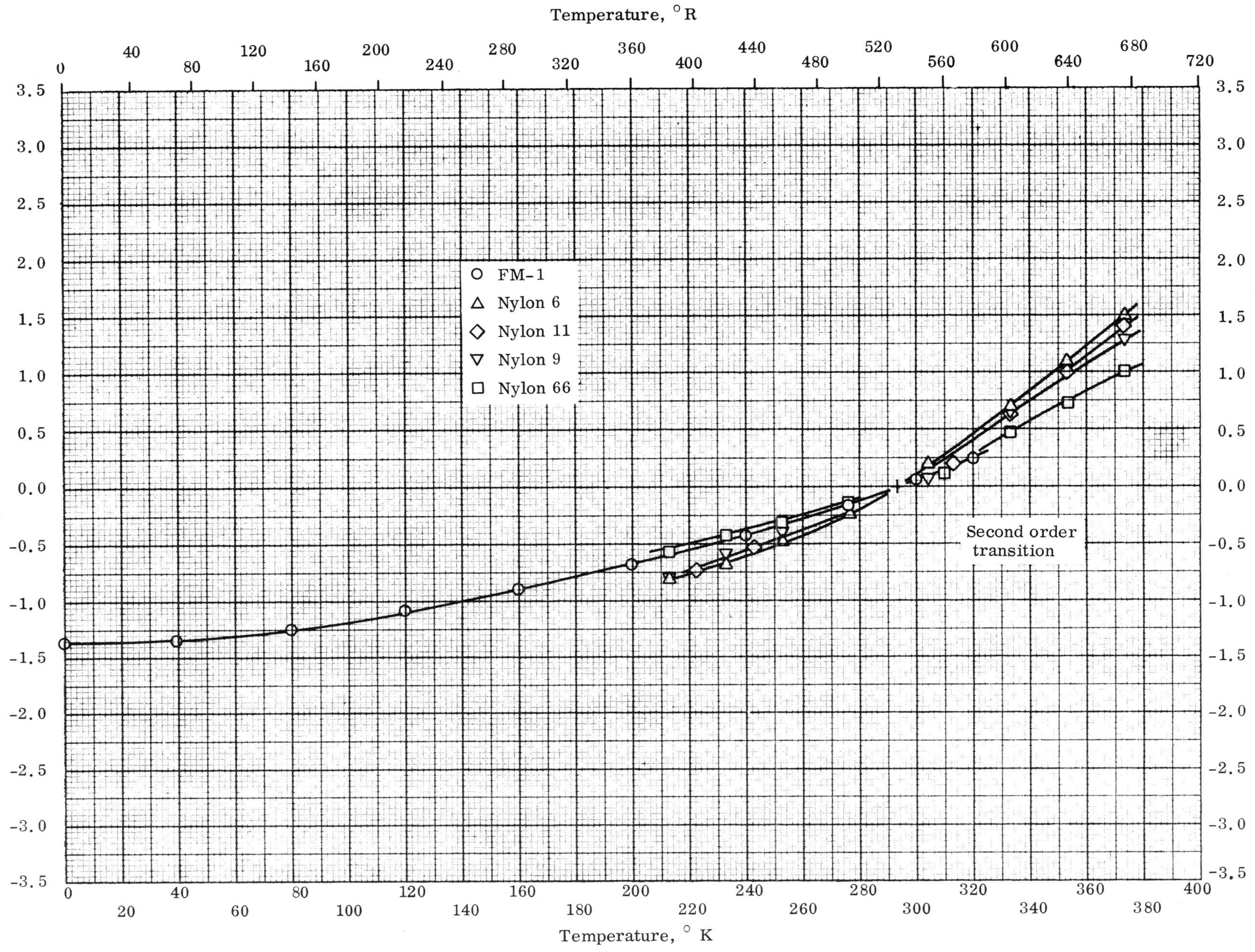

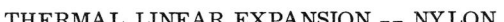

THERMAL LINEAR EXPANSION -- NYLON

THERMAL LINEAR EXPANSION -- NYLON

REFERENCE INFORMATION

Symbol	Ref.	Temp. Range °K	Rept. Error %	Sample Specifications	Remarks
○	52-13	0-320		Extruded Rod (probably E. I. DuPont grade FM-1).	Auth. est. accuracy ± 5% at 0 R and ± 1% at 576 R.
□	57-25	213-373		Nylon 66.	
△	57-25	213-373		Nylon 6.	
◇	57-25	213-373		Nylon 11.	
▽	57-25	213-373		Nylon 9.	

PROPERTIES OF NATURAL AND SYNTHETIC RUBBER

MOST PROBABLE VALUES

Property	C.G.S. Units	Brit. Eng. Units
Density, Neoprene W . . .	1.418	88.5

REPORTED VALUES

Density		$g\ cm^{-3}$	$lb\ ft^{-3}$
	○	1.6367	102.18
	□	1.226 ± 0.004	76.5 ± 0.3
	△	1.223	76.4
	◇	1.418	88.5
	▽	1.356	84.7
	◁	1.186	74.0
	▷	1.22	76.4
	●	1.19	74
	■	1.72	107
	▲	1.223	76.4
	▼	1.232	76.9
	◀	1.235	77.1
	▶	1.175	73.4
	◆	1.269	79.2
	◑	1.237	77.2
	◐	1.35	84
	◈	1.16	72

PROPERTIES OF NATURAL AND SYNTHETIC RUBBER

REFERENCE INFORMATION

Symbol	Ref.	Temp. Range °K	Rept. Error %	Sample Specifications	Remarks
○	57-29	298		Polyfluorobutyl acrylate rubber (1, 1-dihydroperfluorobutyl acrylate): 72.33 polymer, 25.32 philblack A, 0.90 triethylenetetramine, and 0.72 each paraffin, sulfur.	Cured.
□	57-29	298		Natural rubber gaskets.	Large sample.
△	57-29	298		Same as above.	Small sample.
◇	53-19	298		Neoprene W: 64.94 neoprene W, 29.22 SRF black, 3.25 ZnO, 1.30 MgO, 0.65 phenyl β-naphthylamine, and 0.32 each stearic acid, permalux.	Author also reports densities after irradiation.
▽	53-19	298		Neoprene W with dodecyl mercaptan: 62.50 neoprene W, 25.0 SRF black, 6.25 dodecyl mercaptan, 3.13 ZnO, 1.25 each phenyl β-naphthylamine, MgO, and 0.31 each stearic acid, accelerator.	Same as above.
◁	53-19	298		Natural rubber: 52.47 natural rubber, 36.73 SRF black, 5.25 dodecyl mercaptan, 2.62 ZnO, 1.57 S, 0.52 each phenyl β-naphthylamine, stearic acid, and 0.31 captax.	Same as above.
▷	53-19	298		Natural rubber with dodecyl mercaptan: 49.75 natural rubber, 34.83 SRF black, 4.98 each dodecyl mercaptan, PbO, 2.49 each ZnO, chloranil, and 0.5 stearic acid.	Same as above.

(Continued onto next page)

REFERENCE INFORMATION

Symbol	Ref.	Temp. Range °K	Rept. Error %	Sample Specifications	Remarks
●	53-19	298		Natural rubber with dibutyl tin dilaurate: 52.47 natural rubber, 36.73 SRF black, 5.25 dibutyl tin dilaurate, 2.62 ZnO, 1.57 S, 0.52 each phenyl β-naphthylamine, stearic acid, and 0.31 captax.	Same as above.
■	53-19	298		Natural rubber with asbestos filler: 69.33 asbestos filler, 27.73 natural rubber, 1.39 ZnO, 0.83 S, 0.28 each phenyl β-naphthylamine, stearic acid, and 0.17 captax.	Same as above.
▲	53-19	298		50 natural rubber and 50 butyl rubber.	Same as above.
▼	53-19	298		75 butyl rubber and 25 natural rubber.	Same as above.
◀	53-19	298		90 butyl rubber and 10 natural rubber.	Same as above.
▶	53-19	298		62.5 natural rubber and 37.5 butyl reclaim.	Same as above.
◆	53-19	298		Nycar PA-21.	Same as above.
◑	53-19	298		Vulcollan.	Same as above.
◐	40-1	298		Carbon black filled perbunan rubber (butadiene-acrylonitrile copolymer).	
◈	40-1	298		Carbon black filled buna rubber (styrene-butadiene copolymer).	

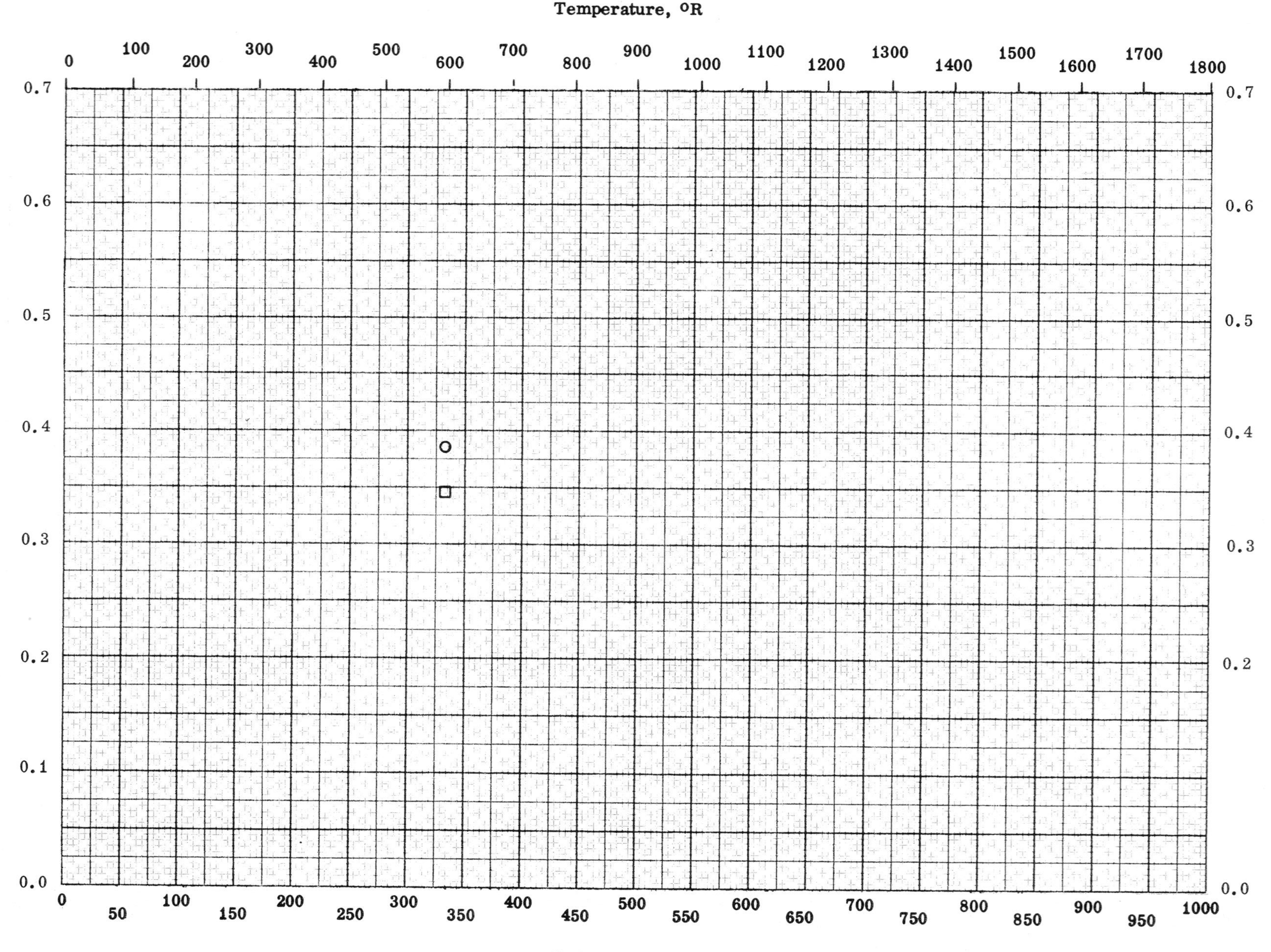

SPECIFIC HEAT -- SYNTHETIC RUBBER

SPECIFIC HEAT -- SYNTHETIC RUBBER

REFERENCE INFORMATION

Symbol	Ref.	Temp. Range °K	Rept. Error %	Sample Specifications	Remarks
○	40-1	333		Buna rubber (styrene-butadiene copolymer) with carbon black.	Author report average C_p between 20 - 100 C.
□	40-1	333		Perbunan rubber (butadiene-acrylonitrile copolymer) with carbon black.	Same as above.

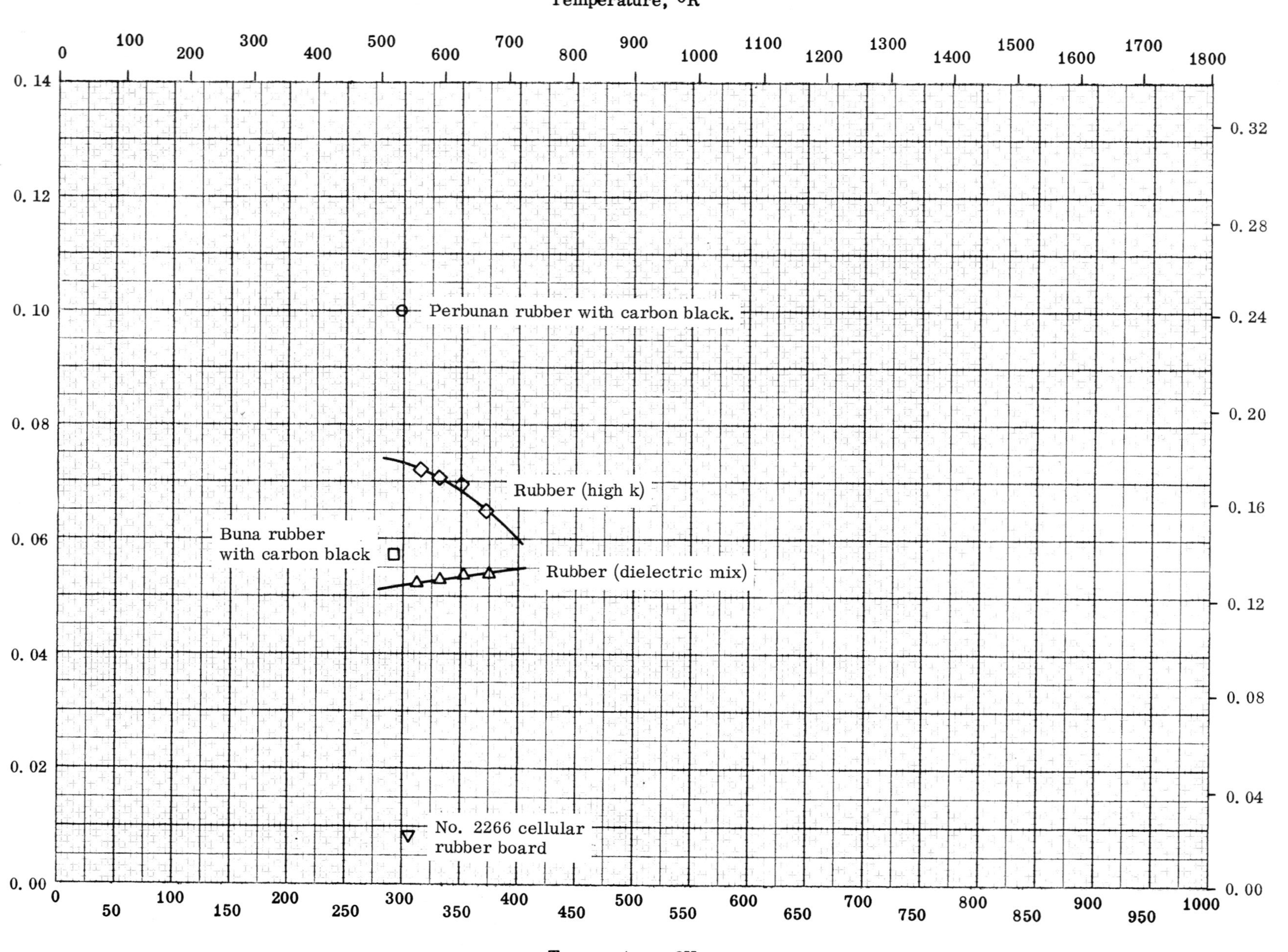

THERMAL CONDUCTIVITY -- NATURAL AND SYNTHETIC RUBBER

REFERENCE INFORMATION

Symbol	Ref.	Temp. Range °K	Rept. Error %	Sample Specifications	Remarks
○	40-1	298		Perbunan rubber with carbon black; density 84 lb ft^{-3}.	Butadiene - acrylonitrile copolymer.
□	40-1	298		Buna rubber with carbon black; density 72 lb ft^{-3}.	Styrene - butadiene copolymer.
△	53-4	293-373		Rubber, typical dielectric mix.	
◇	53-4	293-373		Rubber, designed for high thermal conductivity.	
▽	45-2	308.4		Hard rubber (manufacturer's design.: cellular rubber board No. 2266); from U.S. Rubber Co.; same composition for both skin and core; density 4.3 lb ft^{-3}.	Oven dried 16 hrs at 140-150 F.

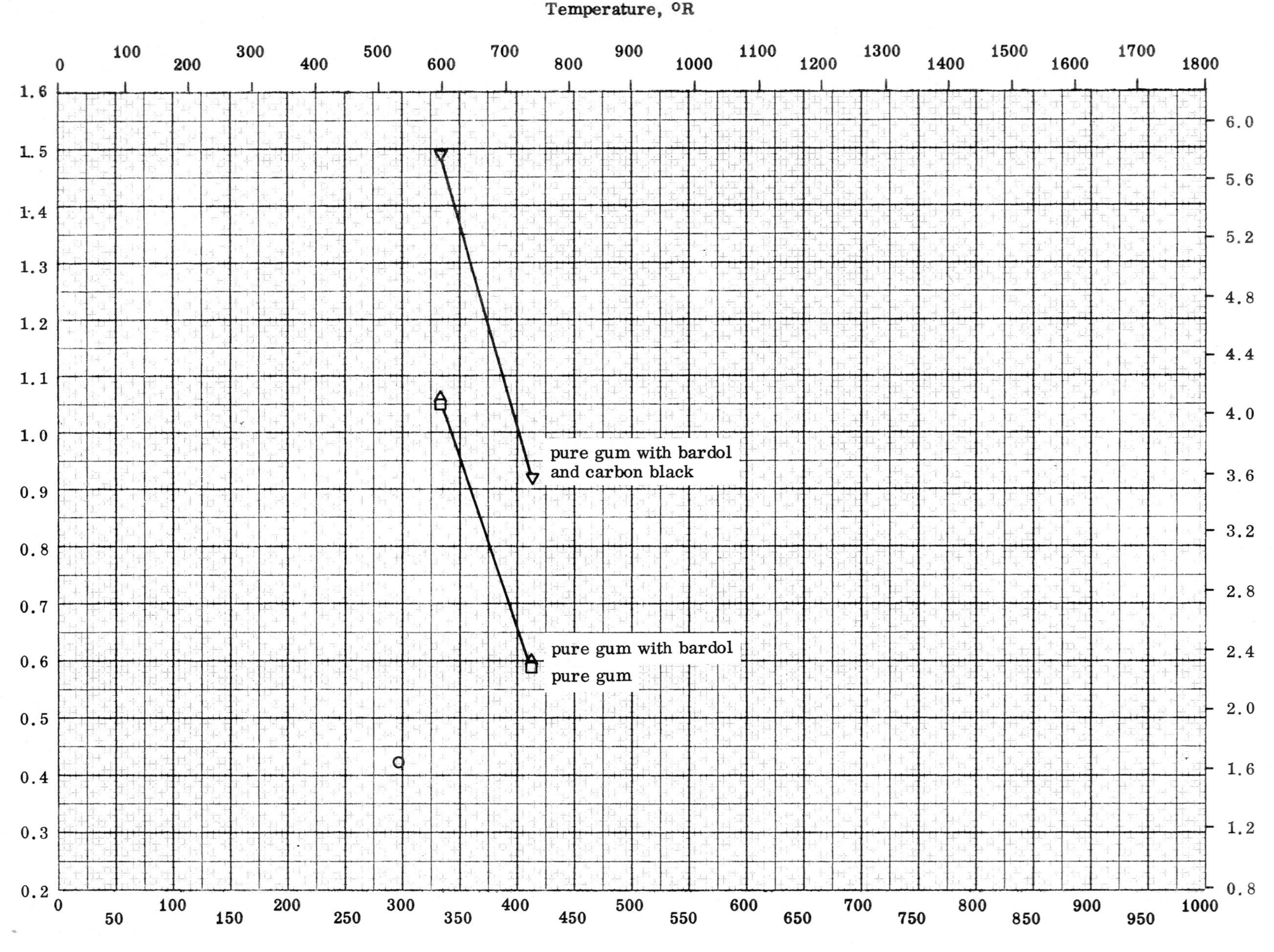

THERMAL DIFFUSIVITY -- NATURAL RUBBER

THERMAL DIFFUSIVITY -- NATURAL RUBBER

REFERENCE INFORMATION

Symbol	Ref.	Temp. Range °K	Rept. Error %	Sample Specifications	Remarks
○	55-1	297		Sample 15.1 mm thick; density 1080 Kg m^{-1}.	
□	47-1	333-413	<5.0	Prepared from 100 parts ribbed smoked sheets, 5 zinc oxide, 1 stearic acid, 1 benzothiazyl disulfide, and 2 sulfur.	Cured at 287 F for 1 hr.
△	47-1	333-413	<5.0	Same as above with 20 parts Bardol (commercial tar distillate) substituted for stearic acid.	Same as above.
▽	47-1	333-413	<5.0	Same as above with 54 Kosmobile 66 carbon black added.	Same as above.

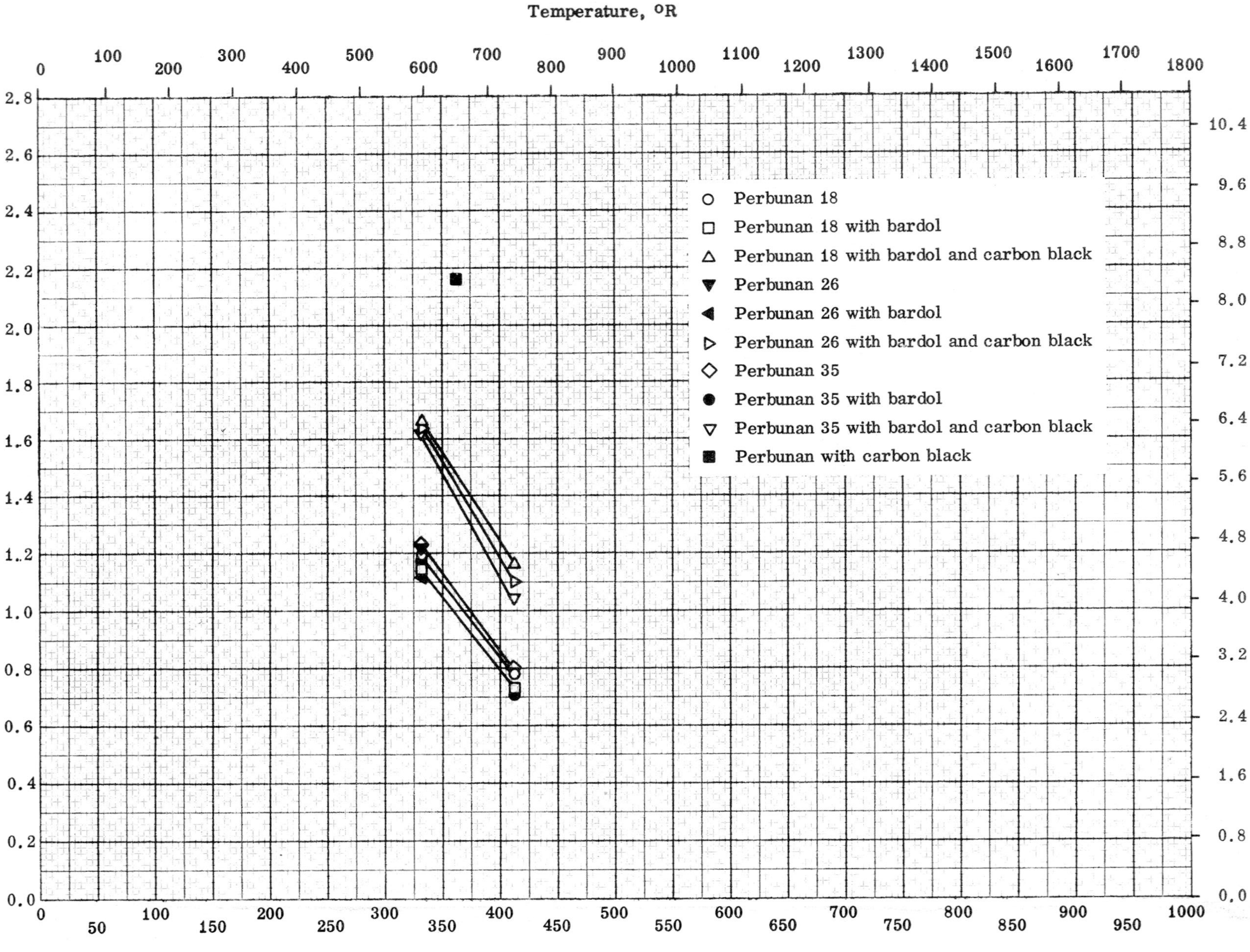

THERMAL DIFFUSIVITY -- SYNTHETIC RUBBER
(Butadiene and acrytonitrile copolymer)

THERMAL DIFFUSIVITY -- SYNTHETIC RUBBER
(Butadiene and acrytonitrile copolymer)

REFERENCE INFORMATION

Symbol	Ref.	Temp. Range °K	Rept. Error %	Sample Specifications	Remarks
○	47-1	333-413	< 5.0	Perbunan 18 (butadiene and 18 acrylonitrile) prepared from 100 parts perbunan 18, 5 zinc oxide, 2 sulfur, 1 stearic acid, and 1 benzothiazyl disulfide.	Cured at 287 F for 1 hr.
□	47-1	333-413	< 5.0	Same as above with 20 parts Bardol substituted for stearic acid.	Same as above.
△	47-1	333-413	< 5.0	Same as above with 54 parts carbon black added.	Same as above.
▼	47-1	333-413	< 5.0	Perbunan 26 (butadiene and 26 acrylonitrile); 5 zinc oxide, 2 sulfur, 1 stearic acid, and 1 benzothiazyl disulfide.	Same as above.
◀	47-1	333-413	< 5.0	Same as above with 20 parts Bordol substituted for stearic acid.	Same as above.
▷	47-1	333-413	< 5.0	Same as above with 54 parts carbon black added.	Same as above.
◇	47-1	333-413	< 5.0	Perbunan 35 (butadiene and 35 acrylonitrile); 5 zinc oxide, 2 sulfur, 1 stearic acid, and 1 benzothiazyl disulfide.	Same as above.
●	47-1	333-413	< 5.0	Same as above with 20 parts Bordol substituted for stearic acid.	Same as above.
▽	47-1	333-413	< 5.0	Same as above with 54 parts of carbon black added.	Same as above.
■	40-1	363		Perbunan rubber with carbon black.	

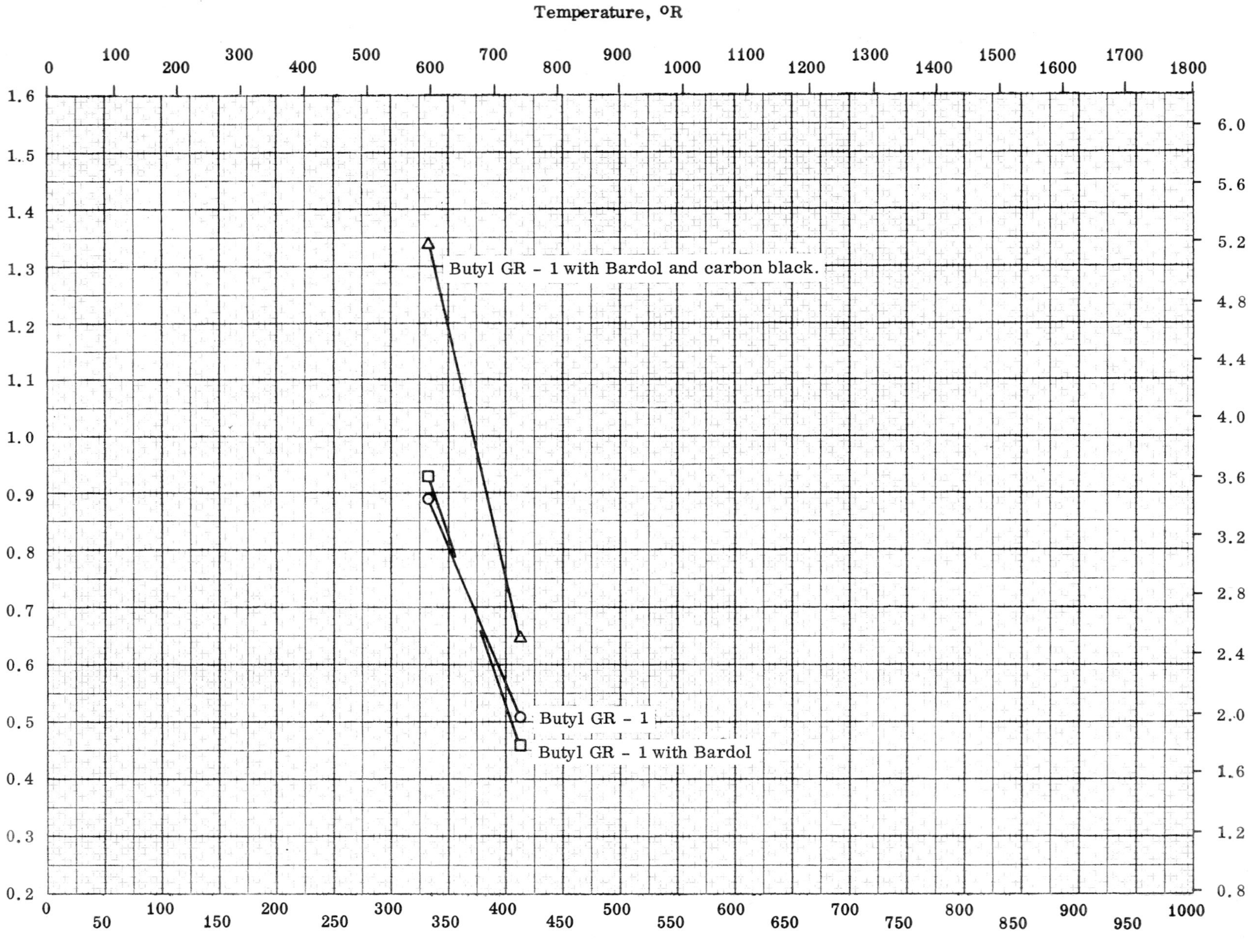

THERMAL DIFFUSIVITY -- SYNTHETIC RUBBER
(Isobutylene and isoprene copolymer)

THERMAL DIFFUSIVITY -- SYNTHETIC RUBBER
(Isobutylene and isoprene copolymer)

REFERENCE INFORMATION

Symbol	Ref.	Temp. Range °K	Rept. Error %	Sample Specifications	Remarks
○	47-1	333-413		Butyl GR-1 (isobutylene -1.0 isoprene units); prepared from 100 parts GR-1, 5 zinc oxide, 2 sulfur, 1 stearic acid, and 1 tetramathylthiuram disulfide.	Cured at 307 F for 1 hr.
□	47-1	333-413		Same as above with 20 parts Bardol (commercial tar distillate) substitute for stearic acid.	Same as above.
△	47-1	333-413		Same as above except 54 parts Kosmobile 66 carbon black added.	Same as above.

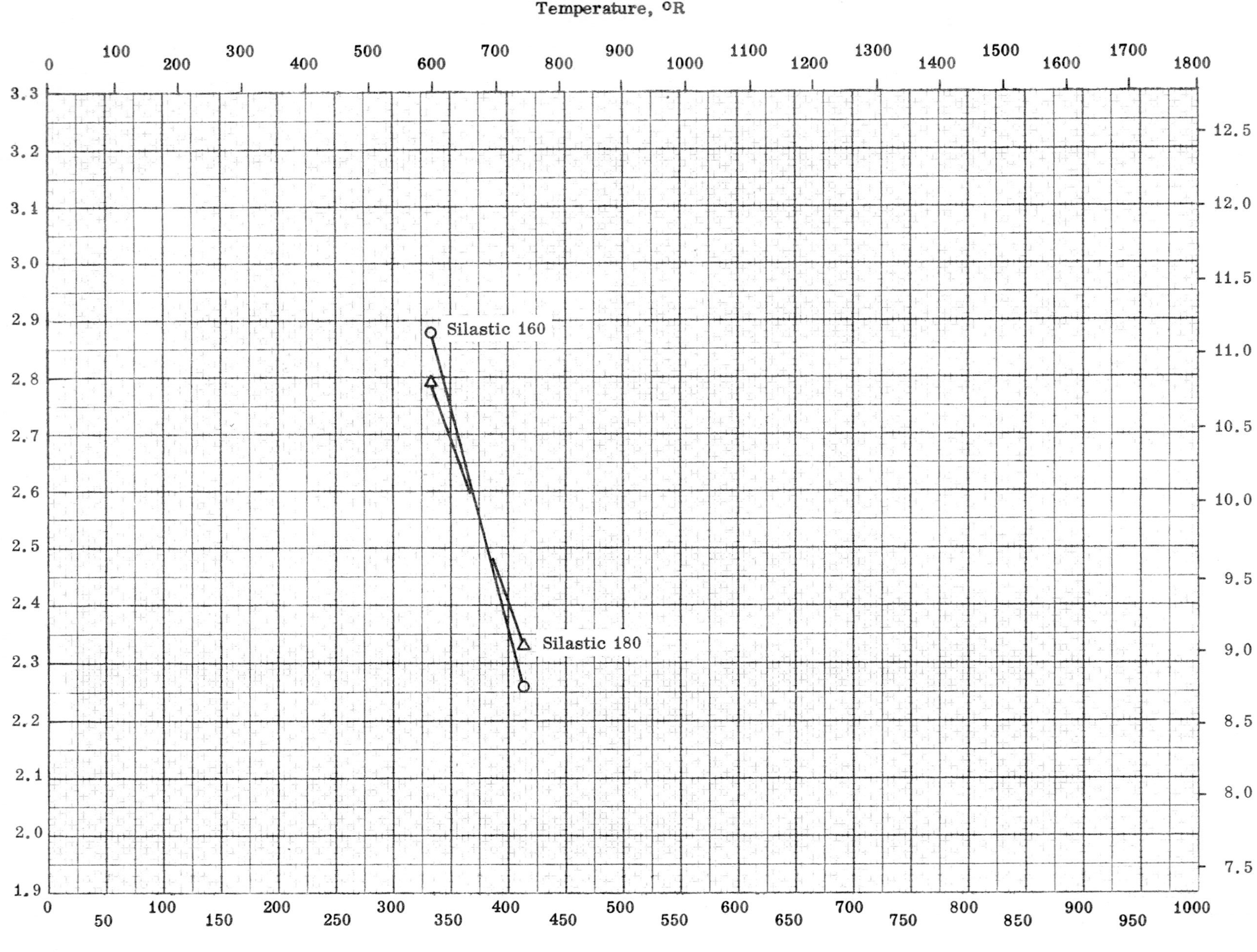

THERMAL DIFFUSIVITY -- SYNTHETIC RUBBER
(Silicone rubber)

THERMAL DIFFUSIVITY -- SYNTHETIC RUBBER
(Silicone rubber)

REFERENCE INFORMATION

Symbol	Ref.	Temp. Range °K	Rept. Error %	Sample Specifications	Remarks
○	47-1	333-413	< 5.0	Silastic 160	Molded at 250 F for 5 min and cured over night in an air oven at 450 F.
△	47-1	333-413	< 5.0	Silastic 180	Same as above.

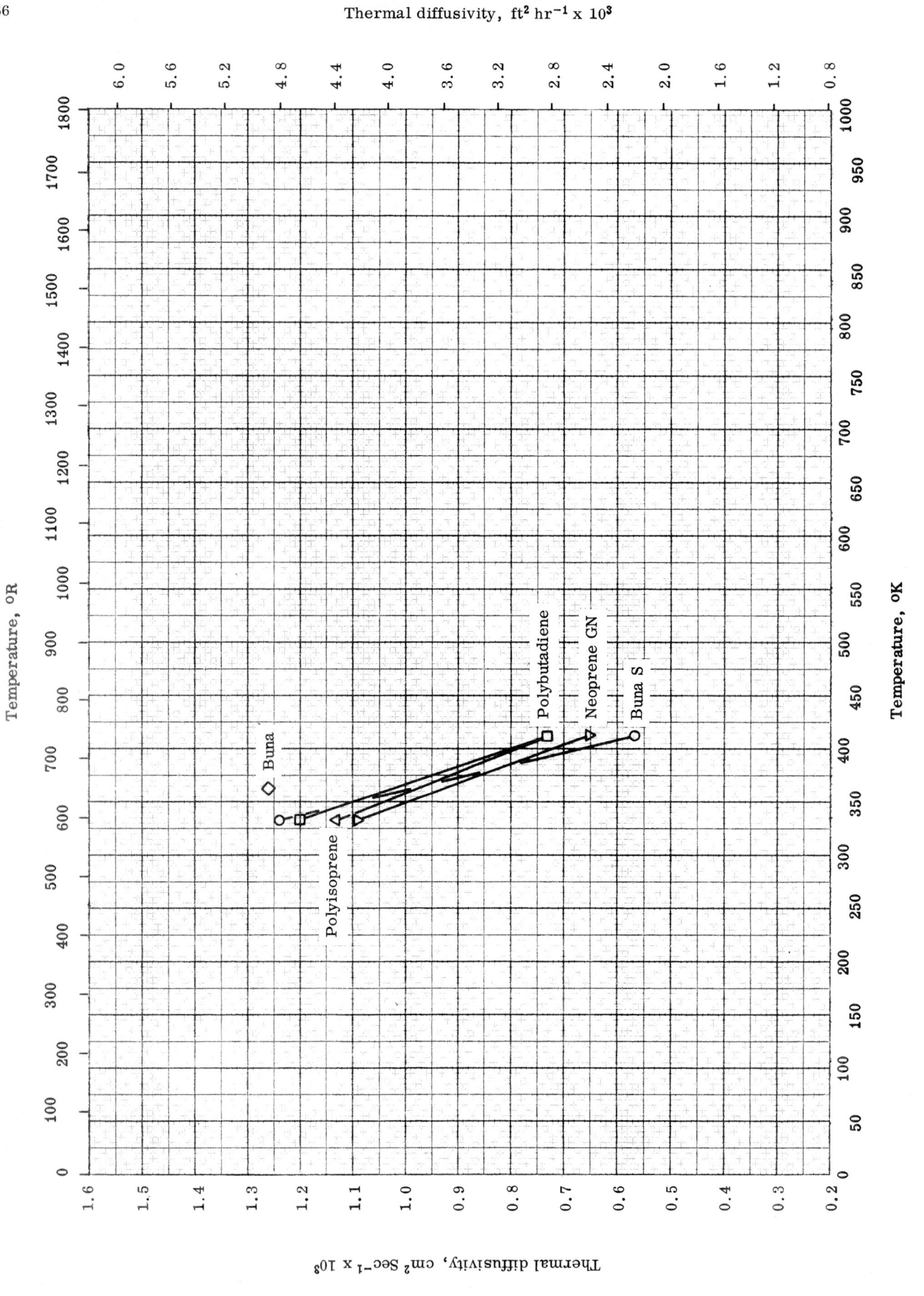

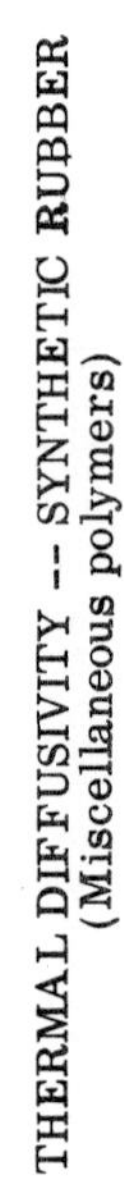

THERMAL DIFFUSIVITY -- SYNTHETIC RUBBER
(Miscellaneous polymers)

Thermal diffusivity, $ft^2\ hr^{-1} \times 10^3$

Temperature, °R

Temperature, °K

Thermal diffusivity, $cm^2\ Sec^{-1} \times 10^3$

Buna

Polybutadiene

Neoprene GN

Buna S

Polyisoprene

THERMAL DIFFUSIVITY -- SYNTHETIC RUBBER
(Miscellaneous polymers)

REFERENCE INFORMATION

Symbol	Ref.	Temp. Range °K	Rept. Error %	Sample Specifications	Remarks
○	47-1	333-413	< 5.0	Buna S (an emulsion copolymer of butadiene and GR-S, containing about 25 styrene units); prepared from 100 parts GR-S, 5 zinc oxide, 2 sulfur, 1 stearic acid, and 1 mercaptobenzothiazole.	Cured at 287 F for 1 hr.
◇	40-1	363		Buna rubber with carbon black.	
□	47-1	333-413	< 5.0	Polybutadiene (an emulsion polymers); prepared from 100 parts polybutadiene, 5 zinc oxide, 2 sulfur, 1 stearic acid, and 1 mercaptobenzothiazole.	Same as above.
△	47-1	333-413	< 5.0	Polyisoprene (an emulsion polymers); prepared from 100 parts polyisoprene, 5 zinc oxide, 2 sulfur, 1 stearic acid, and 1 mercaptobenzothiazole.	Cured at 210 F for 30 min and followed by 60 min at 270-320 F.
▽	47-1	333-413	< 5.0	Neoprene GN; prepared by 100 neoprene GN, 5 zinc oxide, and 4 magnesia.	Cured at 287 F for 30 min.

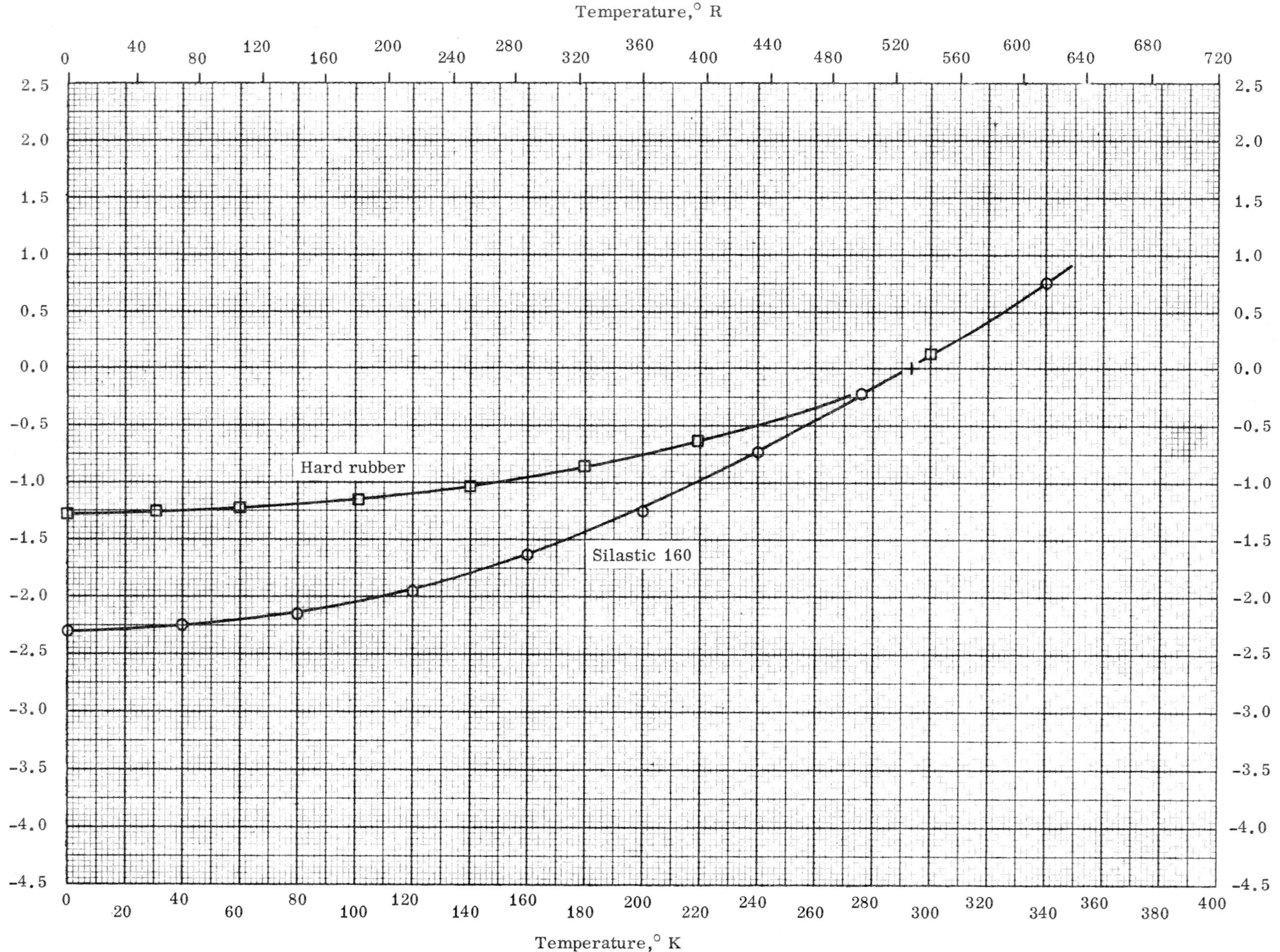

THERMAL LINEAR EXPANSION -- RUBBER AND RUBBERLIKE POLYMERS

REFERENCE INFORMATION

Symbol	Ref.	Temp. Range °K	Rept. Error %	Sample Specifications	Remarks
○	52-13	0-340		Silastic 160 by Dow Corning; shore hardness = 77 on A_2 scale.	Molded at 200 psi and 120 C for 10 min , cured 15 hrs at 150 C; 7 hrs at 200 C; 17 hrs at 250 ; average for 2 or more cycles; auth. estimated accuracy ± 3% at 0 R, ± 6% at 576 R.
□	52-13	0-300		Hard Rubber by W. H. Salesbury Co.; shore hardness = 90 on A_2 scale.	Measured perpendicular to plane of slab; average for 2 or more cycles; author esimated accuracy ± 4% at 0R, ± 3% at 36 R, and ± 6% at 540 R.

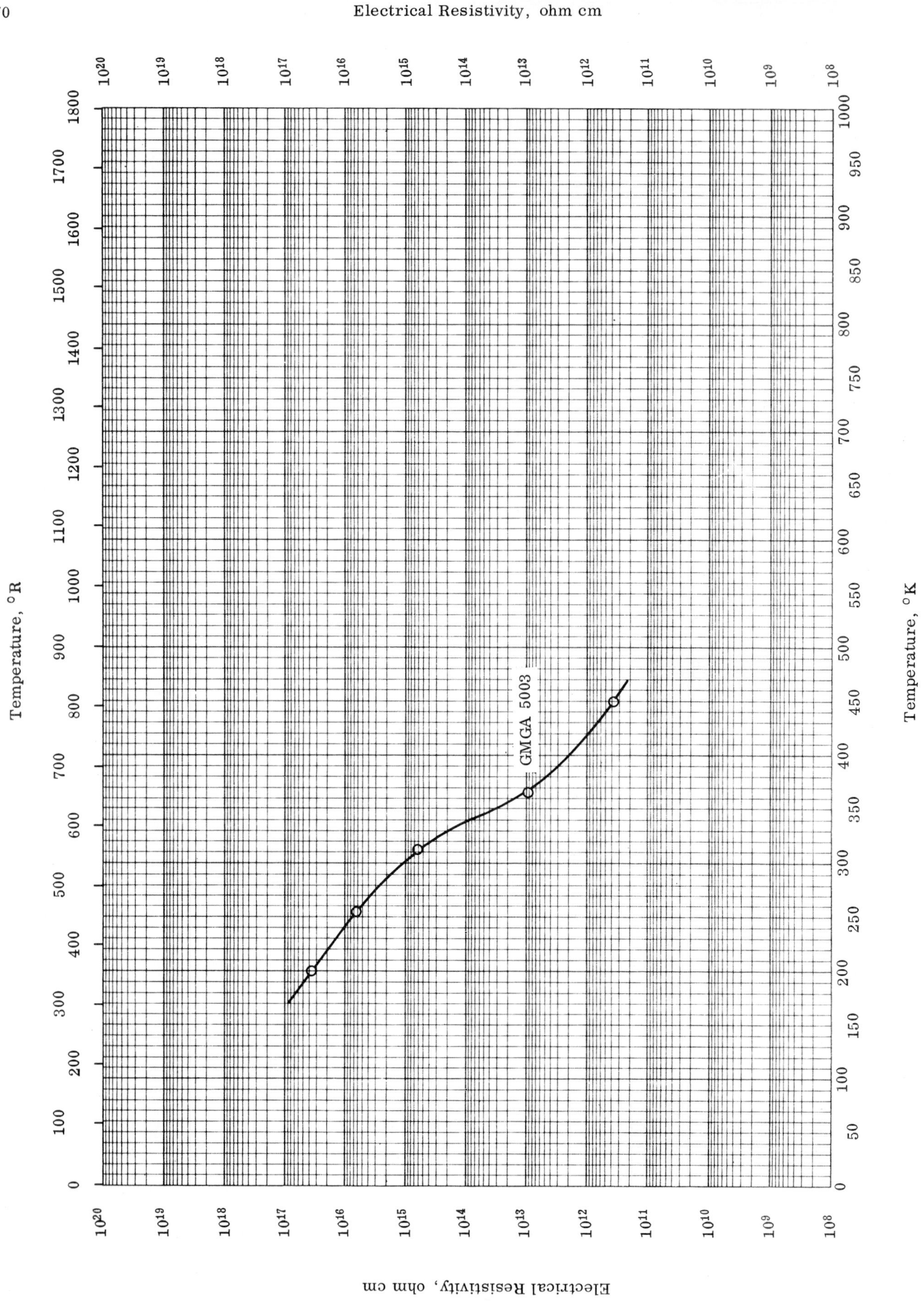

Electrical Resistivity, ohm cm

Temperature, °R

Temperature, °K

GMGA 5003

Electrical Resistivity, ohm cm

ELECTRICAL RESISTIVITY -- FILLED SILICONE

REFERENCE INFORMATION

Symbol	Ref.	Temp. Range °K	Rept. Error %	Sample Specifications	Remarks
○	57-18	200-450		GMGA 5003; mineral filled silicone made by Bakelite Co, Union Carbide and Carbon Corp.	Conditioned 48 hrs at 120 F at 90% humidity; then 7 cycles, ea. of which consists of 12 hrs at 100 F and 100% humidity plus 12 hrs at 120 F and 95% humidity.

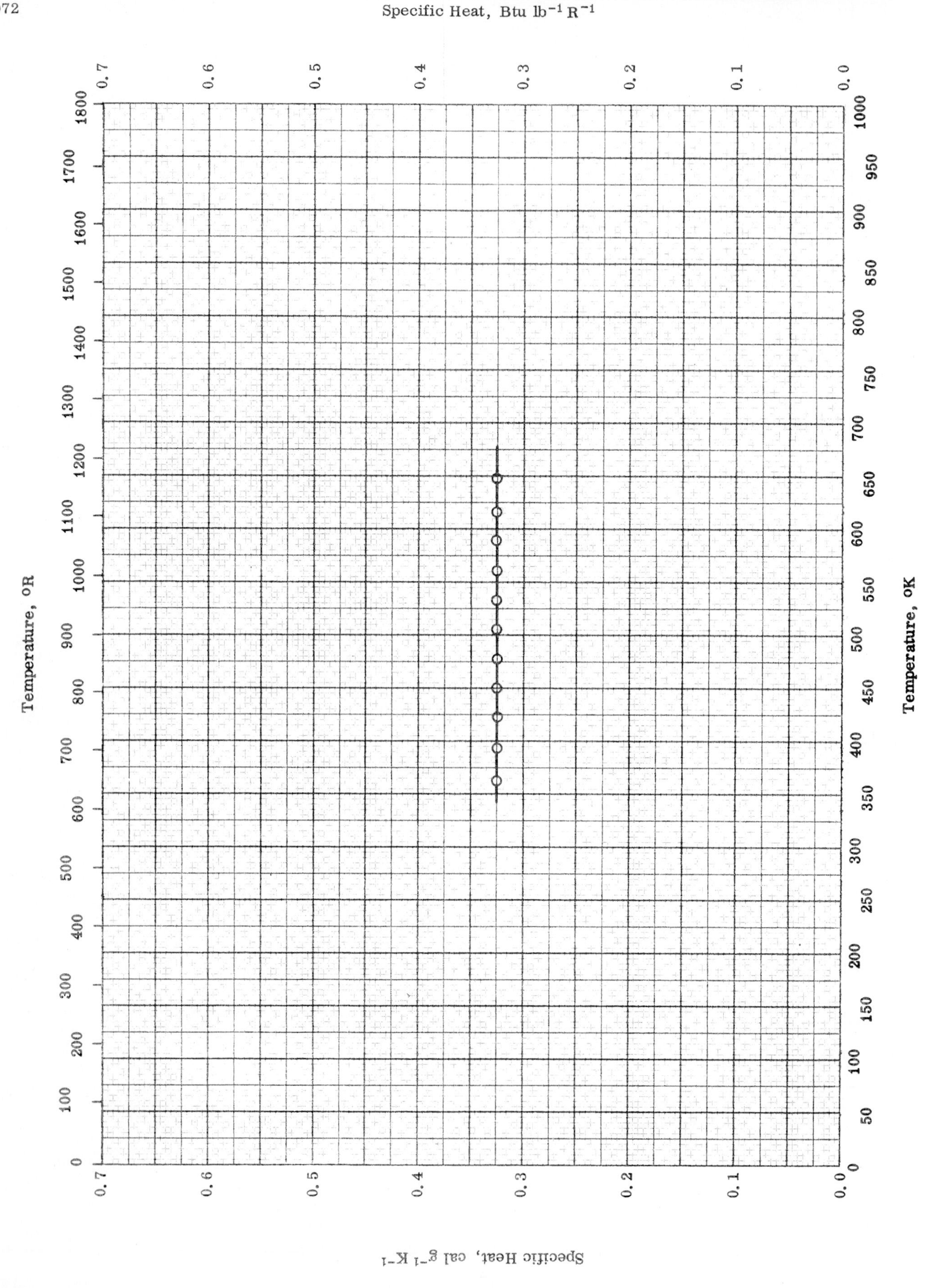

Specific Heat, Btu lb^{-1} R^{-1}

Temperature, °R

Temperature, °K

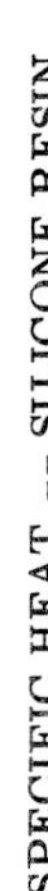

Specific Heat, cal g^{-1} K^{-1}

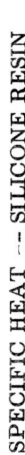

SPECIFIC HEAT -- SILICONE RESIN

REFERENCE INFORMATION

Symbol	Ref.	Temp. Range °K	Rept. Error %	Sample Specifications	Remarks
○	61-13	364-643		SRI No. 3; foam core; Dow Corning silicone R-7002; density 11.6 lb ft^{-3}.	Fabrication and curing; 1 hr at 390 F, 1 hr at 435 F, 24 hrs at 480 F; cooling: 1 hr at 425 F, 1 hr at 390 F, and 1 hr at 150 F.

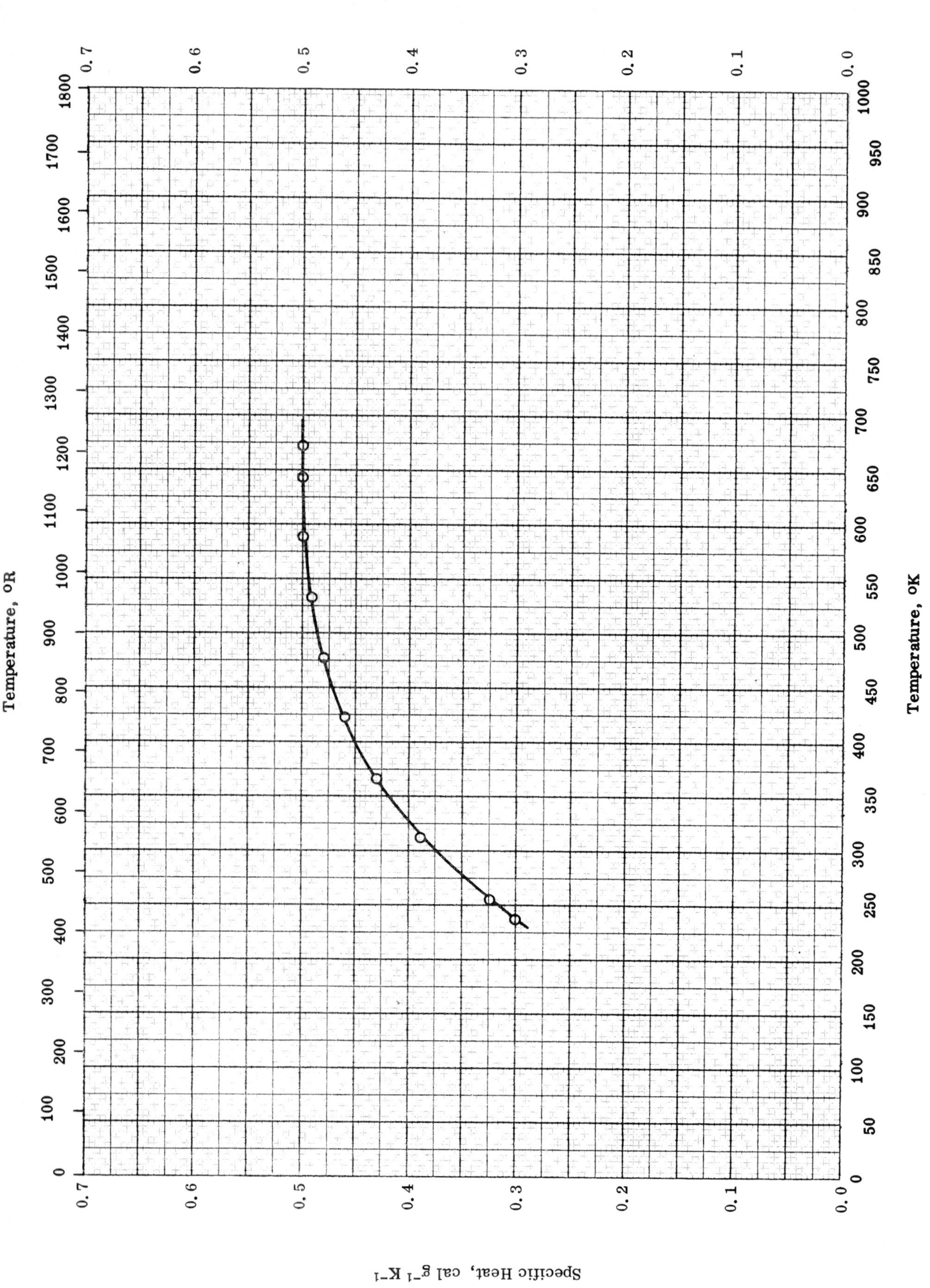

Specific Heat, Btu lb^{-1} R^{-1}

0.7 0.6 0.5 0.4 0.3 0.2 0.1 0.0

Temperature, °R

0 100 200 300 400 500 600 700 800 900 1000 1100 1200 1300 1400 1500 1600 1700 1800

Temperature, °K

0 50 100 150 200 250 300 350 400 450 500 550 600 650 700 750 800 850 900 950 1000

0.7 0.6 0.5 0.4 0.3 0.2 0.1 0.0

Specific Heat, cal g^{-1} K^{-1}

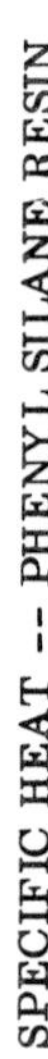

SPECIFIC HEAT -- PHENYL SILANE RESIN

REFERENCE INFORMATION

Symbol	Ref.	Temp. Range °K	Rept. Error %	Sample Specifications	Remarks
○	63-18	228-673		100 resin; Monsanto SC-1013 phenyl silane; density 73 lb ft^{-3}; [Author's design.: f-2].	Cure cycle: 15 hrs at 200 F; post cure cycle: 24 hrs for each at 200, 200 and 325 F.

PROPERTIES OF MISCELLANEOUS PLASTICS

Density	$g\ cm^{-1}$	$lb\ ft^{-1}$
○ Moplen polyproplylene	0.91	57

Softening Point	K	R
○ Moplen polyproplylene	358	645
□ Penton 1215	433	780
△ Polystyrene	393	708
◇ Polyvinyl chloride	393	708

REFERENCE INFORMATION

Symbol	Ref.	Temp. Range °K	Rept. Error %	Sample Specifications	Remarks
○	58-5	441		Moplen: aliphatic olefin polymer, isotactic polypropylene.	Melts at 794 R.
□	56-26	433-448		Hercules Penton 1215 (3, 3 bis-chloromethyl-oxetane).	Flowed at 800 R.
△	56-26	393		Polystyrene (Monsanta Lustrex L-2020).	Flowed at 135 C.
◇	56-26	393		Polyvinyl chloride (Monsanto Opalon 300 FM).	Flowed at 200 C.

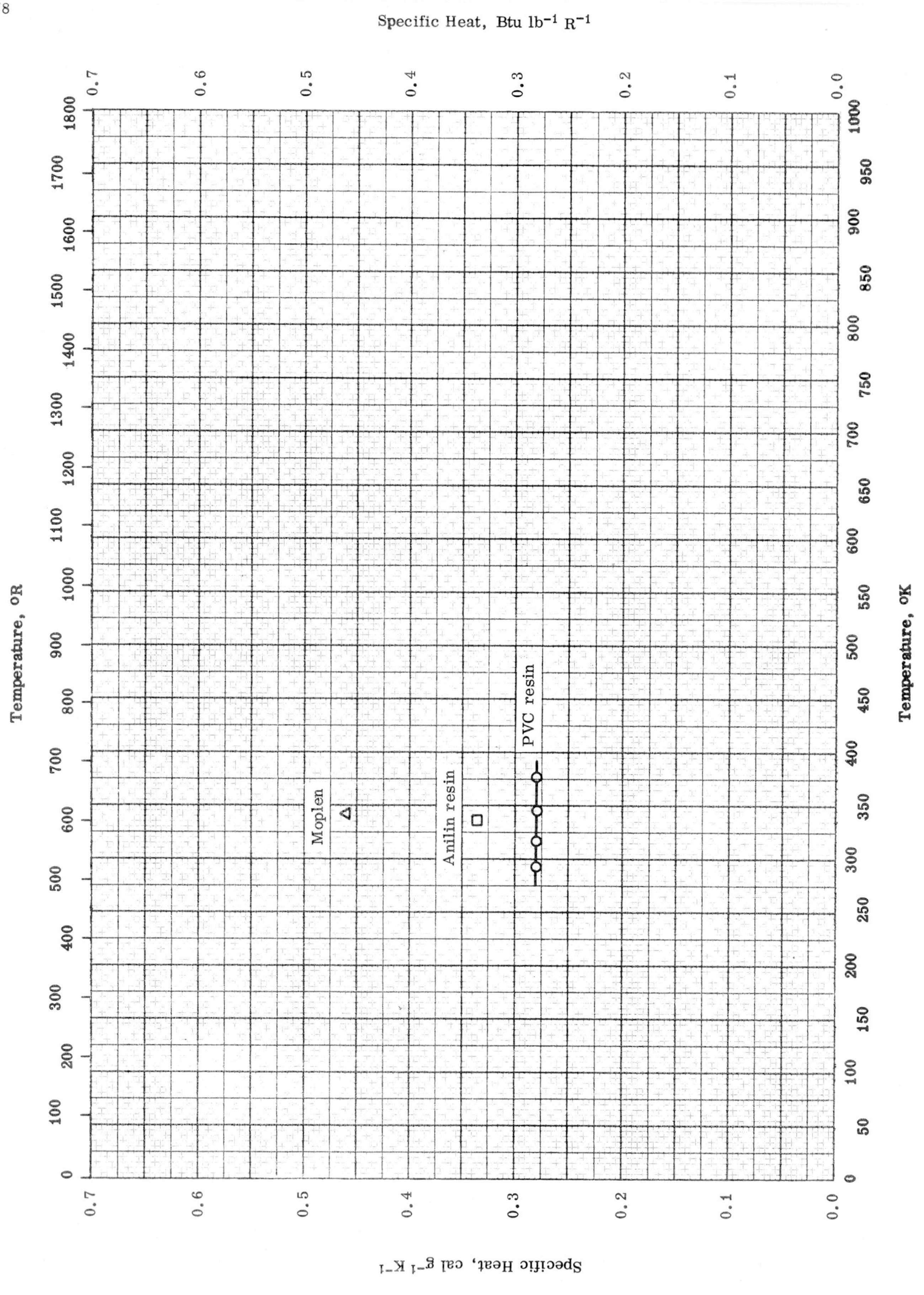

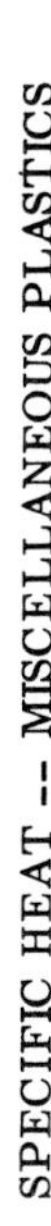

SPECIFIC HEAT -- MISCELLANEOUS PLASTICS

REFERENCE INFORMATION

Symbol	Ref.	Temp. Range °K	Rept. Error %	Sample Specifications	Remarks
○	40-1	293-373		Igelit-PCU; polyvinyl chloride resin of the paste type.	
□	40-1	293-373		Anilin Resin.	Author report mean C_p between 20 - 100 C.
△	58-5	297-395		Moplen: aliphatic olefin polymer, isotactic propylene.	Author reports mean C_p between 75 - 250 F.

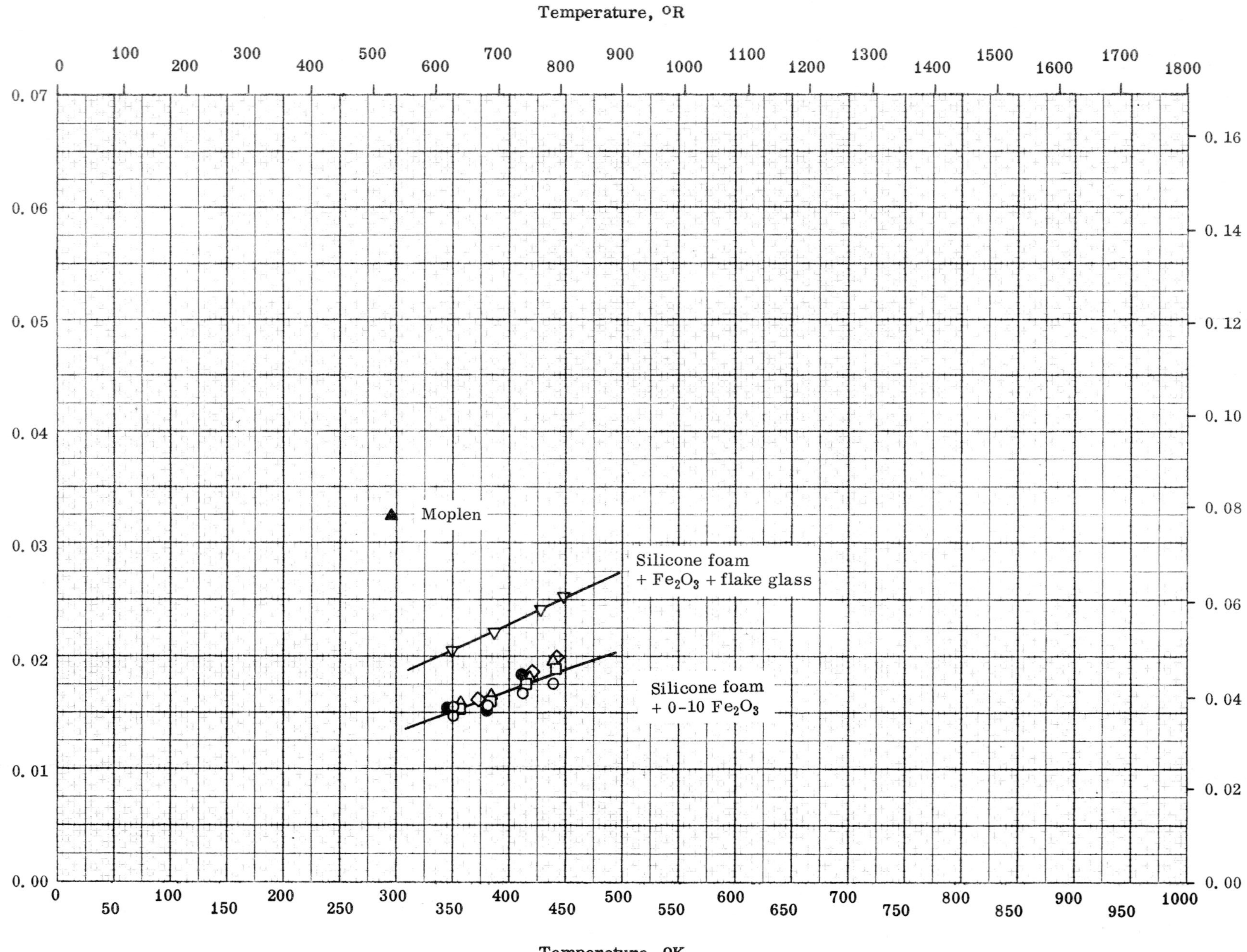

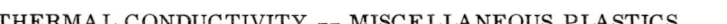

THERMAL CONDUCTIVITY -- MISCELLANEOUS PLASTICS

REFERENCE INFORMATION

Symbol	Ref.	Temp. Range °K	Rept. Error %	Sample Specifications	Remarks
○	ND-1	351-440		Silicone foam of Dow Corning R-7001 (raw material is one component powder); density 18 lb ft^{-3}.	Cured 8 hrs at 300-350 F, 48-72 hrs at 480 F.
□	ND-1	356-442		Silicone foam of Dow Corning R-7002 (raw material is one component powder); density 20 lb ft^{-3}.	Same as above.
△	ND-1	356-439		Silicone foam of Dow Corning R-7091 (raw material is four component liquid); density 15 lb ft^{-3}.	Two cures: (1) 10 hrs at room temperature. (2) 1/2 hr at 250 F and 2 hrs at room temperature.
◇	ND-1	353-441		Silicone foam of Dow Corning R-7091 + 10 Fe_2O_3 (raw material is four component liquid); density 10 lb ft^{-3}.	Same as above.
▽	ND-1	349-438		Silicone foam of Dow Corning R-7091 + 10 Fe_2O_3 and 5 flake glass (raw material is four component liquid); density 16 lb ft^{-3}.	Same as above.
●	ND-1	346-442		Silicone foam (Eccofoam LM) by Emerson and Cumings Inc. (raw material is one component paste); density 22 lb ft^{-3}.	Cured 6 hrs at 200 F, 6 hrs at 350 F, 2 hrs at 550 F.
▲	58-5	294. 5		Moplen; aliphatic olefin polymer, isotactic polypropylene.	

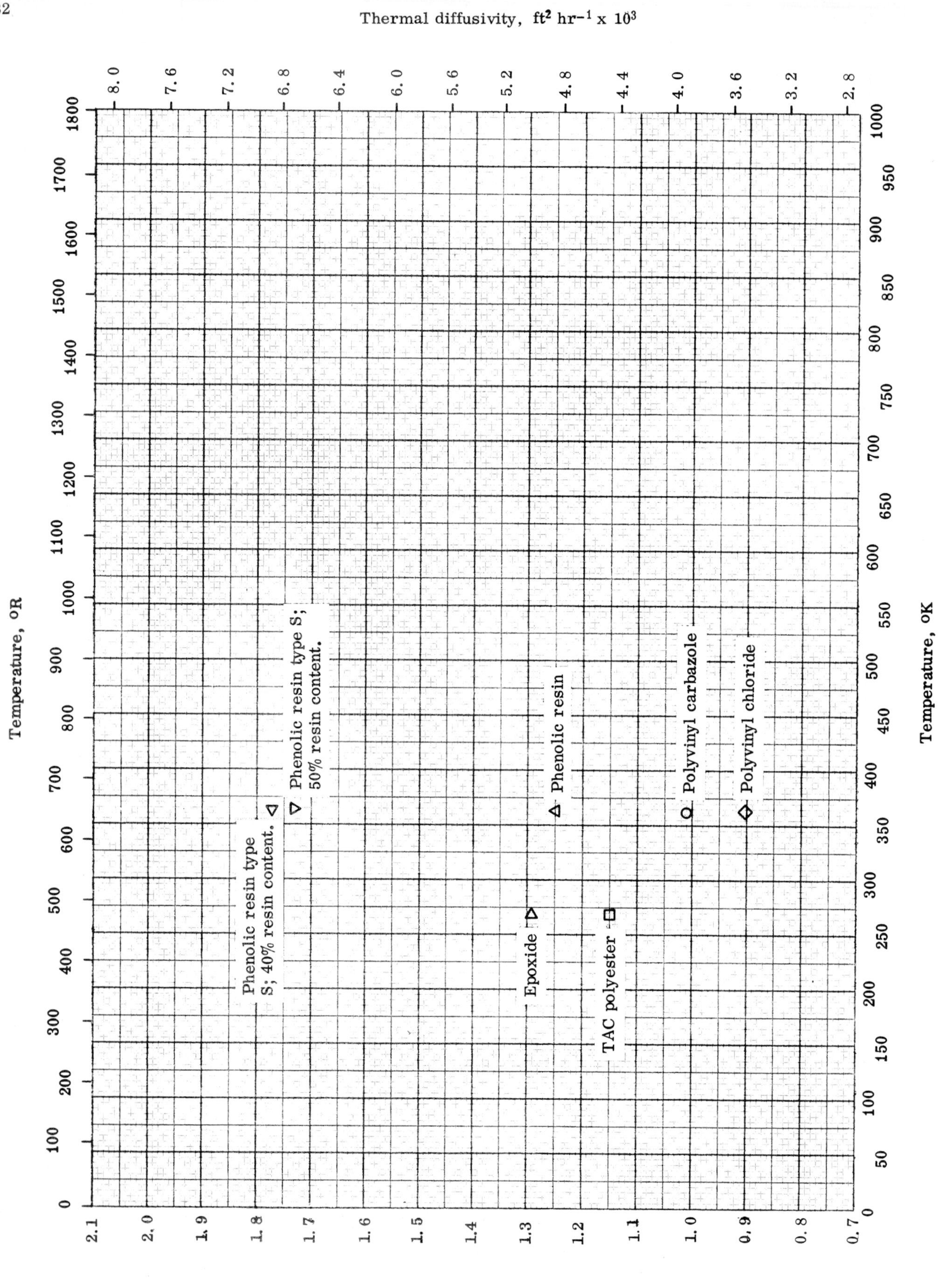

THERMAL DIFFUSIVITY -- MISCELLANEOUS PLASTICS

REFERENCE INFORMATION

Symbol	Ref.	Temp. Range °K	Rept. Error %	Sample Specifications	Remarks
○	40-1	363		Trolitul Luv-M150 (Ger. design.); polyvinyl carbazole; Luvican; polyester; density 74.3 lb ft^{-3}.	
□	57-1	267		Castolite; TAC polyester; density 76.7 lb ft^{-3}.	
△	40-1	363		Phenolic resin; density 79.2 lb ft^{-3}.	Pressed.
▽	40-1	363		Phenolic resin type S; 50% resin content; density 85.5 lb ft^{-3}.	
◁	40-1	363		Phenolic resin type S; 40% resin content; density 87.4 lb ft^{-3}.	
▷	57-1	267		Hysol 6000-op; Epoxide; density 75.3 lb ft^{-3}.	
◇	40-1	363		Igelit-PCU (Ger. design.); polyvinyl chloride resin of the paste type; acrylic; density 86.7 lb ft^{-3}.	

DENSITY -- SILICONE FOAM

Symbol	Material Composition	Density g cm^{-3}	Density lb ft^{-3}
○	Eccofoam LM	0.35	22
□	R-7001	0.29	18
△	R-7002	0.32	20
◇	R-7091	0.24	15
▽	R-7091 + 10 Fe_2O_3	0.16	10
◁	R-7091 + 10 Fe_2O_3 + 5 film glass	0.26	16

REFERENCE INFORMATION

Symbol	Ref.	Temp. Range °K	Rept. Error %	Sample Specifications	Remarks
○	ND-1	298		Eccofoam LM silicone foam.	Made from 1 component paste, cured 6 hrs at 200 F, 6 hrs at 350 F and 2 hrs at 550 F.
□	ND-1	298		Dow Corning R-7001 silicone foam.	Made from 1 component powder, cured 8 hrs at 325 F and 48 - 72 hrs at 480 F.
△	ND-1	298		Dow Corning R-7002 silicone foam.	Same as above.
◇	ND-1	298		Dow Corning R-7091 silicone foam.	Made from 4 component liquids, cured 10 hrs at room temperature, 1/2 hr at 250 F, 2 hrs at room temperature.
▽	ND-1	298		Dow Corning R-7091 silicone foam + 10 Fe_2O_3.	Same as above.
◁	ND-1	298		Dow Corning R-7091 silicone foam + 10 Fe_2O_3 + 5 film glass (a flake glass made by Owens Corning Fiber Glass Co.).	Same as above.

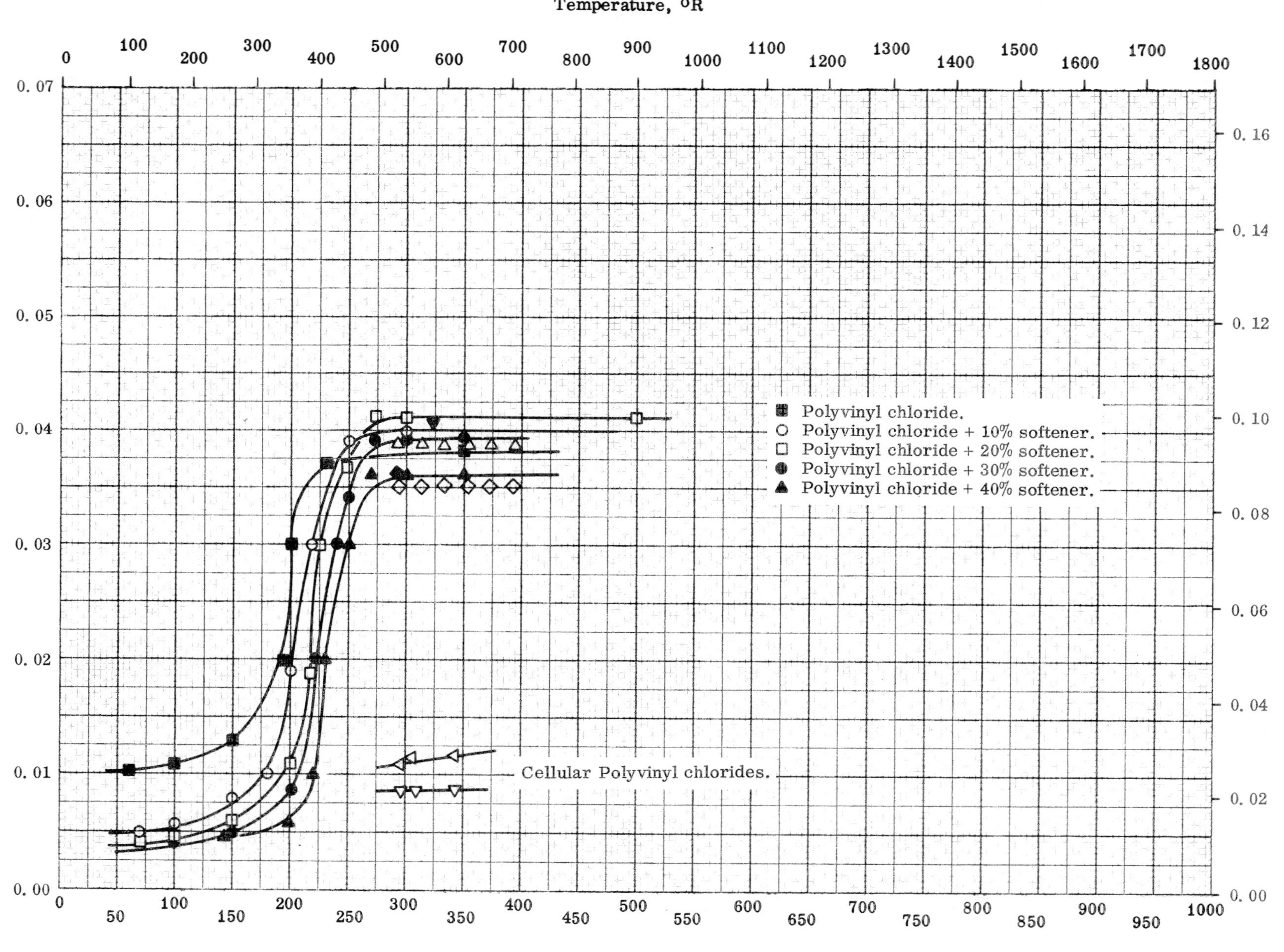

THERMAL CONDUCTIVITY -- POLYVINYL CHLORIDE

REFERENCE INFORMATION

Symbol	Ref.	Temp. Range °K	Rept. Error %	Sample Specifications	Remarks
△	53-4	293-393		Polyvinyl chloride mix; low plasticizer cont. (di-octyl-phthalate).	
◇	53-4	293-393		Polyvinyl chloride mix; high plasticizer cont. (di-octyl-phthalate).	
▽	53-5	296-343		Cellular polyvinyl chloride No. 1 by General Tire and Rubber Co.	
◁	53-5	295-342		Cellular polyvinyl chloride No. 2 by General Tire and Rubber Co.	
■	57-9	60-350	± 6	Polyvinyl chloride.	
○	57-9	70-300	± 6	Polyvinyl chloride + 10% softener (Palatinol AH).	
□	57-9	70-500	± 6	Polyvinyl chloride + 20% softener.	
●	57-9	70-350	± 6	Polyvinyl chloride + 30% softener.	
▲	57-9	70-350	± 6	Polyvinyl chloride + 40% softener.	
◆	40-1	298		Igelit-PCU (Ger. design.): polyvinyl chloride resin of the paste type.	
▼	60-12	323		Polyvinyl chloride rod.	First cooled to 0 C and then brought in boiling water; thermal conductivity calculated from the measurement of temperature and time change.

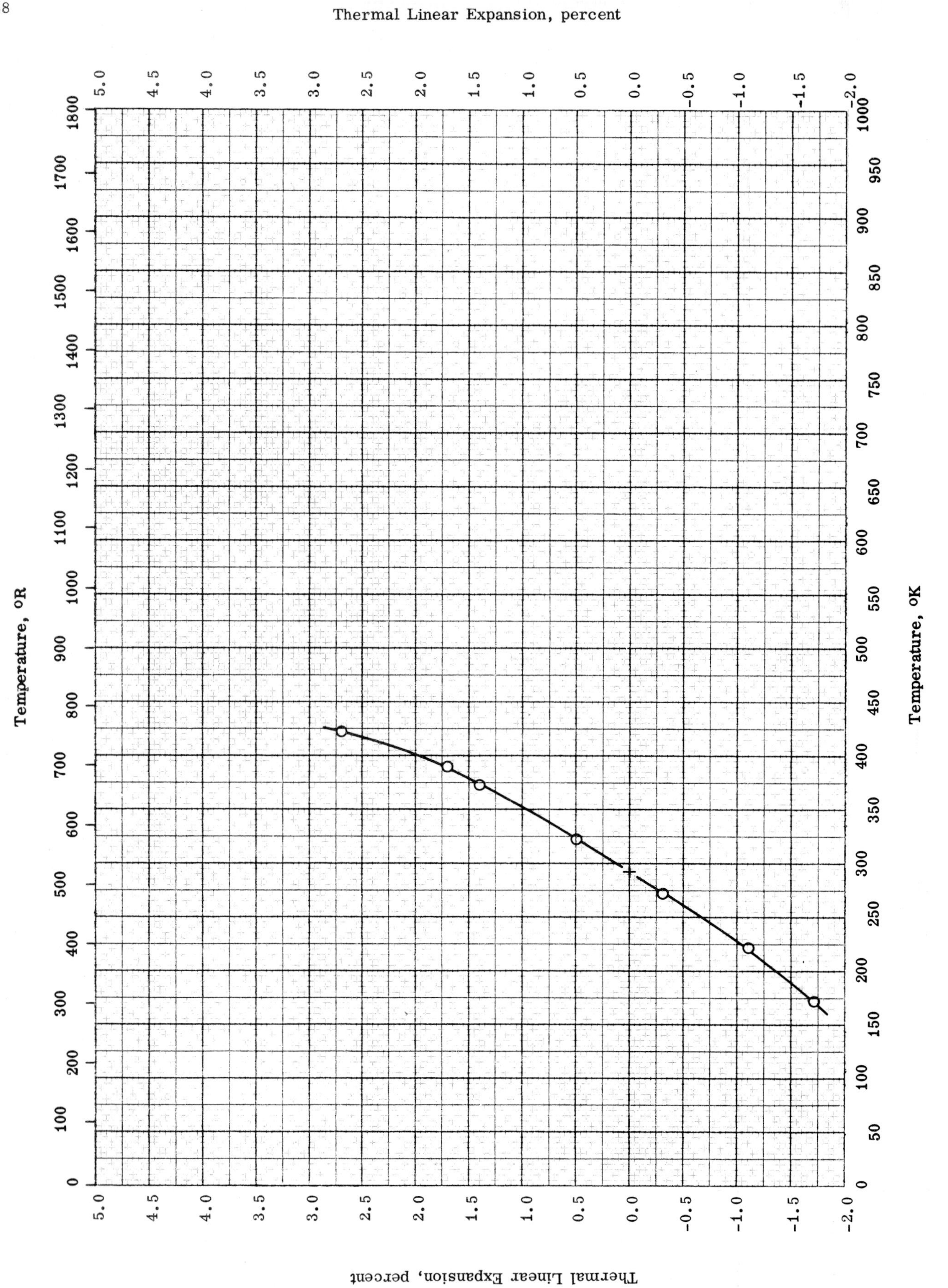

Thermal Linear Expansion, percent
Temperature, °R
Temperature, °K
Thermal Linear Expansion, percent

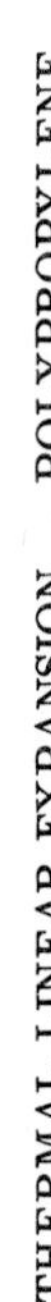

THERMAL LINEAR EXPANSION -- POLYPROPYLENE

REFERENCE INFORMATION

Symbol	Ref.	Temp. Range °K	Rept. Error %	Sample Specifications	Remarks
O	58-5	174-473		Moplen; aliphatic olefin polymer, isotactic polypropylene.	Melts at 792 ± 5 R.

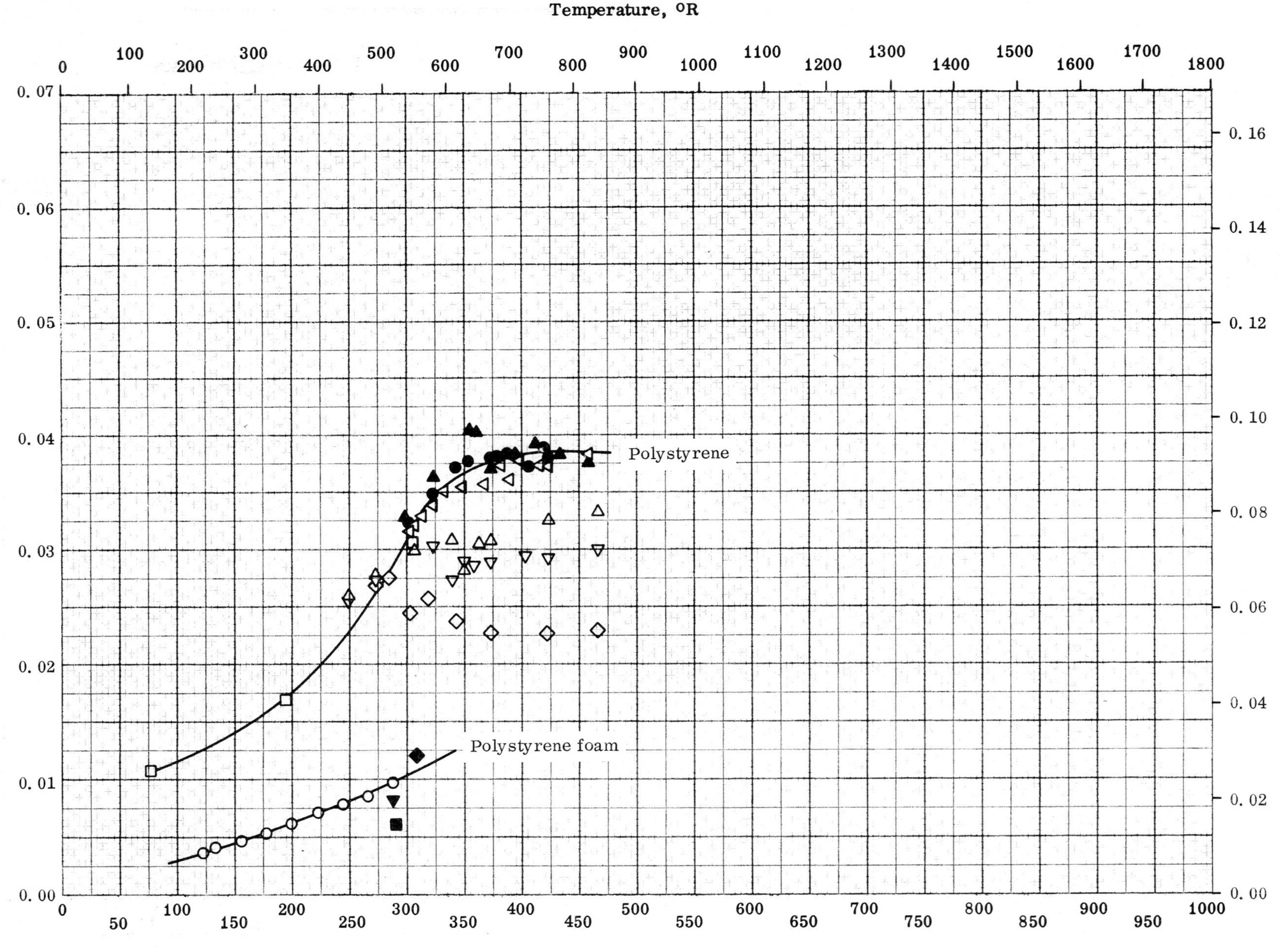

THERMAL CONDUCTIVITY -- POLYSTYRENE

REFERENCE INFORMATION

Symbol	Ref.	Temp. Range °K	Rept. Error %	Sample Specifications	Remarks
○	62-12	122-289		Foam.	Extruded.
□	60-14	70-305		Density 64.4 lb ft^{-3}.	
△	53-7	249-466		Molecular weight 3650.	
▽	53-7	249-466		Molecular weight 2300.	
◇	53-7	249-466		Molecular weight 860.	
◁	53-6	302-458		Pure monostyrene with 5 mole % of pure p-Divinyl benzen.	Polymerized at 200 C without a catalyst.
●	53-6	301-458		Pure monostyrene with 9 mole % of pure p-Divinyl benzen.	Polymerized at 200 C without a catalyst.
▲	53-6	298-460		Pure monostyrene with 15 mole % of pure p-Divinyl benzen.	Polymerized at 200 C without a catalyst.
■	56-4	290		Density 2.75 lb ft^{-3}.	Expanded.
▼	56-4	287		Density 4.0 lb ft^{-3}.	Expanded.
◆	45-2	308		Q-103 Styrofoam of Dow Chem. Co.; density 1.0 lb ft^{-3}.	Oven dried 16 hrs at 140-150 F.

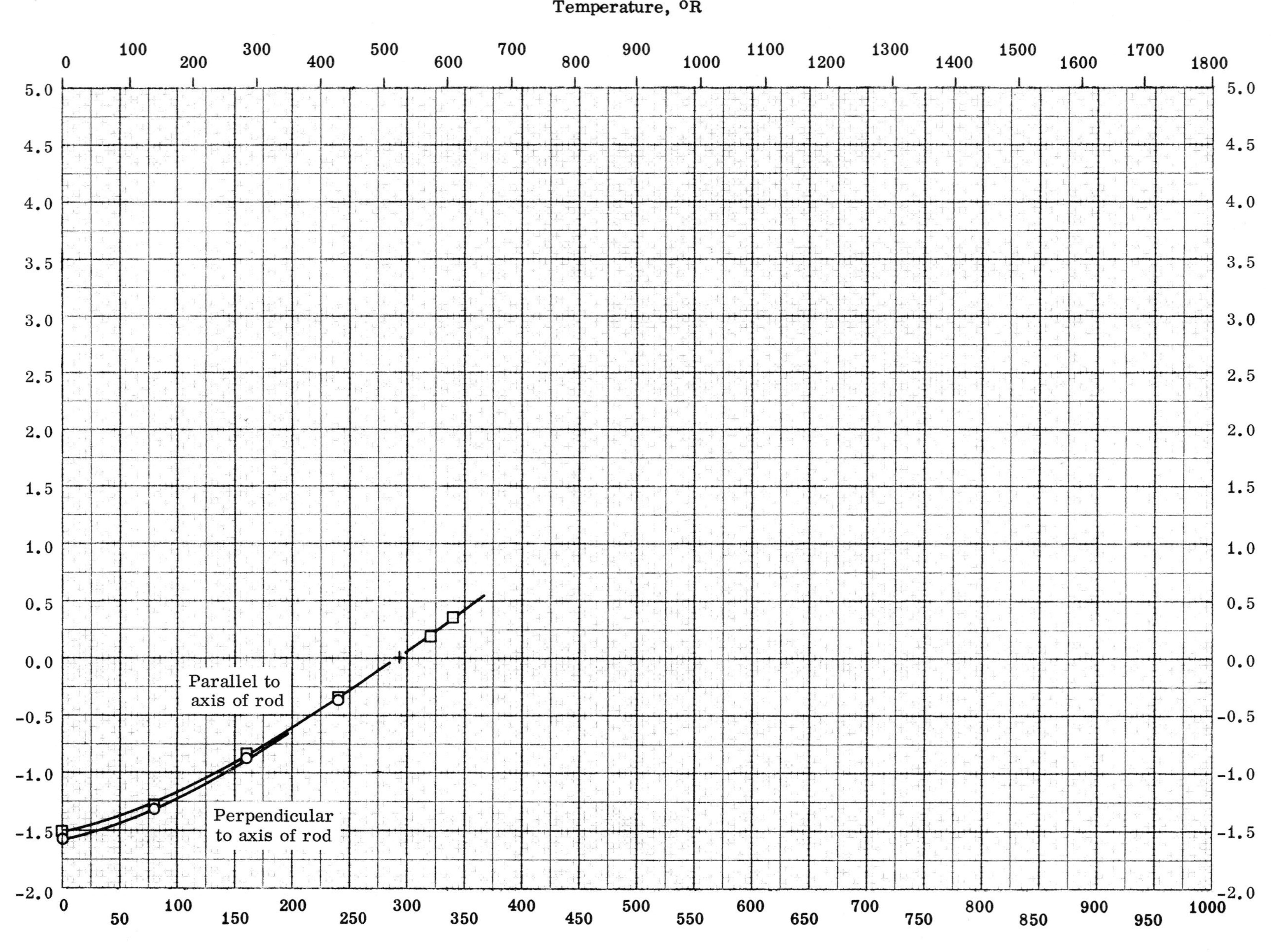

THERMAL LINEAR EXPANSION -- POLYSTYRENE

REFERENCE INFORMATION

Symbol	Ref.	Temp. Range °K	Rept. Error %	Sample Specifications	Remarks
○	52-13	0-340		Polystyrene rod (probably American Phenolic Corp. Grace 912A).	Measured perpendicular to axis of rod; auth.est.accuracy ± 1% at 0 R; values given are average for 2 or more cycles.
□	52-13	0-340		Same as above.	Measured parallel to axis of rod; auth.est.accuracy ± 1% at 0 R; values given are average for 2 or more cycles.

COMPOSITE SYSTEMS

(Materials in combination, with clearly defined boundaries existing between components of the system, or a homogeneous material having a distinct configurations.)

PROPERTIES OF REINFORCED TEFLON

MOST PROBABLE VALUES

Property	C.G.S. Units	Brit. Eng. Units
Density	1.90	118

REPORTED VALUES

Density	g cm^{-3}	lb ft^{-3}
O Duroid 5600	1.90	118

PROPERTIES OF REINFORCED TEFLON

REFERENCE INFORMATION

Symbol	Ref.	Temp. Range °K	Rept. Error %	Sample Specifications	Remarks
○	58-6	298		Duroid 5600; commercial grade, inorganic fiber reinforced Teflon, made by Rogers Corp.	Annealed 4 hrs at 590 F.

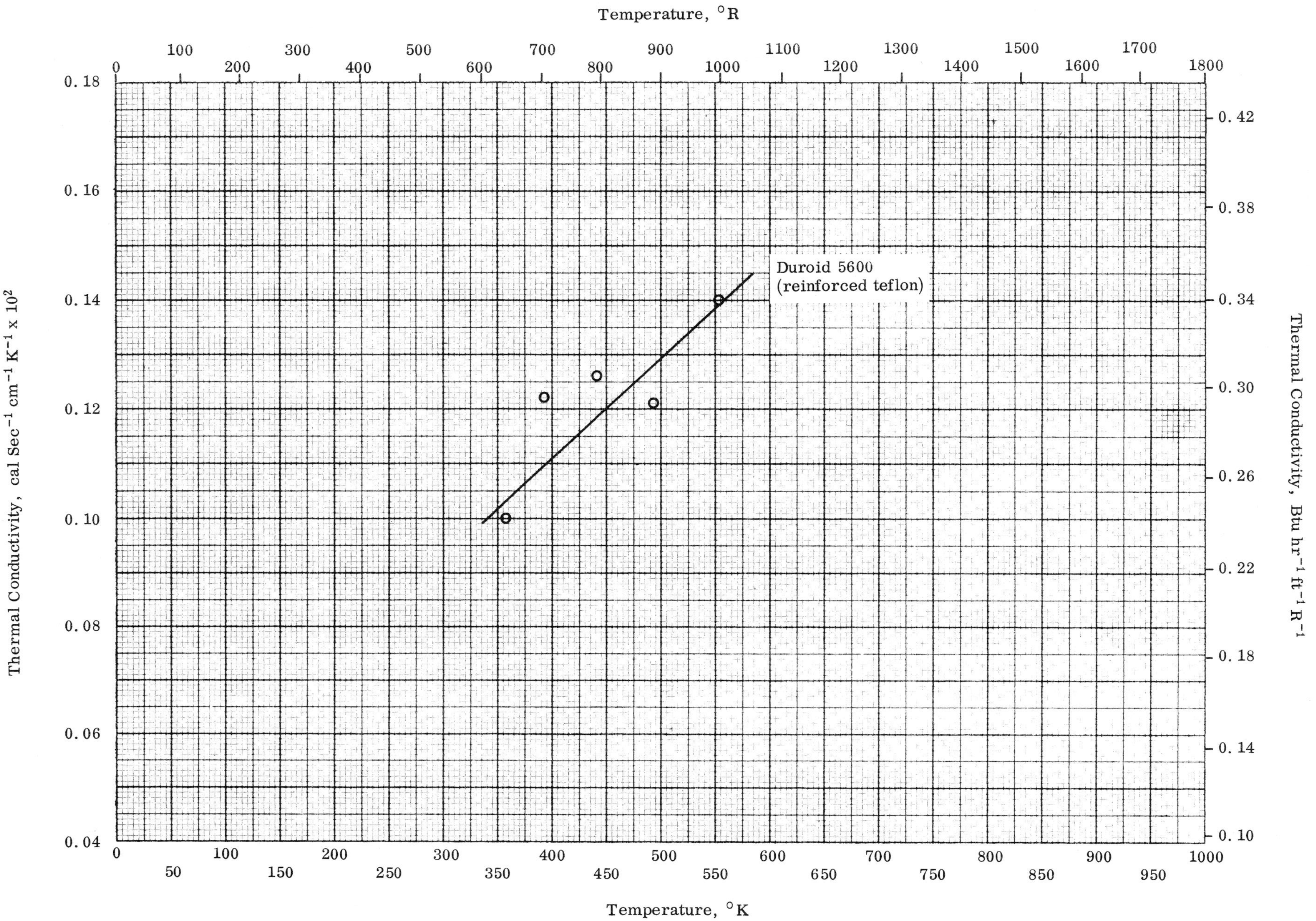

0.42 0.38 0.34 0.30 0.26 0.22 0.18 0.14 0.10

Temperature, °R

1800 1700 1600 1500 1400 1300 1200 1100 1000 900 800 700 600 500 400 300 200 100 0

Duroid 5600 (reinforced teflon)

Temperature, °K

1000 950 900 850 800 750 700 650 600 550 500 450 400 350 300 250 200 150 100 50 0

0.18 0.16 0.14 0.12 0.10 0.08 0.06 0.04

Thermal Conductivity, cal Sec^{-1} cm^{-1} K^{-1} x 10^2

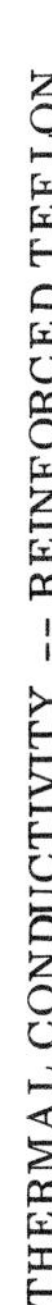

THERMAL CONDUCTIVITY -- REINFORCED TEFLON

REFERENCE INFORMATION

Symbol	Ref.	Temp. Range °K	Rept. Error %	Sample Specifications	Remarks
○	58-6	359-554	<5	Duroid 5600 (inorganic fiber reinforced teflon) by Rogers Corp.; density 1.99 g cm^{-3}.	Annealed 4 hrs at 590 F and cooled in furnace.

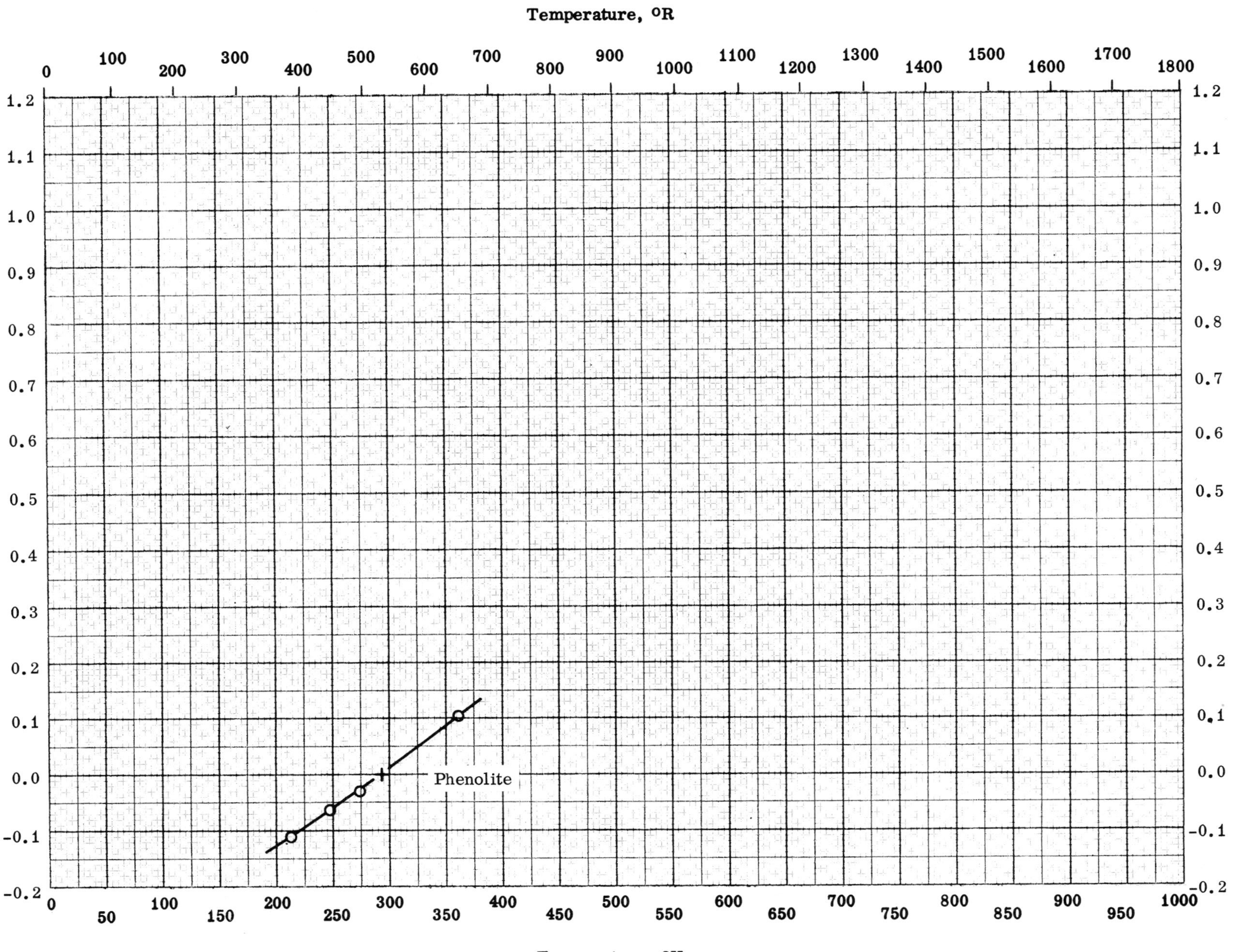

THERMAL LINEAR EXPANSION -- REINFORCED MELAMINE FORMALDEHYDE

THERMAL LINEAR EXPANSION -- REINFORCED MELAMINE FORMALDEHYDE

REFERENCE INFORMATION

Symbol	Ref.	Temp. Range °K	Rept. Error %	Sample Specifications	Remarks
o	54-16	213-361		Phenolite from Nat'l Vulcanized Fibre Co.; glass fabric reinforced; arc resistant grade.	Held at 77 F and 50% humidity for 24-48 hrs before test.

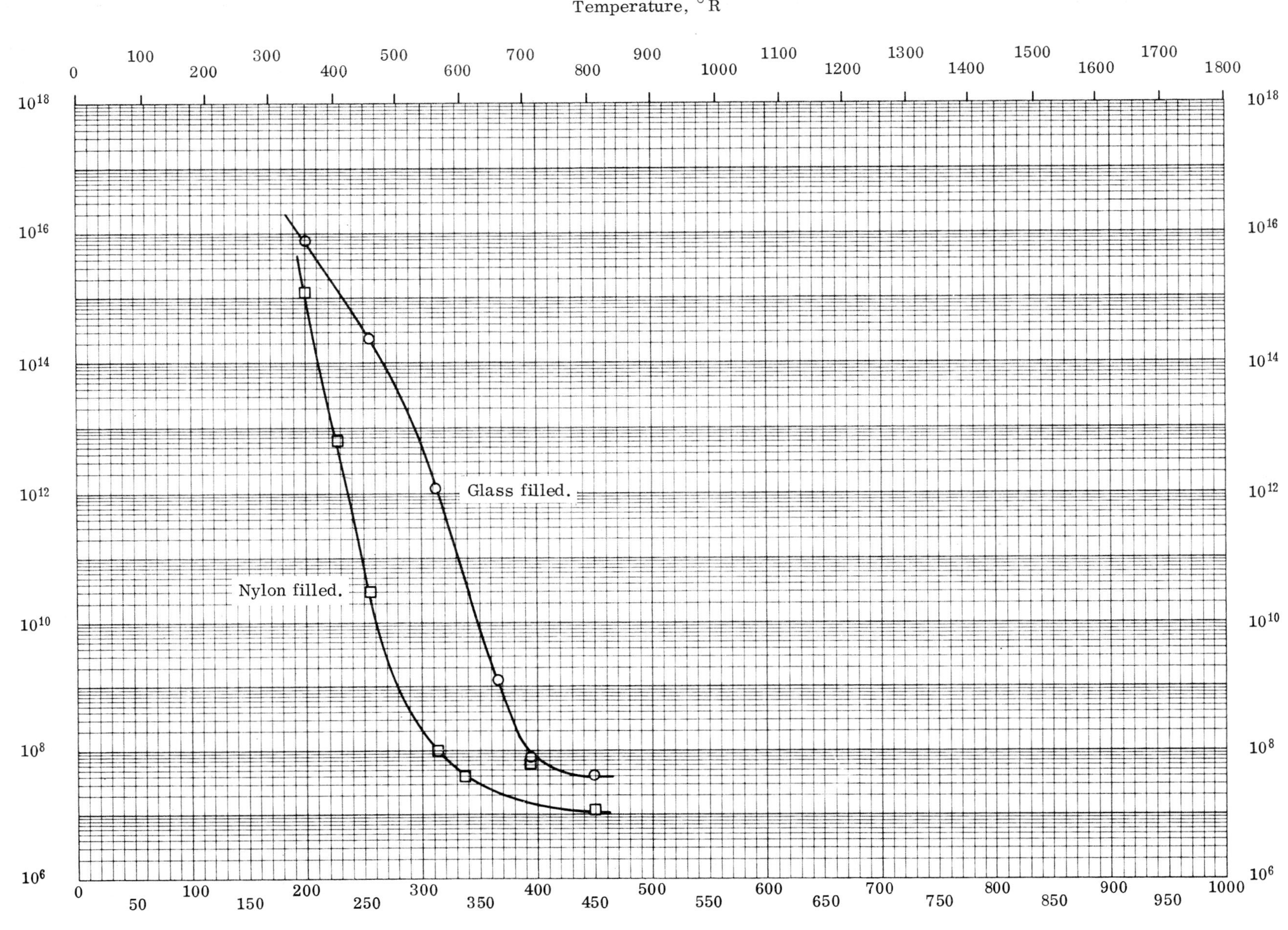

ELECTRICAL RESISTIVITY -- REINFORCED PHENOLIC

ELECTRICAL RESISTIVITY -- REINFORCED PHENOLIC

REFERENCE INFORMATION

Symbol	Ref.	Temp. Range °K	Rept. Error %	Sample Specifications	Remarks
○	57-18	200-450		LMI 304 Nylon flock filled phenolic; made by Loven Chemical.	Conditioned 48 hrs at 120 F at 90% humidity, then 7 cycles, each of which consists of 12 hrs at 100 F and 100% humidity and 12 hour at 120 F and 95% humidity.
□	57-18	200-450		Fiberite 4030-190: long glass fiber reinforced phenolic; same as above.	Conditioned as above.

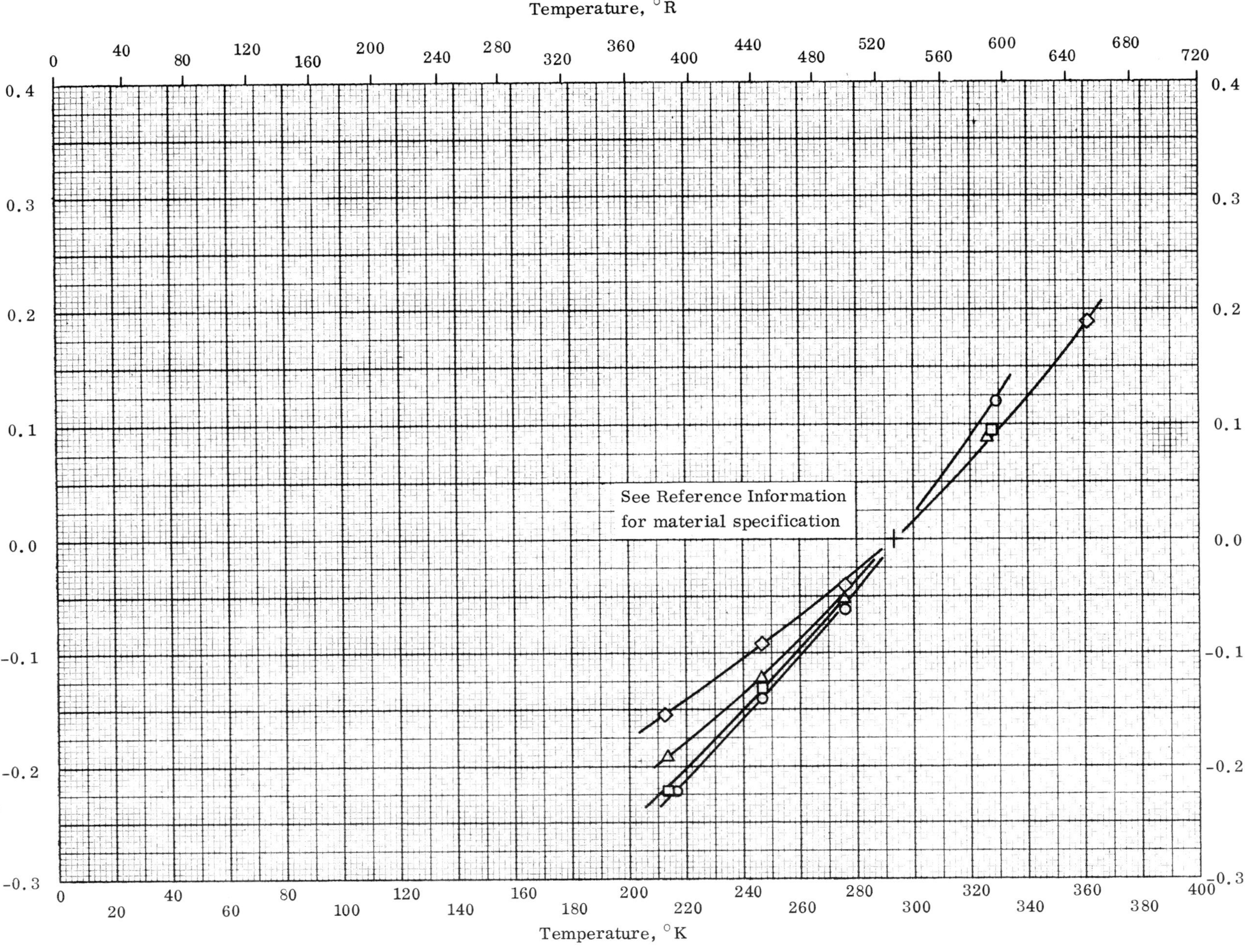

THERMAL LINEAR EXPANSION -- ALPHACELLULOSE PAPER REINFORCED PHENOLIC

THERMAL LINEAR EXPANSION -- ALPHA CELLULOSE PAPER REINFORCED PHENOLIC

REFERENCE INFORMATION

Symbol	Ref.	Temp. Range °K	Rept. Error %	Sample Specifications	Remarks
○	54-16	217-329		Phenolite XXXP from Nat'l. Vulcanized Fibre Co.; min moisture sensitivity; best electrical properties.	Held at 77 F and 502 humidity for 24-48 hrs before test.
□	54-16	215-328		Phenolite NEMA XXXP; 60 resin; high moisture resistance.	Same as above.
△	54-16	215-327		Phenolite NEMA XP; cold punching grade.	Same as above.
◇	54-16	213-361		Phenolite NEMA XXX; 60 resin; max moisture resistance; min impact strength.	Same as above.

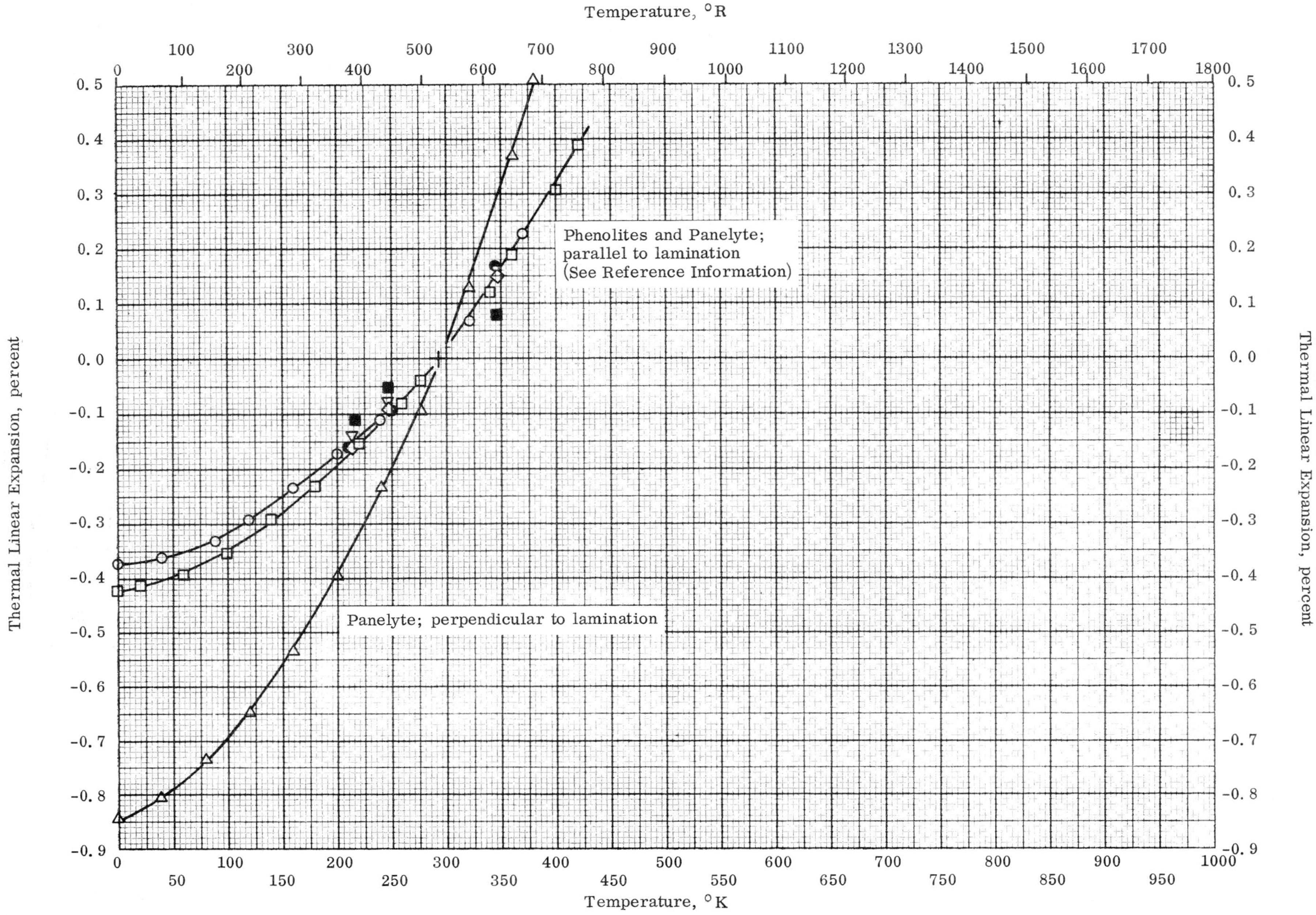
Temperature, °R
Temperature, °K
Thermal Linear Expansion, percent
Phenolites and Panelyte;
parallel to lamination
(See Reference Information)
Panelyte; perpendicular to lamination

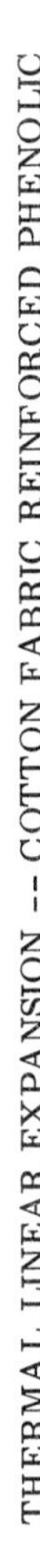

THERMAL LINEAR EXPANSION -- COTTON FABRIC REINFORCED PHENOLIC

THERMAL LINEAR EXPANSION -- COTTON FABRIC REINFORCED PHENOLIC

REFERENCE INFORMATION

Symbol	Ref.	Temp. Range °K	Rept. Error %	Sample Specifications	Remarks
○	52-13	0-420		Panelyte rod grade 942; made by St. Regis Paper Co.	Measured perpendicular to axis of 1 in. diameter rod; parallel to apparent laminations.
□	52-13	0-420		Same as above.	Measured parallel to axis of 1/4 in. rod, laminations appeared as continuous spiral rather than parallel sheets in this case.
△	52-13	0-420		Same as above.	Measured perpendicular to axis of 1 in. diameter rod; perpendicular to laminations.
◇	54-16	213-348		Phenolite NEMA C; 12 oz. fabric; 40 resin; high strength (gear stock).	Held at 77 F and 50% humidity for 24 - 48 hrs before test; made by National Vulcanized Fibre Co.
▽	54-16	213-348		Phenolite NEMA L; 4 oz. fabric; 48 - 54 resin.	Same as above.
●	54-16	213-348		Phenolite NEMA LE; 4 oz. fabric thoroughly dried; electrical grade.	Same as above.
■	54-16	217-346		Phenolite NEMA X; 40 resin.	Same as above.

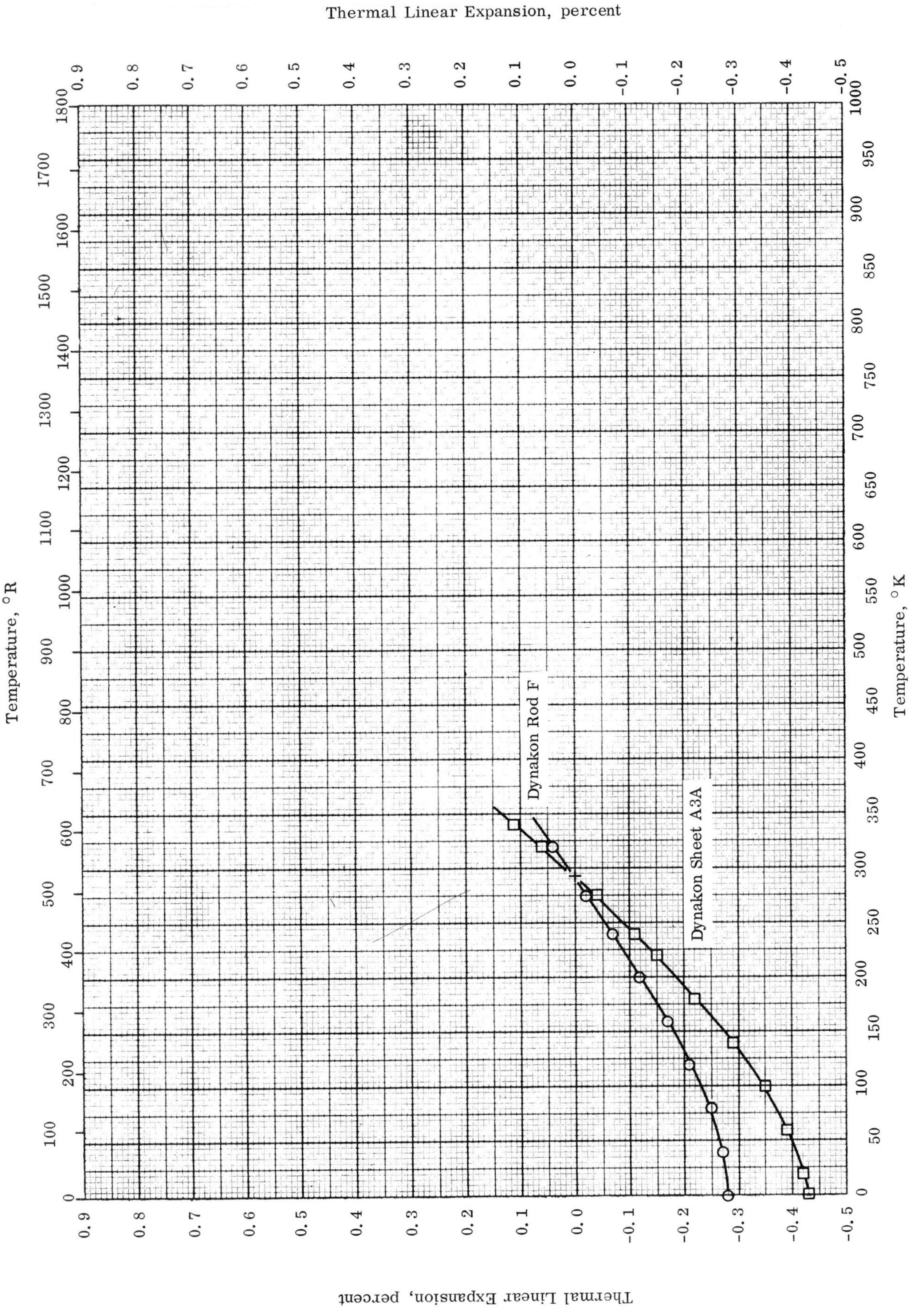

Temperature, °R

Thermal Linear Expansion, percent

Dynakon Rod F

Dynakon Sheet A3A

Thermal Linear Expansion, percent

Temperature, °K

THERMAL LINEAR EXPANSION -- GLASS FIBER REINFORCED POLYESTER

THERMAL LINEAR EXPANSION -- GLASS FIBER REINFORCED POLYESTER

REFERENCE INFORMATION

Symbol	Ref.	Temp. Range °K	Rept. Error %	Sample Specifications	Remarks
○	52-13	0-320		Dynakon Rod F from Dynakon, Inc.	Author estimates accuracy ±3% at 0 R, ±2% at 180 R, ±8% at 576 R.
□	52-13	0-340		Dynakon Sheet A3A.	Author estimates accuracy ±2% at 0 R, ±7% at 576 R.

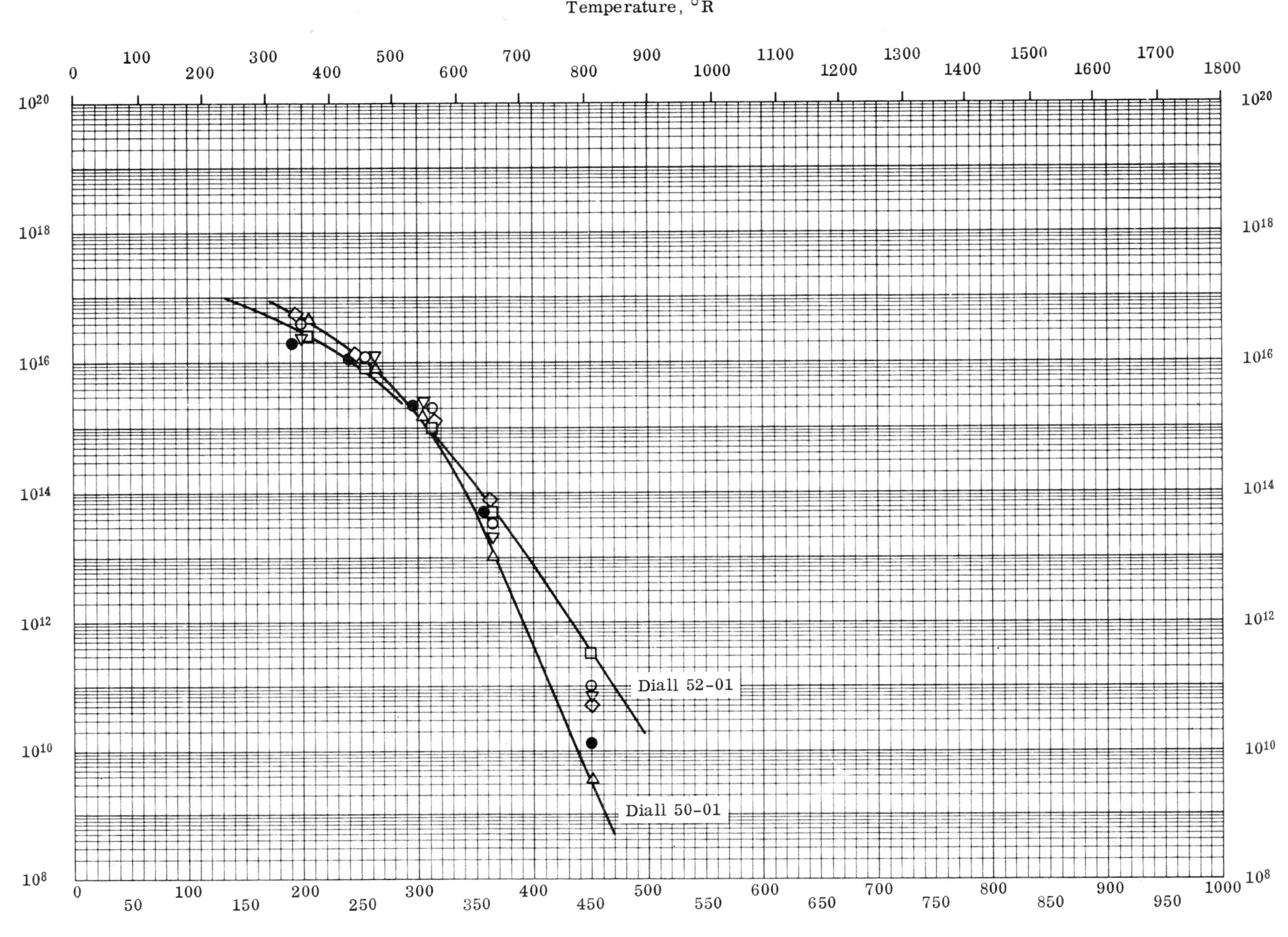

ELECTRICAL RESISTIVITY -- REINFORCED DIALLYLPHTHALATE

ELECTRICAL RESISTIVITY -- REINFORCED DIALLYLPHTHALATE

REFERENCE INFORMATION

Symbol	Ref.	Temp. Range °K	Rept. Error %	Sample Specifications	Remarks
○	57-18	200-450		Diall 52-20-30; long-glass - fiber-filled diallylphthalate; made by Mesa Plastics.	Conditioned 48 hrs at 120 F at 90% humidity; then 7 cycles, ea. of which consists of 12 hrs at 100 F and 100% humidity plus 12 hrs at 120 F and 95% humidity.
□	57-18	200-450		Diall 52-01; short glass-fiber-filled diallylphthalate; same as above.	Same as above.
△	57-18	200-450		Diall 50-01; orlon-fiber-filled diallylphthalate; same as above.	Same as above.
◇	57-18	200-450		Diall 50-52; dacron-fiber-filled diallylphthalate; same as above.	Same as above.
▽	57-18	200-450		Diall 50-51; dacron-fiber-filled diallylphthalate; same as above.	Same as above.
●	57-18	200-450		Dures 16694; orlon fiber-filled diallylphthalate; made by Dures Plastics Div., Hooker Electromechanical Co.	Same as above.

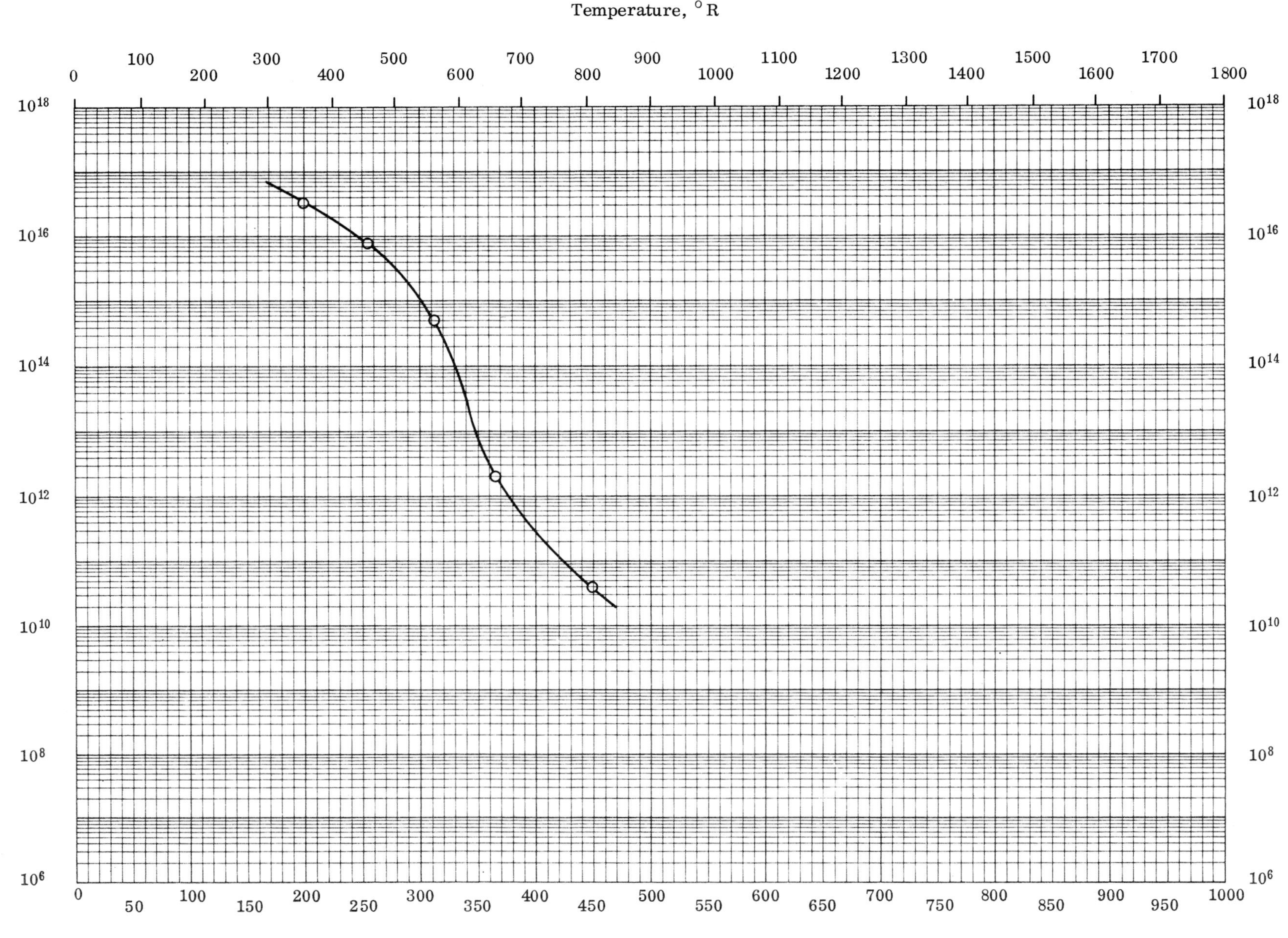

ELECTRICAL RESISTIVITY -- REINFORCED SILICONE

ELECTRICAL RESISTIVITY -- REINFORCED SILICONE

REFERENCE INFORMATION

Symbol	Ref.	Temp. Range °K	Rept. Error %	Sample Specifications	Remarks
○	57-18	200-450		Long glass fiber filled silicone (DC-301 Dow Corning Co.)	Conditioned 48 hrs at 120 F at 90% humidity, then 7 cycles each of which consists of 12 hrs at 100 F and 100% humidity and 12 hrs at 120 F and 95% humidity.

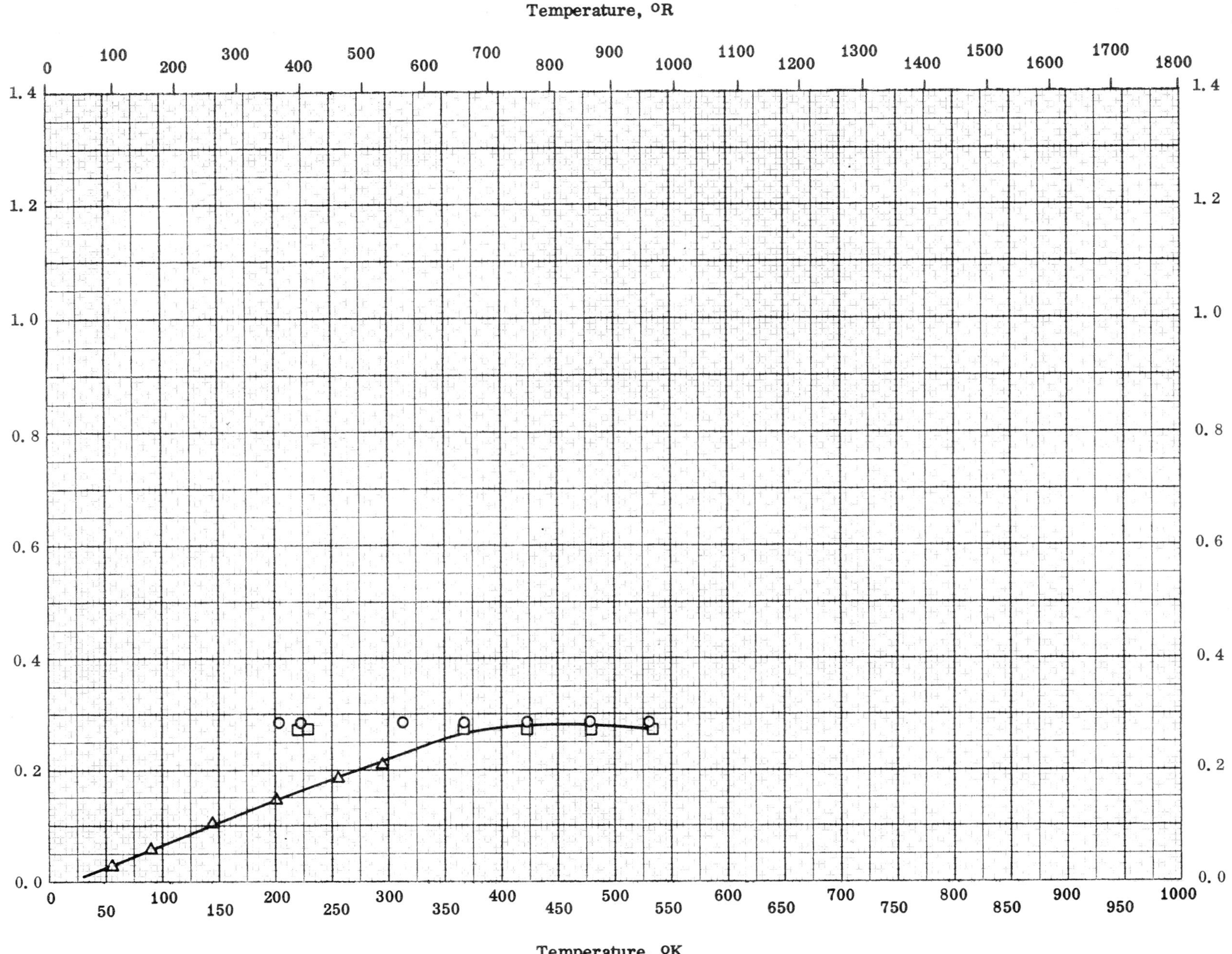

SPECIFIC HEAT -- PLASTIC LAMINATES
(Reinforced Epoxy resin)

SPECIFIC HEAT -- PLASTIC LAMINATES
(Reinforced Epoxy resin)

REFERENCE INFORMATION

Symbol	Ref.	Temp. Range °K	Rept. Error %	Sample Specifications	Remarks
○	61-13	204-530		Isotropic laminate scotch ply; epoxy resin type garan finish with 3M x P-175 catalyst and 60 N roving reinforcing; density 114.9 lb ft^{-3}. [Author's design.: SRI No. 1-2].	Pressed 40 min at 265 - 270 F under 90 psi pressure; cured 16 hrs at 225 F.
□	61-13	220-528		Unidirectional laminate scotch ply; 3M x P-175 epoxy resin system and 60 N roving reinforcing system; density 114.9 lb ft^{-3}. [Author's design.: SRI No. 1-1].	Cure cycle: 90 - 95 psi pressure for 40 min at 275-280 F; post cured 16 hrs at 225 F.
△	65-3	55-294		Cross plied unidirectional glass roving, flat molding simulating a helical wound composite composed of 20 Dow Chemical DER 332 epoxy resin cured with acid anhydride at 80 Owens Corning high modulus YM-31-A glass fiber roving with HTS finish; alternate layers roving cross-plied at 57° horizontal axis.	

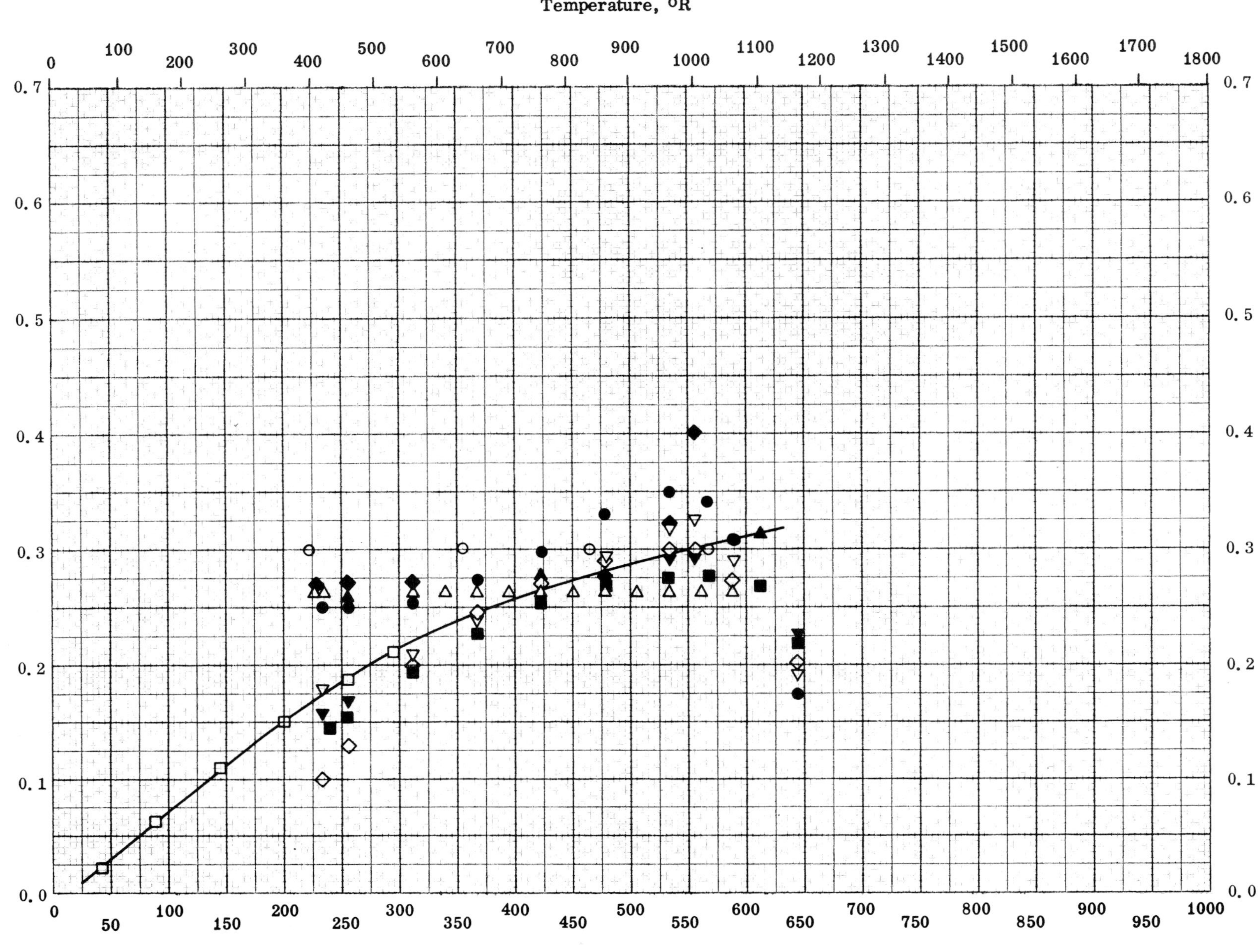

SPECIFIC HEAT -- PLASTIC LAMINATES
(Glass fabric reinforced Epoxide)

SPECIFIC HEAT -- PLASTIC LAMINATES
(Glass fabric reinforced Epoxide)

REFERENCE INFORMATION

Symbol	Ref.	Temp. Range °K	Rept. Error %	Sample Specifications	Remarks
○	57-8	222-567		Fabric No. 181, Volcan A finish; 38 Epon Resin No. 828; CL catalyst; 0.13 in. thick.	Decomposition apparent above 410 F.
□	65-3	43-295		Unidirectional parallel fiber, flat molding composed of 20 Dow Chemical DER-332 epoxy resin cured with acid anhydride and 80 Owens Corning high modulus YM-31-A glass fiber roving containing an HTS finish; void content 5%. [Author's design.: Material D].	
△	61-13	226-587		38 - 40 epoxy resin impregnated; Epon 1031 epoxy resin type and glass type YM-31A weave style 181 reinforcing system; density 137.5 lb ft^{-3}. [Author's design.: SRI No. 12].	Cure cycle: 30 min at 245 psi and 340 F; post cured for 24 hrs at 300 F.
◇	63-19	228-644		60 glass fiber and 40 epoxy; Dow Chemical DER-332 resin system and high modulus YM A glass; layup parallel to surface; unidirectional parallel orientation; density 119 lb ft^{-3}. [Author's design.: Material C-1].	Cure cycle: 2 hrs at 200 psi and 200 F and 2 hrs at 200 psi and 250 F; post cure cycle: 2 hrs at 300 F and 12 hrs at 350 F.
▽	63-19	228-644		70 glass and 30 resin; Dow Chemical DER-332 epoxy resin system with "E" Glass Roving; layup parallel to surface, 40 layers parallel orientation.	Cure cycle: 200 psi for 2 hrs at 200 F and 2 hrs at 250 F; post cure cycle: 2 hrs at 300 F and 24 hrs at 350 F.
●	63-19	228-644		60 glass and 40 resin; Dow Chemical DER-332 epoxy resin system and high modulus YM 31A fiber glass containing beryllia; layup parallel to surface; 40 layers cross plied parallel and 66 degree angle from horizontal axis; density 121 lb ft^{-3}. [Author's design.: C-3]. (Continued onto next page)	Cure cycle: 200 psi for 2 hrs at 200 F and 2 hrs at 250 F; post cure cycle: 2 hrs at 300 F and 12 hrs at 350 F.

SPECIFIC HEAT -- PLASTIC LAMINATES (Continued)
(Glass fabric reinforced Epoxide)

REFERENCE INFORMATION

Symbol	Ref.	Temp. Range °K	Rept. Error %	Sample Specifications	Remarks
■	63-19	228-644		80 glass and 40 resin; Dow Chemical DER-332 epoxy resin system and "E" glass finish HTS reinforcing system; layup parallel to surface; 40 layers cross-plied; density 131 lb ft^{-3}; [Author's design.: C-4].	Cure cycle: 200 psi for 2 hrs at 200 F and 2 hrs at 250 F; post cure cycle: 2 hrs at 300 F and 12 hrs at 250 F.
▼	63-19	228-644		80 glass and 40 resin; Dow Chemical DEN-438 epoxy resin system and "E" glass finish HTS; layup parallel to surface; 40 layers unidirectional orientation; density 128.5 lb ft^{-3}; [Author's design.: C-5].	Cure cycle: 200 psi for 2 hrs at 200 F and 2 hrs at 250 F; post cure cycle: 2 hrs at 300 F and 24 hrs at 250 F.
◆	63-18	228-555		70 glass and 30 resin; NRC 1174/3 epoxy resin system and Owens Corning glass composition E, flakes 2 microns thick, 200 to 2000 microns diameter; random layup; random reinforcement orientation; density 121 lb ft^{-3}. [Author's design.: d-1].	Cure cycle: 800 psi for 120 min at 350 F.
▲	63-18	228-612		77 glass flake and 23 epoxy resin; NRC 1174/3 epoxy and Owen Corning composition E glass flakes 2 microns thick and 200 to 2000 microns diameter; random layup, random reinforcement orientation; density 123 lb ft^{-3}. [Author's design.: d-2].	Cure cycle: 1500 psi for 120 min at 350 F.

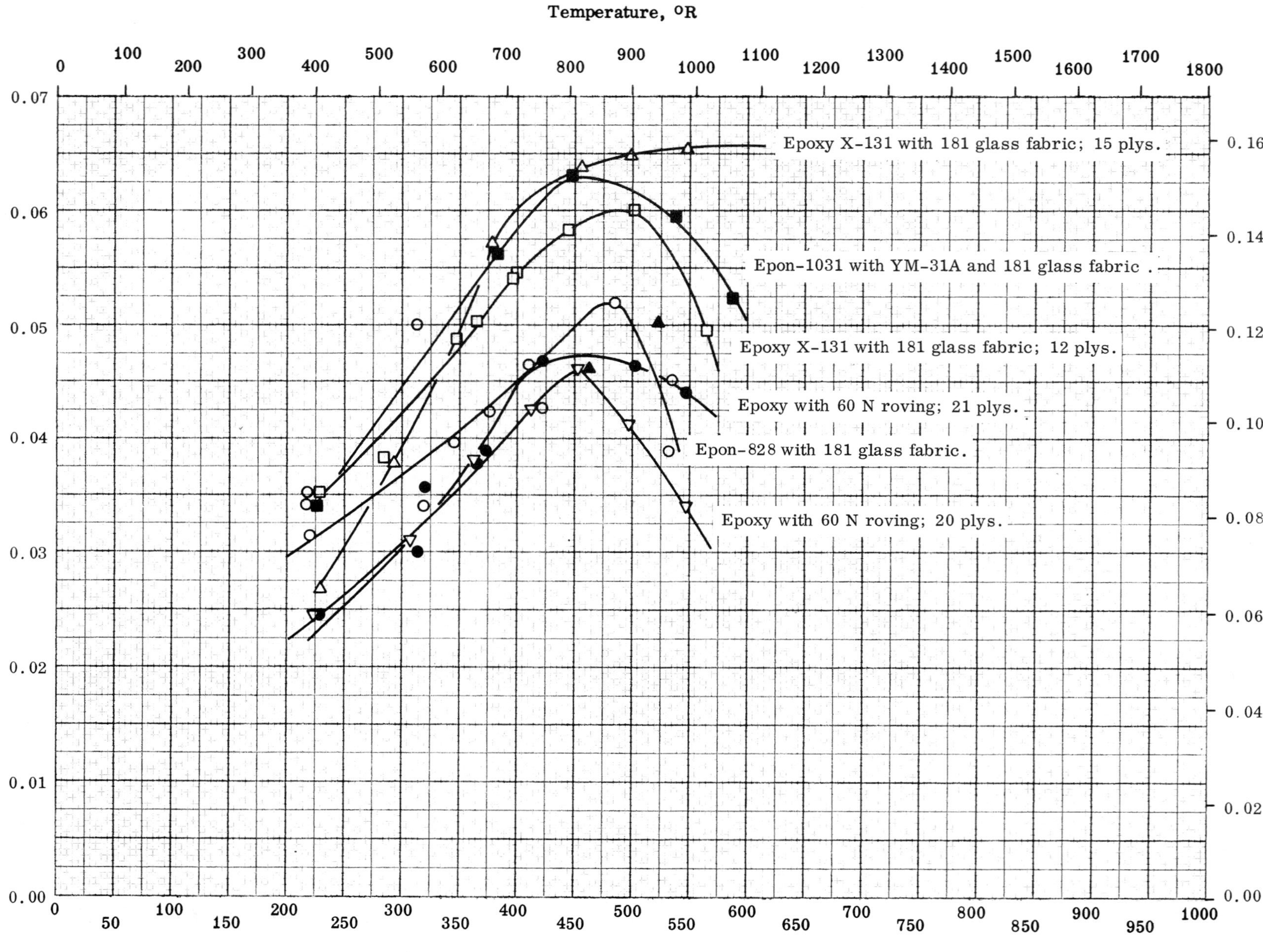

THERMAL CONDUCTIVITY -- PLASTIC LAMINATE
(Reinforced epoxy resin)

THERMAL CONDUCTIVITY -- PLASTIC LAMINATE
(Reinforced epoxy resin)

REFERENCE INFORMATION

Symbol	Ref.	Temp. Range °K	Rept. Error %	Sample Specifications	Remarks
○	57- 8	218-535		Epon - 828 resin reinforced by glass fabric 181 Volan A finish; CL face catalyst.	
□	58 - 8	229-565		Shell Epoxy X-131 resin with 181 glass fabric Volan A finish; 12 plys; 13 wt. pyromellitic dianhydride and 19 wt. maleic anhydride catalyst; density 117 lb ft^{-3} and nominal thickness 1/8 in.	Cured at 200 F for 2 hrs at 25 psi and 300 F for 4 hrs.
△	58 - 8	230-547		Shell Epoxy X-131 resin with 181 glass fabric Volan A finish; 15 plys; 13 wt. maleic anhydride; density 124 lb ft^{-3} and nominal thickness 5/8 in.	Cured at 200 F for 2 hrs under vacuum and post-cured at 300 F for 4 hrs.
▽	61-12	225-548		Unidirectional laminate Scotchply from Minnesota Mining and Manufacturing Co. ; 30 ± 1.5 3MXP-175 catalyst expoxy resin reinforced by 60 N roving; 20 plys; density 114.9 lb ft^{-3}.	Pressed at 275-280 F for 40 min. with a pressure of 90-95 psi; post-cured at 225 F for 16 hrs.
●	61-12	230-548		Isotropic Laminate Scotchply from Minnesota Mining and Manufacturing Co.; same composition as the above sample; 21 plys; density 114.9 lb ft^{-3}.	Pressed at 265-270 F for 40 min with a pressure of 90 psi; post-cured at 225 F for 16 hrs.
■	61-13	227-588		20 Epon - 1031 Epoxy resin reinforced by type YM-31A and weave style 181 glass fabric; density 137.5 lb ft^{-3}.	Pressed at 245 psi; press-cured at 340 F for 30 min.; post-cured at 300 F for 24 hrs.
▲	61-13	463-522		Same as above.	Second run of the above sample.

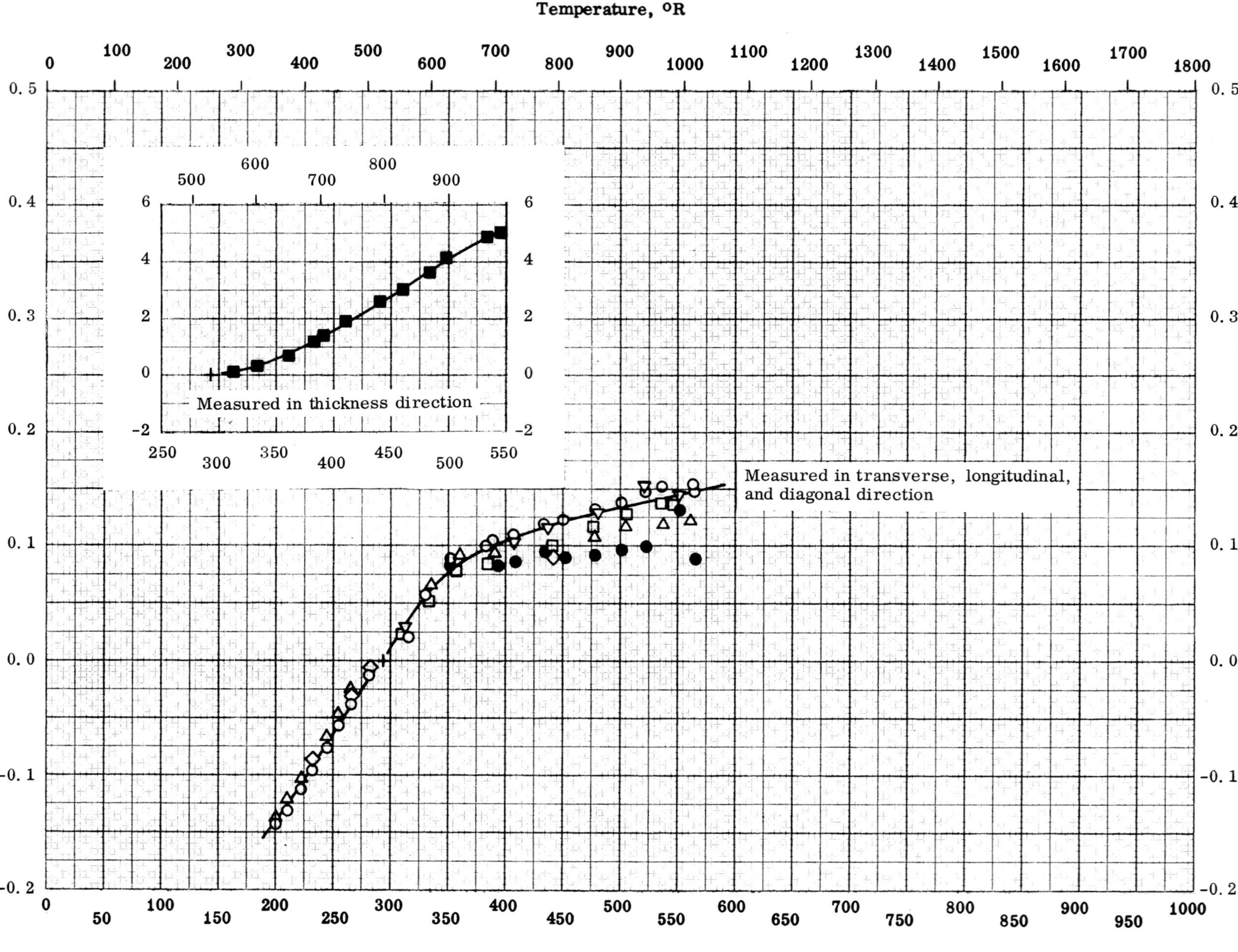

THERMAL LINEAR EXPANSION -- PLASTIC LAMINATES
(Glass fabric reinforced Epoxy Shell X-131 resin)

THERMAL LINEAR EXPANSION -- PLASTIC LAMINATES
(Glass fabric reinforced Epoxy Shell X-131 resin)

REFERENCE INFORMATION

Symbol	Ref.	Temp. Range °K	Rept. Error %	Sample Specifications	Remarks
○	58-8	200-565		Epoxy Shell X-131 resin and 181 glass fabric; fabricated by Brunswick-Balke-Collender Co.; nominal thickness 1/8 in.; sample 1 in. by 7 in. long; density 117 lb ft^{-3}.	Cured at 200 F and 25 psi for 2 hrs and 300 F for 4 hrs; measured in the transverse direction with respect to the fabric lay-up.
□	58-8	299-544		Same as above.	Same as above; second run.
△	58-8	200-563		Same as above.	Same as above except measured in longitudinal direction.
▽	58-8	298-551		Same as above.	Same as above; second run.
◇	58-8	200-563		Same as above.	Same as above excpet measured in diagonal direction.
●	58-8	299-565		Same as above.	Same as above; second run.
■	58-8	293-546		Same as above except sample in disc form with 1 in. in diameter and 7-3/16 in. thick.	Same as above except measured in the thickness direction with respect to fabric lay-up.

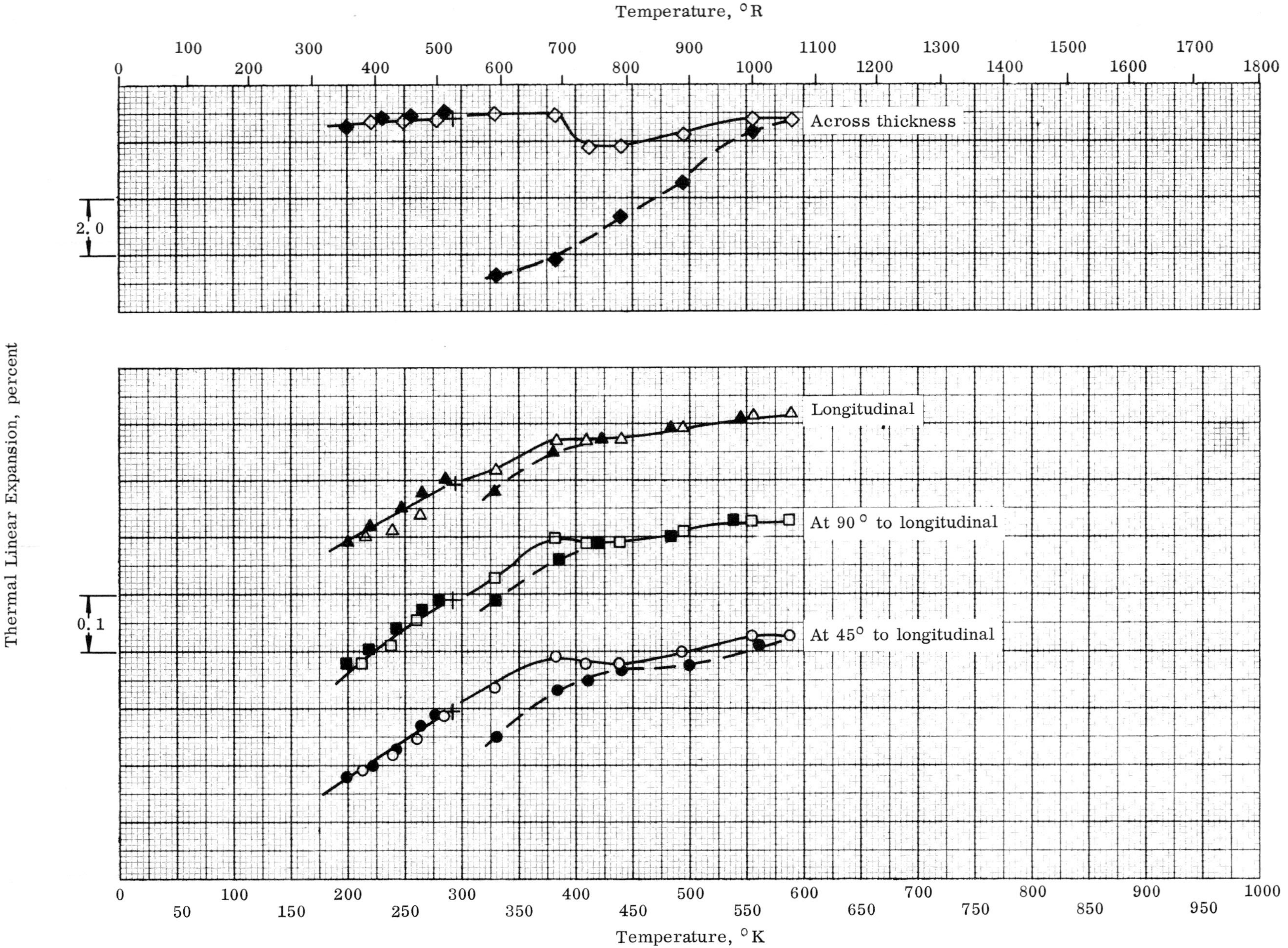

THERMAL LINEAR EXPANSION -- PLASTIC LAMINATES
(Glass fabric reinforced Epon 828 Epoxide resin)

THERMAL LINEAR EXPANSION -- PLASTIC LAMINATES
(Glass fabric reinforced Epon 828 Epoxide resin)

REFERENCE INFORMATION

Symbol	Ref.	Temp. Range °K	Rept. Error %	Sample Specifications	Remarks
○	57-8	200-589		Fabric: No. 181 with Volan A finish; resin: Epon No. 828; catalyst: C. L.; resin content 37. 6; thickness: 0. 126 in.; made by Brunswick-Balke-Collender Co.	Measured at 45 degree to longitudinal direction in plane of laminations; heating.
●	57-8	200-589		Same as above.	Cooling.
□	57-8	200-589		Same as above.	Measured at 90 degree to longitudinal direction in plane of laminations; heating.
■	57-8	200-589		Same as above.	Cooling.
△	57-8	200-589		Same as above.	Measured in longitudinal direction; heating.
▲	57-8	200-589		Same as above.	Cooling.
◇	57-8	200-589		Same as above.	Measured across thickness of sample; heating.
◆	57-8	200-589		Same as above.	Cooling.

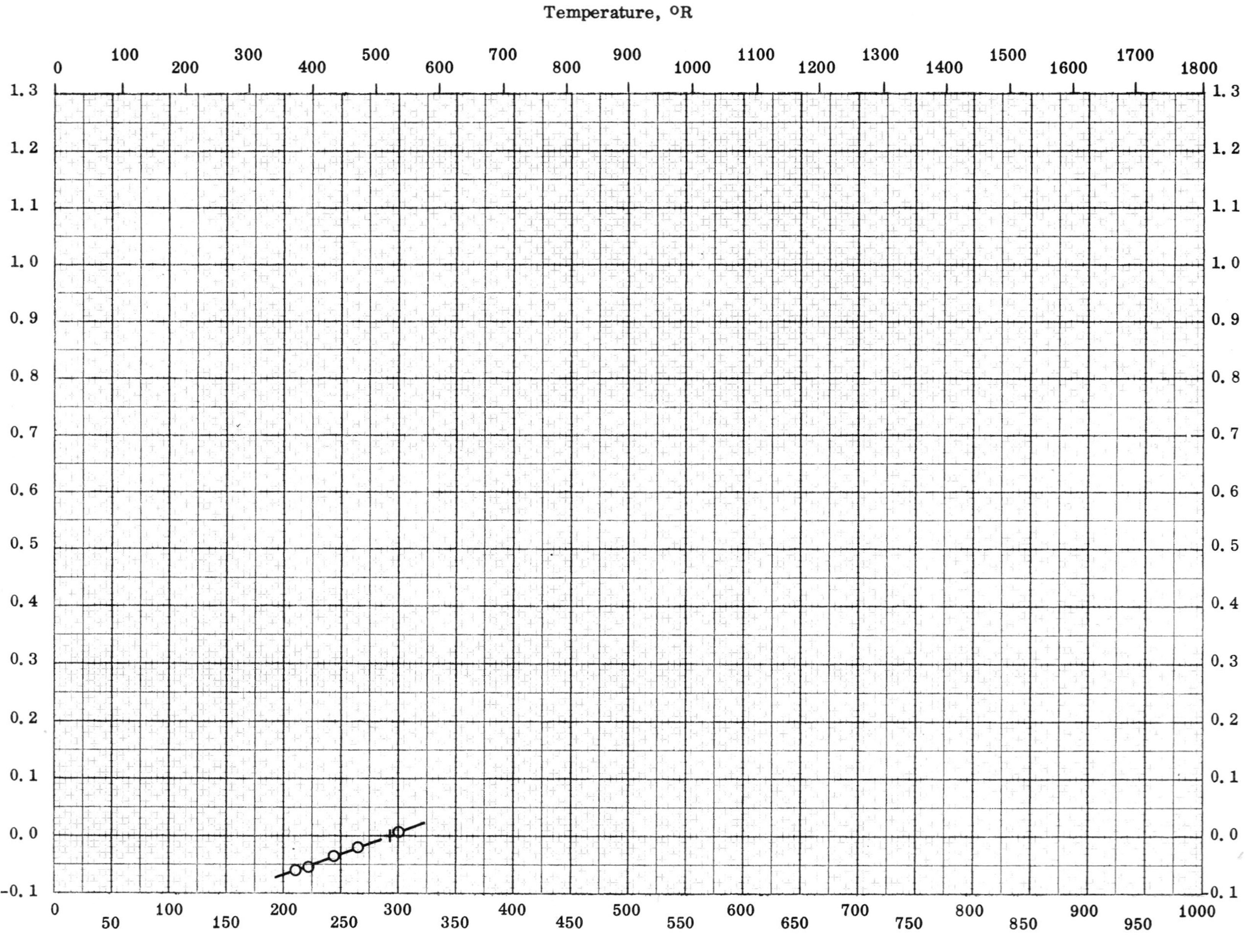

THERMAL LINEAR EXPANSION -- PLASTIC LAMINATES
(Glass fabric reinforced copolymer of phenolic and epoxide resins)

THERMAL LINEAR EXPANSION -- PLASTIC LAMINATES
(Glass fabric reinforced copolymer of phenolic and epoxide resins)

REFERENCE INFORMATION

Symbol	Ref.	Temp. Range °K	Rept. Error %	Sample Specifications	Remarks
○	54-6	211-300		By Shell: Fabric No. 181; 33 Epon/67 Plyophen Resins No. 1001/5023 (24.5 resin content); density 108.6 lb ft^{-3}.	All data taken in plane perpendicular to thickness; effect of angle formed with longitude <± 2%.

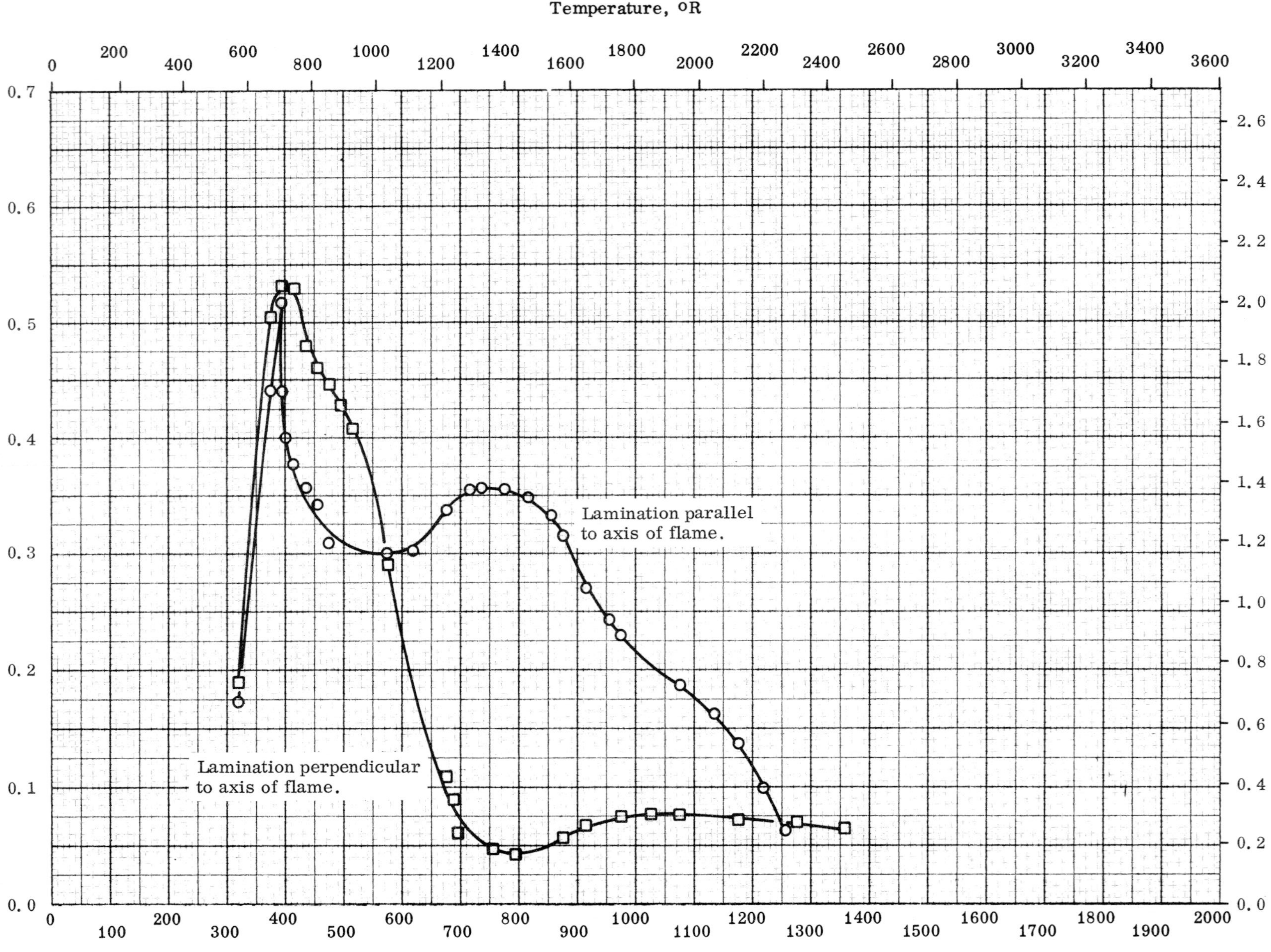

THERMAL DIFFUSIVITY -- PLASTIC LAMINATE
(Glass fabric reinforced melamine - formaldehyde resin)

THERMAL DIFFUSIVITY -- PLASTIC LAMINATE
(Glass fabric reinforced melamine - formaldehyde resin)

REFERENCE INFORMATION

Symbol	Ref.	Temp. Range °K	Rept. Error %	Sample Specifications	Remarks
○	61-3	318-1253		Glass fabric reinforced melamine - formaldehyde resin.	Lamination parallel to axis of flame; data resulted as an average of four specimens.
□	61-3	318-1353		Same as above.	Lamination perpendicular to axis of flame; date resulted as an average of four specimens.

DENSITY -- PLASTIC LAMINATES
(Reinforced phenolic resin)

Symbol	Density	
	g cm^{-3}	lb ft^{-3}
○	1.63	102
□	1.51	94.2
△	1.91	119
◇	1.62	101
▽	1.739	108.6
◁	1.310	81.78
▷	1.340 ± 0.004	83.65 ± 0.25
●	1.3475 ± 0.0035	84.12 ± 0.22

DENSITY -- PLASTIC LAMINATES
(Reinforced phenolic resin)

REFERENCE INFORMATION

Symbol	Ref.	Temp. Range °K	Rept. Error %	Sample Specifications	Remarks
○	55-5	298		Reinforced plastic, laminated by Cincinnati Testing Lab.; fabric: Modiglian; 1 oz. PFM; resin: phenolic; resin code No. CTL-91-LD; 42.2 resin content; thickness: 0.121 in.	
□	55-5	298		Reinforced plastic, laminated by Cincinnati Testing Lab.; fabric: Owens Corning; 3/4 oz. phenolic resin mat; resin: phenolic; resin code No. CTL-91-LD; 44.2 resin content; thickness 0.130 in.	
△	55-5	298		Reinforced plastic, laminated by Cincinnati Testing Lab.; fabric No. 181; finish Volan A; resin: phenolic; resin code No. CTL-91-LD; 28.3 resin content; 14 ply; thickness: 0.120 in.	
◇	55-3	298		Phenolic resin laminate by Narmco, Inc.; fabric: 181 with Volan A finish; phenolic; 12 ply; resin No. Conolon 506 - 33 resin.	
▽	54-6 also 55-5	298		Reinforced plastic, laminated by Shell; fabric No. 181; resin: 33 Epon + 67 Plyophen; resin code No. 1001/5023; 24.5 resin content; thickness: 0.114 in.	
◁	52-9	298		Lamicoid C-6030, cloth-base phenolic laminate.	
▷	52-9	298		Insurok C-T-601, cloth-base phenolic laminate.	
●	52-9	298		Insurok XXX-T-640, paper-base phenolic laminate.	

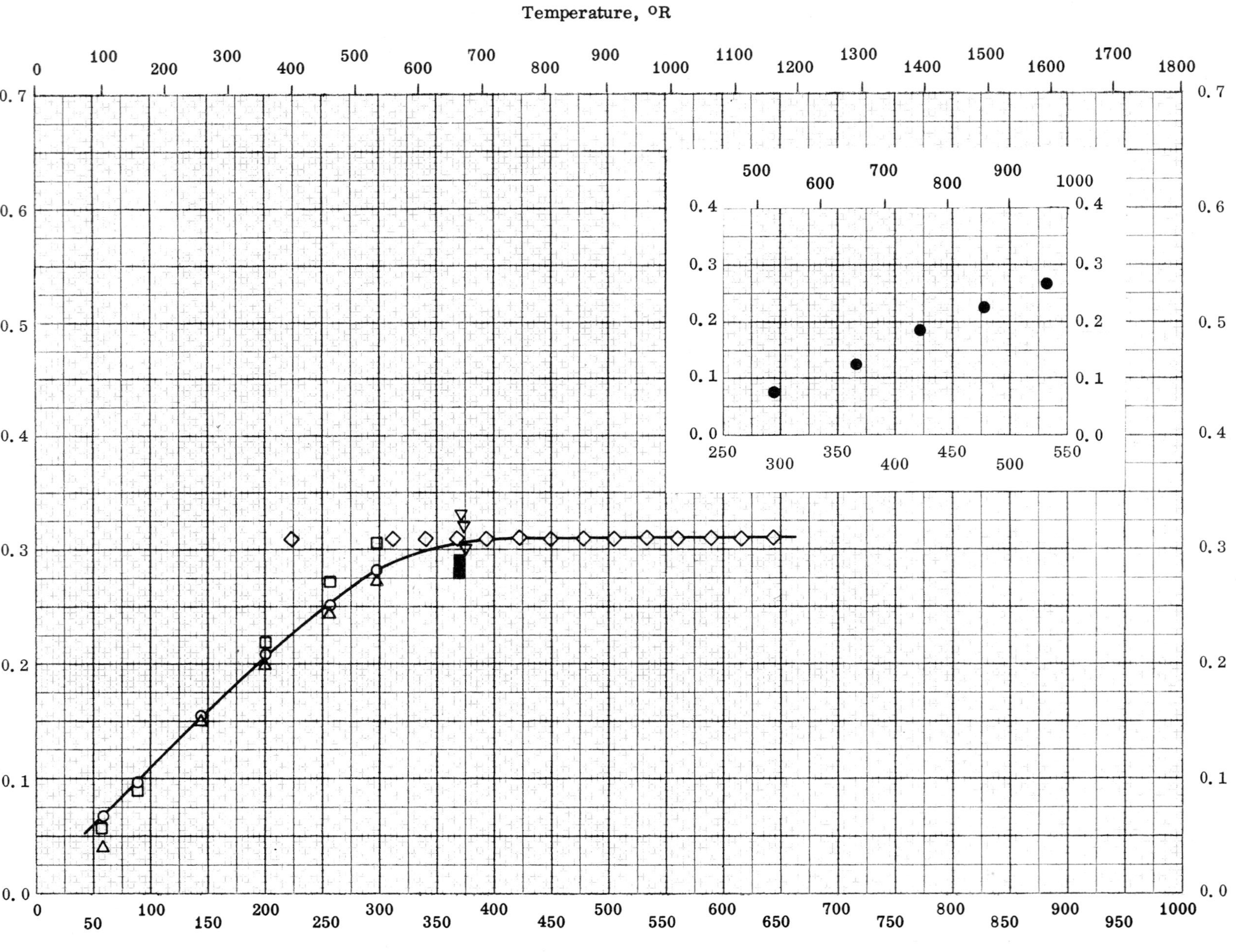

SPECIFIC HEAT -- PLASTIC LAMINATES
(Asbestos reinforced phenolic resin)

SPECIFIC HEAT -- PLASTIC LAMINATES
(Asbestos reinforced phenolic resin)

REFERENCE INFORMATION

Symbol	Ref.	Temp. Range °K	Rept. Error %	Sample Specifications	Remarks
○	65-3	58-297	±5	Chopped asbestos random oriented, Fiberite MX-5700; density 1.4212 g cm^{-3}; void 37.2%. [Author's design.: Material P]	
□	65-3	58-295	±5	Mat construction, Fiberite MX-5700; density 1.4014 g cm^{-3}; void 37.4%. [Author's design.: Material O]	Molded at 200 psi pressure.
△	65-3	57-297	±5	Mat construction, Fiberite MX-5700; density 1.3903 g cm^{-3}; void 62.8%. [Author's design.: Material N]	Molded at 25 psi pressure.
◇	61-13	324-644	±5	Mat construction, asbestos R/M style 42RPD reinforcing; R/M high heat resistant phenolic resin type with 25 - 30% resin; density 117 lb ft^{-3}.	No post cure.
▽	63-3	297-373		Asbestos cloth with one sheet of aluminum foil in center impregnated with 91LD phenolic resin; density 107.8 lb ft^{-3}.	
●	61-5	294-533		Phenolic asbestos laminate.	
■	63-3	297-373		Asbestos cloth with one sheet of silver foil in center impregnated with 91LD phenolic resin; density 113.0 lb ft^{-3}.	

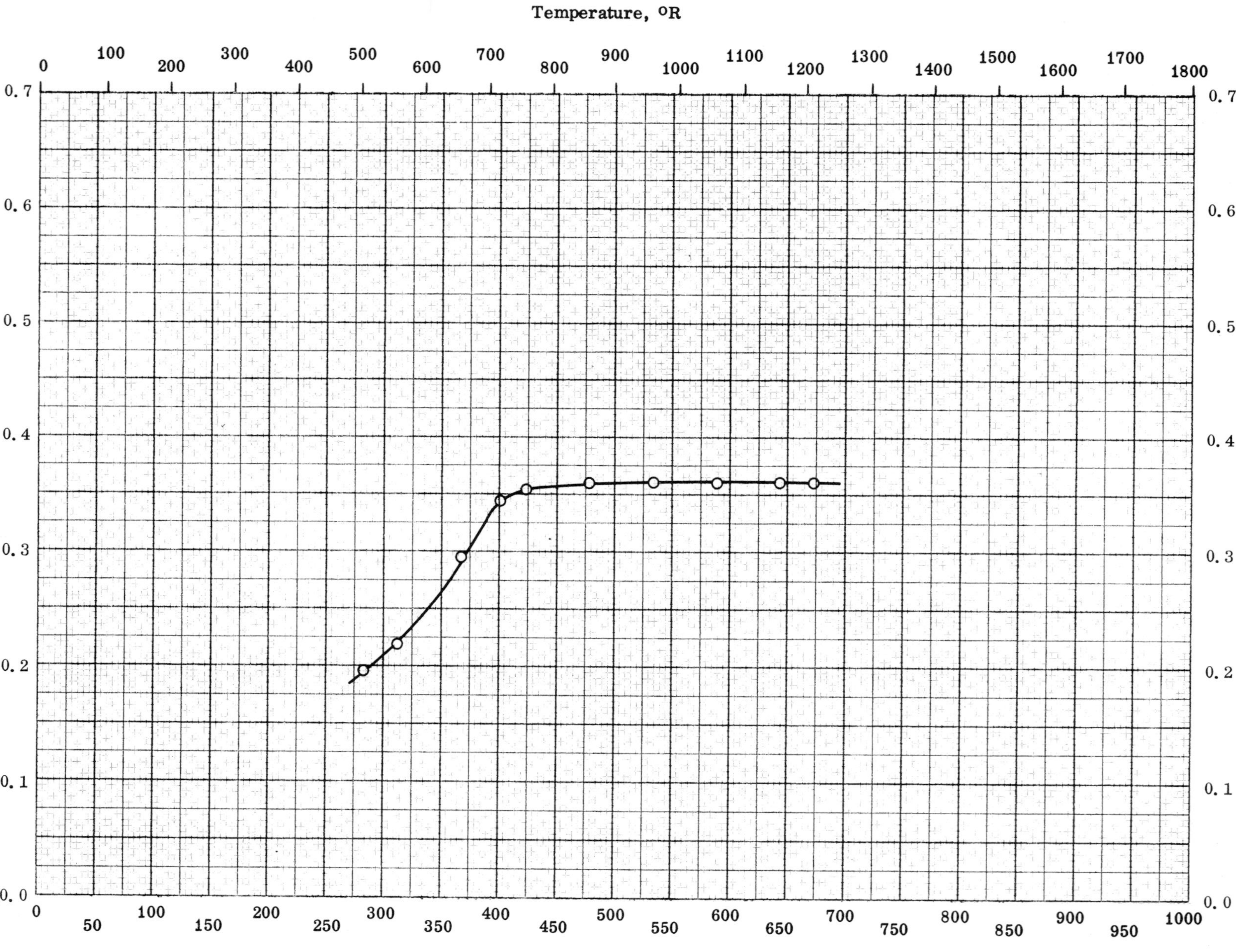

SPECIFIC HEAT -- PLASTIC LAMINATES
(Carbon reinforced phenolic resin)

SPECIFIC HEAT -- PLASTIC LAMINATES
(Carbon reinforced phenolic resin)

REFERENCE INFORMATION

Symbol	Ref.	Temp. Range °K	Rept. Error %	Sample Specifications	Remarks
○	64-10	283-672		MX 4926; 31.5 - 36.5 phenolic resin filled with 96 pure carbon.	Cure cycle: 1/4 in. x 1/2 in. thick panels; 180 F; no pressure for 1 hr; cool down, 1000 psi for 10-20 min, and 300 - 320 F at 400 psi for 3 hrs.

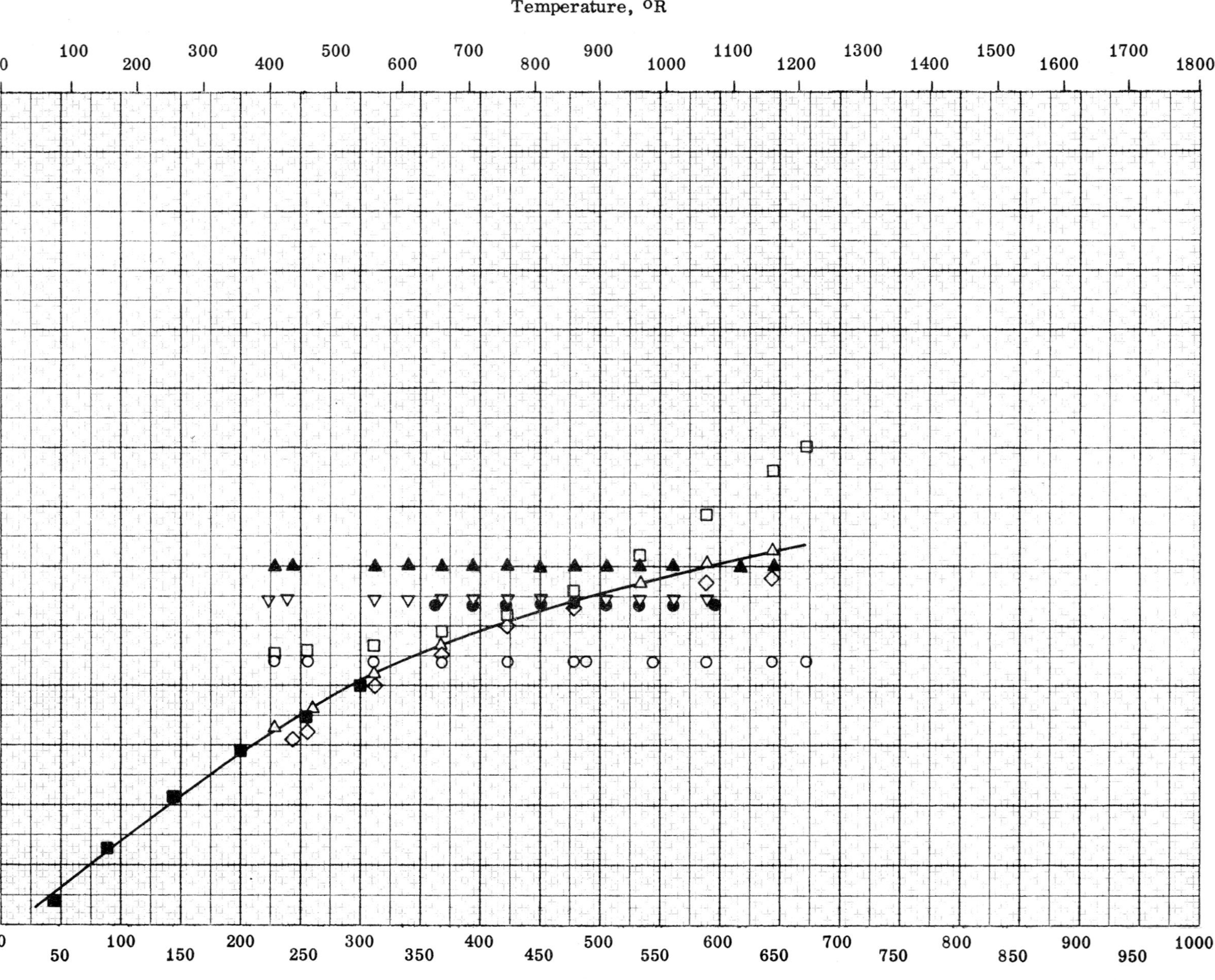

SPECIFIC HEAT -- PLASTIC LAMINATES
(Glass fabric reinforced phenolic resin)

SPECIFIC HEAT -- PLASTIC LAMINATES
(Glass fabric reinforced phenolic resin)

REFERENCE INFORMATION

Symbol	Ref.	Temp. Range °K	Rept. Error %	Sample Specifications	Remarks
○	63-18	228-673		20 phenolic - 80 silica fabric (b-4); after complete fabrication 80.4 silica and 19.6 resin; CTL-91LO resin system and General Electric A1100 finish, 26 plies, 181 style; density 88 lb ft^{-3}.	Cure cycle: 1 hr at 2000 psi and 325 F; post cure cycle: 24 hrs at 350 F; resin system molded at 275 F.
□	63-18	228-673		30 phenolic - 70 silica fabric (b-1); Monsanto SC1008 resin system and reinforcement system General Electric 581-A1100 finish, style 181; density 112 lb ft^{-3}.	Cure cycle: 30 min at 2000 psi and 325 F; post cure cycle: 24 hrs at 350 F; resin system molded at 275 F.
△	63-19	228-644		30 phenolic - 70 silica (b-5); Monsanto SC1008 resin system and reinforcement system General Electric silica A1100 finish; 45° angle to surface layup; style 181; density 106 lb ft^{-3}.	Cure cycle: 1 hr at 2000 psi and 325 F; post cure cycle: 24 hrs at 350 F; 200 F layup temperature.
◇	63-19	244-644		20 phenolic - 80 silica (b-2); Monsanto SC1008 resin system and General Electric fabric design 581-A1100 quartz; 26 plies, style 181; parallel layup; density 88 lb ft^{-3}.	Cure cycle: 1 hr at 2000 psi and 325 F; post cure cycle: 24 hrs at 350 F.
▽	61-13	223-589		38 - 40 phenolic; CTL-91LD resin type and YM-31A glass fabric reinforcement system; density 131 lb ft^{-3}.	Cure cycle: 20 min at 345 psi and 300 F; post cure cycle: 24 hrs at 300 F, 24 hrs at 350 F, and 24 hrs at 400 F.
●	61-13	363-595		Molded panel chopped glass phenolic resin; 35 phenolic - 65 silica; CTL-91LD phenolic resin and chopped glass reinforcing A1100 finish; [Author's design.: SRI No. 2].	Heated for 1 hr to 275 F; post cured for 24 hrs at 275 F.
				(Continued onto next page)	

SPECIFIC HEAT -- PLASTIC LAMINATES (continued)
(Glass fabric reinforced phenolic resin)

REFERENCE INFORMATION

Symbol	Ref.	Temp. Range °K	Rept. Error %	Sample Specifications	Remarks
■	65-3	45-301		Glass fabric reinforced laminate composed of 25 CTL-91LD phenolic resin and 75 "E" glass (spec. MIL-C-9084, type VIII (181) with spec. MIL-F-9118 finish); density 2.0377 g cm^{-3}; 12% void. [Author's design.: Material A]	
▲	63-18	228-612		Glass flakes molding ; 77 glass flake and 23 epoxy; NRC 1174/3 epoxy and Owen Corning Glass flakes composition E; random layup. [Author's design: d-2]	Cure cycle; 1500 psi at 350 F for 120 min.

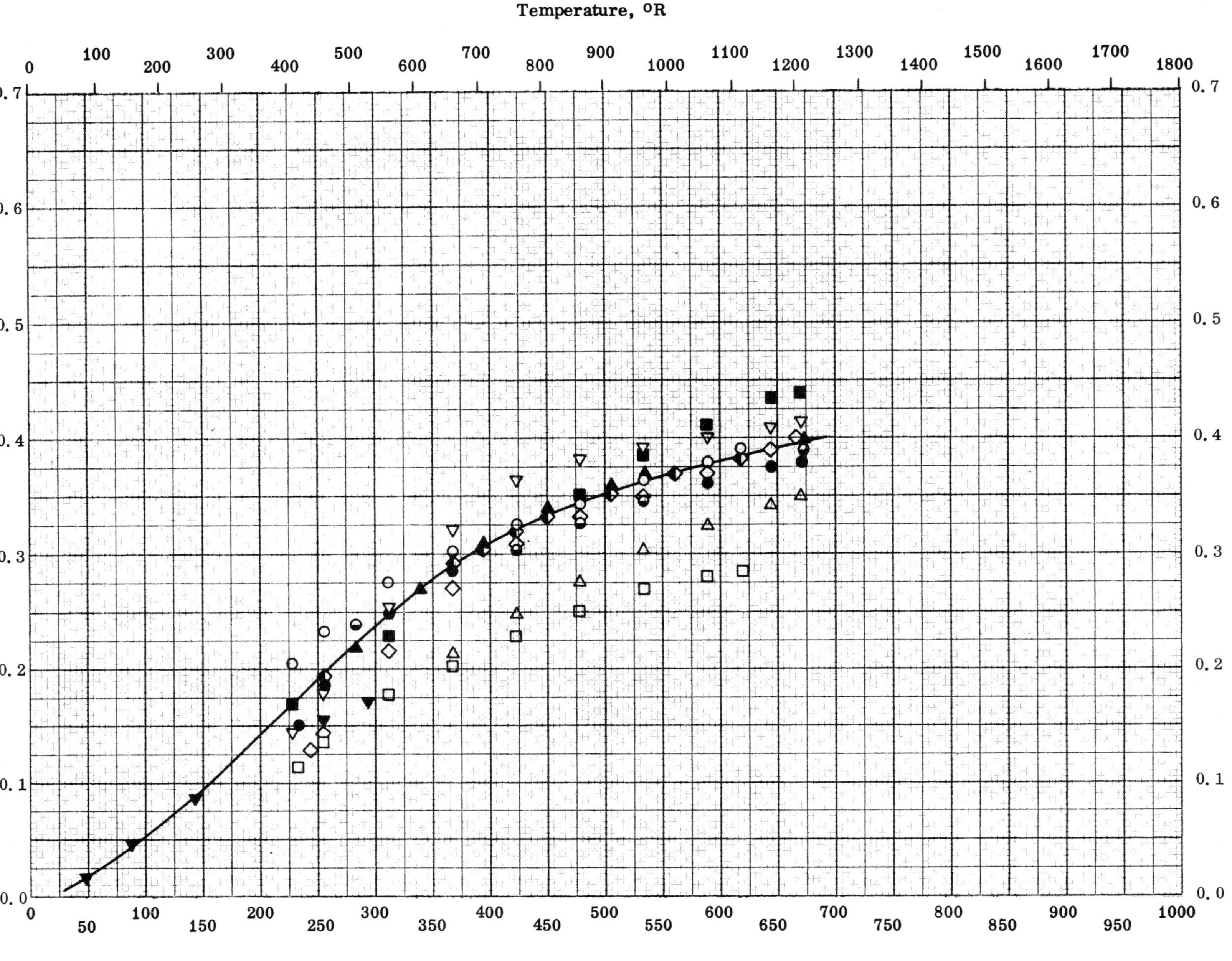

SPECIFIC HEAT -- PLASTIC LAMINATES
(Graphite cloth reinforced phenolic resin)

SPECIFIC HEAT -- PLASTIC LAMINATES
(Graphite cloth reinforced phenolic resin)

REFERENCE INFORMATION

Symbol	Ref.	Temp. Range °K	Rept. Error %	Sample Specifications	Remarks
○	63-19	228-618	±5	56 Resin and 44 graphite; National Carbon WCB reinforcing system with Monsanto Phenolic SC-1008 resin; 45° angle layup; density 84.2 lb ft^{-3}.	
□	63-19	228-644	±5	Graphitized composite "B" Si-SiC coated (g-3); 56 resin and 44 graphite; National Carbon Graphite Cloth reinforcing system with phenolic resin R-120; parallel layup; density 75.5 lb ft^{-3} (normal coated).	Cured 2 hrs at 325 F with 400 psi pressure; heated to 325 F from room temperature in 5 hrs.
△	63-18	228-673	±5	Graphitized composite (g-2); 56 resin and 44 graphite; National Carbon Graphite fabric reinforcing system with phenolic resin R-120; density 74 lb ft^{-3}.	Cured 2 hrs at 325 F with 400 psi pressure; (5 hrs to 325 F from room temperature) post cured 40 hrs to 500 F (23 F/hr from 315 to 500 F).
◇	63-18	228-673	±5	70 graphite fabric squares and 30 SC-1008 phenolic; National Carbon Company WCB reinforcement system with Monsanto Phenolic SC-1008 resin.	Cured 30 min at 300 F with 2000 psi pressure.
▽	63-18	228-673	±5	50 phenolic resin and 50 graphite fabric; National Carbon Co., WCB, reinforcement system with Monsanto Phenolic SC-1008 resin.	
●	63-18	228-673	±5	60 graphite and 40 phenolic; National Carbon Co., WCB graphite reinforcement system with Monsanto Phenolic SC-1008 resin; density 69.2 lb ft^{-3}.	Cured 30 min at 300 F with 1950 psi pressure.
■	63-17	228-673	±5	50 phenolic and 50 graphite fabric squares; National Carbon Co. WCB graphite reinforcement system with Monsanto Phenolic SC-1008 resin; density 86.8 lb ft^{-3}.	Cured 30 min at 300 F with 800 psi pressure.

(Continued onto next page)

SPECIFIC HEAT -- PLASTIC LAMINATES (continued)
(Graphite cloth reinforced phenolic resin)

REFERENCE INFORMATION

Symbol	Ref.	Temp. Range °K	Rept. Error %	Sample Specifications	Remarks
▲	62-30	228-673	±5	60 graphite fabric square 1/2 in. x 1/2 in. and 40 phenolic;	Cured 30 min at 310 F with 1700 psi pressure.
◆	62-30	228-673	±5	70 graphite and 30 phenolic; National Carbon Co. WCB Graphite reinforcement system with Monsanto Phenolic SC-1008 resin.	Cured 30 min at 300 F with 1700 psi pressure.
▼	65-3	49-294		Fabric reinforced laminate composed of 30 Monsanto SC-1008 phenolic resin and 70 National Carbon Co. WCB graphite fabric; density 7.0014 g cm^{-3}, void 37.9%. [Author's design.: Material C].	
◒	64-10	283-672	3.0	Phenolic-graphite material; FM 5064; 35.8 resin.	Cure cycle: pressure: no pressure for 1 hr; 100 psi g 1 hr, and 200 psi y 12 hrs; temperature: 2 hrs at 80 - 180 F, 2 hrs at 180 - 190 F, 4.5 hrs at 190 - 360 F; cooled to 150 in 1.5 hrs; post cycle: 12 hrs at 80 - 300 F, 48 hrs at 300 F, and 10 hrs at 120 F.

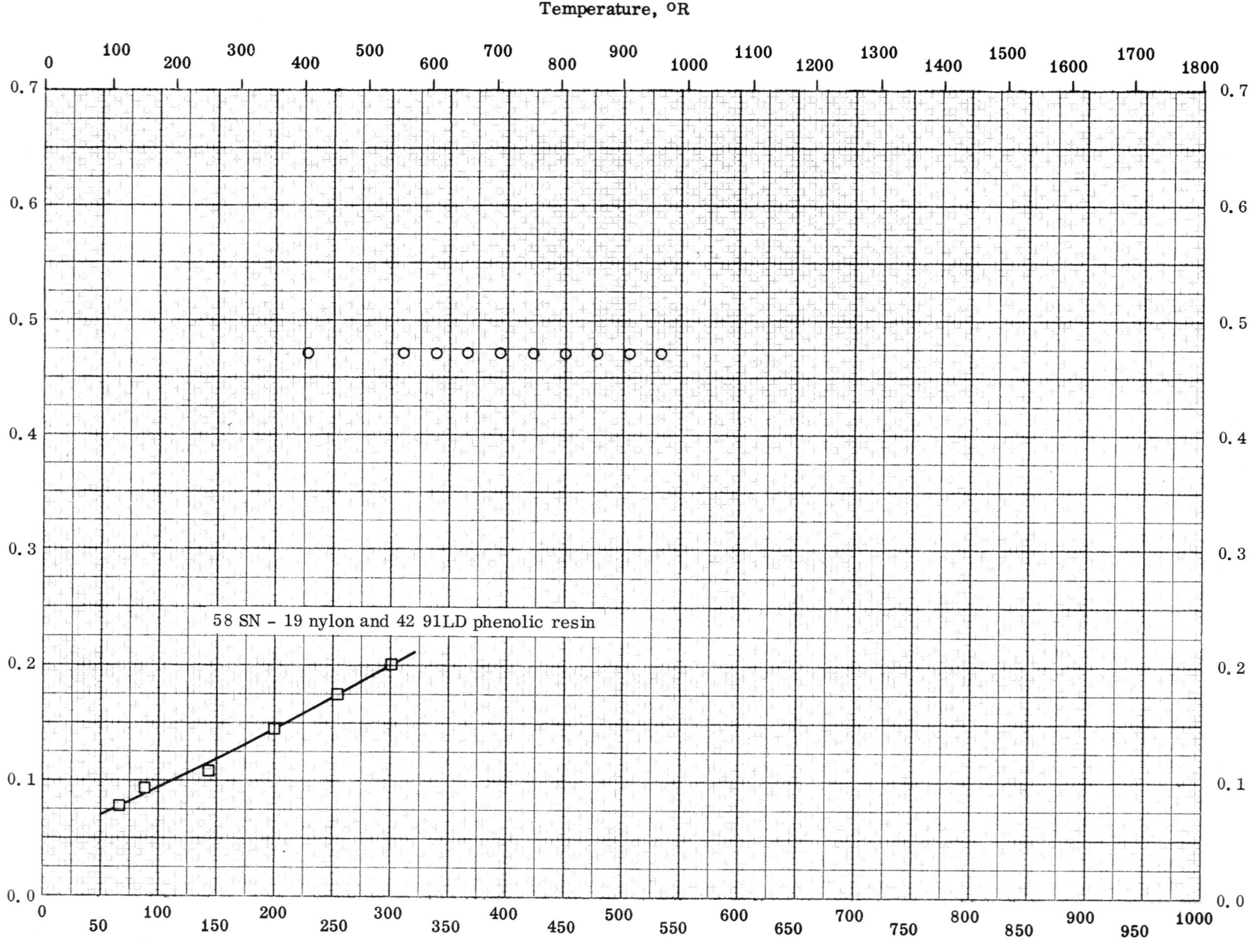

SPECIFIC HEAT -- PLASTIC LAMINATES
(Nylon fabric reinforced phenolic resin)

SPECIFIC HEAT -- PLASTIC LAMINATES
(Nylon fabric reinforced phenolic resin)

REFERENCE INFORMATION

Symbol	Ref.	Temp. Range °K	Rept. Error %	Sample Specifications	Remarks
○	61-13	228-533		Chopped nylon fabric construction YN-25; 42 CTL-91LD phenolic resin and SN-19 nylon heat set and scoured reinforcing system. [Author's design.: SRI No. 9].	Molded 1 hr at 275 F.
□	65-3	66-288		Chopped nylon fabric construction YN-25 composed of 42 CTL-91LD phenolic resin and 58 SN-19 nylon; density 1.1860 g cm^{-1}. [Author's design.: Material B].	Heat set and scoured.

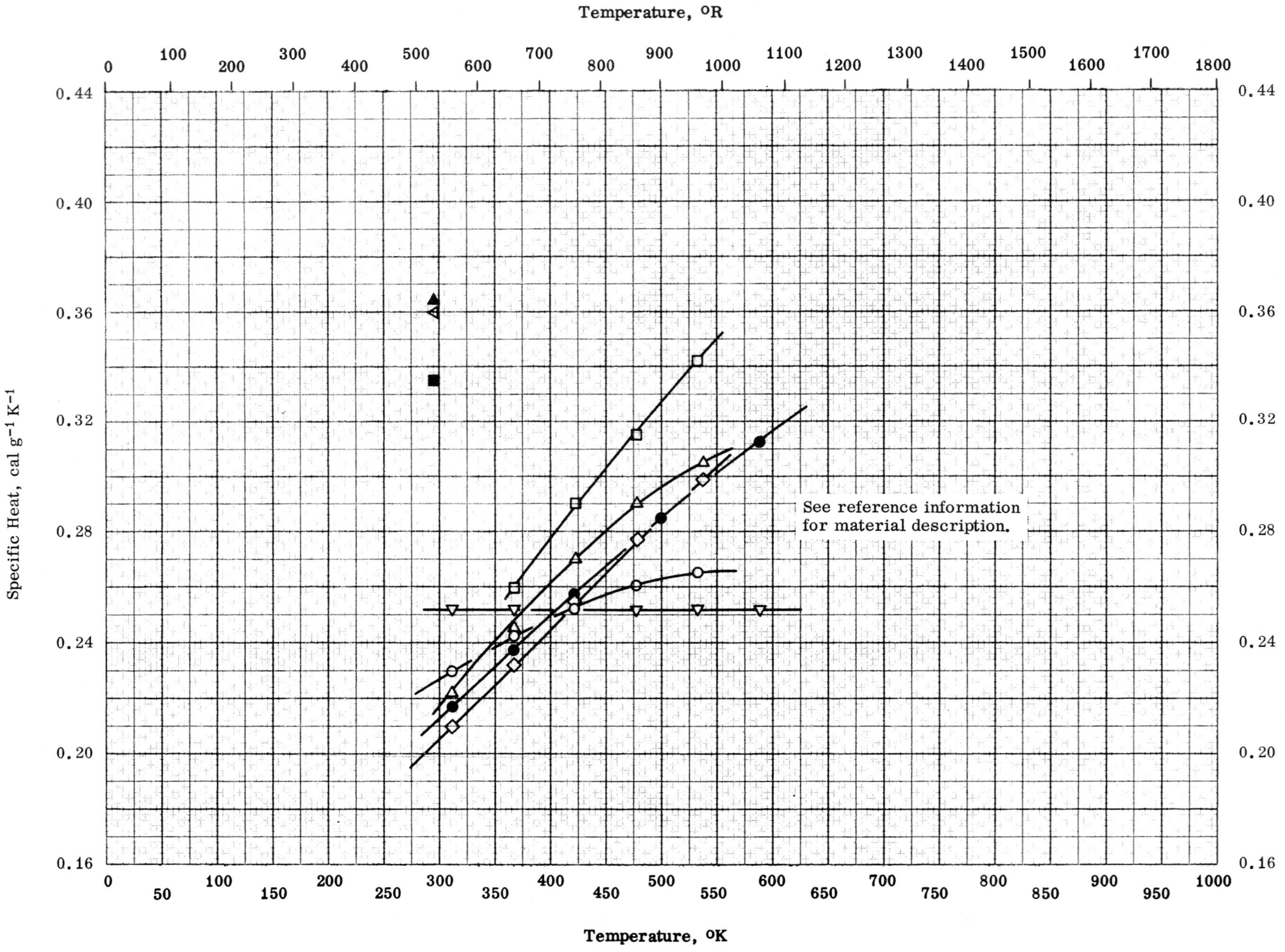

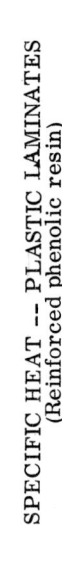

SPECIFIC HEAT -- PLASTIC LAMINATES
(Reinforced phenolic resin)

SPECIFIC HEAT -- PLASTIC LAMINATES
(Reinforced phenolic resin)

REFERENCE INFORMATION

Symbol	Ref.	Temp. Range °K	Rept. Error %	Sample Specifications	Remarks
○	55-5	311-533	±10	By Cincinnati Testing Lab.; fabric: Owens Corning 3/4 oz.; phenolic resin mat; resin No. CTL-91-LD (44.2%); 0.13 in. thick; 94.2 lb ft^{-3}.	
□	55-5	311-533	±10	By Cincinnati Testing Lab.; fabric: Modiglian 1 oz. PFM; resin No. CTL-91-LD (42.2%); 0.12 in. thick; density 102 lb ft^{-3}.	
△	55-5	311-533	±10	By Cincinnati Testing Lab.; fabric 181; volan A finish; resin No. CTL-91-LD (28.3%); 14 ply; 0.12 in. thick; density 119 lb ft^{-3}.	
◇	55-5	311-589	±10	By Narmco Inc.; fabric 181; volan A finish; resin No. Conolon 506 (33%); 12 ply; density 101 lb ft^{-3}.	
▽	54-6	311-589	±10	By Bakelite Co.; fabric 181; resin No. BV 17085 (28.5%); hexasol catalyst; 14 ply.	
●	54-6	311-589	±10	Reinforced copolymer of phenolic and epoxide resins; by Shell; glass fabric No. 181; 33% epon/67% plyophen resin No. 1001/5023 (24.5% total resin content); density 109 lb ft^{-3}.	
■	52-9	298		Cloth base phenolic laminate Insurok C-T-601; density 83.7 lb ft^{-3}.	
▲	52-9	298		Paper base phenolic laminate; Insurok XXX-T-640; density 4.1 lb ft^{-3}.	
◁	52-9	298		Cloth base phenolic laminate; Lamicoid C-6030; density 81.8 lb ft^{-3}.	

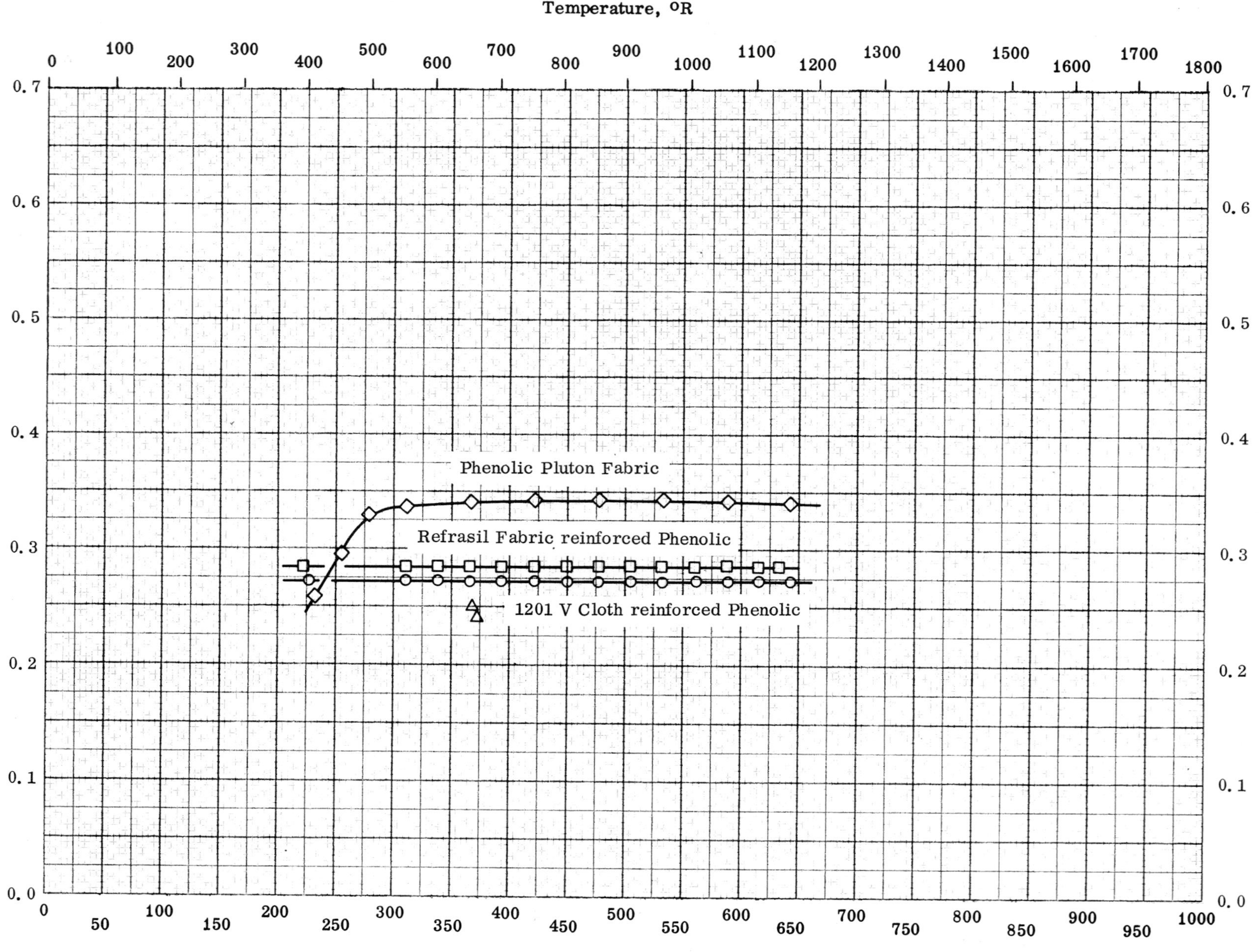

SPECIFIC HEAT -- PLASTIC LAMINATES
(Other materials reinforced phenolic resin)

REFERENCE INFORMATION

Symbol	Ref.	Temp. Range °K	Rept. Error %	Sample Specifications	Remarks
○	61-13	227-645		Laminate random reinforcement 1/2 in. x 1/2 in. squares of 1201 V cloth with 30 - 35 phenolic SC-1008 resin; density 90. 0 lb ft^{-3}.	Cured 2 hrs at 300 F.
□	61-13	223-634		Laminar construction Astrolite parallel layup; refrasil 184 weave with 30 - 35 phenolic SC-1008 resin.	Cured 2 hrs at 300 F.
△	63-3	369-372		Refrasil cloth impregnated with 91LD phenolic resin; density 97. 0 lb ft^{-3}.	
◇	63-19	228-644		62 pluton fabric and 38 resin; Monsanto SC 1008 resin system and 3M Company Pluton B-1 reinforcing system; density 89. 5 lb ft^{-3}; [Author's design.: i-3].	

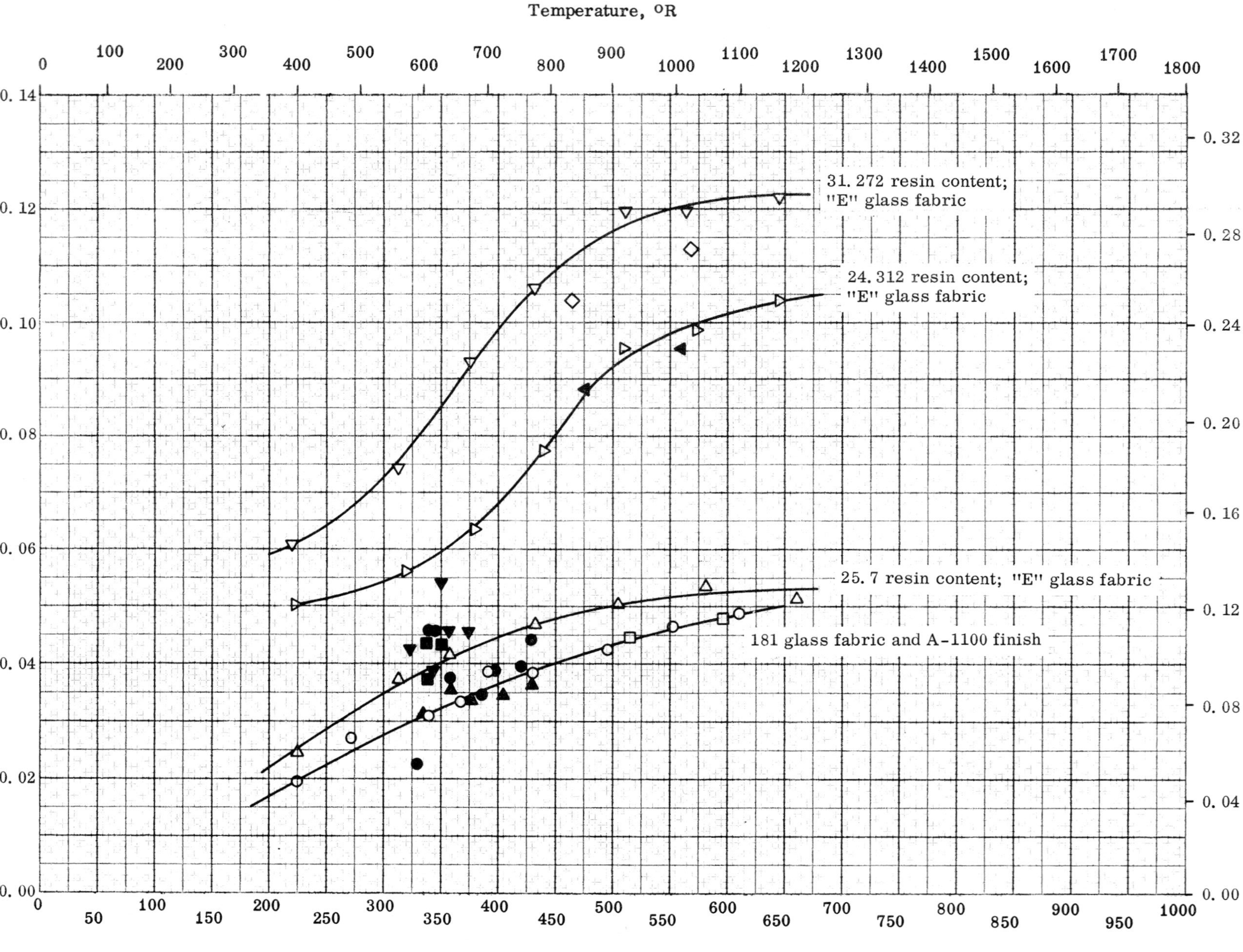

THERMAL CONDUCTIVITY -- PLASTIC LAMINATE
(Reinforced 37-9X phenolic resin)

THERMAL CONDUCTIVITY -- PLASTIC LAMINATE
(Reinforced 37-9X phenolic resin)

REFERENCE INFORMATION

Symbol	Ref.	Temp. Range °K	Rept. Error %	Sample Specifications	Remarks
○	58-8	225-611		Modified phenolic resin 37-9X with 181 glass fabric and A-1100 finish by Cincinnati Testing and Res. Lab.; 12 plies; density 103 lb ft^{-3} and sample nominal thickness 1/8 in.	Cured at 280 F for 1/2 hr at 175 psi and post cured at 250 F for 24 hrs, 300 F for 24 hrs, 350 F for 24 hrs, and then finally 400 F for 24 hrs.
△	61-12	224-661		25.7 37-9X resin with 181 "E" glass fabric reinforcing manufactured by Cincinnati Testing and Res. Lab.; 14 plies; laminar construction regular layup parallel; density 116.5 lb ft^{-3} and sample 1/8 in. thick.	Molded with 100 psi pressure, cured at 280-290 F, and post cured 4 days at 250 F.
□	61-12	515-597		Same as above.	Second run of the above sample.
▽	61-12	220-645		31.272 37-9X resin with 181 "E" glass fabric reinforcing; manufactured by Cincinnati Testing and Res. Lab.; 91 plies in^{-1}; edgewise layup with thickness at 45° of wrap direction; density 111.0 lb ft^{-3} and sample 0.71 in. thick.	Molded with 100 psi pressure, cured at 280-290 F, and post cured 4 days at 250 F.
◇	61-12	465-567		Same as above.	The second run of the above sample.
▷	61-12	223-645		24.312 37-9X resin with 181 "E" glass fabric reinforcing manufactured by Cincinnati Testing and Res. Lab.; edgewise layup with thickness at 45° of wraping direction; density 111.7 lb ft^{-3} and sample 0.7 in. thick.	Augmented-bag type molded with 100 psi, cured 4 hrs at 280-290 F, and post cured 4 days at 250 F.
◀	61-12	475-559		Same as above.	The second run of the above sample.
●	63-3	330-428		7 sheets of 184 Volan finish glass cloth impregnated with 37-9X phenyl silane resin; density (140 F) 121.0 lb ft^{-3} and sample 0.168 in. thick.	Pressed at 100 lb in^{-2} at 350 F for 1 hr and post cured for 16 hrs at 350 F after removing from the press.
				(Continued onto next page)	

THERMAL CONDUCTIVITY -- PLASTIC LAMINATE (continued)
(Reinforced 37-9X phenolic resin)

REFERENCE INFORMATION

Symbol	Ref.	Temp. Range °K	Rept. Error %	Sample Specifications	Remarks
▲	63-3	336-432		Same as above; density (140 F) 120. 5 lb ft^{-3} and sample 0. 170 in. thick.	Same as above.
▼	63-3	323-374		Same as above except a coat of plastic primer and two coats of SAF alkyd resin base paint; density 120. 2 lb ft^{-3} and sample 0. 170 in. thick.	Same as above.
■	63-3	337-351		Same as above except that two SAF paint coatings were replaced by two coats of TIC water base paint; density 120. 2 lb ft^{-3} and sample 0. 172 in. thick.	Same as above.

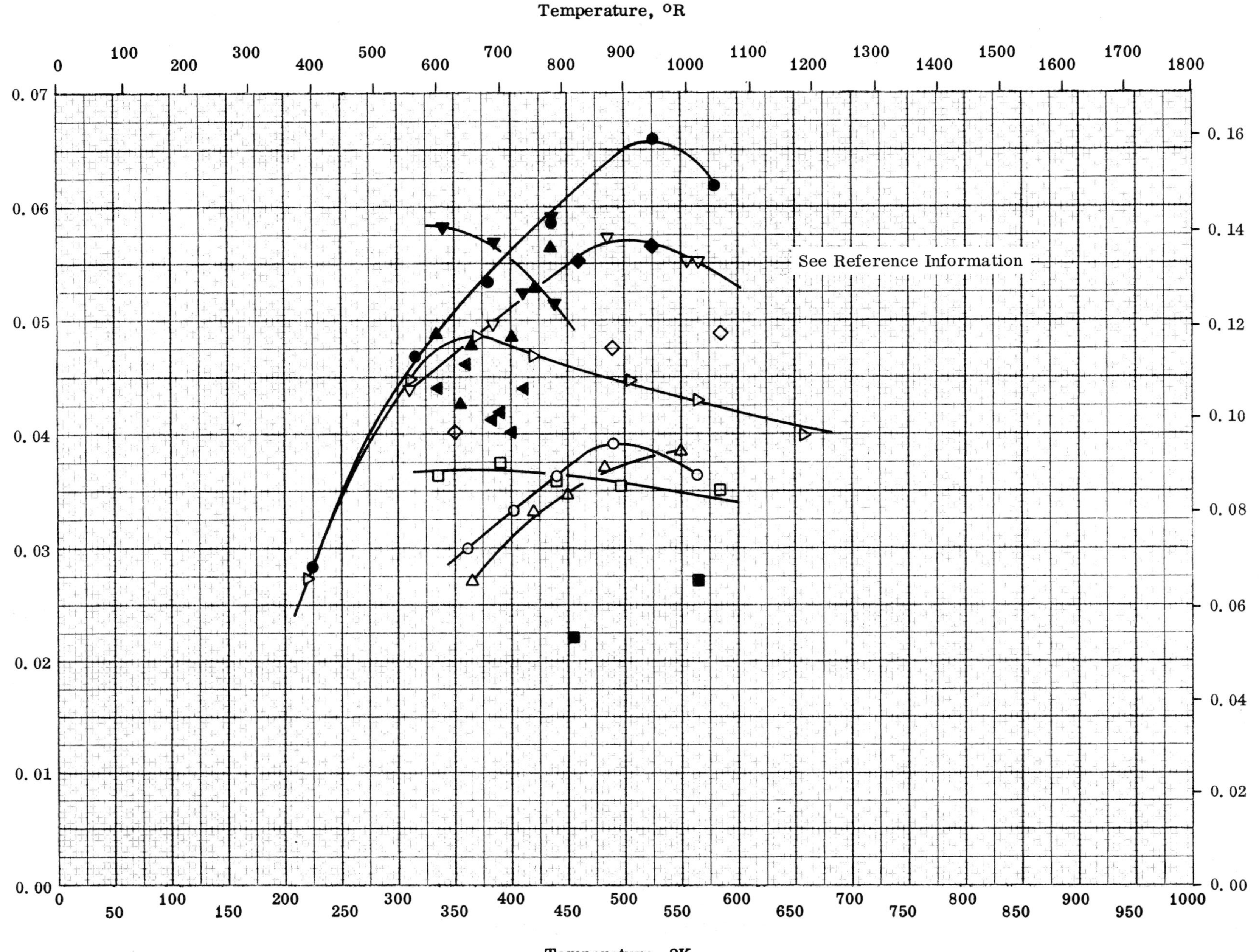

THERMAL CONDUCTIVITY -- PLASTIC LAMINATE
(Reinforced 91-LD phenolic resin)

THERMAL CONDUCTIVITY -- PLASTIC LAMINATE
(Reinforced 91-LD phenolic resin)

REFERENCE INFORMATION

Symbol	Ref.	Temp. Range °K	Rept. Error %	Sample Specifications	Remarks
○	55-5	362-564		91-LD phenolic resin with 181 volan A finish glass fabric; resin content 28.3 and 14 plies; density 119.18 lb ft^{-3}.	Placed in a constant temperature humidity cabinet at 73 F - 50% RH for a minimum of 1 week prior to testing.
□	55-5	336-584		91-LD phenolic resin reinforced with 3/4 oz. phenolic resin mat; resin content 44.2 and viscosity 850 cps at 77 F; density 94.22 lb ft^{-3}.	Same as above.
△	55-5	366-552		91-LD phenolic resin with Modigliana 1 oz. PFM; resin content 42.2; density 102.34 lb ft^{-3}.	Same as above.
▽	61-12	312-585		91-LD phenolic resin reinforced with chopped 181 glass by Reinhold Engr. and Plastic Co., Inc.; resin content 35 ± 5 and density 114.2 lb ft^{-3}.	Fabricated 1 hr at 275 F and post-cured 24 hrs at 275 F.
◇	61-12	348-585		Same as above.	Second run of above sample.
▷	61-12	218-662		91-LD phenolic resin with SN-19 Nylon heat set and scoured reinforcing from U. S. Polymaric Chem. Inc.; chopped fabric construction YN25; resin content 42 and density 72.0 lb ft^{-3}; sample 0.25 in. thick.	Molded 1 hr at 275 F.
■	61-12	457-566		Same as above.	Second run of the above sample.
●	61-12	224-581		91-LD phenolic resin reinforced by 181 weave and YM-31 A type glass fabric; resin content 38 - 40 prior to molding and 31 after molding; density 131.0 lb ft^{-3} and sample 0.125 in. thick.	Pressed at 345 psi, press-cured 20 min at 300 F, and post-cured 24 hrs at 300 F, 24 hrs at 350 F, and 24 hrs at 400 F.
◆	61-12	461-526		Same as above. (Continued onto next page)	Second run of the above sample.

THERMAL CONDUCTIVITY -- PLASTIC LAMINATE (continued)
(Reinforced 91-LD phenolic resin)

REFERENCE INFORMATION

Symbol	Ref.	Temp. Range °K	Rept. Error %	Sample Specifications	Remarks
▼	63-3	343-438		Asbestos cloth with one sheet of silver foil in center impregnated with 91-LD phenolic resin; density 113.0 lb ft^{-3} at 140 F and sample 0.254 in. thick.	Pressed at 100 lb in^{-2} at 350 F for 1 hr and post-cured for 16 hrs at 350 F after removing from the press.
▲	63-3	334-433		Asbestos cloth with one sheet of aluminum foil in the center impregnated with 91-LD phenolic resin; density 107.8 lb ft^{-3} at 140 F.	Same as above.
◀	63-3	337-407		Refrasil cloth impregnated with 91-LD phenolic resin; density 97.0 lb ft^{-3} at 140 F and sample 0.170 in. thick.	Same as above.

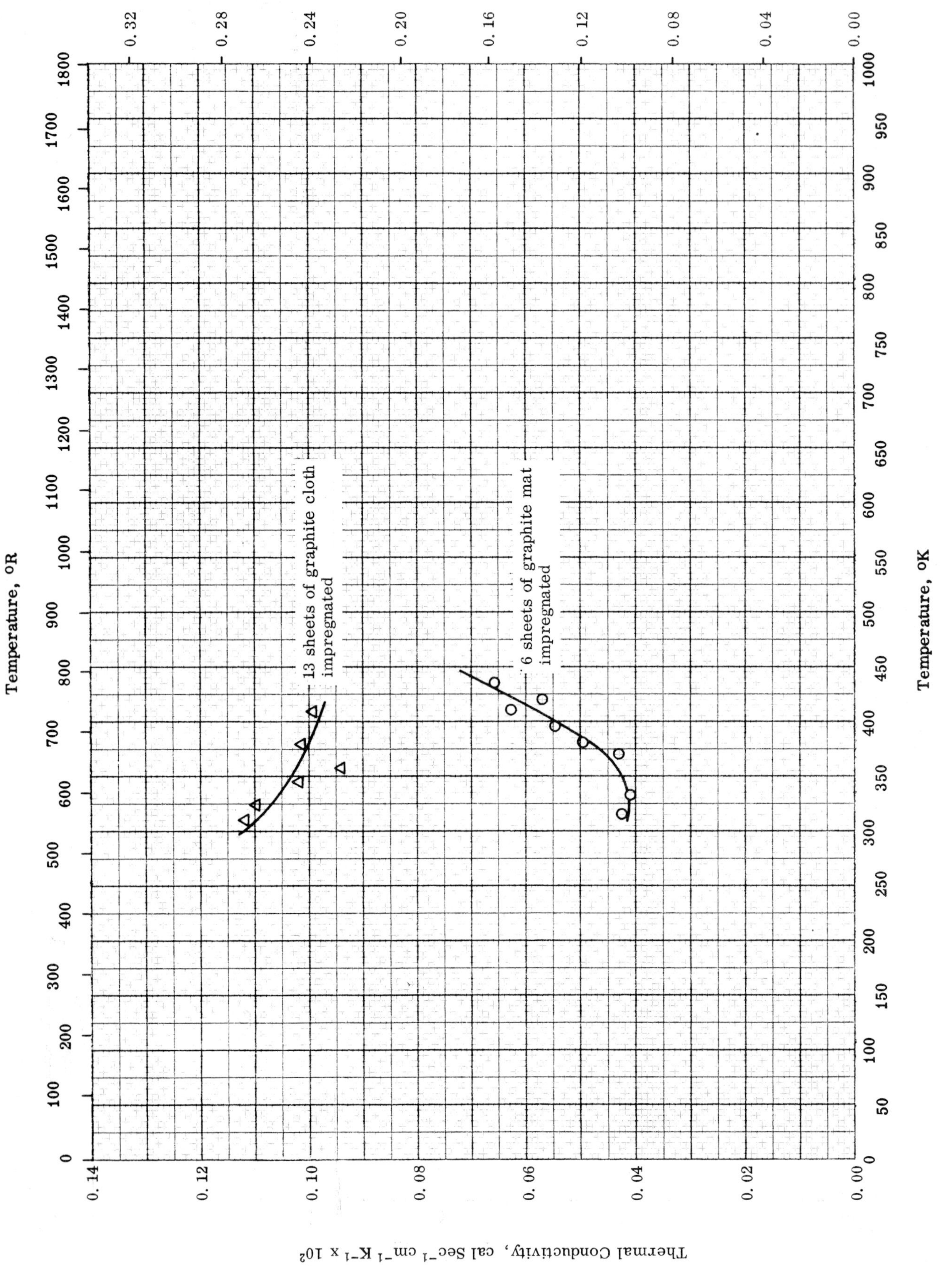

Temperature, °R

0 100 200 300 400 500 600 700 800 900 1000 1100 1200 1300 1400 1500 1600 1700 1800

Thermal Conductivity, cal Sec^{-1} cm^{-1} K^{-1} x 10^2

0.14 0.12 0.10 0.08 0.06 0.04 0.02 0.00

13 sheets of graphite cloth impregnated

6 sheets of graphite mat impregnated

Thermal Conductivity, Btu hr^{-1} ft^{-1} R^{-1}

0.32 0.28 0.24 0.20 0.16 0.12 0.08 0.04 0.00

0 50 100 150 200 250 300 350 400 450 500 550 600 650 700 750 800 850 900 950 1000

Temperature, °K

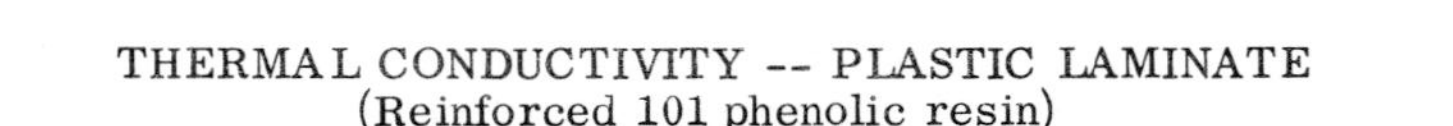

THERMAL CONDUCTIVITY -- PLASTIC LAMINATE
(Reinforced 101 phenolic resin)

THERMAL CONDUCTIVITY -- PLASTIC LAMINATE
(Reinforced 101 phenolic resin)

REFERENCE INFORMATION

Symbol	Ref.	Temp. Range °K	Rept. Error %	Sample Specifications	Remarks
○	63-3	315-434		6 sheets of graphite mat impregnated with 101 phenolic resin; density 66.4 lb ft^{-3} at 140 F and sample 0.141 in. thick.	Pressed at 100 lb in^{-2} at 350 F for 1 hr and post-cured at 350 F for 16 hrs after removing from the press.
△	63-3	312-409		13 sheets of WC-001 graphite cloth impregnated with 101 phenolic resin; density 79.6 lb ft^{-3} at 140 F and sample 0.163 in. thick.	Same as above.

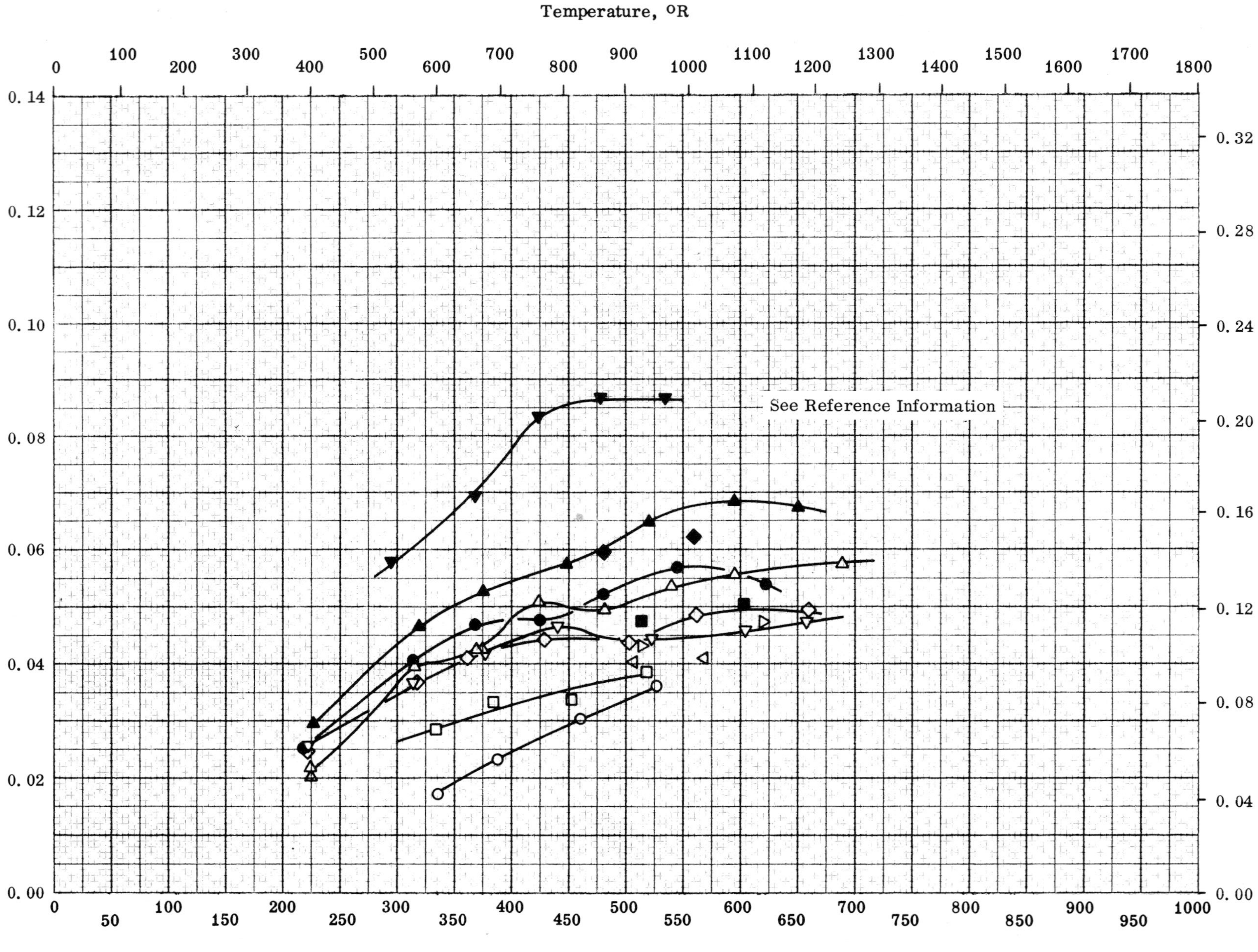

THERMAL CONDUCTIVITY -- PLASTIC LAMINATE
(Other types of reinforced phenolic resins)

THERMAL CONDUCTIVITY --PLASTIC LAMINATE
(Other types of reinforced phenolic resins)

REFERENCE INFORMATION

Symbol	Ref.	Temp. Range °K	Rept. Error %	Sample Specifications	Remarks
○	55-3	336-527		Phenolic BV 17085 resin with 181 glass fabric; resin content 27.6 and 28.5 by author; hexasol catalyst; 14 plies and 0.119 thick.	
□	55-3	334-519		Phenolic conolon 506 resin with 181 glass fabric Volan A finish; resin content 25 - 27 and 33 by author; 12 plies, 0.119 in. thick, and density 1.62 g cm^{-3}.	
△	61-12	225-689		48 - 53 phenolic R 181 resin with glass roving no. F 846 reinforcing manufactured by Fiberite Corp., fiberite 4030 - 190; density 107.9 lb ft^{-3} and 1/4 in. thick; C-205 catalyst.	Curing in hydraulic press at 2000 psi, and cured for 20 min. at 350 F.
▽	61-12	222-685		30 - 35 phenolic SC-1008 resin with 1201 V cloth manufactured by H. I. Thompson; laminate random reinforcement; density 90 lb ft^{-3}.	Molded; cured 2 hrs at 300 F.
◁	61-12	508-568		Same as above.	Second run of the above sample.
◇	61-12	222-661		Same as above except reinforced by refrasil 184 weave fabric; laminar construction parallel layup; 6 plies and density 90 lb ft^{-3}.	Cured 2 hrs at 300 F.
▷	61-12	514-620		Same as above.	Second run of the above sample.
●	61-12	219-623		Same as above; edgewise layup with thickness in warp direction; 50 plies in^{-1}; density 90 lb ft^{-3} and 0.125 in. thick.	Cured 1 hr at 200 F, 1 hr at 250 F, and 2 hrs at 300 F.
■	61-12	514-603		Same as above.	Second run of above sample.
				(Continued onto next page)	

THERMAL CONDUCTIVITY -- PLASTIC LAMINATE (continued)
(Other types of reinforced phenolic resins)

REFERENCE INFORMATION

Symbol	Ref.	Temp. Range °K	Rept. Error %	Sample Specifications	Remarks
▲	61-12	227-648		25 - 30 R/M high resistant phenolic resin reinforced by asbestos R/M style 42 RPD mat manufactured by Raybestos-Manhatten, Inc.; density 117.0 lb ft^{-3} and 0.125 in. thick.	Not post cured.
◆	61-12	481-559		Same as above.	The second run of the above sample.
▼	61-5	294-533		Phenolic-asbestos.	

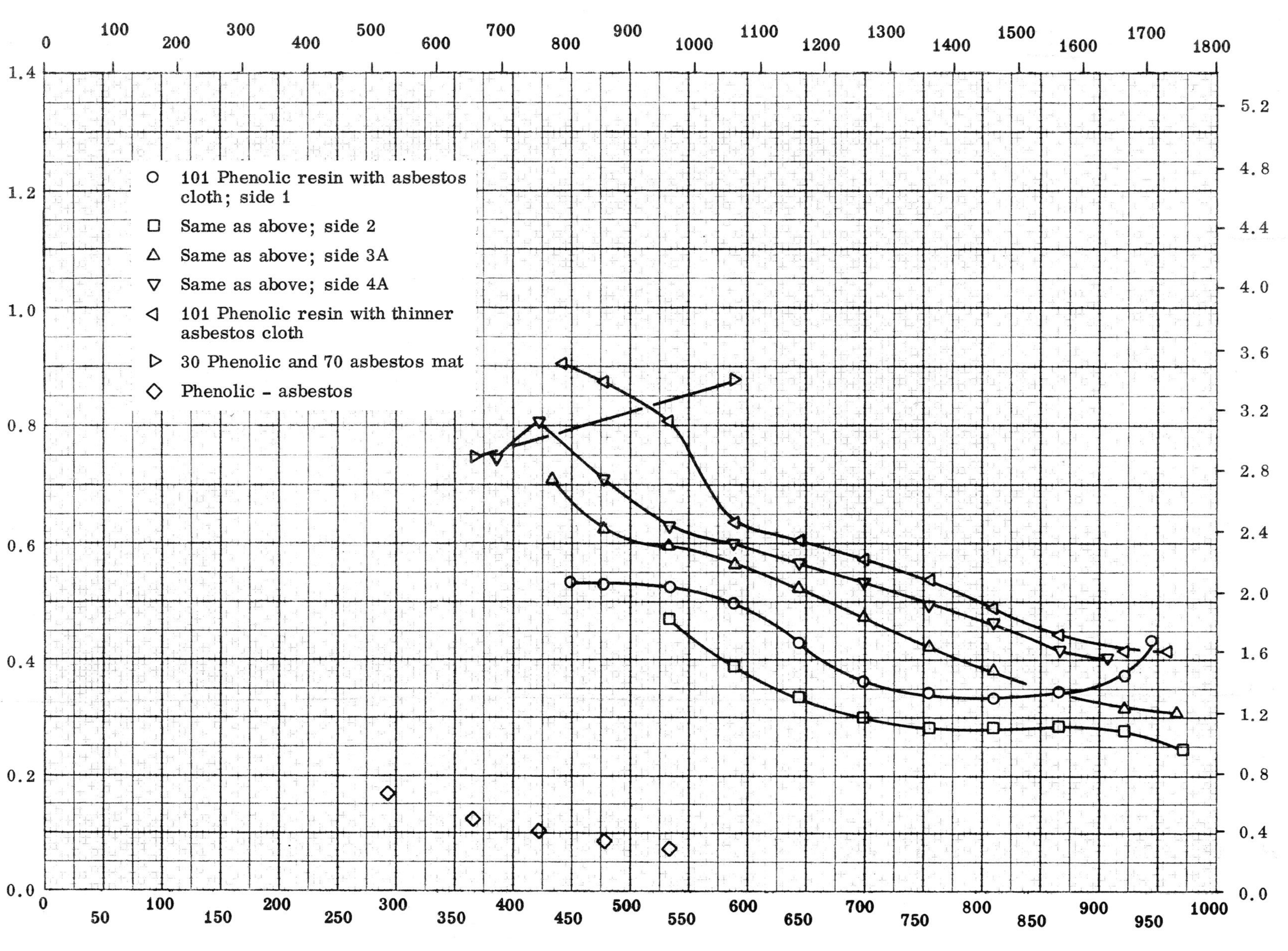

THERMAL DIFFUSIVITY -- PLASTIC LAMINATE
(Asbestos fabric reinforced phenolic resin)

THERMAL DIFFUSIVITY -- PLASTIC LAMINATE
(Asbestos fabric reinforced phenolic resin)

REFERENCE INFORMATION

Symbol	Ref.	Temp. Range °K	Rept. Error %	Sample Specifications	Remarks
○	63-2	450-944		Ironsides no. 101 phenolic resin reinforced by 0.125 in. thick asbestos cloth; resin content 47 to 53%; sample size 4.5 by 4.5 by 0.180 in. [Author's design.: panel 1].	Prepared by using 100 lb in^{-2} laminating pressure at a curing temperature of 375 F for 1 hr and then post-cured for 12 hrs in an oven at 375 F; measured at side 1.
□	63-2	533-972		Same as above.	The above specimen measured at side 2.
△	63-2	433-967		Same as above. [Author's design.: panel 2].	Same as above except measured at the side author designated as 3A.
▽	63-2	386-908		Same as above.	Same as above except measured at the side author designated as 4A.
◁	63-2	442-958		Same as above sample except reinforced by 0.0625 in. thick asbestos cloth. [Author's design.: 2A].	Same as above; measured at side 1.
▷	61-4	367-589		30 phenolic and 70 asbestos mat.	
◇	61-5	294-533		1/8 in. thick phenolic-asbestos laminate.	

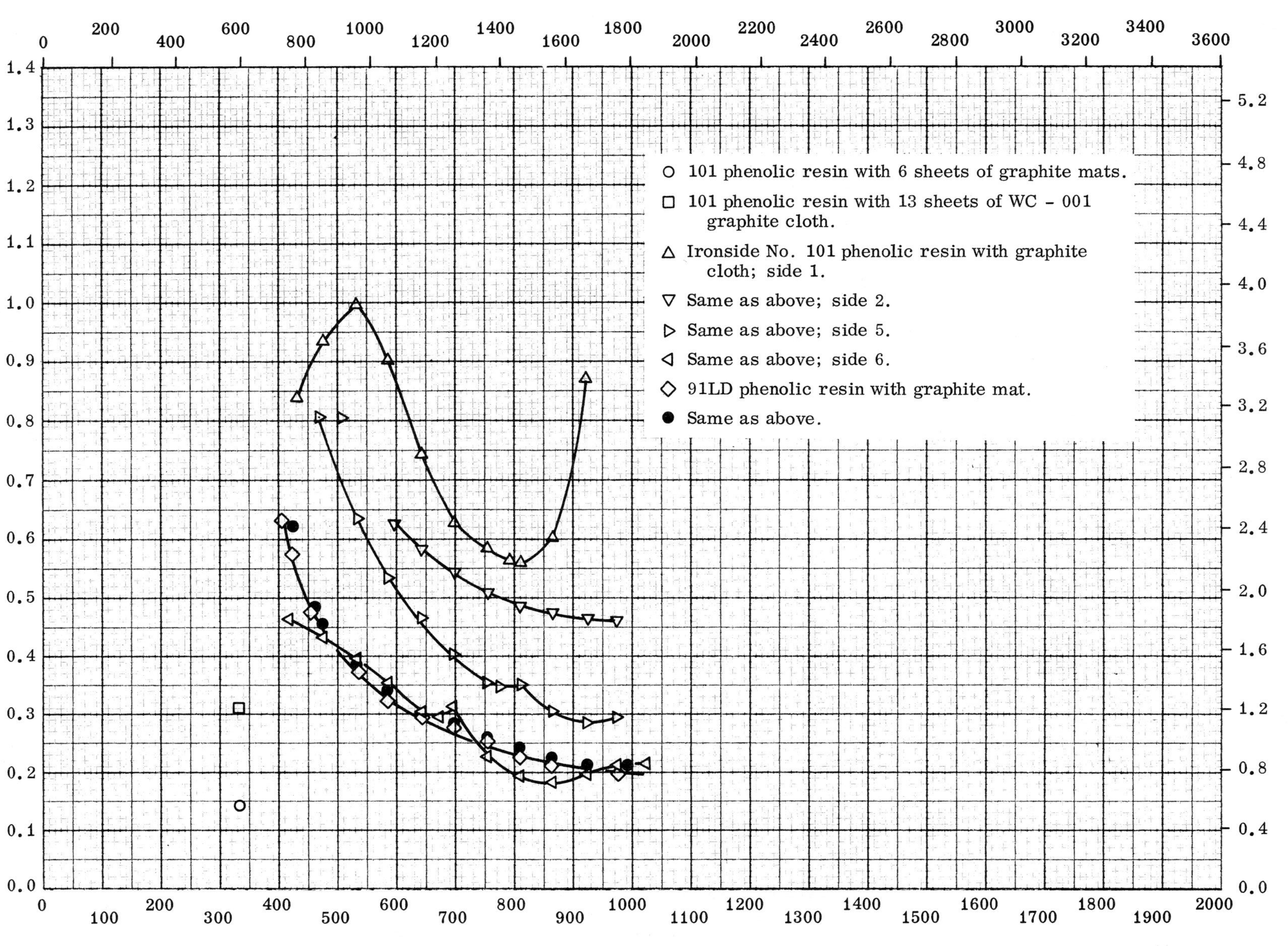

THERMAL DIFFUSIVITY -- PLASTIC LAMINATE
(Graphite fabric reinforced phenolic resin)

THERMAL DIFFUSIVITY -- PLASTIC LAMINATE
(Graphite fabric reinforced phenolic resin)

REFERENCE INFORMATION

Symbol	Ref.	Temp. Range °K	Rept. Error %	Sample Specifications	Remarks
○	63-3	333		101 phenolic resin with 6 sheets of graphite mat impregnated; sample 0.34 ft^2 circular area with 0.141 in. thick; density 66.4 lb ft^{-3}. [Author's design.: 1].	Pressed at 100 lb in^{-2} at 350 F for 1 hr and then post-cured for 16 hrs at 350 F.
□	63-3	333		101 phenolic resin with 13 sheets of WC-001 graphite cloth impregnated; sample 0.34 ft^2 and 0.163 in. thick; density 79.6 lb ft^{-3}. [Author's design.: 2].	Same as above.
△	63-2	430-922		Ironside no. 101 phenolic resin with 0.012 in. thick graphite cloth reinforced; resin content within 47 to 53%. [Author's design.: panel 1].	Pressed at 100 lb in^{-2} at a curing temperature of 375 F for 1 hr and then post-cured for 12 hrs in an oven at 375 F; measured at side 1.
▽	63-2	597-972		Same as above.	Same as above; measured at side 2.
▷	63-2	469-972		Same as above. [Author's design.: panel 3].	Same as above; measured at side 5.
◁	63-2	419-1022		Same as above.	Same as above; measured at side 6.
◇	63-2	405-978		91 LD phenolic resin with 0.5 in. thick graphite mat reinforced; resin content 47 to 53%; sample size 4.5 by 4.5 by 0.180 in. [Author's design.: panel 2].	Same as above.
●	63-2	422-994		Same as above [Author's design.: panel 3].	Same as above.

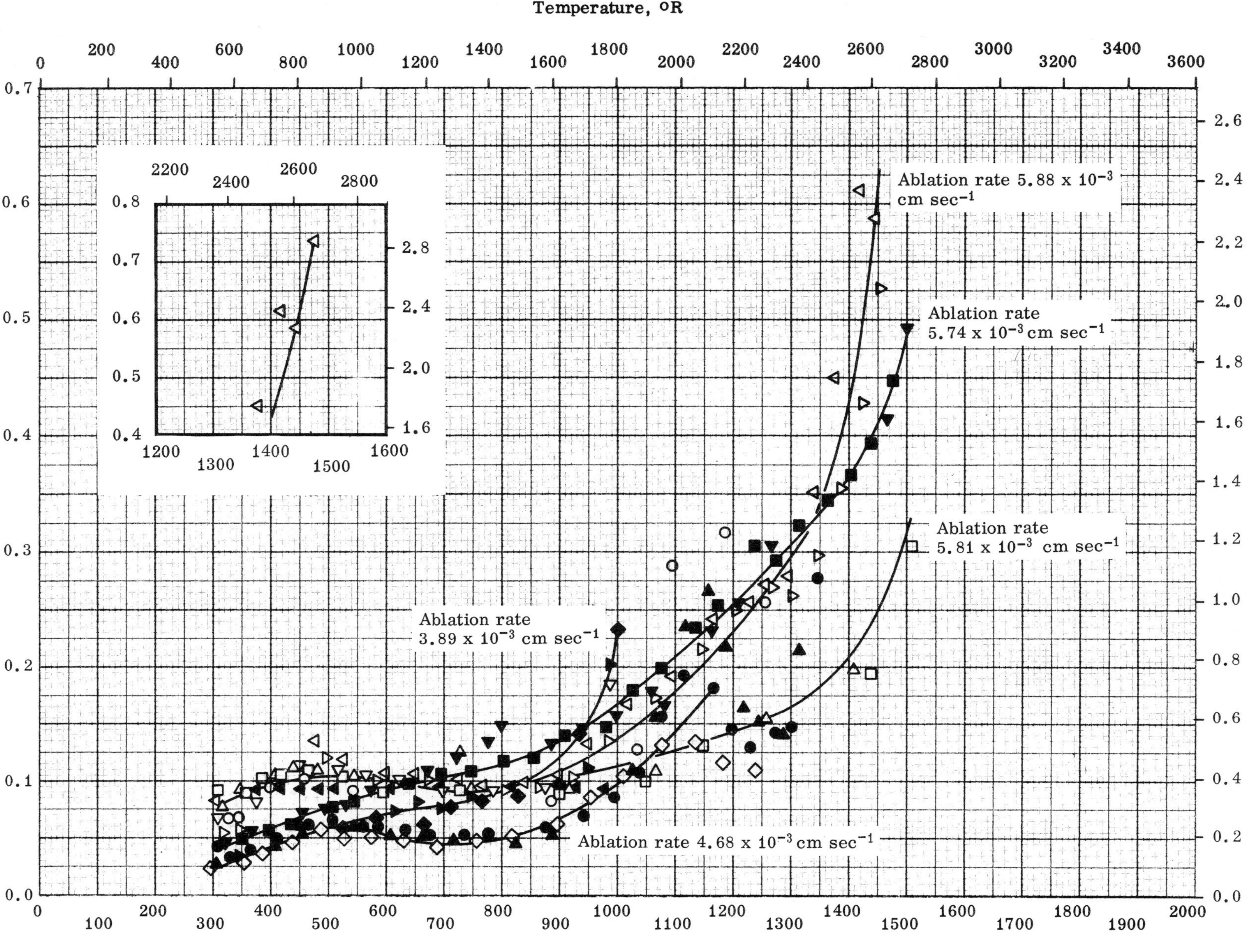

THERMAL DIFFUSIVITY -- PLASTIC LAMINATE
(Adhesive bonded glass cloth reinforced phenolic resin)

THERMAL DIFFUSIVITY -- PLASTIC LAMINATE
(Adhesive bonded glass cloth reinforced phenolic resin)

REFERENCE INFORMATION

Symbol	Ref.	Temp. Range °K	Rept. Error %	Sample Specifications	Remarks
○	60-5	328-1255		Bakelite BLL 3085 resin reinforced with 181 glass cloth NOL24 finish bonded by Shell Epon 422 adhesive; ablation rate 5.81x 10^{-3} cm sec^{-1}. [Author's design.: 1].	Measured with lamination prependicular to central axis of the cylindrical specimen by using Pt-Pt 10 Rh thermocouple.
□	60-5	308-1509		Same as above.	Same as above except measured by Cr-Al thermocouple.
△	60-5	313-1408		Same as above.	Same as above; second run.
▽	60-5	308-986		Same description as the above sample except ablation rate 5.88x 10^{-3} cm sec^{-1}. [Author's design.: 2].	Measured by using Pt-Pt 10 Rh thermocouple under the same condition as above specimen.
◁	60-5	303-1473		Same as above.	Same as above except measured by using Cr-Al thermocouple.
▷	60-5	318-1453		Same as above.	Same as above; second run.
◇	60-5	294-1238		Same description as the above sample except ablation rate 4.68x 10^{-3} cm sec^{-1}. [Author's design.: 3].	Same as above except measured by Pt-Pt 10 Rh thermocouple.
●	60-5	308-1346		Same as above.	Same as above except measured by using Cr-Al thermocouple.
▲	60-5	308-1318		Same as above.	Same as above; second run.
■	60-5	309-1478		Same description as the above sample except ablation rate 5.74x 10^{-3} cm sec^{-1}. [Author's design.: 4].	Measured with lamination parallel to central axis of the cylindrical specimen by using Cr-Al thermocouple.
▼	60-5	320-1500		Same as above.	Same as above; second run.

(Continued onto next page)

THERMAL DIFFUSIVITY -- PLASTIC LAMINATE (Continued)
(Adhesive bonded glass cloth, reinforced phenolic resin)

REFERENCE INFORMATION

Symbol	Ref.	Temp. Range °K	Rept. Error %	Sample Specifications	Remarks
◆	60-5	310-1000		Same description as the above sample except ablation rate 3.89x 10^{-3} cm sec^{-1}. [Author's design.: 5].	Same as above except using Pt-Pt 10Rh thermocouple.
▶	60-5	320-986		Same as above.	Same as above except using Cr-Al thermocouple.
◀	60-5	313-978		Same as above.	Same as above; second run.

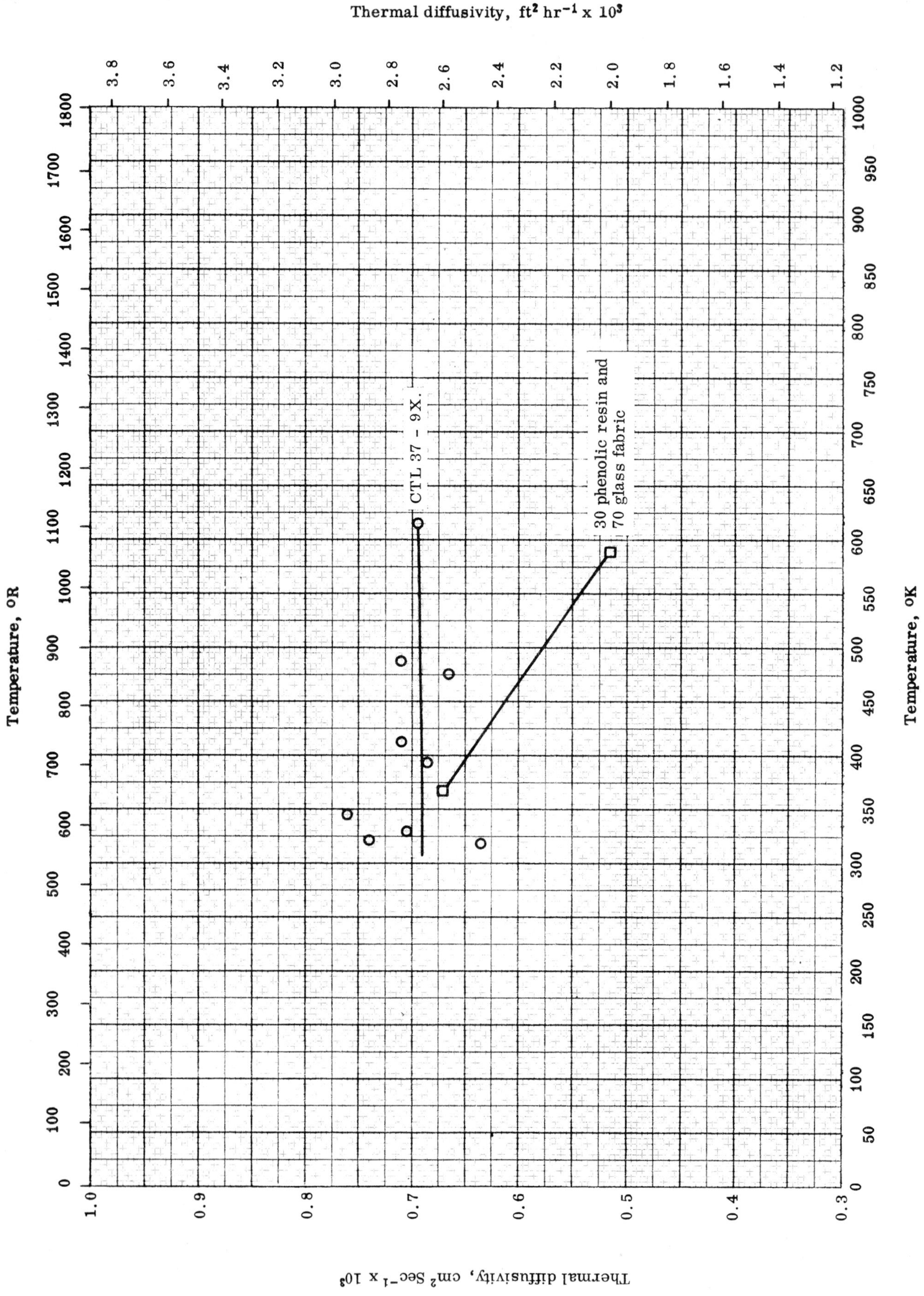

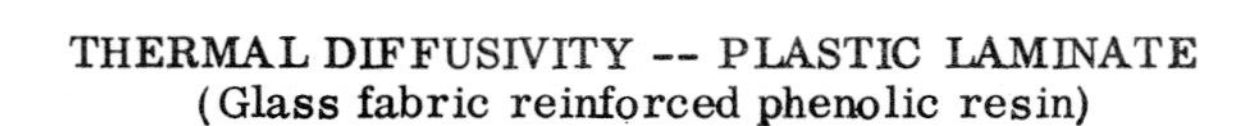

THERMAL DIFFUSIVITY -- PLASTIC LAMINATE
(Glass fabric reinforced phenolic resin)

THERMAL DIFFUSIVITY -- PLASTIC LAMINATE
(Glass fabric reinforced phenolic resin)

REFERENCE INFORMATION

Symbol	Ref.	Temp. Range °K	Rept. Error %	Sample Specifications	Remarks
○	60-6	319-615	9-11	CTL 37-9X; modified phenolic resin with 181 glass fabric.	
□	61-4	367-589		30 phenolic and 70 glass fabric.	

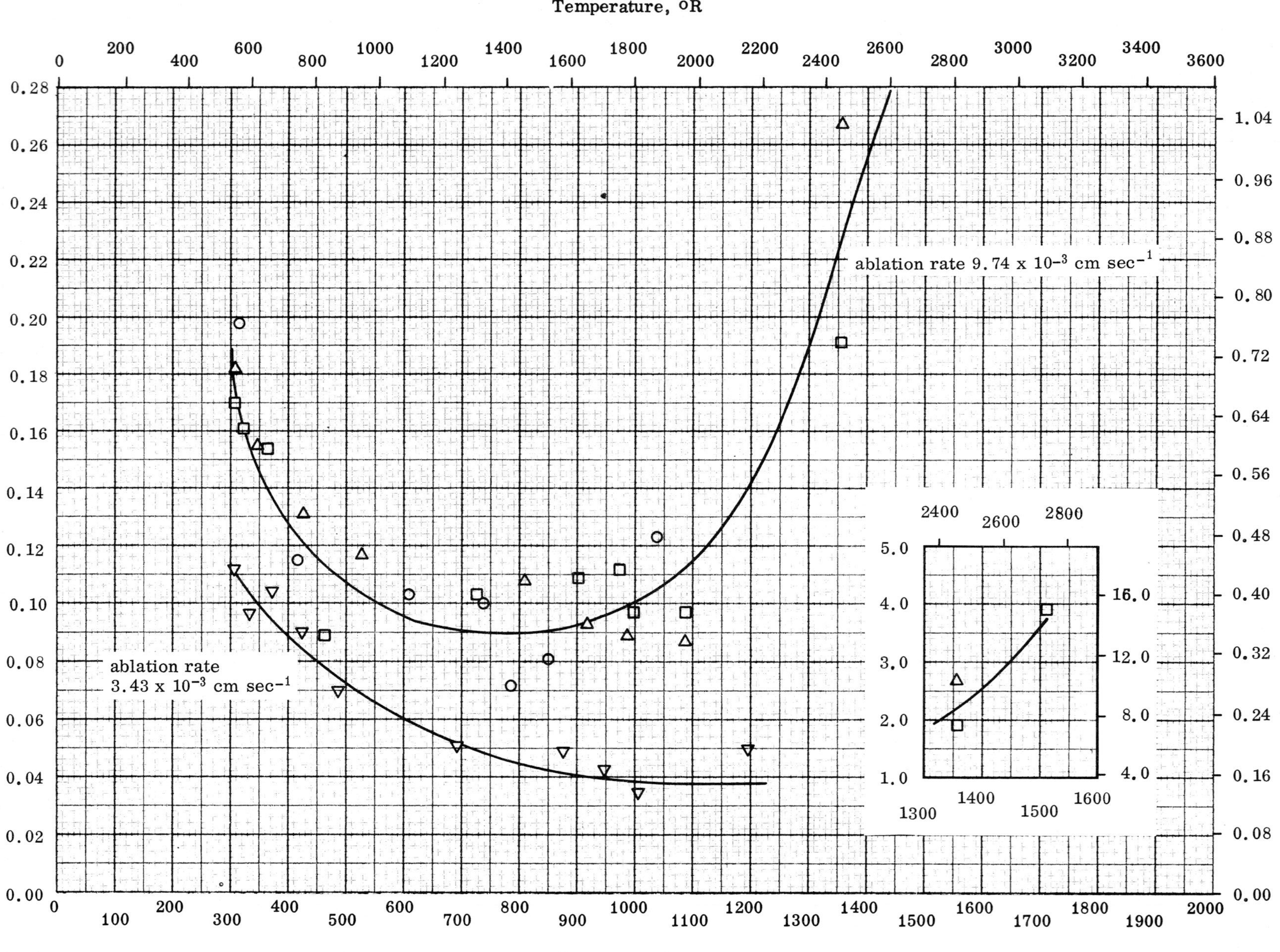

THERMAL DIFFUSIVITY -- PLASTIC LAMINATE
(Adhesive bonded nylon fabric reinforced phenolic resin)

THERMAL DIFFUSIVITY -- PLASTIC LAMINATE
(Adhesive bonded nylon fabric reinforced phenolic resin)

REFERENCE INFORMATION

Symbol	Ref.	Temp. Range °K	Rept. Error %	Sample Specifications	Remarks
○	60-5	318-1039		Formica no. YN-25 nylon reinforced phenolic resin bonded by shell Epon 422 adhesive; ablation rate 9.74×10^{-3} cm sec^{-1}. [Author's design.: 6].	Measured with lamination perpendicular to the central axis of the cylindrical specimen by using pt-pt 10Rh thermocouple.
□	60-5	308-1511		Same as above.	Same as above but measured by using Cr-Al thermocouple.
△	60-5	309-1359		Same as above.	Same as above.
▽	60-5	308-1196		Same description as the above sample except ablation rate 3.43×10^{-3} cm sec^{-1}. [Author's design.: 7].	Measured with laminate parallel to central axis of the cylindrical specimen by using pt-pt 10Rh thermocouple.

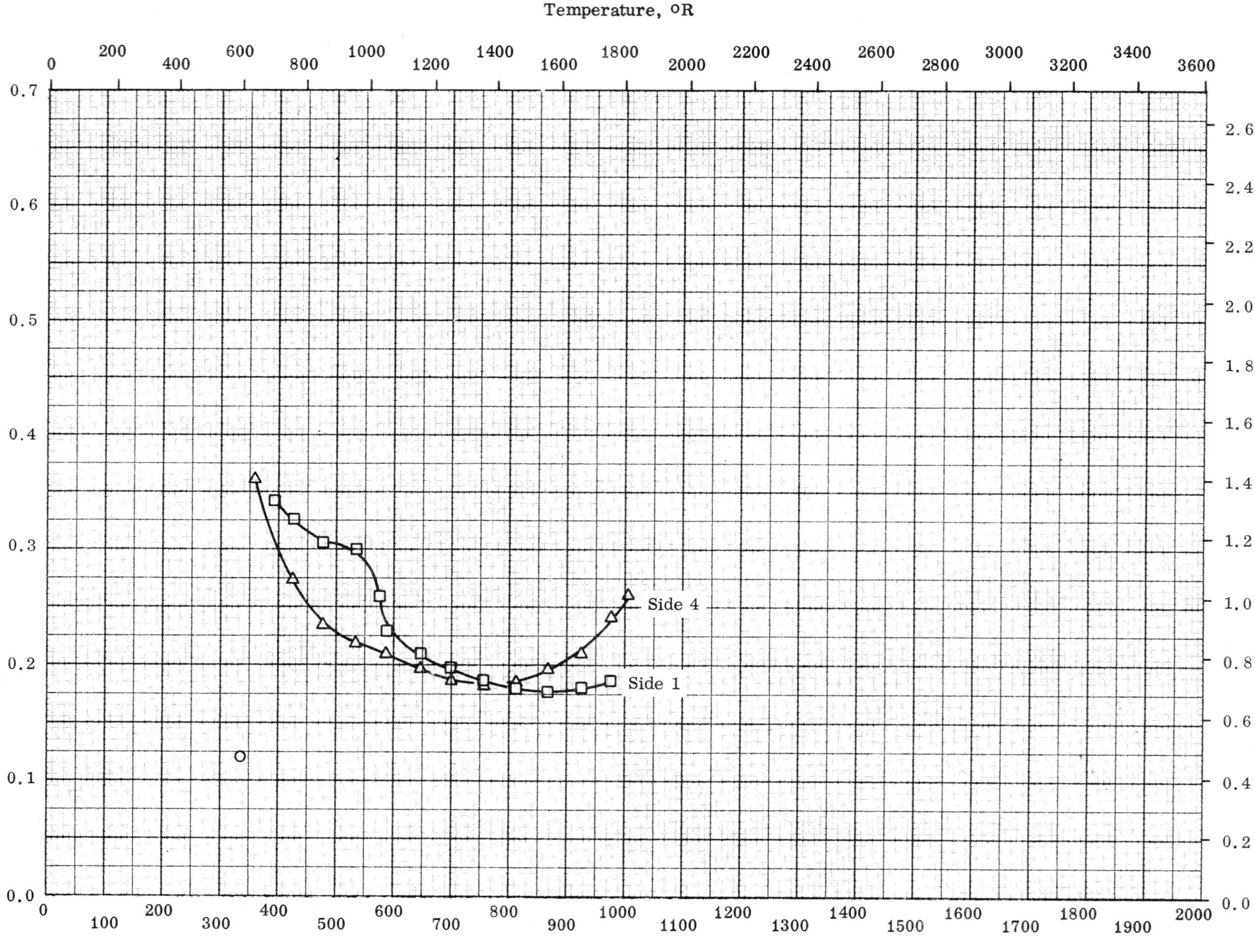

THERMAL DIFFUSIVITY -- PLASTIC LAMINATE
(Refrasil fabric reinforced phenolic resin)

THERMAL DIFFUSIVITY -- PLASTIC LAMINATE
(Refrasil fabric reinforced phenolic resin)

REFERENCE INFORMATION

Symbol	Ref.	Temp. Range °K	Rept. Error %	Sample Specifications	Remarks
○	63-3	333		91LD phenolic resin with refrasil cloth impregnated; sample circular area 0.34 ft^2 and 0.170 in. thick; density 97.0 lb ft^{-3}.	Pressed at 100 lb in^{-2} at 350 F for 1 hr and post-cured for 16 hrs at 350 F.
□	63-2	392-975		91LD phenolic resin with 0.15 in. thick refrasil cloth; resin content within 47 to 53%; sample 4.5 by 4.5 by 0.180 in. [Author's design.: panel 1].	Pressed at 100 lb in^{-2} at 375 F for 1 hr and post-cured for 12 hrs in an oven at 375 F; measured at side 1.
△	63-2	358-1003		Same as above. [Author's design.: panel 2].	Same as above; measured at side 4.

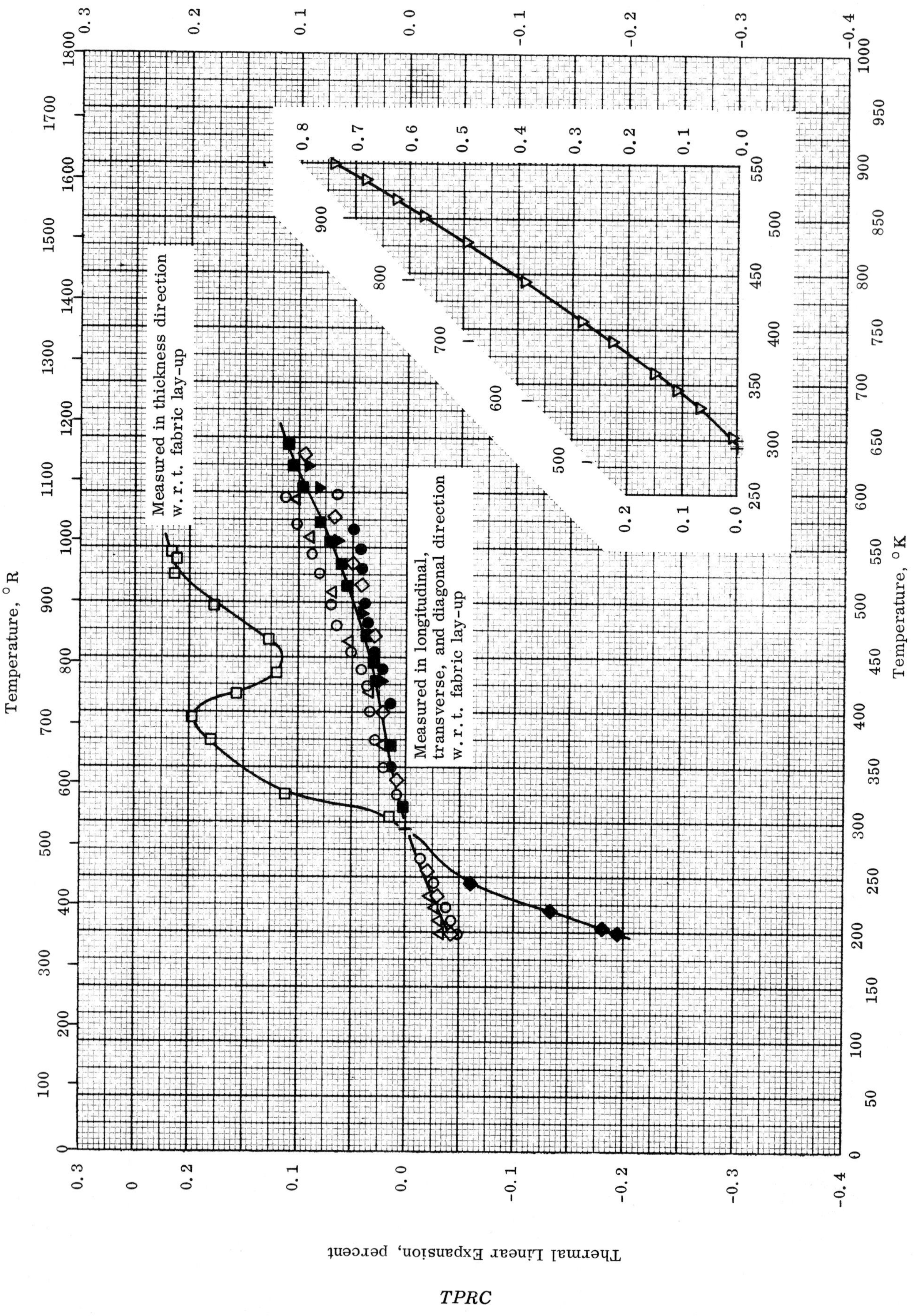

THERMAL LINEAR EXPANSION -- PLASTIC LAMINATES
(Asbestos reinforced phenolic resin)

THERMAL LINEAR EXPANSION -- PLASTIC LAMINATES
(Asbestos reinforced phenolic resin)

REFERENCE INFORMATION

Symbol	Ref.	Temp. Range °K	Rept. Error %	Sample Specifications	Remarks
○	58-8	200-596		Phenolic and Raybestos-Manhattan 9526 D fabric; fabricated by Brunswick-Balke-Collender Co.; nominal thickness 1/8 in.; sample 1 in. wide, 7 in. long, and 78 lb ft^{-3} density.	Cured at 300 F and 400 psi for 30 min and post-cured 300 F for 4 hrs and 350 F for 8 hrs; measured in longitudinal direction with respect to the fabric lay-up.
■	58-8	313-643		Same as above.	Second run of the above sample.
△	58-8	200-593		Same as above.	Same as above except measured in transverse direction.
▼	58-8	296-629		Same as above.	Second run of the above sample.
◇	58-8	200-635		Same as above.	Same as above except measured in diagonal direction.
●	58-8	300-598		Same as above.	Second run of the above sample.
□	58-8	293-545		Same as above except sample 1 in. in dia and 7-1/6 in. in thickness.	Same as above except measured in thickness direction with respect to fabric lay-up.
▽	58-8	293-549		Same as above.	Second run of the above sample.
◆	58-8	199-293		Same as above except sample 5-1/4 in. thick.	Same as above except measured in thickness direction with respect to the fabric lay-up.

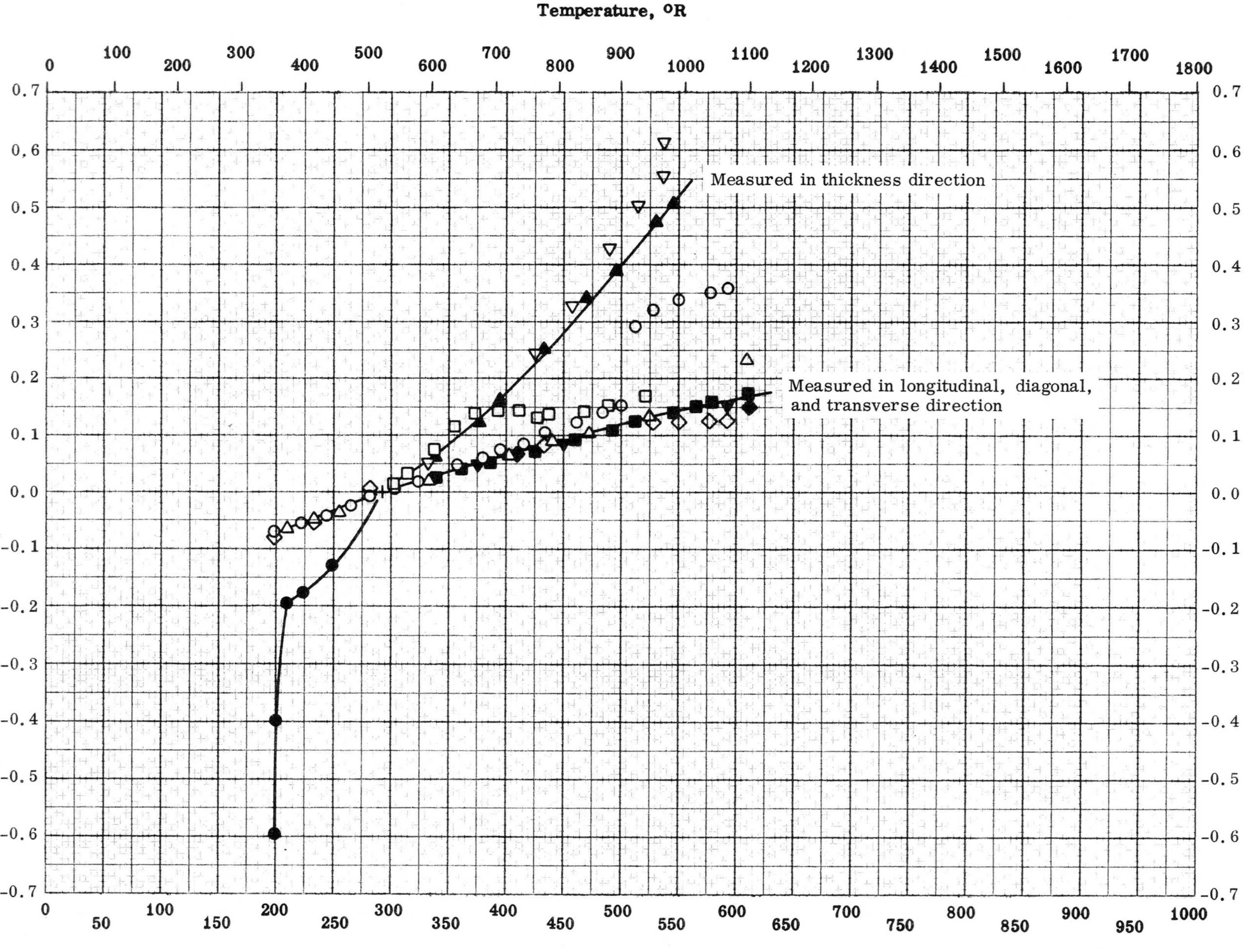

THERMAL LINEAR EXPANSION -- PLASTIC LAMINATES
(Glass fabric reinforced 37-9X phenolic resin)

THERMAL LINEAR EXPANSION -- PLASTIC LAMINATES
(Glass fabric reinforced 37-9X phenolic resin)

REFERENCE INFORMATION

Symbol	Ref.	Temp. Range °K	Rept. Error %	Sample Specifications	Remarks
○	58-8	200-593		Modified phenolic CTL-37-9X resin and 181 glass fabric; fabricated by Brunswick-Balke-Collender Co.; nominal thickness 1/8 in., 1 in. wide, and 7 in. long; calculated density 103 lb ft^{-3}.	Cured at 280 F and 175 psi for 30 min and post-cured 250 F, 300 F, 350 F, and 400 F each for 24 hrs; measured in longitudinal direction with respect to the fabric lay-up.
■	58-8	296-609		Same as above.	Second run of above sample.
△	58-8	200-608		Same as above.	Same as above; measured in transverse direction with respect to fabric lay-up.
▼	58-8	302-593		Same as above.	Second run of above sample.
◇	58-8	200-593		Same as above.	Same as above; measured in diagonal direction with respect to fabric lay-up.
◆	58-8	295-611		Same as above.	Second run of the above sample.
□	58-8	293-575		Same as above except sample 1 in. in dia and 7-1/4 in. thick.	Same as above; measured in thickness direction.
▲	58-8	293-545		Same as above.	Second run of above sample.
▽	58-8	293-536		Same as above.	Third run of above sample.
●	58-8	200-293		Same as above except 5-1/4 in. thick.	Same as above; first run.

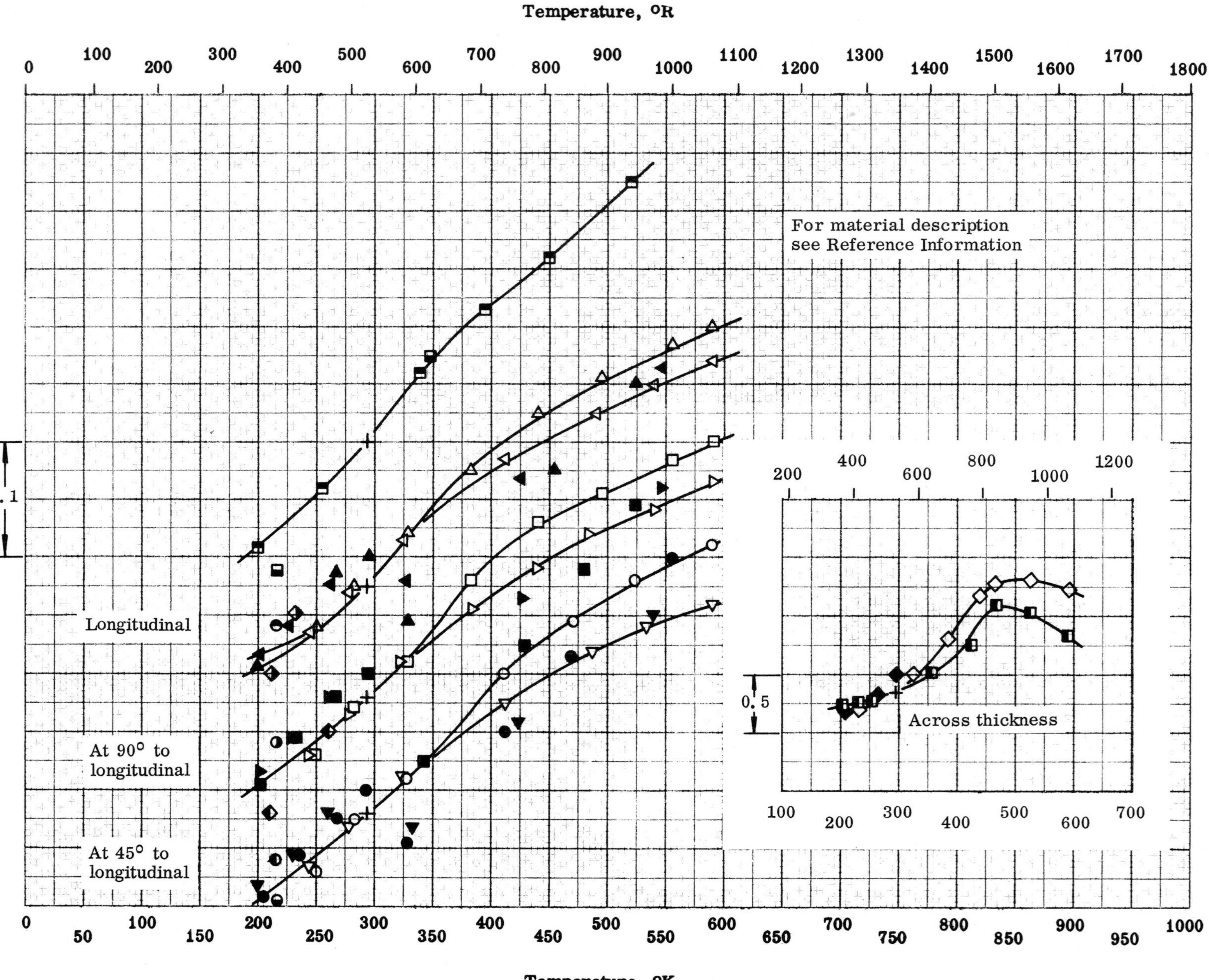

THERMAL LINEAR EXPANSION -- PLASTIC LAMINATES
(Glass fabric reinforced other phenolic resins)

THERMAL LINEAR EXPANSION -- PLASTIC LAMINATES
(Glass fabric reinforced other phenolic resins)

REFERENCE INFORMATION

Symbol	Ref.	Temp. Range °K	Rept. Error %	Sample Specifications	Remarks
○	55-3	200-589		Phenolic Resin Laminate; made by Narmco Inc.; fabric: 181 with Volan A finish, 12 ply; resin: Phenolic, Conolon 506; resin content 33 ; density 101 lb ft^{-3}.	Measured at 45 degree to longitudinal direction in plane of laminations; heating.
●	55-3	200-589		Same as above.	Cooling.
□	55-3	200-589		Same as above.	Measured at 90 degree to longitudinal direction in plane of laminations; heating.
■	55-3	200-589		Same as above.	Cooling.
△	55-3	200-589		Same as above.	Measured in longitudinal direction; heating.
▲	55-3	200-589		Same as above.	Cooling.
◇	55-3	200-589		Same as above.	Measured across thickness; heating.
◆	55-3	200-589		Same as above.	Cooling.
▽	55-3	200-589		Phenolic Resin Laminate; made by Bakelite Co.; fabric: 181; 14 ply; resin: Phenolic No. BV17085; resing content 28.5 ; catalyst: Hexasol.	Measured at 45 degree to longitudinal direction in plane of laminations; heating.
▼	55-3	200-589		Same as above.	Cooling.
▷	55-3	200-589		Same as above.	Measured at 90 degree to longitudinal direction in plane of laminations; heating.
▶	55-3	200-589		Same as above.	Cooling.
				(Continued onto next page)	

THERMAL LINEAR EXPANSION -- PLASTIC LAMINATES (Continued)
(Glass fabric reinforced other phenolic resins)

REFERENCE INFORMATION

Symbol	Ref.	Temp. Range °K	Rept. Error %	Sample Specifications	Remarks
◁	55-3	200-589		Same as above.	Measured in longitudinal direction; heating.
◀	55-3	200-589		Same as above.	Cooling.
◧	55-3	200-589		Same as above.	Measured across thickness; heating.
◨	55-3	200-589		Same as above.	Cooling.
⬒	51-4	200-533		Conolon N-1 Laminate; fabric: No. 181 - 114 Fiberglass cloth, 11 ply; resin: Nylon phenolic; resin content: 33. 8 .	Impregnated cloth heated 45 min at 250 F, pressed 5 hrs at 10 psi and 330 F, cooled in press to 150 F, heated 5 hrs at 350 F; measured parallel to laminations.
⬓	54-16	217-346		Phenolite made by National Vulcanized Fibre Co.; phenol-formaldehyde laminate with glass fabric base.	Held at 77 F and 50% relative humidity for 24 to 48 hrs; direction of measurement not specified.
◐	54-6	222-300		Phenolic resin No. 91-LD reinforced with 3/4 oz. phenolic resin mat laminated by Cincinnati Testing and Res. Lab.; resin content 44. 2 and 0. 130 in. thick; density 94 lb ft^{-3}.	Cured 30 min at 250 F, pressed at 200 psi, heated 108 hrs at 250 - 300 F; measured at 45 degree to longitudinal direction in plane of laminations.
◑	54-6	222-300		Same as above.	Same as above except measured at 90 degree to longitudinal direction in plane of laminations.
◓	54-6	222-300		Same as above.	Same as above except measured in longitudinal direction.
◒	54-6	211-300		Same resin reinforced by Modigliani PRM fabric laminated by Cincinnati Testing and Res. Lab.; resin content 47 and 0. 121 in. thick; density 102 lb ft^{-3}.	Same as above except second heating for 60 hrs at 250 - 300 F.; measured at 45 degree to longitudinal direction in plane of laminations.

(Continued onto next page)

THERMAL LINEAR EXPANSION -- PLASTIC LAMINATES (Continued)
(Glass fabric reinforced other phenolic resins)

REFERENCE INFORMATION

Symbol	Ref.	Temp. Range °K	Rept. Error %	Sample Specifications	Remarks
◆	54-6	211-300		Same as above.	Same as above except measured at 90 degree to longitudinal direction in plane of laminations.
◆	54-6	211-300		Same as above.	Same as above except measured in longitudinal direction.

DENSITY -- PLASTIC LAMINATES
(Reinforced polyesters and TAC polyester resins)

Symbol	Density	
	g cm^{-3}	lb ft^{-3}
○	1.62	101
□	1.82	114
△	1.83	114
◇	1.83	114
▽	1.71	107
◁	1.76	110
▷	1.76	110
●	1.86	116
■	1.91	119

DENSITY -- PLASTIC LAMINATES
(Reinforced polyesters and TAC polyester resins)

REFERENCE INFORMATION

Symbol	Ref.	Temp. Range °K	Rept. Error %	Sample Specifications	Remarks
○	55-5	298		Reinforced plastic laminated by Goodyear; fabric No. 181; Volan A finish; 11 ply; resin: Selectron; resin code No. 5003; 34.1 resin content; thickness: 0.127 in.	
□	55-5	298		Same as above except: 42.8 resin content; 12 ply; thickness: 0.135 in.	
△	55-5	298		Same as above except: 40.8 resin content; 12 ply; thickness: 0.123 in.	
◇	55-5	298		Same as above except: 37.5 resin content; 12 ply; thickness: 0.116 in.	
▽	55-5	298		Reinforced plastic, laminated by Goodyear; fabric No. 143; Garan finish; 11 ply; resin: Selectron; resin code No. 5003; 43.5 resin content; thickness: 0.136 in.	
◁	55-3	298		TAC-polyester resin, laminated by Naugatuck Chem. Co.; fabric No. 181; 301 finish; resin TAC-polyester resin No. Vibrin 135; 39.3 resin content; catalyst: benzoyl peroxide; thickness: 0.129 in.	
▷	55-5	298		Reinforced plastic, laminated by Goodyear; fabric No. 116; Garan finish; 30-32 ply; resin: Selectron; resin code No. 5003; 39.5 resin content; thickness: 0.127 in.	
				(Continued onto next page)	

DENSITY -- PLASTIC LAMINATES (Continued)
(Reinforced polyesters and TAC polyester resins)

REFERENCE INFORMATION

Symbol	Ref.	Temp. Range °K	Rept. Error %	Sample Specifications	Remarks
●	54-6 also 55-5	298		Reinforced plastic, laminated by American Cyanimid; fabric No. 181; OC 137 finish; resin: Laminac; resin code No. PDL7-669; 33.9 resin content; catalyst: Luperco ATC 1%; total thickness: 0.110 in.	
■	55-5	298		Reinforced plastic, laminated by Goodyear; fabric No. 181; Volan A finish; resin: Selectron; resin code No. 5005; 24.5 resin content; 4 ply; thickness: 0.036 in.	

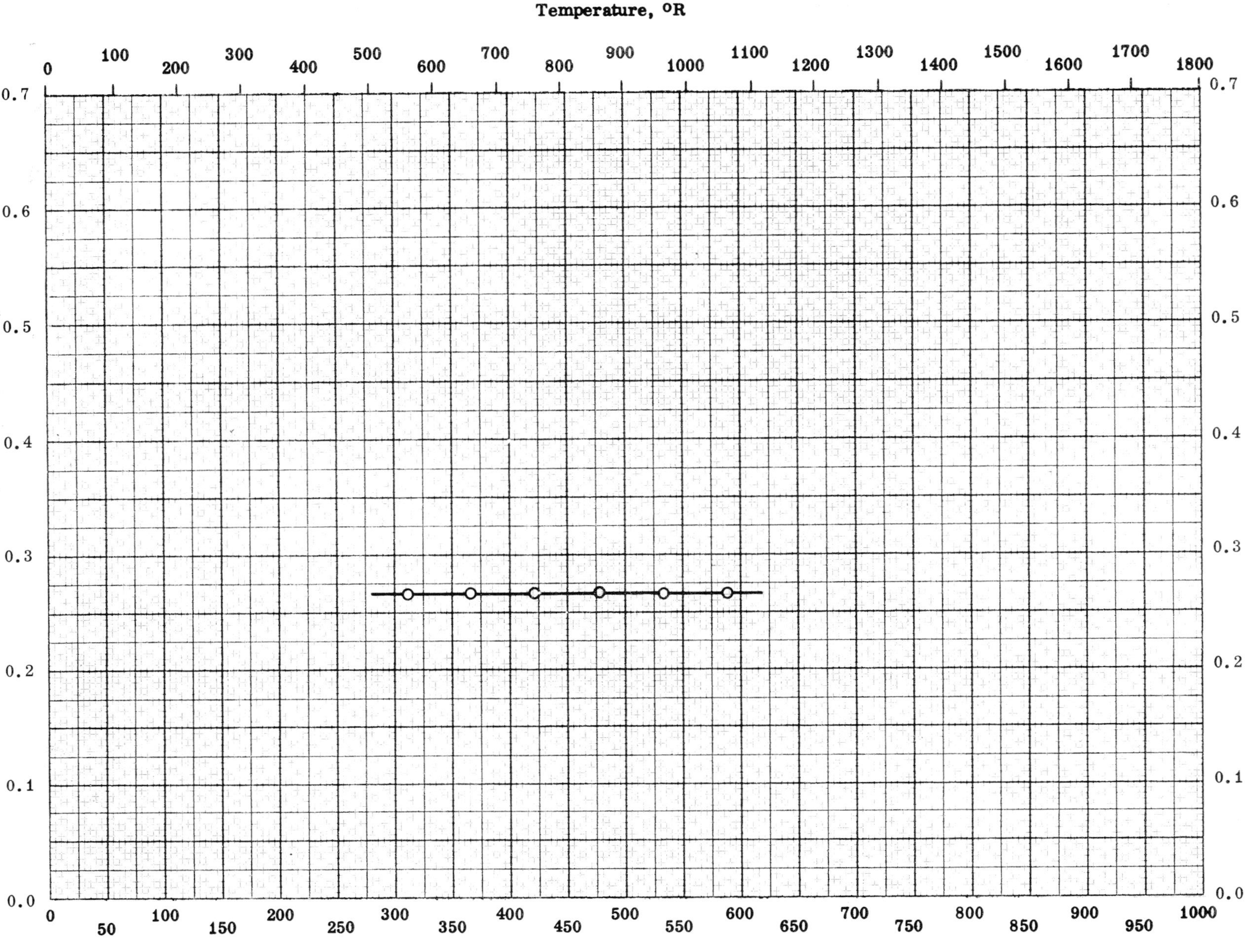

SPECIFIC HEAT -- PLASTIC LAMINATES
(Reinforced TAC polyester)

SPECIFIC HEAT -- PLASTIC LAMINATES
(Reinforced TAC polyester)

REFERENCE INFORMATION

Symbol	Ref.	Temp. Range °K	Rept. Error %	Sample Specifications	Remarks
○	55-3	311-589		By Naugatuck Chem. Co.; glass fabric 181; 301 finish; resin No. vibrin 135 (39.3%); Benzoyl peroxide catalyst; 14 ply; density 110 lb ft^{-3}.	

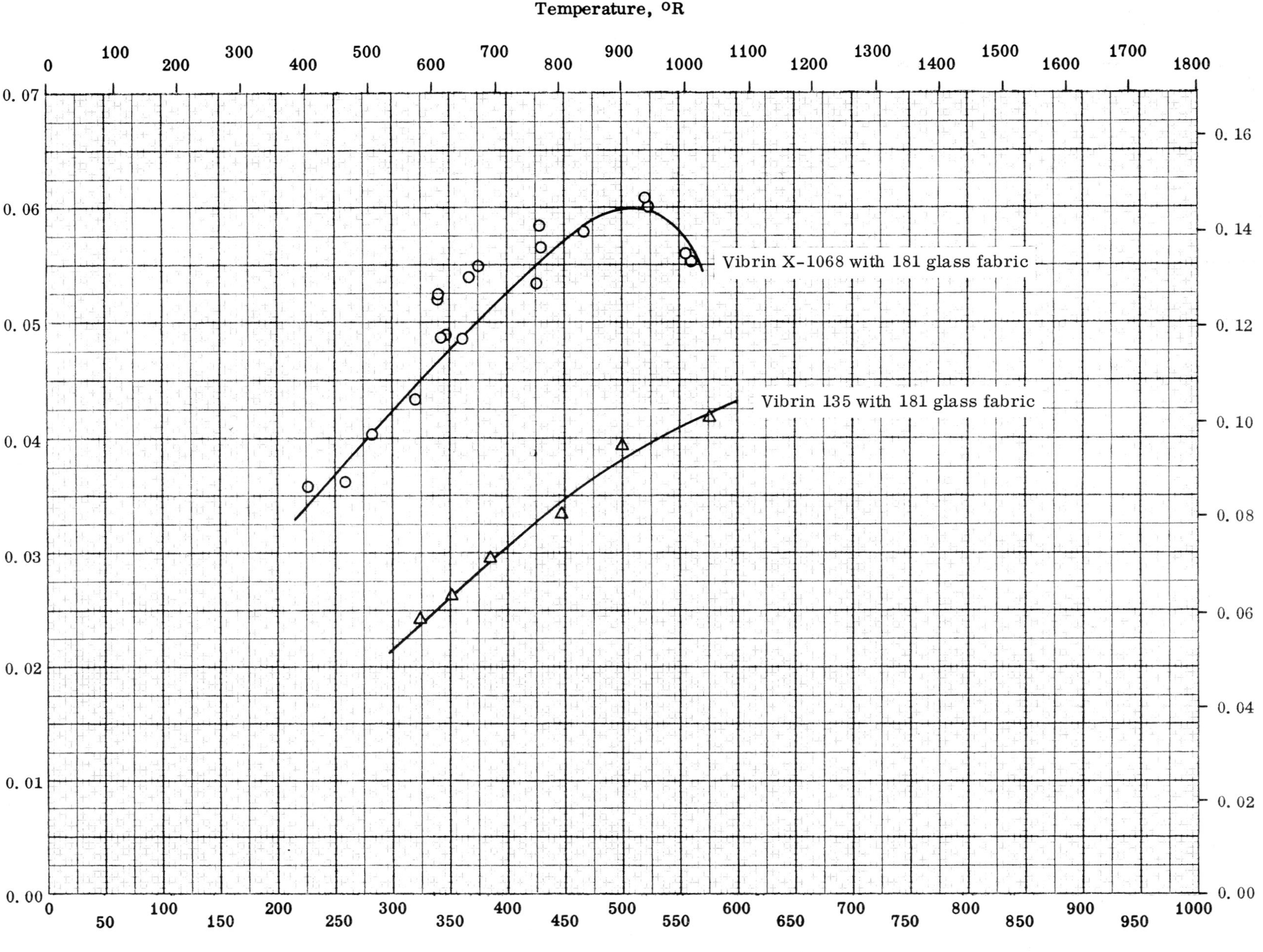

THERMAL CONDUCTIVITY -- PLASTIC LAMINATE
(Reinforced TAC polyester resin)

THERMAL CONDUCTIVITY -- PLASTIC LAMINATE
(Reinforced TAC polyester resin)

REFERENCE INFORMATION

Symbol	Ref.	Temp. Range °K	Rept. Error %	Sample Specifications	Remarks
○	58-8	227-560		TAC polyester vibrin X-1068 with 181 glass fabric and garan finish; 13 plies; catalyst 1. 5%benzoyl peroxide; density 112 lb ft^{-3} and nominal thickness 0. 125 in.	Cured at 200 F for 12 hrs and 250 F for 3 hrs in vacuum and post-cured 300 F for 1 hr, 350 F for 5 hrs, and 400 F for 1 hr.
△	55-3	324-575		TAC polyester vibrin 135 resin with 181 glass fabric 301 finish; resin content 39. 4 by weight and 39. 3 by author; 14 plies; catalyst benzoyl peroxide.	

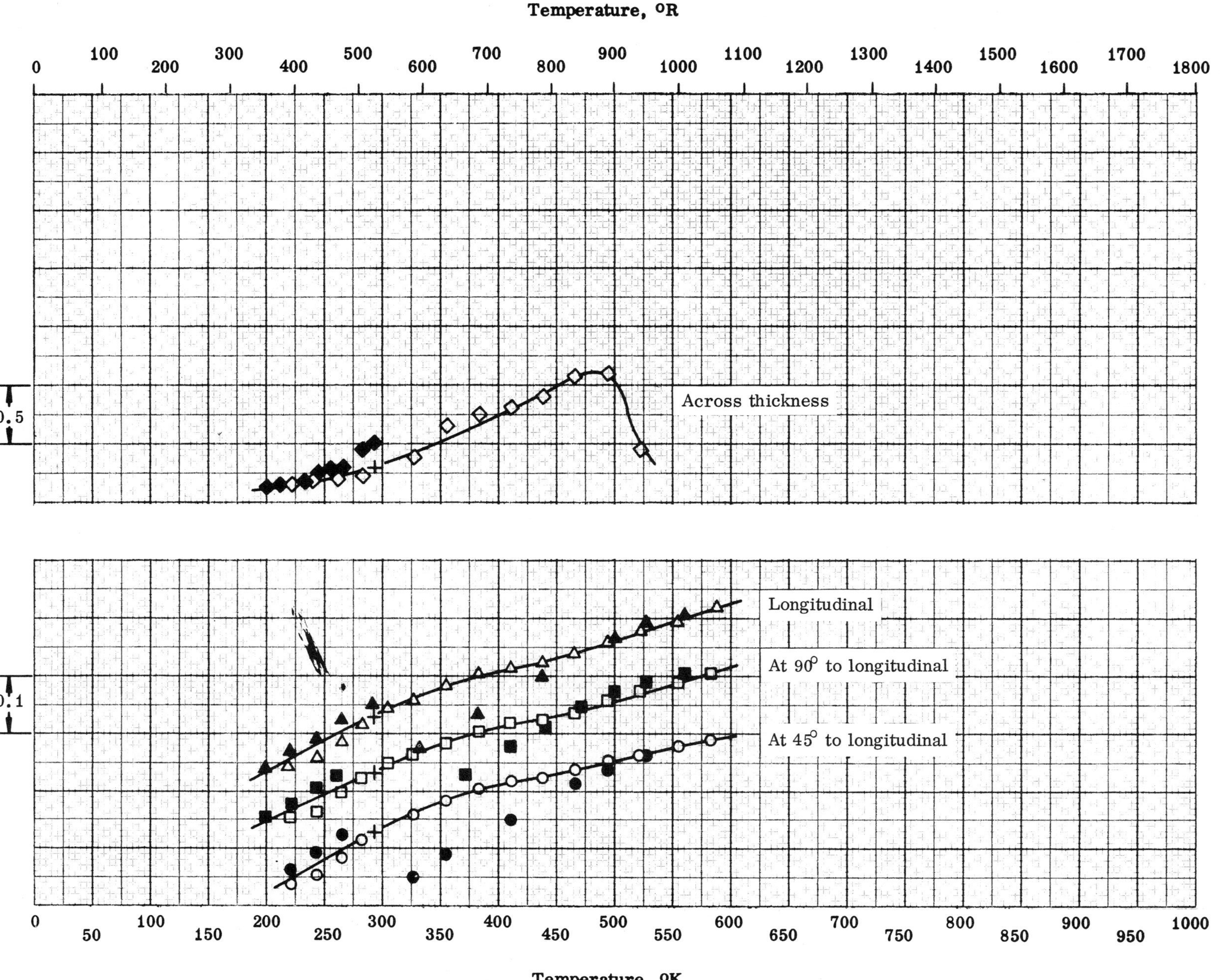

THERMAL LINEAR EXPANSION -- PLASTIC LAMINATES
(Glass fabric reinforced TAC Polyester Vibrin 135 resin)

THERMAL LINEAR EXPANSION -- PLASTIC LAMINATES
(Glass fabric reinforced TAC Polyester Vibrin 135 resin)

REFERENCE INFORMATION

Symbol	Ref.	Temp. Range °K	Rept. Error %	Sample Specifications	Remarks
○	55-3	200-589		TAC - Polyester Resin Laminate; fabric: 181 with 301 Finish; resin: TAC - Polyester No. Vibrin 135; Catalyst: Benzoyl Peroxide: Resin Content 39 made by Naugatuck Chem. Co.	Measured at 45° to the longitudinal direction in plane of laminations; heating.
●	55-3	200-589		Same as above.	Cooling.
□	55-3	200-589		Same as above.	Measured at 90° to the longitudinal direction in plane of laminations; heating.
■	55-3	200-589		Same as above.	Cooling.
△	55-3	200-589		Same as above.	Measured in longitudinal direction; heating.
▲	55-3	200-589		Same as above.	Cooling.
◇	55-3	200-589		Same as above.	Measured across thickness of sample; heating.
◆	55-3	200-589		Same as above.	Cooling.

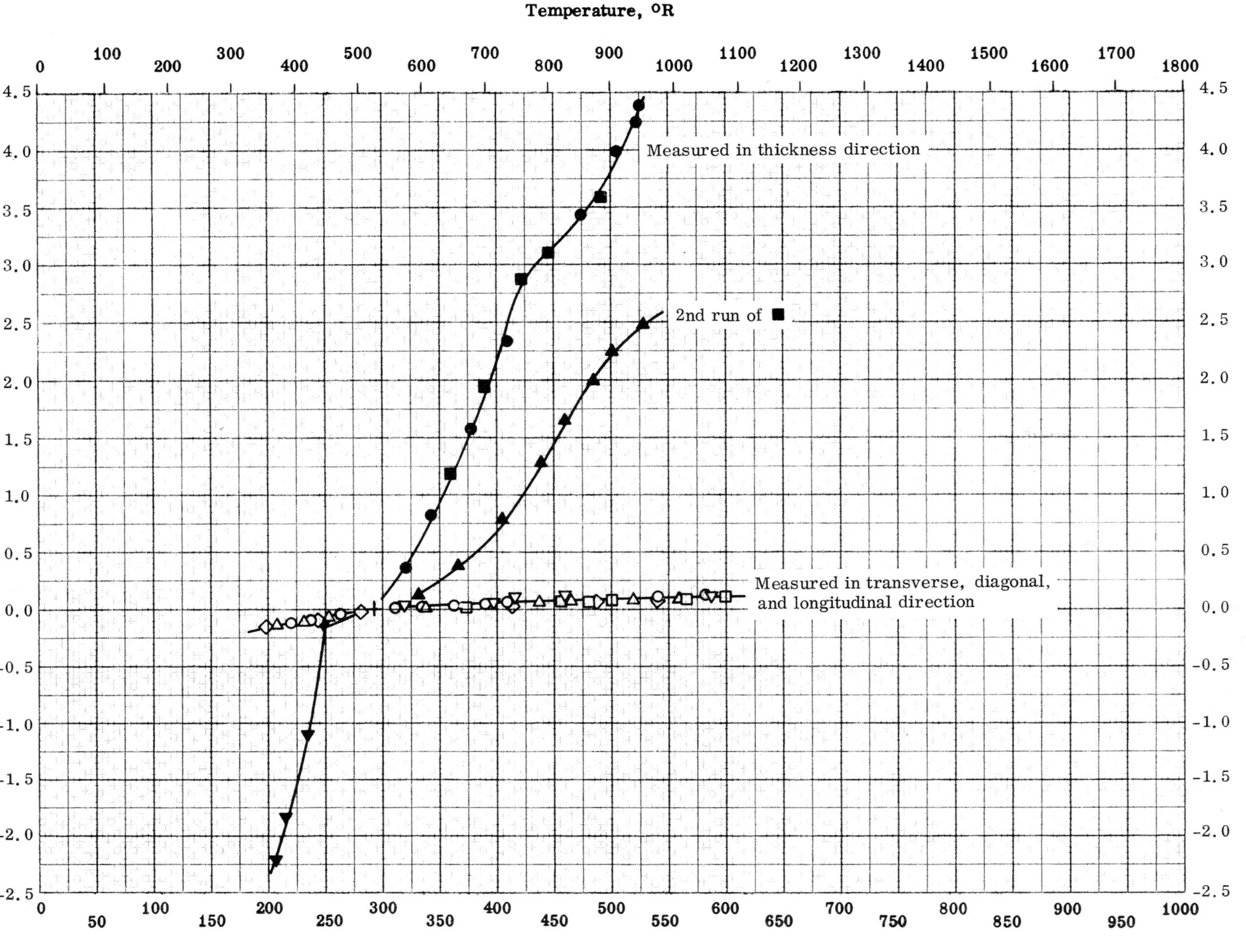

THERMAL LINEAR EXPANSION -- PLASTIC LAMINATES
(Glass fabric reinforced TAC Polyester Vibrin X-1068 resin)

THERMAL LINEAR EXPANSION -- PLASTIC LAMINATES
(Glass fabric reinforced TAC Polyester Vibrin X-1068 resin)

REFERENCE INFORMATION

Symbol	Ref.	Temp. Range °K	Rept. Error %	Sample Specifications	Remarks
○	58-8	200-584		TAC Polyester Vibrin X-1068 resin and 181 glass fabric; fabricated by Brunswick-Balke-Collender Co.; nominal thickness 1/8 in.; density 112 lb ft^{-3}.	Cured at 200 F for 12 hrs and 250 F for 3 hrs under vacuum and post-cured 300 F for 1 hr, 350 F for 5 hrs and 400 F for 1 hr; measured in transverse direction with respect to the fabric lay-up.
□	58-8	294-602		Same as above.	Second run of above sample.
△	58-8	200-585		Same as above.	Same as above except measured in longitudinal direction.
▽	58-8	294-604		Same as above.	Second run of above sample.
◇	58-8	200-585		Same as above.	Same as above except measured in diagonal direction.
●	58-8	293-526		Same as above except in disc form of 1 in. dia and 3-15/16 in. thick.	Same as above except measured in the direction of thickness with respect to fabric lay-up.
■	58-8	293-468		Same as above except 3-1/2 in. thick.	Same as above.
▲	58-8	293-529		Same as above.	Second run of above sample.
▼	58-8	208-293		Same as above except disc 2-7/8 in. thick.	Same curing and measuring process as above.

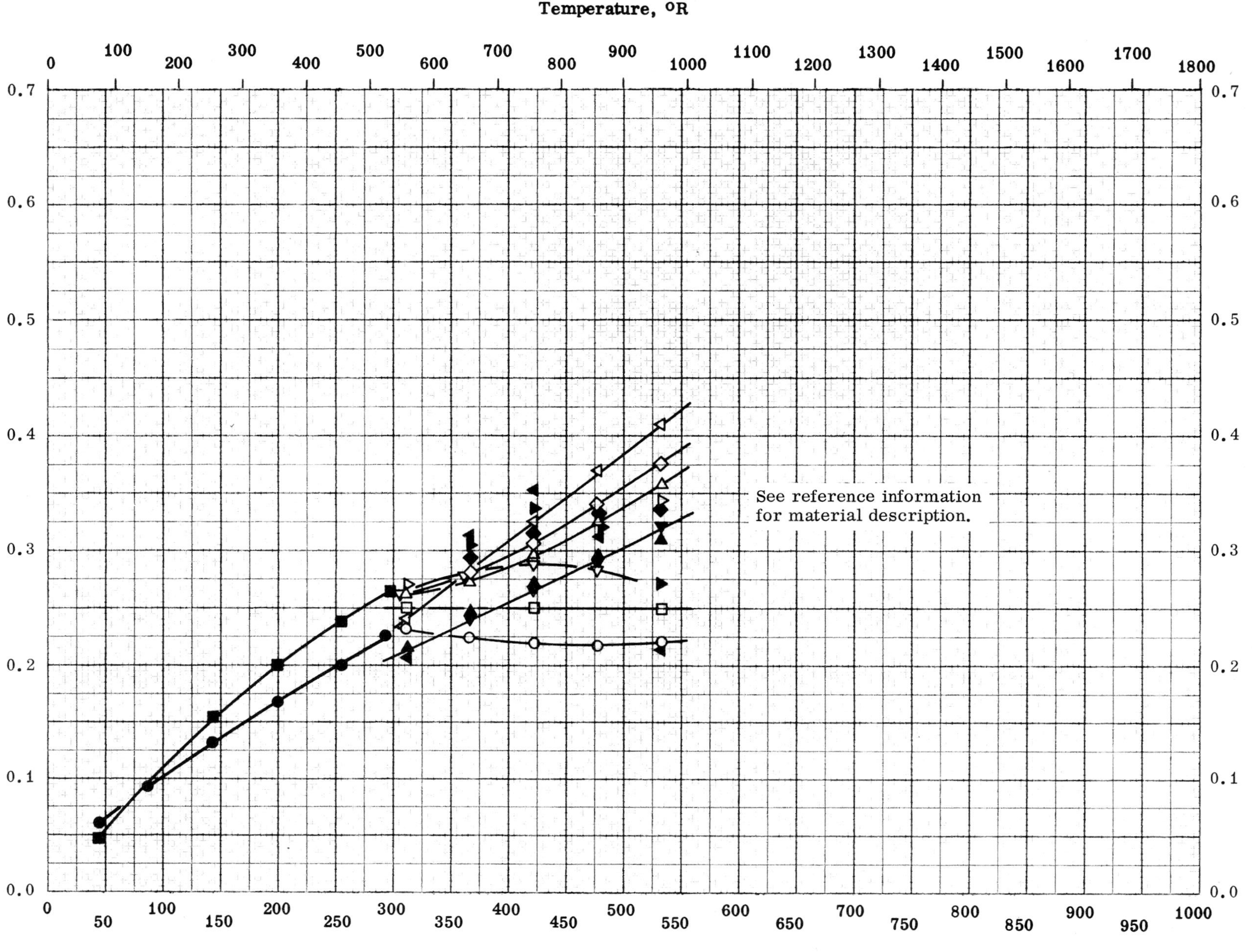

SPECIFIC HEAT -- PLASTIC LAMINATE
(Glass fabric reinforced polyester)

SPECIFIC HEAT -- PLASTIC LAMINATES
(Glass fabric reinforced polyester)

REFERENCE INFORMATION

Symbol	Ref.	Temp. Range °K	Rept. Error %	Sample Specifications	Remarks
○	55-5	311-533	±10	Material GY-H; Reinforced plastic laminated by Goodyear; fabric No. 181; finish: Volan A; resin: Selectron; resin code No. 5003; 24.5% resin content; 4 ply; 0.036 in. thick; density 119 lb ft^{-3}.	
□	55-5	311-533	±10	Material GY-E; Reinforced plastic laminated by Goodyear; fabric No. 181; finish: Volan A; resin: Selectron; resin code No. 5003; 29.2% resin content; 12 ply; 0.109 in. thick; density 120 lb ft^{-3}.	
△	55-5	311-533	±10	Material GY-D; Reinforced plastic laminated by Goodyear; fabric No. 143; finish: Garan; resin: Selectron; resin code No. 5003; 43.5% resin content; 11 ply; 0.136 in. thick; density 107 lb ft^{-3}.	
◇	55-5	311-533	±10	Material GY-A; Reinforced plastic laminated by Goodyear; fabric No. 116; finish: Garan; resin: Selectron; resin code No. 5003; 39.5% resin content; 30 - 32 ply; 0.127 in. thick; density 110 lb ft^{-3}.	
▽	55-5	311-533	±10	Material GY-G; Reinforced plastic laminated by Goodyear; fabric No. 181; finish: Volan A; resin: Selectron; resin code No. 5003; 42.8% resin content; 12 ply; 0.135 in. thick; density 114 lb ft^{-3}.	
				(Continued onto next page)	

SPECIFIC HEAT -- PLASTIC LAMINATES (continued)
(Glass fabric reinforced polyester)

REFERENCE INFORMATION

Symbol	Ref.	Temp. Range °K	Rept. Error %	Sample Specifications	Remarks
◁	55-5	311-533	±10	Material GY-C. Reinforced plastic laminated by Goodyear; fabric No. 181; finish: Volan A; resin: Selectron; resin code No. 5003; 40.8% resin content; 12 ply; 0.123 in. thick; density 114 lb ft^{-3}.	
▷	55-5	311-533	±10	Material GY-F. Reinforced plastic laminated by Goodyear; fabric No. 181; finish: Volan A; resin: Selectron; resin code No. 5003; 37.5% resin content; 12 ply; 0.116 in. thick; density 114 lb ft^{-3}.	
▲	55-5	311-533	±10	Material GY-I. Reinforced plastic laminated by Goodyear; fabric No. 181; finish: Volan A; resin: Selectron; resin code No. 5003; 34.1% resin content; 11 ply; 0.127 in. thick; density 101 lb ft^{-3}.	
▼	55-5	311-533	±10	Material GY-B. Reinforced plastic laminated by Goodyear; fabric No. 128; finish: Volan A; resin: Selectron; resin code No. 5003; 39.2% resin content; 0.115 in. thick; density 115 lb ft^{-3}.	
◆	55-5	311-533	±10	Reinforced plastic laminated by American Cyanamid; fabric No. 181; finish: OC 136; resin: Laminac; resin code No. PDL-669; 33.9% resin content; catalyst: Luperco ATC 1%; 12 ply; 0.118 in. thick; density 116 lb ft^{-3}.	

(Continued onto next page)

SPECIFIC HEAT -- PLASTIC LAMINATES (continued)
(Glass fabric reinforced polyester)

REFERENCE INFORMATION

Symbol	Ref.	Temp. Range °K	Rept. Error %	Sample Specifications	Remarks
◀	54-6	311-533	±10	Reinforced plastic laminated by Goodyear; fabric No. 116; finish: Garan; resin: Selectron; resin code No. 5003; 30 - 32 ply; 0.127 in. thick.	
▶	54-6	311-589	±10	Reinforced plastic laminated by American Cyanamid; fabric No. 181; finish: OC 136; resin: Laminac; resin code No. PDL7-669; 33.9% resin content; catalyst: Luperco ATC 1%; 12 ply; 0.118 in. thick.	
●	65-3	45-293	± 5	Glass fabric reinforced polyester laminate compound of 38 paraplex P-43 polyester resin and 62 E glass (spec. MIL-C-9084; type VIII (181) with spec MIL-F-8118 finish); density 1.8298 g cm^{-3}; void 2-1%; [Author's design.: Material H].	
■	65-3	55-299	± 5	Formed and slow cooled polyethelene terephthalale film (MYLAR); density 86.59 lb ft^{-3}.	

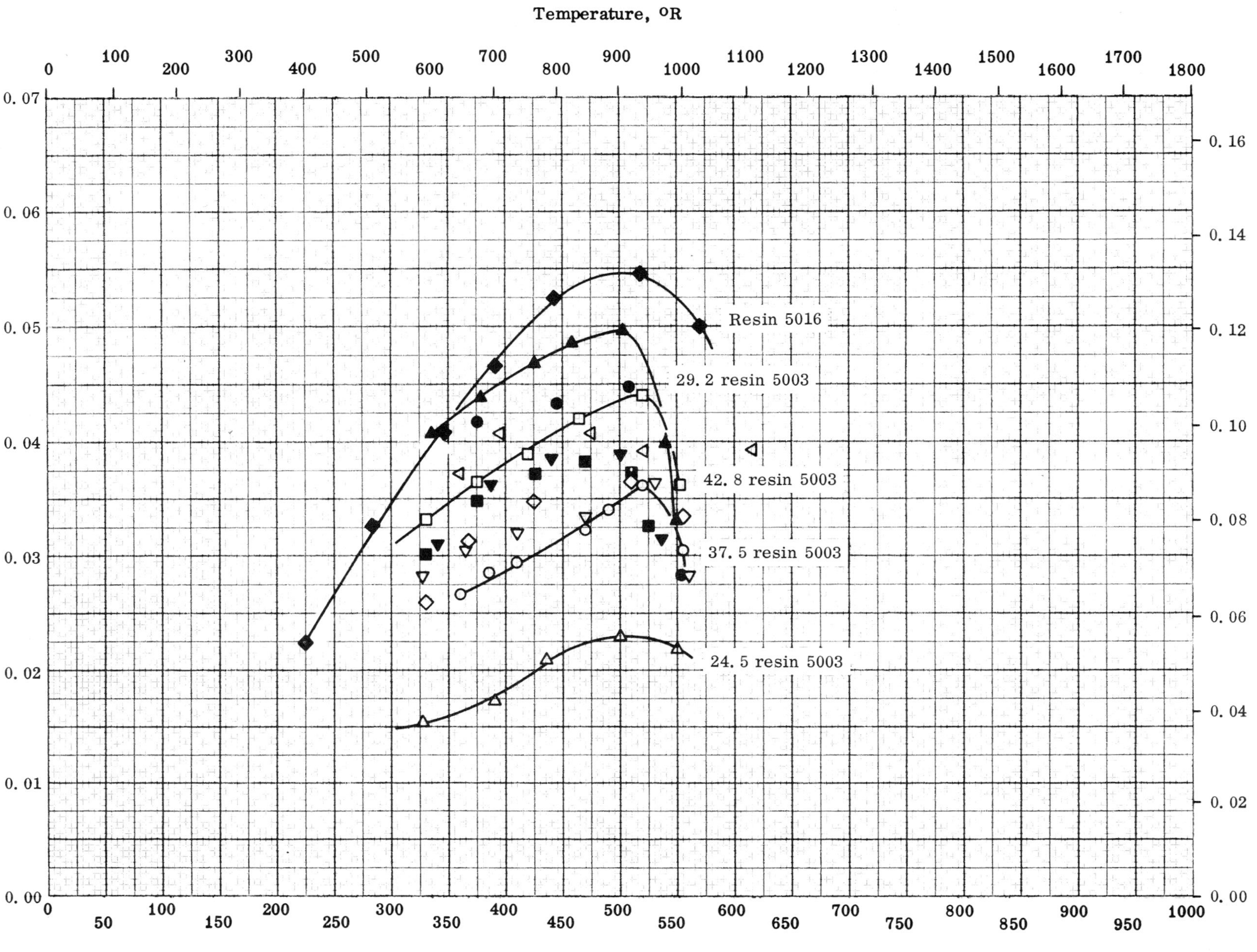

THERMAL CONDUCTIVITY -- PLASTIC LAMINATE
(Reinforced polyester Selectron resin)

THERMAL CONDUCTIVITY -- PLASTIC LAMINATE
(Reinforced polyester Selectron resin)

REFERENCE INFORMATION

Symbol	Ref.	Temp. Range °K	Rept. Error %	Sample Specifications	Remarks
○	55-5	361-555		Selectron 5003 resin with 181 glass fabric volan A finish from Goodyear; resin content 37. 5; 11-12 plies; density 114. 3 lb ft^{-3} and viscosity 850 cps at 77 F.	Placed in a constant temperature-humidity cabinet at 73 F - 50% RH for a minimum of one week prior to testing.
□	55-5	332-552		Same as above except resin content 42. 8 and density 113. 5 lb ft^{-3}.	Same as above.
△	55-5	327-550		Same as above except resin content 24. 5, 4 plies, and density 118. 99 lb ft^{-3}.	Same as above.
▽	55-5	328-560		Same as above except resin content 34. 1, 11 plies, and density 101. 15 lb ft^{-3}.	Same as above.
◁	55-5	361-613		Same as above except resin content 37. 5, 11-12 plies, and density 114. 50 lb ft^{-3}.	Same as above.
◇	55-5	330-557		Selectron 5003 resin with 116 glass fabric with garan finish from Goodyear; resin content 39. 5; 30-32 plies; density 110. 12 lb ft^{-3} and viscosity 850 cps at 77 F.	Same as above.
●	55-5	375-553		Selectron 5003 resin with 181 glass fabric volan A finish from Goodyear; resin content 40. 8; 12 plies; density 114. 70 lb ft^{-3} and viscosity 850 cps at 77 F.	Same as above.
■	55-5	331-523		Selectron 5003 resin with 143 glass fabric of garan finish; resin content 43. 5; 11 ples; density 107. 08 lb ft^{-3} and viscosity 850 cps at 77 F.	Same as above.

(Continued onto next page)

THERMAL CONDUCTIVITY -- PLASTIC LAMINATE (continued)
(Reinforced polyester Selectron resin)

REFERENCE INFORMATION

Symbol	Ref.	Temp. Range °K	Rept. Error %	Sample Specifications	Remarks
▲	54-6	335-551		Selectron 5003 resin with glass fabric 181 of volan finish from Goodyear; resin content 29. 2; 11 plies; density 119. 75 lb ft^{-3} and viscosity 850 cps at 77 F.	Same as above.
▼	54-6	340-537		Selectron 5003 resin with 128 glass fabric volan A finish from Goodyear; resin content 39. 2; 18 plies; density 115. 32 lb ft^{-3} and viscosity 850 cps at 77 F.	Same as above.
◆	58-8	227-569		Selectron 5016 resin with 181 fabric glass and volan A finish; 15 plies on both sides; 2% benzoyl peroxide catalyst; density 105 lb ft^{-3}.	Cured at 250 F from 5 hrs.

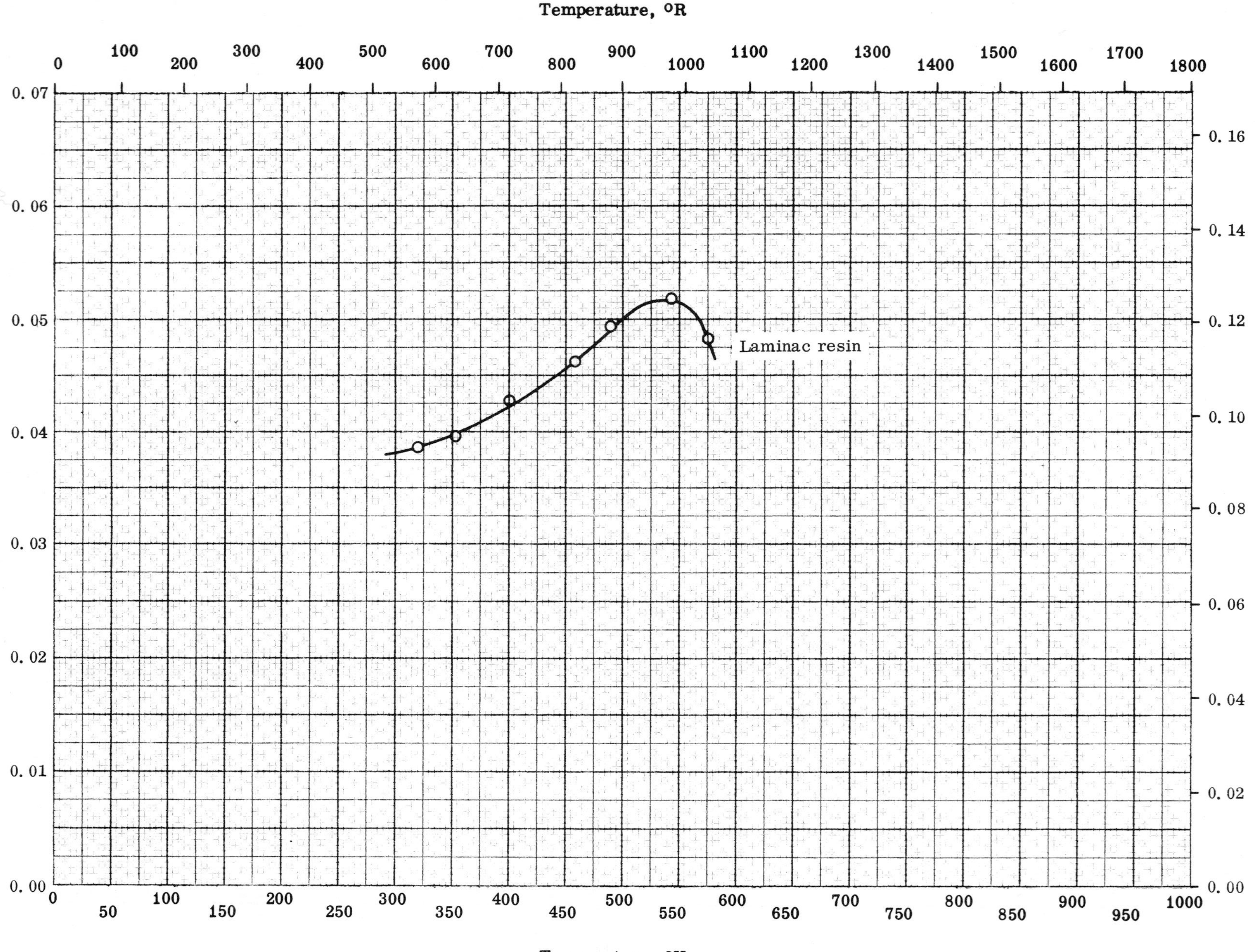

THERMAL CONDUCTIVITY -- PLASTIC LAMINATE
(Reinforced polyester resin)

THERMAL CONDUCTIVITY -- PLASTIC LAMINATE
(Reinforced polyester resin)

REFERENCE INFORMATION

Symbol	Ref.	Temp. Range °K	Rept. Error %	Sample Specifications	Remarks
○	54-6	320-575		Laminac resin PDL-7-669 with 181 glass fabric of OC 136 finish from American Cyanamid; resin content 33.9; 12 plies; luperco ATC - 1% catalyst; density 116.38 lb ft^{-3} and viscosity 45 poises.	Placed in a constant temperature-humidity cabinet at 73 F - 50% RH for a minimum of one week prior to testing.

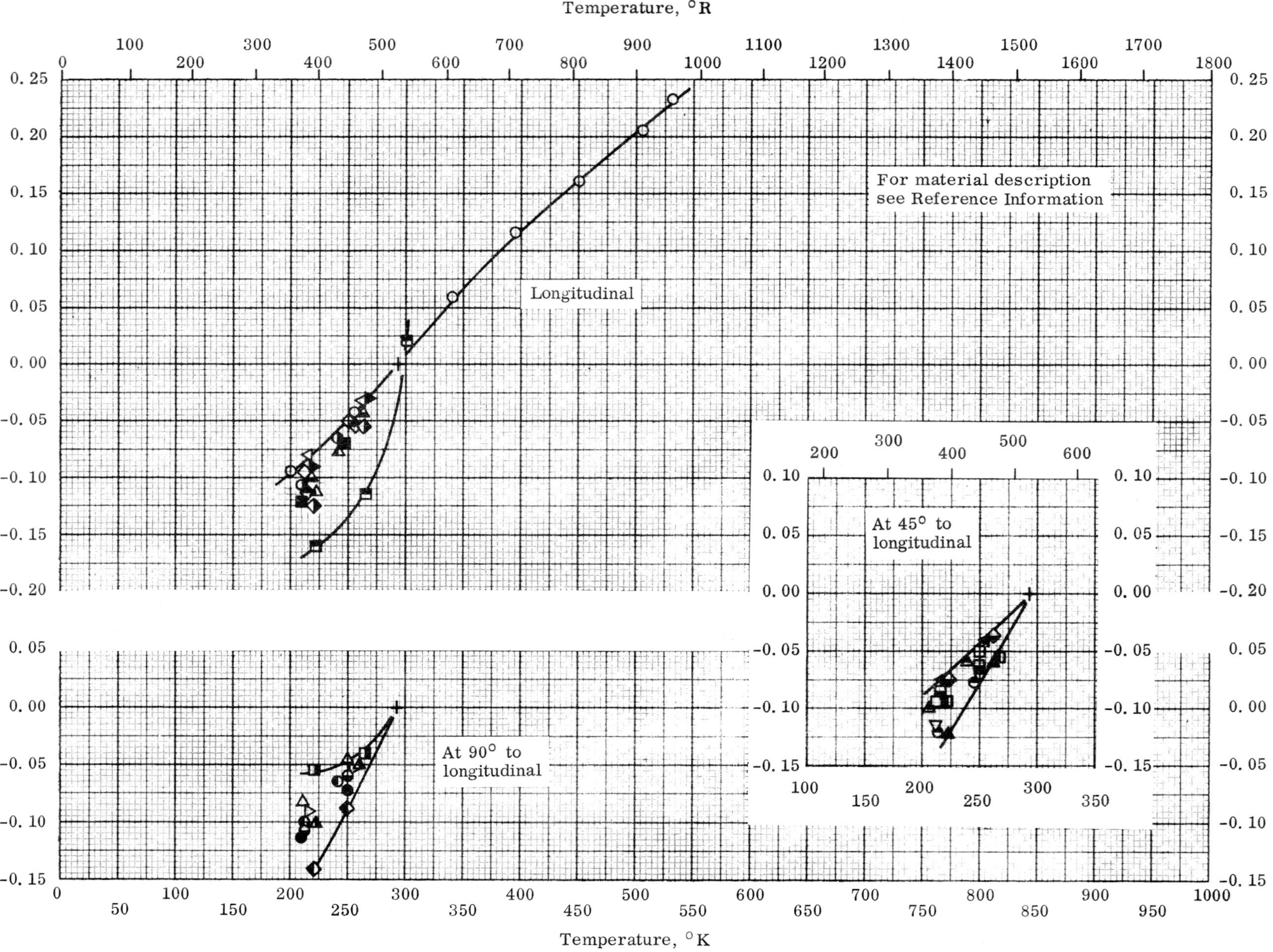

THERMAL LINEAR EXPANSION -- PLASTIC LAMINATES
(Glass fabric reinforced polyester)

REFERENCE INFORMATION

Symbol	Ref.	Temp. Range °K	Rept. Error %	Sample Specifications	Remarks
○	51-4	200-533		11 Ply Laminate; fabric: No. 181-114 fiber glass cloth; resin: Polyester, Selectron 5016; catalyst: 1.5% benzoyl peroxide; resin content: 38.5 .	Cured at 10 psi for 1/2 hr at 180 F, 1/2 hr at 200 F, 1/2 hr at 225 F, cooled in press to 150 F, heat treated in oven 16 hrs at 350 F; measured parallel to laminations.
□	54-6	211-300		30 - 32 ply reinforced plastic (by Goodyear Corp.); fabric: No. 116 with Garan finish; resin: Selectron 5003; total thickness: 0.127 in.	Measured at 45 degree to the longitudinal direction in the plane of laminations.
△	54-6	211-300		Same as above.	Measured at 90 degree to the longitudinal direction in the plane of laminations.
◇	54-6	211-300		Same as above.	Measured in longitudinal direction.
▽	54-6	211-300		18 ply reinforced plastic (by Goodyear Corp.); fabric: No. 128 with Volan finish; resin: Selectron 5003; total thickness: 0.115 in.	Measured at 45 degree to the longitudinal direction in plane of laminations.
●	54-6	211-300		Same as above.	Measured at 90 degree to the longitudinal direction in plane of laminations.
■	54-6	211-300		Same as above.	Measured in longitudinal direction.
▲	54-6	222-300		12 ply reinforced plastic (by Goodyear Corp.); fabric: No. 181 with Volan finish; resin: Selectron 5003; total thickness: 0.123 in.	Measured at 45 degree to the longitudinal direction in plane of laminations.
▲	54-6	222-300		Same as above.	Measured at 90 degree to the longitudinal direction in plane of laminations.

(Continued onto next page)

THERMAL LINEAR EXPANSION -- PLASTIC LAMINATES (Continued)
(Glass fabric reinforced polyester)

REFERENCE INFORMATION

Symbol	Ref.	Temp. Range °K	Rept. Error %	Sample Specifications	Remarks
◭	54-6	222-300		Same as above.	Measured in longitudinal direction.
◧	54-6	222-300		11 ply reinforced plastic (by Goodyear Corp.); fabric: No. 143 with Garan finish; resin: Selectron 5003; total thickness: 0.136 in.	Measured at 45 degree to the longitudinal direction in plane of laminations.
◨	54-6	222-300		Same as above.	Measured at 90 degree to the longitudinal direction in plane of laminations.
⬒	54-6	222-300		Same as above.	Measured in longitudinal direction.
⬓	54-6	214-300		11 ply reinforced plastic (by Goodyear Corp.); fabric: No. 181 with Volan A finish; resin: Selectron 5003; resin content: 34.5 ; total thickness: 0.109 in.	Measured at 45 degree to the longitudinal direction in plane of laminations.
◐	54-6	214-300		Same as above.	Measured at 90 degree to the longitudinal direction in plane of laminations.
◑	54-6	214-300		Same as above	Measured in longitudinal direction.
◒	54-6	214-300		11 or 12 ply reinforced plastic (by Goodyear Corp.); fabric: No. 181 with Volan A finish; resin: Selectron 5003; resin content: 38 ; total thickness: 0.116 in.	Measured at 45 degree to the longitudinal direction in plane of laminations.
◓	54-6	214-300		Same as above.	Measured at 90 degree to the longitudinal direction in plane of laminations.
⬘	54-6	214-300		Same as above.	Measured in longitudinal direction.

(Continued onto next page)

THERMAL LINEAR EXPANSION -- PLASTIC LAMINATES (Continued)
(Glass fabric reinforced polyester)

REFERENCE INFORMATION

Symbol	Ref.	Temp. Range °K	Rept. Error %	Sample Specifications	Remarks
⬙	54-6	222-300		12 ply reinforced plastic (by Goodyear Corp.); fabric: No. 181 with Volan A finish; resin: Selectron 5003; resin content: 42 ; total thickness: 0.135 in.	Measured at 45 degree to the longitudinal direction in plane of laminations.
◐	54-6	222-300		Same as above.	Measured at 90 degree to the longitudinal direction in plane of laminations.
◑	54-6	222-300		Same as above.	Measured in longitudinal direction.
△	54-6	214-300		4 ply reinforced plastic (by Goodyear Corp.); fabric: No. 181 with Volan A finish; resin: Selectron 5003; total thickness: 0.036 in.	Measured at 45 degree to the longitudinal direction in plane of laminations.
▲	54-6	214-300		Same as above.	Measured at 90 degree to the longitudinal direction in plane of laminations.
◁	54-6	214-300		Same as above.	Measured in longitudinal direction.
◀	54-6	217-300		11 ply reinforced plastic (by Goodyear Corp.); fabric: No. 181 with Volan A finish; resin: Selectron 5003; resin content: 34.1 ; total thickness: 0.127 in.	Measured at 45 degree to the longitudinal direction in plane of laminations.
▷	54-6	217-300		Same as above.	Measured at 90 degree to the longitudinal direction in plane of laminations.
▶	54-6	217-300		Same as above.	Measured in longitudinal direction.

DENSITY -- PLASTIC LAMINATES
(Reinforced silicone resin)

Symbol	Density	
	$g\ cm^{-3}$	$lb\ ft^{-3}$
○	1.62	101

DENSITY -- PLASTIC LAMINATES
(Reinforced silicone resin)

REFERENCE INFORMATION

Symbol	Ref.	Temp. Range °K	Rept. Error %	Sample Specifications	Remarks
○	54-6 also 57-8	298		Reinforced plastic - laminated by Dow Corning; fabric No. 181; finish: OC 112; 14 ply; resin: silicone; resin code No. 2104; 32 - 35 resin content; total thickness: 0. 141 in.	

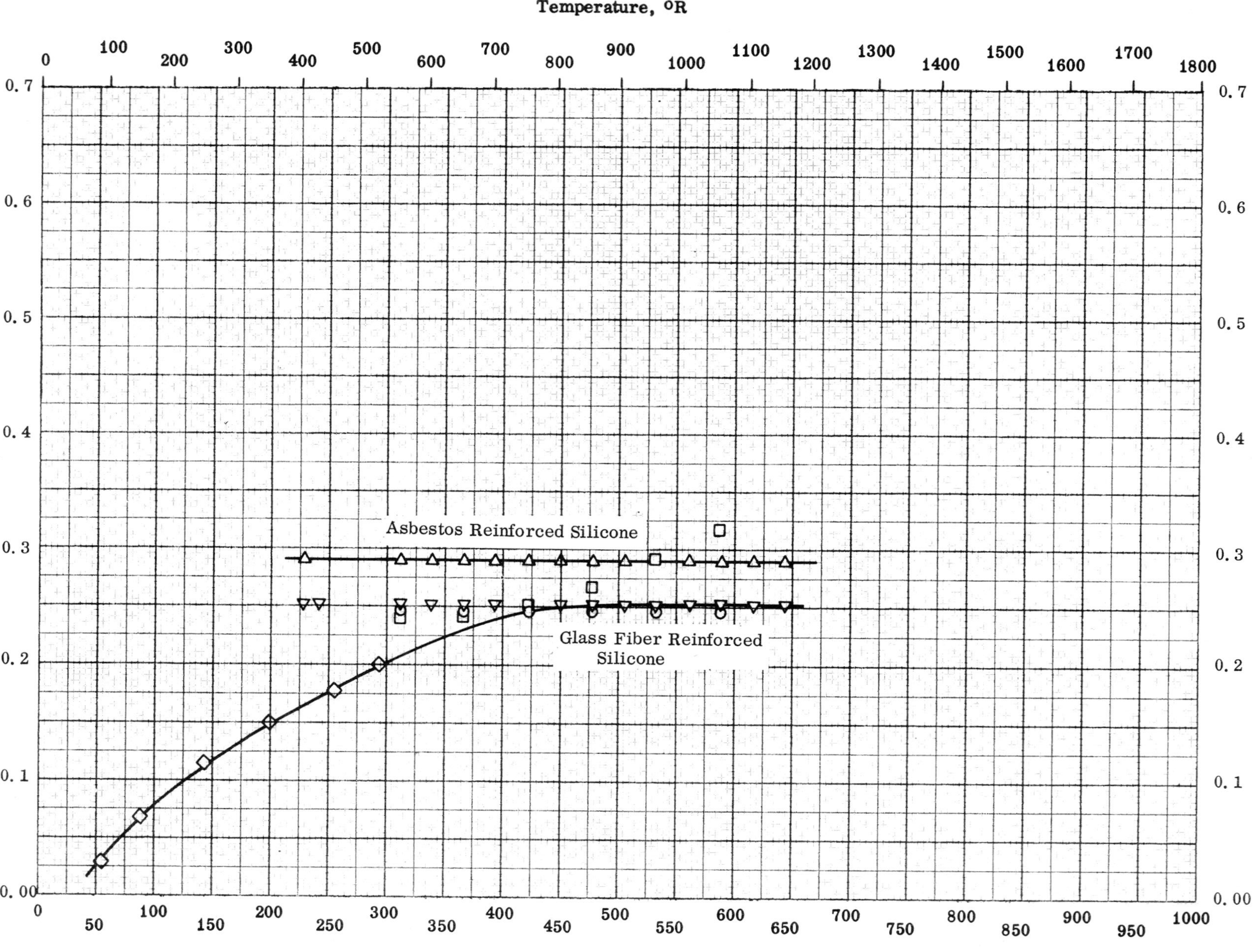

SPECIFIC HEAT -- PLASTIC LAMINATES
(Reinforced Silicone Resin)

SPECIFIC HEAT -- PLASTIC LAMINATES
(Reinforced Silicone Resin)

REFERENCE INFORMATION

Symbol	Ref.	Temp. Range °K	Rept. Error %	Sample Specifications	Remarks
○	55-3	311-589		Glass fabric No. 181, 112 finish by Dow Corning; resin No. 2 2106; XY-15 catalyst, 12 ply.	
□	55-5	311-589	±10	Glass fabric No. 181, OC112 finish; resin No. 2104; 14 ply, 0.14 thick; resin content 32 - 35; density 101 lb ft^{-3}.	
△	61-13	228-645		40 RPD asbestos and DC-2106 silicone; density 113.6 lb ft^{-3}. [Author's design.: SRI No. 10].	Loaded at 330 F for 20 sec; full pressure applied and bumped after 20 sec; cured 1-1/2 hrs at 330 F and 850 psi.
◇	65-3	55-294		Glass fiber roving reinforced laminate composed of 31 Dow Corning DC-2106 silicone resin and 69 heat cleaned "E" glass fiber roving; density 2.1770 g cm^{-3}; void 11.0%; [Author's design.: Material F].	
▽	61-13	242-645		Molded panel coast F130R; 30 silicone 4P020, DC 2106 resin and chopped glass 1B603 reinforcing system; density 106-109.7 lb ft^{-3}. [Author's design.: SRI No. 5].	

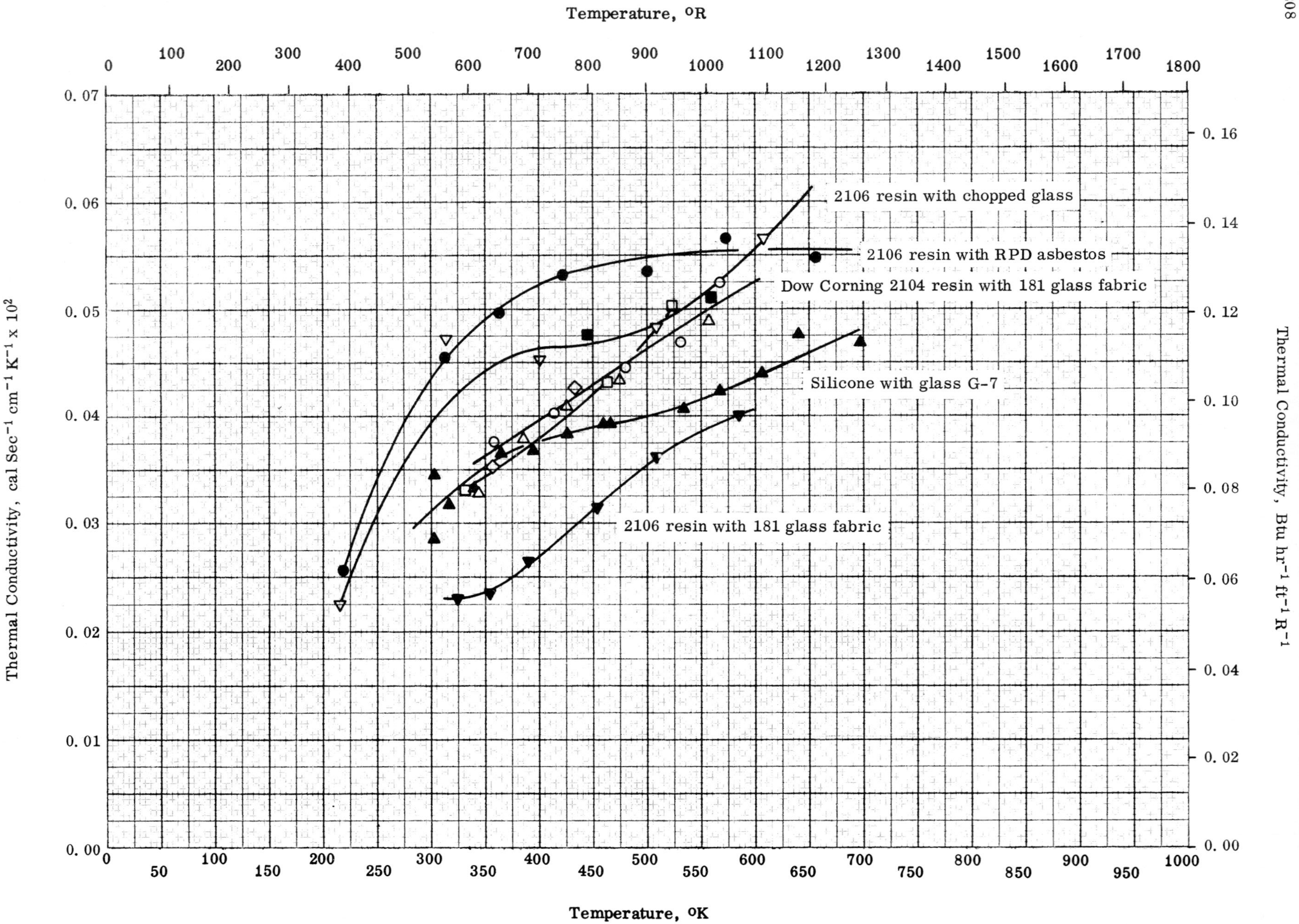

Thermal Conductivity, Btu hr^{-1} ft^{-1} R^{-1}

0.16 0.14 0.12 0.10 0.08 0.06 0.04 0.02 0.00

2106 resin with chopped glass

2106 resin with RPD asbestos

Dow Corning 2104 resin with 181 glass fabric

Silicone with glass G-7

2106 resin with 181 glass fabric

Temperature, °R

0 100 200 300 400 500 600 700 800 900 1000 1100 1200 1300 1400 1500 1600 1700 1800

Temperature, °K

0 50 100 150 200 250 300 350 400 450 500 550 600 650 700 750 800 850 900 950 1000

Thermal Conductivity, cal Sec^{-1} cm^{-1} K^{-1} x 10^2

0.07 0.06 0.05 0.04 0.03 0.02 0.01 0.00

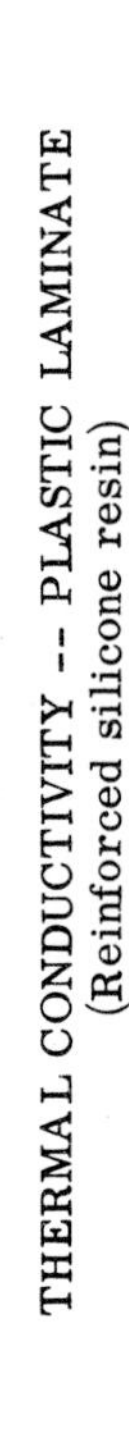

THERMAL CONDUCTIVITY -- PLASTIC LAMINATE
(Reinforced silicone resin)

THERMAL CONDUCTIVITY -- PLASTIC LAMINATE
(Reinforced silicone resin)

REFERENCE INFORMATION

Symbol	Ref.	Temp. Range °K	Rept. Error %	Sample Specifications	Remarks
○	57-8	358-566		Dow Corning 2104 silicone resin 181 glass fabric.	
□	57-8	331-532		Dow Corning 2106 silicone resin 181 glass fabric.	
▼	55-3	325-585		0. 105 in. thick silicone 2106 resin with 181 glass fabric of 112 finish; XY-15 catalyst and 12 plies.	
△	54-6	344-556		Dow Corning 2104 silicone resin with OC 112 finish; 32-35 resin content and 14 plies; sample 0. 1415 in. thick, 64 $in.^2$ area, and density 101. 03 lb ft^{-3}.	Placed in a constant temperature-humidity cabinet at 73 F - 50% RH for a minimum of one week prior to testing.
▽	61-12	215-607		Silicone 4 P 020 F 130 RDC-2106 resin reinforced by 1B603 chopped glass manufactured by Coast Manufacturing and Supply Co.; density 106 to 109. 7 lb ft^{-3}; resin content 35 ± 3.	Fabricated by heating at 200 F for 16 hrs, 260 F 2 hrs, 300 F 2 hrs, 350 F 2 hrs, 400 F 2hrs, 440 F 2 hrs, 482 F 12 hrs, and then cooled to 200 F before removing from oven.
◇	61-12	357-433		Same as above.	Second run of the above sample.
●	61-12	219-656		DC-2106 Silicone resin with 40 RPD asbestos reinforcing by U. S. Polymeric Chem., Inc.; 37 plies and 113. 6 lb ft^{-3}.	Pressed at 330 F and cured at 330 F for 1-1/2 hrs at a pressure of 850 psi.
■	61-12	449-559		Same as above.	Second run of the above sample.
▲	56-5	302-697		Silicone - glass G-7 laminates.	

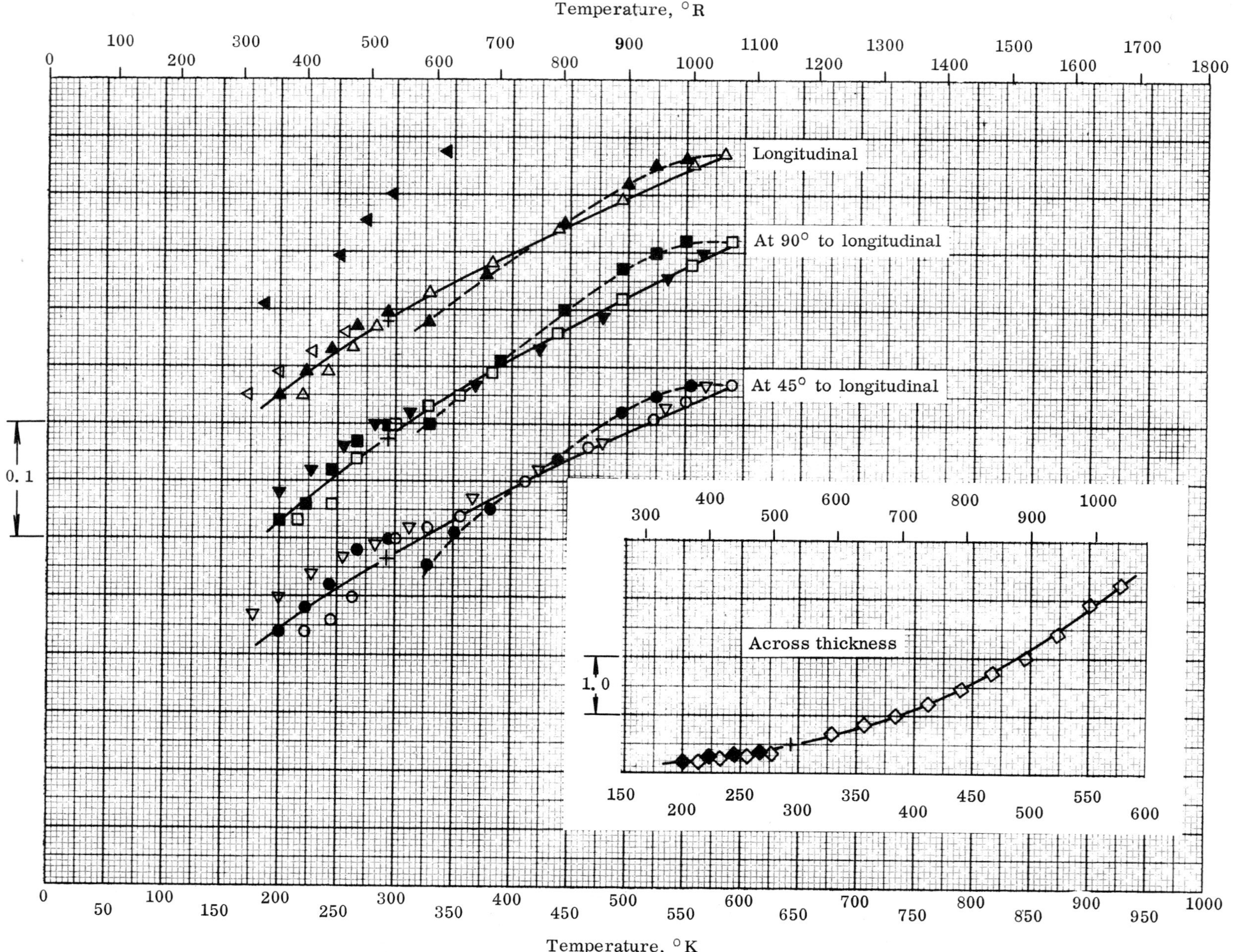

THERMAL LINEAR EXPANSION -- PLASTIC LAMINATES
(Glass fabric reinforced silicone)

THERMAL LINEAR EXPANSION -- PLASTIC LAMINATES
(Glass fabric reinforced silicone)

REFERENCE INFORMATION

Symbol	Ref.	Temp. Range °K	Rept. Error %	Sample Specifications	Remarks
○	55-3	200-589		12 ply silicone-resin laminate, made by Dow Corning; fabric: 181 with a 112 finish; resin: silicone No. 2106; catalyst: XY-15	Measured at 45 degree to the longitudinal direction in plane of laminations; heating.
●	55-3	200-589		Same as above.	Cooling.
□	55-3	200-589		Same as above.	Measured at 90 degree to the longitudinal direction in plane of laminations; heating.
■	55-3	200-589		Same as above.	Cooling.
△	55-3	200-589		Same as above.	Measured in longitudinal direction; heating.
▲	55-3	200-589		Same as above.	Cooling.
◇	55-3	200-589		Same as above.	Measured across thickness of sample; heating.
◆	55-3	200-589		Same as above.	Cooling.
▽	54-6	172-561		14 ply reinforced plastic made by Dow Corning; fabric: 181 with OC 112 finish; resin: silicone No. 2104; resin content: 32 - 35%; thickness: 0.141 in.; density 101 lb ft^{-3}.	Measured at 45 degree to longitudinal direction in plane of face.
▼	54-6	200-561		Same as above.	Measured at 90 degree to longitudinal direction in plane of face.
◀	54-6	172-256		Same as above.	Measured in longitudinal direction.
◁	54-6	215-343		Silicone glass laminate; fabric: medium weave fiber glass.	Made by National Vulcanized Fibre Co.; held at 77 F and 50% relative humidity for 24 to 48 hrs; direction of measurement not specified.

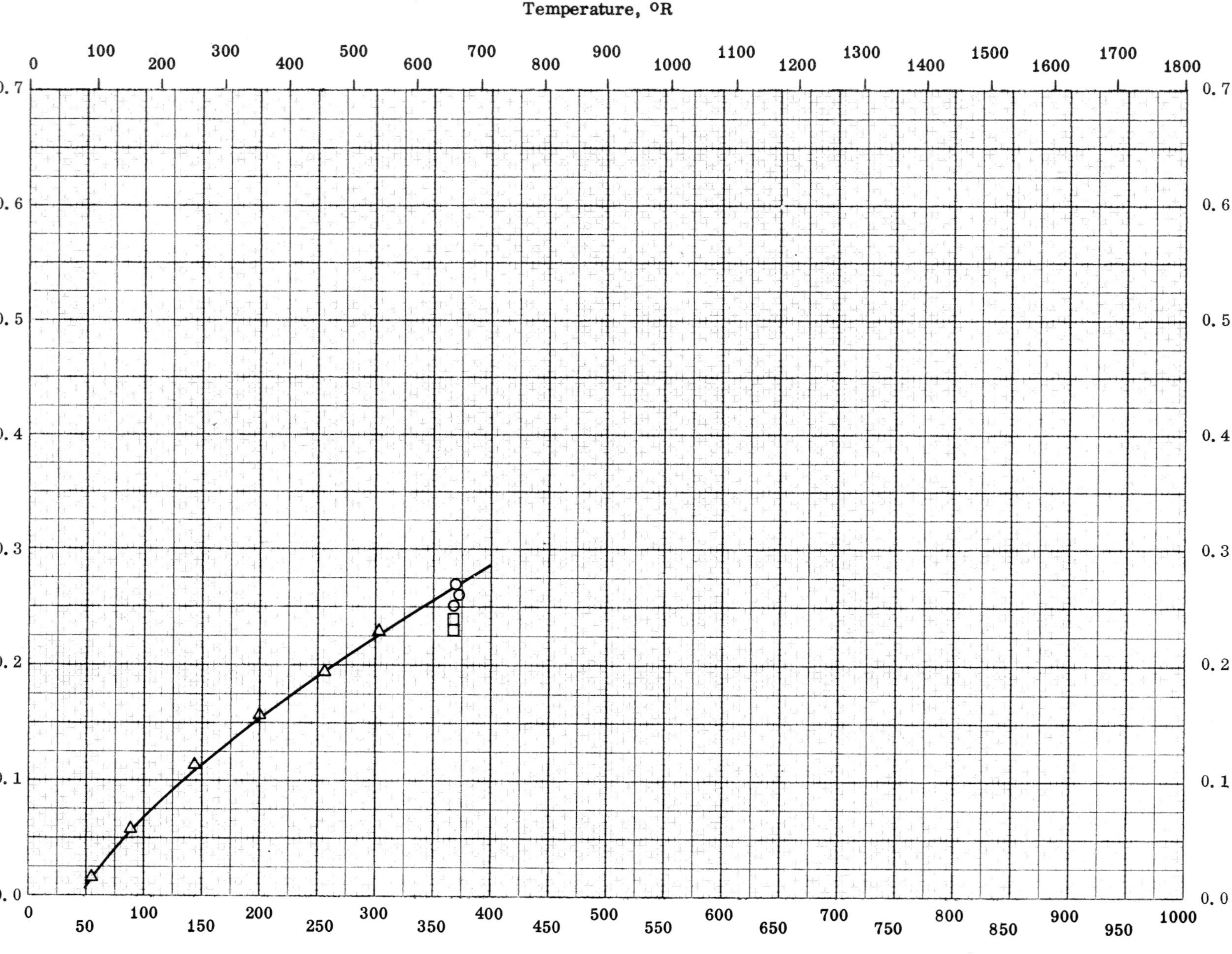

SPECIFIC HEAT -- PLASTIC LAMINATES
(Reinforced phenyl silane resin)

SPECIFIC HEAT -- PLASTIC LAMINATES
(Reinforced phenyl silane resin)

REFERENCE INFORMATION

Symbol	Ref.	Temp. Range °K	Rept. Error %	Sample Specifications	Remarks
○	63-3	368-371		Volcan impregnated with phenyl silane resin; 7 sheets of 184 volcan impregnated with 37 - 9X phenyl silane resin; glass cloth with volcan finish; density 121 lb ft^{-3}.	
□	63-3	367-369		Same as above; density 120.5 lb ft^{-3}.	
△	65-3	55-302	±5	Fabric reinforced laminate composed of 31 Monsanto SC-1013 phenyl silane resin and 69 Owens Corning X-994 woven glass fabric containing A-1100 finish; density 1.7587 g cm^{-3}; void 8.4%. [Author's design.: Material G].	

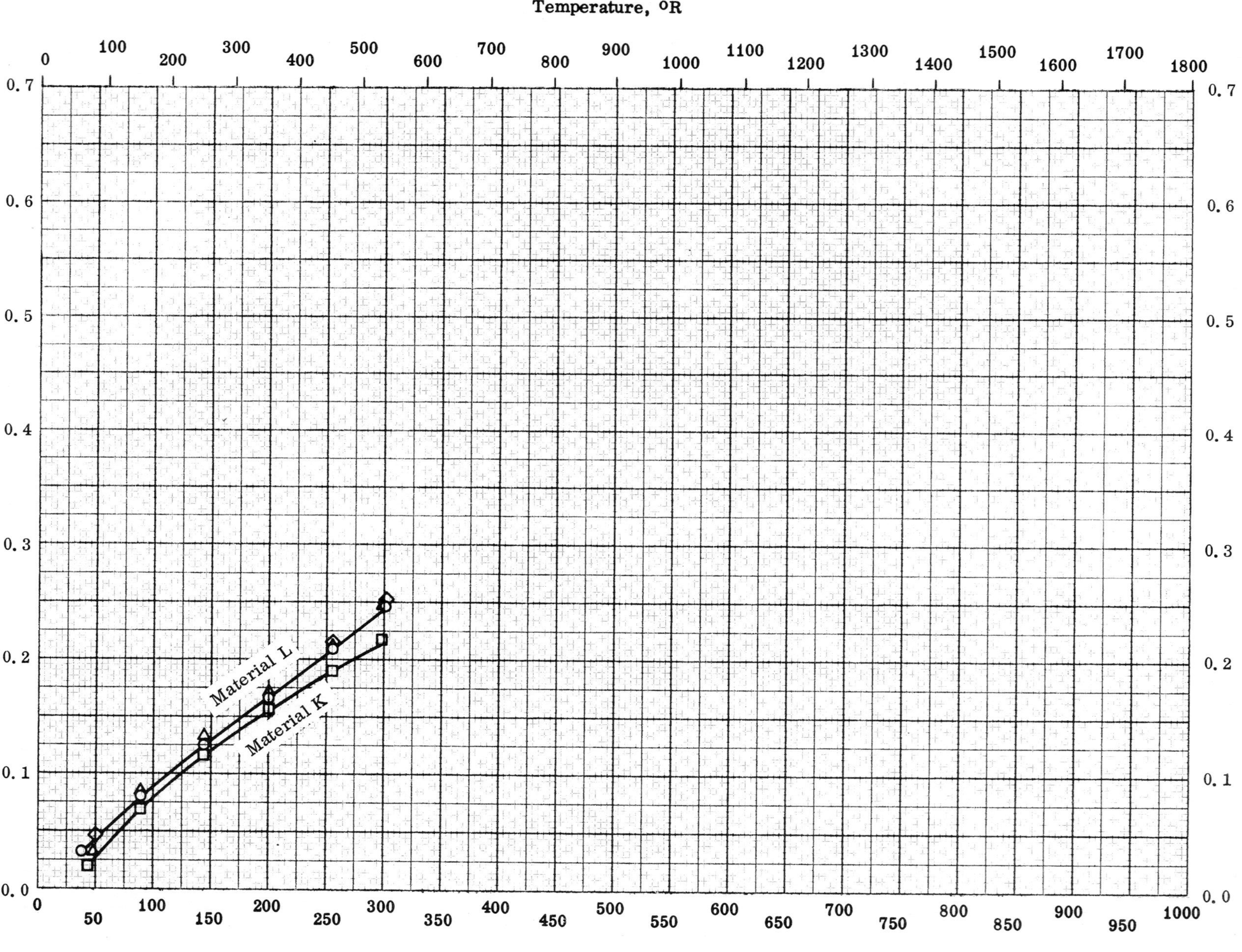

SPECIFIC HEAT -- PLASTIC LAMINATES
(Reinforced Teflon)

SPECIFIC HEAT -- PLASTIC LAMINATES
(Reinforced Teflon)

REFERENCE INFORMATION

Symbol	Ref.	Temp. Range °K	Rept. Error %	Sample Specifications	Remarks
○	65-3	38-301	±5	Mat construction panel composed of 70 DuPont low crystallinity TFE teflon and 30 Raybestos-Manhattan style 42 RPD asbestos; density 1.9032 g cm^{-3}; [Author's design.: Material C].	
□	65-3	44-298	±5	Chopped graphite fabric reinforced molded panel composed of 80 DuPont low crystallinity TFE teflon and 20 National Carbon Co. WCB graphite fabric in 1/2 in.x 1/2 in. squares; density 1.8848 g cm^{-3}. [Author's design.: Material K].	
△	65-3	42-298	±5	Chopped glass fiber reinforced molded panel composed of 75 DuPont low crystallinity TFE teflon and 25 "E" glass fibers; density 2.1727 g cm^{-3}; void 1.5%. [Author's design.: Material J].	
◇	65-3	50-301	±5	Glass fabric reinforced molded panel composed of 75 low crystallinity DePont TFE teflon and 25 style 116 "E" glass cloth; density 2.2445 g cm^{-3}; void 0.6%. [Author's design.: Material I].	

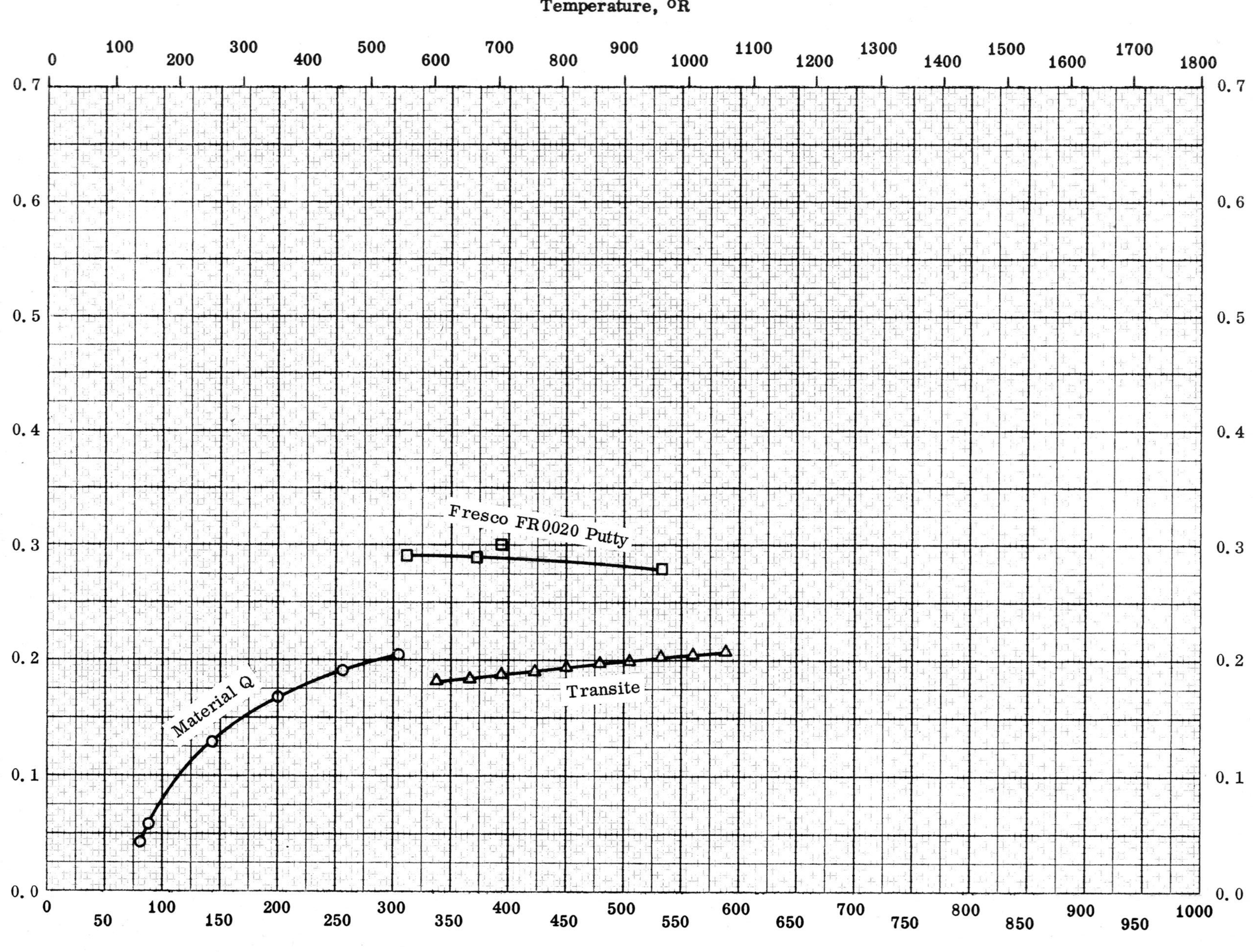

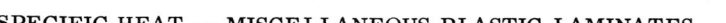

SPECIFIC HEAT -- MISCELLANEOUS PLASTIC LAMINATES

REFERENCE INFORMATION

Symbol	Ref.	Temp. Range °K	Rept. Error %	Sample Specifications	Remarks
○	65-3	82-304	±5	Micro-Quartz type II; density 8 lb ft^{-3}. [Author's design.: Material Q].	
□	62-29	311-543		Fresco FR0020; 71.0 putty, 25.8 aluminum coated beads, and 3.2 accelerator.	
△	61-5	340-590		Transite.	Preheated to remove moisture.

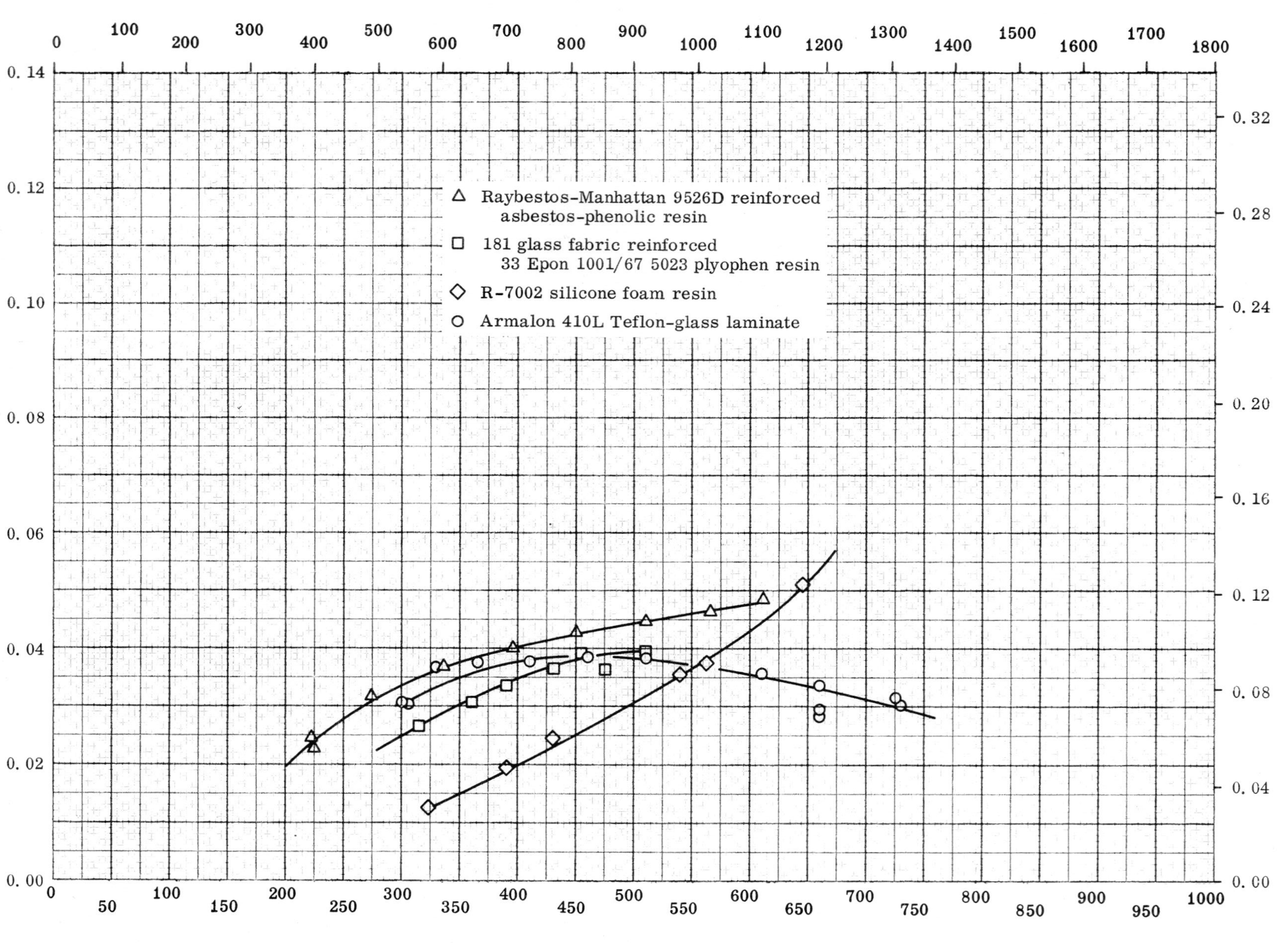

THERMAL CONDUCTIVITY -- MISCELLANEOUS PLASTIC LAMINATE

REFERENCE INFORMATION

Symbol	Ref.	Temp. Range °K	Rept. Error %	Sample Specifications	Remarks
△	58-8	222-609		Raybestos-Manhattan 9526 D glass fabric reinforced asbestos-phenolic resin; 3 plies; density 78 lb ft^{-3} and sample nominal thickness 0. 125 in.	Cured at 300 F for 1/2 hr at a pressure of 400 psi and post-cured at 300 F for 4 hrs and 350 F for 8 hrs.
□	55-5	314-507		181 glass fabric reinforced Epon 1001/5023 plyophen 33/67 resin from Shell; resin content 24. 5 and density 108. 58 lb ft^{-3}.	
◇	61-12	323-647		R-7002 silicone foam resin by Dow Corning Corp. ; density 11. 60 lb ft^{-3} and sample 0. 5 in. thick.	Cured at 390 F for 1 hr, 435 F for 1 hr, 480 F for 24-48 hrs, 435 F for 1 hr, 390 for 1 hr, and 150 F for 1 hr; fully cured.
○	56-5	301-728		Armalon 410L Teflon-glass laminate.	

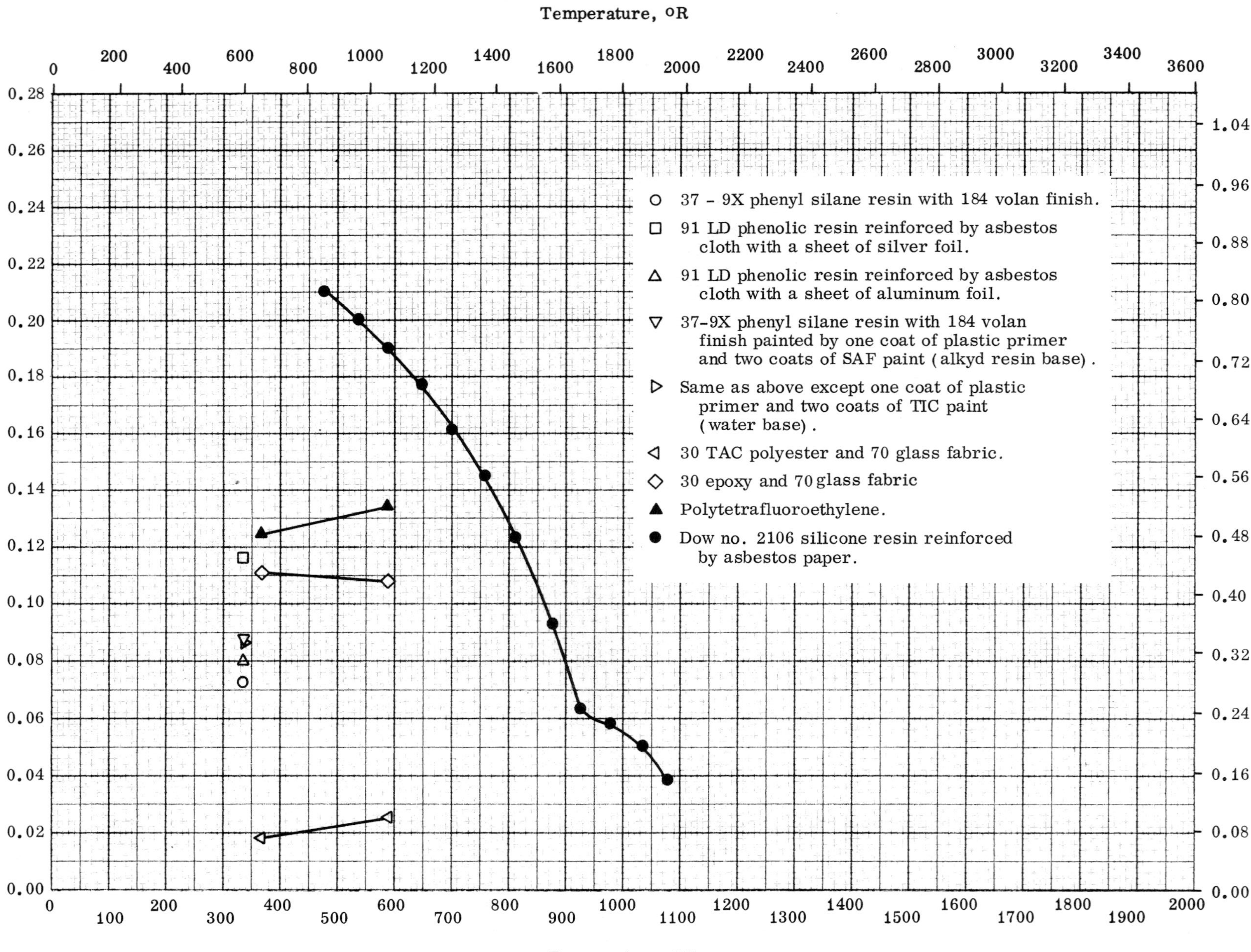

Temperature, °R
Temperature, °K
Thermal diffusivity, $cm^2\ Sec^{-1} \times 10^2$
Thermal diffusivity, $ft^2\ hr^{-1} \times 10^2$
○ 37 – 9X phenyl silane resin with 184 volan finish.
□ 91 LD phenolic resin reinforced by asbestos cloth with a sheet of silver foil.
△ 91 LD phenolic resin reinforced by asbestos cloth with a sheet of aluminum foil.
▽ 37-9X phenyl silane resin with 184 volan finish painted by one coat of plastic primer and two coats of SAF paint (alkyd resin base).
▷ Same as above except one coat of plastic primer and two coats of TIC paint (water base).
◁ 30 TAC polyester and 70 glass fabric.
◇ 30 epoxy and 70 glass fabric
▲ Polytetrafluoroethylene.
● Dow no. 2106 silicone resin reinforced by asbestos paper.

THERMAL DIFFUSIVITY -- PLASTIC LAMINATE
(Miscellaneous)

THERMAL DIFFUSIVITY -- PLASTIC LAMINATE
(Miscellaneous)

REFERENCE INFORMATION

Symbol	Ref.	Temp. Range °K	Rept. Error %	Sample Specifications	Remarks
○	63-3	333		37-9X phenyl silane resin with 7 sheets of 184 volan (glass cloth with a volan finish) impregnated; sample circular area 0.34 ft^2 and 0.168 in. thick; density 121.0 lb ft^{-3}. [Author's design.: 3].	Pressed at 100 lb in^{-2} at 350 F for 1 hr and then post-cured for 16 hrs at 350 F.
▽	63-3	333		Similar to above sample except one coat of plastic primer and two coats of SAF paint (alkyd resin base) and density 120.2 lb ft^{-3}. [Author's design.: 9].	Same as above.
▷	63-3	333		Similar to sample 3 above except one coat of plastic primer and two coats of TIC paint (water base); sample circular area 0.34 ft^2 and 0.172 in. thick; density 120.2 lb ft^{-3}. [Author's design.: 10].	Same as above.
□	63-3	333		91LD phenolic resin reinforced by asbestos cloth with one sheet of silver foil impregnated in the center; sample circular area 0.34 ft^2 and 0.254 in. thick; density 113.0 lb ft^{-3}. [Author's design.: 6].	Same as above.
△	63-3	333		Same as above except with an aluminum foil impregnated; sample circular area 0.34 ft^2 and 0.281 in. thick; density 107.8 lb ft^{-3}. [Author's design.: 7].	Same as above.
◁	61-4	367-589		30 TAC polyester and 70 glass fabric.	
◇	61-4	367-589		30 epoxy and 70 glass fabric.	
▲	61-4	367-589		Polytetrafluoroethylene.	
				(Continued onto next page)	

THERMAL DIFFUSIVITY -- PLASTIC LAMINATE (Continued)
(Miscellaneous)

REFERENCE INFORMATION

Symbol	Ref.	Temp. Range °K	Rept. Error %	Sample Specifications	Remarks
●	63-2	472-1075		Dow no. 2106 silicone resin reinforced by 0.010 in. thick asbestos paper; resin content 47 to 53% sample 4.5x4.5x 0.180 in.	Pressed by 100 lb in^{-2} pressure at a curing temperature of 375 F for 1 hr and then post-cured for 12 hrs in an oven at 375 F.

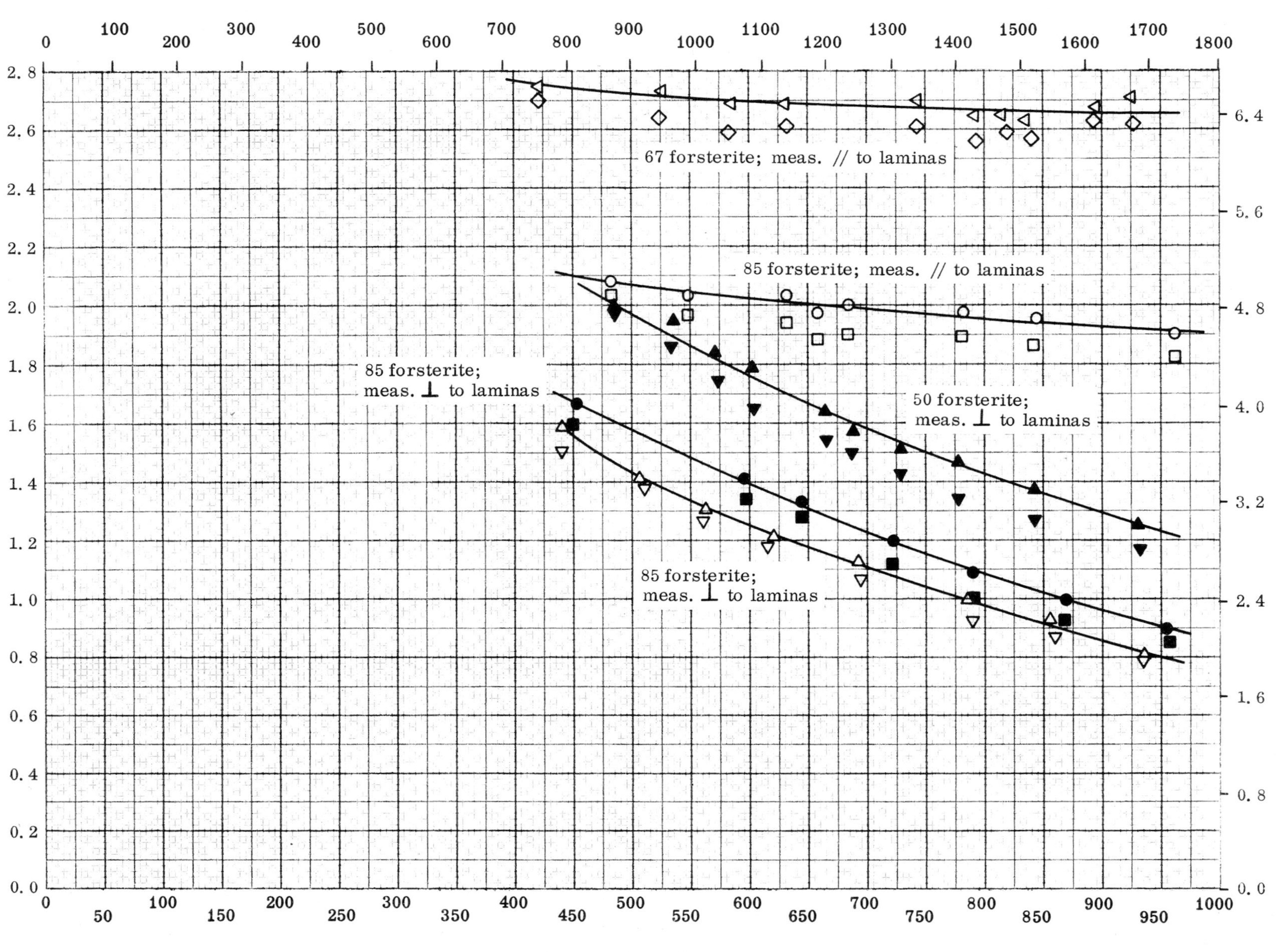

THERMAL CONDUCTIVITY -- FORSTERITE - STAINLESS STEEL LAMINATE

THERMAL CONDUCTIVITY -- FORSTERITE - STAINLESS STEEL LAMINATE

REFERENCE INFORMATION

Symbol	Ref.	Temp. Range °K	Rept. Error %	Sample Specifications	Remarks
○	60-13	483-963	±3	85 forsterite and 15 stainless steel 430, corresponding to 4 layers of forsterite and 3 layers of stainless steel.	Measured parallel to laminas.
□	60-13	483-963	±3	Same as above.	Second run of the above sample.
△	60-13	441-936	±3	Same as above.	Measured normal to laminas.
▽	60-13	440-936	±3	Same as above.	Second run of the above sample.
◁	60-13	420-924	±3	67 forsterite and 33 stainless steel 430, corresponding to 2 layers of forsterite and 1 layer of stainless steel.	Measured parallel to laminas.
◇	60-13	420-928	±3	Same as above.	Second run of the above sample.
●	60-13	453-956	±3	Same as above.	Measured normal to laminas.
■	60-13	451-958	±3	Same as above.	Second run of the above sample.
▲	60-13	485-931	±3	50 forsterite and 50 stainless steel 430, corresponding to 1 layer of forsterite and 1 layer of stainless steel 430.	Measured normal to laminas.
▼	60-13	486-932	±3	Same as above.	Second run of the above sample.

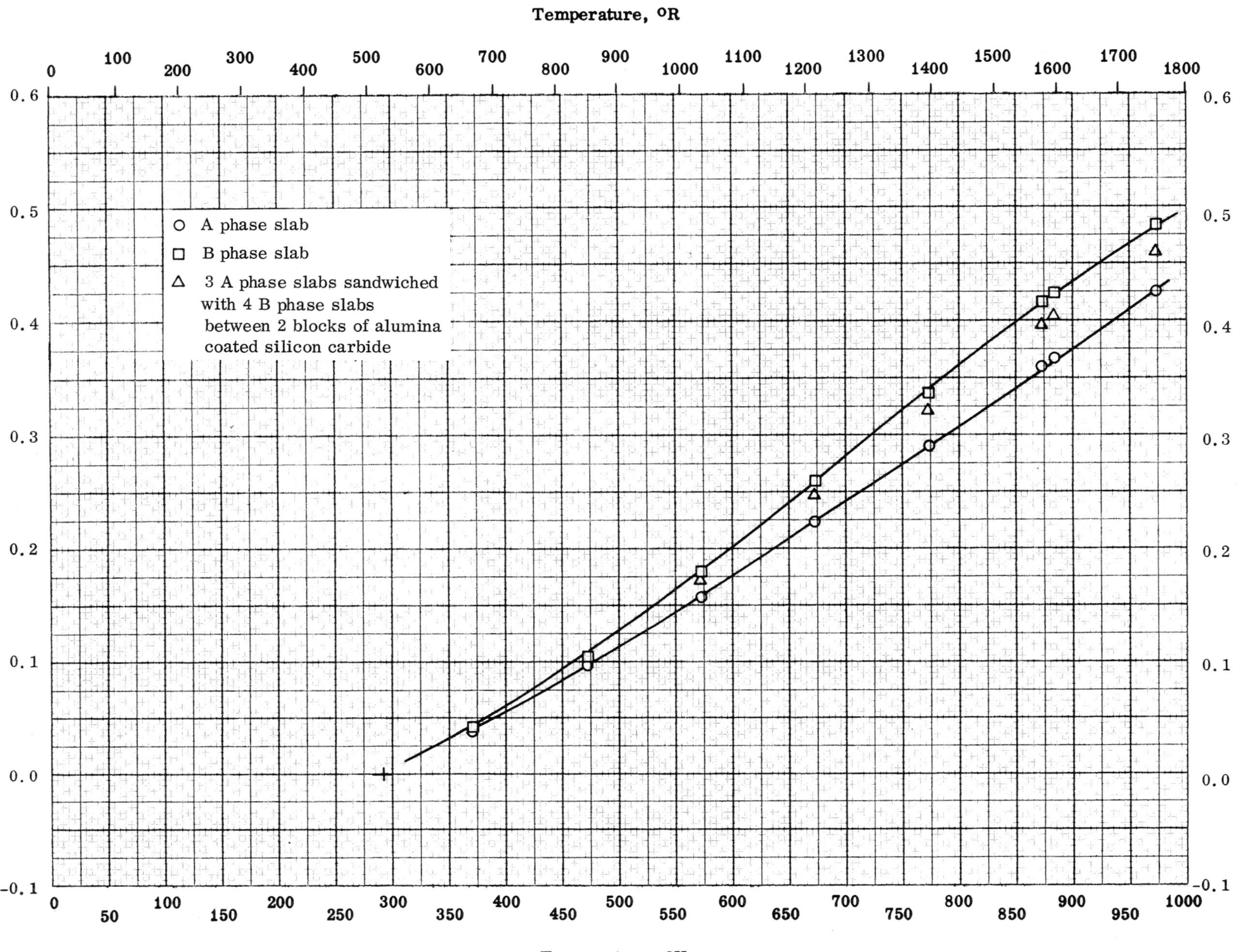

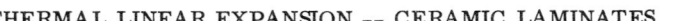

THERMAL LINEAR EXPANSION -- CERAMIC LAMINATES

THERMAL LINEAR EXPANSION -- CERAMIC LAMINATES

REFERENCE INFORMATION

Symbol	Ref.	Temp. Range °K	Rept. Error %	Sample Specifications	Remarks
○	59-20	293-973		50 A-270 Nepheline Syenite, 25 Air-floated Pioneer Kaolin, and 25 Air-floated Imperial Ball clay; sample 0.5 in. square by 3 in. long. [Author's design.: A-phase slab].	Dry ball-milled for 6 hrs, mixed with 8 water and 1 polyvinyl alcohol, passed through a 20 mesh screen, stored in a sealed-container over night, pressed at 3000 psi into slabs, and dried at 110 C at least 24 hrs; fired at 2130 F at a rate of 100 F hr^{-1} and soaked 1 hr at peak temperature (a load of 100 lbs applied at last 20 min of soaking), and then ground and cut to size.
□	59-20	293-973		50 A-270 Nepheline Syenite, 17 Air-floated Pioneer Kaolin, 25 Air-floated Imperial Ball clay, and 8 200-mesh potters flint; same size as above. [Author's design.: B-phase slab].	Same as above.
△	59-20	293-973		Same as above. [Author's design.: composites].	3 A-phase slabs sandwiched with 4 B-phase slabs between 2 blocks of alumina-coated silicon carbide and heat-treated as above.

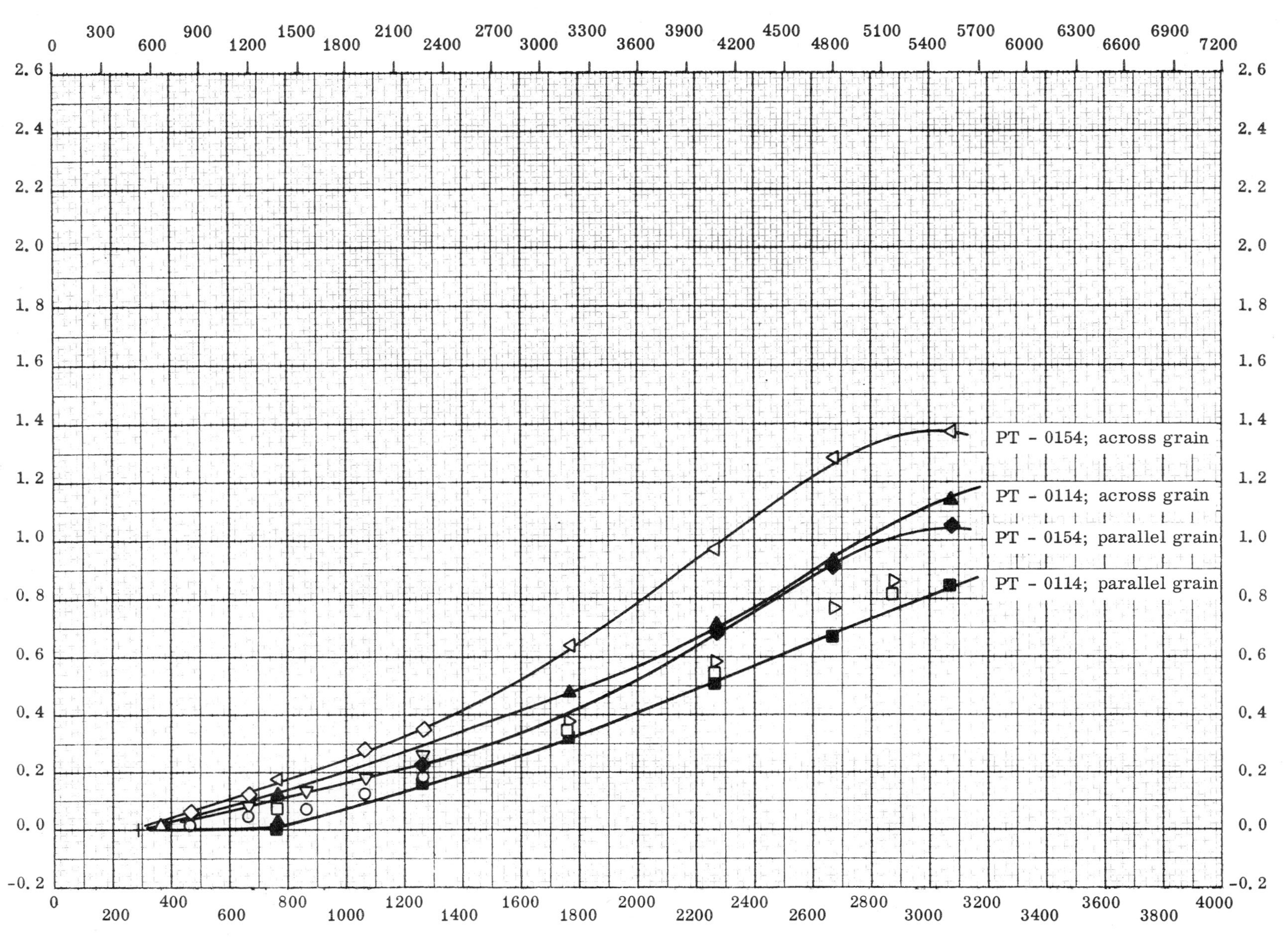

THERMAL LINEAR EXPANSION -- GRAPHITE - CLOTH LAMINATES

THERMAL LINEAR EXPANSION -- GRAPHITE - CLOTH LAMINATES

REFERENCE INFORMATION

Symbol	Ref.	Temp. Range °K	Rept. Error %	Sample Specifications	Remarks
○	64-19	293-1273		PT-0110 graphite-cloth from National Carbon Co.; bulk density 1.14 g cm^{-3} at room temperature; sample 1/2 in. by 1/2 in. by 5 in.	Layers bonded by a carbonaceous binder and baked to 800 C; measured parallel to grain; average data over several runs.
□	64-19	293-2873		PT-0111 graphite-cloth from National Carbon Co.; bulk density 1.11 g cm^{-3} at room temperature; sample size same as above.	Layers bonded by a carbonaceous binder and graphitized; same as above.
△	64-19	293-373		PT-0113 graphite-cloth from National Carbon Co.; bulk density 1.18 g cm^{-3} at room temperature; sample 0.3 in. by 3/8 in. by 5 in.	Contained shredded or macerated graphite-cloth filler; final process temperature 800 C; measured parallel to grain.
▽	64-19	293-1273		Same as above except size 0.5 in. by 0.5 in. by 5in.	Same as above.
◇	64-19	293-1273		Same as above.	Same as above except measured across grain.
●	64-19	293-373		PT-0114 graphite-cloth from National Carbon Co.; bulk density 1.15 g cm^{-3} at room temperature; sample size 0.3 in. by 3/8 in. by 5 in.	Contained a macerated graphite-cloth filler and baked to graphitizing temperature; measured parallel to the grain; of several runs.
■	64-19	293-3073		Same as above except 0.5 in. by 0.5 in. by 5 in. size.	Same as above.
▲	64-19	293-3073		Same as above.	Same as above except measured across grain.
▼	64-19	293-373		PT-0154 graphite-cloth from National Carbon Co., bulk density 1.38 g cm^{-3} at room temperature; sample size 0.3 in. by 3/8 in. by 5 in.	Contained shredded graphite-cloth filler; fully graphitized, then impregnated and rebaked; measured parallel to grain; average of several runs.
◆	64-19	293-3073		Same as above except sample size 0.5 in. by 0.5 in. by 5 in.	Same as above.

(Continued onto next page)

THERMAL LINEAR EXPANSION -- GRAPHITE - CLOTH LAMINATES (Continued)

REFERENCE INFORMATION

Symbol	Ref.	Temp. Range °K	Rept. Error %	Sample Specifications	Remarks
◁	64-19	293-3073		Same as above.	Same as above except measured across grain.
▷	64-19	293-2873		PT-0156 graphite-cloth from National Carbon Co.; bulk density 1.29 g cm^{-3} at room temperature; sample size 0.5 in. by 0.5 in. by 5 in.	Layers of graphite-cloth bonded together by a suitable carbonaceous binder and graphitized; measured parallel to the grain; average data over several runs.

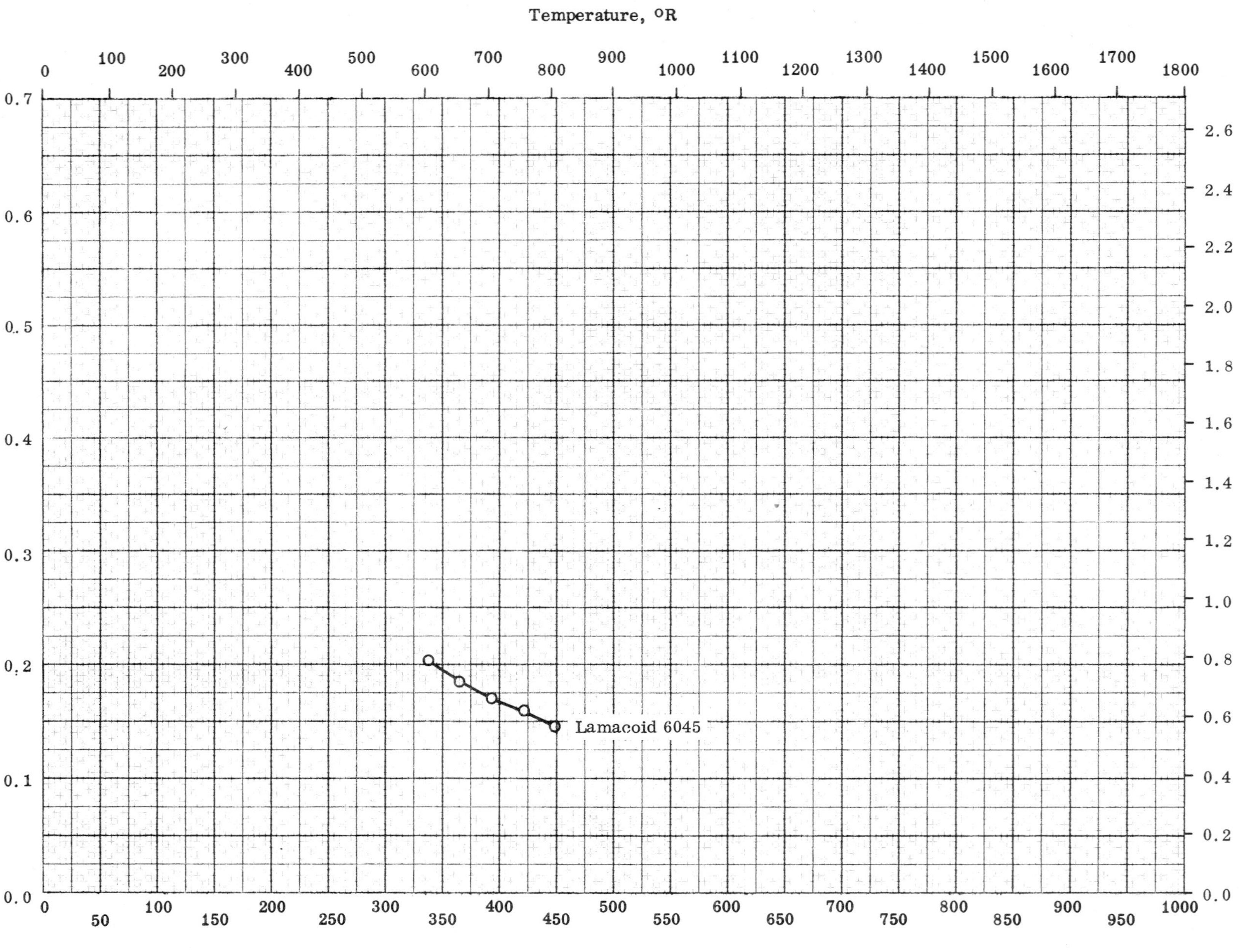

THERMAL DIFFUSIVITY -- PLASTIC + MICA
(Lamacoid)

THERMAL DIFFUSIVITY -- PLASTIC + MICA
(Lamacoid)

REFERENCE INFORMATION

Symbol	Ref.	Temp. Range °K	Rept. Error %	Sample Specifications	Remarks
○	61-5	339-450		Lamacoid no. 6045; mica in powder form.	

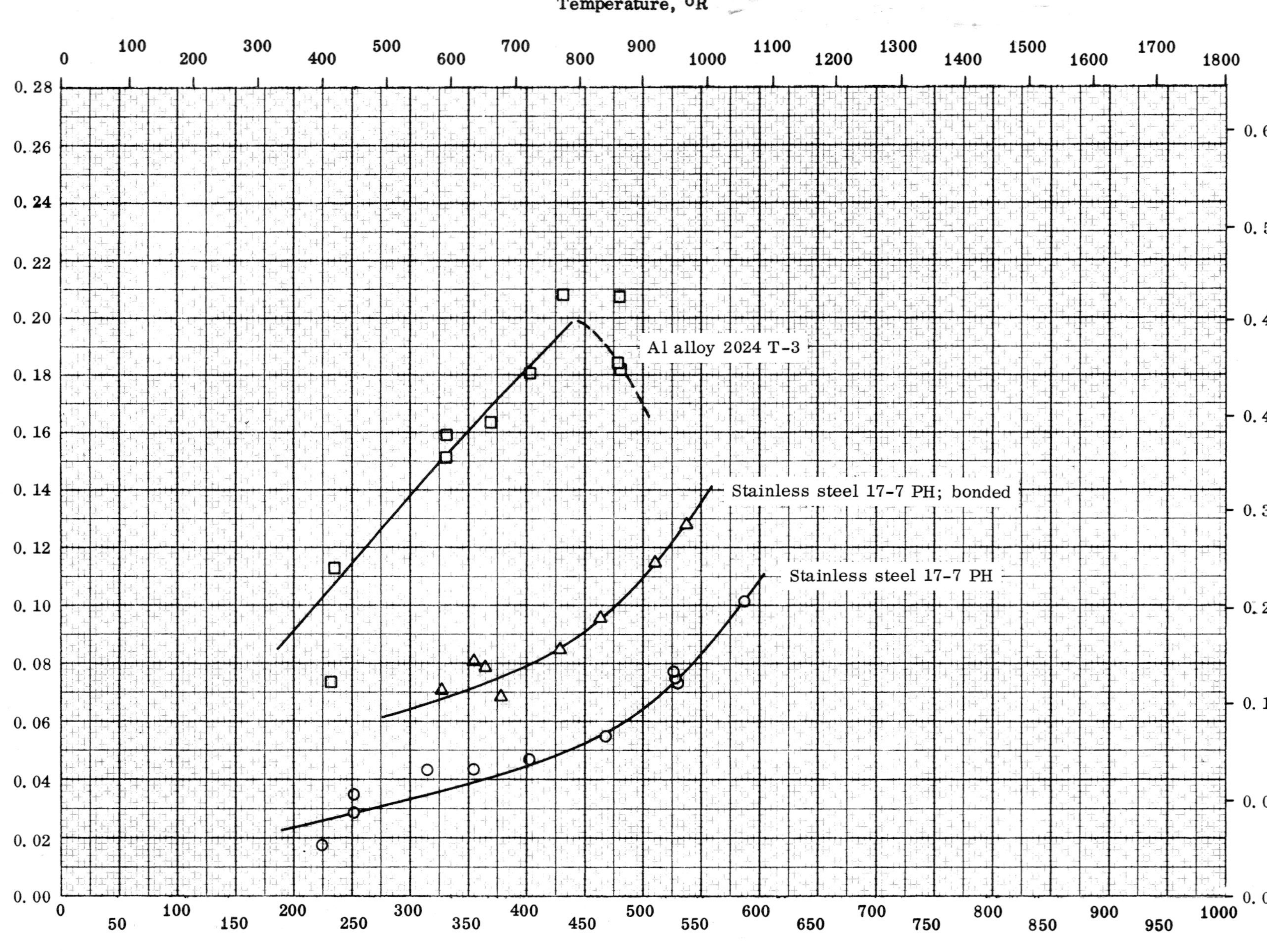

THERMAL CONDUCTIVITY -- HONEYCOMB
(Metal skin and metal core)

REFERENCE INFORMATION

Symbol	Ref.	Temp. Range °K	Rept. Error %	Sample Specifications	Remarks
○	57-8	225-587		3 ply panel - faces: 0.032 in. stainless steel 17-7 PH; core: 0.0015 in. stainless steel 17-7 PH honeycomb (3/8 in. cells x 5/8 in. thick) by Glenn L. Martin Co.	
□	57-8	232-480		3 ply panel - faces: 0.020 in. Al alloy 2024 T-3; core: 0.002 in. Al alloy 2024 T-3 honeycomb (1/4 in. cells x 5/8 in. thick, density 4.3 lb ft^{-3}); by Brunswick Balke Collender Co.; resin bonded (15.5% total wt.); 0.66 in. total thickness.	Decomposition evident above 310 F.
△	59-8	329-537		17-7 PH stainless steel panel with Shell adhesive No. 422 as bonding agent; overall hight 0.622 in. with 0.052 in. face thickness; solidity of core 0.135 in., cell size 0.25 $in.^2$, and core density 6.48 lb ft^{-3}.	

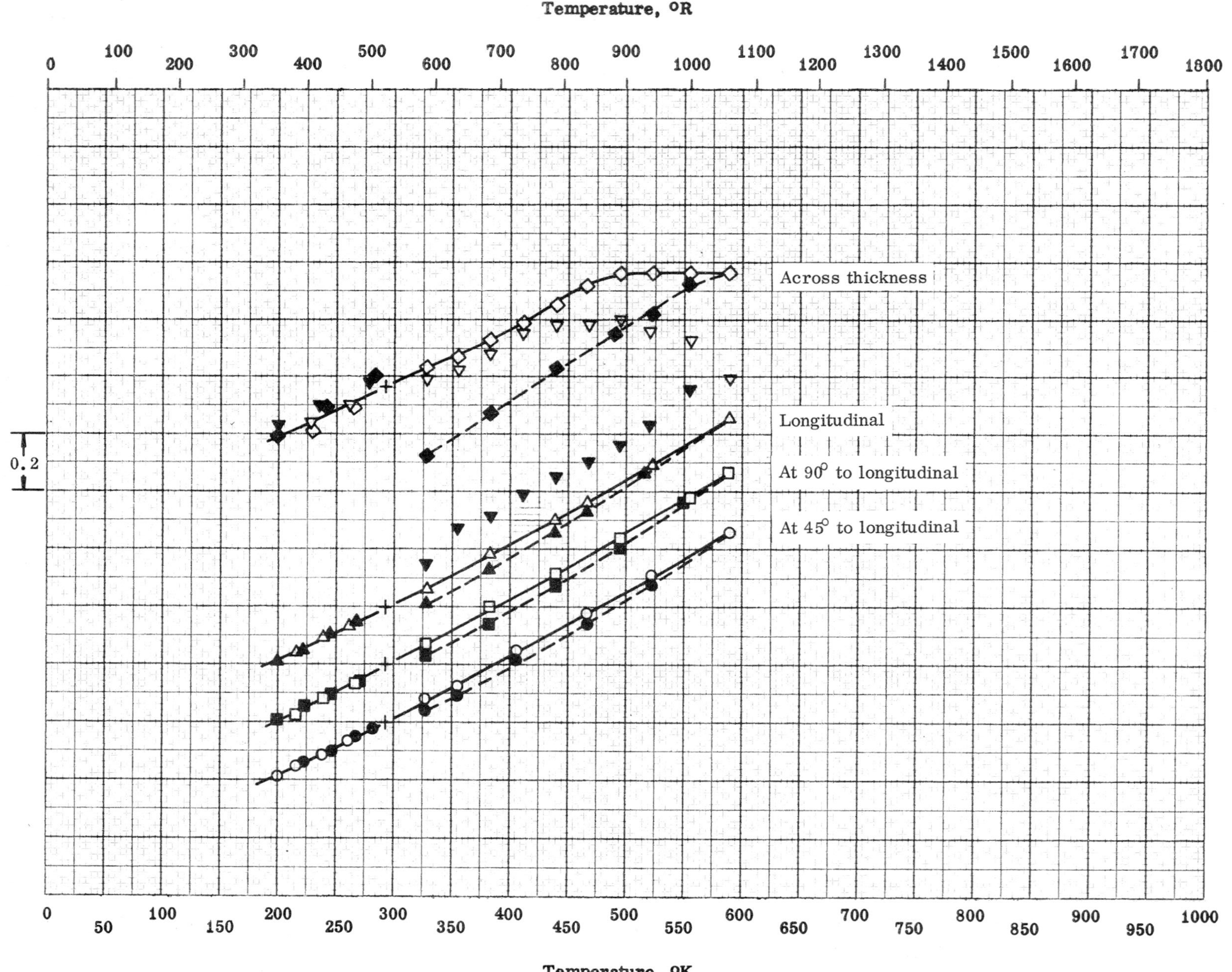

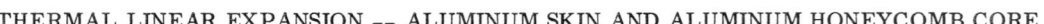

THERMAL LINEAR EXPANSION -- ALUMINUM SKIN AND ALUMINUM HONEYCOMB CORE

REFERENCE INFORMATION

Symbol	Ref.	Temp. Range °K	Rept. Error %	Sample Specifications	Remarks
○	57-8	200-589		Skin-Aluminum 2024-T3, 0.020 in. thick Core - Aluminum 2024-T3 Honeycomb (Brunswick-Balke Collender Co.); thickness: 5/8 in.; cell size: 1/4 in.; density: 4.3 lb ft^{-3}; total thickness: 0.6611 in.; resin content: 15.5.	Measured at 45° to longitudinal direction in plane of face; heating.
●	57-8	200-589		Same as above.	Cooling.
□	57-8	200-589		Same as above.	Measured at 90° to longitudinal direction in plane of face; heating.
■	57-8	200-589		Same as above.	Cooling.
△	57-8	200-589		Same as above.	Measured in longitudinal direction in plane of face; heating.
▲	57-8	200-589		Same as above.	Cooling.
◇	57-8	200-589		Same as above.	Measured across thickness of sample; heating.
◆	57-8	200-589		Same as above.	Cooling.
▽	57-8	200-589		0.002 in. Aluminum 2024-T3 Honeycomb (Brunswick-Balke Collender Co.); thickness: 5/8 in.; cell size: 1/4 in.; density 4.3 lb ft^{-3}; resin content: 0.9 (binder).	Measured across thickness of sample; heating.
▼	57-8	200-589		Same as above.	Cooling.

Thermal Linear Expansion, percent

Temperature, °R

Temperature, °K

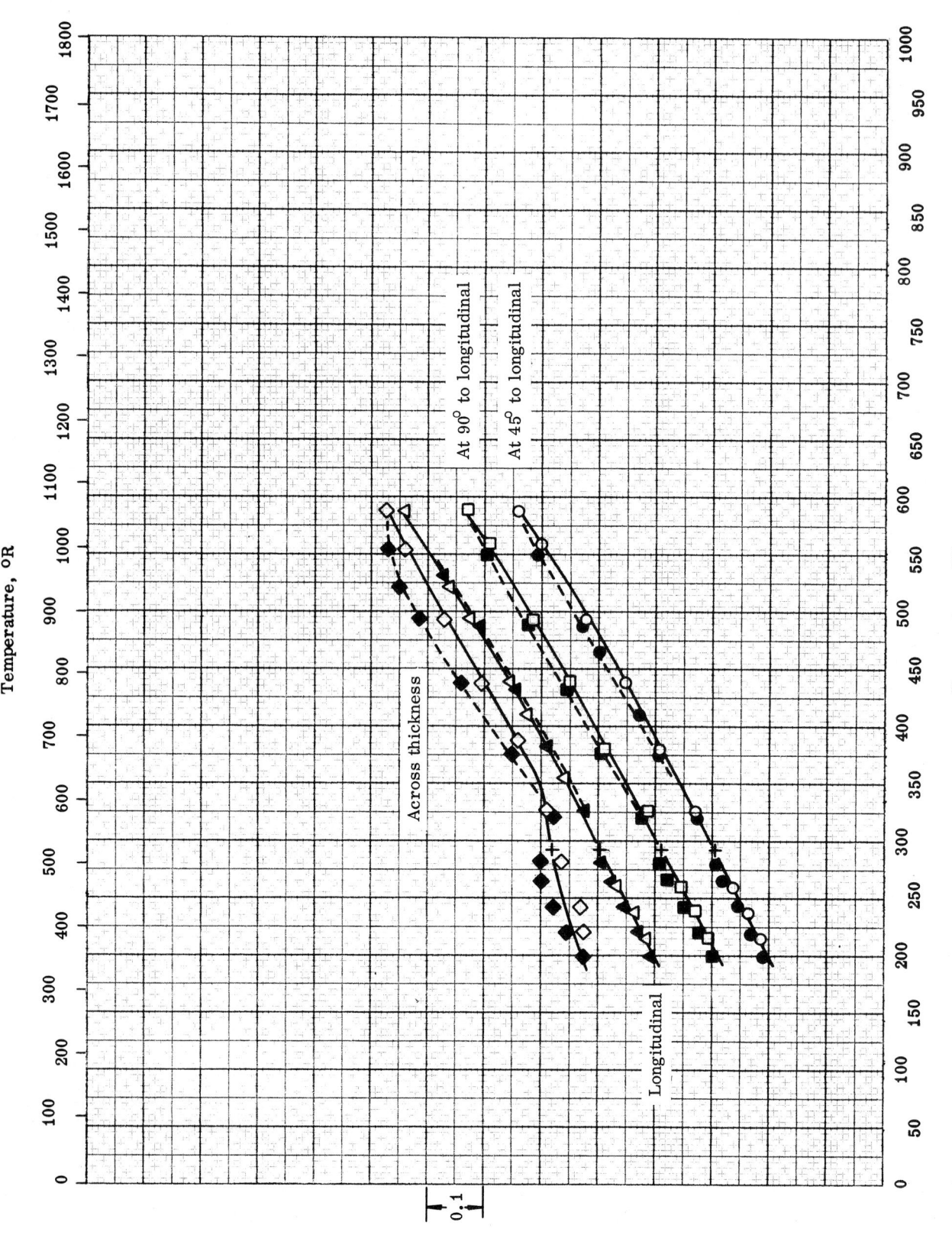

At 90° to longitudinal

At 45° to longitudinal

Across thickness

Longitudinal

0.1

Thermal Linear Expansion, percent

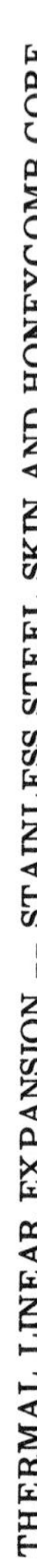

THERMAL LINEAR EXPANSION -- STAINLESS STEEL SKIN AND HONEYCOMB CORE

REFERENCE INFORMATION

Symbol	Ref.	Temp. Range °K	Rept. Error %	Sample Specifications	Remarks
○	57-8	200-589		Skin - stainless steel 17-7 PH; thickness: 0.032 in.; core - 0.0015 in. thick stainless steel 17-7PH honeycomb (by Glenn L. Martin Co.); thickness: 5/8 in. and cell size: 3/8 in.	Measured at 45° to longitudinal direction in plane of face; heating.
●	57-8	200-589		Same as above.	Cooling.
□	57-8	200-589		Same as above.	Measured at 90° to longitudinal direction in plane of face; heating.
■	57-8	200-589		Same as above.	Cooling.
△	57-8	200-589		Same as above.	Measured in longitudinal direction in plane of face; heating.
▲	57-8	200-589		Same as above.	Cooling.
◇	57-8	200-589		Same as above.	Measured across thickness of sample; heating.
◆	57-8	200-589		Same as above.	Cooling.

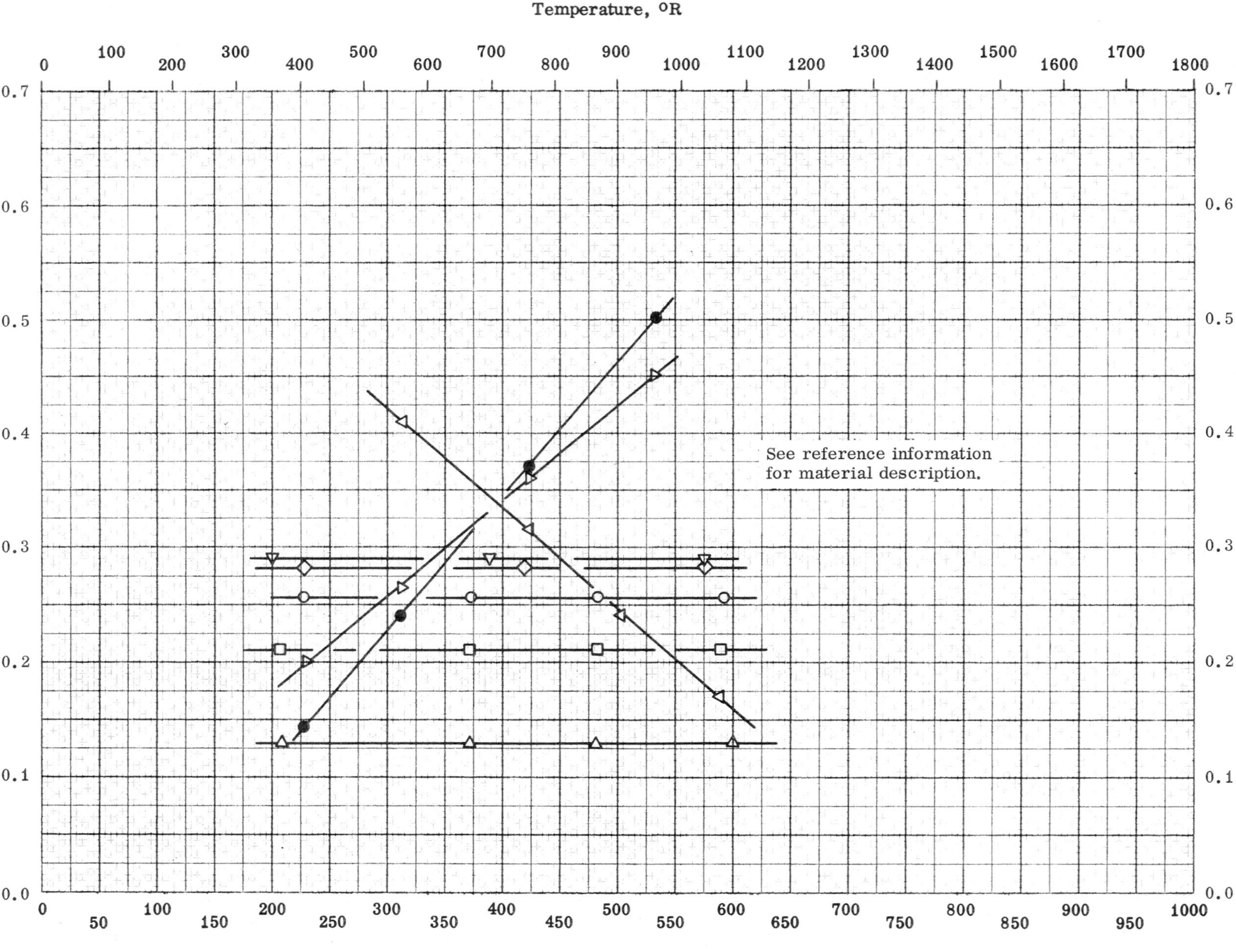

SPECIFIC HEAT -- HONEYCOMBS
(Plastic and metal composites)

SPECIFIC HEAT -- HONEYCOMBS
(Plastic and metal composites)

REFERENCE INFORMATION

Symbol	Ref.	Temp. Range °K	Rept. Error %	Sample Specifications	Remarks
○	57-8	228-589		Al alloy 2024-T3 skin with 0.020 in. thick; 5/8 in. thick honeycomb of 0.002 in. Al alloy 2024-T3 with 1/4 in. cell size; core density 4.3 lb ft^{-3}; total thickness 0.6611 in.; resin content 15.5.	Made by Brunswick-Balke Collender Co.
□	57-8	211-589		5/8 in. thick honeycomb panel of 0.002 in. Al alloy 2024-T3 with 1/4 in. cell size.	Same as above.
△	57-8	211-600		Stainless steel 17-7 PH skin with 0.032 in. thick; 5/8 in. thick honeycomb of 0.0015 in. stainless steel 17-7 PH core with 3/8 in. cell size.	Made by Glenn L. Martin Co.
▽	57-8	200-575		Fabric: 181 skin with Volan A finish; polyester P-43 resin; catalyst: 2% ATC; 0.002 in. thick aluminum 2024T-3 honeycomb core (by Brunswick-Balke Collender Co.); thickness: 5/8 in.; density: 4.3 lb ft^{-3}; total thickness 0.5591 in.; resing content: 34.9%.	C_p of the core 0.212 Btu lb^{-1} R^{-1} from 380 to 1060 R.
◇	57-8	228-575		Aluminum 2024T-3 sking with thickness 0.020 in.; phenolic honeycomb core (Brunswick-Balke Collender Co.) thickness: 5/8 in., cell size: 1/9 in.; catalyst: agent A; density 9 lb ft^{-3}; total thickness: 0.6694 in.; resin content: 54.4%.	C_p of core is 0.300 Btu lb^{-1} R^{-1} from 380 to 1040 R.
●	57-8	228-533		Al alloy 2024-T3 skin with thickness 0.020 in.; alkyd isocyanate foam core (by Brunswick-Balke Collender Co.) with thickness 5/8 in.; catalyst: Agent Z; density: 10 lb ft^{-3}; total thickness: 0.6656 in.; resin content: 51.9%. (Continued onto next page)	C_p Btu lb^{-1} F^{-1} = $0.175 \pm 6.5 \times 10^{-4}$ t (F) for range (-50 to 600 F); decomposition apparent above 320 F.

SPECIFIC HEAT -- HONEYCOMBS (continued)
(Plastic and metal composites)

REFERENCE INFORMATION

Symbol	Ref.	Temp. Range °K	Rept. Error %	Sample Specifications	Remarks
▷	57-8	228-533		Fabric No. 181 faces with Volan A; polyester resin No. P-43; catalyst: 2% ATC; polyester honeycomb core 5/8 in. thick with 1/4 in. cells; overall thickness 0.6548 in.; 62.9% resin content; density of core 9 lb ft^{-3}.	Made by Brunswick Balke Collender Co.; C_p for core 0.323; Btu lb^{-1} F^{-1} for 380 - 1000 R; decomposition apparent above 400 F.
◁	55-3	311-589		Phenolic honeycomb panel, 3 ply TAC - polyester Vibrin 135 and 181 fabric faces; phenolic honeycomb core with density 9.9 lb ft^{-3}.	Made by Goodyear Co.

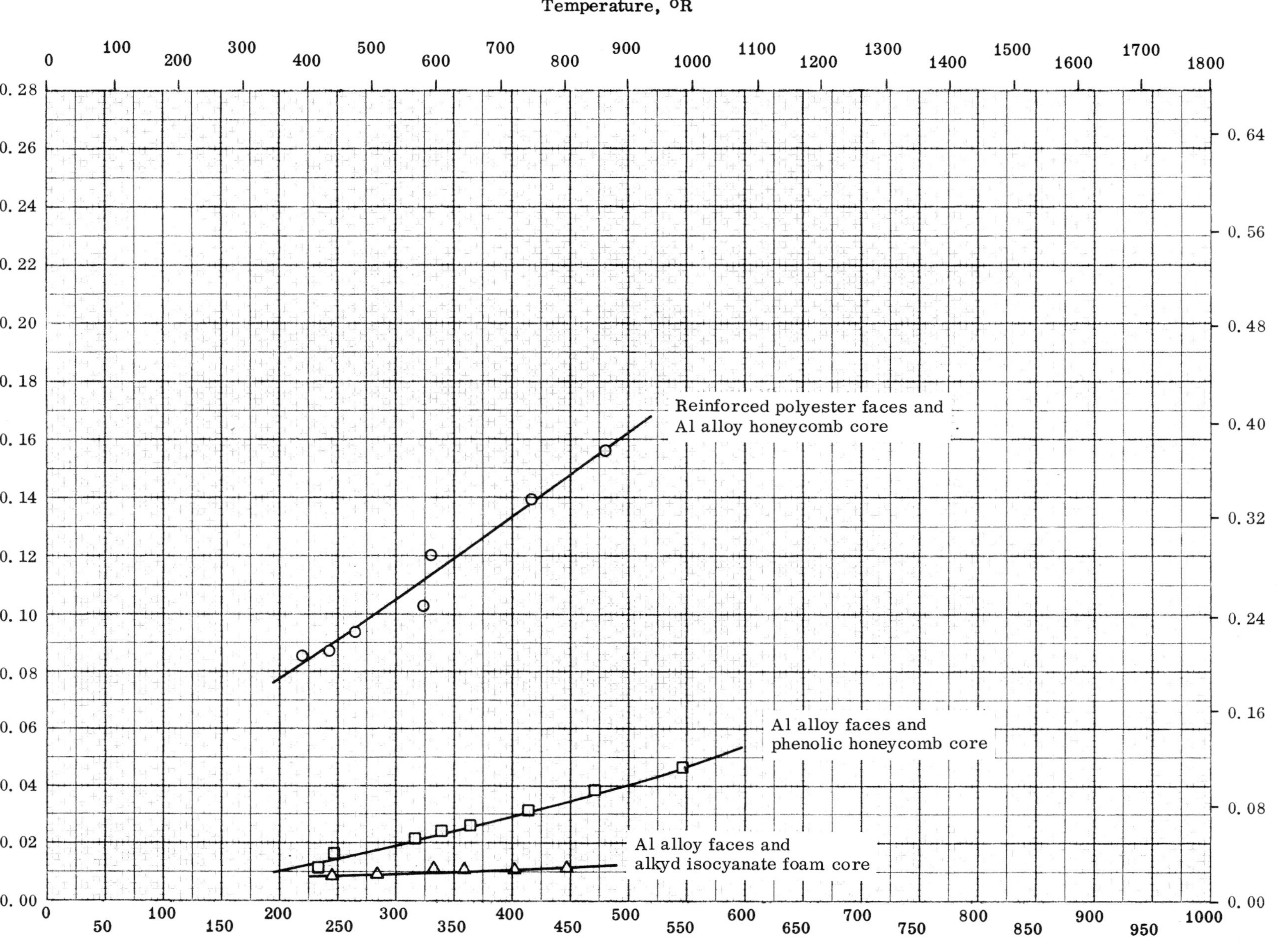

THERMAL CONDUCTIVITY -- HONEYCOMB
(Plastic and metal composites)

THERMAL CONDUCTIVITY -- HONEYCOMB
(Plastic and metal composites)

REFERENCE INFORMATION

Symbol	Ref.	Temp. Range °K	Rept. Error %	Sample Specifications	Remarks
○	57-8	220-480		3 ply panel - faces: glass fabric No. 181, Volan A finish reinforced polyester resin No. P-43 (2% A. T. C. catalyst); core: 0. 002 in. thick Al alloy 2024 T-3 Honeycomb by Brunswick-Balke Collender Co. (4. 3 lb ft^{-3}) 5/8 in. core thickness; 0. 66 in. total thickness; resin content 34. 9% total wt.	
□	57-8	233-547		3 ply panel - faces: 0. 020 in. thick Al alloy 2024 T-3; core: Phenolic Honeycomb by Brunswick-Balke Collender Co. (9 lb ft^{-3}); 1/9 in. cell size; agent A catalyst; 5/8 in. core thickness; 0. 67 in. total thickness; resin content 51. 9 total wt.	Decomposition evident above 390 F.
△	57-8	245-445		3 ply panel - faces: as above; core: Alkyd Isocyanate Foam by Brunswick-Balke Collender Co. (10 lb ft^{-3}); agent Z catalyst 5/8 in. core thickness; 0. 67 in. total thickness; resin content 51. 9% total wt.	Decomposition evident above 275 F; after test, sample completely charred, melted and had begun to flow out between warped Al faces.

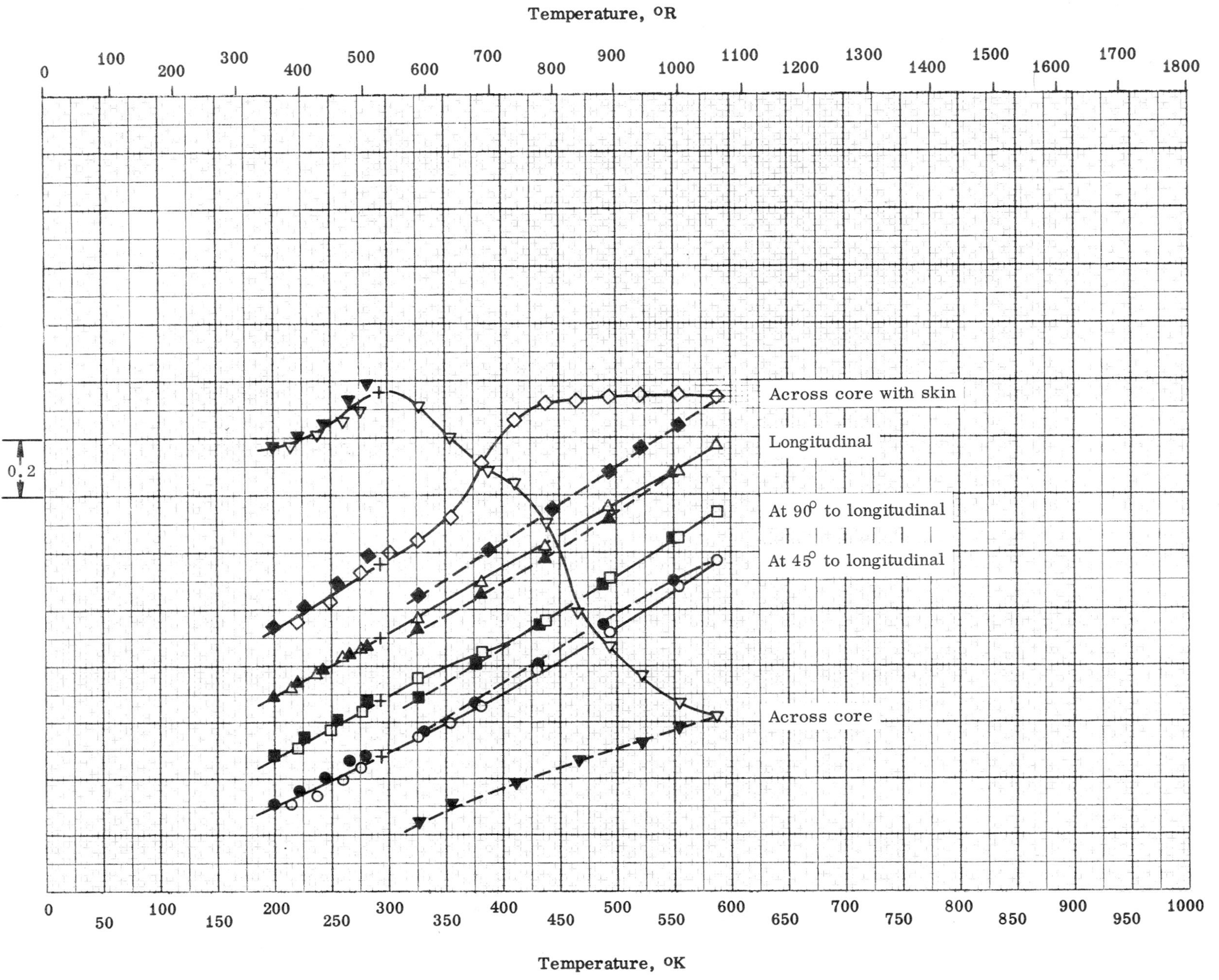

THERMAL LINEAR EXPANSION -- ALUMINUM SKIN, PHENOLIC HONEYCOMB CORE

THERMAL LINEAR EXPANSION -- ALUMINUM SKIN, PHENOLIC HONEYCOMB CORE

REFERENCE INFORMATION

Symbol	Ref.	Temp. Range °K	Rept. Error %	Sample Specifications	Remarks
○	57-8	200-589		Skin: 0.020 in. thick Al alloy 2024 T-3; core: Phenolic honeycome; thickness: 5/8 in.; cell size: 1/9 in.; catalyst: Agent A; density: 9 lb ft^{-3}; total thickness: 0.6694 in.; resin content: 54.4 made by Brunswick-Balke Collender Co.	Measured at 45° to longitudinal direction in plane of face; heating.
●	57-8	200-589		Same as above.	Cooling.
□	57-8	200-589		Same as above.	Measured at 90° to longitudinal direction in plane of face; heating.
■	57-8	200-589		Same as above.	Cooling.
△	57-8	200-589		Same as above.	Measured in longitudinal direction in plane of face; heating.
▲	57-8	200-589		Same as above.	Cooling.
◇	57-8	200-589		Same as above.	Measured across thickness of sample; heating.
◆	57-8	200-589		Same as above.	Cooling.
▽	57-8	200-589		Phenolic honeycomb panel (Brunswick-Balke Collender Co.); thickness: 5/8 in.; cell size: 1/9 in.; catalyst: 2%A.T.C.; density: 9 lb ft^{-3}; resin content 77.5 .	Measured across thickness of sample; heating.
▼	57-8	200-589		Same as above.	Cooling.

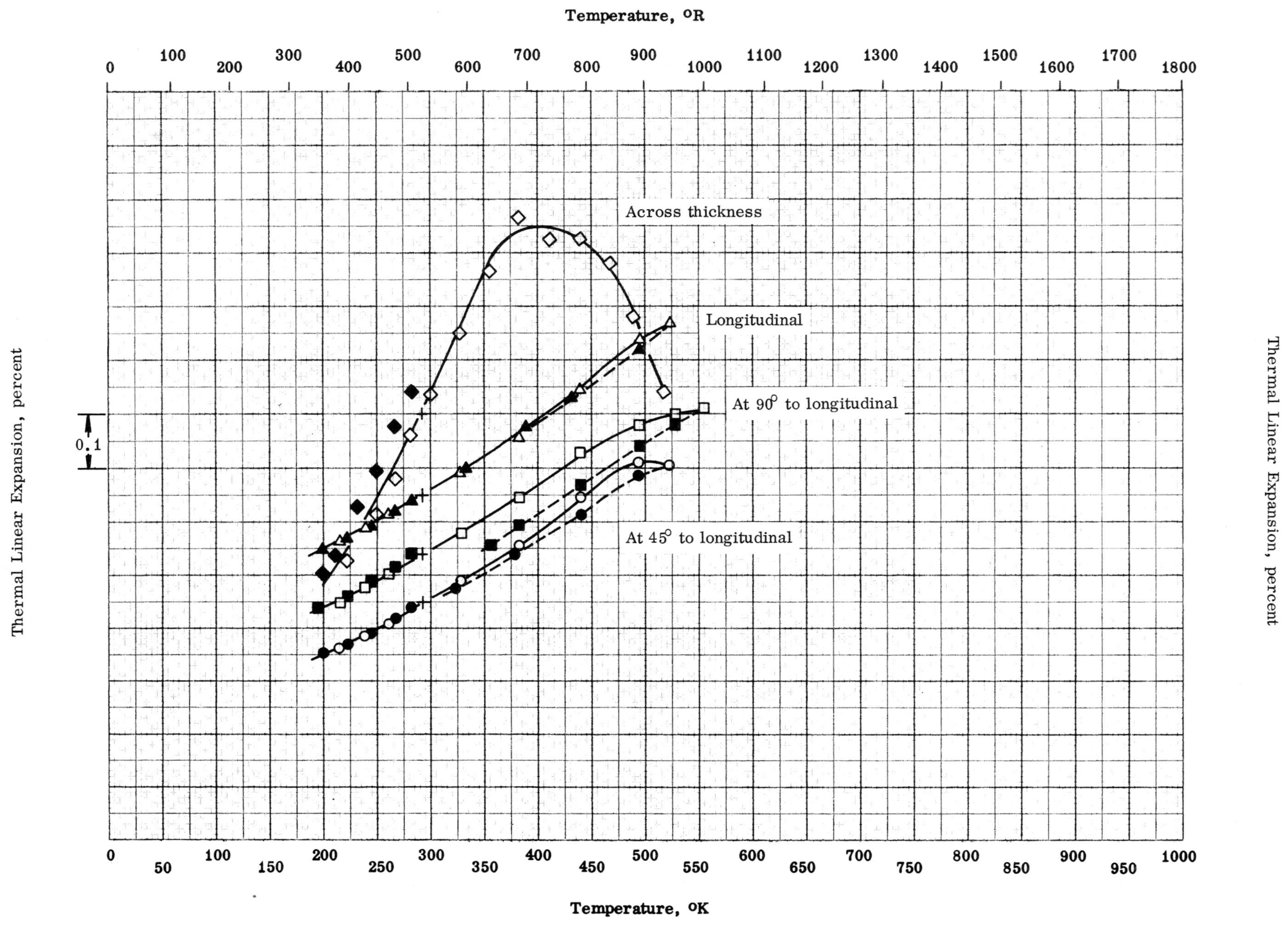

THERMAL LINEAR EXPANSION -- ALUMINUM SKIN, PLASTIC FOAM CORE

THERMAL LINEAR EXPANSION -- ALUMINUM SKIN, PLASTIC FOAM CORE

REFERENCE INFORMATION

Symbol	Ref.	Temp. Range °K	Rept. Error %	Sample Specifications	Remarks
○	57-8	200-522		Skin - Aluminum 2024 - T3; thickness: 0.020 in.; Core-Alkyd Isocyanate Foam (by Brunswick-Balke Collender Co.); thickness: 5/8 in; catalyst: Agent Z; density 10 lb ft^{-3}.	Measured at 45° direction to longitudinal direction in plane of face; heating.
●	57-8	200-522		Same as above.	Cooling.
□	57-8	200-556		Same as above.	Measured at 90° to longitudinal direction in plane of face; heating.
■	57-8	200-556		Same as above.	Cooling.
△	57-8	200-495		Same as above.	Measured in longitudinal direction in plane of face; heating.
▲	57-8	200-495		Same as above.	Cooling.
◇	57-8	200-522		Same as above.	Measured across thickness of sample.
◆	57-8	200-522		Same as above.	Cooling.

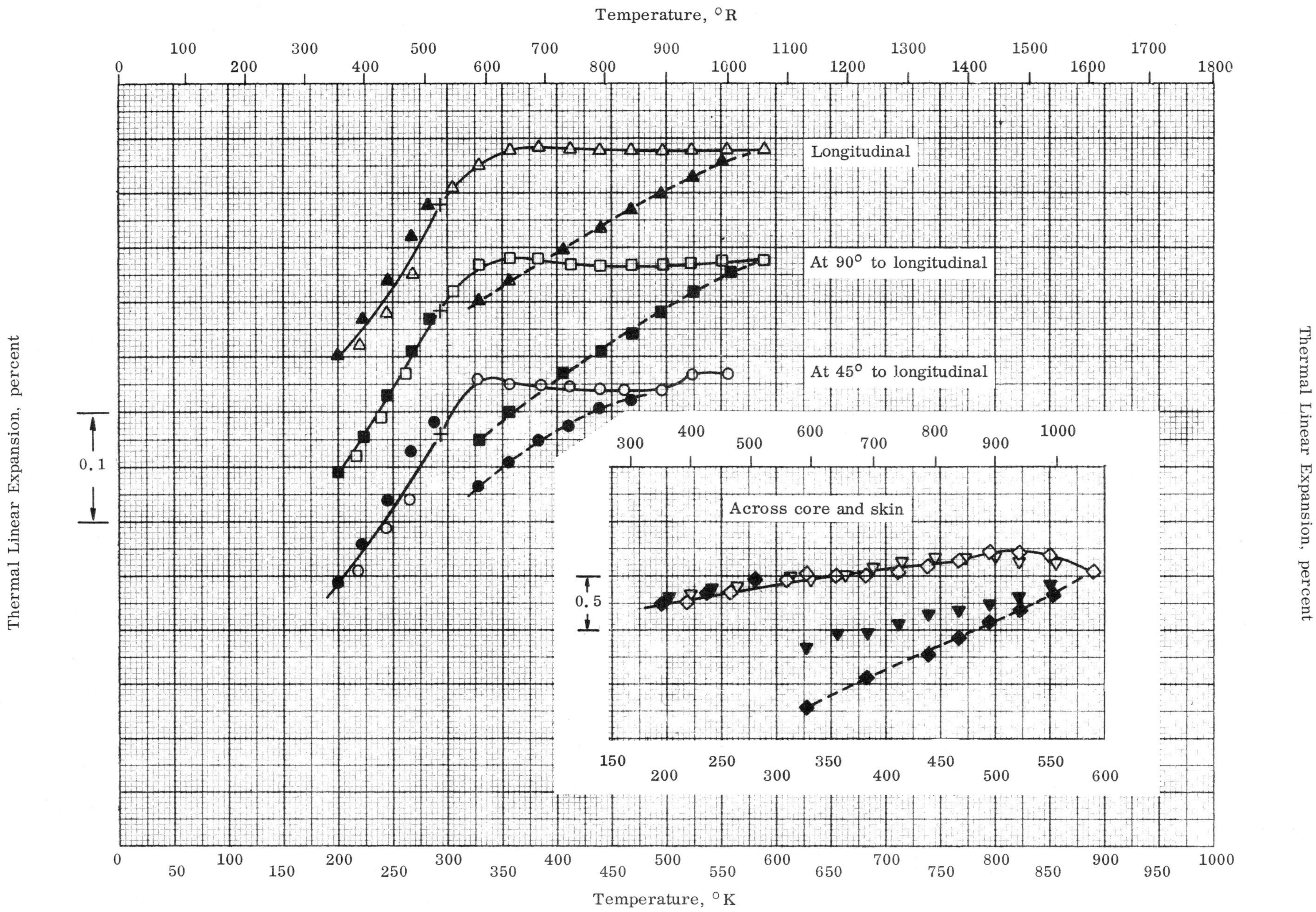

Thermal Linear Expansion, percent

THERMAL LINEAR EXPANSION -- REINFORCED POLYESTER SKIN, ALUMINUM HONEYCOMB CORE

THERMAL LINEAR EXPANSION -- REINFORCED POLYESTER SKIN, ALUMINUM HONEYCOMB CORE

REFERENCE INFORMATION

Symbol	Ref.	Temp. Range °K	Rept. Error %	Sample Specifications	Remarks
○	57-8	200-589		Skin - Fabric: 181 with Volan A finish; resin: Polyester No. P-43; catalyst: 2% A. T. C.; core - 0.002 in. thick aluminum 2024T-3 honeycomb; thickness: 5/8 in.; core by Brunswick-Balke-Collender Co.; density of core 4.3 lb ft^{-3}.	Measured at 45 degree to the longitudinal direction in plane of face; heating.
●	57-8	200-589		Same as above.	Cooling.
□	57-8	200-589		Same as above.	Measured at 90 degree to the longitudinal direction in plane of face; heating.
■	57-8	200-589		Same as above.	Cooling.
△	57-8	200-589		Same as above.	Measured in longitudinal direction in plane of face; heating.
▲	57-8	200-589		Same as above.	Cooling.
◇	57-8	200-589		Same as above.	Measured across thickness of sample; heating.
◆	57-8	200-589		Same as above.	Cooling.
▽	57-8	200-589		0.002 in. aluminum 2024T-3 honeycomb; 5/8 in. thick; 1/4 in. cells; resin content 0.9 ; density 4.3 lb ft^{-3}.	Measured across thickness of sample; heating.
▼	57-8	200-589		Same as above.	Cooling.

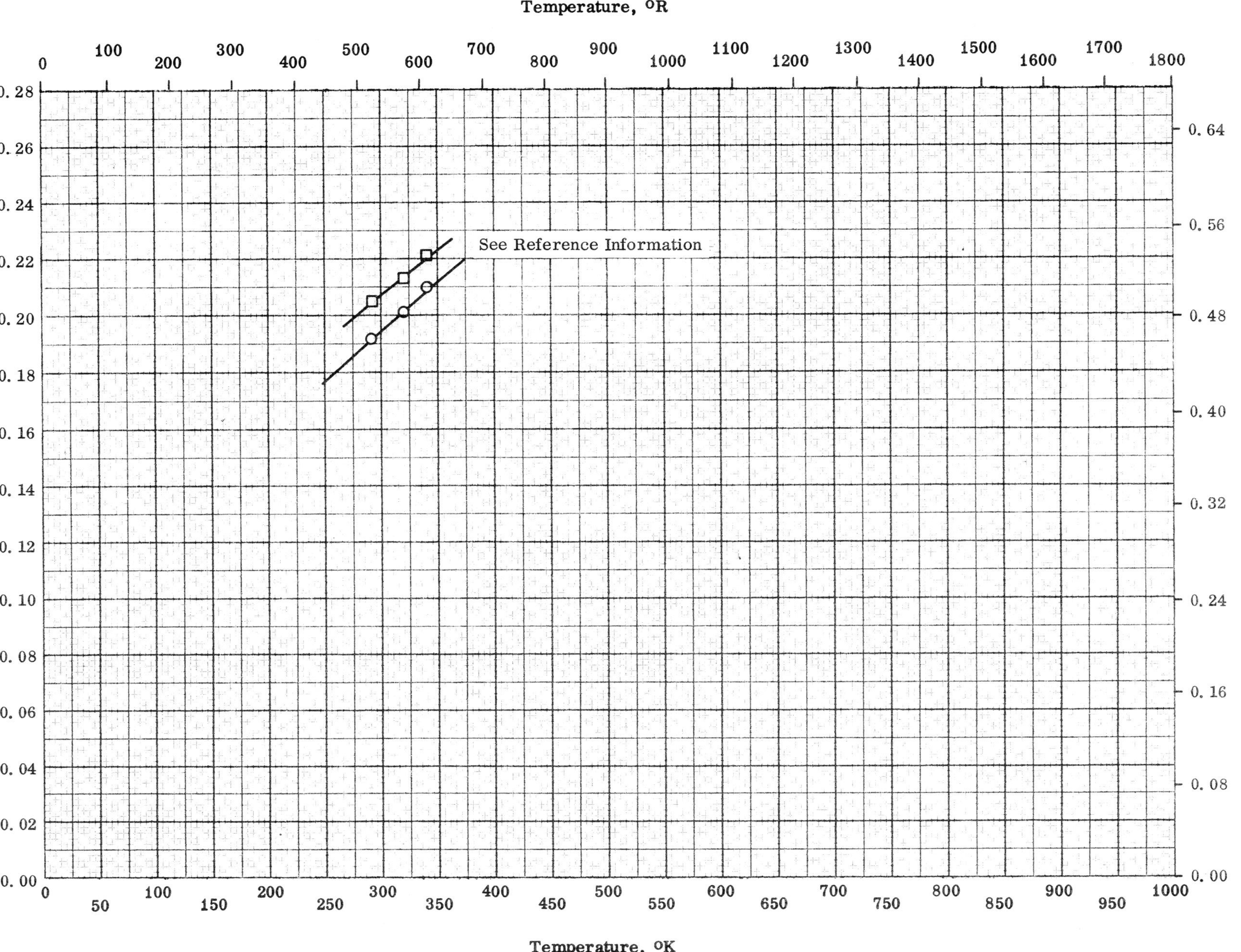

THERMAL CONDUCTIVITY -- HONEYCOMB
(Plastic skin and plastic core)

THERMAL CONDUCTIVITY -- HONEYCOMB
(Plastic skin and plastic core)

REFERENCE INFORMATION

Symbol	Ref.	Temp. Range °K	Rept. Error %	Sample Specifications	Remarks
○	57-7	290-339		Skins 0.034 in. thick of glass fabric impregnated with polyester resin; honeycomb (hexag. cyl. normal to skins) 0.309 in. thick of nylon phenolic having density 4 lb ft^{-3}; skins bonded to core with epoxy resin.	
□	57-7	291-333		As above, except honeycomb 0.311 in. thick made of CTL (glass fabric) phenolic having density 6 lb ft^{-3}.	

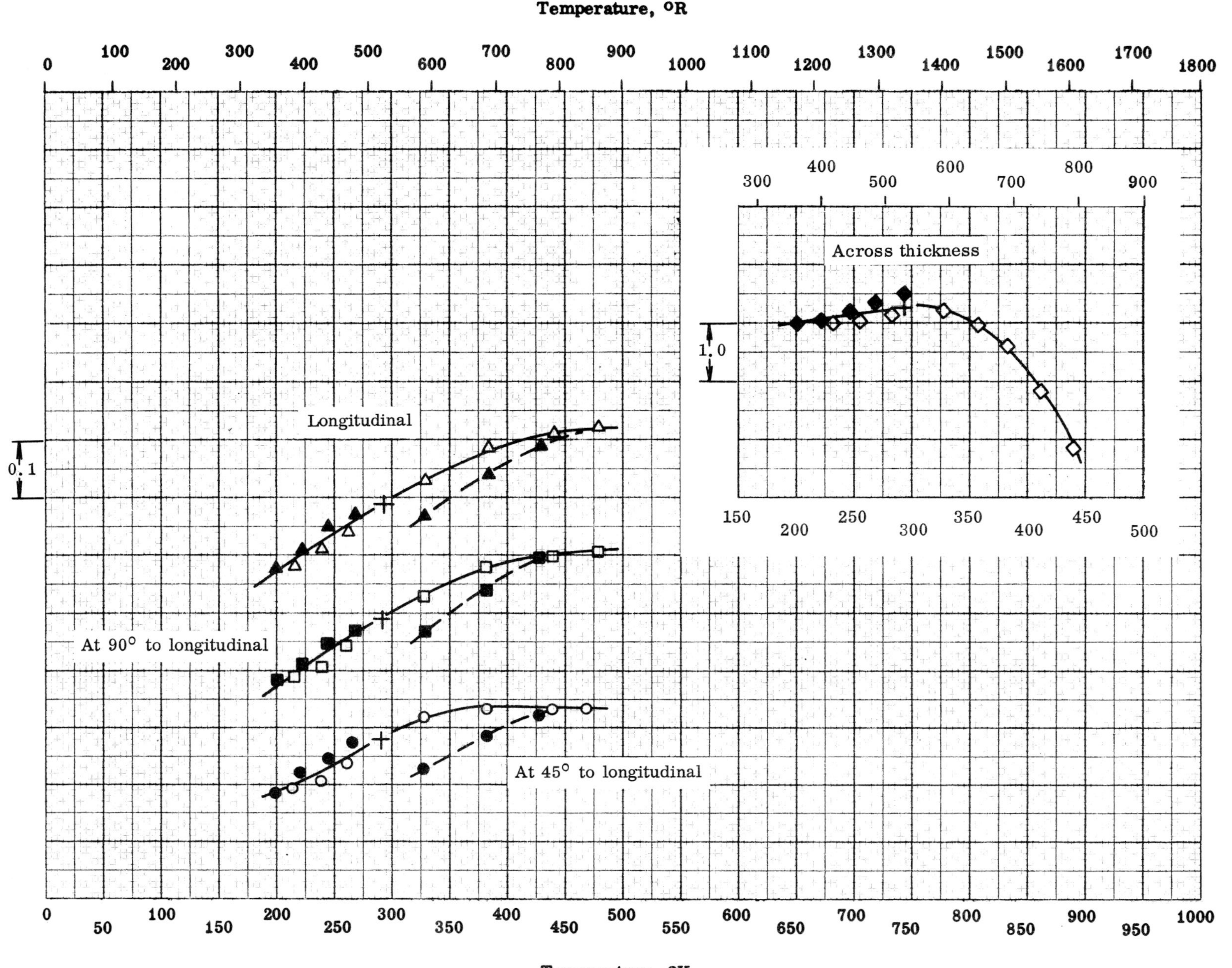

THERMAL LINEAR EXPANSION -- REINFORCED TAC POLYESTER SKIN, ALKYD ISOCYANATE FOAM CORE

THERMAL LINEAR EXPANSION -- REINFORCED TAC POLYESTER SKIN, ALKYD ISOCYANATE FOAM CORE

REFERENCE INFORMATION

Symbol	Ref.	Temp. Range °K	Rept. Error %	Sample Specifications	Remarks
○	55-3	200-478		3 ply foam sandwich panel made by Goodyear; skin: TAC polyester Vibrin 135 and 181 fabric; core: Alkyd Isocyanate Foam; density of core 10 lb ft^{-3}.	Measured at 45 degree angle to longitudinal direction in plane of face; heating curve.
●	55-3	200-478		Same as above.	Cooling curve of the above sample.
□	55-3	200-478		Same as above.	Measured at 90 degree angle to longitudinal direction in plane of face; heating data.
■	55-3	200-478		Same as above.	Cooling data of the above sample.
△	55-3	200-478		Same as above.	Same as above except measured in longitudinal direction in plane of face; heating data.
▲	55-3	200-478		Same as above.	Cooling data of the above sample.
◇	55-3	200-478		Same as above.	Measured across thickness of sample; heating data.
◆	55-3	200-478		Same as above.	Cooling data of the above sample.

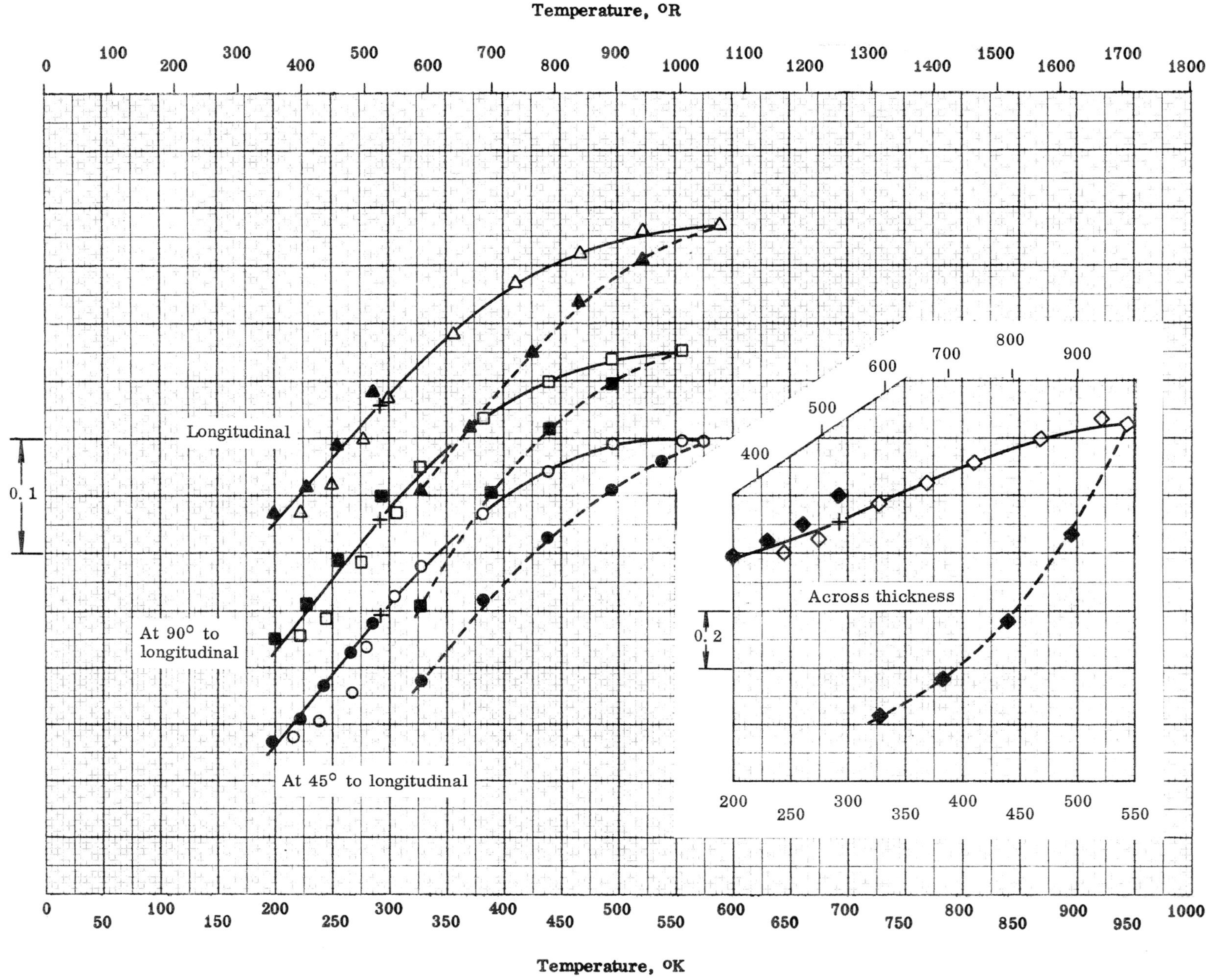

THERMAL LINEAR EXPANSION -- REINFORCED TAC POLYESTER SKIN, PHENOLIC HONEYCOMB CORE

THERMAL LINEAR EXPANSION -- REINFORCED TAC POLYESTER SKIN, PHENOLIC HONEYCOMB CORE

REFERENCE INFORMATION

Symbol	Ref.	Temp. Range °K	Rept. Error %	Sample Specifications	Remarks
○	55-3	200-589		3 ply phenolic honeycomb panel (made by Goodyear); skin: TAC-polyester Vibrin 135 and 181 fabric; core: phenolic honeycomb with dentisy 9.9 lb ft^{-3}.	Measured at 45 degree to longitudinal direction in plane of face; heating.
●	55-3	200-589		Same as above.	Cooling.
□	55-3	200-589		Same as above.	Measured at 90 degree to longitudinal direction in plane of face; heating.
■	55-3	200-589		Same as above.	Cooling.
△	55-3	200-589		Same as above.	Measured in longitudinal direction in plane of face; heating.
▲	55-3	200-589		Same as above.	Cooling.
◇	55-3	200-589		Same as above.	Measured across thickness of sample; heating.
◆	55-3	200-589		Same as above.	Cooling.

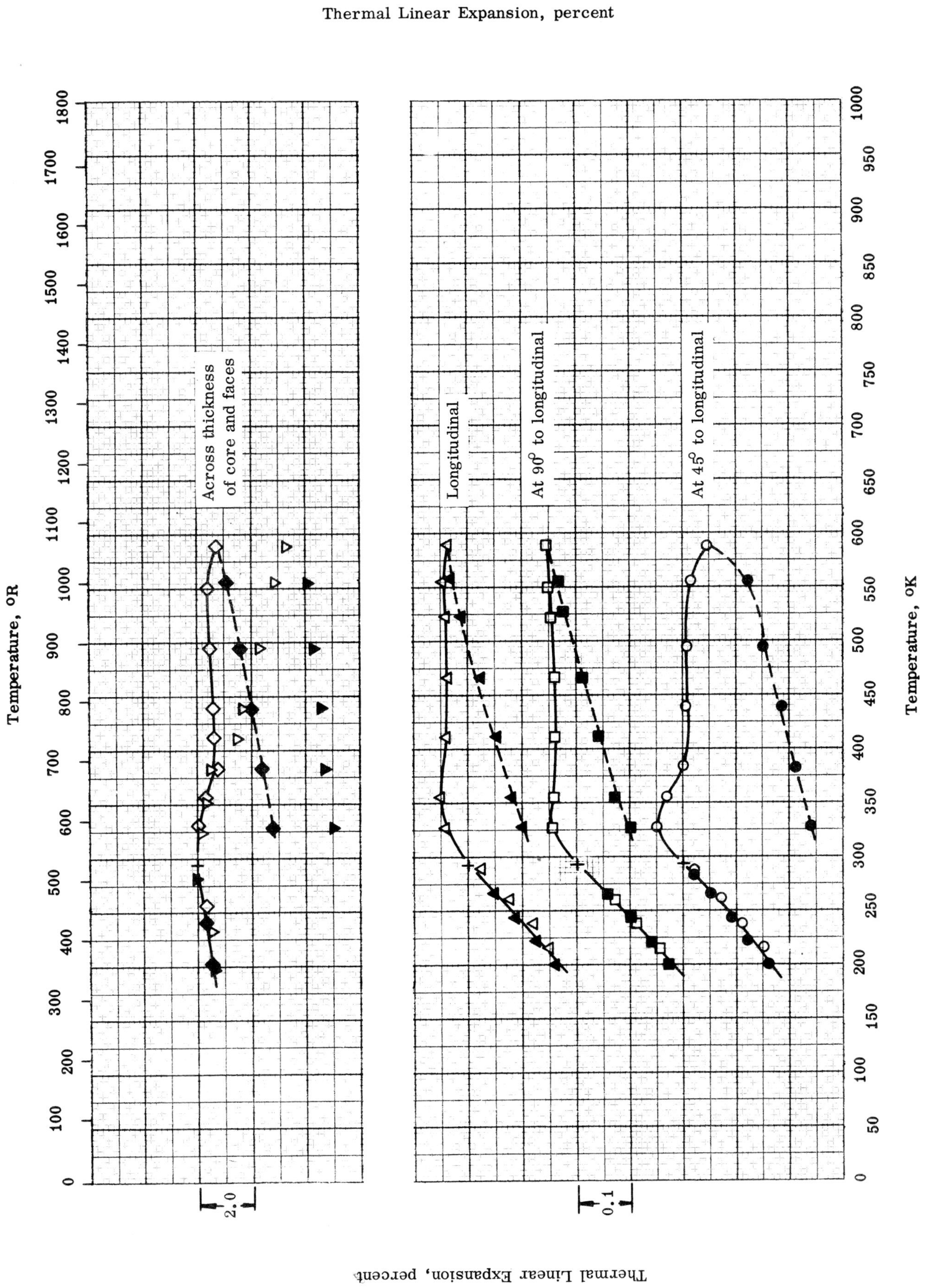

Temperature, °R

0 100 200 300 400 500 600 700 800 900 1000 1100 1200 1300 1400 1500 1600 1700 1800

Across thickness of core and faces

Longitudinal

At 90° to longitudinal

At 45° to longitudinal

2.0

0.1

Thermal Linear Expansion, percent

Thermal Linear Expansion, percent

0 50 100 150 200 250 300 350 400 450 500 550 600 650 700 750 800 850 900 950 1000

Temperature, °K

THERMAL LINEAR EXPANSION -- REINFORCED POLYESTER SKIN, POLYESTER HONEYCOMB CORE

THERMAL LINEAR EXPANSION -- REINFORCED POLYESTER SKIN, POLYESTER HONEYCOMB CORE

REFERENCE INFORMATION

Symbol	Ref.	Temp. Range °K	Rept. Error %	Sample Specifications	Remarks
○	57-8	200-589		Faces: No. 181 Fabric, Volan A Finish No. P-43 Polyester Resin, 2%A.T.C. Catalyst; Core: Polyester Honeycomb, 5/8 in. thick with 1/4 in. cells; total thickness 0.655 in.; resin content 62.9 by wt.	Core by Brunswick-Balke Collender Co.; density of core 9 lb ft^{-3}; measured at 45^{0} to longitudinal direction in plane of face; heating.
●	57-8	200-589		Same as above.	Cooling.
□	57-8	200-589		Same as above.	Same as above except measured at 90^{0} to longitudinal direction in plane of face; heating.
■	57-8	200-589		Same as above.	Cooling.
△	57-8	200-589		Same as above.	Same as above except measured in longitudinal direction in plane of face; heating.
▲	57-8	200-589		Same as above.	Cooling.
◇	57-8	200-589		Same as above.	Same as above except measured across thickness of sample; heating.
◆	57-8	200-589		Same as above.	Cooling.
▽	57-8	200-589		Polyester Honeycomb Panel (No faces): 5/8 in. thick with 1/4 in. cells, 2%A.T.C. Catalyst; Resin content 79.2; density 9 lb ft^{-3}.	By Brunswick-Balke Collender Co.; measured across thickness of sample; heating.
▼	57-8	200-589		Same as above.	Cooling.

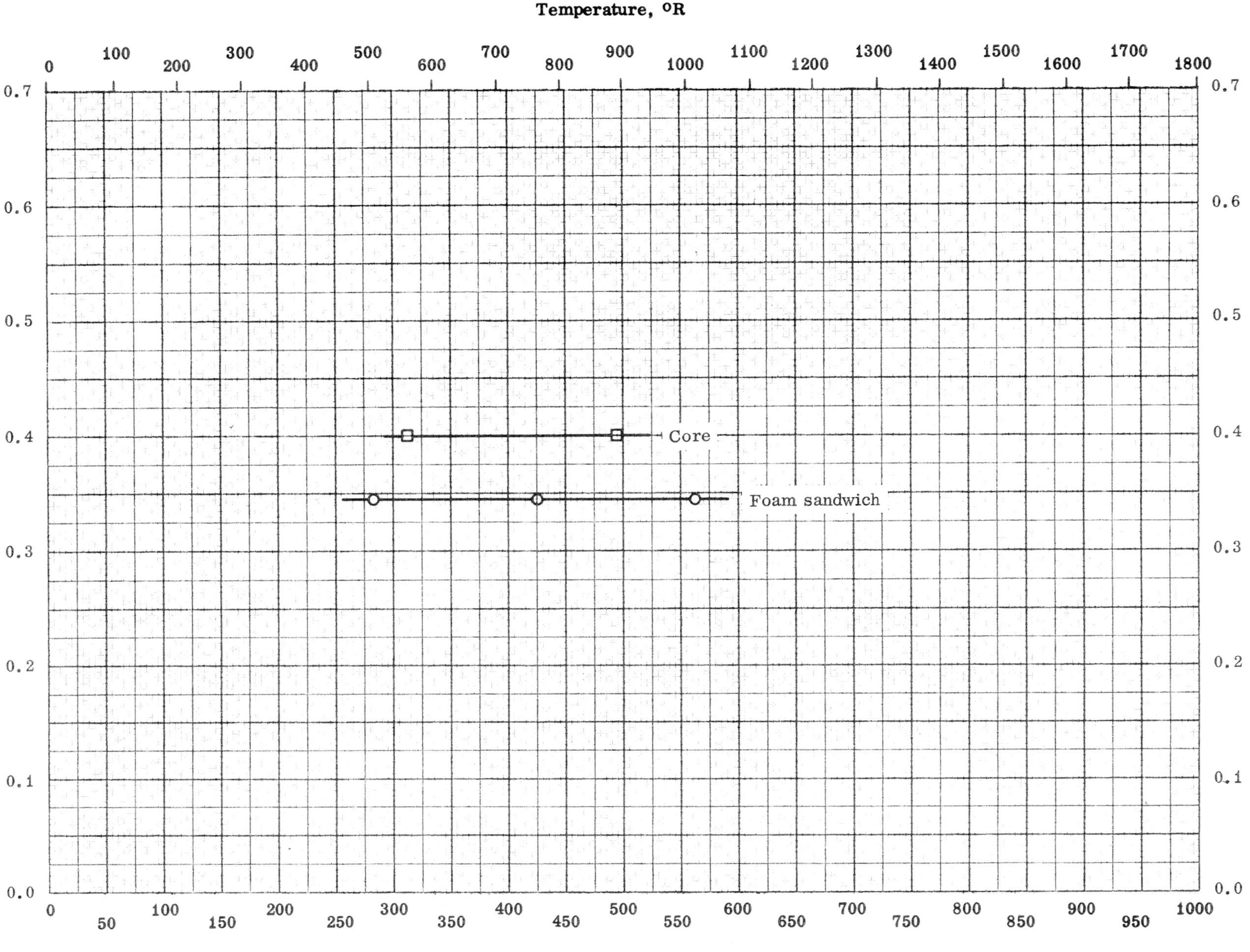

SPECIFIC HEAT -- SANDWICH PANEL
(Plastic skin and plastic foam core)

SPECIFIC HEAT -- SANDWICH PANEL
(Plastic skin and plastic foam core)

REFERENCE INFORMATION

Symbol	Ref.	Temp. Range °K	Rept. Error %	Sample Specifications	Remarks
○	55-3	283-561		3 ply foam sandwich panel; skin: TAC-Polyester Vibrin 135 and 181 fabric; core: alkyd isocyanate foam, core density 10 lb ft^{-3}.	Made by Goodyear.
□	55-3	311-495		Alkyd isocyanate foam core, density 10 lb ft^{-3}.	

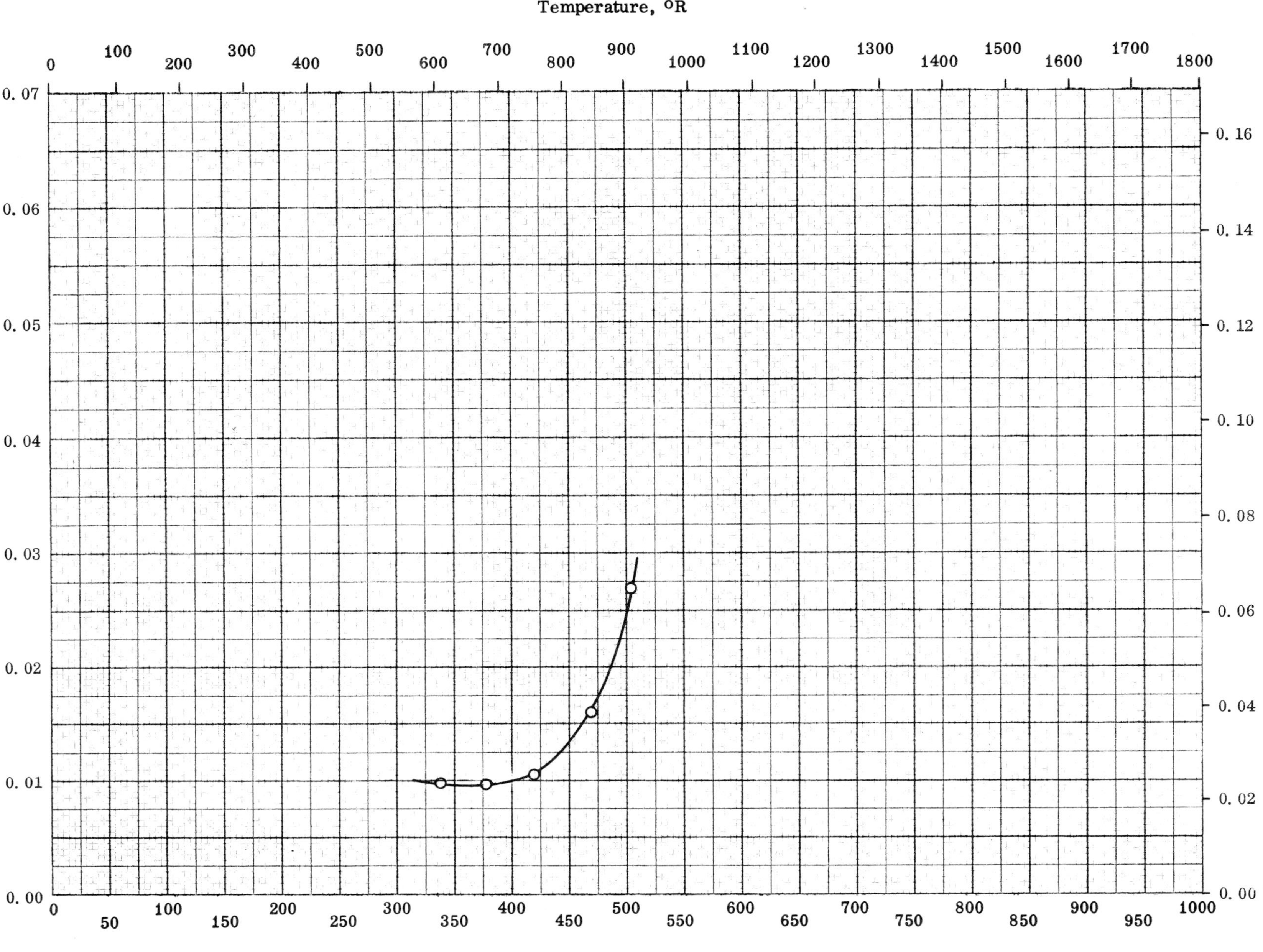

THERMAL CONDUCTIVITY -- SANDWICH PANEL
(Plastic skin and plastic foam core)

THERMAL CONDUCTIVITY -- SANDWICH PANEL
(Plastic skin and plastic foam core)

REFERENCE INFORMATION

Symbol	Ref.	Temp. Range °K	Rept. Error %	Sample Specifications	Remarks
○	55-3	337-504		3 ply panel by Goodyear; faces: glass fabric No. 181 reinforced Vibrin 135 (TAC polyester); core: Alkyd Isocyanate Foam (10 lb ft^{-3}); total thickness: 0.36 in.	Decomposition evident above 300 F.

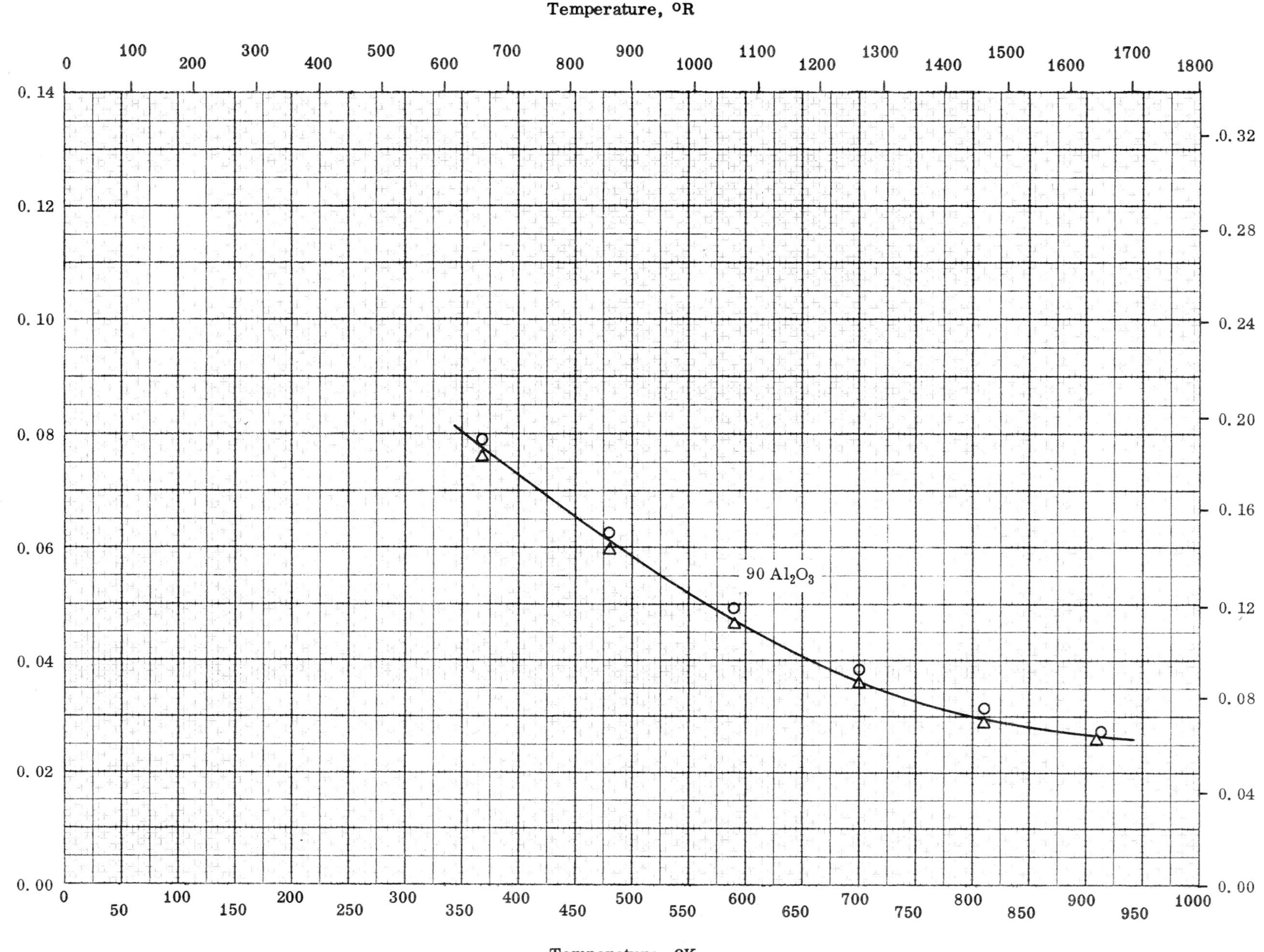

THERMAL CONDUCTIVITY -- MOLYBDENUM FIBERS REINFORCED ALUMINUM OXIDE

THERMAL CONDUCTIVITY -- MOLYBDENUM FIBERS REINFORCED ALUMINUM OXIDE

REFERENCE INFORMATION

Symbol	Ref.	Temp. Range °K	Rept. Error %	Sample Specifications	Remarks
○	58-7	361-922		Alumina reinforced with Mo fibers; 90 alumina (Norton 38-900) and 10 molybdenum fibers (0.002 in. dia. by 1/8 in. long, unannealed); alumina grain size 5 to 9 microns; density above 90% of theoretical.	Hot pressed at 3000 F under 3000 psi; meas. normal to fiber.
△	58-7	367-900		Same as above.	Same as above; meas. parallel to fiber.

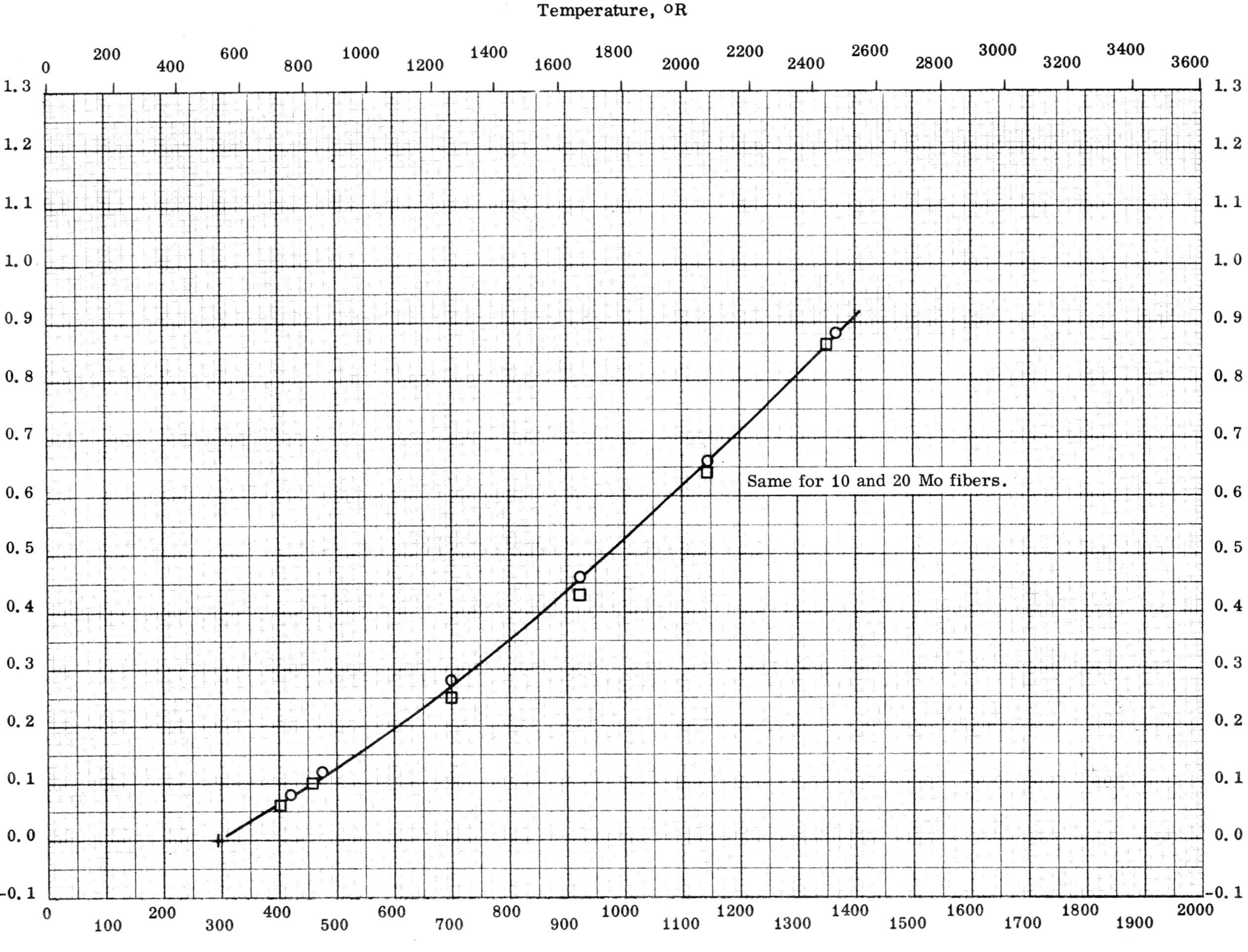

THERMAL LINEAR EXPANSION -- MOLYBDENUM FIBERS REINFORCED ALUMINUM OXIDE

THERMAL LINEAR EXPANSION -- MOLYBDENUM FIBER REINFORCED ALUMINUM OXIDE

REFERENCE INFORMATION

Symbol	Ref.	Temp. Range °K	Rept. Error %	Sample Specifications	Remarks
○	58-7	422-1367		Norton 38-900 alumina and 10 Mo fibers; alumina grain size 5 - 9 μ.	As received; hot pressed at 3000 F and 3000 psi; Mo fibers unannealed.
□	58-7	422-1367		Norton 38 - 900 alumina and 20 Mo fibers; alumina grain size 5 - 9 μ.	Same as above.

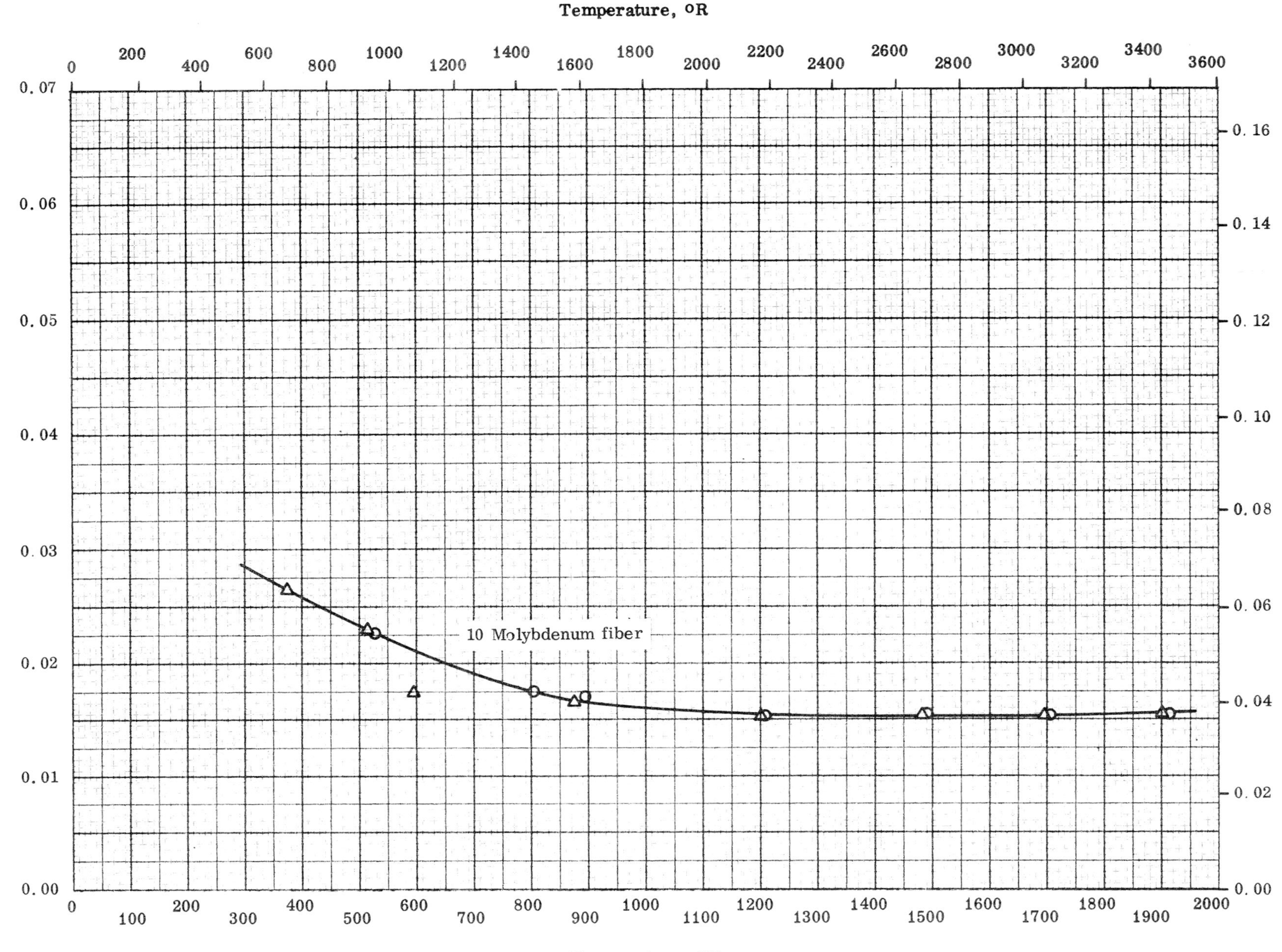

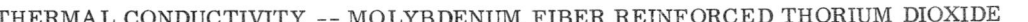

THERMAL CONDUCTIVITY -- MOLYBDENUM FIBER REINFORCED THORIUM DIOXIDE

THERMAL CONDUCTIVITY -- MOLYBDENUM FIBER REINFORCED THORIUM DIOXIDE

REFERENCE INFORMATION

Symbol	Ref.	Temp. Range °K	Rept. Error %	Sample Specifications	Remarks
○	57-11	529-1913		10 Molybdenum fiber and 0.5 CaF_2; Mo fiber 0.002 in. dia and 1/8 in. nominal length; average bulk density 9.26 g cm^{-3}.	Hot-pressed at 1500 ± 50 C and a pressure of ca. 100 psi for 30 min.
△	62-16	373-1903		Reinforced with 10 molybdenum fiber of 0.005 cm dia and 0.5 cm long.	

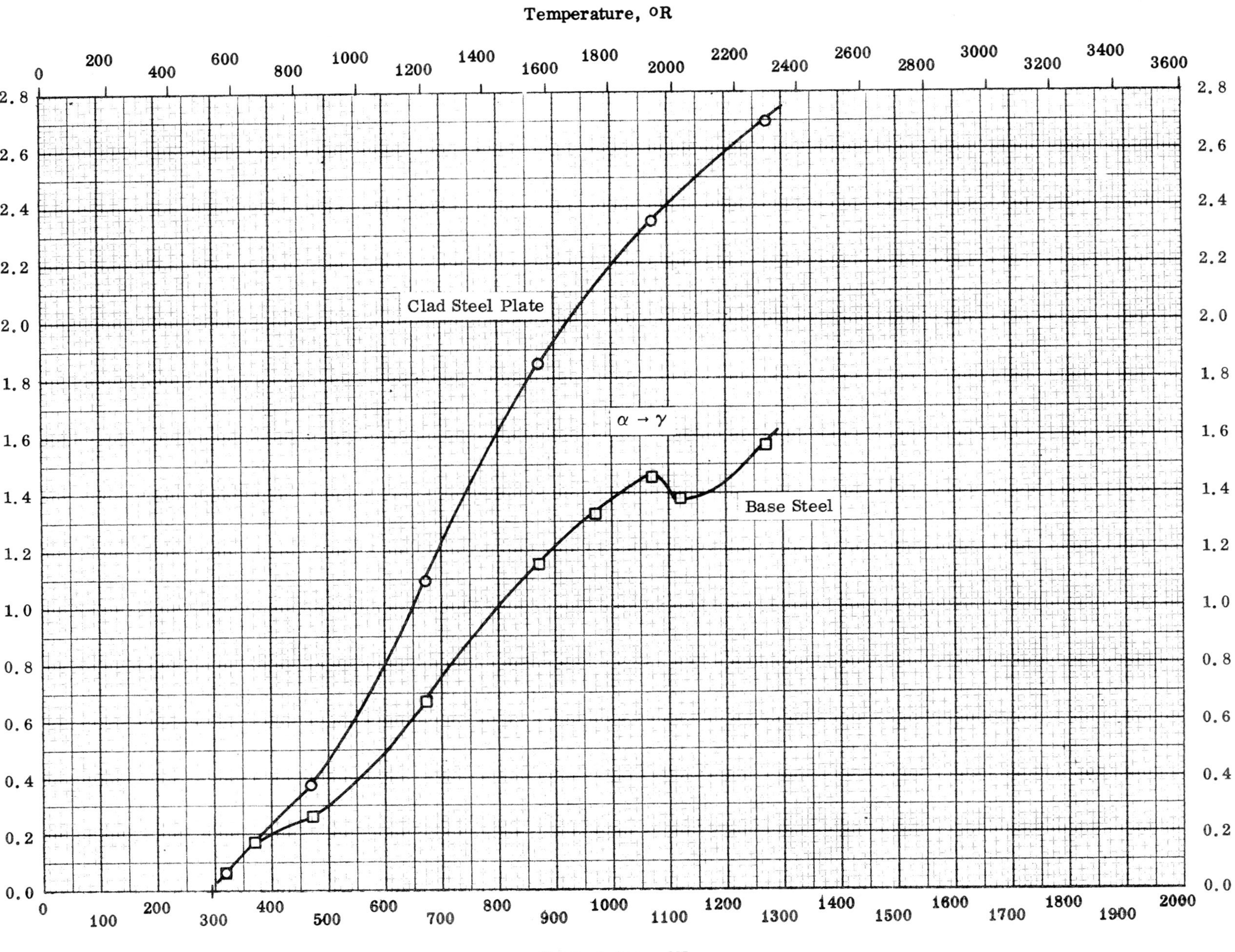

THERMAL LINEAR EXPANSION -- STAINLESS STEEL CLAD STEEL PLATE

THERMAL LINEAR EXPANSION -- STAINLESS STEEL CLAD STEEL PLATE

REFERENCE INFORMATION

Symbol	Ref.	Temp. Range °K	Rept. Error %	Sample Specifications	Remarks
○	52-14	293-1273		Clad steel; 18.81 Cr, 8.46 Ni, 0.45 Si, 0.05 C, 0.04 Cu, 0.028 P, 0.021 S, and traces of Mn and Mo.	
□	52-14	293-1273		Base metal; low carbon steel.	

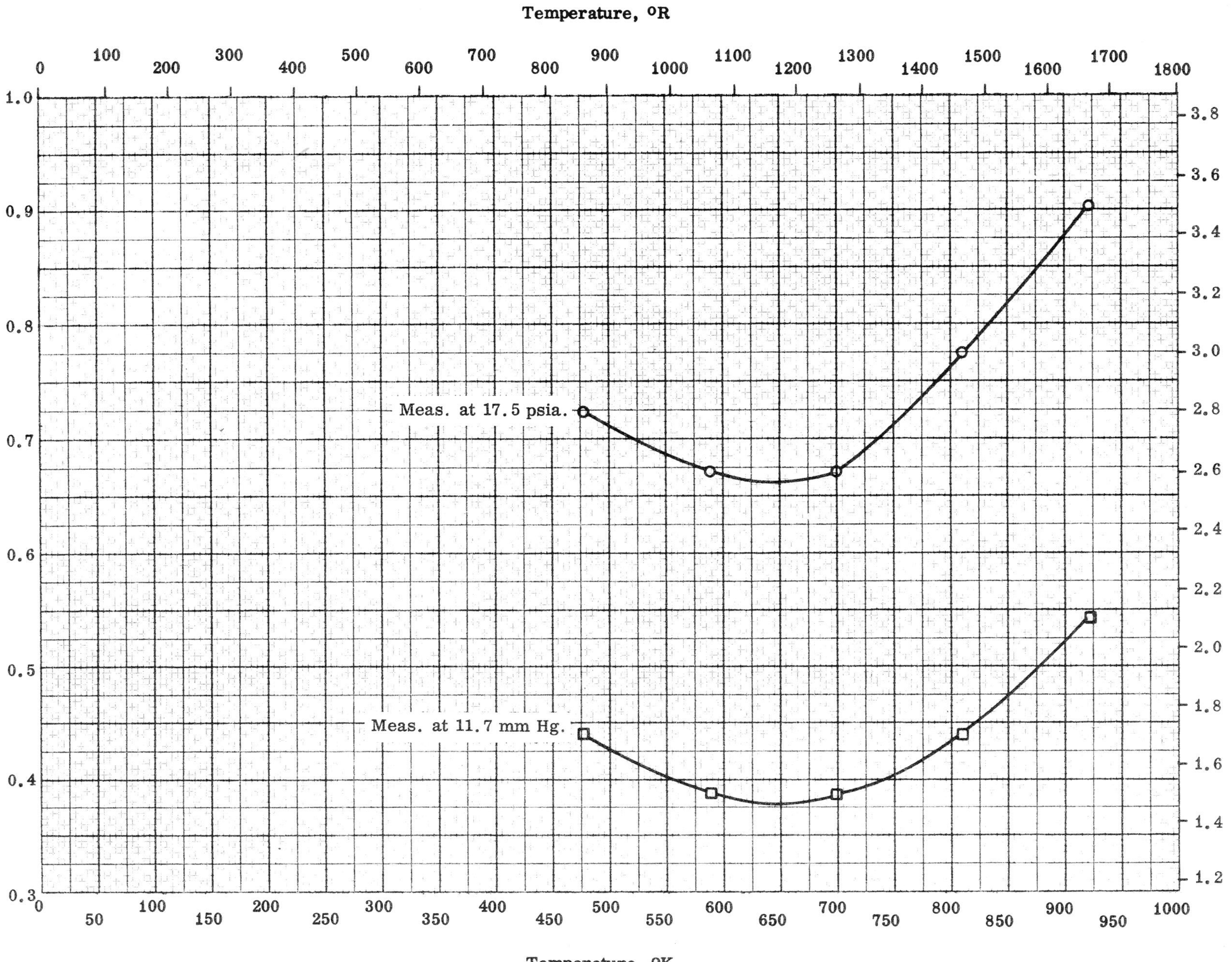

THERMAL DIFFUSIVITY -- FABRICS
(Fiber glass cloth)

THERMAL DIFFUSIVITY -- FABRICS
(Fiber glass cloth)

REFERENCE INFORMATION

Symbol	Ref.	Temp. Range °K	Rept. Error %	Sample Specifications	Remarks
○	62-1	478-922		Supplied by Owens Corning Co.; 8 harness satin type weave with 57 yarns in^{-1} ends and 54 picks in^{-1}; A - 1100 finish 112 and non-coated; weight 8.9 oz. yd^{-2} and average thickness 0.01660 in.	Measured in an average ambient pressure 17.5 psia
□	62-1	478-922		Same as above.	Measured in vacuum of 11.7 mm Hg average ambient pressure.

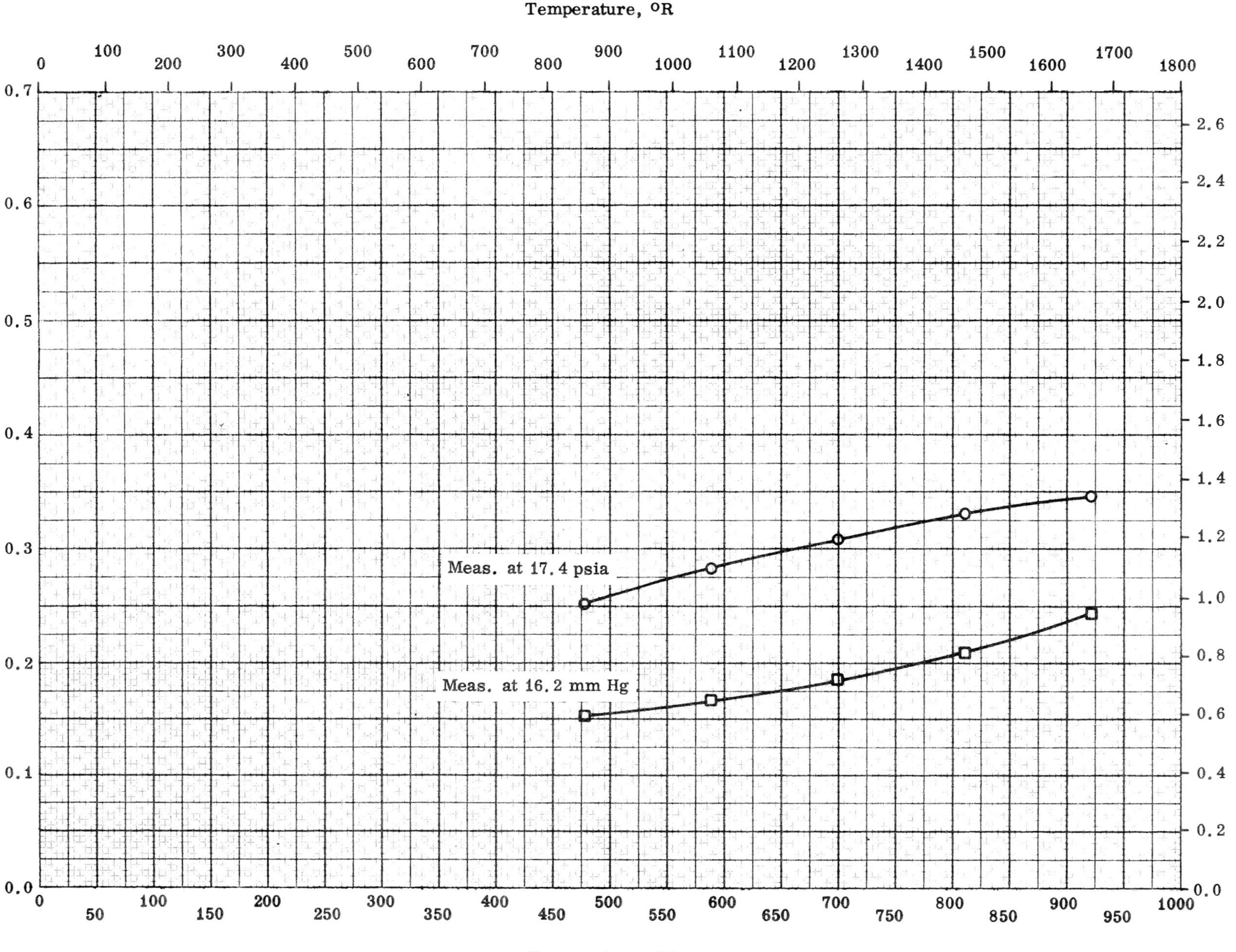

THERMAL DIFFUSIVITY -- FABRICS
(Graphite cloth)

THERMAL DIFFUSIVITY -- FABRICS
(Graphite cloth)

REFERENCE INFORMATION

Symbol	Ref.	Temp. Range °K	Rept. Error %	Sample Specifications	Remarks
○	62-1	478-922		Supplied by National Carbon Co.; plain weave type with 26.9 wrap and 22.7 filling yarns in^{-1}; non-coated; weight 7.6 oz yd^{-2} and average thickness 0.02430 in.	Measured in an average ambient pressure of 17.4 psia.
□	62-1	478-922		Same as above.	Measured in a vacuum of an average ambient pressure 16.2 mm Hg.

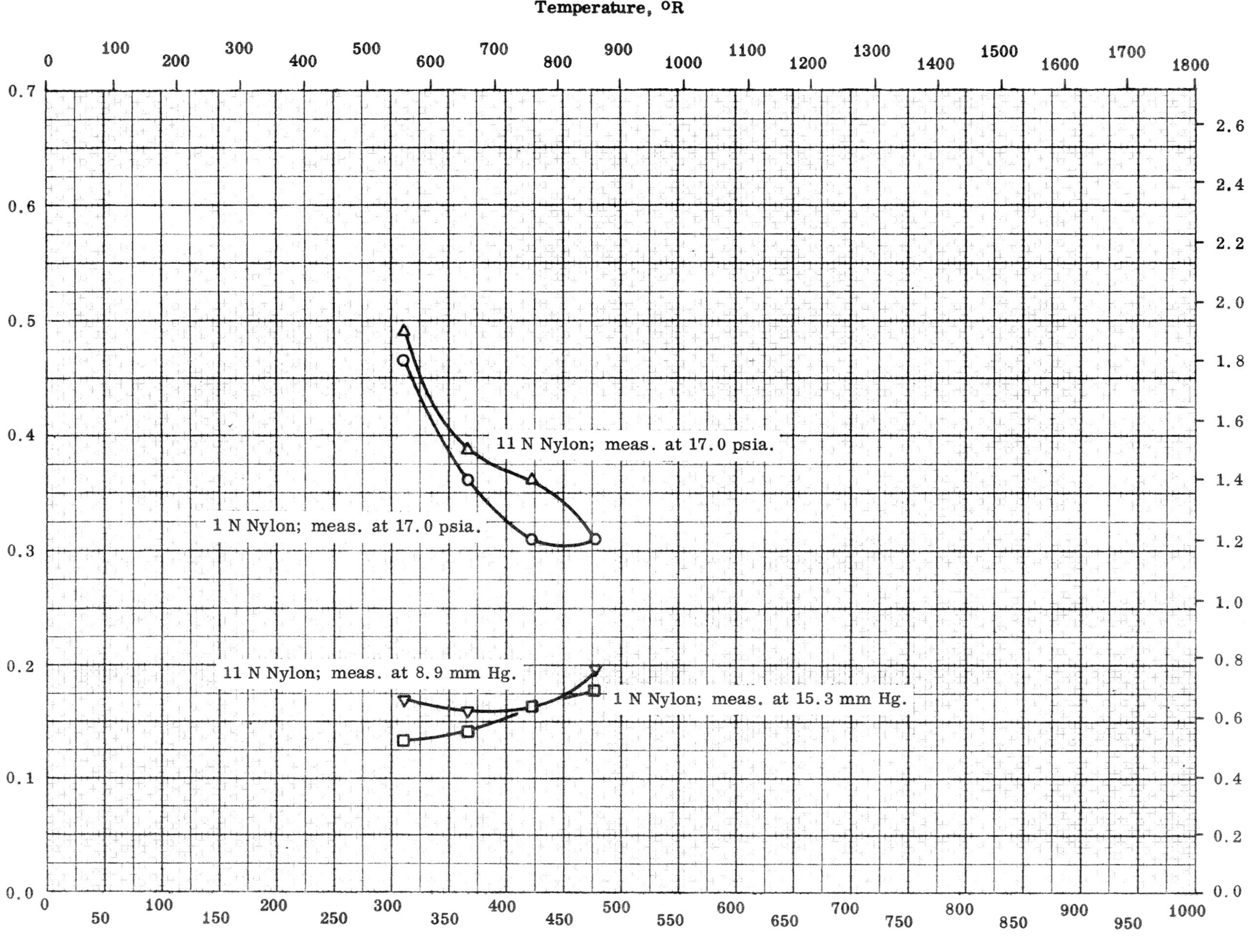

THERMAL DIFFUSIVITY -- FABRICS
(Nylon cloth)

THERMAL DIFFUSIVITY -- FABRICS
(Nylon cloth)

REFERENCE INFORMATION

Symbol	Ref.	Temp. Range °K	Rept. Error %	Sample Specifications	Remarks
○	62-1	311-478		1N nylon; MIL-C-7350 type I by E. I. DuPont; plain weave with 64 yarns per in. ends and 68 picks in. $^{-1}$; nominal twist 0.75 wrap in. $^{-1}$ and filling each; non-calendered finish and non-coated; weight 2.10 oz. yd $^{-2}$ and average thickness 0.00531 in	Measured in an average ambient pressure 17.0 psia.
□	62-1	311-478		Same as above.	Measured in a vacuum of 15.3 mm Hg average ambient pressure.
△	62-1	311-478		11 N nylon; MIL-C-7350 type I by E. I. DuPont; twill (2 x 1) weave with 64 yarns in.$^{-1}$ ends and 68 picks in.$^{-1}$; nominal twish 5.75 wrap in.$^{-1}$ and filling each; non-calendered finish and non-coated; weight 2.06 oz yd^{-2} and average thickness 0.00656 in.	Measured in a average ambient pressure 17.0 psia.
▽	62-1	311-478		Same as above.	Measured in vacuum of 8.9 mm Hg average ambient pressure.

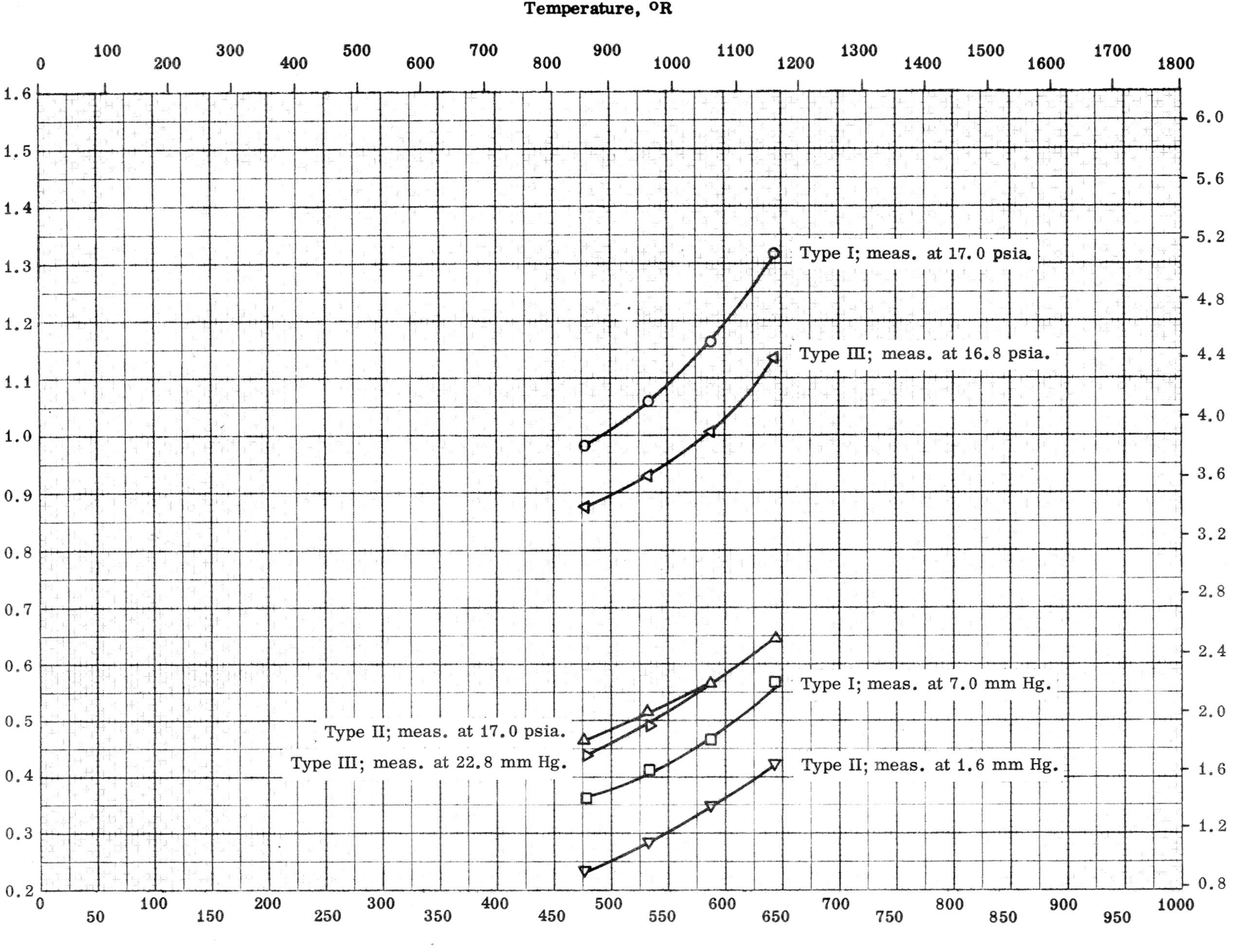

THERMAL DIFFUSIVITY -- FABRICS
(Organic fiber cloth)

THERMAL DIFFUSIVITY -- FABRICS
(Organic fiber cloth)

REFERENCE INFORMATION

Symbol	Ref.	Temp. Range °K	Rept. Error %	Sample Specifications	Remarks
○	62-1	478-644		HT - 1 type I; MIL - C - 7350 type I and II by E. I. DuPont; with 74 yarns in^{-1} end and 71 picks in^{-1}; nominal twist 6.3 in^{-1} warp and filling each; non-finished and non coated; weight 1.95 oz. yd^{-2} and average thickness 0.00675 in.	Measured in an average ambient pressure of 17.0 psia.
□	62-1	478-644		Same as above.	Measured in vacuum of 7.0 mm Hg average ambient pressure.
△	62-1	478-644		HT - 1 type II; MIL - C - 7350 type I and II; with 58 yarns in^{-1} ends and 52 picks in^{-1}; nominal twist 6.0 warp in^{-1} and 6.5 filling; non-finished and non-coated; weight 3.07 oz. yd^{-2} and average thickness 0.01187 in.	Measured in an average ambient pressure of 17.0 psia.
▽	62-1	478-644		Same as above.	Measured in vacuum of 1.6 mm Hg average ambient pressure.
◁	62-1	478-644		HT - 1 type III; MIL - C - 8021 type I by E. I. DuPont; non-finished and non-coated; weight 6.02 oz. yd^{-2} and average thickness 0.01636 in.	Measured in an average ambient pressure of 16.8 psia.
▷	62-1	478-644		Same as above.	Measured in a vacuum of 22.8 mm Hg average ambient pressure.

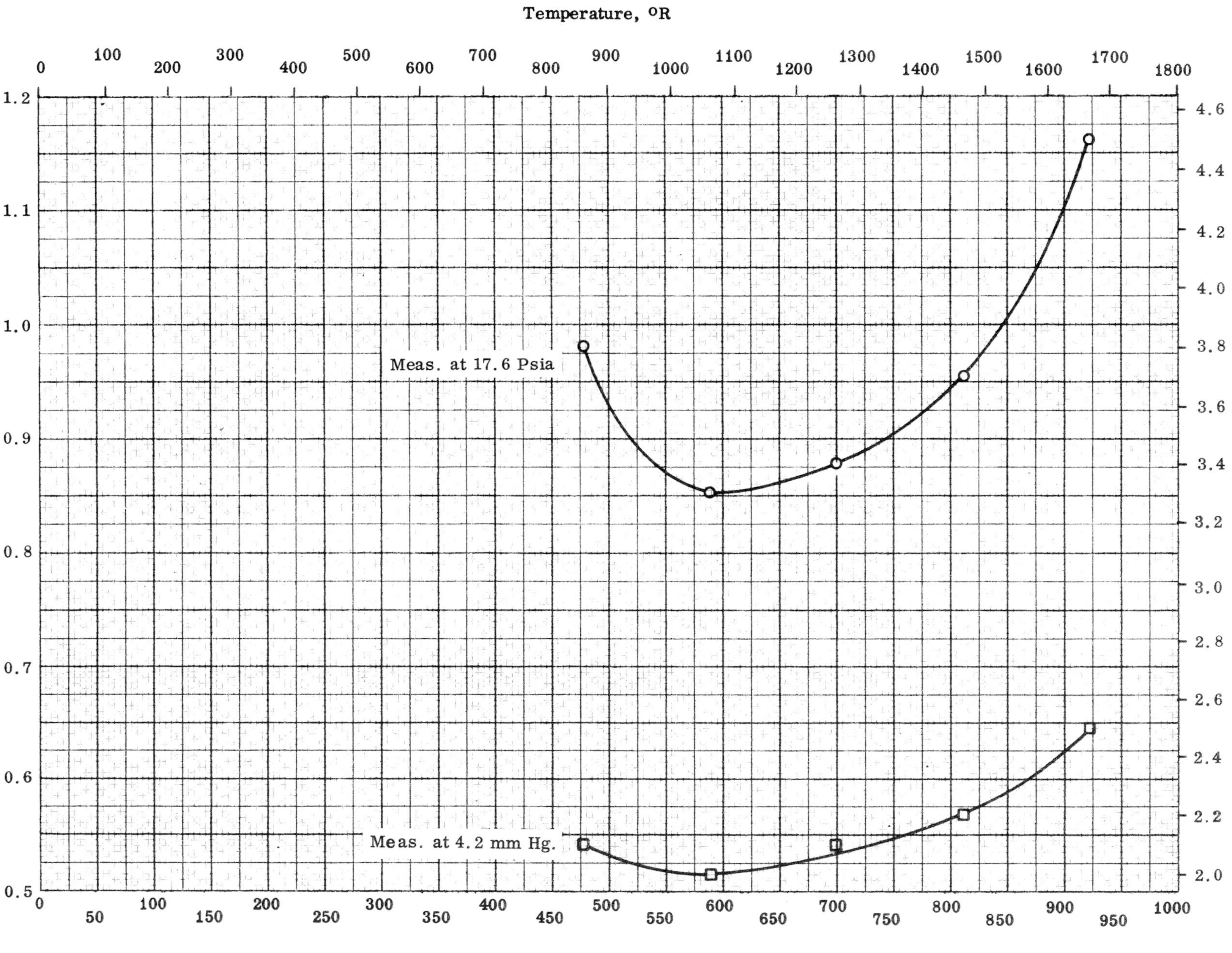

THERMAL DIFFUSIVITY -- FABRICS
(Silica cloth)

THERMAL DIFFUSIVITY -- FABRICS
(Silica cloth)

REFERENCE INFORMATION

Symbol	Ref.	Temp. Range °K	Rept. Error %	Sample Specifications	Remarks
○	62-1	478-922		FRLG 2502 - 1 by Fabric Res. Lab., Inc.; vitrous silica; 7/1 twill type weave with 57 warp and 52 filling yarns in $^{-1}$; non-coated; weight 7.56 oz. yd.$^{-2}$ and average thickness 0.01947 in.	Measured in an average ambient pressure 17.6 psia
□	62-1	478-922		Same as above.	Measured in a vacuum of 4.2 mm Hg average ambient pressure.

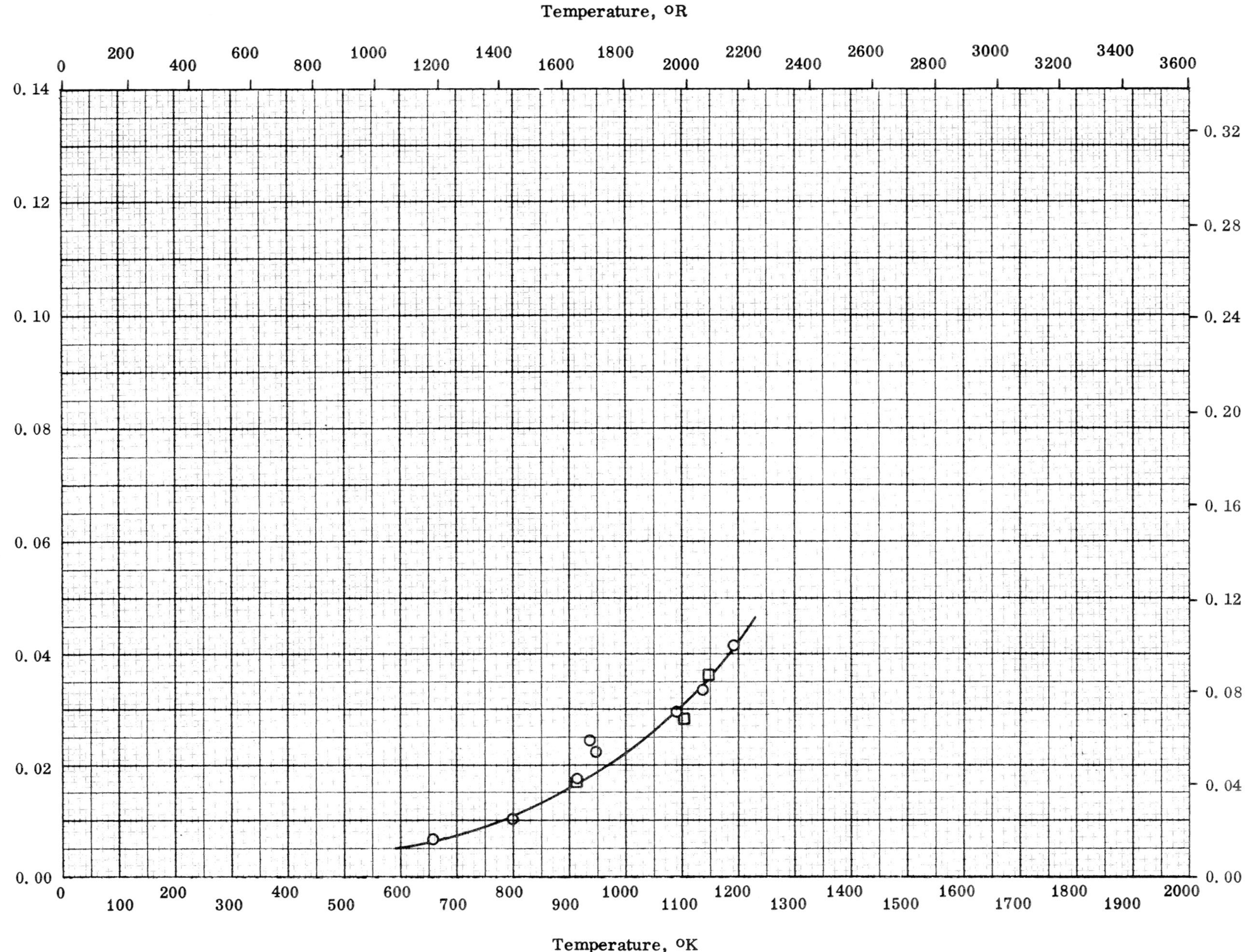

THERMAL CONDUCTIVITY -- ALUMINA BUBBLES - GRAPHITE FIBERS COMPOSITE SYSTEM

THERMAL CONDUCTIVITY -- ALUMINA BUBBLES - GRAPHITE FIBERS COMPOSITE SYSTEM

REFERENCE INFORMATION

Symbol	Ref.	Temp. Range °K	Rept. Error %	Sample Specifications	Remarks
○	63-5	655-1189		Alumina bubbles with 250-350μ dia and 66 lb ft^{-3} density and 2 layers graphite matting with 14μ average dia fiber and 5.15 lb ft^{-3} density.	Measured in 0.7×10^{-6} to 1.2×10^{-4} mm Hg pressure range.
□	63-5	911-1144		Same as above.	Measured when cooling.

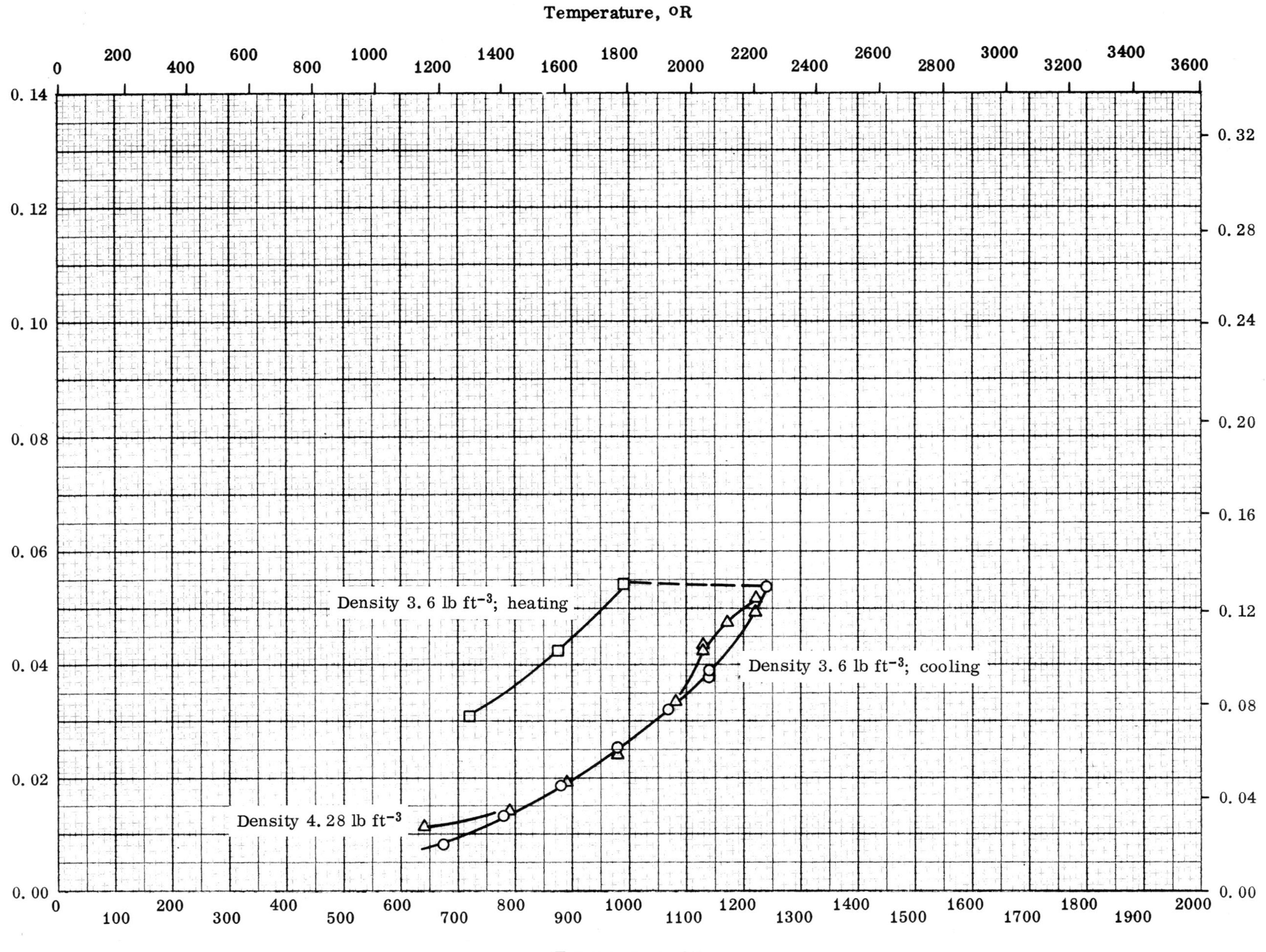

THERMAL CONDUCTIVITY -- GRAPHITE FIBERS - TANTALUM SHIELD COMPOSITE SYSTEM

THERMAL CONDUCTIVITY -- GRAPHITE FIBERS - TANTALUM SHIELD COMPOSITE SYSTEM

REFERENCE INFORMATION

Symbol	Ref.	Temp. Range °K	Rept. Error %	Sample Specifications	Remarks
○	63-5	672-1239		Type WDF and 14 μ average dia graphite fiber mats and 0.0005 in. thick tantalum; graphite fibers 3.6 lb ft^{-3} density.	Prepared by wrapping four spiral layers of graphite fiber mats ($\approx$0.25 in. thick) alternated with three tantalum shield; measured in 1.6×10^{-6} to 1.5×10^{-4} mm Hg pressure range.
□	63-5	722-989		Same as above.	Same as above except measured in cooling.
△	63-5	639-1222		Same as above except graphite fiber 4.28 lb ft^{-3} density.	Same as above except that tantalum foil had a 5% open area made by spacing 3/12 in. dia holes in regular array.

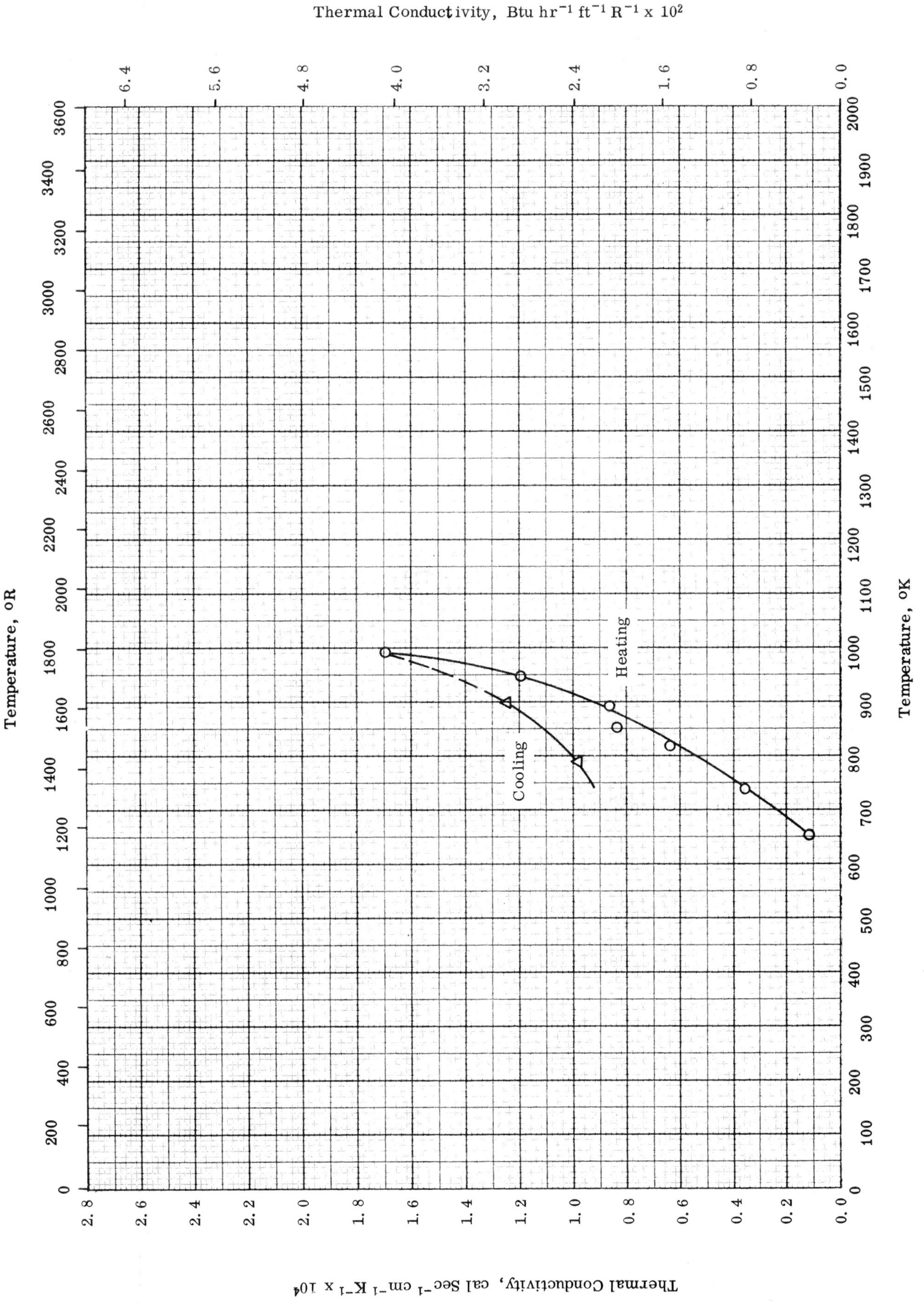

Temperature, °R

0 200 400 600 800 1000 1200 1400 1600 1800 2000 2200 2400 2600 2800 3000 3200 3400 3600

Thermal Conductivity, cal Sec^{-1} cm^{-1} K^{-1} x 10^4

2.8 2.6 2.4 2.2 2.0 1.8 1.6 1.4 1.2 1.0 0.8 0.6 0.4 0.2 0.0

Cooling

Heating

Thermal Conductivity, Btu hr^{-1} ft^{-1} R^{-1} x 10^2

6.4 5.6 4.8 4.0 3.2 2.4 1.6 0.8 0.0

0 100 200 300 400 500 600 700 800 900 1000 1100 1200 1300 1400 1500 1600 1700 1800 1900 2000

Temperature, °K

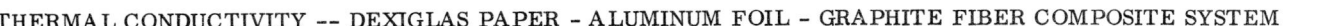

THERMAL CONDUCTIVITY -- DEXIGLAS PAPER - ALUMINUM FOIL - GRAPHITE FIBER COMPOSITE SYSTEM

THERMAL CONDUCTIVITY -- DEXIGLAS PAPER - ALUMINUM FOIL - GRAPHITE FIBER COMPOSITE SYSTEM

REFERENCE INFORMATION

Symbol	Ref.	Temp. Range °K	Rept. Error %	Sample Specifications	Remarks
○	63-5	655-994		"Dexiglas" (Dexter) paper, 0.002 in. Aluminum foil, and 14 μ average dia. type WDF graphite fibers; graphite fiber density 5.5 lb ft^{-3}.	Formed by wrapping 13 layers of paper and 10 layers of aluminum foil alternately around the heater and then wrapping 4 layers of graphite fiber mats outside; measured in 1.4×10^{-7} to 2.0×10^{-5} mm Hg pressure range.
△	63-5	789-900		Same as above.	Same as above except measured cooling.

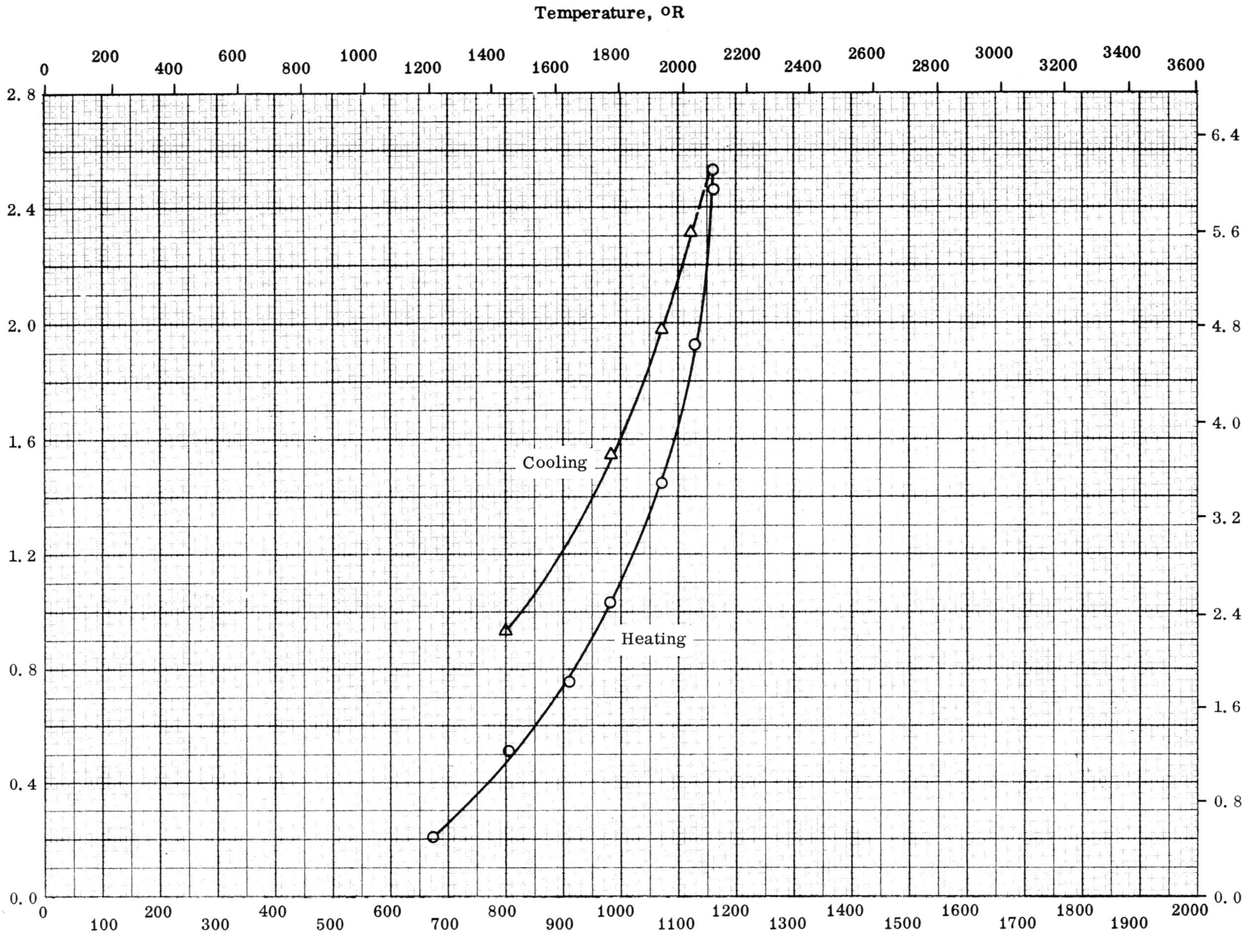

THERMAL CONDUCTIVITY -- FIBERFRAX PAPER - TANTALUM SHIELD - GRAPHITE FIBERS COMPOSITE SYSTEM

THERMAL CONDUCTIVITY -- FIBERFRAX PAPER - TANTALUM SHIELD - GRAPHITE FIBERS COMPOSITE SYSTEM

REFERENCE INFORMATION

Symbol	Ref.	Temp. Range °K	Rept. Error %	Sample Specifications	Remarks
○	63-5	672-1161		"Fiberfrax" paper, 0. 0005 in. and 0. 005 in. tantalum foil, and 10 μ average dia type WDF graphite fibers.	Formed by wrapping ten layers of Fiberfrax paper, nine layers slit 0. 0005 in. Ta foils around the heater with 0. 005 in. Ta foil as outer layer and then three layers of graphite fibers with tantalum foils to separate them; measured 1×10^{-6} to 6×10^{-4} mm Hg pressure range.
△	63-5	800-1119		Same as above.	Same as above; measured cooling.

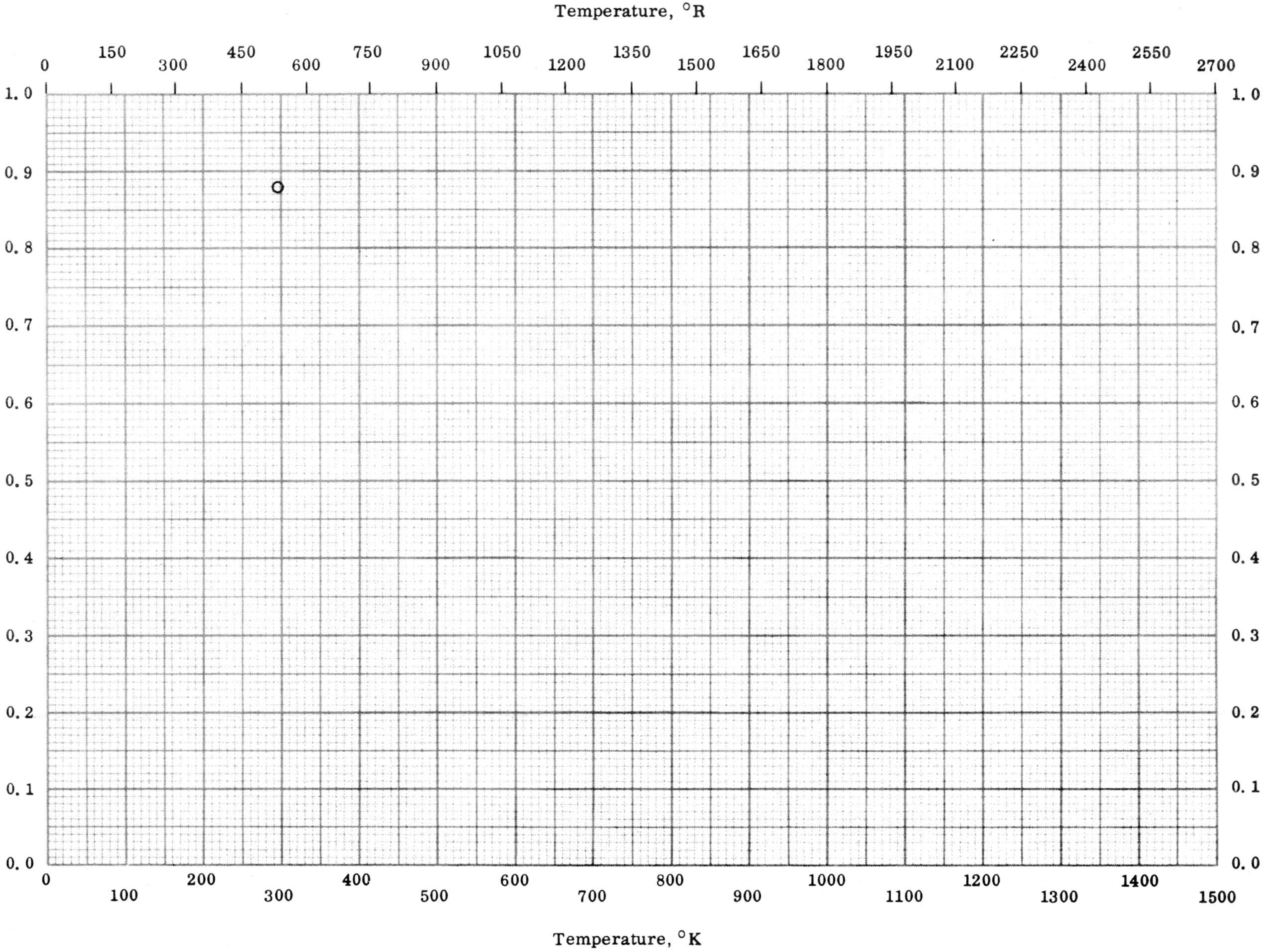

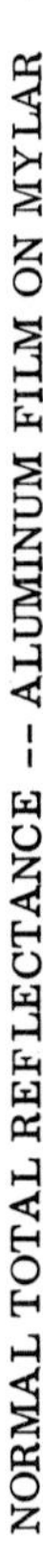

NORMAL TOTAL REFLECTANCE -- ALUMINUM FILM ON MYLAR

Temperature, °R

Temperature, °K

Normal Total Reflectance

NORMAL TOTAL REFLECTANCE -- ALUMINUM FILM ON MYLAR

REFERENCE INFORMATION

Symbol	Ref.	Temp. Range °K	Rept. Error %	Sample Specifications	Remarks
○	62-33	298		Aluminum film on 0.00025 in. mylar.	Using integrating hemispherical radiometer; data for normal incidence solar radiation.

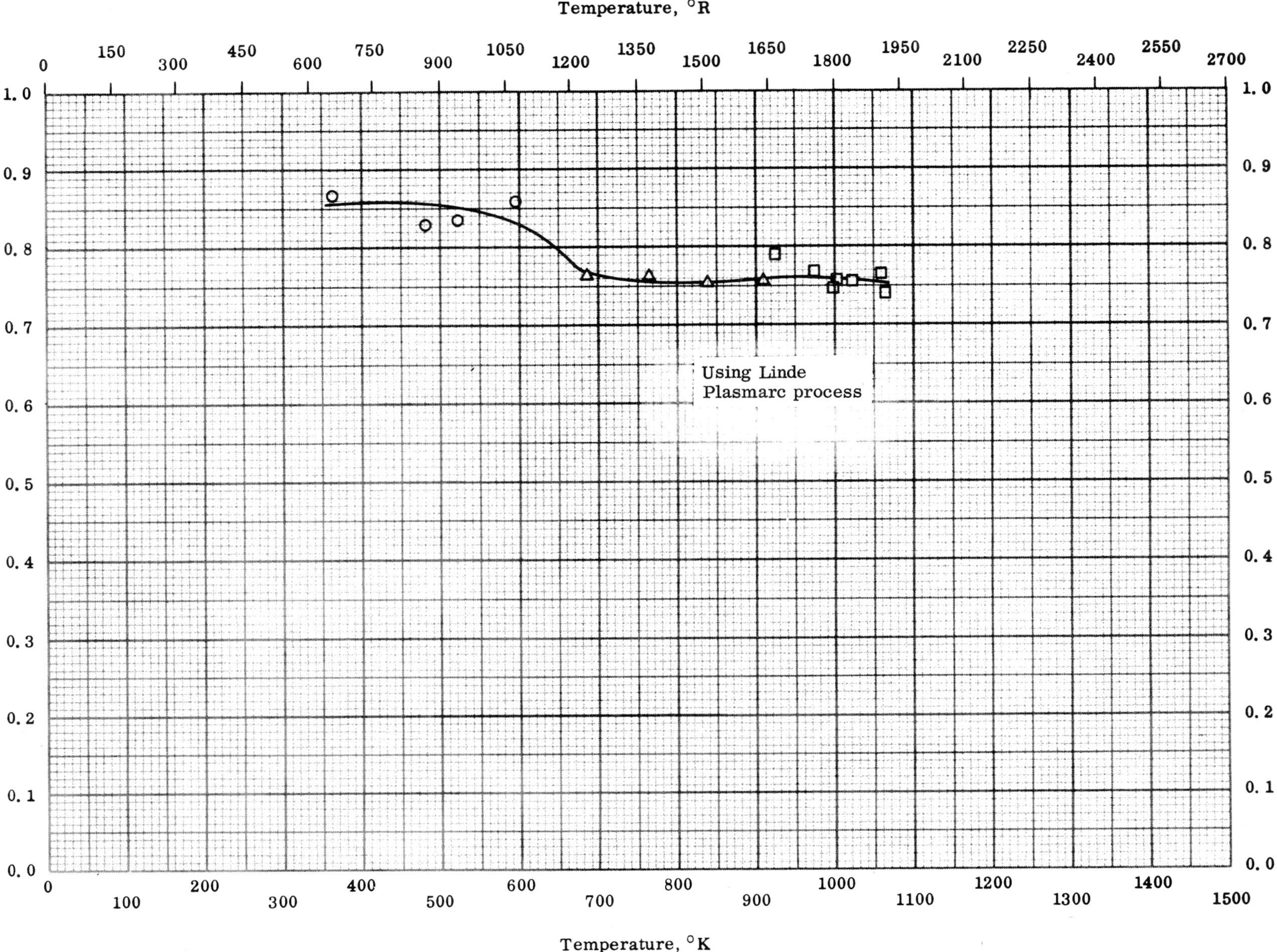

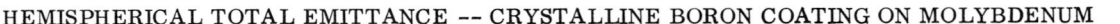

HEMISPHERICAL TOTAL EMITTANCE -- CRYSTALLINE BORON COATING ON MOLYBDENUM

HEMISPHERICAL TOTAL EMITTANCE -- CRYSTALLINE BORON COATING ON MOLYBDENUM

REFERENCE INFORMATION

Symbol	Ref.	Temp. Range °K	Rept. Error %	Sample Specifications	Remarks
○	60-25	363-595		Coating thickness 0.003 in.	By Linde Plasmarc process; measured in vacuum; run No. 1.
△	60-25	688-909		Same as above.	Same as above; run No. 2.
□	60-25	927-1066		Same as above.	Same as above; run No. 3.

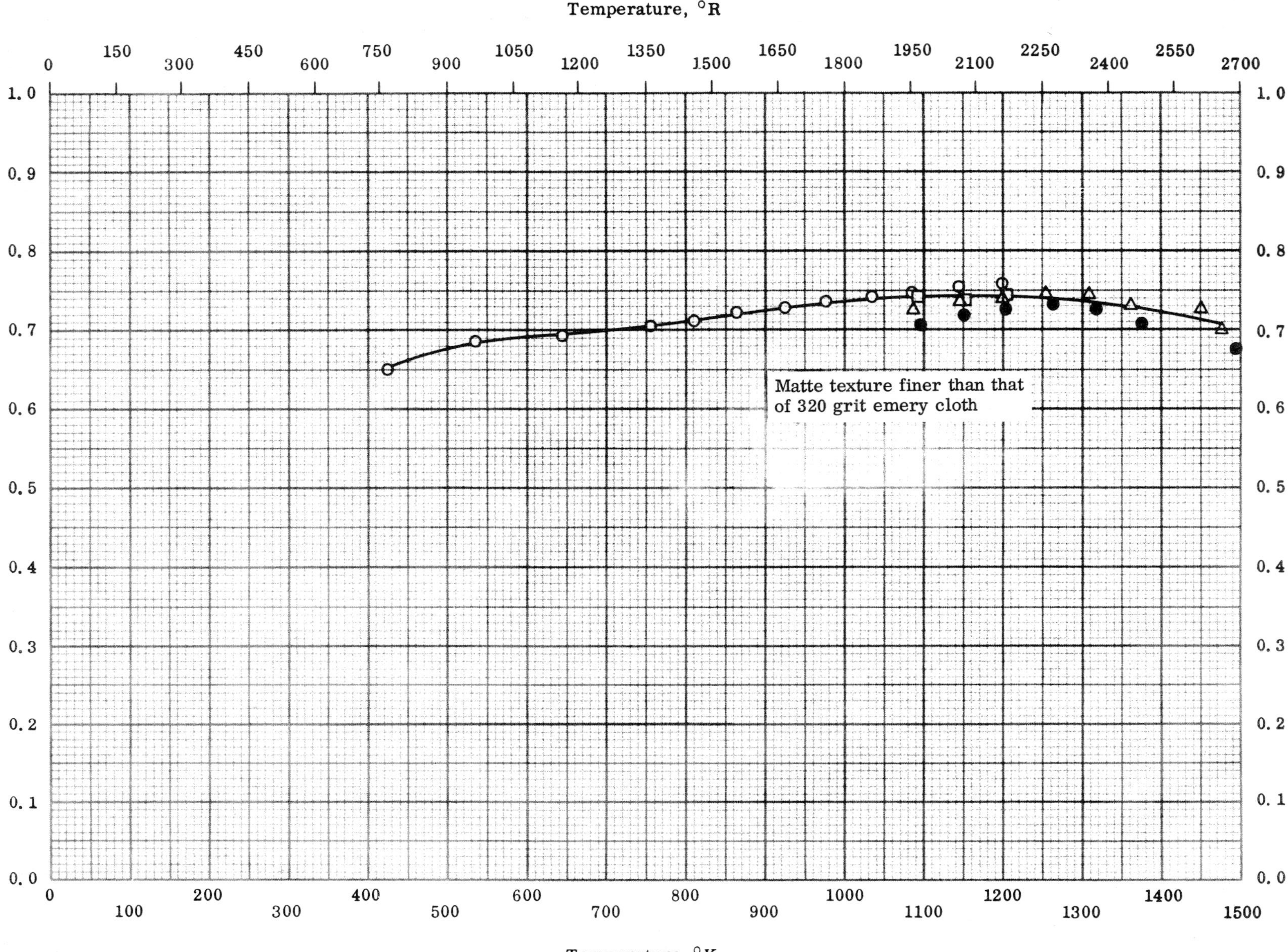

HEMISPHERICAL TOTAL EMITTANCE -- CRYSTALLINE BORON COATING ON NIOBIUM ALLOY

HEMISPHERICAL TOTAL EMITTANCE -- CRYSTALLINE BORON COATING ON NIOBIUM ALLOY

REFERENCE INFORMATION

Symbol	Ref.	Temp. Range °K	Rept. Error %	Sample Specifications	Remarks
○	63-23	422-1199		99 Nb and 1 Zr; coating thickness < 0.001 in. with a matte texture finer than that of 320 grit emery cloth.	Plasma-arc sprayed; measured in vacuum; using thermocouple; first run.
△	63-23	1088-1477		Same as above.	Same as above; second run.
□	63-23	1091-1205		Same as above.	Same as above; using optical pyrometer; first run.
●	63-23	1096-1491		Same as above.	Same as above; second run.

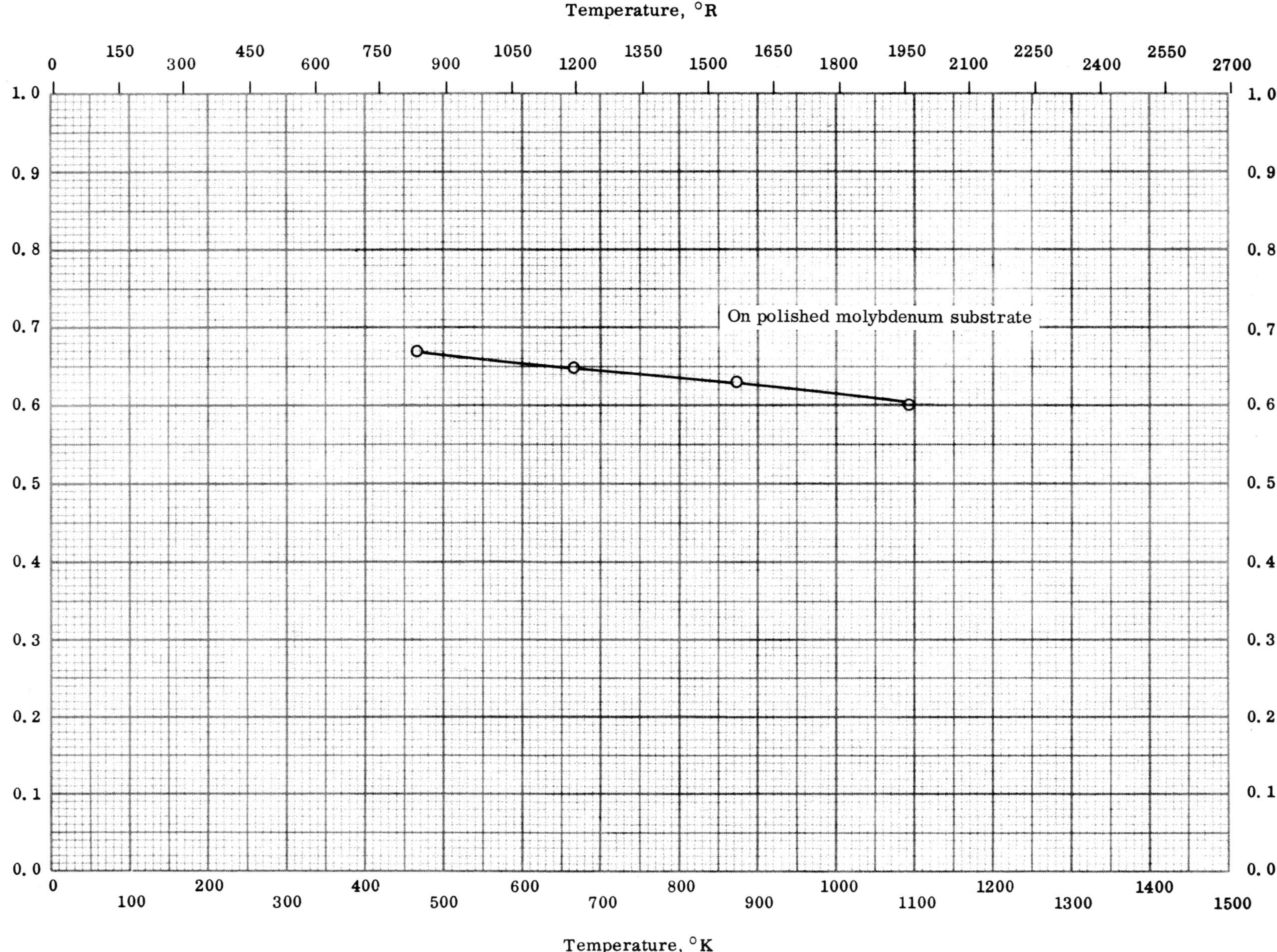

SOLAR ABSORPTANCE -- CARBON COATING ON MOLYBDENUM

SOLAR ABSORPTANCE -- CARBON COATING ON MOLYBDENUM

REFERENCE INFORMATION

Symbol	Ref.	Temp. Range °K	Rept. Error %	Sample Specifications	Remarks
○	61-24	468-1093	≤10	Very thin coating of carbon black.	Deposited on a polished molybdenum from the flame of buring kerosene; measured in vacuum (10^{-5} mm. Hg).

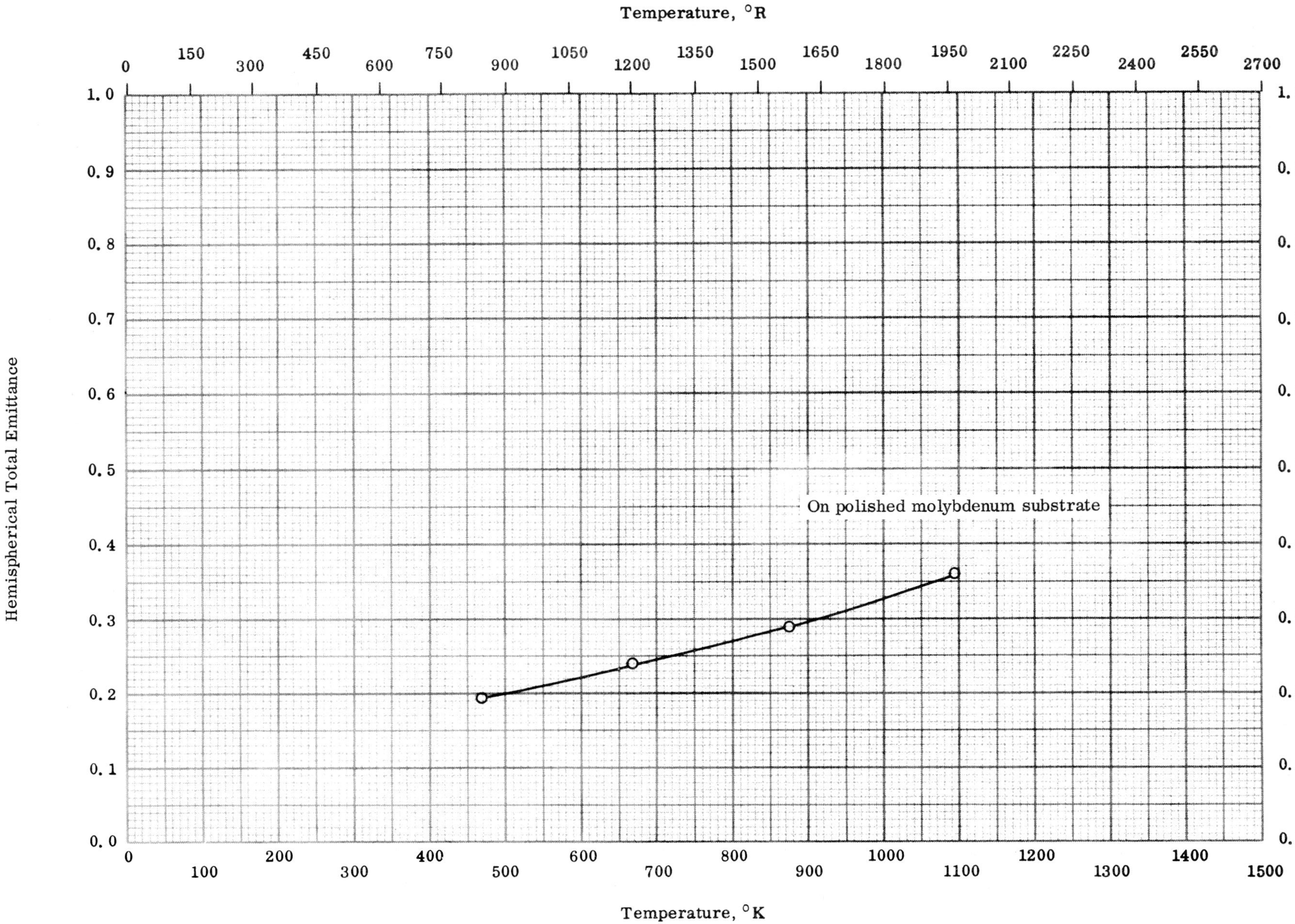

HEMISPHERICAL TOTAL EMITTANCE -- CARBON COATING ON MOLYBDENUM

On polished molybdenum substrate

Temperature, °R

Temperature, °K

Hemispherical Total Emittance

HEMISPHERICAL TOTAL EMITTANCE -- CARBON COATING ON MOLYBDENUM

REFERENCE INFORMATION

Symbol	Ref.	Temp. Range °K	Rept. Error %	Sample Specifications	Remarks
o	61-24	468-1093	≤10	Very thin coating of carbon black.	Deposited on a polished molybdenum from the flame of burning kerosene; measured in vacuum (10^{-5} mm Hg).

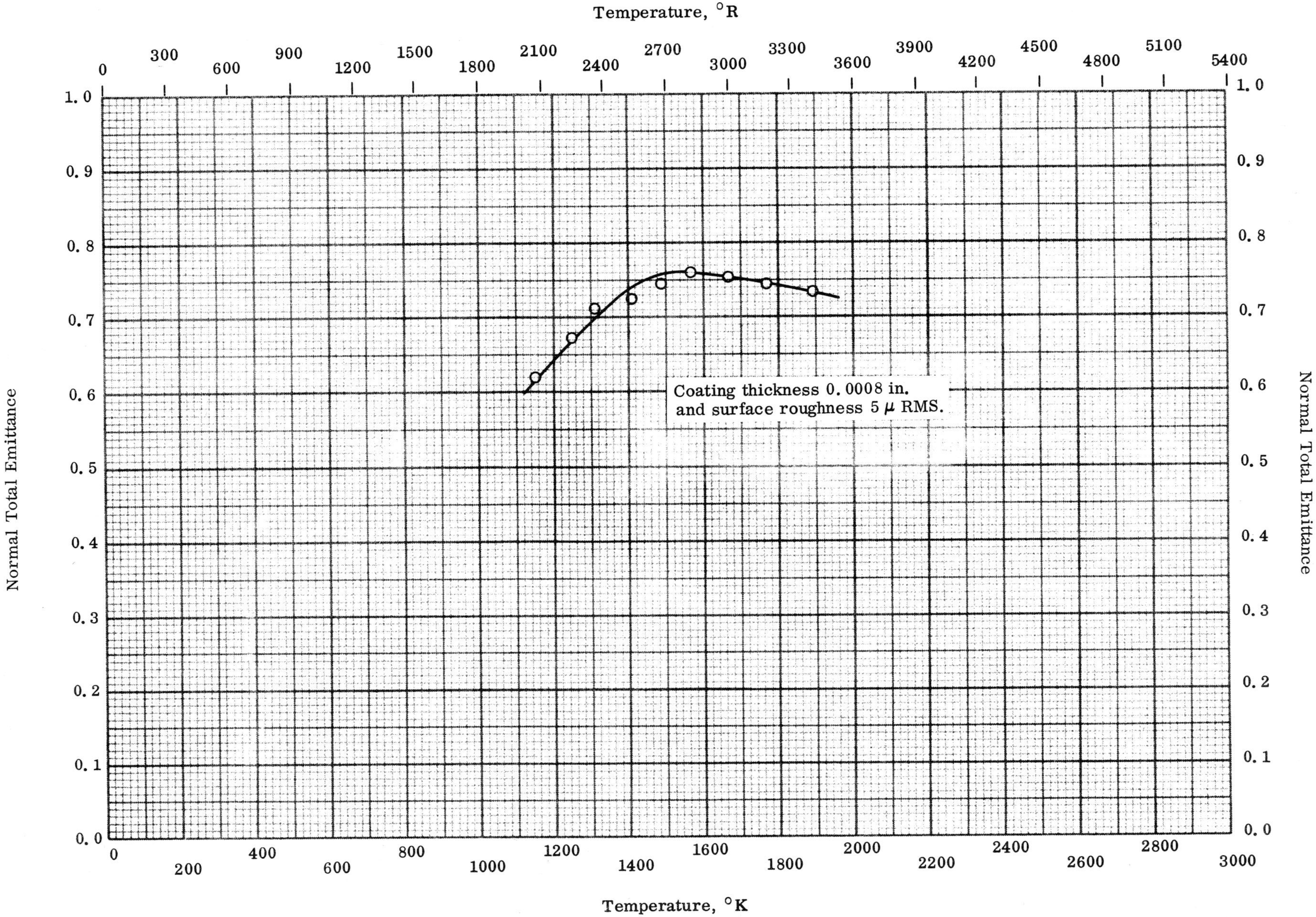

Normal Total Emittance

Normal Total Emittance

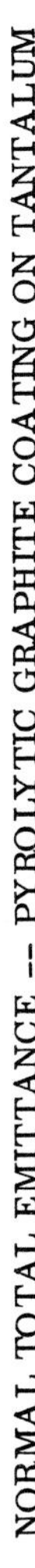
NORMAL TOTAL EMITTANCE -- PYROLYTIC GRAPHITE COATING ON TANTALUM

NORMAL TOTAL EMITTANCE -- PYROLYTIC GRAPHITE COATING ON TANTALUM

REFERENCE INFORMATION

Symbol	Ref.	Temp. Range °K	Rept. Error %	Sample Specifications	Remarks
○	63-22	1157-1897		Coating thickness 0.0008 in. and surface roughness 5 μ RMS.	Vapor deposit; measured in vacuum (3 - 4 μ Hg).

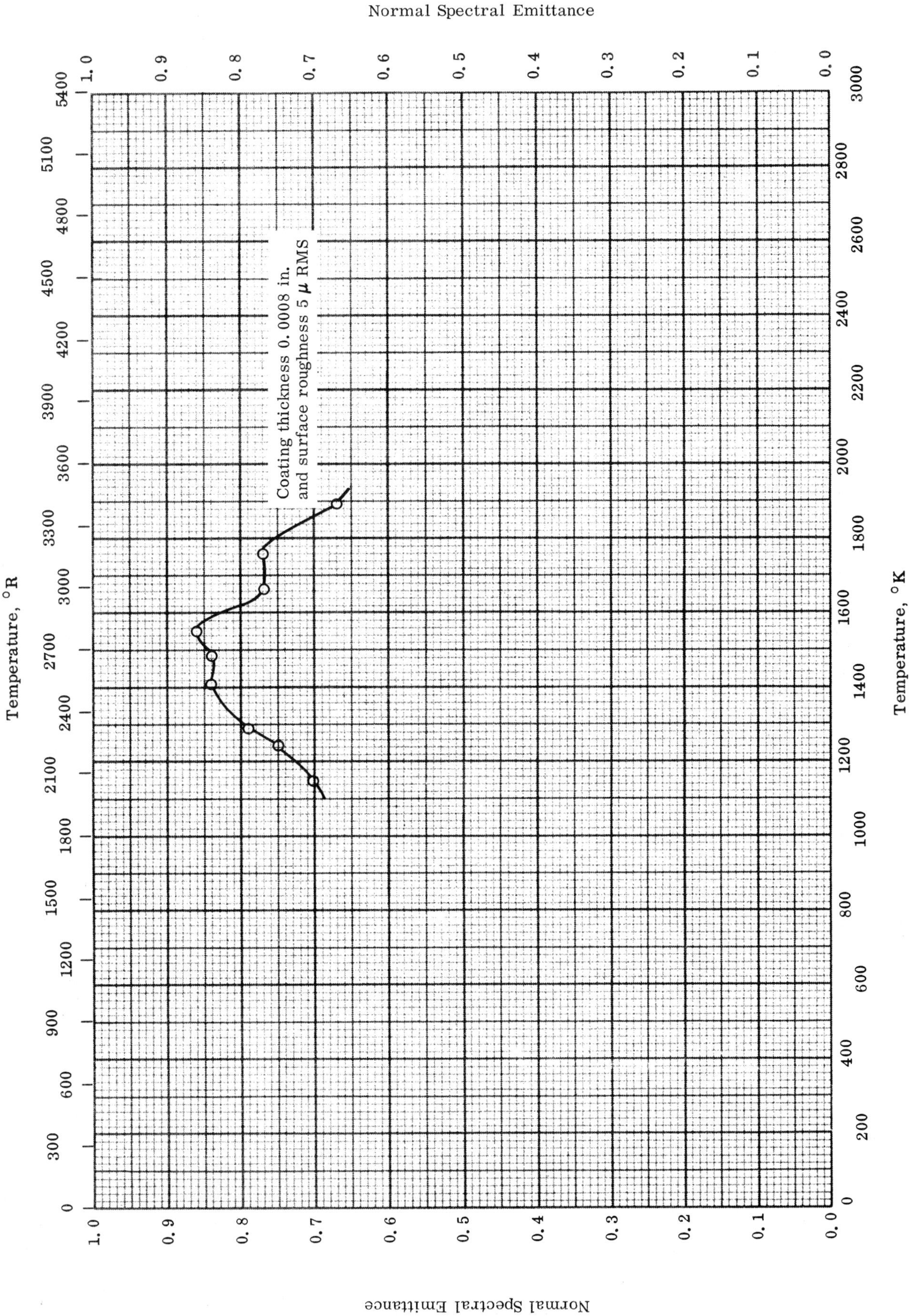

Temperature, °R

Coating thickness 0. 0008 in.
and surface roughness 5 μ RMS

Temperature, °K

Normal Spectral Emittance

NORMAL SPECTRAL EMITTANCE -- PYROLYTIC GRAPHITE COATING ON TANTALUM

NORMAL SPECTRAL EMITTANCE -- PYROLYTIC GRAPHITE COATING ON TANTALUM

REFERENCE INFORMATION

Symbol	Ref.	Wavelength μ	Temp. Range °K	Rept. Error %	Sample Specifications	Remarks
○	63-22	0.65	1155-1899		Coating thickness 0.0008 in. and surface roughness 5 μ RMS.	Vapor deposit; measured in vacuum (3 - 4 μ Hg).

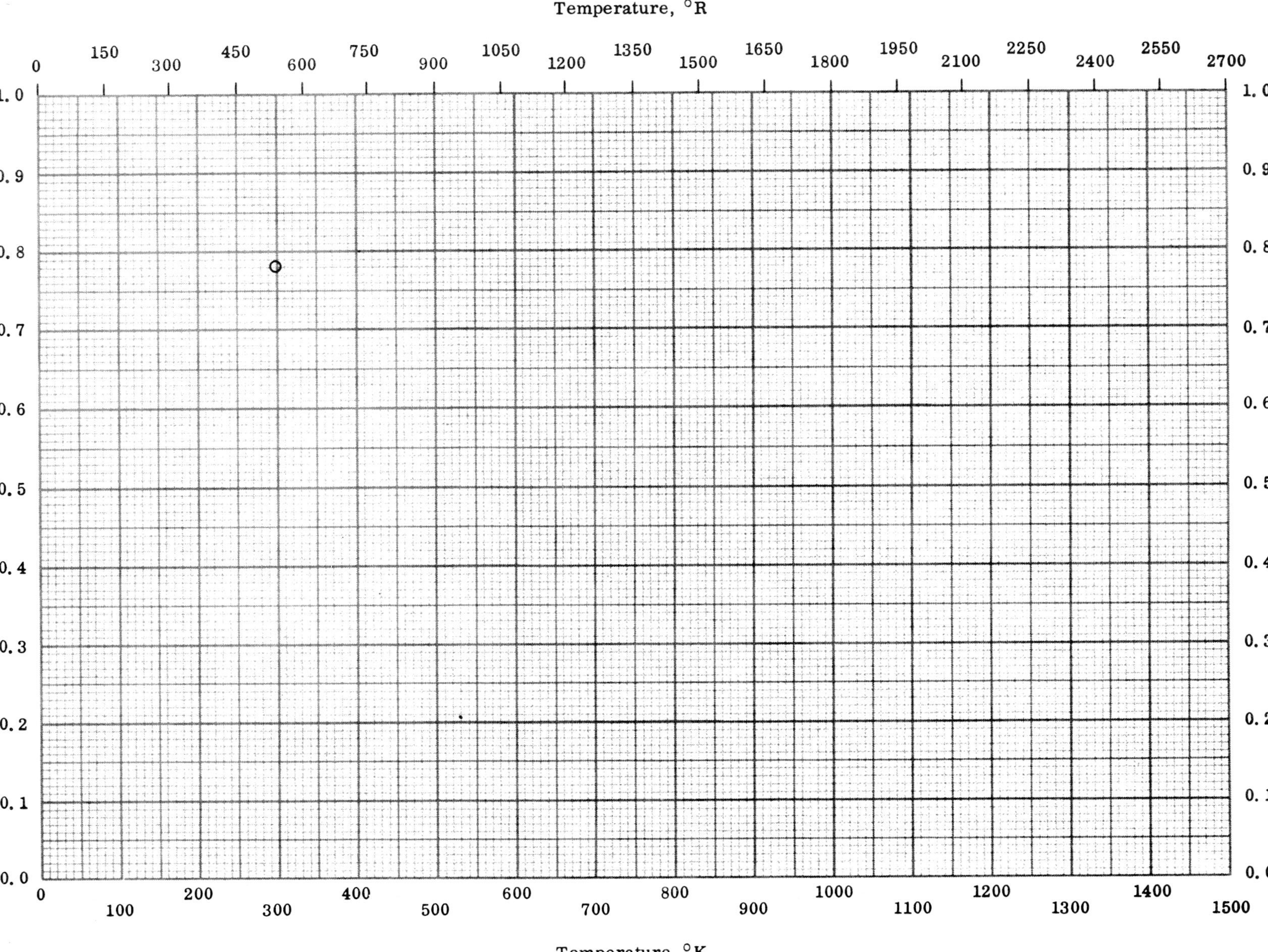

NORMAL TOTAL REFLECTANCE -- COPPER FILM ON MYLAR

NORMAL TOTAL REFLECTANCE -- COPPER FILM ON MYLAR

REFERENCE INFORMATION

Symbol	Ref.	Temp. Range °K	Rept. Error %	Sample Specifications	Remarks
○	62-33	298		Copper film on 0.00025 in. mylar.	Using integrating hemispherical radiometer; data for normal incidence solar radiation.

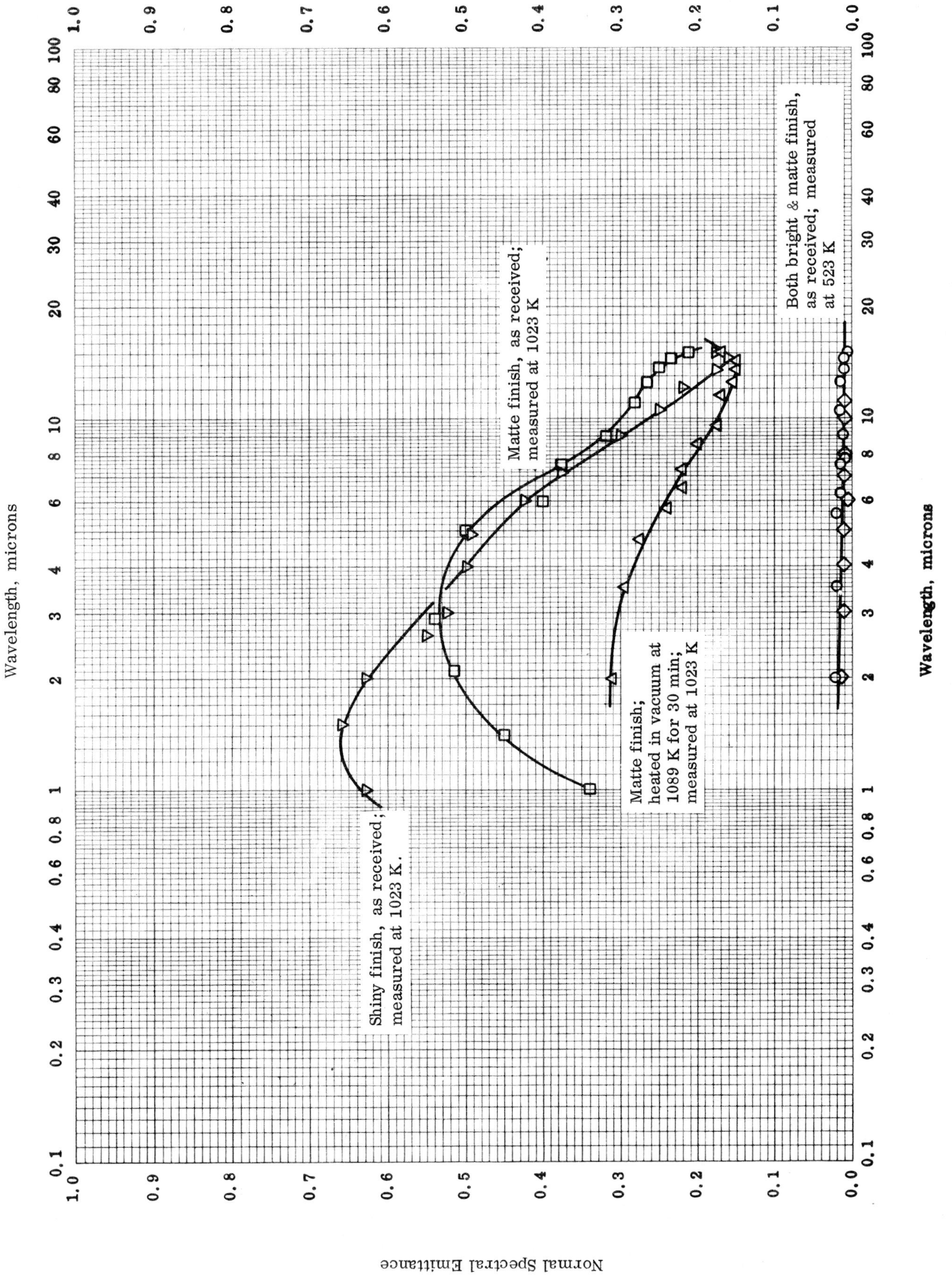

Wavelength, microns

0.1 0.2 0.3 0.4 0.6 0.8 1 2 3 4 6 8 10 20 30 40 60 80 100

Normal Spectral Emittance

0.0 0.1 0.2 0.3 0.4 0.5 0.6 0.7 0.8 0.9 1.0

Shiny finish, as received; measured at 1023 K.

Matte finish, as received; measured at 1023 K

Matte finish; heated in vacuum at 1089 K for 30 min; measured at 1023 K

Both bright & matte finish, as received; measured at 523 K

Wavelength, microns

NORMAL SPECTRAL EMITTANCE -- GOLD COATING ON TITANIUM

NORMAL SPECTRAL EMITTANCE -- GOLD COATING ON TITANIUM

REFERENCE INFORMATION

Symbol	Ref.	Temp. °K	Wavelength Range, μ	Rept. Error %	Sample Specifications	Remarks
○	62-34	523	2-15		Bright gold No. 6854.	Applied by spray and fired at 873 K for 5 min.; matte finish, as received; data taken from smooth curve.
□	62-34	1023	1-15		Same as above.	Same as above; different specimen.
△	62-34	1023	2-15		Same as above.	Same as above; matte finish, heated in vacuum (6.8 x 10^{-5} mm Hg) at 1089 K for 30 min.; data taken from smooth curve.
◇	62-34	523	2-15		Same as above.	Same as above; shiny finish, as received; data taken from smooth curve.
▽	62-34	1023	1-15		Same as above.	Same as above.

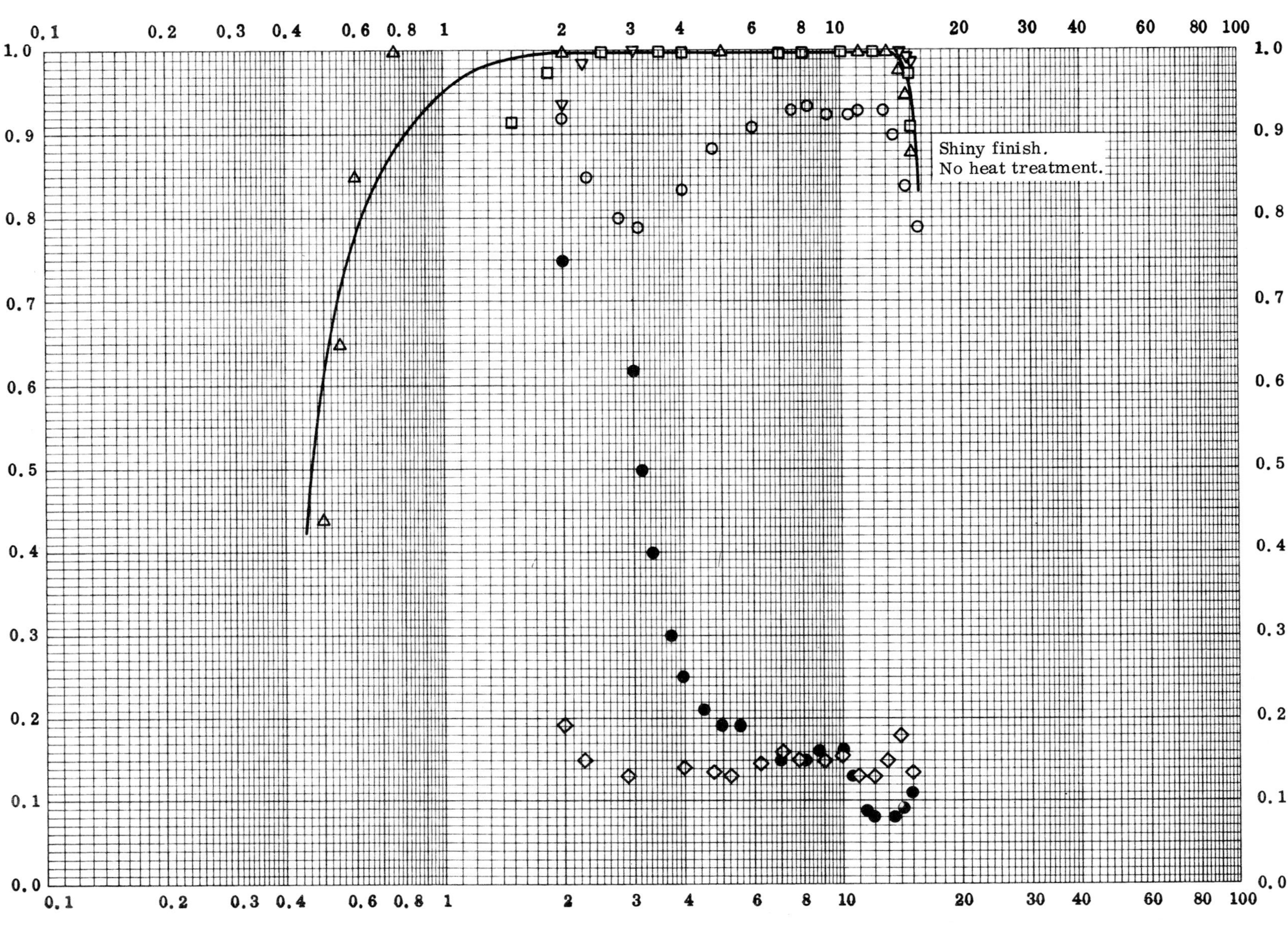

NORMAL SPECTRAL REFLECTANCE -- GOLD COATING ON TITANIUM

NORMAL SPECTRAL REFLECTANCE -- GOLD COATING ON TITANIUM

REFERENCE INFORMATION

Symbol	Ref.	Temp. °K	Wavelength Range, μ	Rept. Error %	Sample Specifications	Remarks
□	62-34	<322	1.5-15	<±2	Bright gold No. 6854.	Applied by spray and fired at 873 K for 5 min.; shiny finish, as received; data taken from smooth curve; hemispherical illumination, normal viewing; 523 K source temperature.
△	62-34	<322	0.5-15	<±2	Same as above.	Same as above; 1273 K source temperature.
○	62-34	<322	2-15	<±2	Same as above.	Same as above except heated in vacuum (6.8×10^{-5} mm Hg) at 1089 K for 30 min.; data taken from smooth curve; hemispherical illumination, normal viewing; 523 K source temperature.
◇	62-34	<322	2-15	<±2	Same as above.	Same as above except heated in air at 1089 K for 30 min.
▽	62-34	<322	2-15	<±2	Same as above.	Applied by spray and fired at 873 K for 5 min.; matte finish, as received; data taken from smooth curve; hemispherical illumination, normal viewing; 523 K source temperature.
●	62-34	<322	2-15	<±2	Same as above.	Same as above except heated in vacuum (6.8×10^{-5} mm Hg) at 1089 K for 30 min.

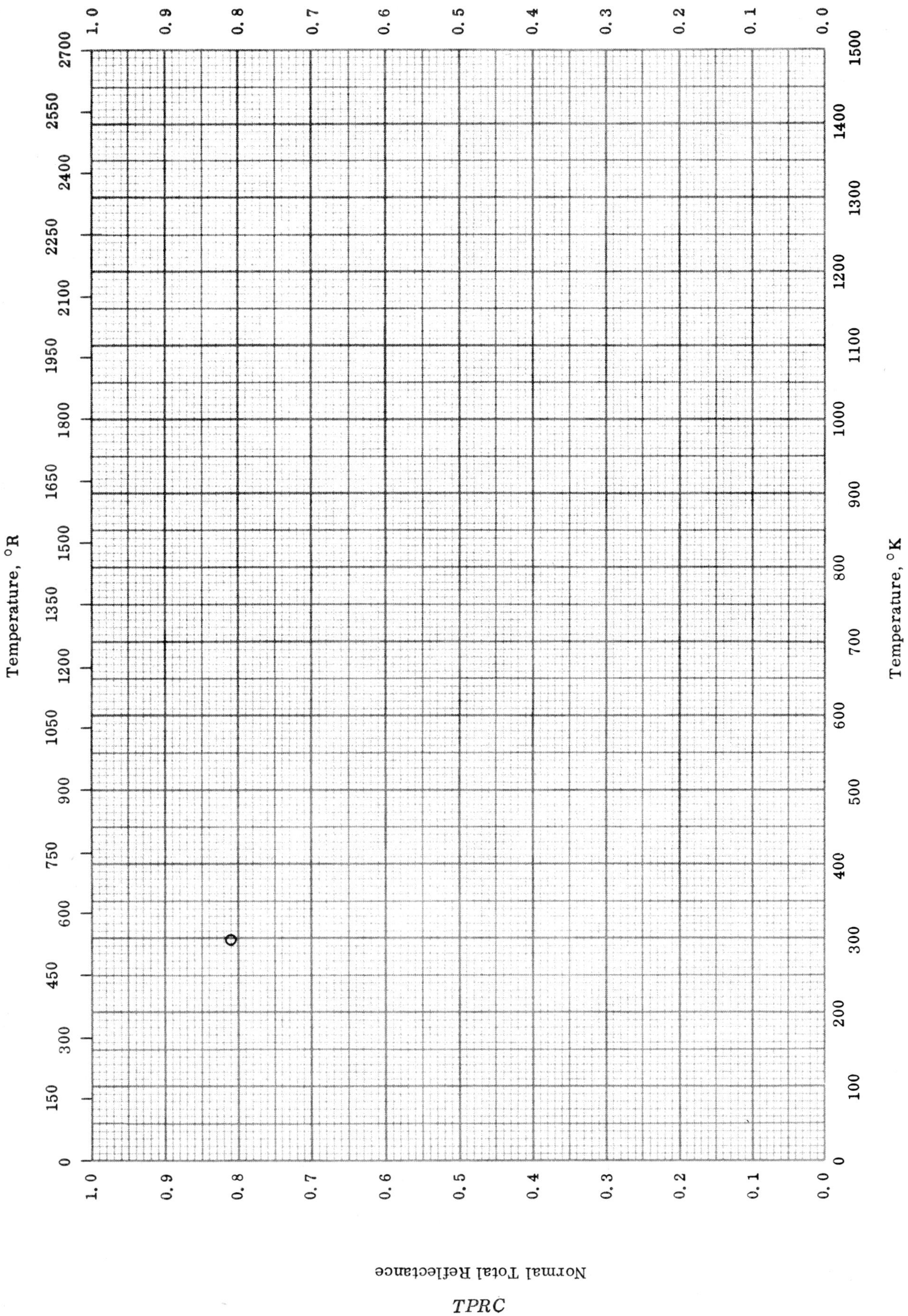

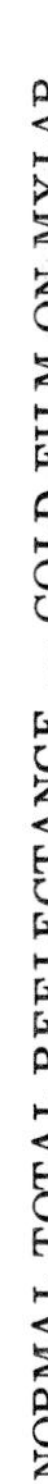

Temperature, °R
0
150
300
450
600
750
900
1050
1200
1350
1500
1650
1800
1950
2100
2250
2400
2550
2700
Temperature, °K
0
100
200
300
400
500
600
700
800
900
1000
1100
1200
1300
1400
1500
Normal Total Reflectance
1.0
0.9
0.8
0.7
0.6
0.5
0.4
0.3
0.2
0.1
0.0

NORMAL TOTAL REFLECTANCE -- GOLD FILM ON MYLAR

NORMAL TOTAL REFLECTANCE -- GOLD FILM ON MYLAR

REFERENCE INFORMATION

Symbol	Ref.	Temp. Range °K	Rept. Error %	Sample Specifications	Remarks
○	62-33	298		Gold film on 0.00025 in. mylar.	Using integrating hemispherical radiometer; data for normal incidence solar radiation.

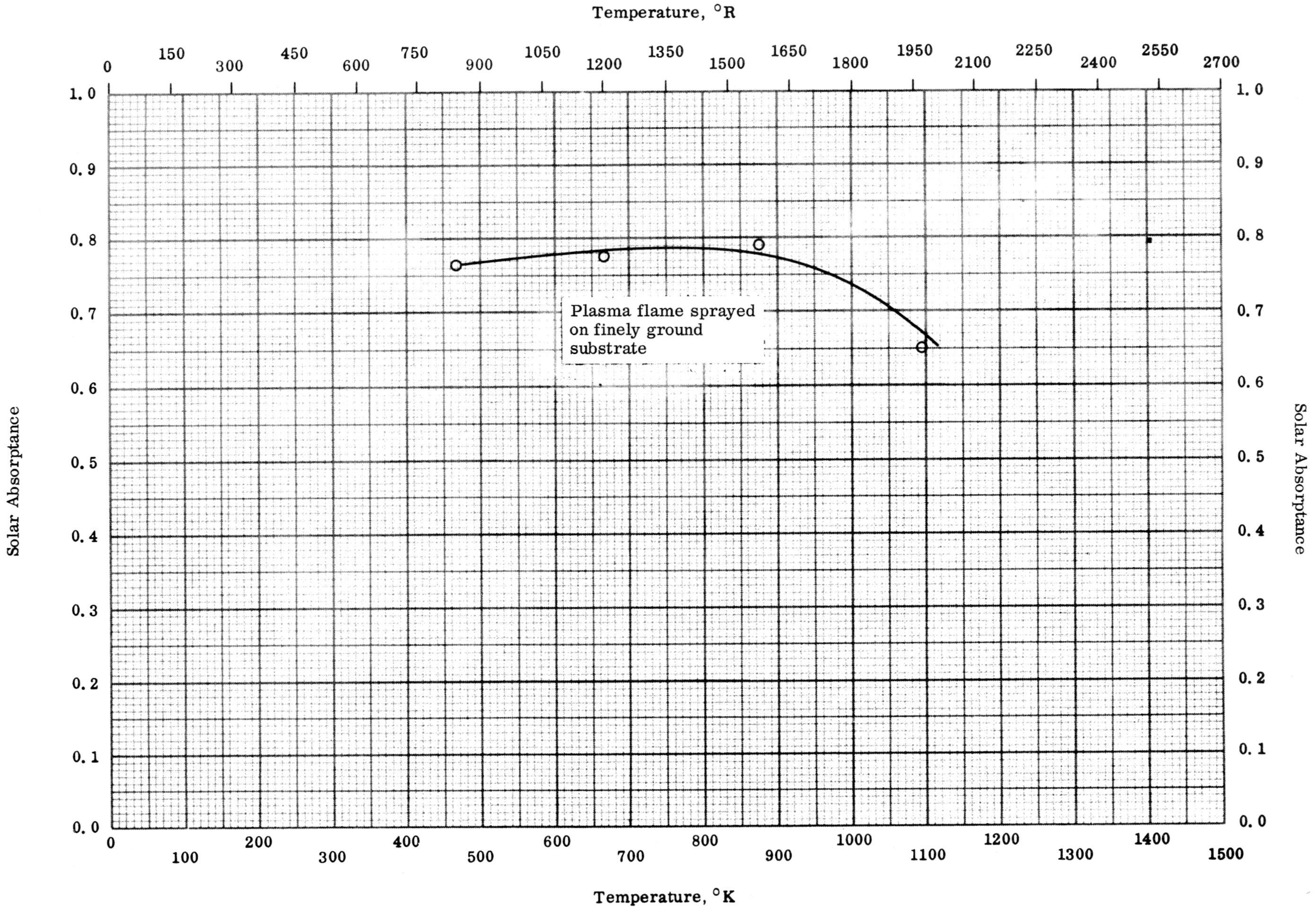

SOLAR ABSORPTANCE -- MOLYBDENUM COATING ON ARMCO IRON

Solar Absorptance

Temperature, °R

Temperature, °K

Plasma flame sprayed on finely ground substrate

SOLAR ABSORPTANCE -- MOLYBDENUM COATING ON ARMCO IRON

REFERENCE INFORMATION

Symbol	Ref.	Temp. Range °K	Rept. Error %	Sample Specifications	Remarks
○	61-24	468-1093	≤10	Granular molybdenum, -140 mesh ± 325 mesh, Metco XP-1103.	Substrate finely ground; plasma flame sprayed; measured in vacuum (10^{-5} mm Hg).

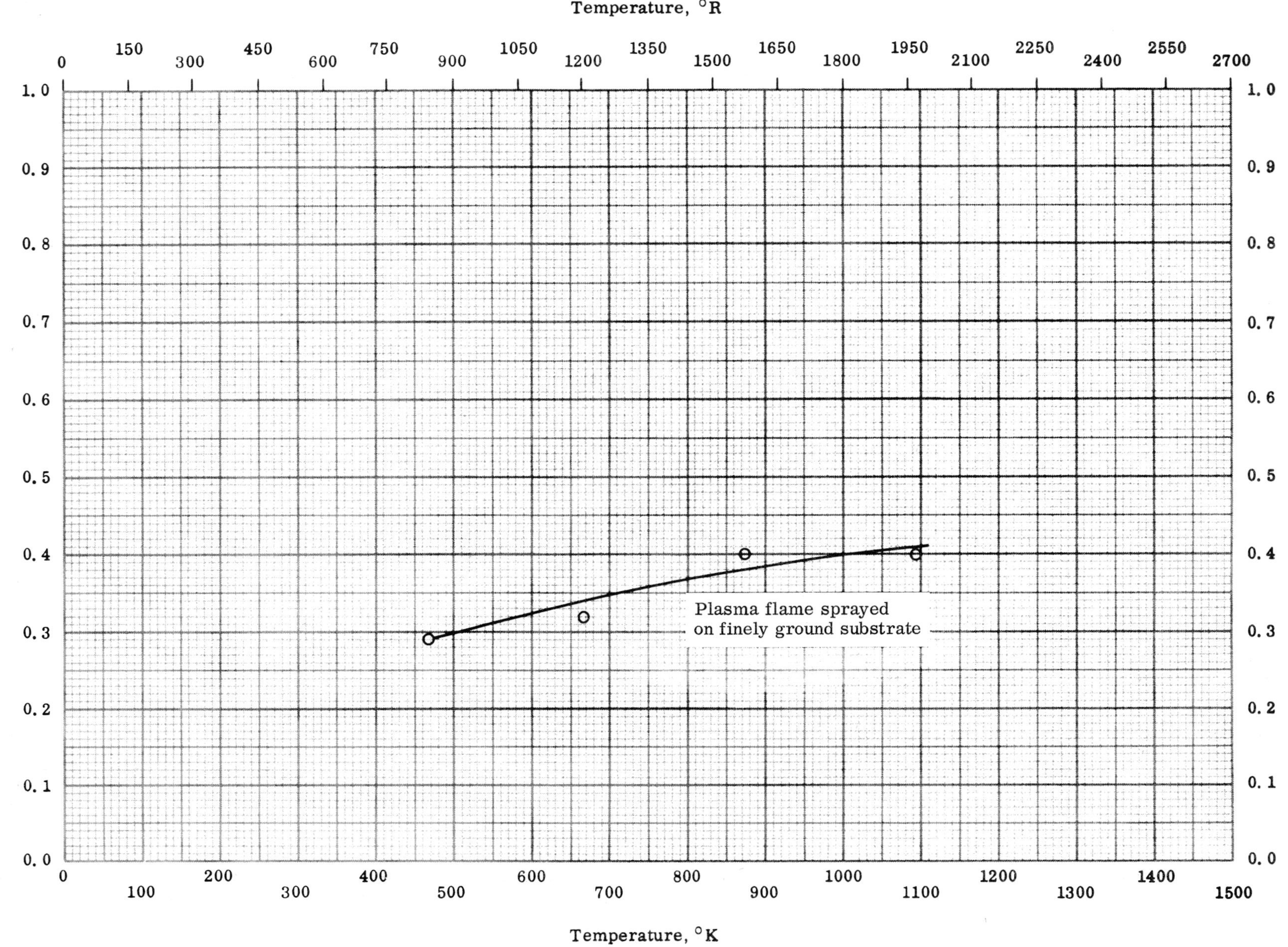

HEMISPHERICAL TOTAL EMITTANCE -- MOLYBDENUM COATING ON ARMCO IRON

HEMISPHERICAL TOTAL EMITTANCE -- MOLYBDENUM COATING ON ARMCO IRON

REFERENCE INFORMATION

Symbol	Ref.	Temp. Range °K	Rept. Error %	Sample Specifications	Remarks
○	61-24	468-1093	≤10	Granular molybdenum, -140 mesh ± 325 mesh, Metco XP-1103.	Substrate finely ground; plasma flame sprayed; measured in vacuum (10^{-5} mm Hg).

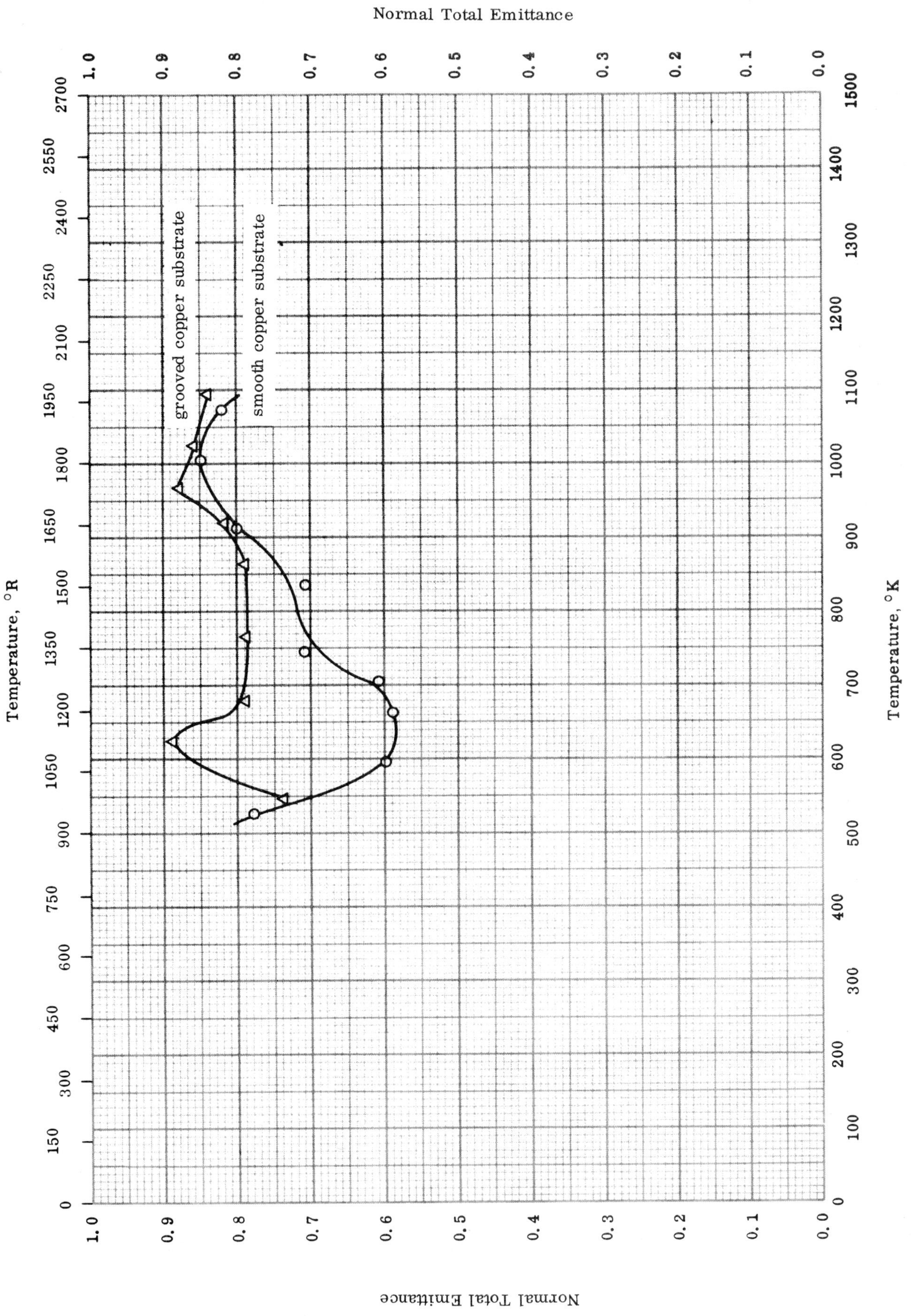

Temperature, °R

Normal Total Emittance

grooved copper substrate

smooth copper substrate

Temperature, °K

NORMAL TOTAL EMITTANCE -- PLATINUM BLACK COATING ON COPPER

NORMAL TOTAL EMITTANCE -- PLATINUM BLACK COATING ON COPPER

REFERENCE INFORMATION

Symbol	Ref.	Temp. Range °K	Rept. Error %	Sample Specifications	Remarks
○	63-25	527-1078	± 10	Smooth copper disc.	Measured in dry air.
△	63-25	545-1098	± 10	Grooved copper disc.	Same as above.

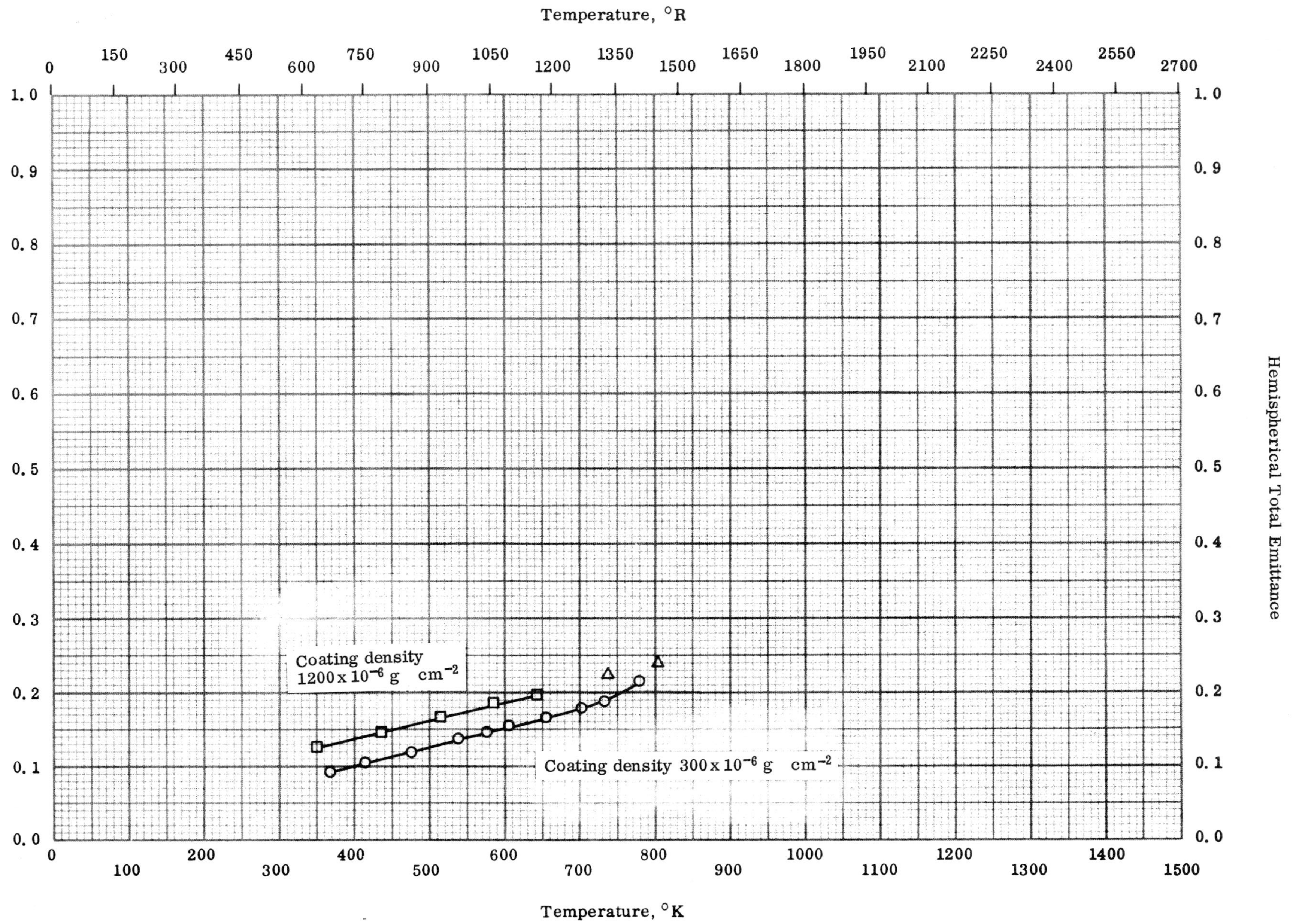

Temperature, °R

Temperature, °K

Hemispherical Total Emittance

Coating density 300×10^{-6} g cm^{-2}

Coating density 1200×10^{-6} g cm^{-2}

HEMISPHERICAL TOTAL EMITTANCE -- PLATINUM BLACK COATING ON STAINLESS STEEL

HEMISPHERICAL TOTAL EMITTANCE -- PLATINUM BLACK COATING ON STAINLESS STEEL

REFERENCE INFORMATION

Symbol	Ref.	Temp. Range °K	Rept. Error %	Sample Specifications	Remarks
○	60-25	368-780		Coating density 300 x 10^{-6} g cm^{-3}.	Measured in vacuum.
△	60-25	737-802		Coating density 600 x 10^{-6} g cm^{-3}.	Same as above.
□	60-25	349-642		Coating density 1200 x 10^{-6} g cm^{-3}.	Same as above.

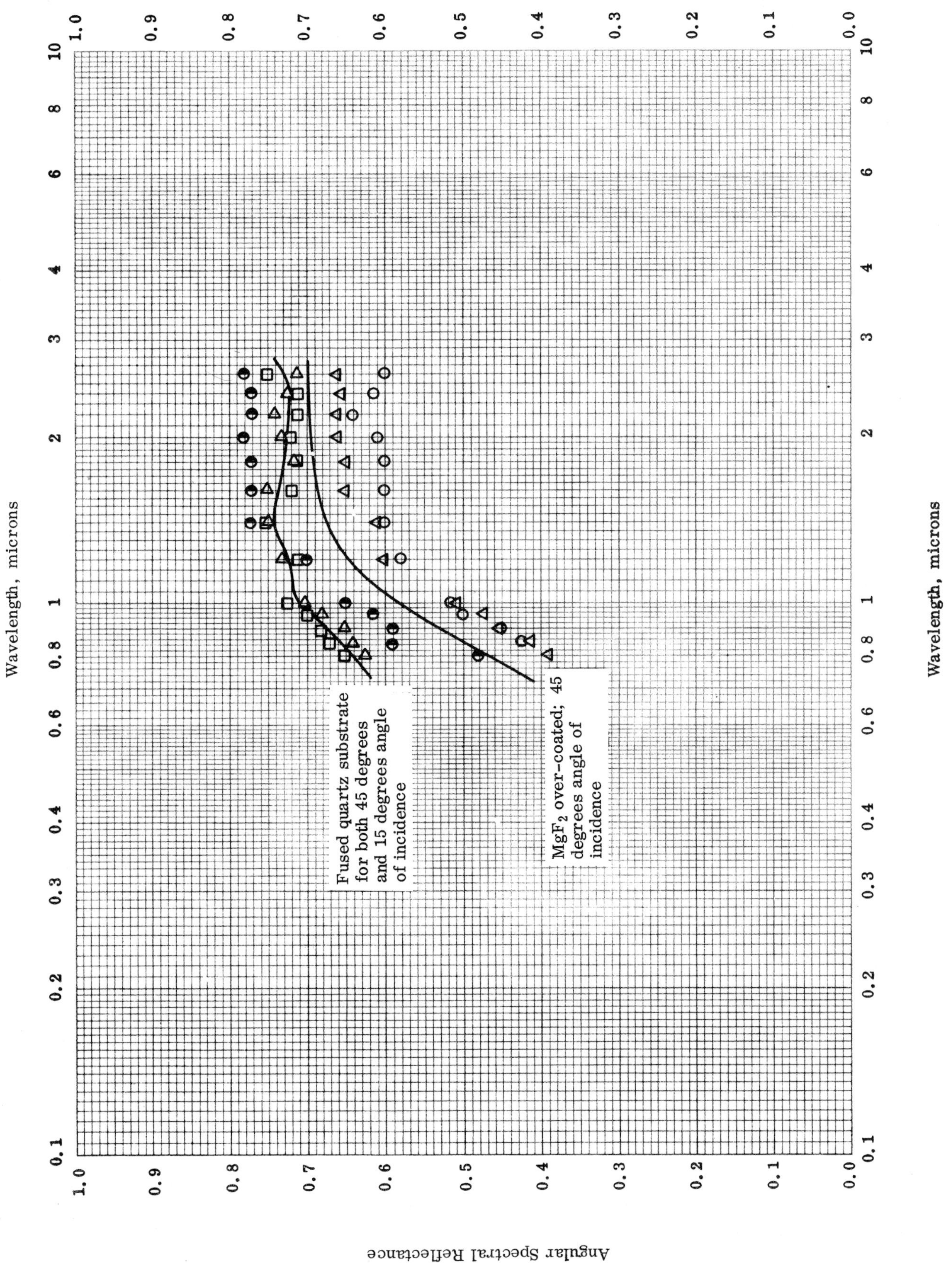

Wavelength, microns
Angular Spectral Reflectance
Fused quartz substrate for both 45 degrees and 15 degrees angle of incidence
MgF2 over-coated; 45 degrees angle of incidence
0.1
0.2
0.3
0.4
0.6
0.8
1
2
3
4
6
8
10
0.0
0.1
0.2
0.3
0.4
0.5
0.6
0.7
0.8
0.9
1.0

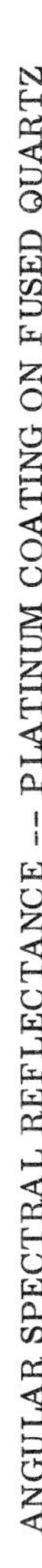

ANGULAR SPECTRAL REFLECTANCE -- PLATINUM COATING ON FUSED QUARTZ

ANGULAR SPECTRAL REFLECTANCE -- PLATINUM COATING ON FUSED QUARTZ

REFERENCE INFORMATION

Symbol	Ref.	Temp. °K	Wavelength Range, μ	Rept. Error %	Sample Specifications	Remarks
○	64-11	298	0.8-2.6		Mg F_2 over-coated both sides and Pt on one side.	Measurement taken on the Pt-coated side; evaporated aluminum as reference standard; 45° incidence, 45° viewing.
◑	64-11	298	0.8-2.6		Same as above.	Same as above; another sample.
△	64-11	298	0.8-2.6		Same as above.	Same as above; 15° incidence, 15° viewing.
□	64-11	298	0.8-2.6		Fused quartz substrate.	Same as above; evaporated aluminum as reference standard; 45° incidence, 45° viewing.
▷	64-11	298	0.8-2.6		Same as above.	Same as above; 15° incidence, 15° viewing.

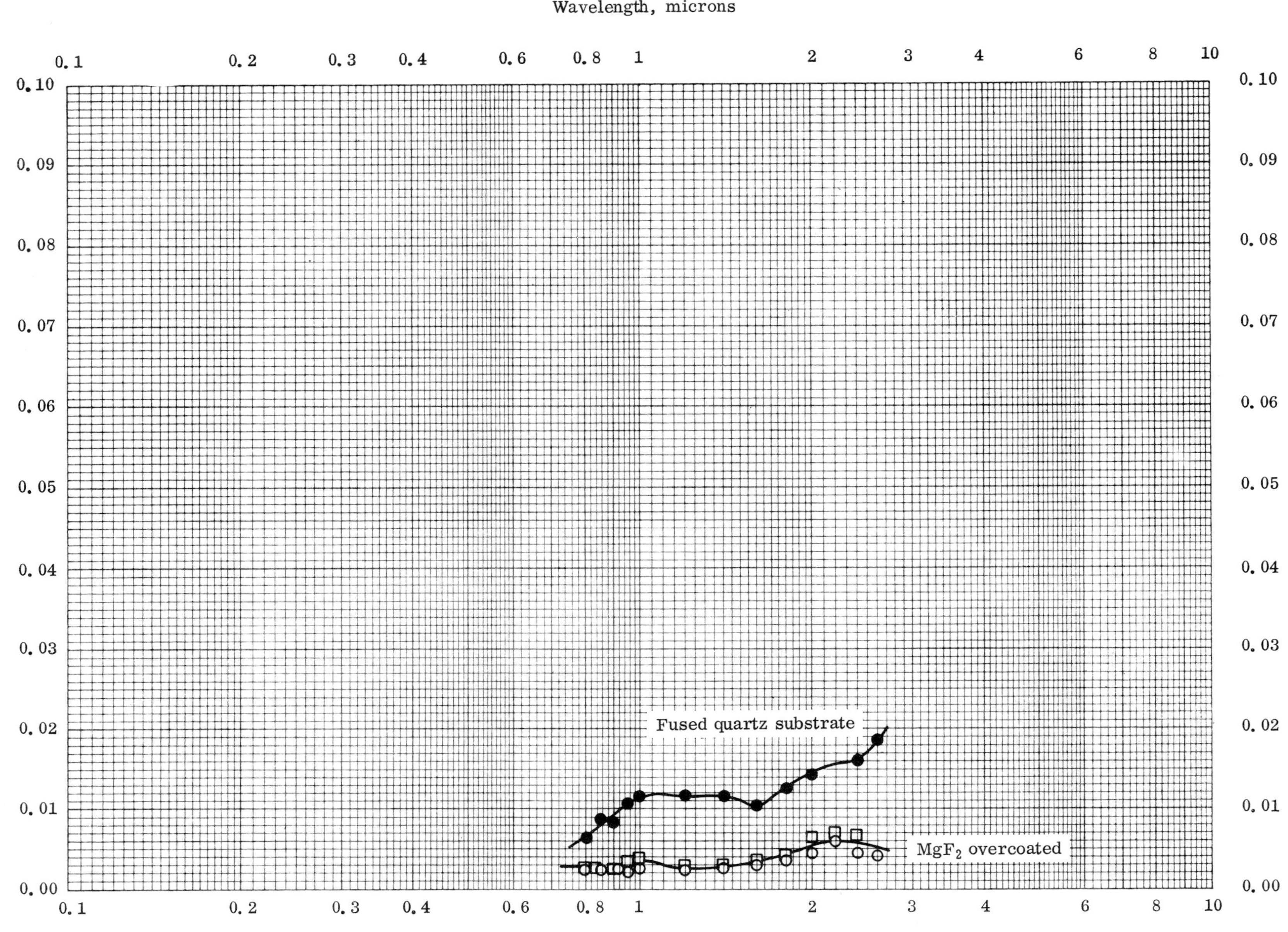

NORMAL SPECTRAL TRANSMITTANCE -- PLATINUM COATING ON FUSED QUARTZ

NORMAL SPECTRAL TRANSMITTANCE -- PLATINUM COATING ON FUSED QUARTZ

REFERENCE INFORMATION

Symbol	Ref.	Temp. °K	Wavelength Range, μ	Rept. Error %	Sample Specifications	Remarks
○	64-11	298	0.8-2.6		MgF_2 over-coated both sides and Pt on one side.	Measured in air on Pt-coated side.
□	64-11	298	0.8-2.4		Same as above.	Same as above; another sample.
●	64-11	298	0.8-2.6		Fused quartz substrate.	Same as above; another sample.

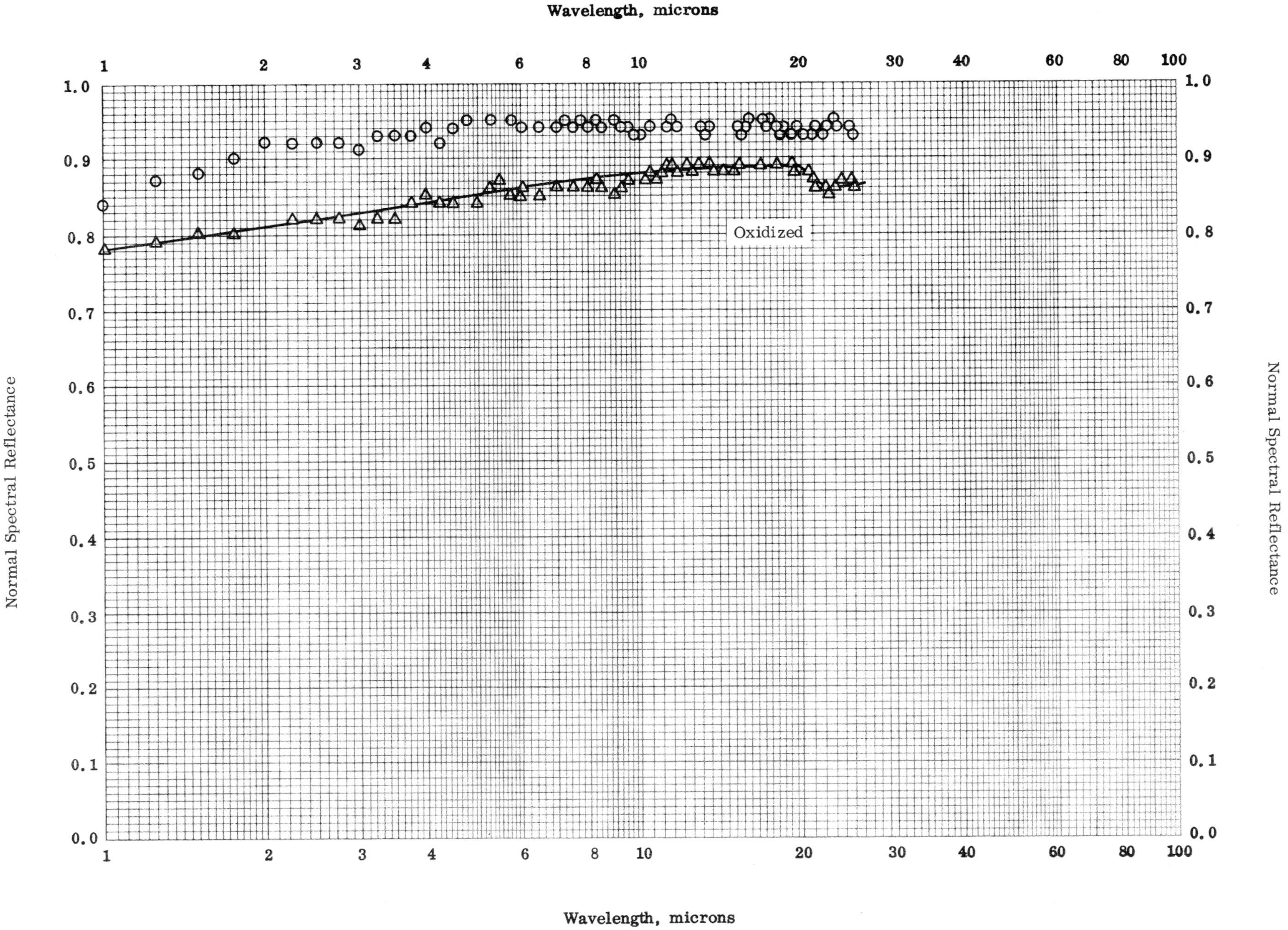

Wavelength, microns

Normal Spectral Reflectance

Oxidized

NORMAL SPECTRAL REFLECTANCE -- SILVER PLATED AISI 321 STEEL

NORMAL SPECTRAL REFLECTANCE -- SILVER PLATED AISI 321 STEEL

REFERENCE INFORMATION

Symbol	Ref.	Temp. °K	Wavelength Range, μ	Rept. Error%	Sample Specifications	Remarks
○	58-13	311	1-25	± 2.4	Type 321 corrosion resistant steel substrate, MIL-S-6721.	Hemispherical illumination, normal viewing.
△	58-13	311	1-25	±2.6	Same as above.	Oxidized at 634 K for 303 hrs.

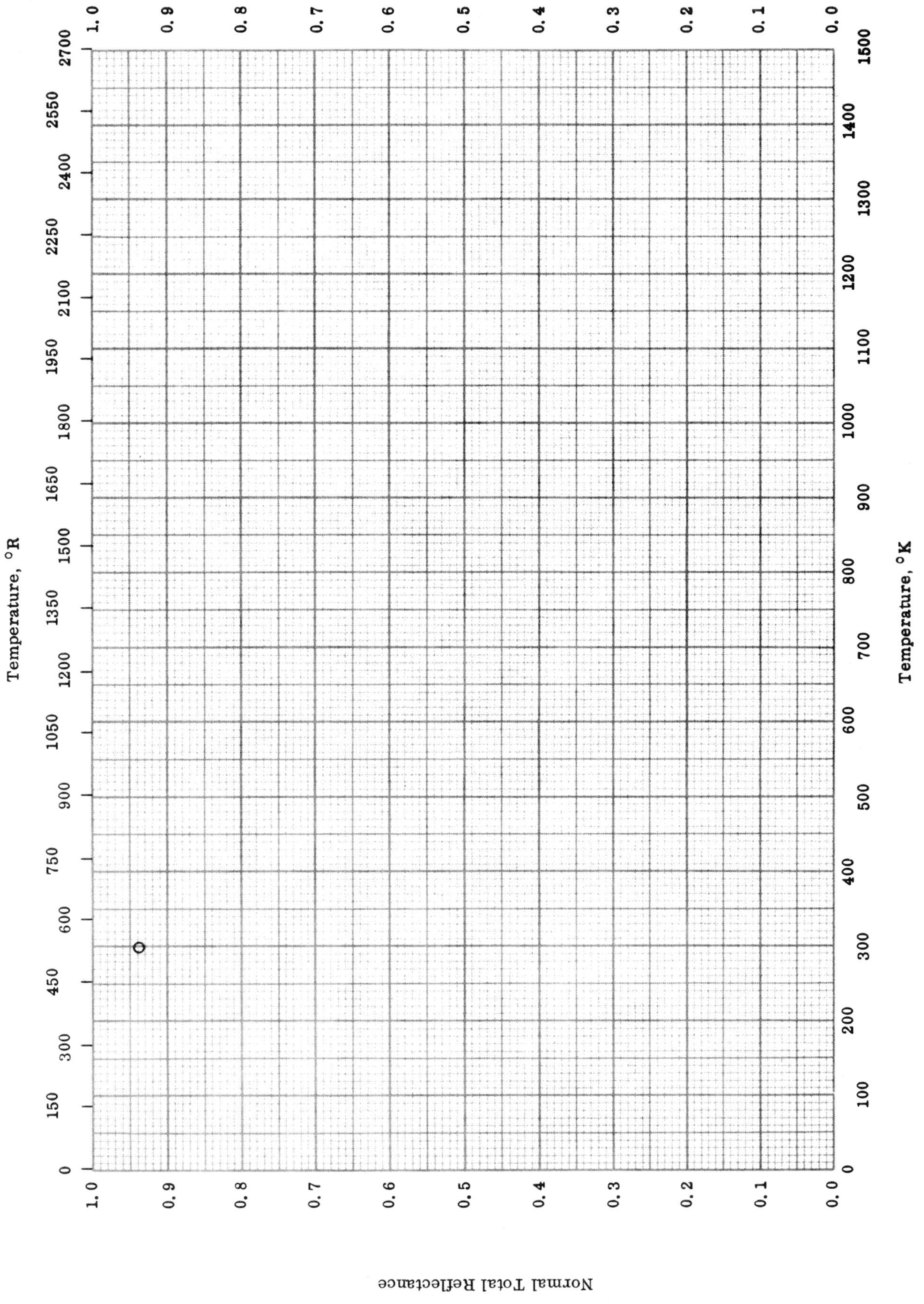

NORMAL TOTAL REFLECTANCE -- SILVER FILM ON MYLAR

NORMAL TOTAL REFLECTANCE -- SILVER FILM ON MYLAR

REFERENCE INFORMATION

Symbol	Ref.	Temp. Range °K	Rept. Error %	Sample Specifications	Remarks
○	62-33	298		Silver film on 0.00025 in. mylar.	Using integrating hemispherical radiometer; data for normal incidence solar radiation.

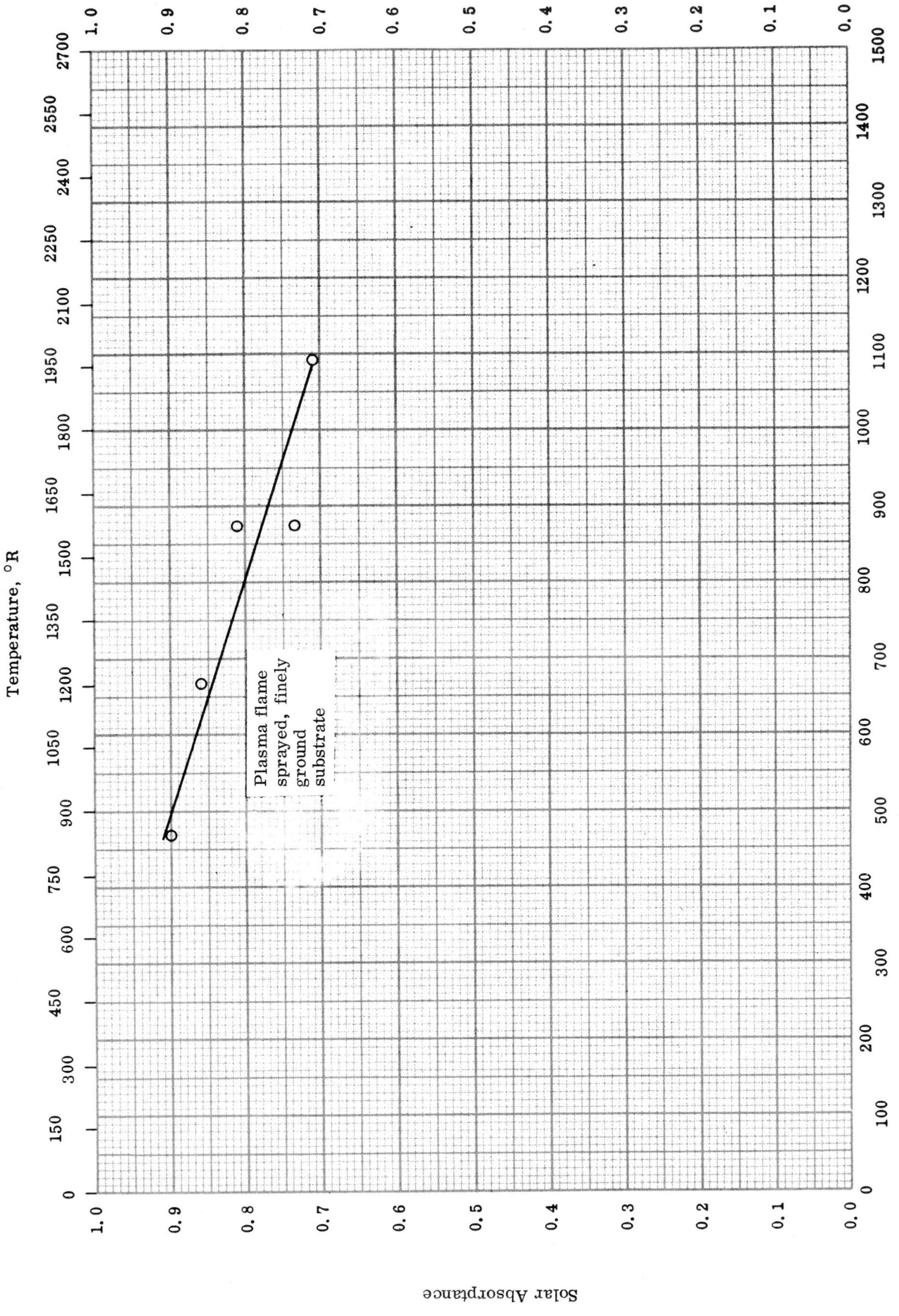

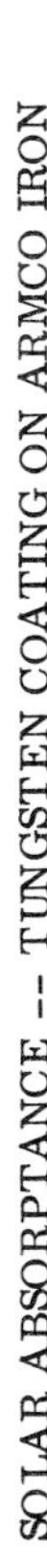
SOLAR ABSORPTANCE -- TUNGSTEN COATING ON ARMCO IRON

Solar Absorptance
1.0
0.9
0.8
0.7
0.6
0.5
0.4
0.3
0.2
0.1
0.0
Temperature, °R
0
150
300
450
600
750
900
1050
1200
1350
1500
1650
1800
1950
2100
2250
2400
2550
2700
Temperature, °K
0
100
200
300
400
500
600
700
800
900
1000
1100
1200
1300
1400
1500
Plasma flame sprayed, finely ground substrate

SOLAR ABSORPTANCE -- TUNGSTEN COATING ON ARMCO IRON

REFERENCE INFORMATION

Symbol	Ref.	Temp. Range °K	Rept. Error %	Sample Specifications	Remarks
○	61-24	468-1093	≤10	Crystalline tungsten, -200 mesh + 30 micron, Metco XP-1106.	Substrate finely ground, plasma flame sprayed; measured in vacuum (10^{-5} mm Hg).

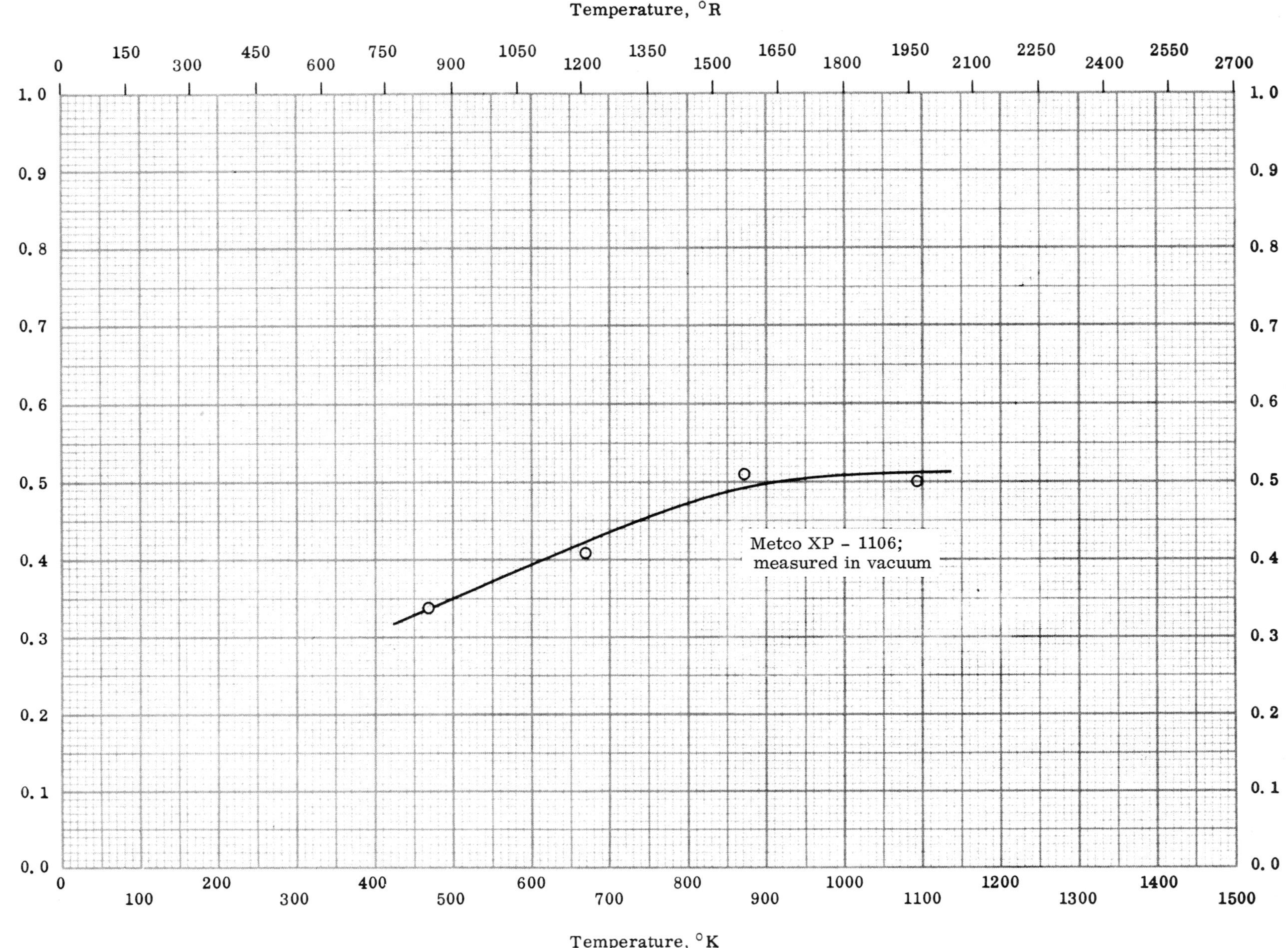

HEMISPHERICAL TOTAL EMITTANCE -- TUNGSTEN COATING ON ARMCO IRON

HEMISPHERICAL TOTAL EMITTANCE -- TUNGSTEN COATING ON ARMCO IRON

REFERENCE INFORMATION

Symbol	Ref.	Temp. Range °K	Rept. Error %	Sample Specifications	Remarks
○	61-24	468-1093	≤10	Crystalline tungsten, -200 mesh + 30 micron, Metco XP-1106.	Substrate finely ground, plasma flame sprayed; measured in vacuum (10^{-5} mm Hg).

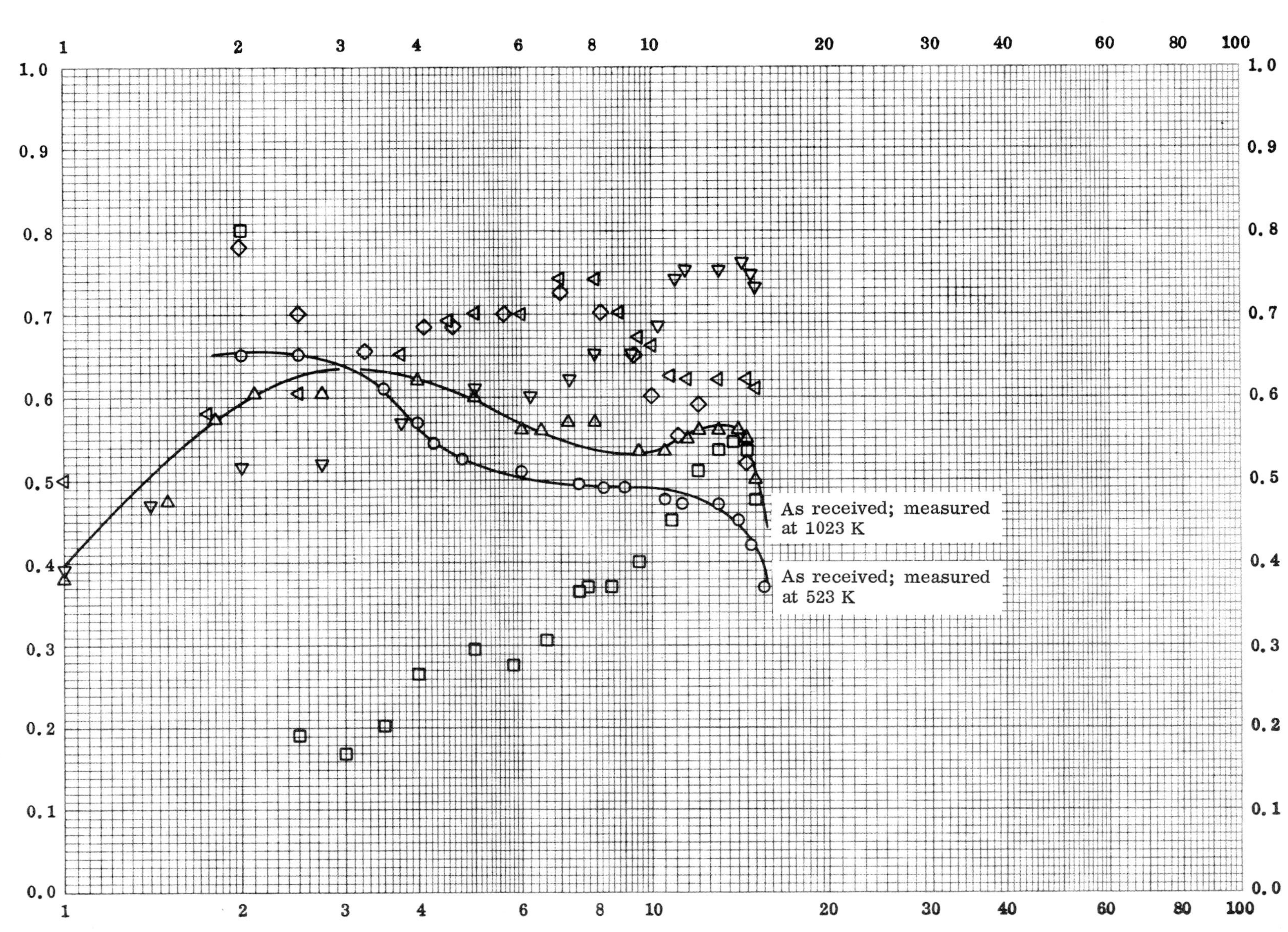

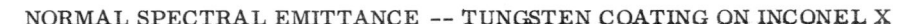

NORMAL SPECTRAL EMITTANCE -- TUNGSTEN COATING ON INCONEL X

NORMAL SPECTRAL EMITTANCE -- TUNGSTEN COATING ON INCONEL X

REFERENCE INFORMATION

Symbol	Ref.	Temp. °K	Wavelength Range, μ	Rept. Error %	Sample Specifications	Remarks
○	62-34	523	2-15		Flame sprayed on sandblasted Inconel X using a Plasmatron.	As received; data taken from smooth curve.
△	62-34	1023	1-15		Same as above.	Same as above; different specimen.
□	62-34	523	2-15		Same as above.	Heated in vacuum (6.8×10^{-5} mm Hg) at 1089 K for 30 min.; data taken from smooth curve.
▽	62-34	1023	1-15		Same as above.	Same as above.
◇	62-34	523	2-15		Same as above.	Heated in air at 1089 K for 30 min.
◁	62-34	1023	1-15		Same as above.	Same as above; data taken from smooth curve.

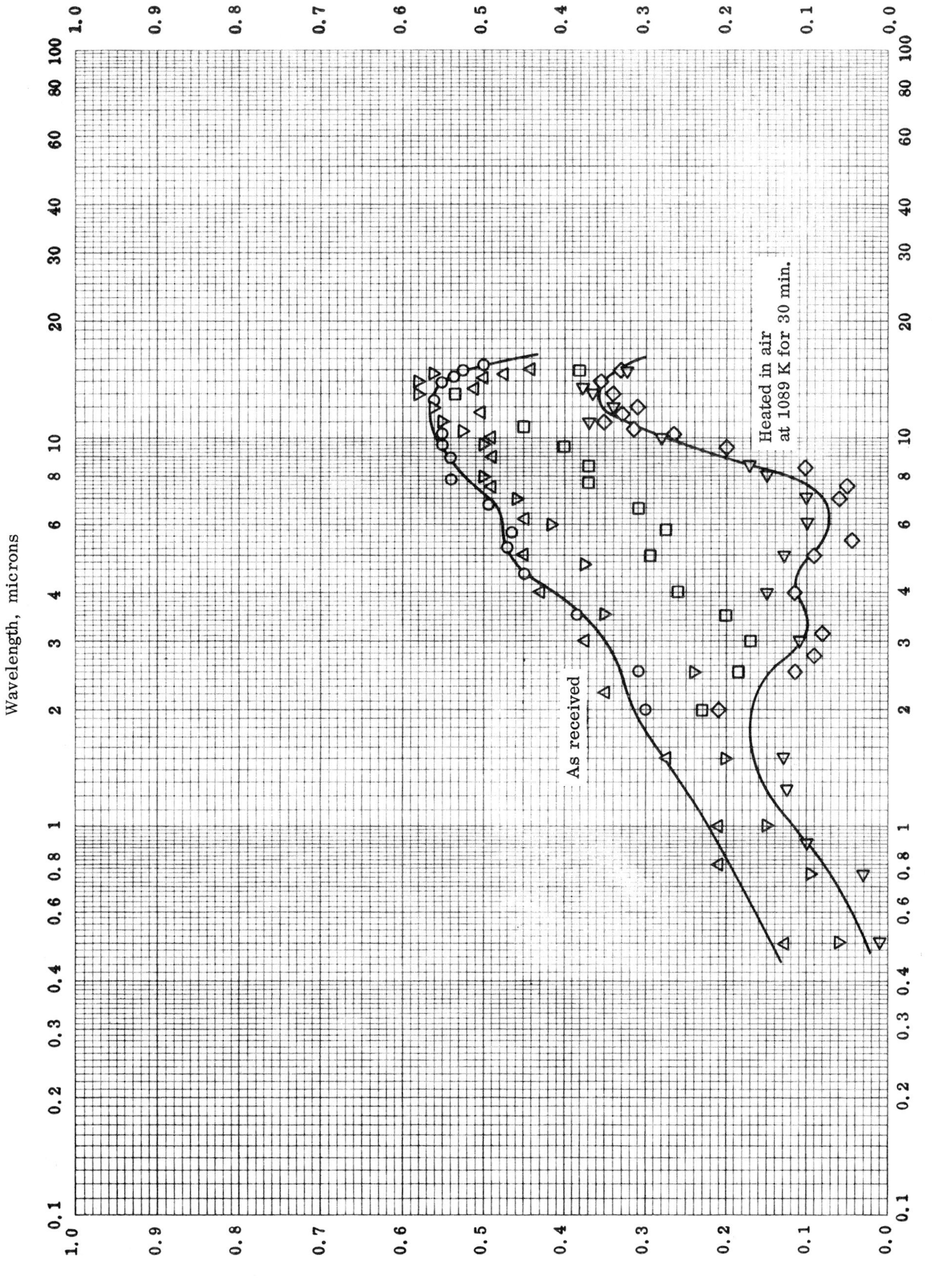

NORMAL SPECTRAL REFLECTANCE -- TUNGSTEN COATING ON INCONEL X

NORMAL SPECTRAL REFLECTANCE -- TUNGSTEN COATING ON INCONEL X

REFERENCE INFORMATION

Symbol	Ref.	Temp. °K	Wavelength Range, μ	Rept. Error %	Sample Specifications	Remarks
○	62-34	<322	2-15.5	<±2	Flame sprayed on sandblasted Inconel X using a Plasma-tron.	As received; data taken from smooth curve; hemispherical illumination, normal viewing; 523 K source temperature.
△	62-34	<322	0.5-15	<±2	Same as above.	Same as above; 1273 K source temperature.
□	62-34	<322	2-15	<±2	Same as above.	Heated in vacuum (6.8×10^{-5} mm Hg) at 1089 K for 30 min.; data taken from smooth curve; hemispherical illumination, normal viewing; 523 K source temperature.
▽	62-34	<322	0.5-15	<±2	Same as above.	Same as above; 1273 K source temperature.
◇	62-34	<322	2-15	<±2	Same as above.	Heated in air at 1089 K for 30 min.; data taken from smooth curve; hemispherical illumination, normal viewing; 523 K source temperature.
◁	62-34	<322	0.5-15	<±2	Same as above.	Same as above; 1273 K source temperature.

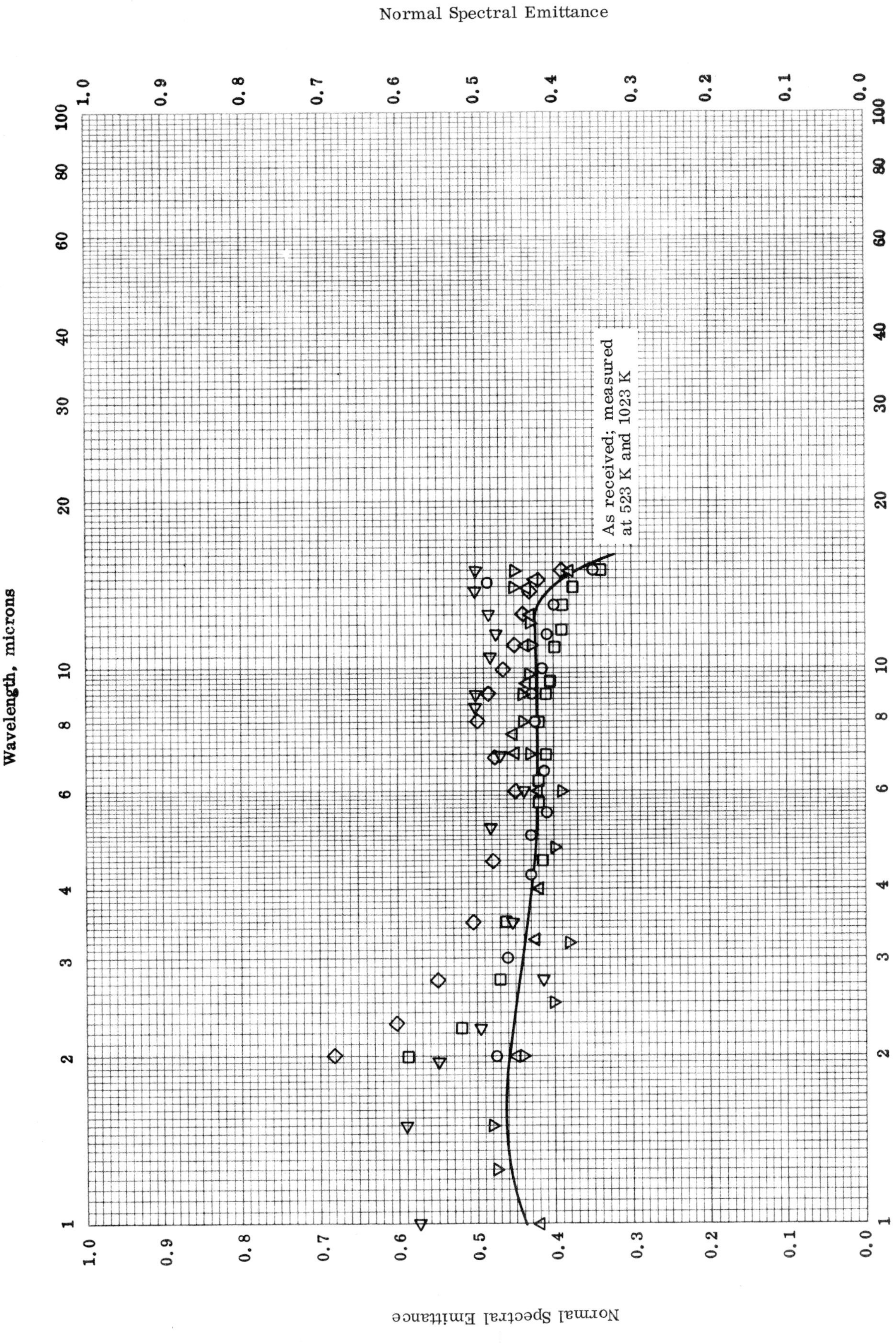

Normal Spectral Emittance
Wavelength, microns
As received; measured at 523 K and 1023 K
1.0
0.9
0.8
0.7
0.6
0.5
0.4
0.3
0.2
0.1
0.0
1
2
3
4
6
8
10
20
30
40
60
80
100

NORMAL SPECTRAL EMITTANCE -- NICKEL AND CHROMIUM ALLOY COATING ON INCONEL X

NORMAL SPECTRAL EMITTANCE -- NICKEL AND CHROMIUM ALLOY COATING ON INCONEL X

REFERENCE INFORMATION

Symbol	Ref.	Temp. °K	Wavelength Range, μ	Rept. Error %	Sample Specifications	Remarks
○	62-34	523	2-15		80 Ni and 20 Cr coating; flame sprayed on sandblasted Inconel X using a Plasmatron.	As received; data taken from smooth curve.
△	62-34	1023	1-15		Same as above.	Same as above; different specimen.
□	62-34	523	2-15		Same as above.	Heated in vacuum (6.8×10^{-5} mm Hg) at 1089 K for 30 min., data taken from smooth curve.
▽	62-34	1023	1-15		Same as above.	Same as above.
◇	62-34	523	2-15		Same as above.	Heated in air at 1089 K for 30 min.
◁	62-34	1023	1-15		Same as above.	Same as above; data taken from smooth curve.

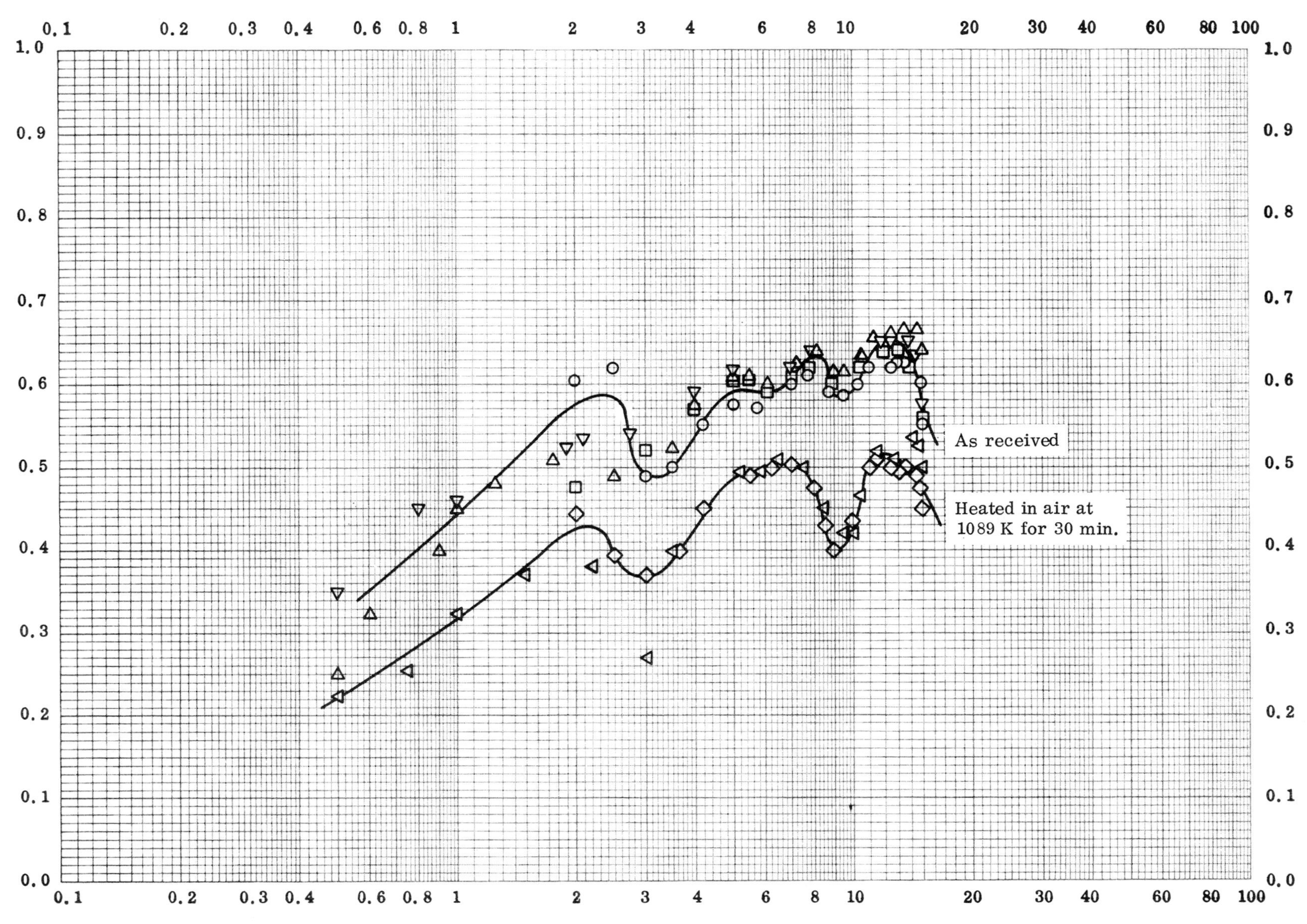

NORMAL SPECTRAL REFLECTANCE -- NICKEL AND CHROMIUM ALLOY COATING ON INCONEL X

NORMAL SPECTRAL REFLECTANCE -- NICKEL AND CHROMIUM ALLOY COATING ON INCONEL X

REFERENCE INFORMATION

Symbol	Ref.	Temp. °K	Wavelength Range, μ	Rept. Error %	Sample Specifications	Remarks
○	62-34	<322	2-15	<±2	80 Ni and 20 Cr coating flame sprayed on sandblasted Inconel X using a plasmatron.	As received; data taken from smooth curve; hemispherical illumination, normal viewing; 523 K source temperature.
△	62-34	<322	0.5-15	<±2	Same as above.	Same as above; 1273 K source temperature.
□	62-34	<322	2-15	<±2	Same as above.	Heated in vacuum (6.8 x 10^{-5} mm Hg) at 1089 K for 30 min.; data taken from smooth curve, hemispherical illumination, normal viewing; 523 K source temperature.
▽	62-34	<322	0.5-15	<±2	Same as above.	Same as above; 1273 K source temperature.
◇	62-34	<322	2-15	<±2	Same as above.	Heated in air at 1089 K for 30 min.; data taken from smooth curve; hemispherical illumination, normal viewing; 523 K source temperature.
◁	62-34	<322	0.5-15	<±2	Same as above.	Same as above; 1273 K source temperature.

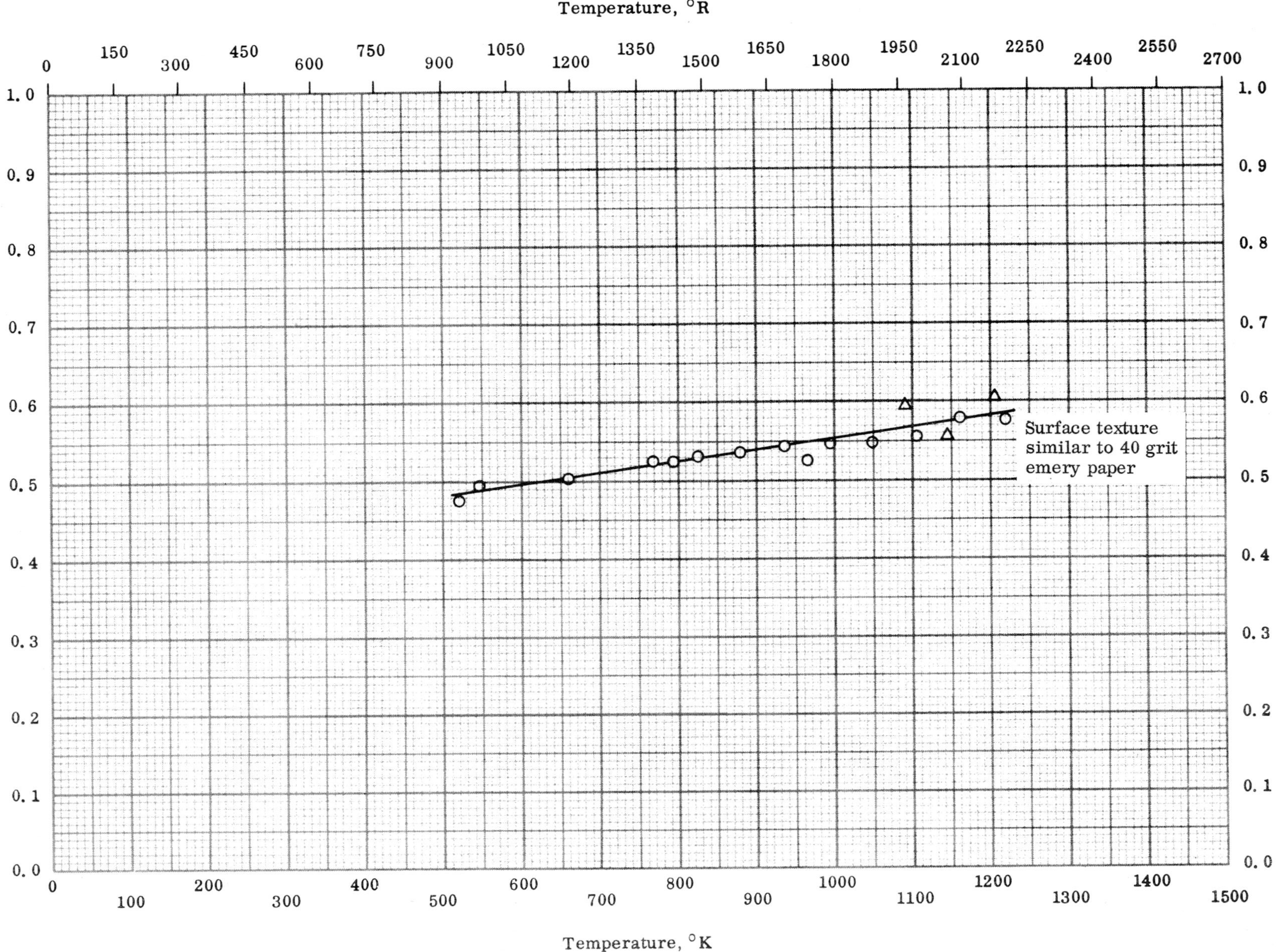

HEMISPHERICAL TOTAL EMITTANCE -- HASTELLOY C COATING ON STAINLESS STEEL

HEMISPHERICAL TOTAL EMITTANCE -- HASTELLOY C COATING ON STAINLESS STEEL

REFERENCE INFORMATION

Symbol	Ref.	Temp. Range °K	Rept. Error %	Sample Specifications	Remarks
○	63-23	519-1219		Partially oxidized Hastelloy C powder on AISI-310 stainless steel; coating thickness 0.007 in. with a texture similar to that of 40 grit emery cloth.	Plasma-arc sprayed; measured in vacuum.
△	63-23	1091-1205		Same as above.	Same as above.

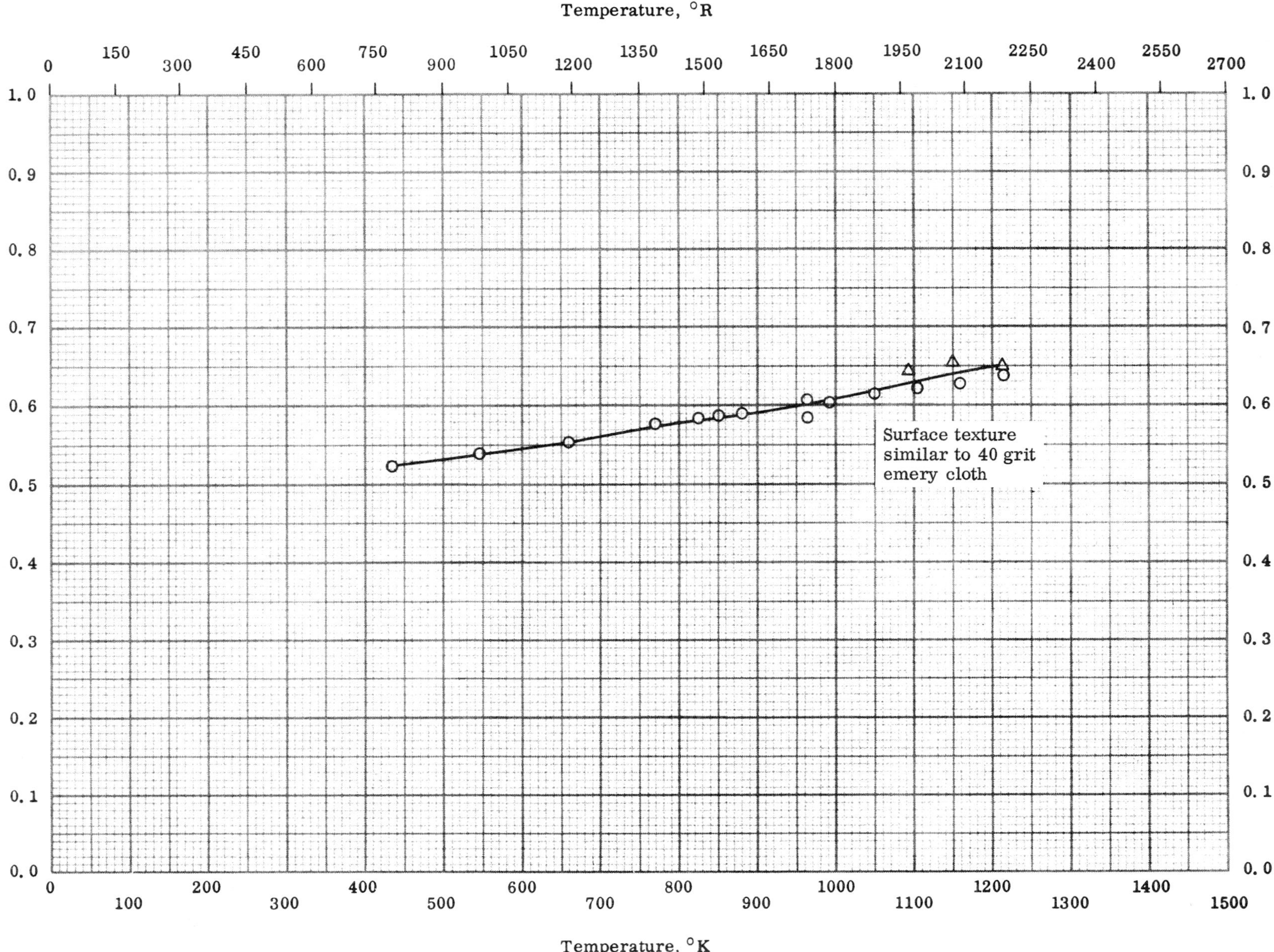

HEMISPHERICAL TOTAL EMITTANCE -- HASTELLOY X COATING ON STAINLESS STEEL

HEMISPHERICAL TOTAL EMITTANCE -- HASTELLOY X COATING ON STAINLESS STEEL

REFERENCE INFORMATION

Symbol	Ref.	Temp. Range °K	Rept. Error %	Sample Specifications	Remarks
○	63-23	434-1217		Partially oxidized Hastelloy X powder on AISI 310 stainless steel; coating thickness 0.008 in. with a texture similar to 40 grit emery cloth.	Plasma-arc sprayed; measured in vacuum.
△	63-23	1095-1214		Same as above.	Same as above.

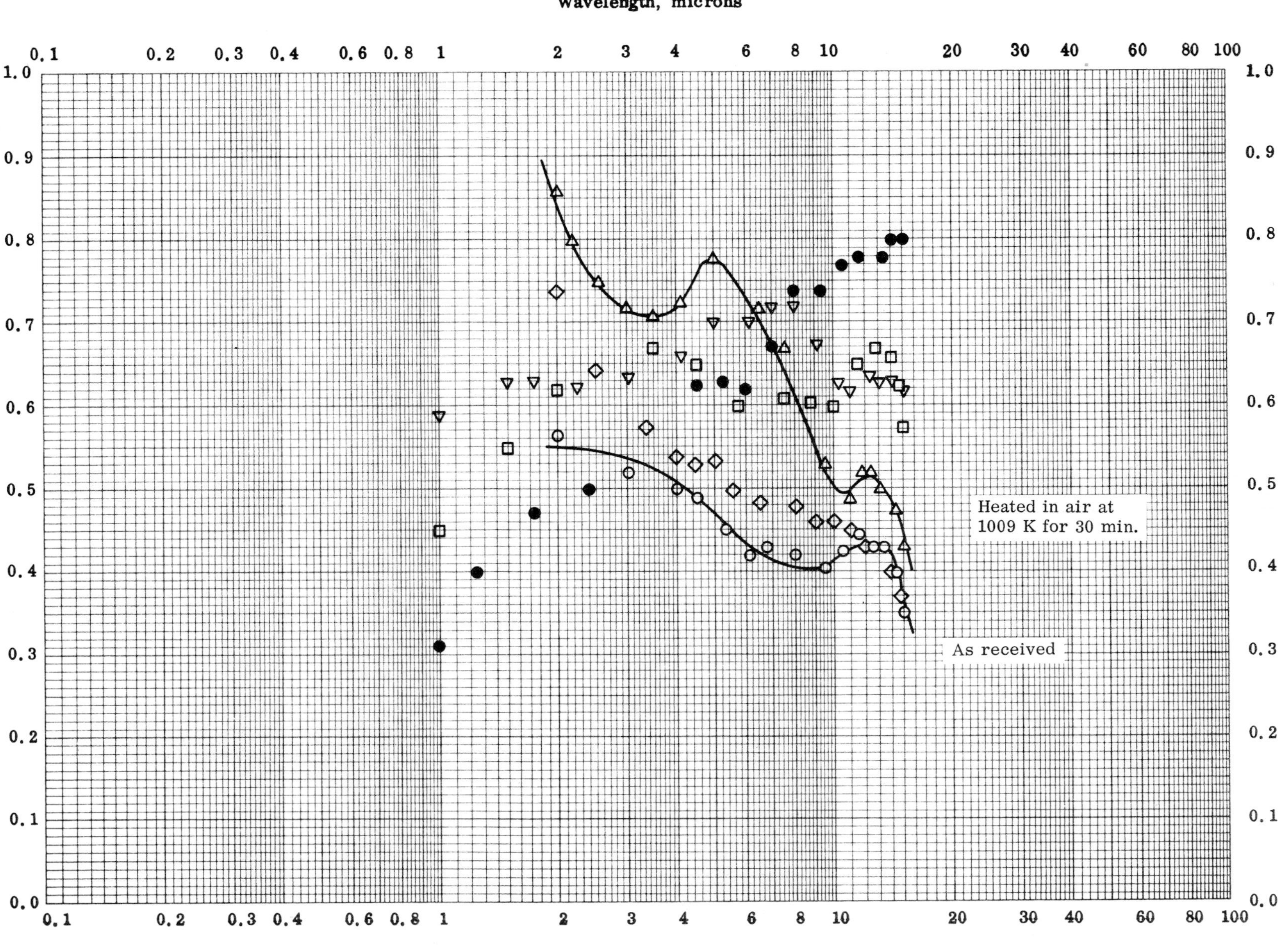

NORMAL SPECTRAL EMITTANCE -- TUNGSTEN AND COBALT ALLOY COATING ON INCONEL X

NORMAL SPECTRAL EMITTANCE -- TUNGSTEN AND COBALT ALLOY COATING ON INCONEL X

REFERENCE INFORMATION

Symbol	Ref.	Temp. °K	Wavelength Range, μ	Rept. Error %	Sample Specifications	Remarks
○	62-34	523	2-15		50 W and 50 Co flame sprayed on sandblasted Inconel X using a Plasmatron.	As received; data taken from smooth curve.
□	62-34	1023	1-15		Same as above.	Same as above; different specimen.
△	62-34	523	2-15		Same as above.	Heated in air at 1089 K for 30 min.; data taken from smooth curve.
▽	62-34	1023	1-15		Same as above.	Same as above.
◇	62-34	523	2-15		Same as above.	Heated in vacuum (6.8×10^{-5} mm Hg) at 1089 K for 30 min.; data taken from smooth curve.
●	62-34	1023	1-15		Same as above.	Same as above.

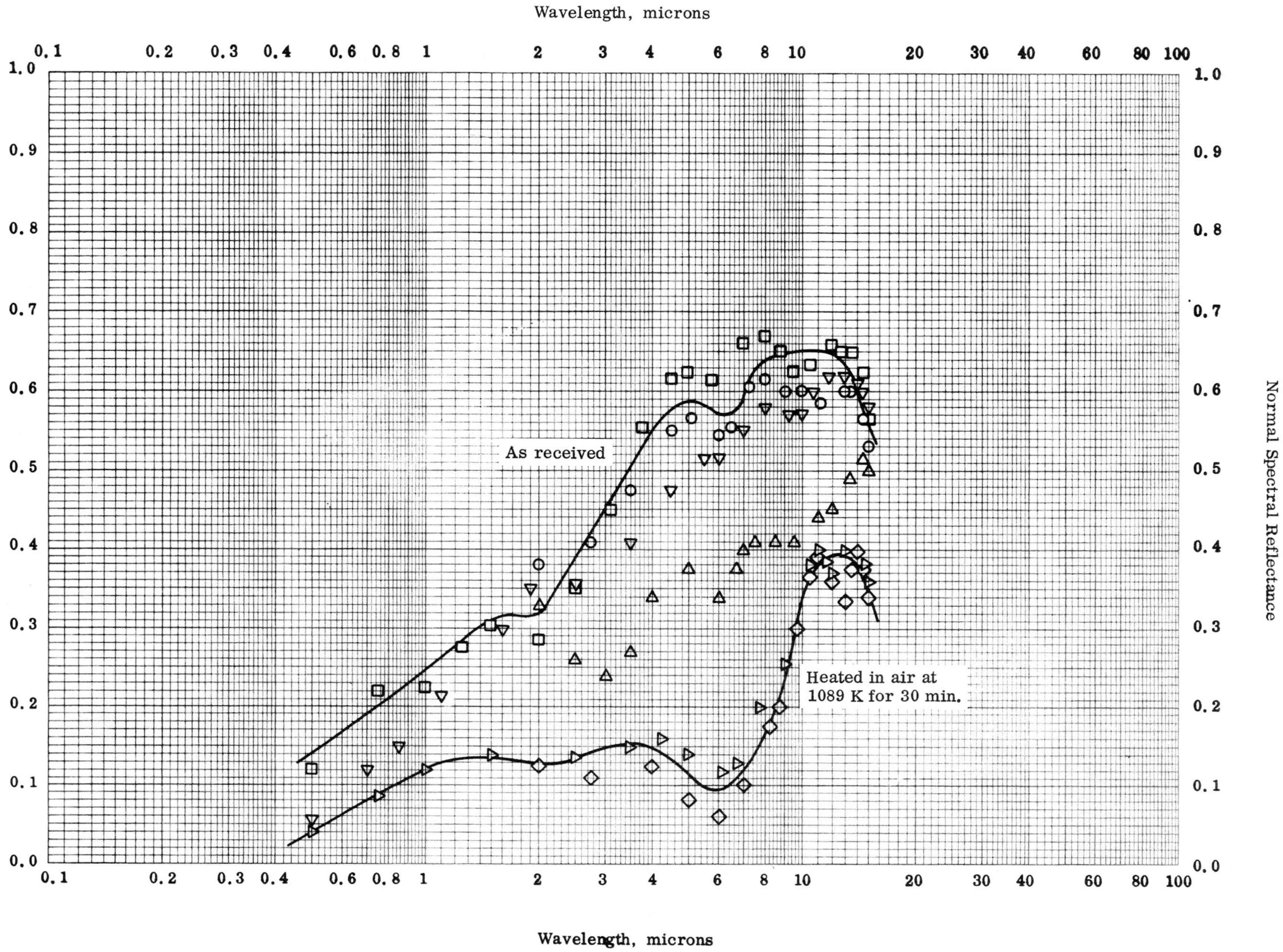

NORMAL SPECTRAL REFLECTANCE -- TUNGSTEN AND COBALT ALLOY COATING ON INCONEL X

NORMAL SPECTRAL REFLECTANCE -- TUNGSTEN AND COBALT ALLOY COATING ON INCONEL X

REFERENCE INFORMATION

Symbol	Ref.	Temp. °K	Wavelength Range, μ	Rept. Error %	Sample Specifications	Remarks
○	62-34	<322	2-15	<±2	50 W and 50 Co flame sprayed on sandblasted Inconel X using a Plasmatron.	As received; data taken from smooth curve; hemispherical illumination, normal viewing; 523 K source temperature.
□	62-34	<322	0.5-15	<±2	Same as above.	Same as above; 1273 K source temperature.
△	62-34	<322	2-15	<±2	Same as above.	Heated in vacuum (6.8 x 10^{-5} mm Hg) at 1089 K for 30 min.; data taken from smooth curve; hemispherical illumination, normal viewing; 523 K source temperature.
▽	62-34	<322	0.5-15	<±2	Same as above.	Same as above; 1273 K source temperature.
◇	62-34	<322	2-15	<±2	Same as above.	Heated in air at 1089 K for 30 min.; data taken from smooth curve; hemispherical illumination, normal viewing; 523 K source temperature.
▷	62-34	<322	0.5-15	<±2	Same as above.	Same as above; 1273 K source temperature.

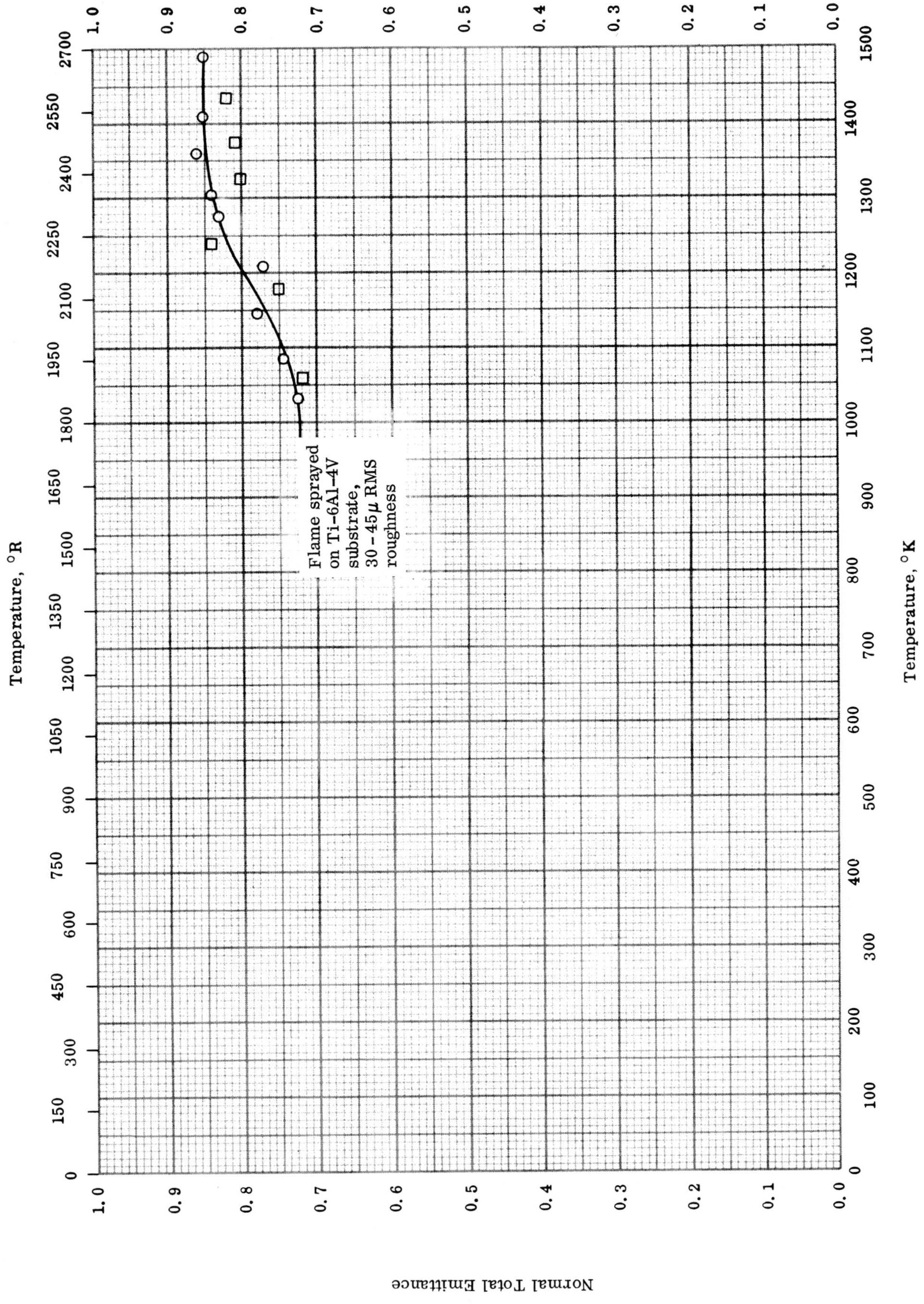

NORMAL TOTAL EMITTANCE -- ROKIDE C COATING ON TITANIUM ALLOY

NORMAL TOTAL EMITTANCE -- ROKIDE C COATING ON TITANIUM ALLOY

REFERENCE INFORMATION

Symbol	Ref.	Temp. Range °K	Rept. Error %	Sample Specifications	Remarks
○	63-22	1033-1490		Flame sprayed on Ti - 6 Al - 4 V; coating thickness 0.004 in.; surface roughness 30 - 45 μ RMS.	Measured in a vacuum of 3 - 4 μ Hg; ascending temperature.
□	63-22	1066-1435		Same as above.	Same as above; descending temperature.

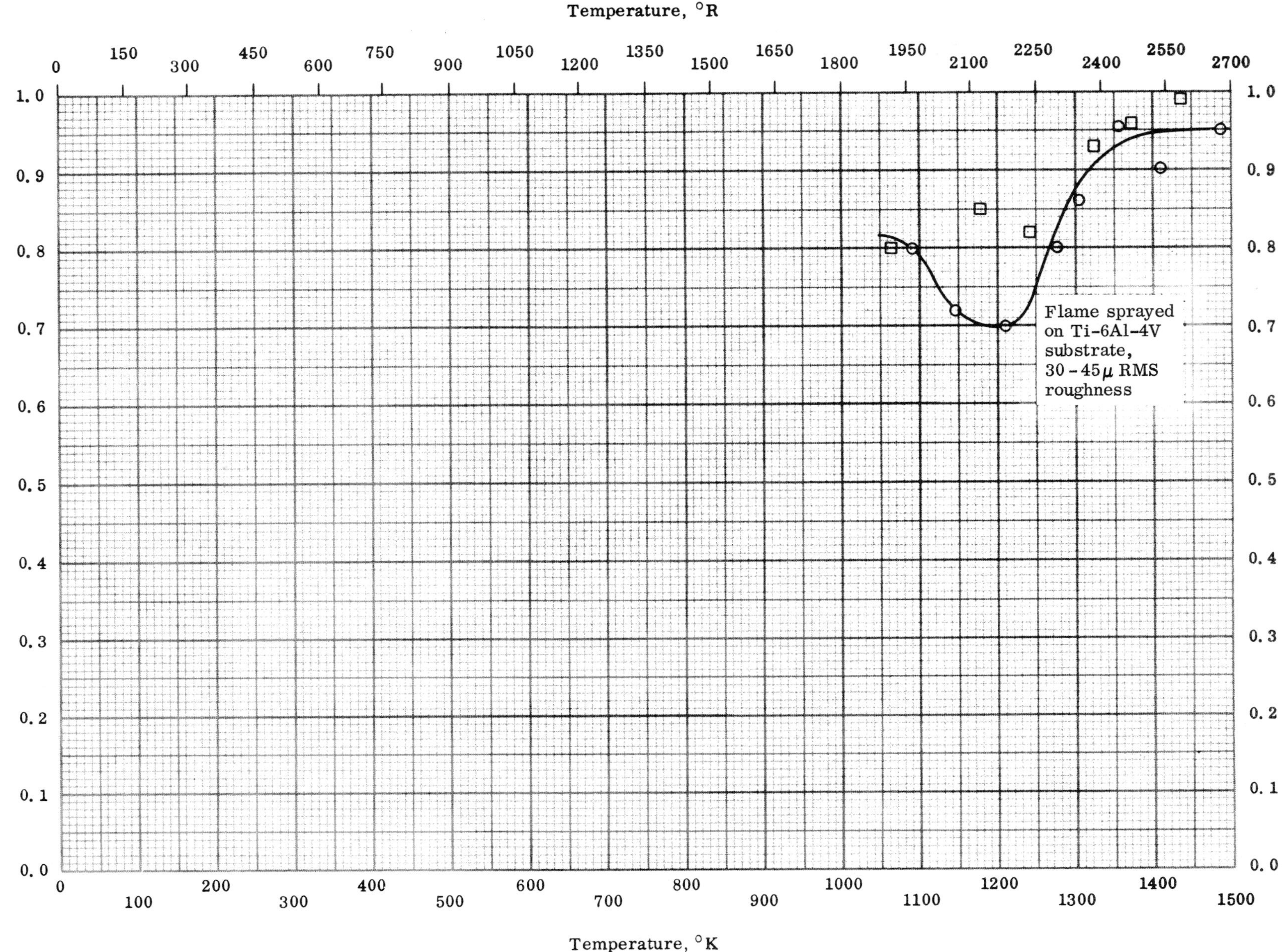

NORMAL SPECTRAL EMITTANCE -- ROKIDE C COATING ON TITANIUM ALLOY

NORMAL SPECTRAL EMITTANCE -- ROKIDE C COATING ON TITANIUM ALLOY

REFERENCE INFORMATION

Symbol	Ref.	Wavelength μ	Temp. Range °K	Rept. Error %	Sample Specifications	Remarks
○	63-22	0.65	1091-1488		Flame sprayed Rokide C on Ti - 6 Al - 4 V; coating thickness 0.004 in.; surface roughness 30 - 45 μ RMS.	Measured in a vacuum of 3 - 4 μ Hg; ascending temperature.
□	63-22	0.65	1066-1438		Same as above.	Same as above; descending temperature.

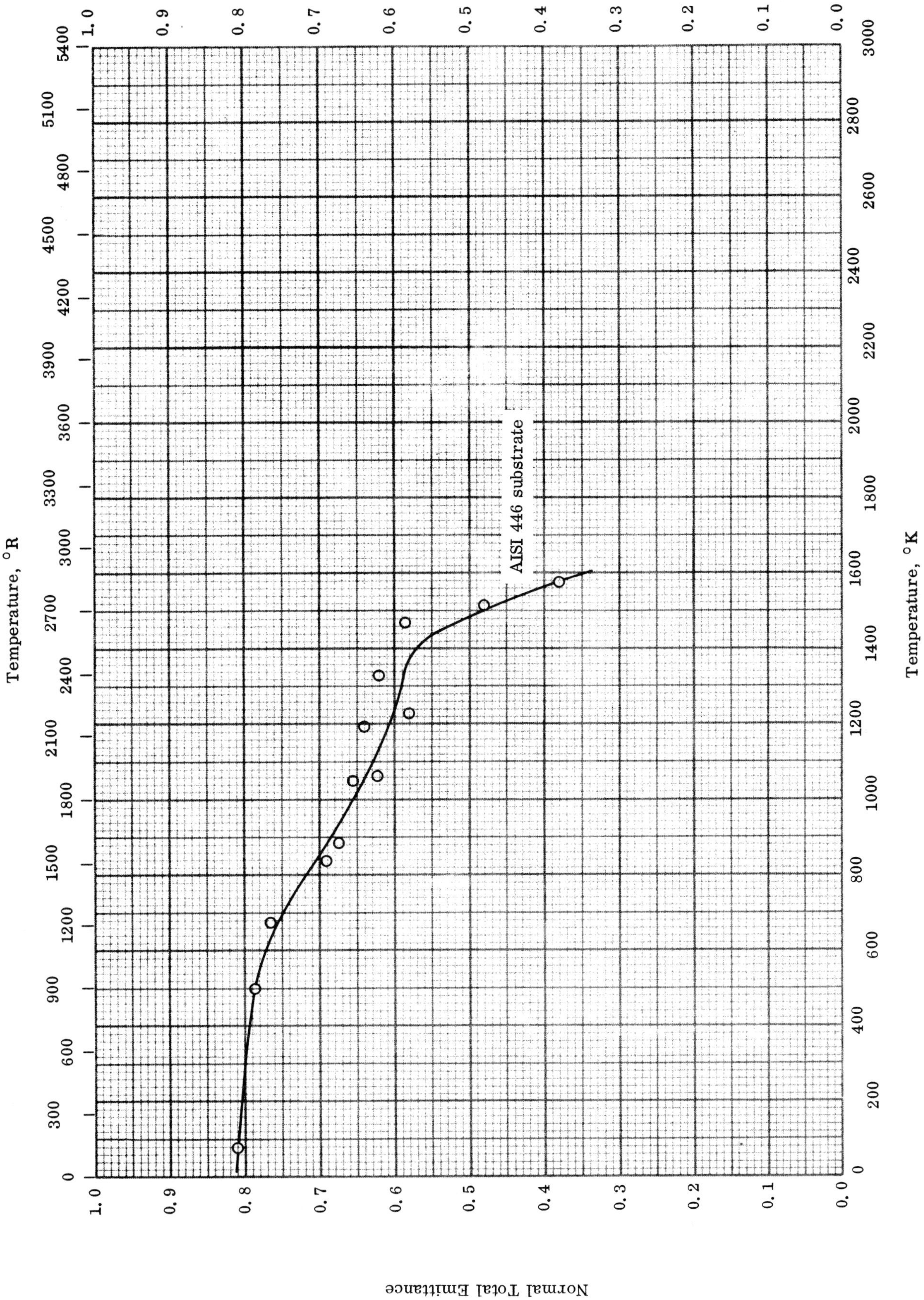

NORMAL TOTAL EMITTANCE -- ALUMINUM OXIDE ON STAINLESS STEEL

NORMAL TOTAL EMITTANCE -- ALUMINUM OXIDE ON STAINLESS STEEL

REFERENCE INFORMATION

Symbol	Ref.	Temp. Range °K	Rept. Error %	Sample Specifications	Remarks
○	59-19	77-1578		Stainless steel AISI 446 substrate.	Measured in air.

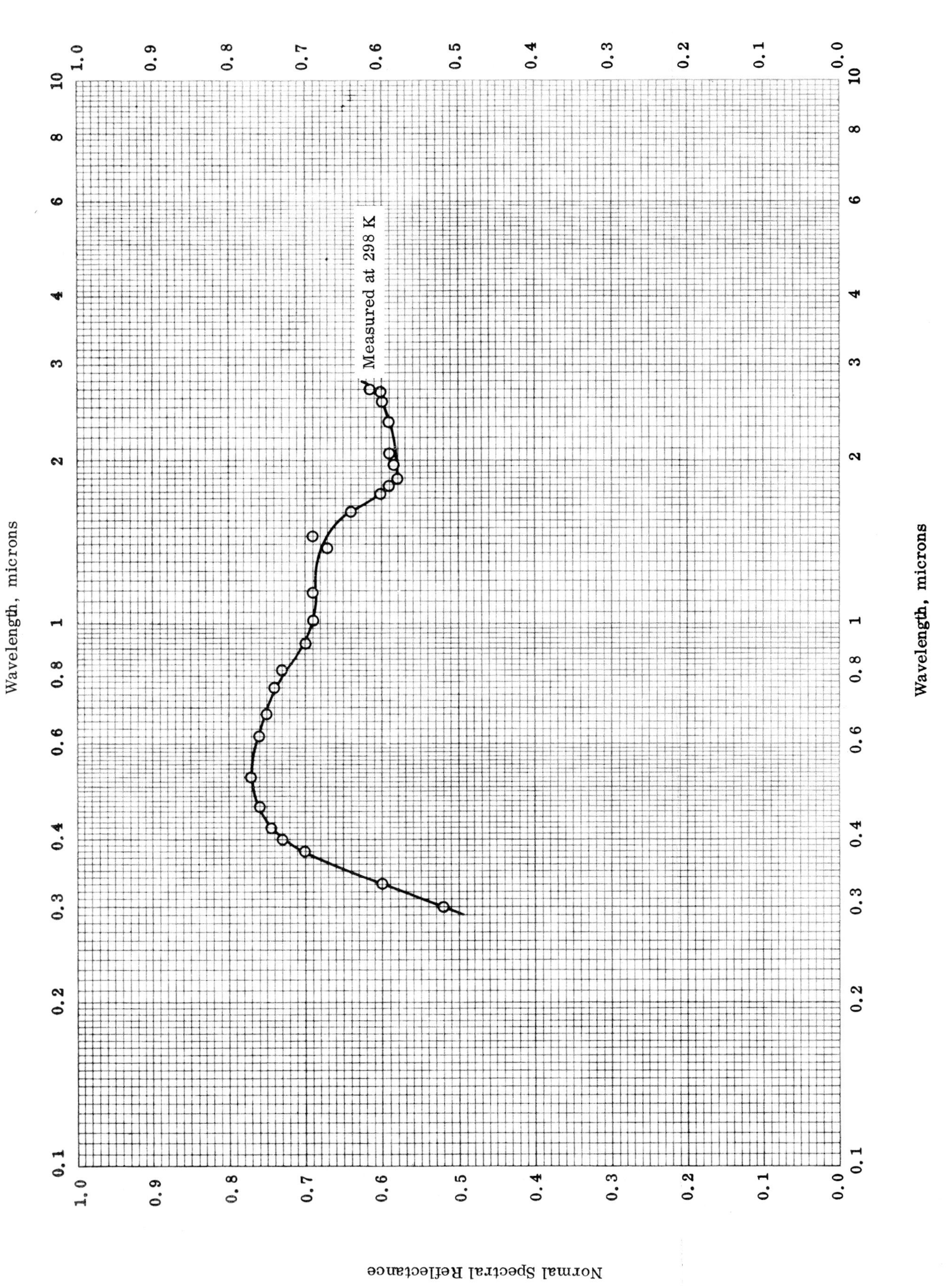

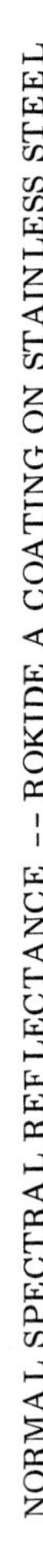

NORMAL SPECTRAL REFLECTANCE -- ROKIDE A COATING ON STAINLESS STEEL

NORMAL SPECTRAL REFLECTANCE -- ROKIDE A COATING ON STAINLESS STEEL

REFERENCE INFORMATION

Symbol	Ref.	Temp. °K	Wavelength Range, μ	Rept. Error %	Sample Specifications	Remarks
○	59-19	298	0.3-2.7	4	Substrate AISI 446 stainless steel.	Data taken from smooth curve, $MgCO_3$ as reference standard; normal incidence, hemispherical viewing.

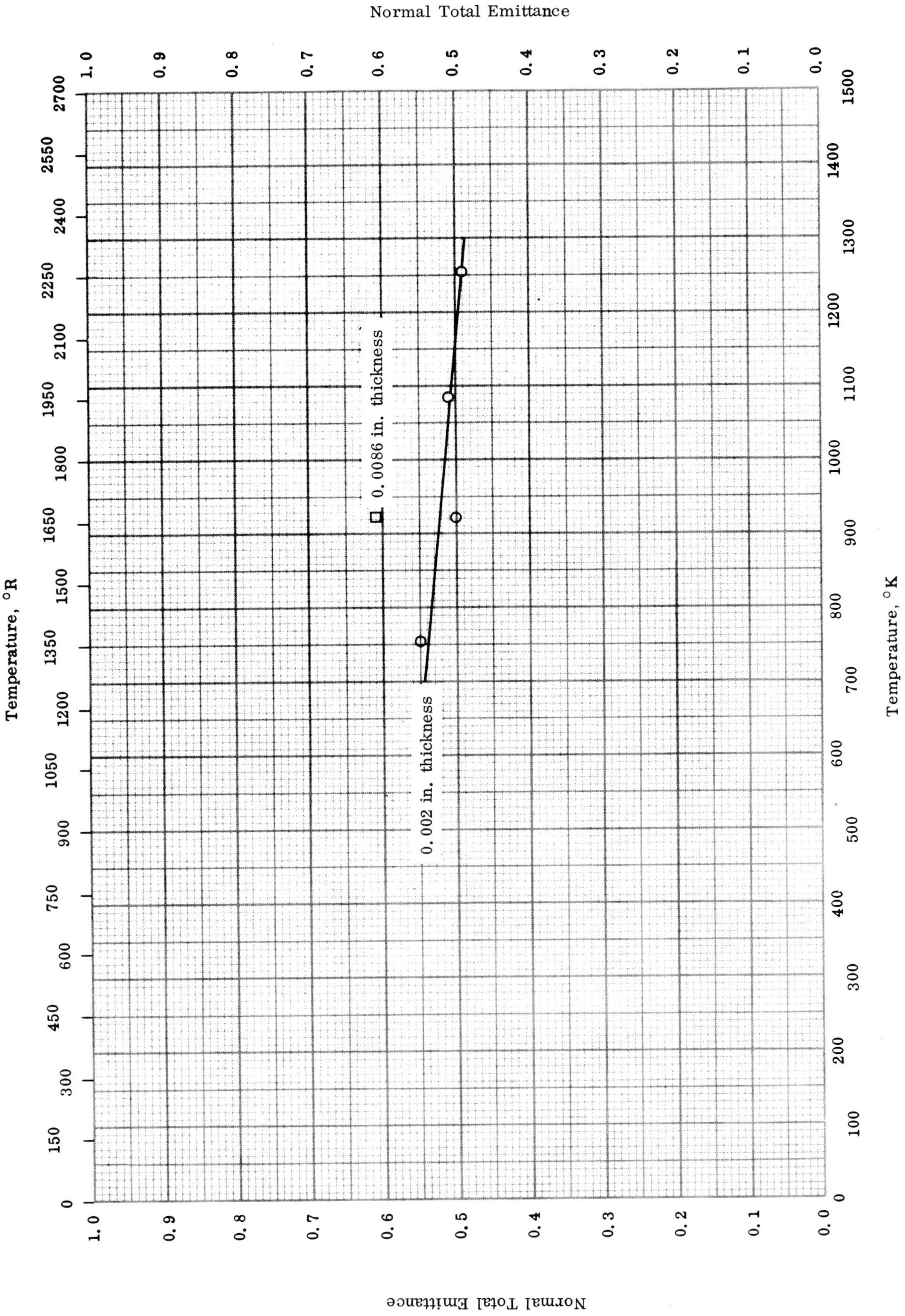

Normal Total Emittance
Temperature, °R
Temperature, °K
0.0086 in. thickness
0.002 in. thickness
Normal Total Emittance

NORMAL TOTAL EMITTANCE -- NBS COATING N-143 ON INCONEL

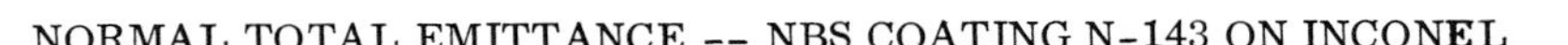

NORMAL TOTAL EMITTANCE -- NBS COATING N-143 ON INCONEL

REFERENCE INFORMATION

Symbol	Ref.	Temp. Range °K	Rept. Error %	Sample Specifications	Remarks
○	59-18	955-1256	<8	Coating consists of a boron-free barium beryllium silicate frit with a refractory mill addition of cerium oxide; coating thickness 0.002 in.; substrate composition 80 Ni, 14 Cr, and 6 Fe.	
□	59-18	922	<8	Same as above except coating thickness 0.0086 in.	

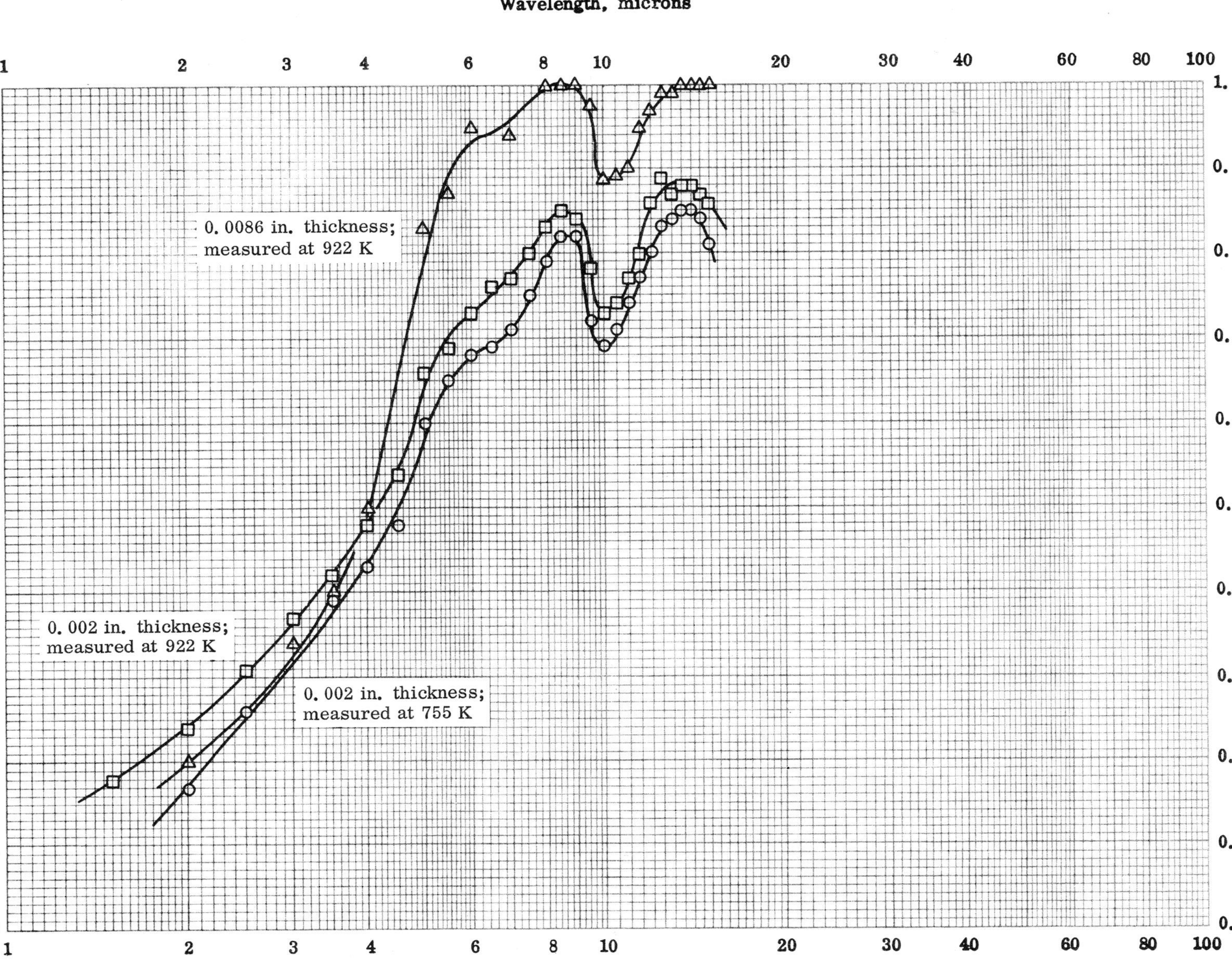

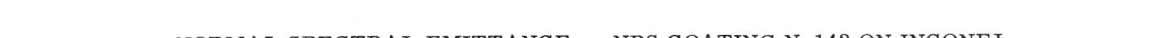

NORMAL SPECTRAL EMITTANCE -- NBS COATING N-143 ON INCONEL

NORMAL SPECTRAL EMITTANCE -- NBS COATING N-143 ON INCONEL

REFERENCE INFORMATION

Symbol	Ref.	Temp. °K	Wavelength Range, μ	Rept. Error %	Sample Specifications	Remarks
○	59-18	755	2.0-15.0	<8	Coating consists of a boron-free barium beryllium silicate frit with a refractory mill addition of cerium oxide; coating thickness 0.002 in.; substrate composition 80 Ni, 14 Cr, and 6 Fe.	
□	59-18	922	1.5-15	<8	Same as above.	
△	59-18	922	2.0-15	<8	Same as above except coating thickness 0.0086 in.	

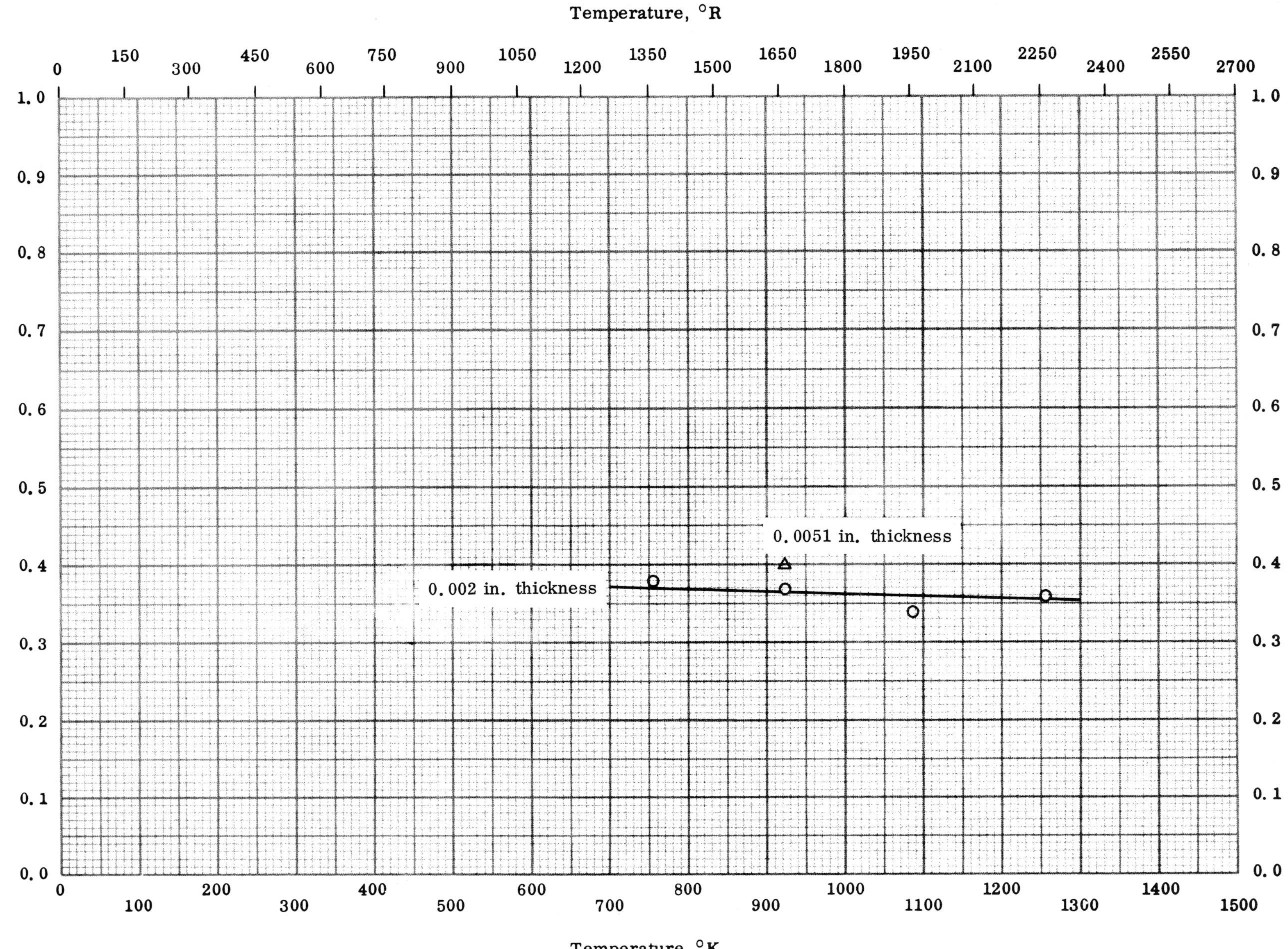

NORMAL TOTAL EMITTANCE -- NBS COATING N-143 ON STAINLESS STEEL

NORMAL TOTAL EMITTANCE -- NBS COATING N-143 ON STAINLESS STEEL

REFERENCE INFORMATION

Symbol	Ref.	Temp. Range °K	Rept. Error %	Sample Specifications	Remarks
○	59-18	755-1255	<8	Coating consists of a boron-free barium beryllium silicate frit with a refractory mill addition of cerium oxide; coating thickness 0.002 in.; substrate composition 74 Fe, 18 Cr, and 8 Ni.	
△	59-18	922	<8	Same as above except coating thickness 0.0051 in.	

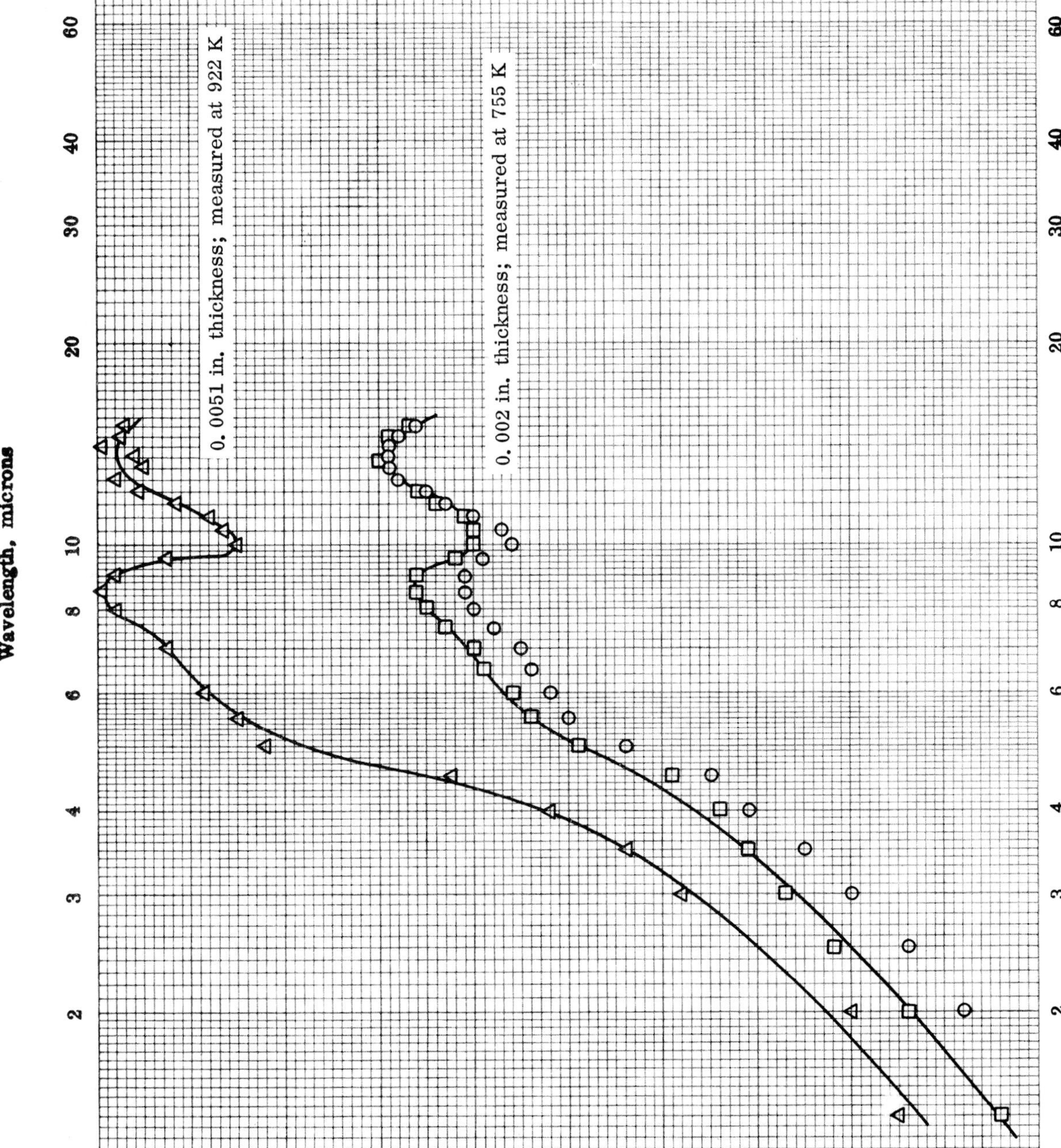

NORMAL SPECTRAL EMITTANCE -- NBS COATING N-143 ON STAINLESS STEEL

NORMAL SPECTRAL EMITTANCE -- NBS COATING N-143 ON STAINLESS STEEL

REFERENCE INFORMATION

Symbol	Ref.	Temp. °K	Wavelength Range, μ	Rept. Error %	Sample Specifications	Remarks
○	59-18	755	2.0-15.0	< 8	Coating consists of a boron-free barium beryllium silicate frit with a refractory mill addition of cerium oxide; coating thickness 0.002 in.; substrate composition 74 Fe, 18 Cr, and 8 Ni.	
□	59-18	922	1.5-15.0	< 8	Same as above.	
△	59-18	922	1.5-15.0	< 8	Same as above except coating thickness 0.0051 in.	

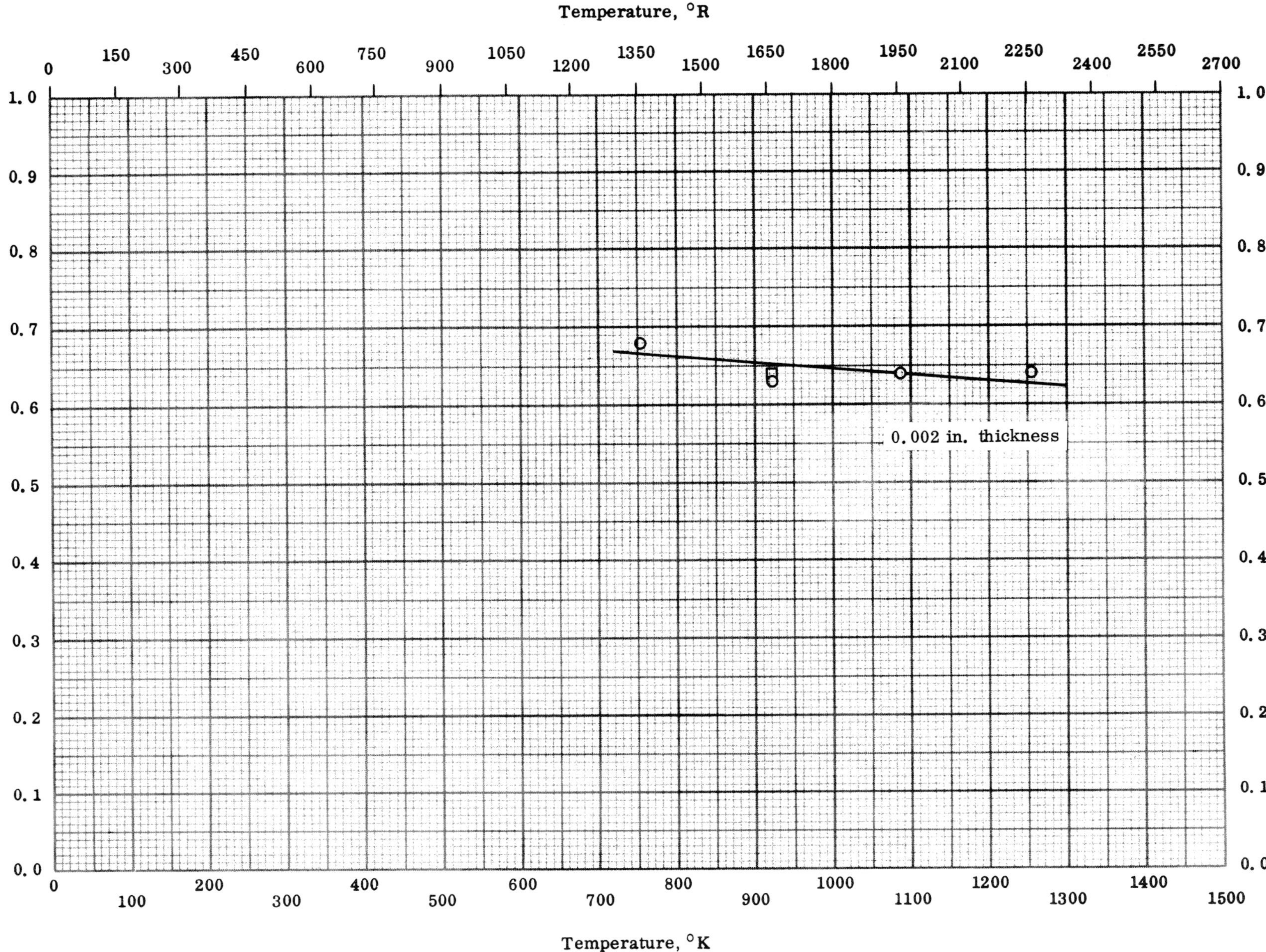

NORMAL TOTAL EMITTANCE -- NBS COATING A-418 ON INCONEL

NORMAL TOTAL EMITTANCE -- NBS COATING A-418 ON INCONEL

REFERENCE INFORMATION

Symbol	Ref.	Temp. Range °K	Rept. Error %	Sample Specifications	Remarks
○	59-18	755-1256	< 8	Coating consists of alkali free barium borosilicate frit with a refractory mill addition of chromic oxide; coating thickness 0.002 in.; substrate composition 80 Ni, 14 Cr, and 6 Fe.	
□	59-18	922	< 8	Same as above except coating thickness 0.0048 in.	

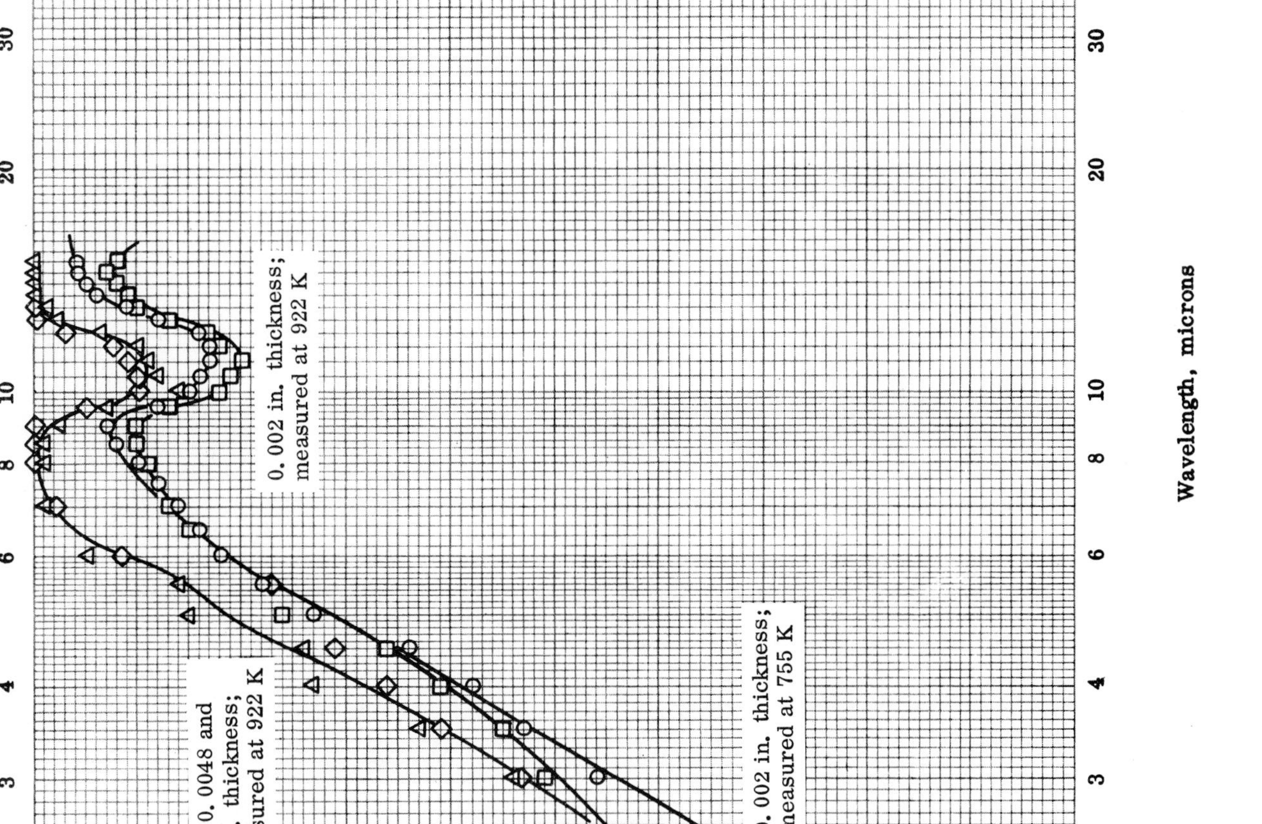

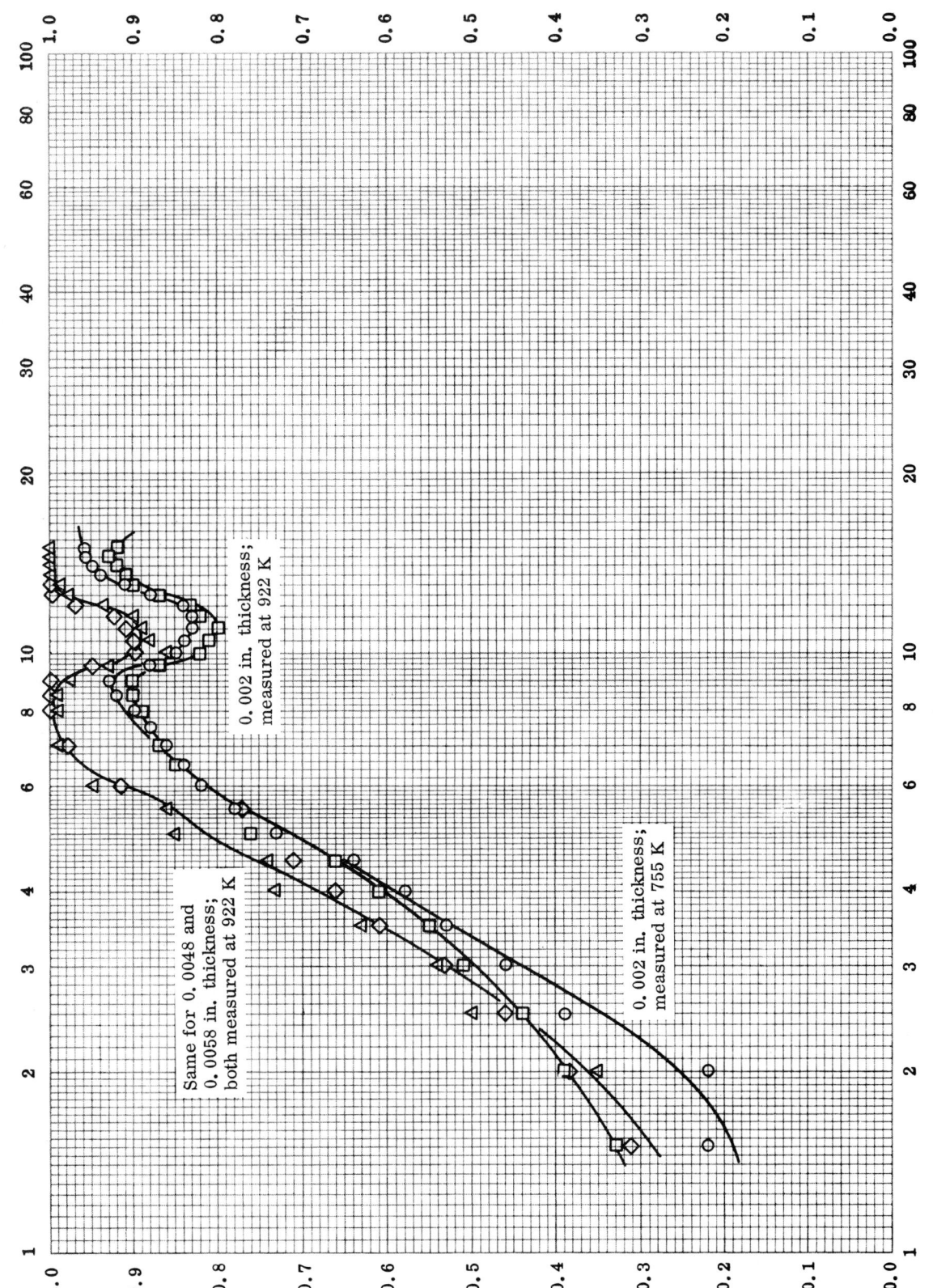

NORMAL SPECTRAL EMITTANCE -- NBS COATING A-418 ON INCONEL

NORMAL SPECTRAL EMITTANCE -- NBS COATING A-418 ON INCONEL

REFERENCE INFORMATION

Symbol	Ref.	Temp. °K	Wavelength Range, μ	Rept. Error %	Sample Specifications	Remarks
○	59-18	755	1.5-15	<8	Coating consists of alkali free barium borosilicate frit with a refractory mill addition of chromic oxide, coating thickness 0.002 in; substrate composition 80 Ni, 14 Cr, and 6 Fe.	
□	59-18	922	1.5-15	<8	Same as above.	
△	59-18	922	2.0-15	<8	Same as above except coating thickness 0.0048 in.	
◇	59-18	922	1.5-15	<8	Same as above except coating thickness 0.0058 in.	

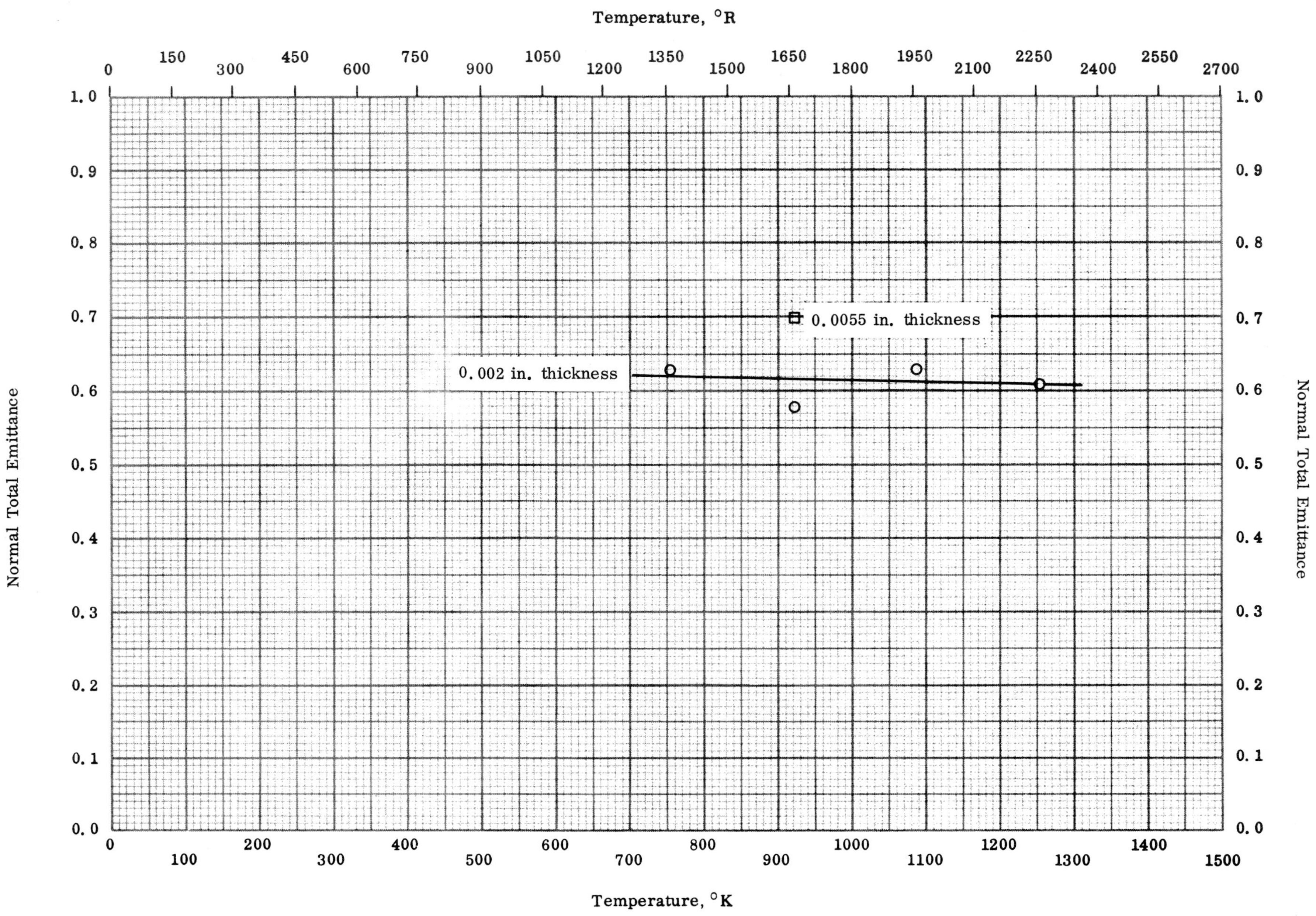

Temperature, °R

Normal Total Emittance

0.0055 in. thickness

0.002 in. thickness

Temperature, °K

NORMAL TOTAL EMITTANCE -- NBS COATING A-418 ON STAINLESS STEEL

NORMAL TOTAL EMITTANCE -- NBS COATING A-418 ON STAINLESS STEEL

REFERENCE INFORMATION

Symbol	Ref.	Temp. Range °K	Rept. Error %	Sample Specifications	Remarks
○	59-18	755-1255	< 8	Coating consists of alkali free barium borosilicate frit with a refractory mill addition of chromic oxide; coating thickness 0.002 in.; substrate composition 74 Fe, 18 Cr, and 8 Ni.	
□	59-18	922	< 8	Same as above except coating thickness 0.0055 in.	

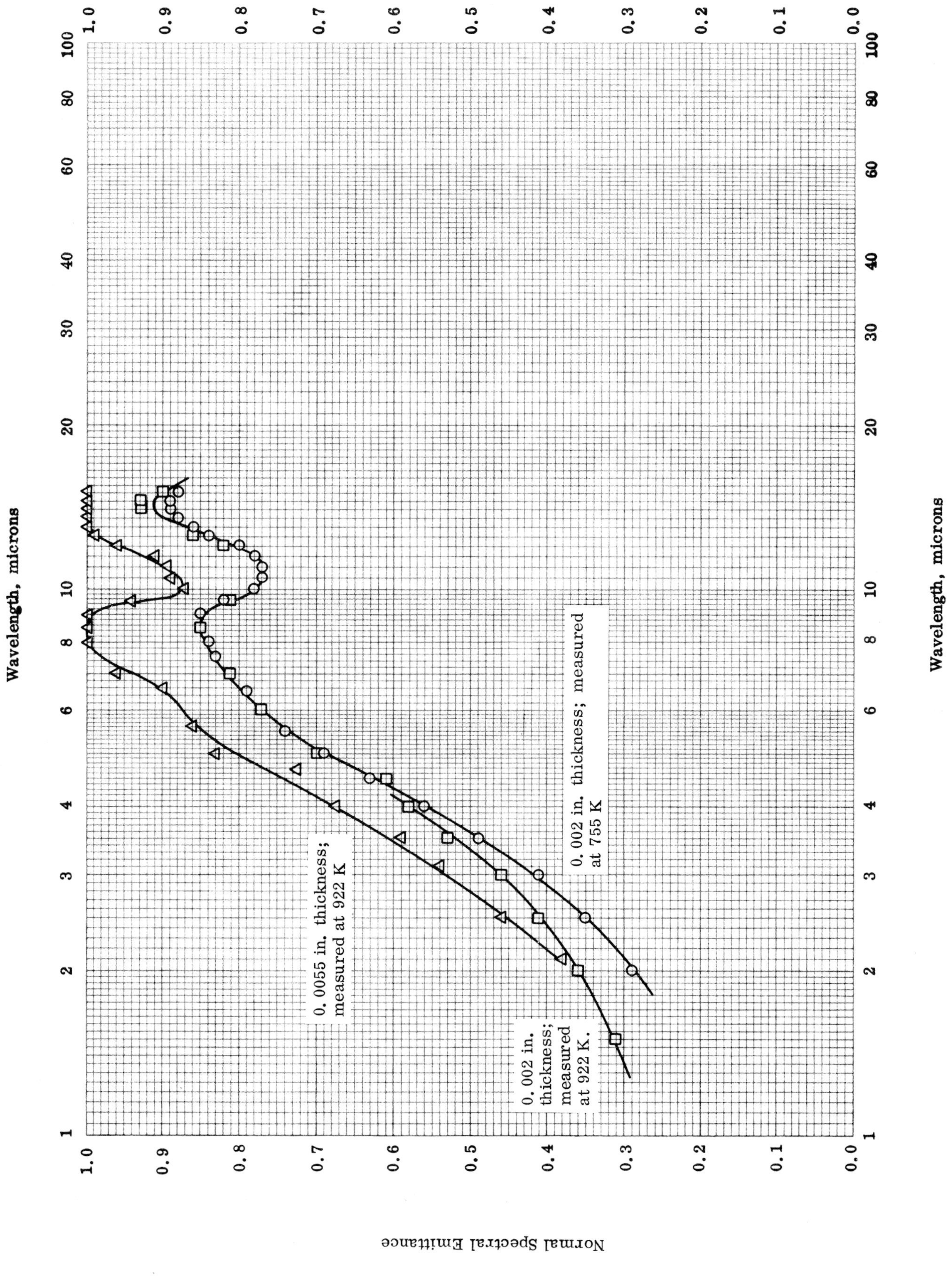

NORMAL SPECTRAL EMITTANCE -- NBS COATING A-418 ON STAINLESS STEEL

NORMAL SPECTRAL EMITTANCE -- NBS COATING A-418 ON STAINLESS STEEL

REFERENCE INFORMATION

Sym bol	Ref.	Temp. °K	Wavelength Range, μ	Rept. Error%	Sample Specifications	Remarks
○	59-18	755	2.0-15.0	<8	Coating consists of alkali free barium borosilicate frit with a refractory mill addition of chromic oxide; coating thickness 0.002 in.; substrate composition 74 Fe, 18 Cr, and 8 Ni.	
□	59-18	922	1.5-15.00	<8	Same as above.	
△	59-18	922	2.1-15.0	<8	Same as above except coating thickness 0.0055 in.	

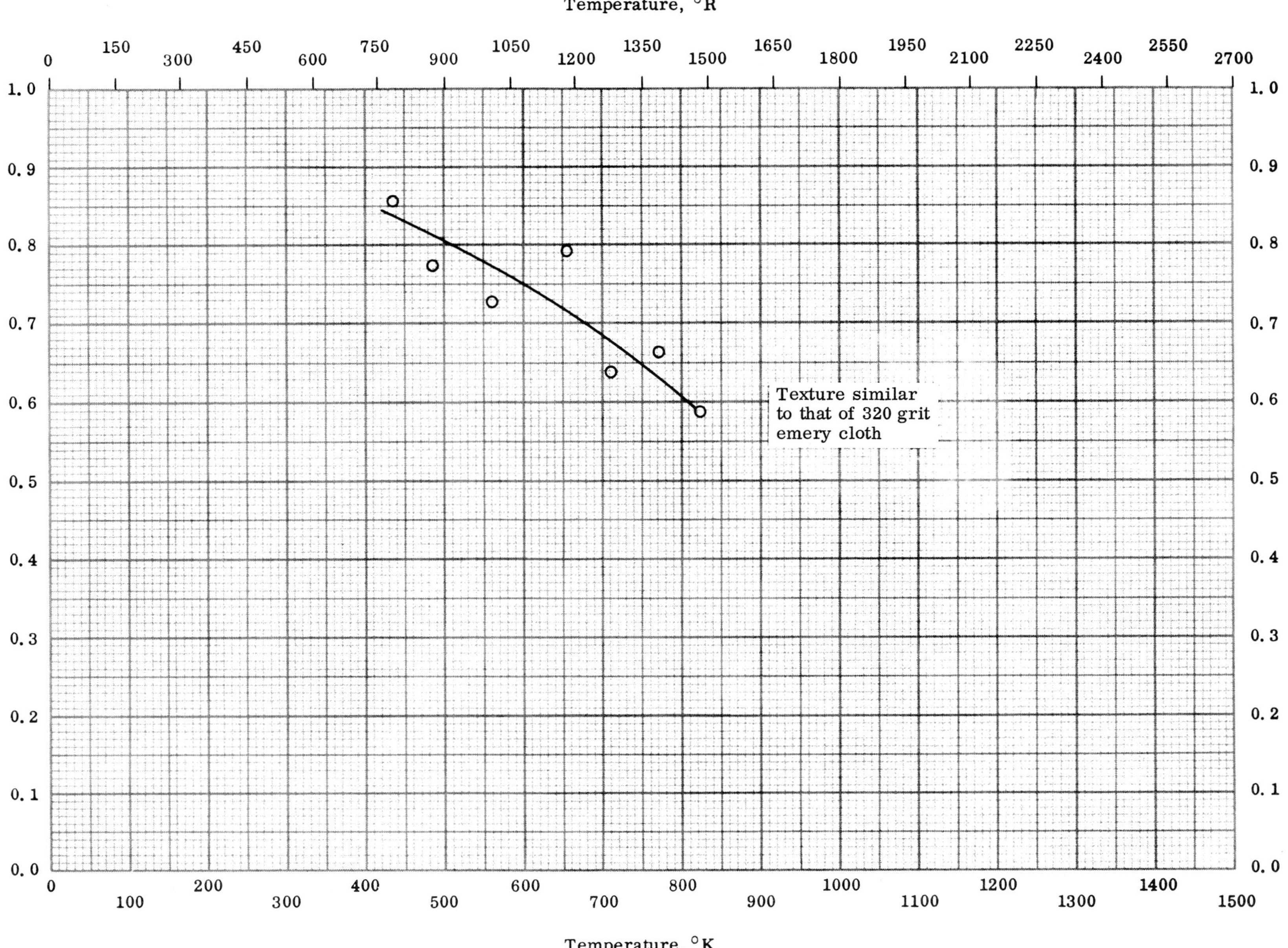

HEMISPHERICAL TOTAL EMITTANCE -- BARIUM TITANATE COATING ON NIOBIUM ALLOY

HEMISPHERICAL TOTAL EMITTANCE -- BARIUM TITANATE COATING ON NIOBIUM ALLOY

REFERENCE INFORMATION

Symbol	Ref.	Temp. Range °K	Rept. Error %	Sample Specifications	Remarks
○	63-23	434-825		BaO · TiO_2 coating; aluminum phosphate bonded to 99 Nb and 1 Zr; coating thickness 0.007 in. with texture similar to that of 320 grit emery cloth.	Measured in vacuum.

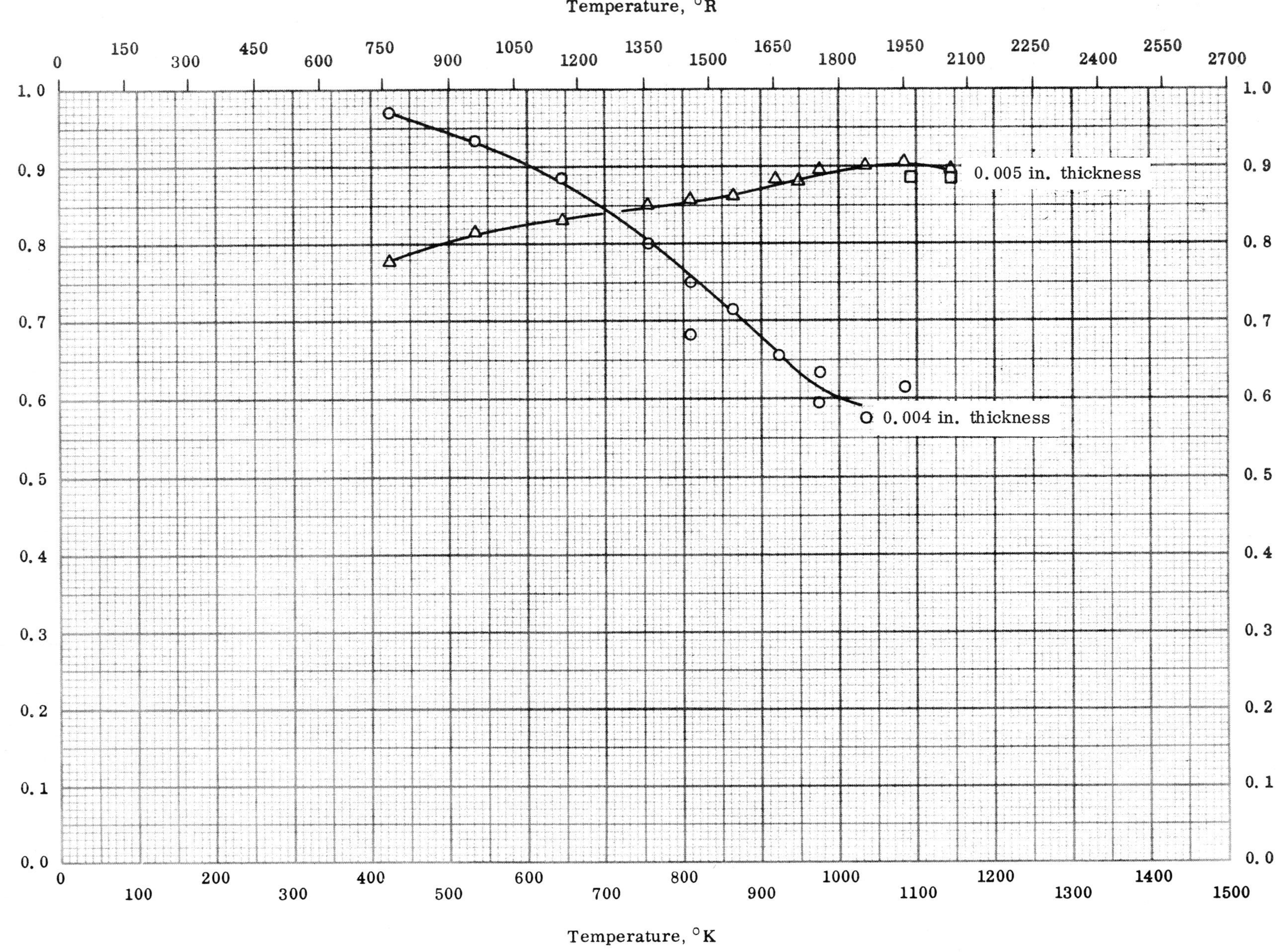

HEMISPHERICAL TOTAL EMITTANCE -- CALCIUM TITANATE COATING ON NIOBIUM ALLOYS

HEMISPHERICAL TOTAL EMITTANCE -- CALCIUM TITANATE COATING ON NIOBIUM ALLOYS

REFERENCE INFORMATION

Symbol	Ref.	Temp. Range °K	Rept. Error %	Sample Specifications	Remarks
○	63-23	421-1088		99 Nb and 1 Zr substrate; coating thickness 0.004 in. with a texture similar to that of 320 grit emery cloth.	Plasma-arc sprayed; measured in vacuum; using thermocouple.
△	63-23	422-1144		Same as above; coating thickness 0.005 in.	Same as above.
□	63-23	1094-1148		Same as above.	Same as above; using optical pyrometer.

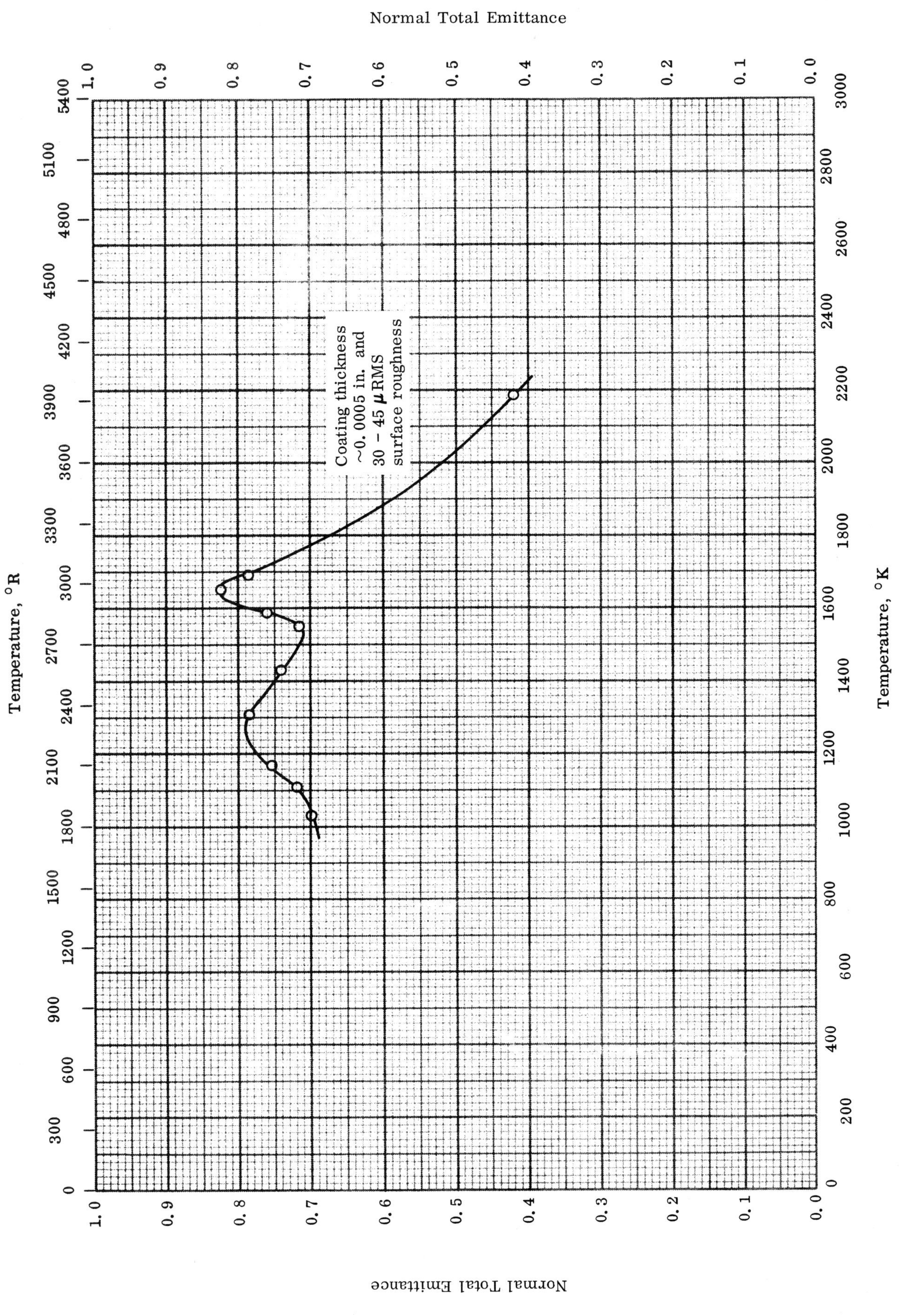

Normal Total Emittance
Temperature, °R
Temperature, °K
Coating thickness
~0.0005 in. and
30 - 45 μRMS
surface roughness
Normal Total Emittance

NORMAL TOTAL EMITTANCE -- COBALT OXIDE COATING ON TANTALUM

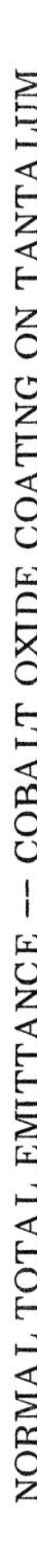

NORMAL TOTAL EMITTANCE -- COBALT OXIDE COATING ON TANTALUM

REFERENCE INFORMATION

Symbol	Ref.	Temp. Range °K	Rept. Error %	Sample Specifications	Remarks
o	63-22	1033-2188		Coating thickness ~ 0.0005 in. and surface roughness 30 - 45 μ RMS.	Plasma sprayed; measured in vacuum (3 - 4 μ Hg).

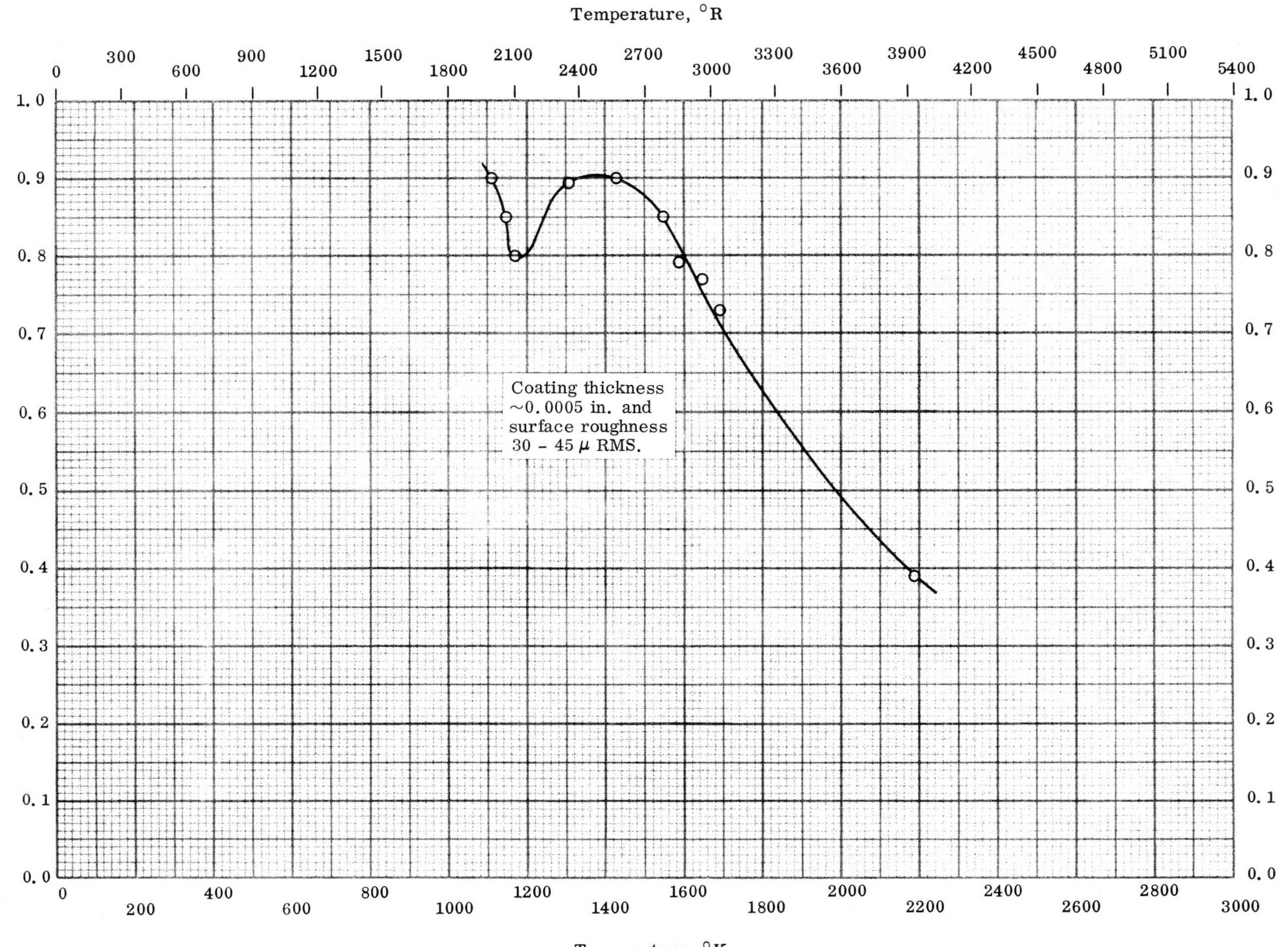

NORMAL SPECTRAL EMITTANCE -- COBALT OXIDE COATING ON TANTALUM

NORMAL SPECTRAL EMITTANCE -- COBALT OXIDE COATING ON TANTALUM

REFERENCE INFORMATION

Symbol	Ref.	Wavelength μ	Temp. Range °K	Rept. Error %	Sample Specifications	Remarks
○	63-22	0.65	1110-2188		Coating, thickness ~0.0005 in. and surface roughness 30 - 45 μ RMS.	Plasma sprayed; measured in vacuum (3 - 4 μ Hg).

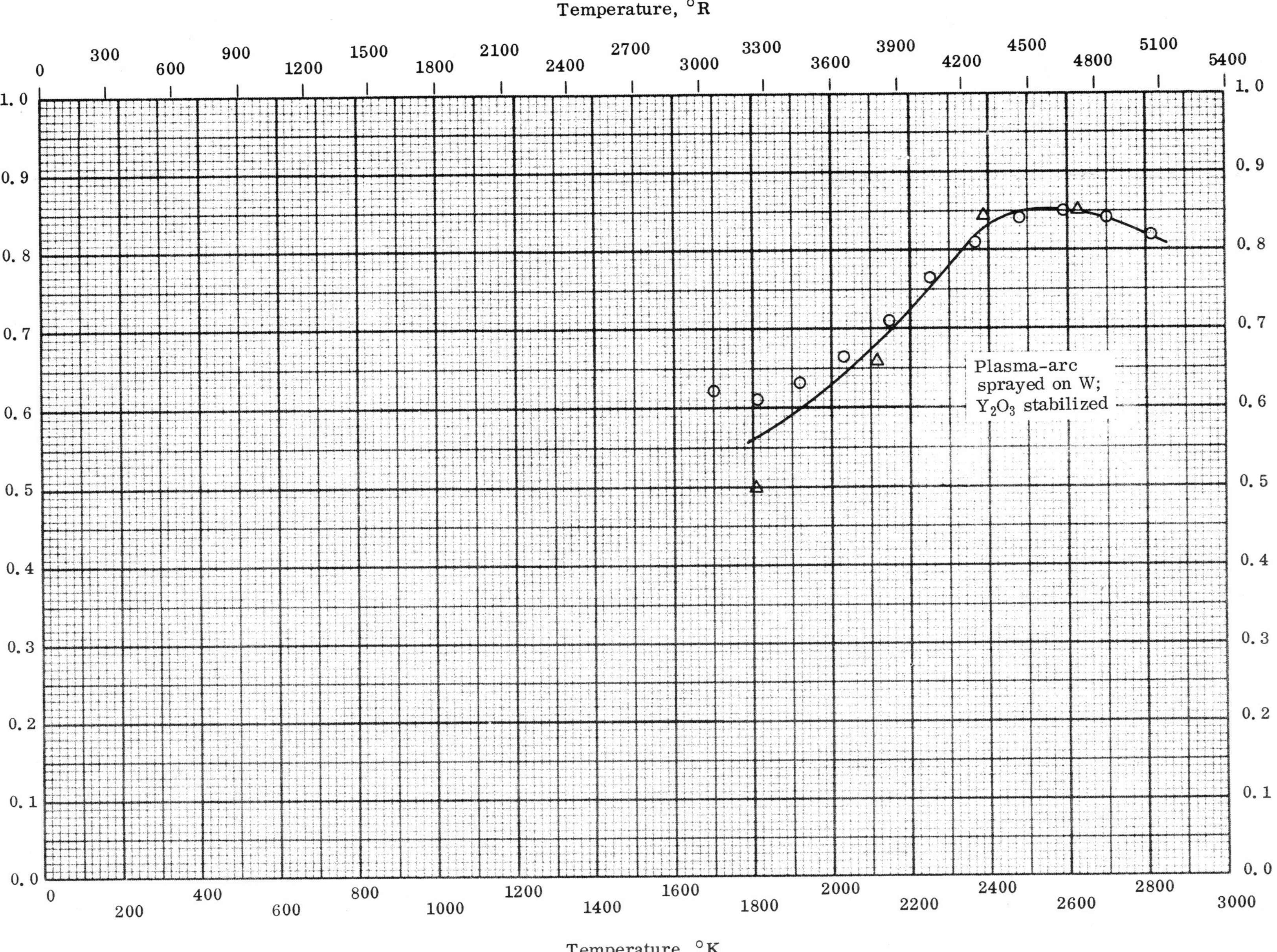

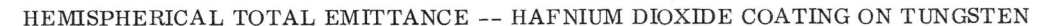

HEMISPHERICAL TOTAL EMITTANCE -- HAFNIUM DIOXIDE COATING ON TUNGSTEN

HEMISPHERICAL TOTAL EMITTANCE -- HAFNIUM DIOXIDE COATING ON TUNGSTEN

REFERENCE INFORMATION

Symbol	Ref.	Temp. Range °K	Rept. Error %	Sample Specifications	Remarks
○	63-21	1700-2700		Tungsten substrate with HfO_2 coating.	Plasma-arc sprayed and Y_2O_3 stabilized; measured in vacuum; resistometric readings.
△	63-21	1803-2622		Same as above.	Same as above; optical readings.

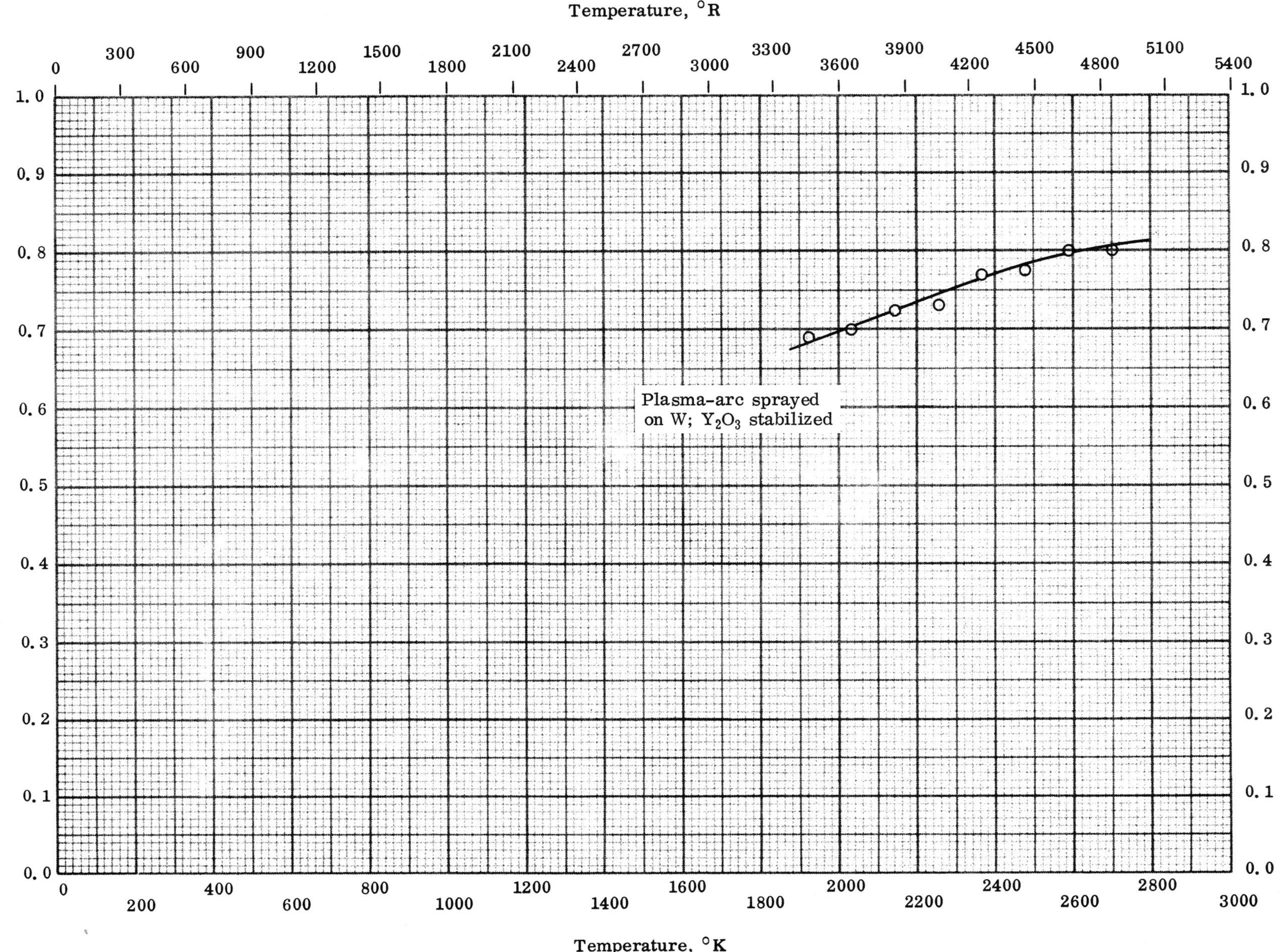

HEMISPHERICAL SPECTRAL EMITTANCE -- HAFNIUM DIOXIDE COATING ON TUNGSTEN

HEMISPHERICAL SPECTRAL EMITTANCE -- HAFNIUM DIOXIDE COATING ON TUNGSTEN

REFERENCE INFORMATION

Symbol	Ref.	Wavelength μ	Temp. Range °K	Rept. Error %	Sample Specifications	Remarks
○	63-21	0.65	1922-2700		Tungsten substrate with HfO_2 coating.	Plasma-arc sprayed and Y_2O_3 stabilized; measured in vacuum; optical readings.

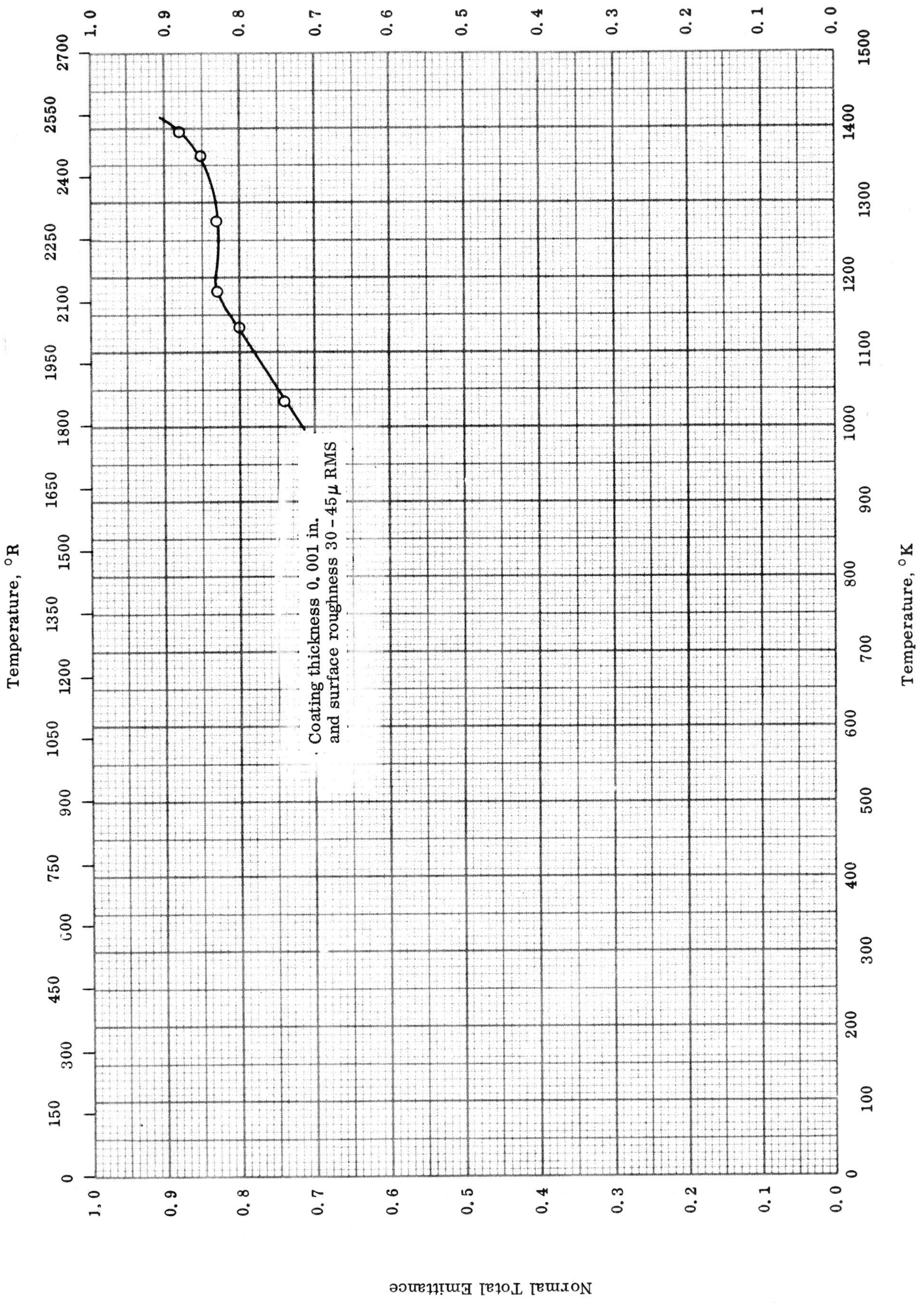

Temperature, °R

Temperature, °K

Normal Total Emittance

Coating thickness 0.001 in. and surface roughness 30 - 45 μ RMS

NORMAL TOTAL EMITTANCE -- IRON (IC) OXIDE COATING ON HAYNES ALLOY NO. 25

NORMAL TOTAL EMITTANCE -- IRON (IC) OXIDE COATING ON HAYNES ALLOY NO. 25

REFERENCE INFORMATION

Symbol	Ref.	Temp. Range °K	Rept. Error %	Sample Specifications	Remarks
○	63-22	1035-1397		Fe_2O_3 on Haynes Alloy 25 (L-605); coating thickness 0.001 in. and surface roughness 30 - 45 μ RMS.	Plasma-sprayed; measured in vacuum (3 - 4 μHg).

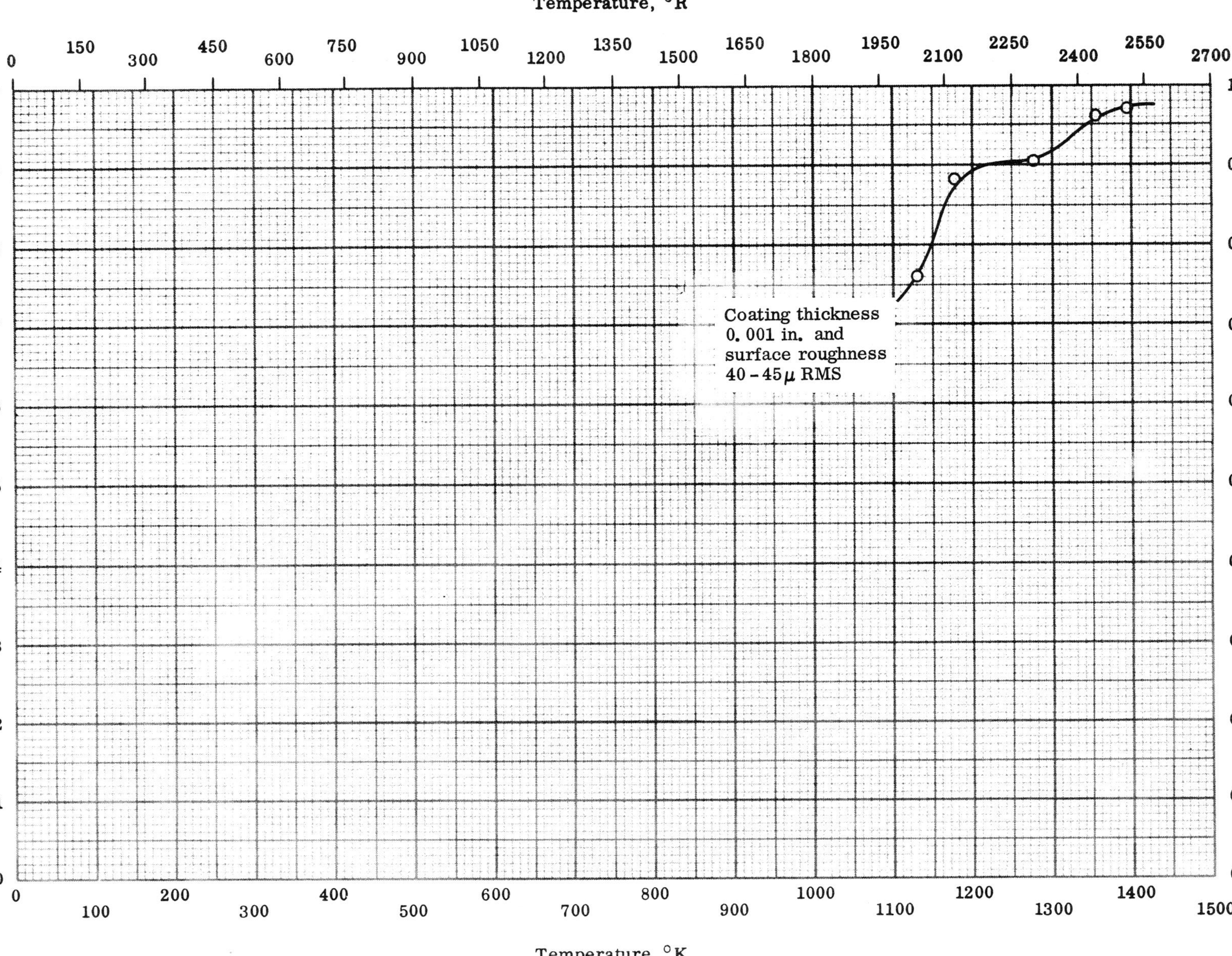

NORMAL SPECTRAL EMITTANCE -- IRON (IC) OXIDE COATING ON HAYNES ALLOY NO. 25

NORMAL SPECTRAL EMITTANCE -- IRON (IC) OXIDE COATING ON HAYNES ALLOY NO. 25

REFERENCE INFORMATION

Symbol	Ref.	Wavelength μ	Temp. Range °K	Rept. Error %	Sample Specifications	Remarks
○	63-22	0.65	1133-1394		Fe_2O_3 on Haynes Alloy 25 (L-605); coating thickness 0.001 in. and surface roughness 30 - 45 μ RMS.	Plasma-sprayed; measured in vacuum (3 - 4 μ Hg).

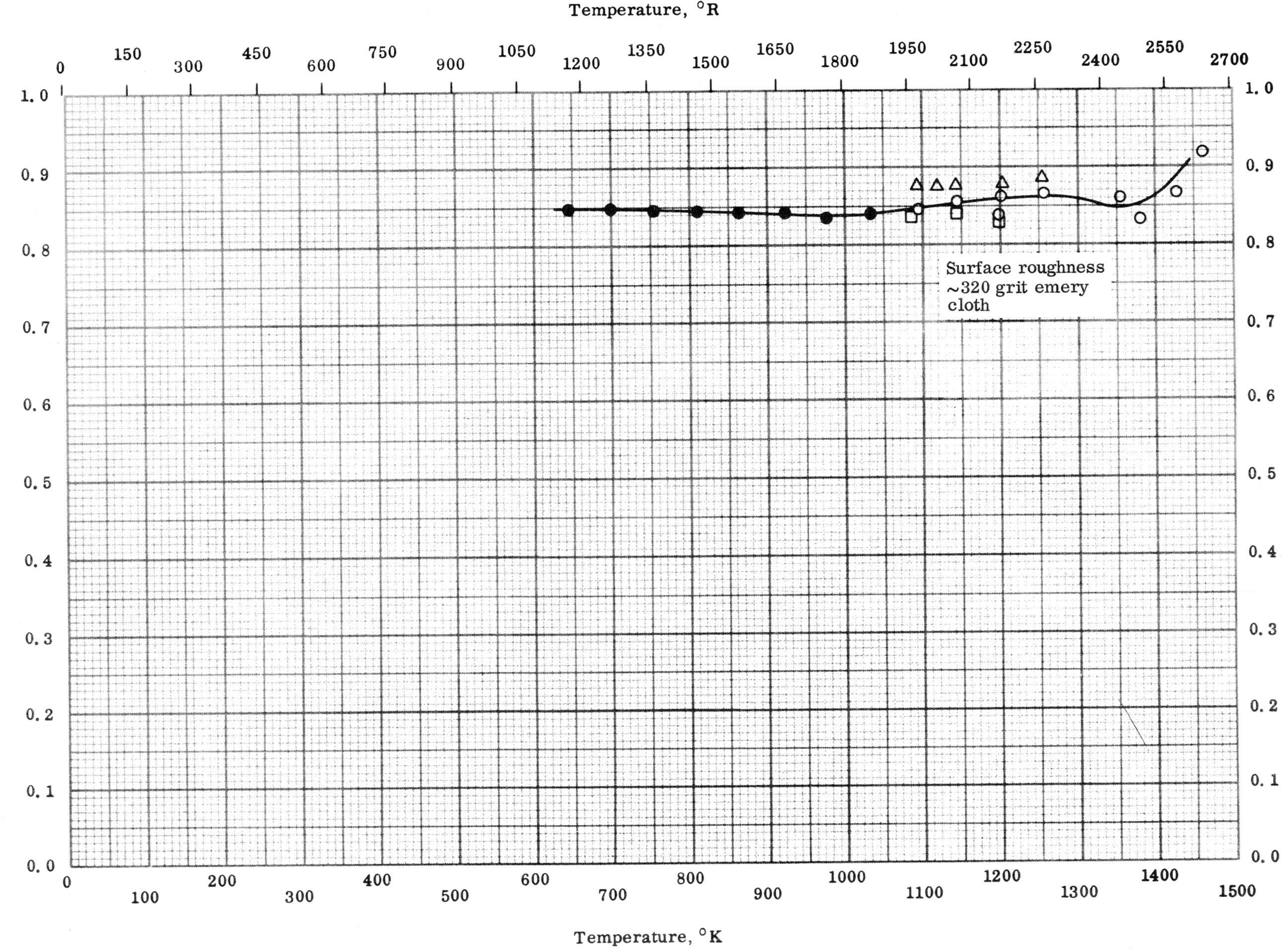

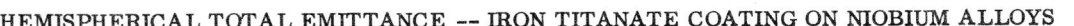

HEMISPHERICAL TOTAL EMITTANCE -- IRON TITANATE COATING ON NIOBIUM ALLOYS

HEMISPHERICAL TOTAL EMITTANCE -- IRON TITANATE COATING ON NIOBIUM ALLOYS

REFERENCE INFORMATION

Symbol	Ref.	Temp. Range °K	Rept. Error %	Sample Specifications	Remarks
○	63-23	1097-1462		99 Nb and 1 Zr substrate; surface roughness equivalent to that of 320 grit emery cloth; coating thickness 0.005 in.	Plasma-arc sprayed; measured in vacuum.
△	63-23	1092-1257		Same as above except coating thickness 0.002 in.	Same as above.
□	63-23	1088-1200		Same as above except coating thickness 0.004 in.	Same as above.
●	63-23	644-1199		Same as above.	Same as above.

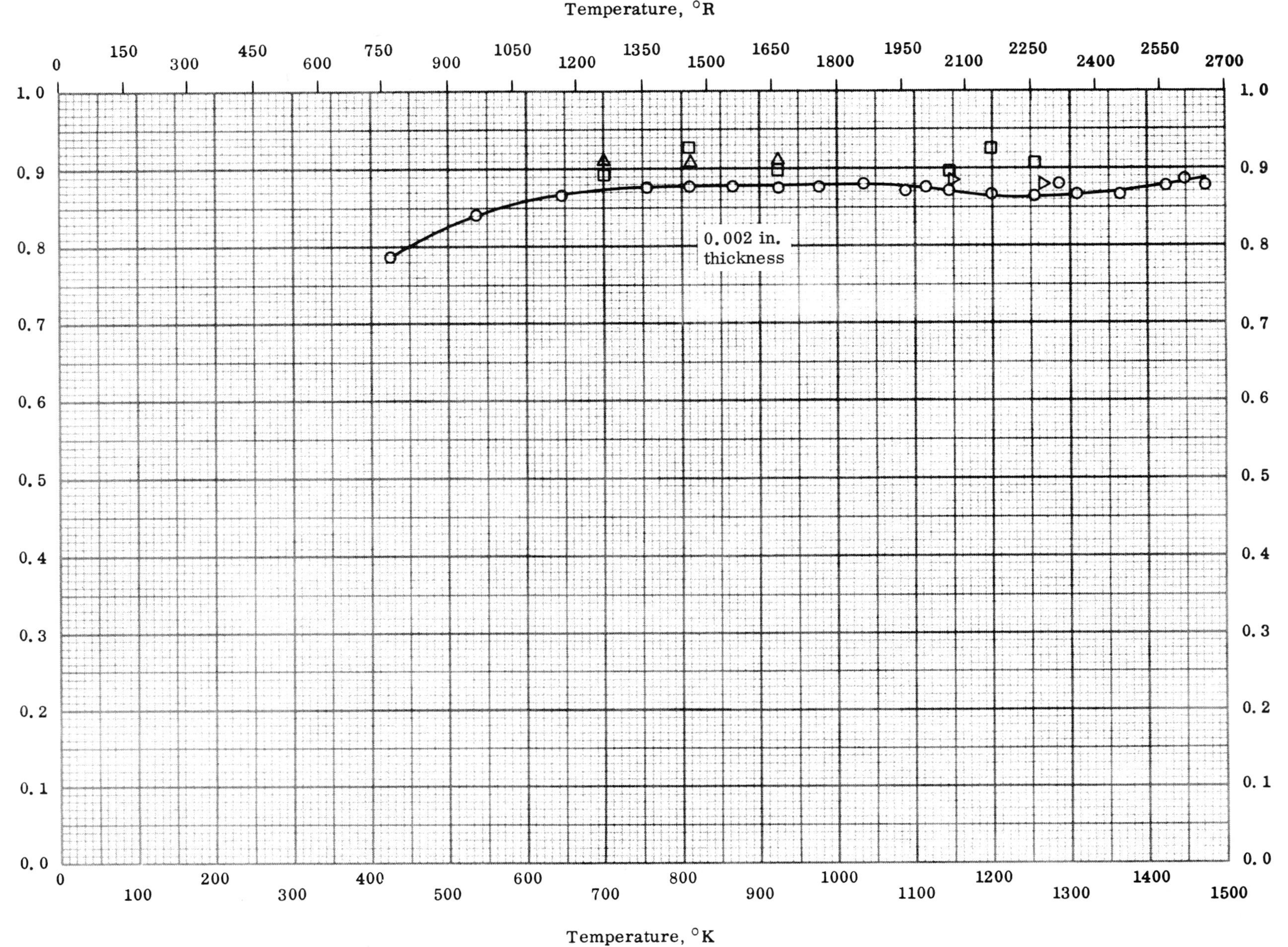

HEMISPHERICAL TOTAL EMITTANCE -- NICKEL CHROME SPINEL COATING ON NIOBIUM ALLOY

HEMISPHERICAL TOTAL EMITTANCE -- NICKEL CHROME SPINEL COATING ON NIOBIUM ALLOY

REFERENCE INFORMATION

Symbol	Ref.	Temp. Range °K	Rept. Error %	Sample Specifications	Remarks
○	63-23	422-1477		Spinel ($NiO \cdot Cr_2O_3$) on 99 Nb and 1 Zr alloy; coating thickness 0.002 in. with matte texture similar to that of 240 grit emery cloth.	Plasma-arc spray; measured in vacuum; using thermocouple.
△	63-23	699-922		Same as above, coating thickness 0.004 in.	Same as above; first run.
□	63-23	699-1255		Same as above.	Same as above; second run.
▷	63-23	1148-1264		Same as above.	Same as above; using optical pyrometer.

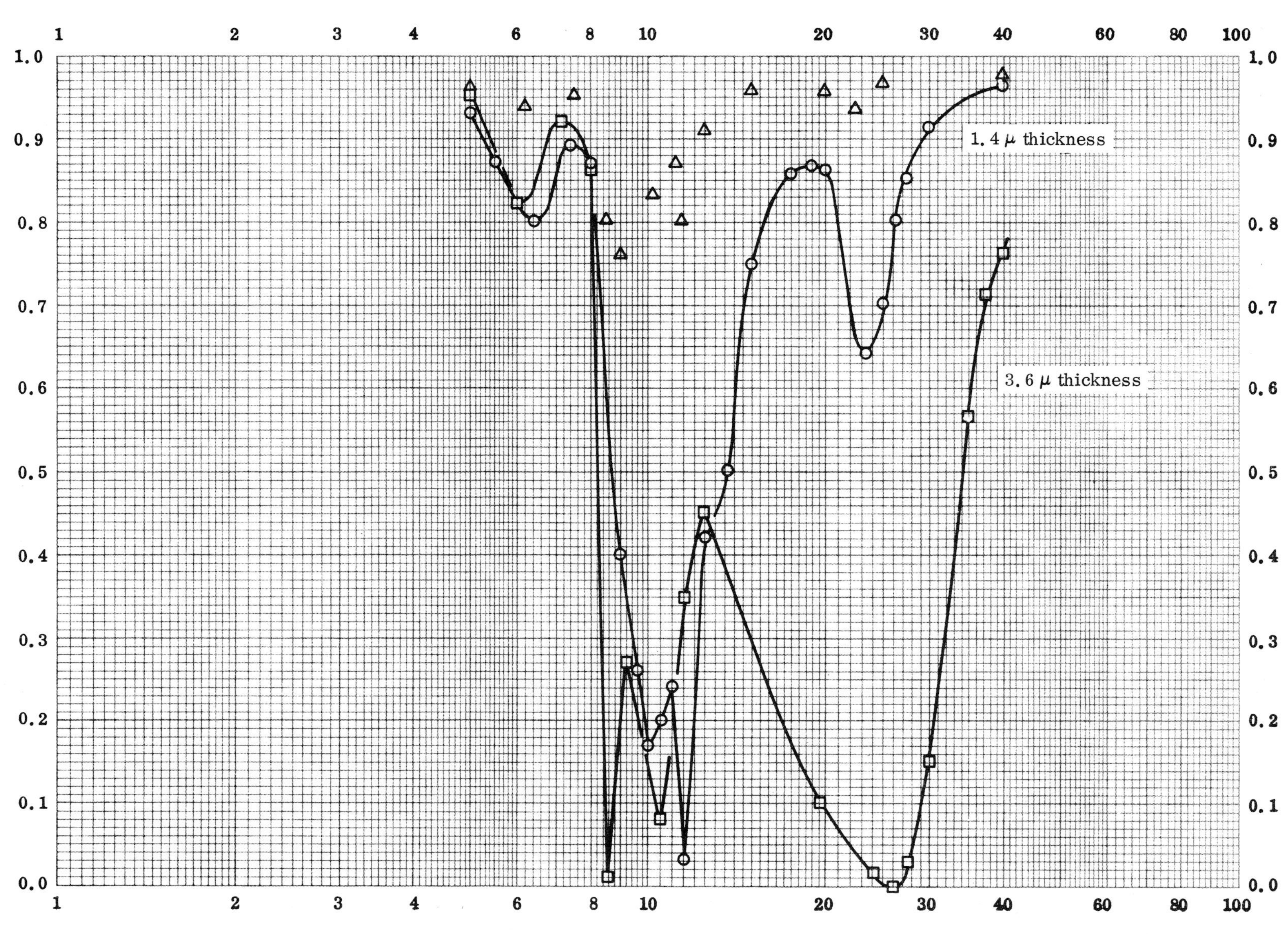

NORMAL SPECTRAL REFLECTANCE -- SILICON MONOXIDE COATING ON ALUMINUM

NORMAL SPECTRAL REFLECTANCE -- SILICON MONOXIDE COATING ON ALUMINUM

REFERENCE INFORMATION

Symbol	Ref.	Temp. °K	Wavelength Range, μ	Rept. Error %	Sample Specifications	Remarks
○	64-12	298	5-40		Strongly oxidized SiO on Al substrate; coating thickness 1.4 μ.	Evaporated; normal incidence, hemispherical viewing; data taken from smooth curve.
△	64-12	298	5-40		Same as above, coating thickness 0.7 μ.	Same as above.
□	64-12	298	5-40		Same as above, coating thickness 3.6 μ.	Same as above.

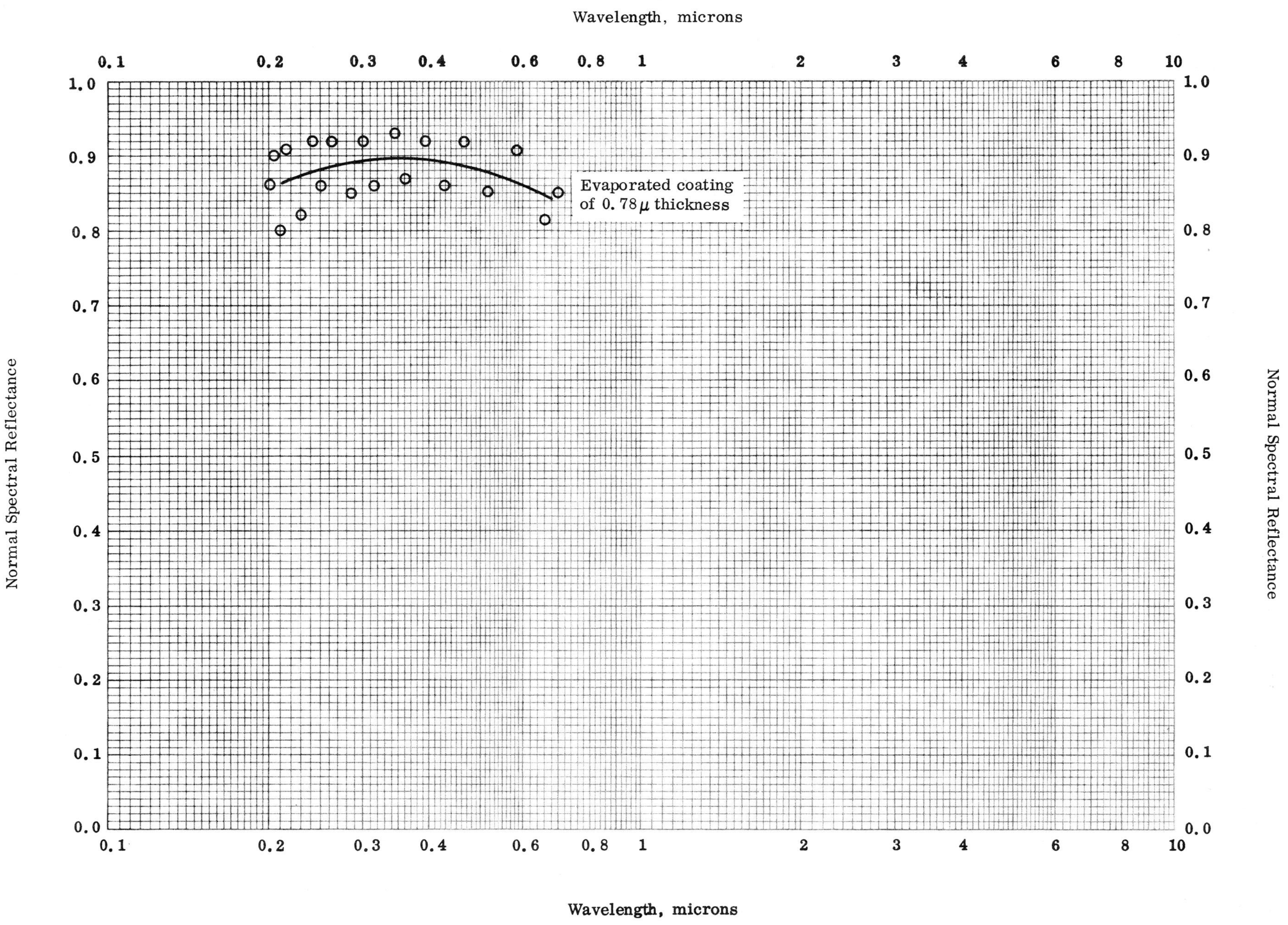

Wavelength, microns

Normal Spectral Reflectance

Evaporated coating of 0.78 μ thickness

Wavelength, microns

NORMAL SPECTRAL REFLECTANCE -- SILICON DIOXIDE COATING ON ALUMINUM

NORMAL SPECTRAL REFLECTANCE -- SILICON DIOXIDE COATING ON ALUMINUM

REFERENCE INFORMATION

Symbol	Ref.	Temp. °K	Wavelength Range, μ	Rept. Error %	Sample Specifications	Remarks
○	64-12	298	0.2-0.7		SiO_2 on aluminum; coating thickness 0.78 μ.	Evaporated; normal incidence, hemispherical viewing; data taken from smooth curve.

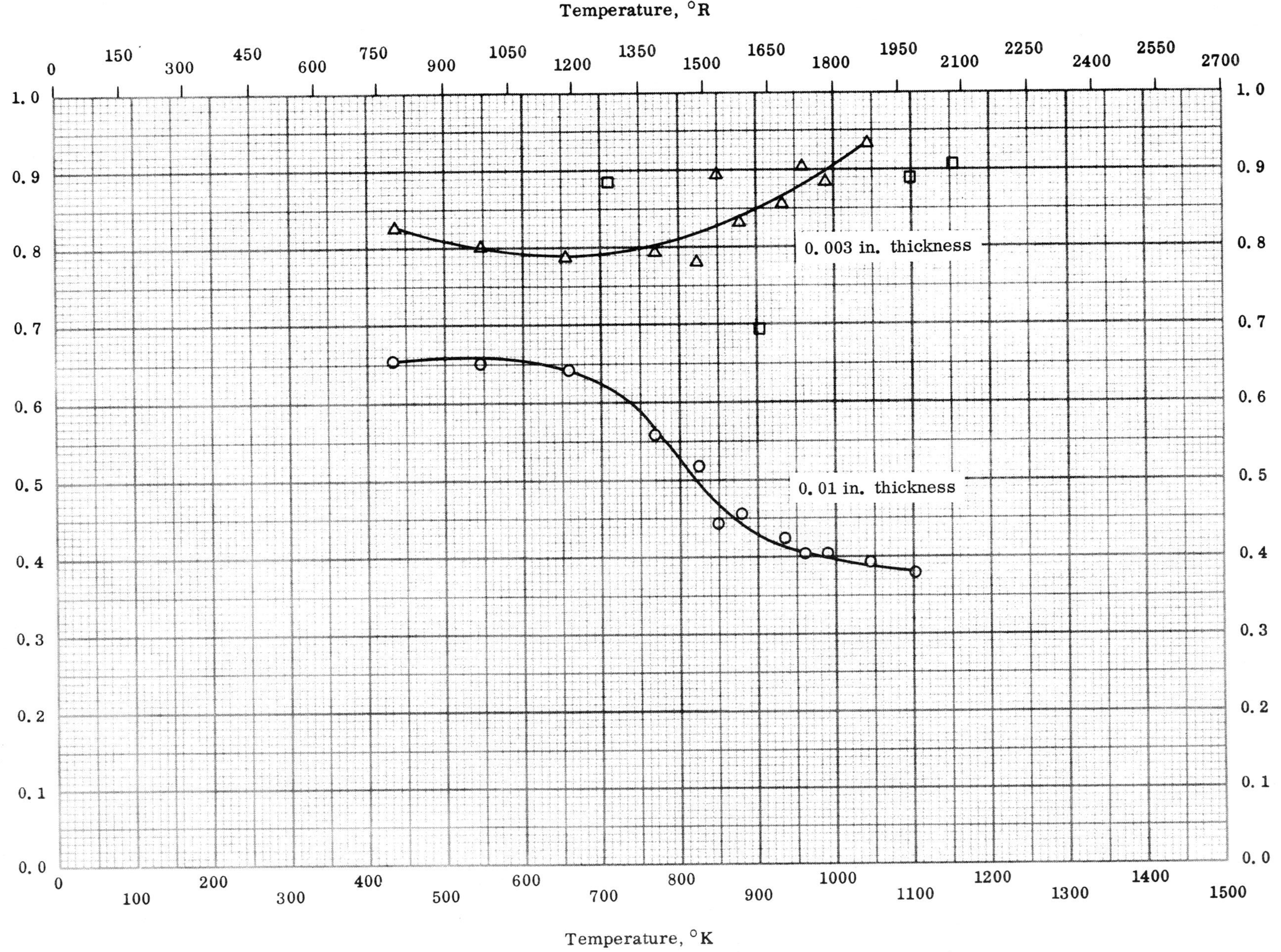

HEMISPHERICAL TOTAL EMITTANCE -- STRONTIUM TITANATE COATING ON STAINLESS STEEL

HEMISPHERICAL TOTAL EMITTANCE -- STRONTIUM TITANATE COATING ON STAINLESS STEEL

REFERENCE INFORMATION

Symbol	Ref.	Temp. Range °K	Rept. Error %	Sample Specifications	Remarks
○	63-23	434-1102		Commercial grade strontium titanate; aluminum-phosphate bonded to AISI-310 stainless steel, coating thickness 0.01 in. with a texture of 40 grit emery cloth.	Measured in vacuum; using thermocouple.
△	63-23	434-1101		High purity grade of strontium titanate on AISI-310 stainless steel; coating thickness 0.003 in. with a texture equivalent to that of 80 grit emery cloth.	Plasma-arc sprayed; same as above; first run.
□	63-23	710-1156		Same as above.	Same as above; second run.

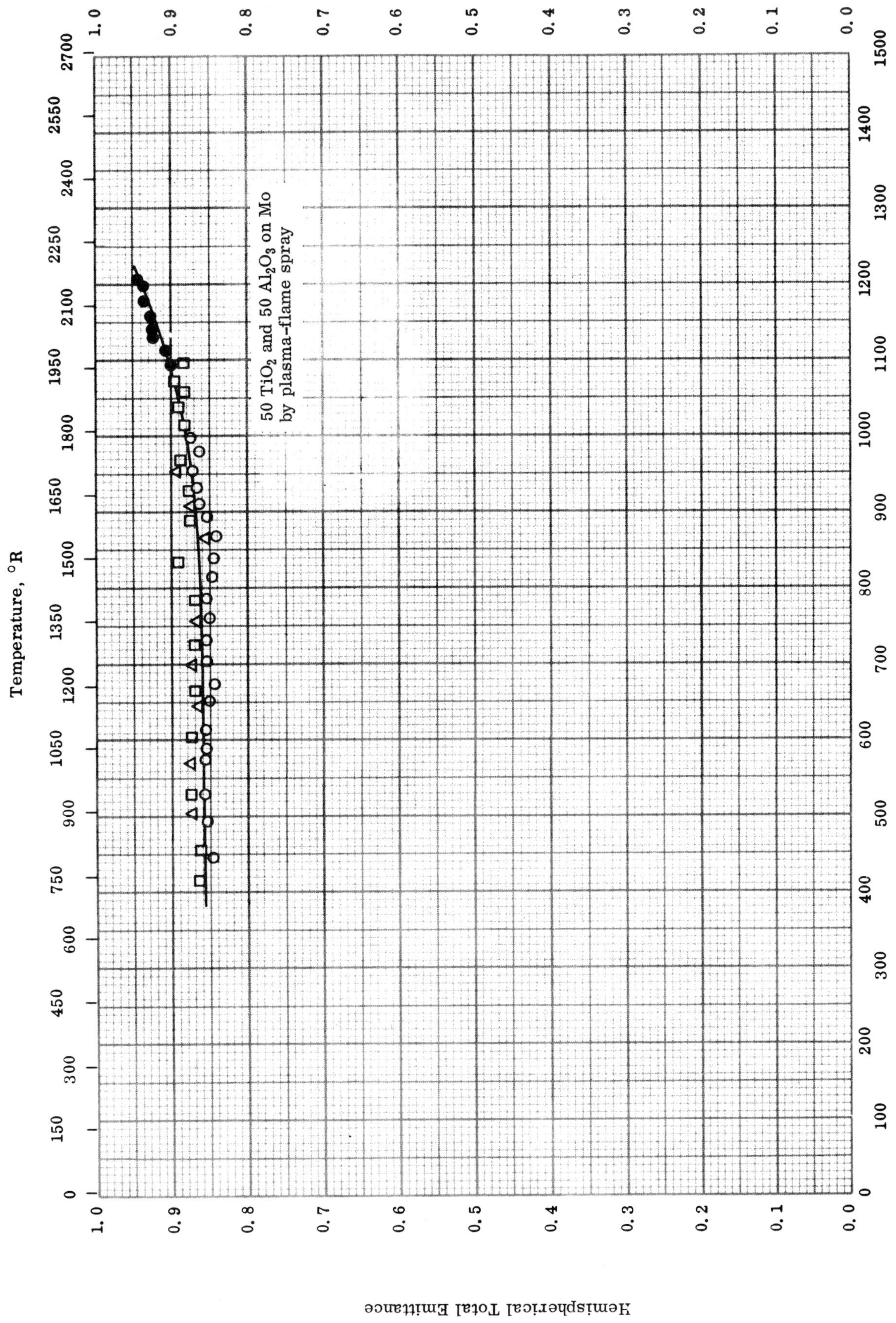

Temperature, °R

50 TiO_2 and 50 Al_2O_3 on Mo by plasma-flame spray

Hemispherical Total Emittance

Temperature, °K

HEMISPHERICAL TOTAL EMITTANCE -- TITANIUM DIOXIDE AND ALUMINUM OXIDE COATING ON MOLYBDENUM

HEMISPHERICAL TOTAL EMITTANCE -- TITANIUM DIOXIDE AND ALUMINUM OXIDE COATING ON MOLYBDENUM

REFERENCE INFORMATION

Symbol	Ref.	Temp. Range °K	Rept. Error %	Sample Specifications	Remarks
○	60-25	447-1000		50 TiO_2 and 50 Al_2O_3 coating on molybdenum strip; coating thickness 0.0024 in.	Coated by plasma-flame spray process; measured in vacuum; run No. 1.
△	60-25	954-502		Same as above.	Same as above; run No. 2A.
□	60-25	418-1099		Same as above.	Same as above; run No. 2B.
●	60-25	1094-1210		Same as above.	Same as above; run No. 2C.

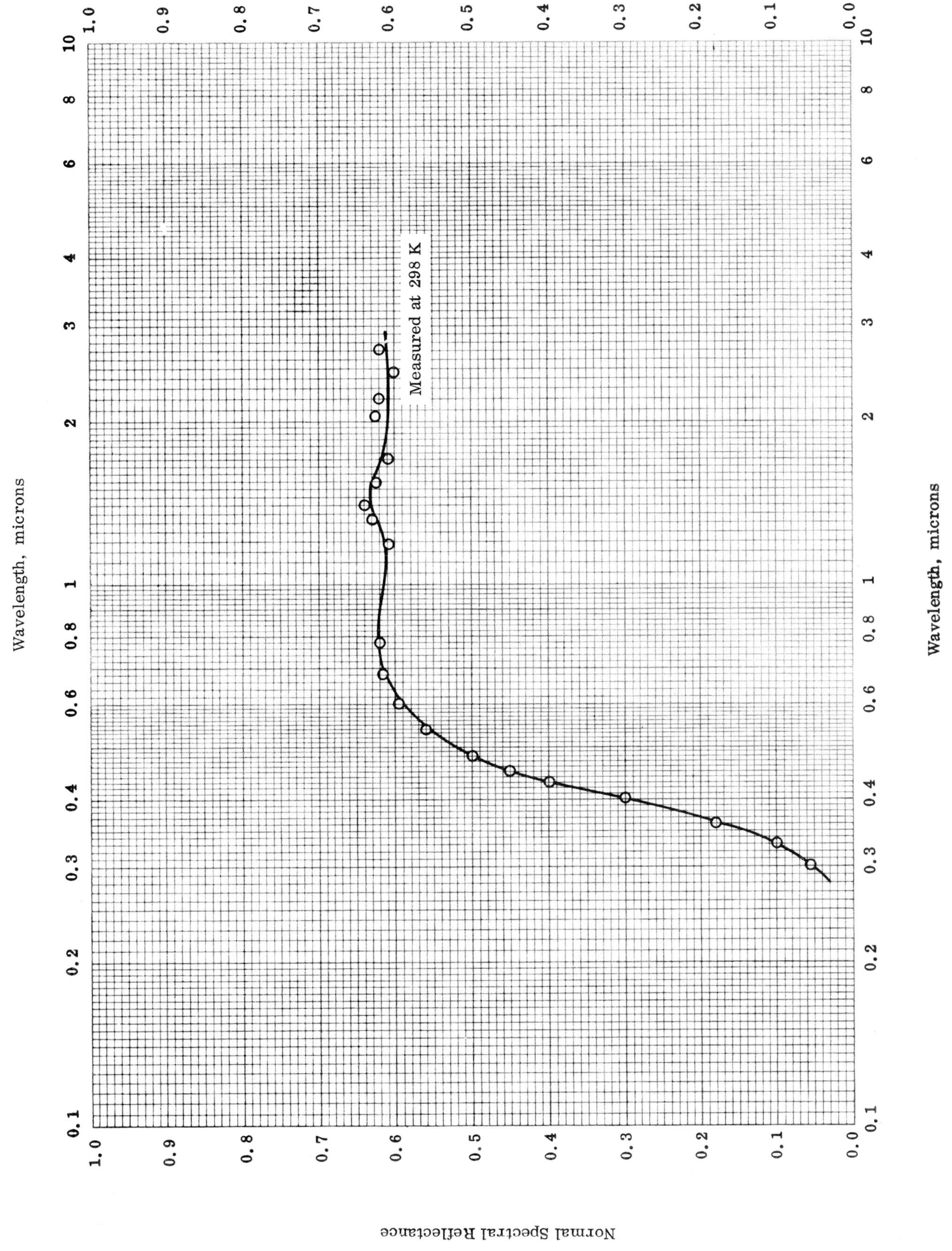

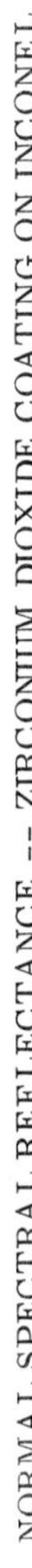

Wavelength, microns

Normal Spectral Reflectance

Measured at 298 K

NORMAL SPECTRAL REFLECTANCE -- ZIRCONIUM DIOXIDE COATING ON INCONEL

REFERENCE INFORMATION

Symbol	Ref.	Temp. °K	Wavelength Range, μ	Rept. Error %	Sample Specifications	Remarks
○	59-19	298	0.3-2.71	4	Flame sprayed on Inconel.	Data taken from smooth curve; Mg CO_2, as reference standard; normal incidence, hemispherical viewing.

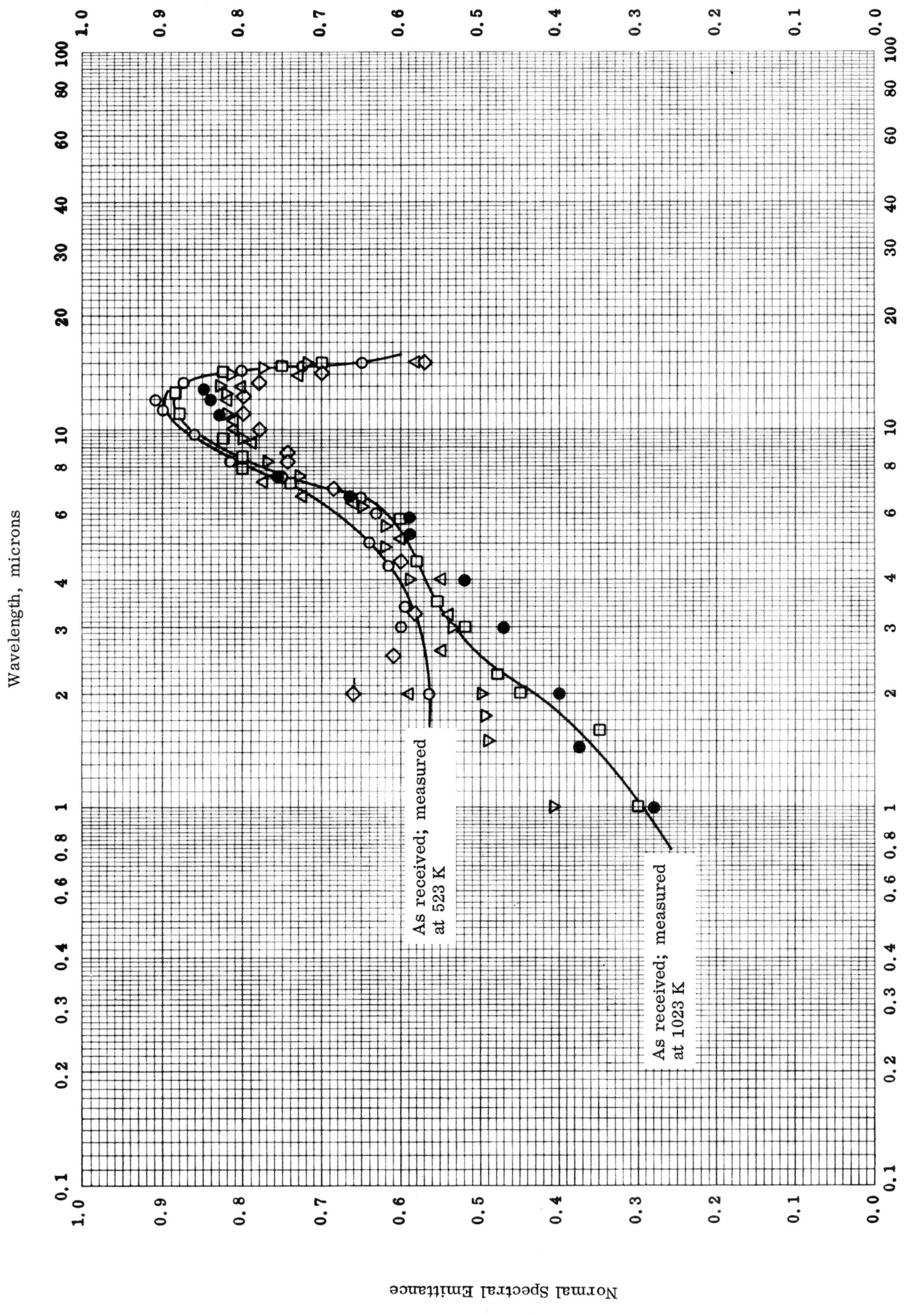

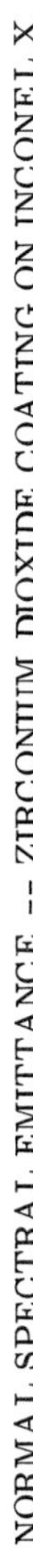

Normal Spectral Emittance
Wavelength, microns
As received; measured at 523 K
As received; measured at 1023 K
0.1 0.2 0.3 0.4 0.6 0.8 1 2 3 4 6 8 10 20 30 40 60 80 100
0.0 0.1 0.2 0.3 0.4 0.5 0.6 0.7 0.8 0.9 1.0

NORMAL SPECTRAL EMITTANCE -- ZIRCONIUM DIOXIDE COATING ON INCONEL X

NORMAL SPECTRAL EMITTANCE -- ZIRCONIUM DIOXIDE COATING ON INCONEL X

REFERENCE INFORMATION

Symbol	Ref.	Temp. °K	Wavelength Range, μ	Rept. Error %	Sample Specifications	Remarks
○	62-34	523	2-15		ZrO_2 flame sprayed on sandblasted Inconel X by using a Plasmatron.	As received; data taken from smooth curve.
□	62-34	1023	1-15		Same as above.	Same as above; different specimen.
△	62-34	523	2-15		Same as above.	Heated in air at 1089 K for 30 min.; data taken from smooth curve.
▽	62-34	1023	1-15		Same as above.	Same as above.
◇	62-34	523	2-15		Same as above.	Heated in vacuum (6.8 x 10^{-5} mm Hg) at 1089 K for 30 min.; data taken from smooth curve.
●	62-34	1023	1-15		Same as above.	Same as above.

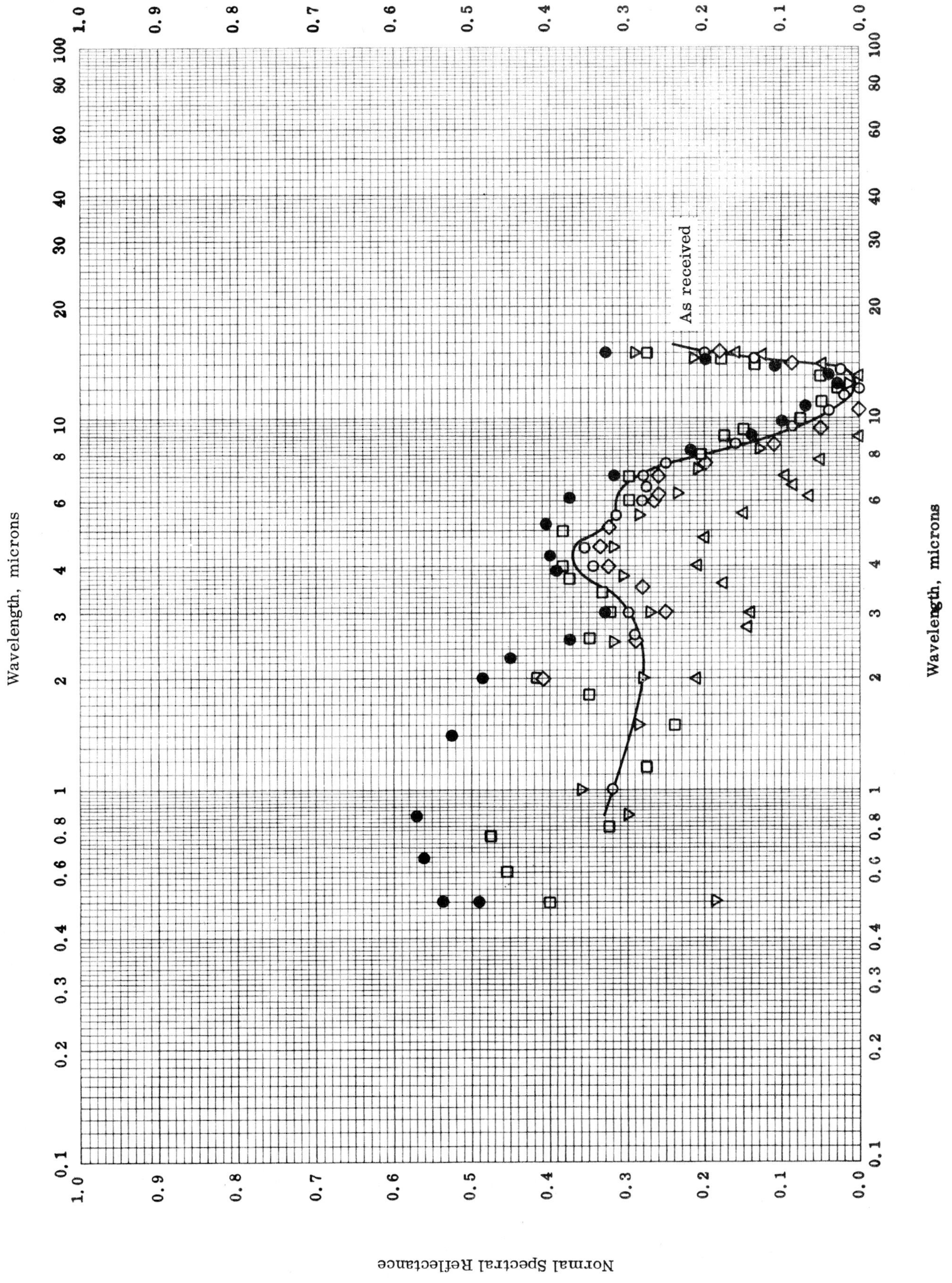

NORMAL SPECTRAL REFLECTANCE -- ZIRCONIUM DIOXIDE COATING ON INCONEL X

NORMAL SPECTRAL REFLECTANCE -- ZIRCONIUM DIOXIDE COATING ON INCONEL X

REFERENCE INFORMATION

Symbol	Ref.	Temp. °K	Wavelength Range, μ	Rept. Error %	Sample Specifications	Remarks
○	62-34	<322	1-15	<±2	ZrO_2 flame sprayed on sandblasted Inconel X using a Plasmatron.	As received; data taken from smooth curve; hemispherical illumination, normal viewing; 523 K source temperature.
□	62-34	<322	0.5-15	<±2	Same as above.	Same as above; 1273 K source temperature.
△	62-34	<322	2-15	<±2	Same as above.	Heated in vacuum (6.8×10^{-5} mm Hg) at 1089 K for 30 min.; data taken from smoth curve; hemispherical illumination, normal viewing; 523 K source temperature.
▽	62-34	<322	0.5-15	<±2	Same as above.	Same as above; 1273 K source temperature.
◇	62-34	<322	2-15	<±2	Same as above.	Heated in air at 1089 K for 30 min.; data taken from smooth curve; hemispherical illumination, normal viewing; 523 K source temperature.
●	62-34	<322	0.5-15	<±2	Same as above.	Same as above; 1273 K source temperature.

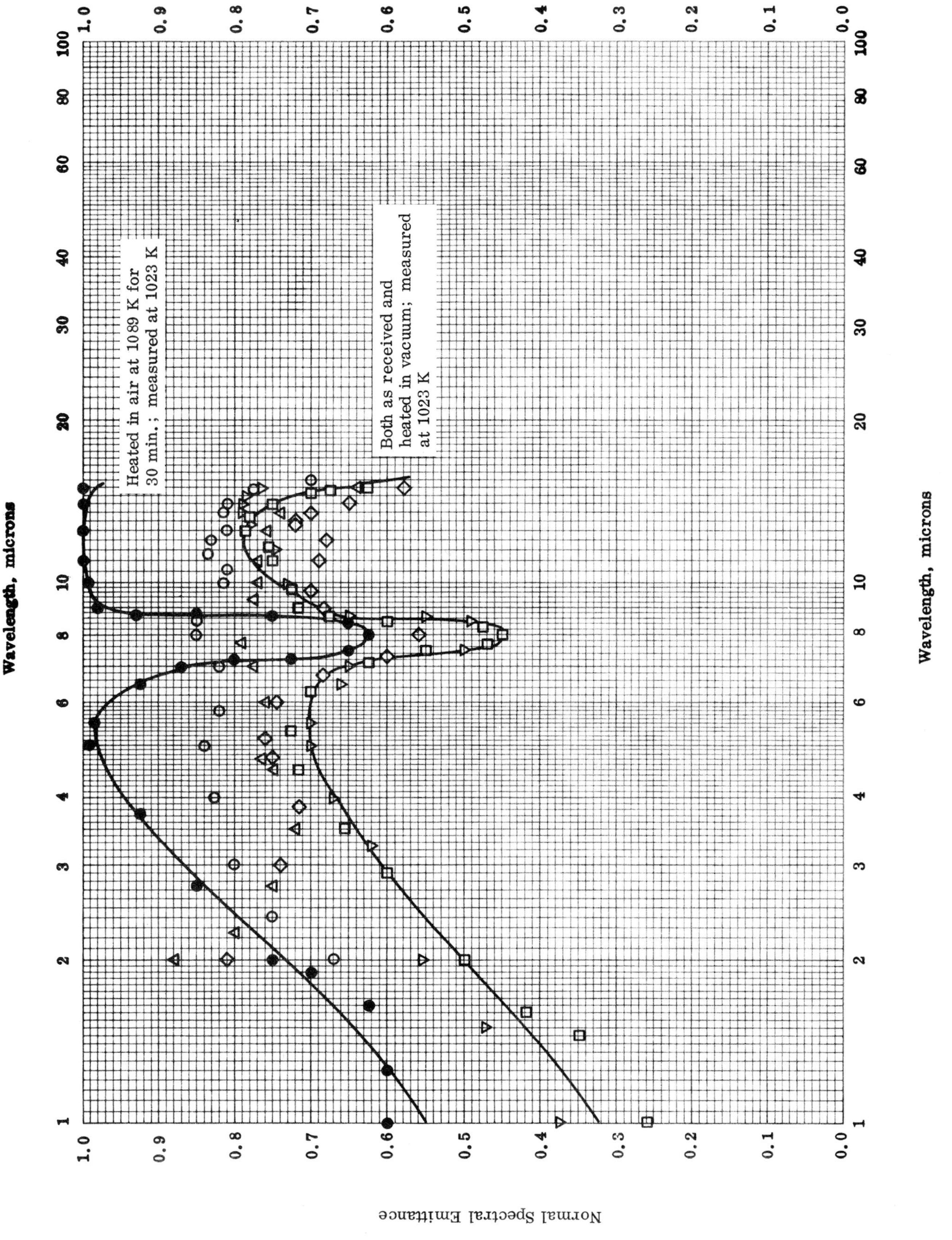

Wavelength, microns

Normal Spectral Emittance

Heated in air at 1089 K for 30 min.; measured at 1023 K

Both as received and heated in vacuum; measured at 1023 K

NORMAL SPECTRAL EMITTANCE -- BORON CARBIDE COATING ON INCONEL X

NORMAL SPECTRAL EMITTANCE -- BORON CARBIDE COATING ON INCONEL X

REFERENCE INFORMATION

Symbol	Ref.	Temp. °K	Wavelength Range, μ	Rept. Error %	Sample Specifications	Remarks
○	62-34	523	2-15		B_4C flame sprayed on sandblasted Inconel X using a Plasmatron.	As received; data taken from smooth curve.
□	62-34	1023	1-15		Same as above.	Same as above; different specimen.
△	62-34	523	2-15		Same as above.	Heated in vacuum (6.8×10^{-5} mm Hg) at 1089 K for 30 min.; data taken from smooth curve.
▽	62-34	1023	1-15		Same as above.	Same as above.
◇	62-34	523	2-15		Same as above.	Heated in air at 1089 K for 30 min.; data taken from smooth curve.
●	62-34	1023	1-15		Same as above.	Same as above.

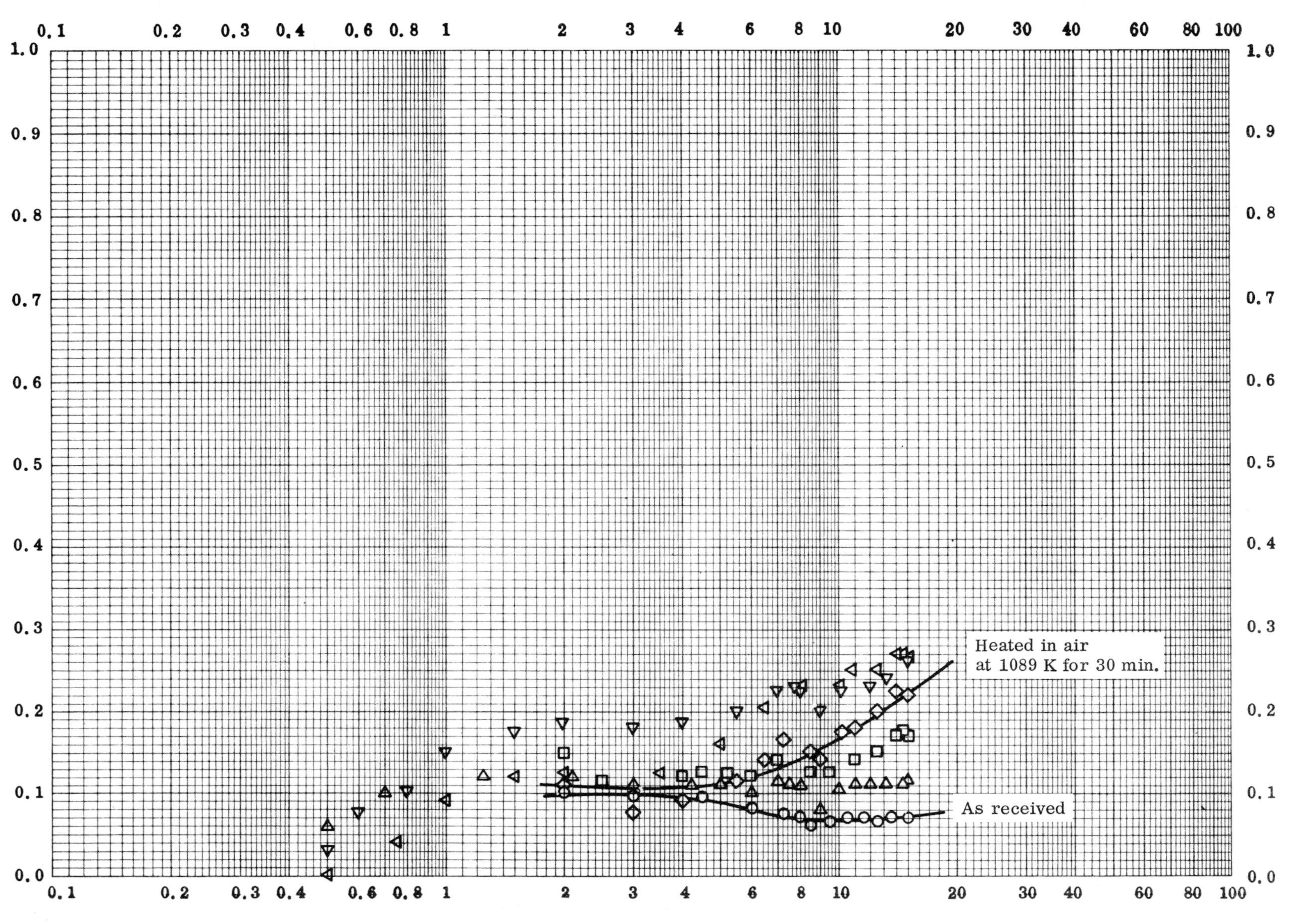

NORMAL SPECTRAL REFLECTANCE -- BORON CARBIDE COATING ON INCONEL X

NORMAL SPECTRAL REFLECTANCE -- BORON CARBIDE COATING ON INCONEL X

REFERENCE INFORMATION

Symbol	Ref.	Temp. °K	Wavelength Range, μ	Rept. Error %	Sample Specifications	Remarks
○	62-34	<322	2-15	<± 2	B_4C flame sprayed on sandblasted Inconel X using a Plasmatron.	As received; data taken from smooth curve; hemispherical illumination, normal viewing; 523 K source temperature.
△	62-34	<322	0.5-15	<± 2	Same as above.	Same as above; 1273 K source temperature.
□	62-34	<322	2-15	<± 2	Same as above.	Heated in vacuum (6.8×10^{-5} mm Hg) at 1089 K for 30 min.; data taken from smooth curve; hemispherical illumination, normal viewing; 523 K source temperature.
▽	62-34	<322	0.5-15	<± 2	Same as above.	Same as above; 1273 K source temperature.
◇	62-34	<322	2-15	<± 2	Same as above.	Heated in air at 1089 K for 30 min.; data taken from smooth curve; hemispherical illumination, normal viewing; 523 K source temperature.
◁	62-34	<322	0.5-15	<± 2	Same as above.	Same as above; 1273 K source temperature.

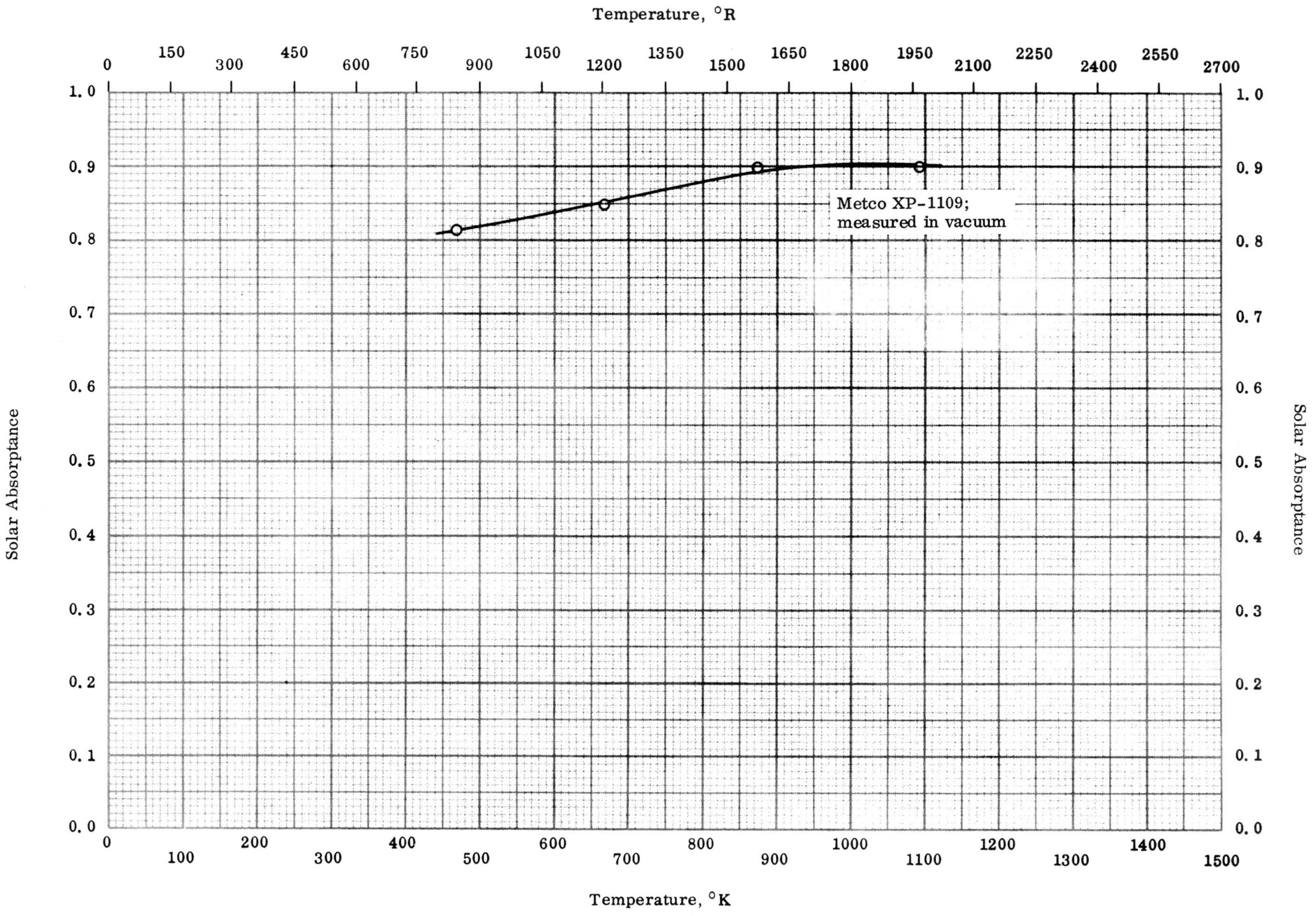

SOLAR ABSORPTANCE -- CHROMIUM CARBIDE - COBALT BLEND COATING ON ARMCO IRON

SOLAR ABSORPTANCE -- CHROMIUM CARBIDE - COBALT BLEND COATING ON ARMCO IRON

REFERENCE INFORMATION

Symbol	Ref.	Temp. Range °K	Rept. Error %	Sample Specifications	Remarks
○	61-24	468-1093	≤10	60 Chromium carbide - cobalt blend, Metco XP-1109, coating.	Substrate finely ground, plasma flame sprayed; measured in vacuum (10^{-5} mm Hg) .

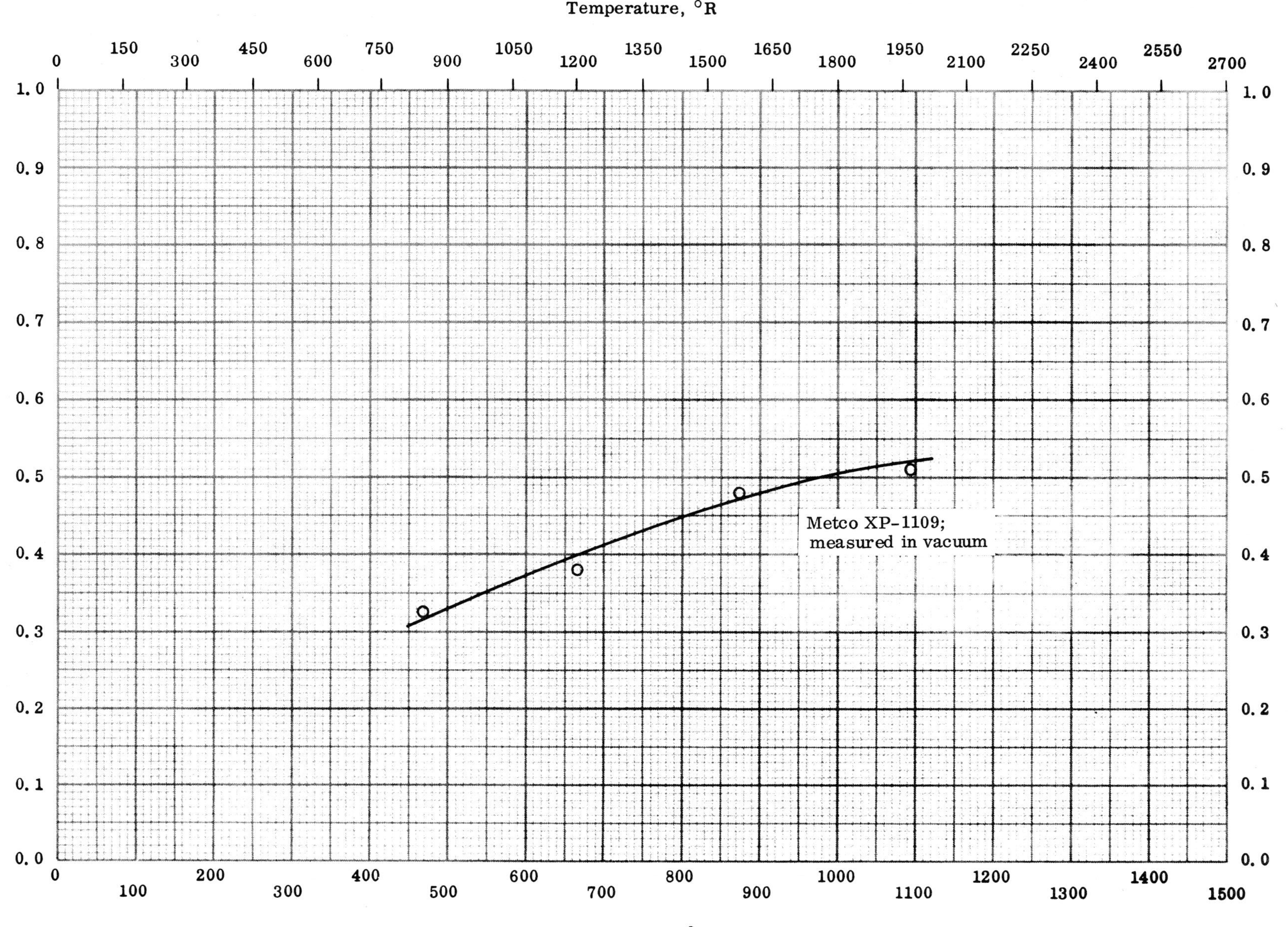

HEMISPHERICAL TOTAL EMITTANCE -- CHROMIUM CARBIDE - COBALT BLEND COATING ON ARMCO IRON

HEMISPHERICAL TOTAL EMITTANCE -- CHROMIUM CARBIDE - COBALT BLEND COATING ON ARMCO IRON

REFERENCE INFORMATION

Symbol	Ref.	Temp. Range °K	Rept. Error %	Sample Specifications	Remarks
O	61-24	468-1093	≤ 10	60 Chromium carbide - cobalt blend, Metco XP-1109, coating.	Substrate finely ground; plasma flame sprayed; measured in vacuum (10^{-5} mm Hg).

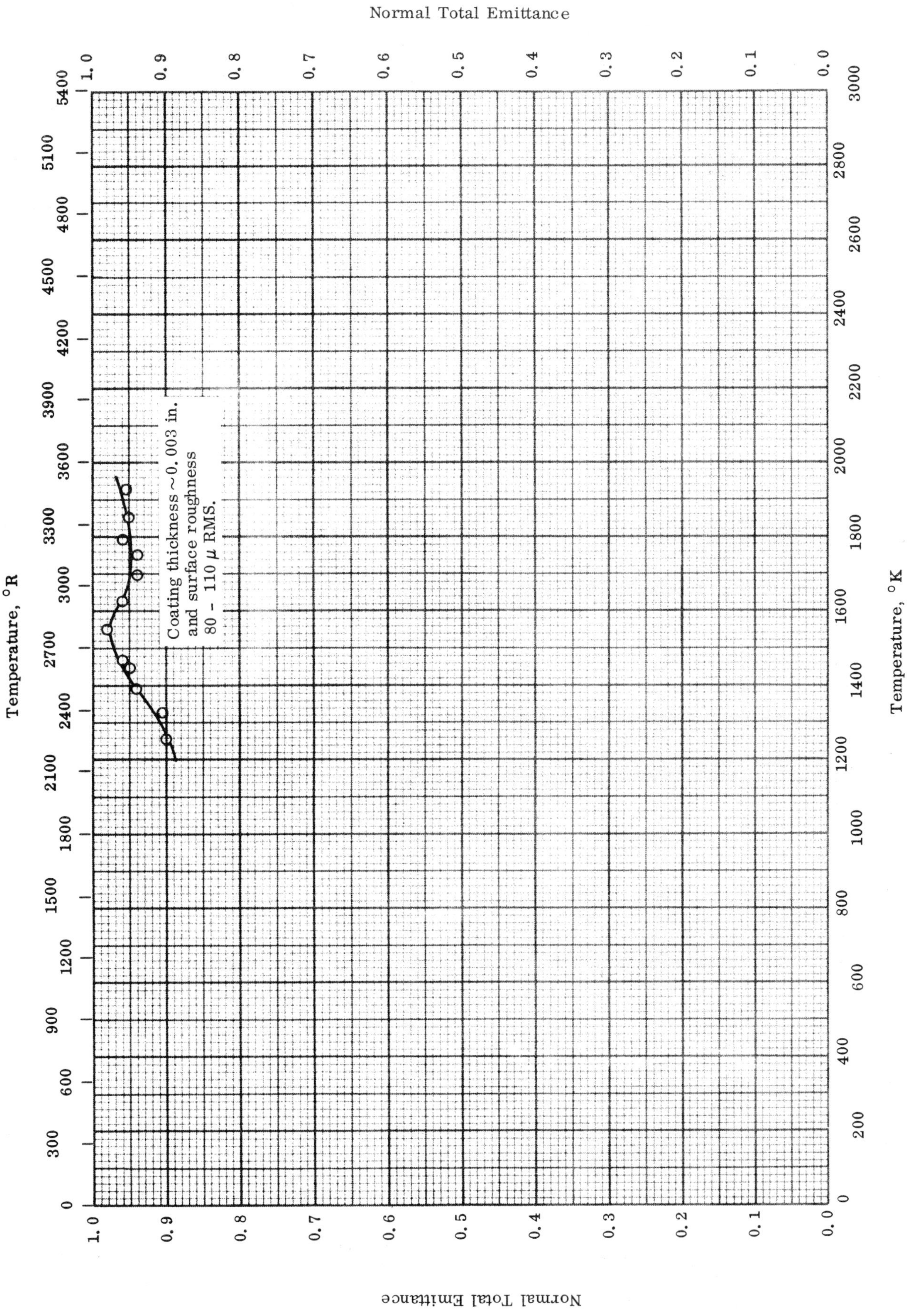

NORMAL TOTAL EMITTANCE -- SILICON CARBIDE COATING ON TANTALUM

NORMAL TOTAL EMITTANCE -- SILICON CARBIDE COATING ON TANTALUM

REFERENCE INFORMATION

Symbol	Ref.	Temp. Range °K	Rept. Error %	Sample Specifications	Remarks
○	63-22	1255-1922		Coating thickness ~ 0.003 in. and surface roughness 80 - 110 μ RMS.	Vapor deposit; measured in vacuum (3 - 4 μ Hg).

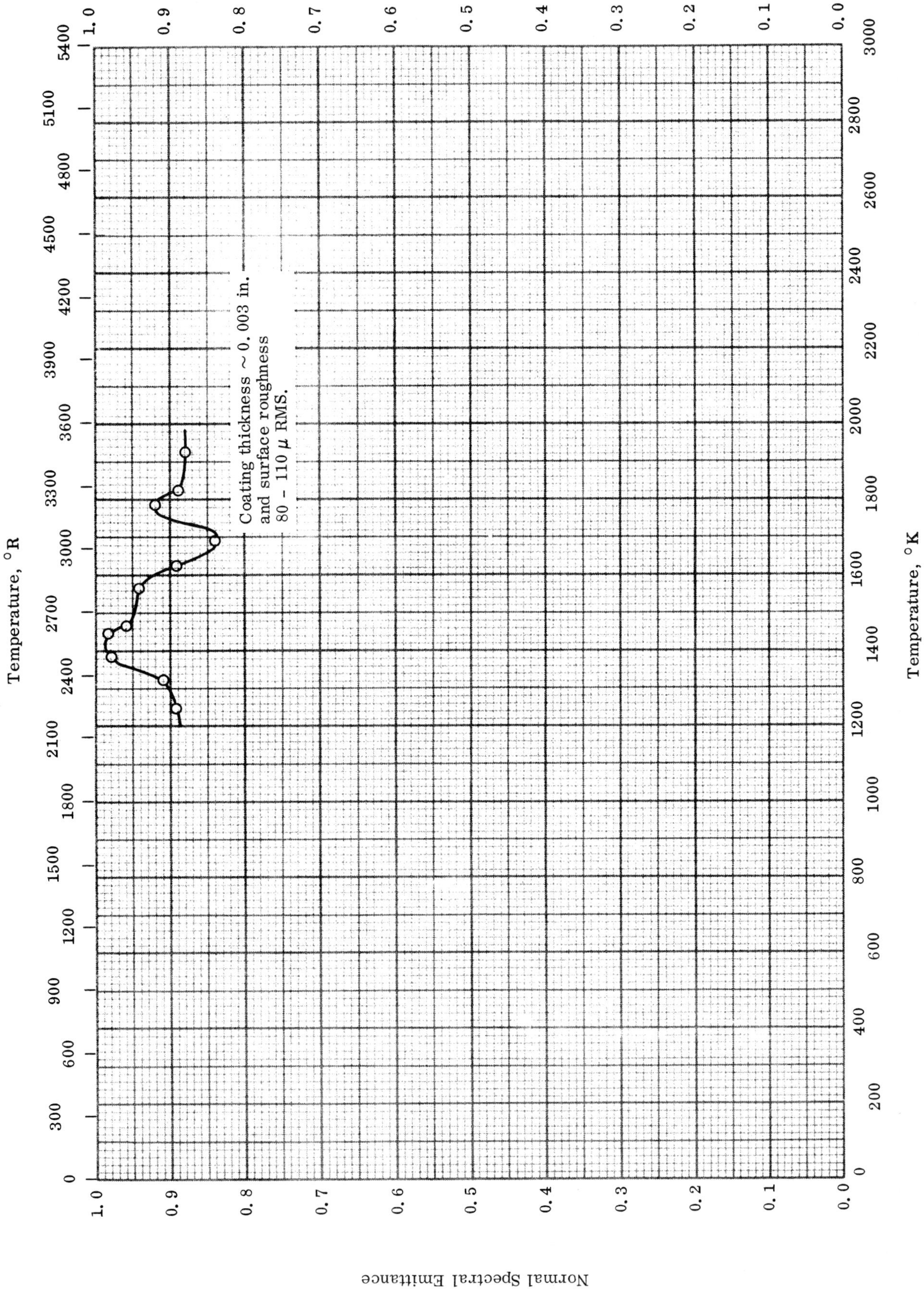

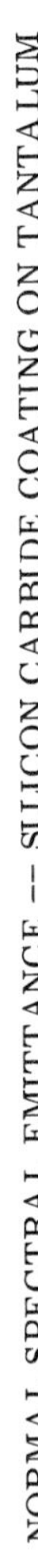

Coating thickness ~ 0.003 in. and surface roughness 80 - 110 μ RMS.

NORMAL SPECTRAL EMITTANCE -- SILICON CARBIDE COATING ON TANTALUM

NORMAL SPECTRAL EMITTANCE -- SILICON CARBIDE COATING ON TANTALUM

REFERENCE INFORMATION

Symbol	Ref.	Wavelength μ	Temp. Range °K	Rept. Error %	Sample Specifications	Remarks
○	63-22	0.65	1255-1923		Coating thickness ~ 0.003 in. and surface roughness 80 - 110 μ RMS.	Vapor deposit; measured in vacuum (3 - 4 μ Hg).

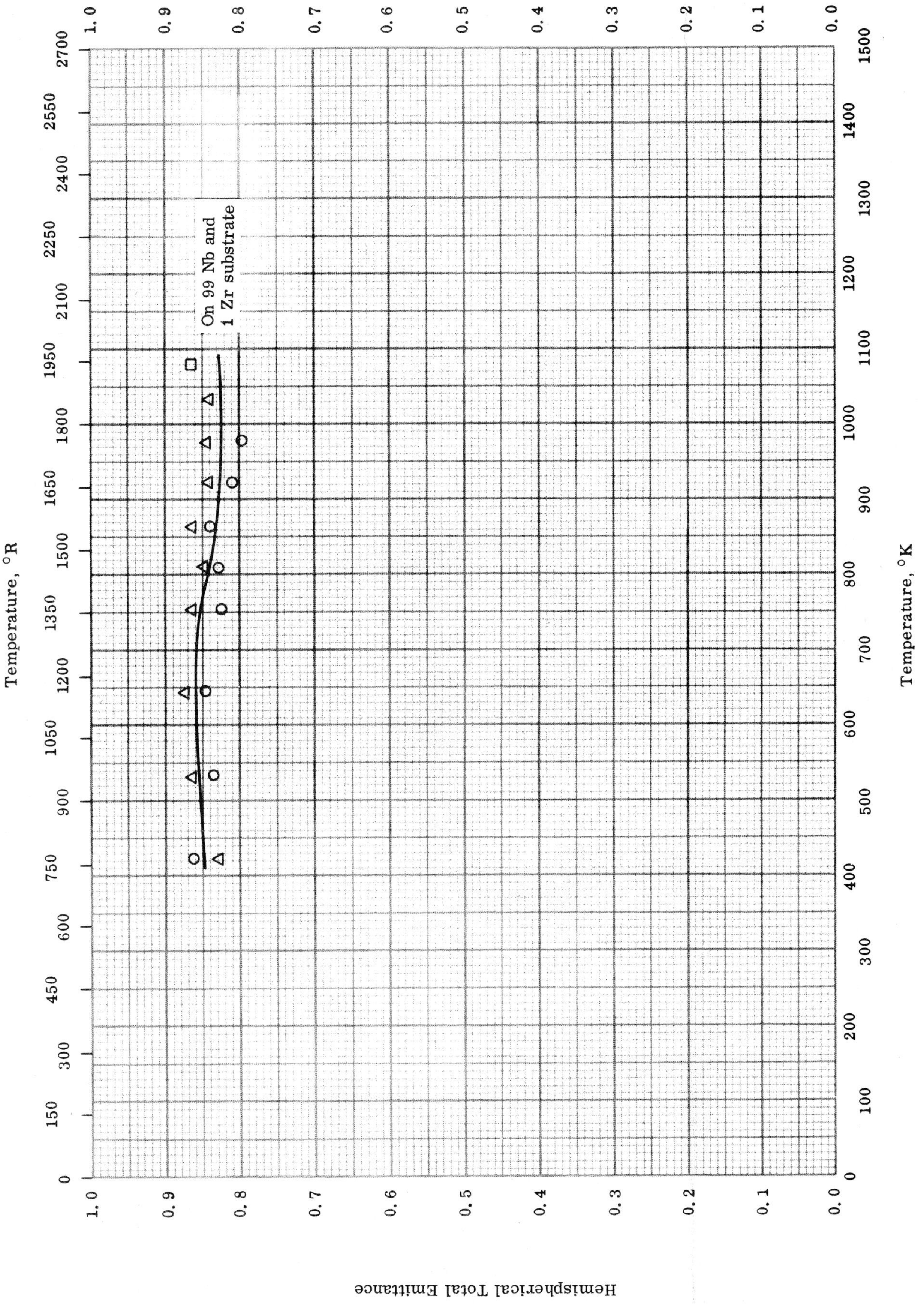

Temperature, °R

On 99 Nb and 1 Zr substrate

Temperature, °K

Hemispherical Total Emittance

HEMISPHERICAL TOTAL EMITTANCE -- SILICON CARBIDE COATING ON NIOBIUM ALLOY

HEMISPHERICAL TOTAL EMITTANCE -- SILICON CARBIDE COATING ON NIOBIUM ALLOY

REFERENCE INFORMATION

Symbol	Ref.	Temp. Range °K	Rept. Error %	Sample Specifications	Remarks
○	63-23	422-977		99 Nb and 1 Zr substrate; coating thickness 0.007 in.	Using aluminum-phosphate bonding procedure; measured in vacuum; using thermocouple.
△	63-23	422-1034		Same as above, coating thickness 0.004 in.	Same as above.
□	63-23	1080		Same as above.	Same as above; using optical pyrometer.

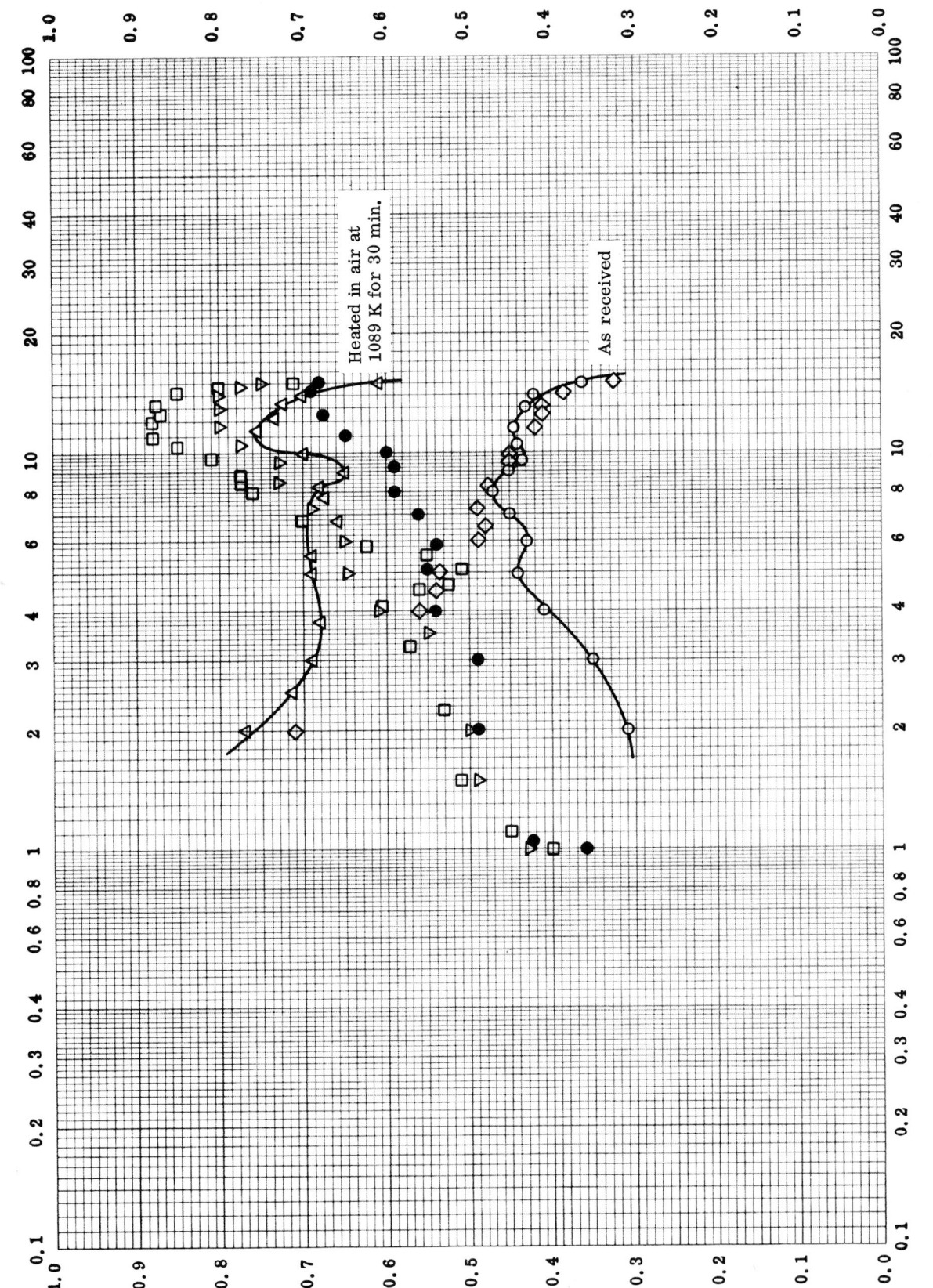

NORMAL SPECTRAL EMITTANCE -- TANTALUM CARBIDE COATING ON INCONEL X

NORMAL SPECTRAL EMITTANCE -- TANTALUM CARBIDE COATING ON INCONEL X

REFERENCE INFORMATION

Symbol	Ref.	Temp. °K	Wavelength Range, μ	Rept. Error %	Sample Specifications	Remarks
○	62-34	523	2-15		TaC flame-sprayed on sandblasted Inconel X using a Plasmatron.	As received; data taken from smooth curve.
□	62-34	1023	1-15		Same as above.	Same as above; different specimen.
△	62-34	523	2-15		Same as above.	Heated in air at 1089 K for 30 min.; data taken from smooth curve.
▽	62-34	1023	1-15		Same as above.	Same as above.
◇	62-34	523	2-15		Same as above.	Heated in vacuum (6.8×10^{-5} mm Hg) at 1089 K for 30 min.; data taken from smooth curve.
●	62-34	1023	1-15		Same as above.	Same as above.

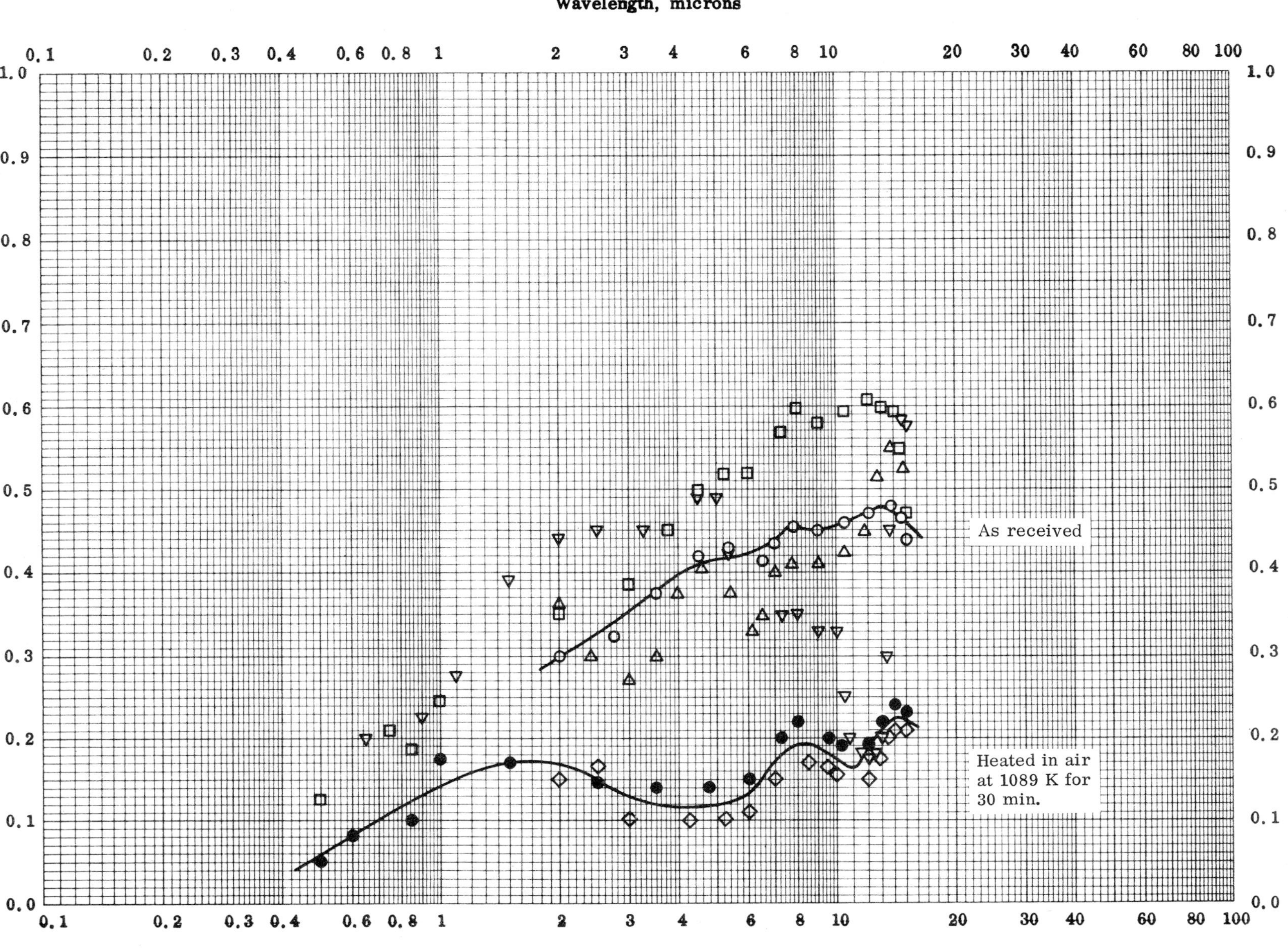

NORMAL SPECTRAL REFLECTANCE — TANTALUM CARBIDE COATING ON INCONEL X

NORMAL SPECTRAL REFLECTANCE -- TANTALUM CARBIDE COATING ON INCONEL X

REFERENCE INFORMATION

Symbol	Ref.	Temp. °K	Wavelength Range, μ	Rept. Error %	Sample Specifications	Remarks
○	62-34	<322	2-15	<±2	TaC flame-sprayed on sandblasted Inconel X using a Plasmatron.	As received; data taken from smooth curve; hemispherical illumination, normal viewing; 523 K source temperature.
□	62-34	<322	0.5-15	<±2	Same as above.	Same as above; 1273 K source temperature.
△	62-34	<322	2-15	<±2	Same as above.	Heated in vacuum (6.8 x 10^{-5} mm Hg) at 1089 K for 30 min.; data taken from smooth curve; hemispherical illumination, normal viewing; 523 K source temperature.
▽	62-34	<322	0.5-15	<±2	Same as above.	Same as above; 1273 K source temperature.
◇	62-34	<322	2-15	<±2	Same as above.	Heated in air at 1089 K for 30 min.; data taken from smooth curve; hemispherical illumination, normal viewing; 523 K source temperature.
●	62-34	<322	0.5-15	<±2	Same as above.	Same as above; 1273 K source temperature.

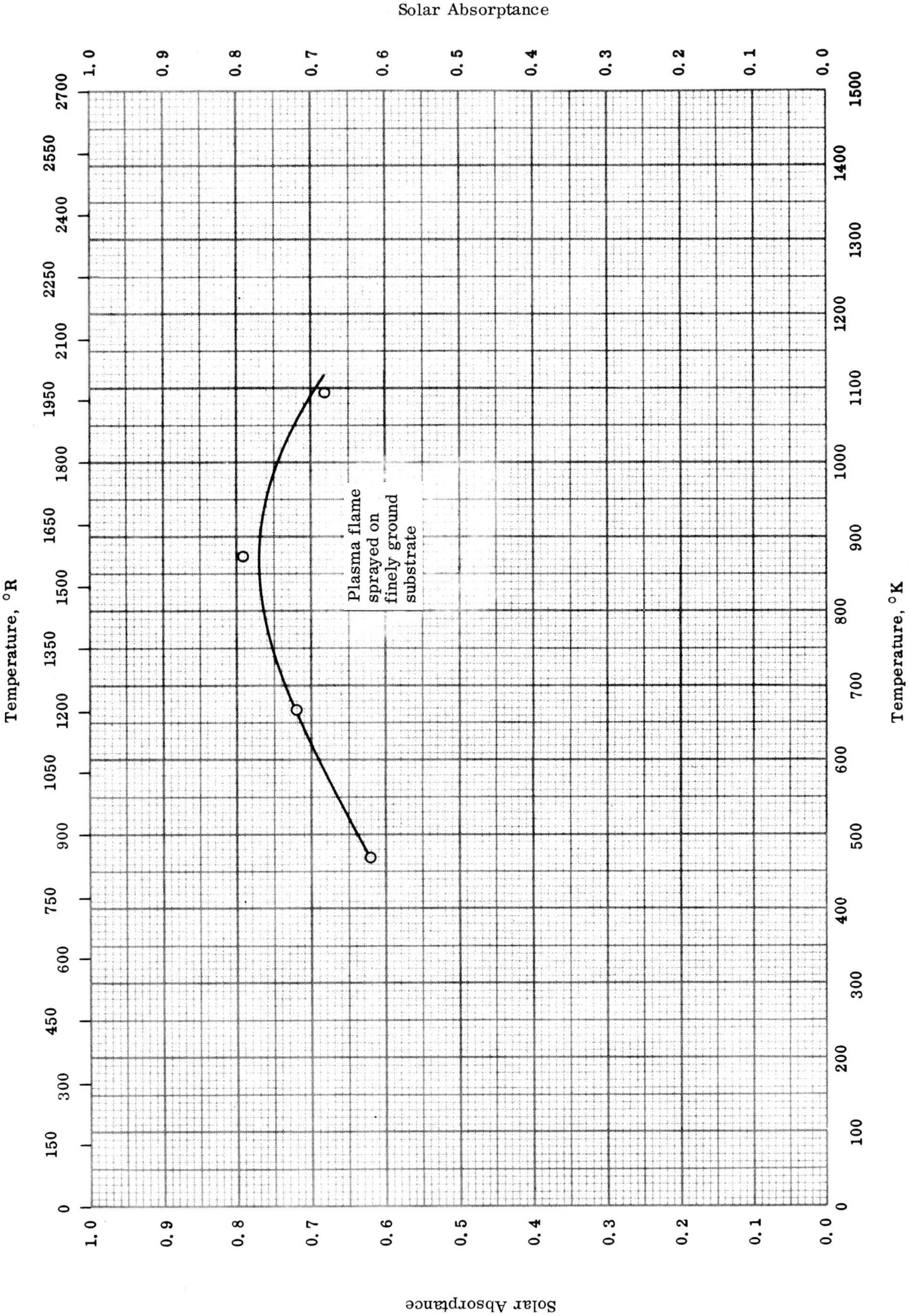

SOLAR ABSORPTANCE -- TUNGSTEN CARBIDE COATING ON ARMCO IRON

SOLAR ABSORPTANCE -- TUNGSTEN CARBIDE COATING ON ARMCO IRON

REFERENCE INFORMATION

Symbol	Ref.	Temp. Range °K	Rept. Error %	Sample Specifications	Remarks
○	61-24	468-1093	≤ 10	Tungsten carbide coating with 12 cobalt aggregate, -270 mesh + 15 micron, Metco XP-1110	Substrate finely ground; plasma flame sprayed; measured in vacuum (10^{-5} mm Hg)

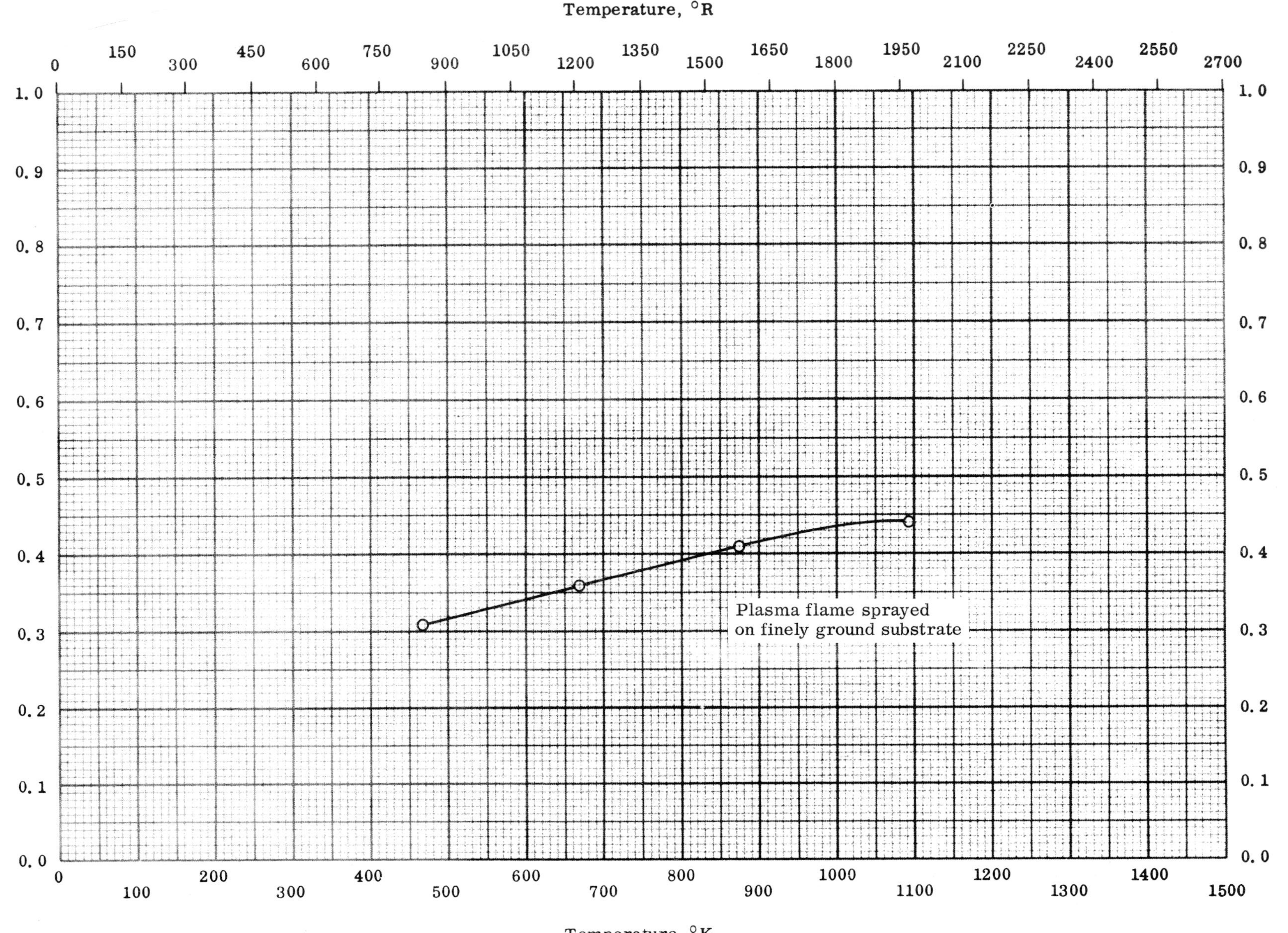

HEMISPHERICAL TOTAL EMITTANCE -- TUNGSTEN CARBIDE COATING ON ARMCO IRON

HEMISPHERICAL TOTAL EMITTANCE -- TUNGSTEN CARBIDE COATING ON ARMCO IRON

REFERENCE INFORMATION

Symbol	Ref.	Temp. Range °K	Rept. Error %	Sample Specifications	Remarks
○	61-24	468-1093	≤10	Tungsten carbide coating with 12 cobalt aggregate, -270 mesh + 15 micron, Metco XP-1110.	Substrate finely ground, plasma flame sprayed; measured in vacuum (10^{-5} mm Hg).

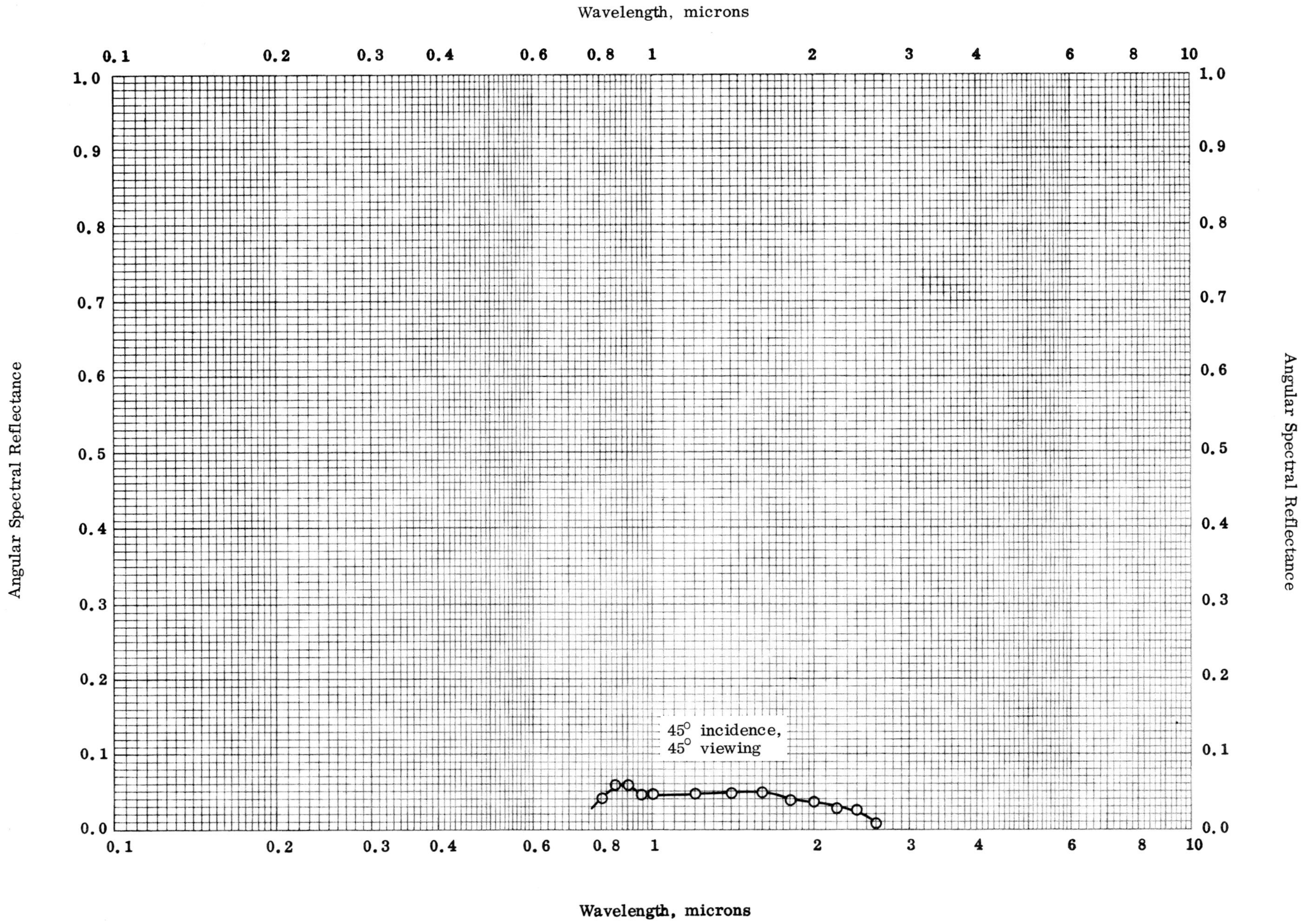

Wavelength, microns
0.1
0.2
0.3
0.4
0.6
0.8
1
2
3
4
6
8
10
1.0
0.9
0.8
0.7
0.6
0.5
0.4
0.3
0.2
0.1
0.0
Angular Spectral Reflectance
45° incidence,
45° viewing
Wavelength, microns

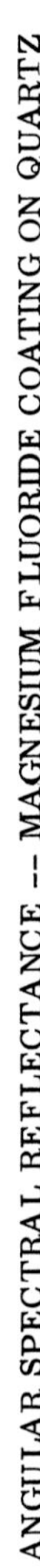

ANGULAR SPECTRAL REFLECTANCE -- MAGNESIUM FLUORIDE COATING ON QUARTZ

ANGULAR SPECTRAL REFLECTANCE -- MAGNESIUM FLUORIDE COATING ON QUARTZ

REFERENCE INFORMATION

Symbol	Ref.	Temp. °K	Wavelength Range, μ	Rept. Error %	Sample Specifications	Remarks
○	64-11	298	0.8-2.6		MgF_2 on clear fused quartz substrate.	Measured in air, evaporated aluminum as reference standard; 45° incidence, 45° viewing.

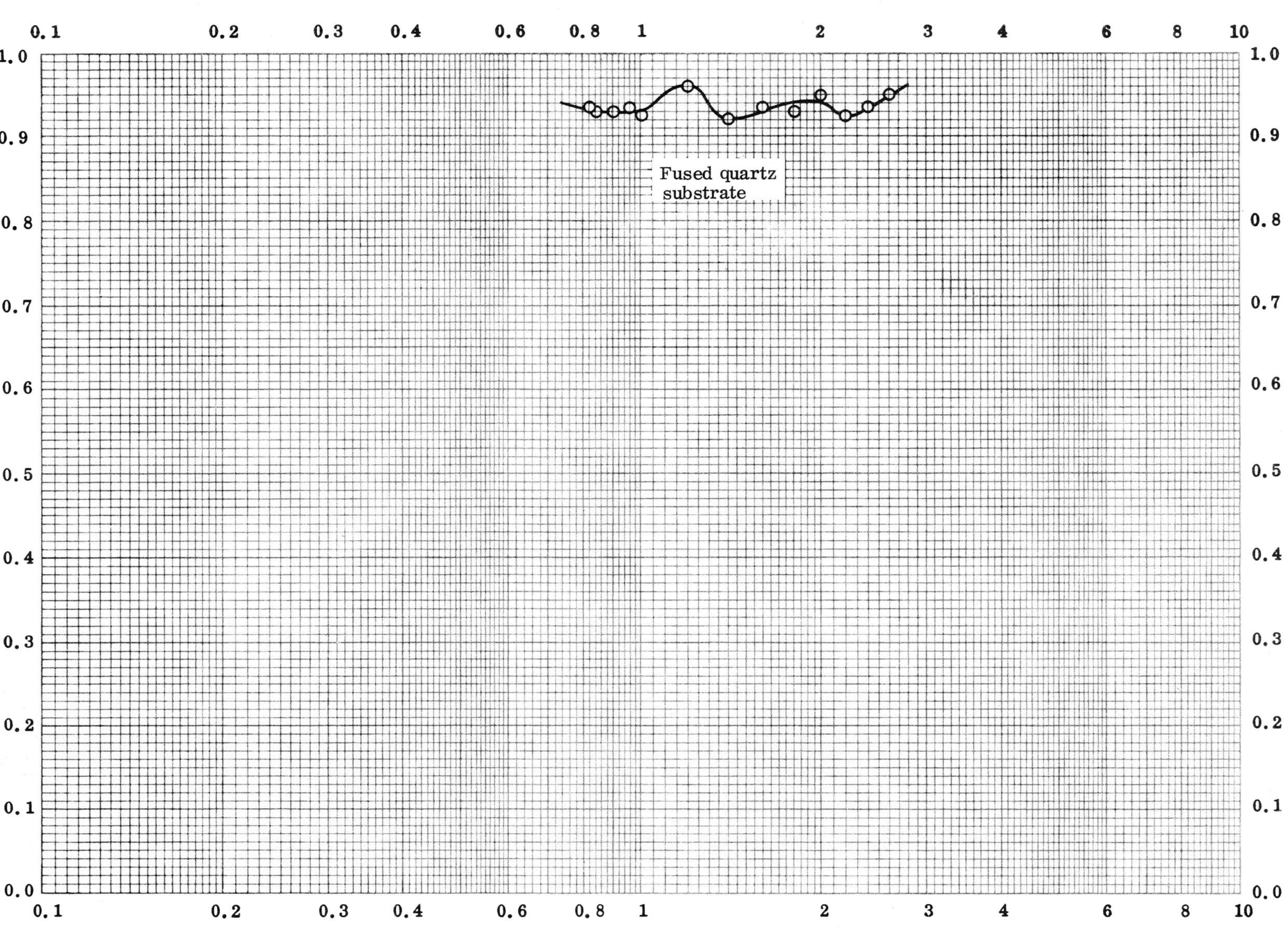

NORMAL SPECTRAL TRANSMITTANCE -- MAGNESIUM FLUORIDE CQATING ON QUARTZ

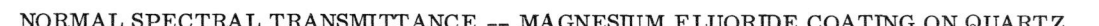

NORMAL SPECTRAL TRANSMITTANCE -- MAGNESIUM FLUORIDE COATING ON QUARTZ

REFERENCE INFORMATION

Symbol	Ref.	Temp. °K	Wavelength Range, μ	Rept. Error %	Sample Specifications	Remarks
○	64-11	298	0.8-2.6		MgF_2 on clear, fused quartz substrate.	Measured in air.

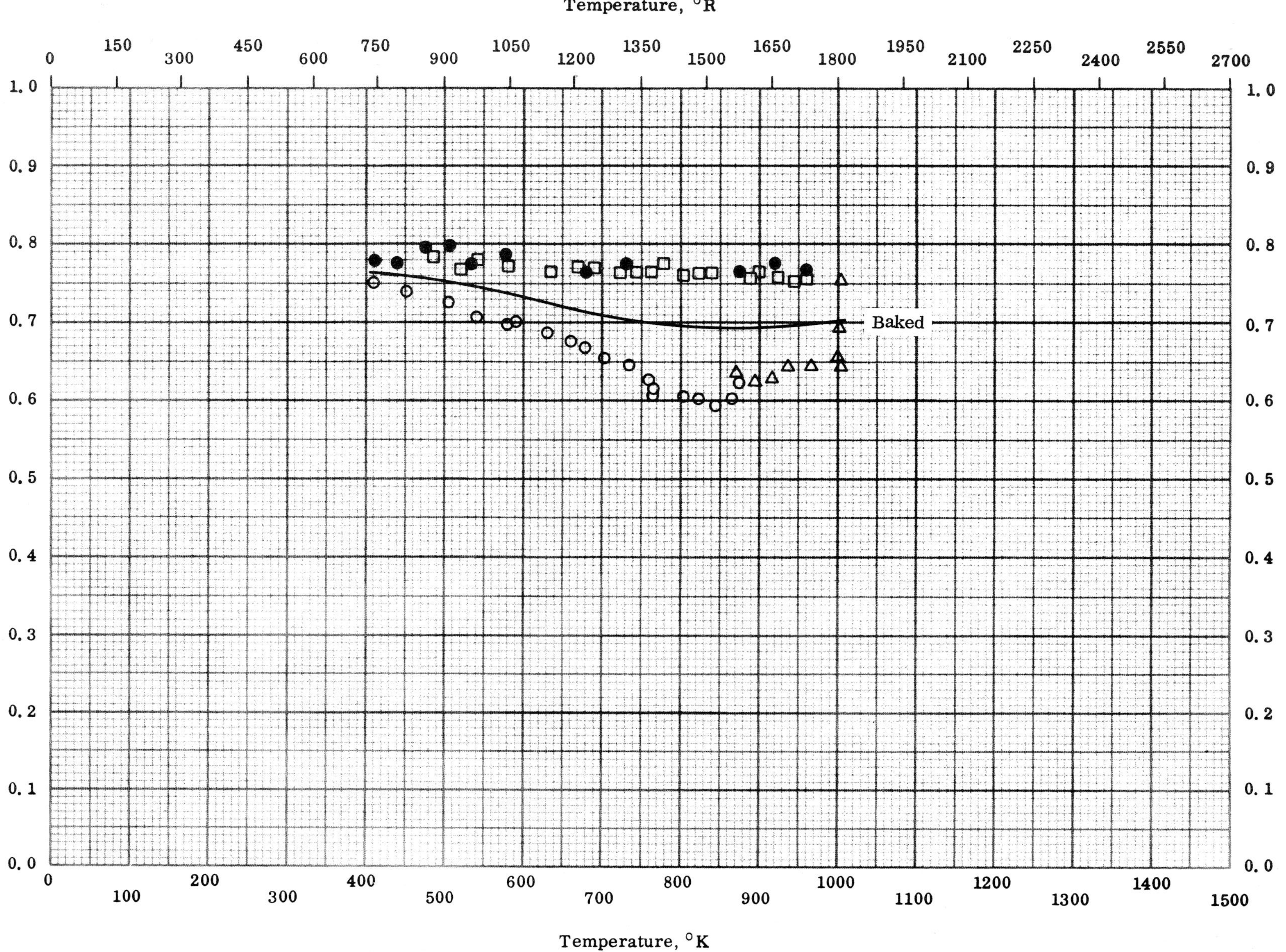

HEMISPHERICAL TOTAL EMITTANCE -- ALUMINUM PHOSPHATE COATING ON NICKEL

HEMISPHERICAL TOTAL EMITTANCE -- ALUMINUM PHOSPHATE COATING ON NICKEL

REFERENCE INFORMATION

Symbol	Ref.	Temp. Range °K	Rept. Error %	Sample Specifications	Remarks
○	60-25	408-874		Water base slurry containing 240 g Al_2O_3, 24 g Ferro Black Label clay, 24 g H_3PO_4, and 8 g ferric oxide sprayed on a nickel strip; coating thickness 0.0018 in.	Baked 1 hr at every 100 degree increment up to 800 F; measured in vacuum; run No. 1A.
△	60-25	870-1002		Same as above.	Same as above; run No. 1B.
□	60-25	961-487		Same as above.	Same as above; run No. 2A.
●	60-25	409-959		Same as above.	Same as above; run No. 2B.

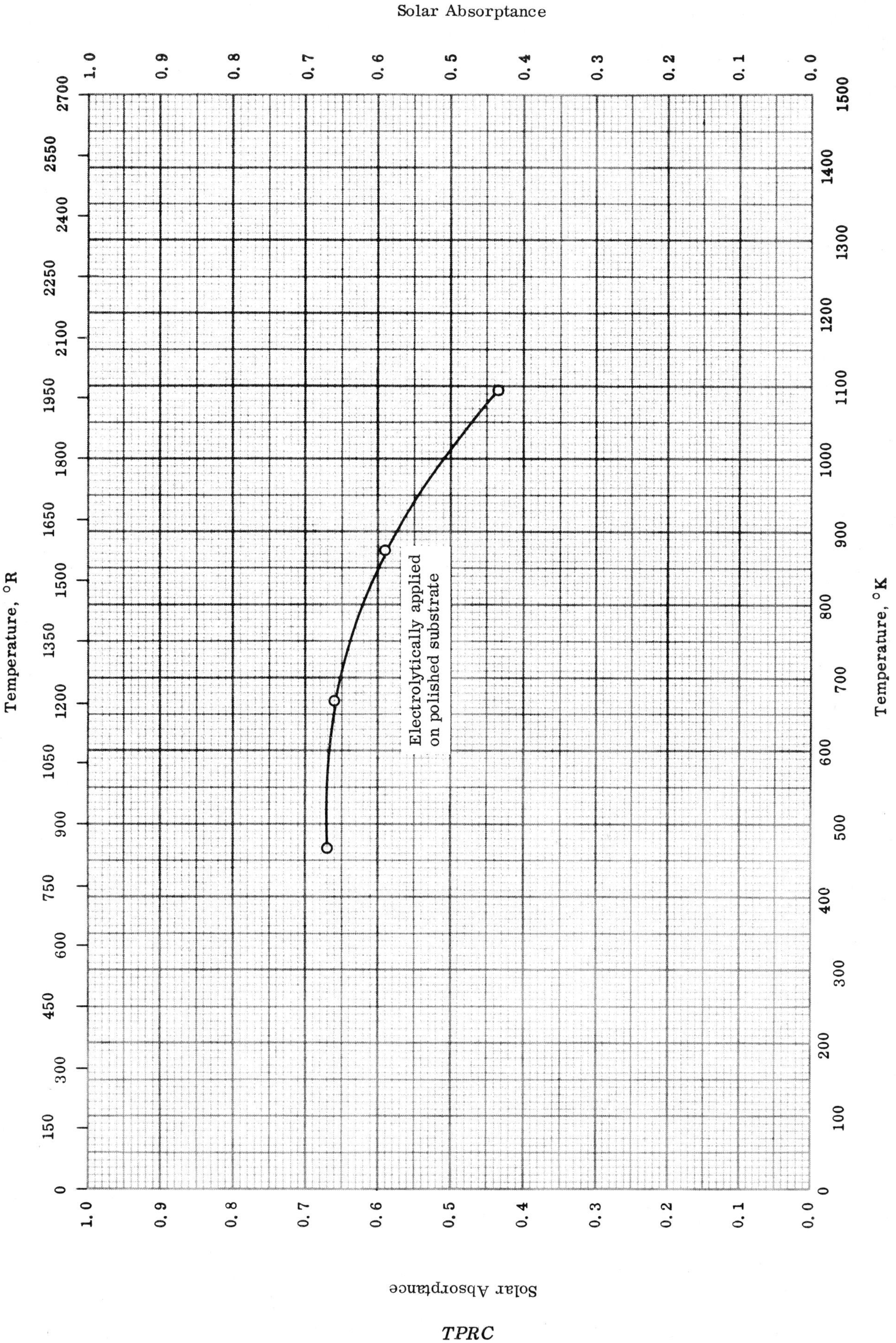

SOLAR ABSORPTANCE -- SILVER SULFIDE COATING ON SILVER

SOLAR ABSORPTANCE -- SILVER SULFIDE COATING ON SILVER

REFERENCE INFORMATION

Symbol	Ref.	Temp. Range °K	Rept. Error %	Sample Specifications	Remarks
○	61-24	468-1093	≤10	Silver sulfide coating on silver.	Substrate polished, applied electrolytically at a potential of 9 volts for 45 sec., dried, and buffed; measured in vacuum (10^{-5} mm Hg).

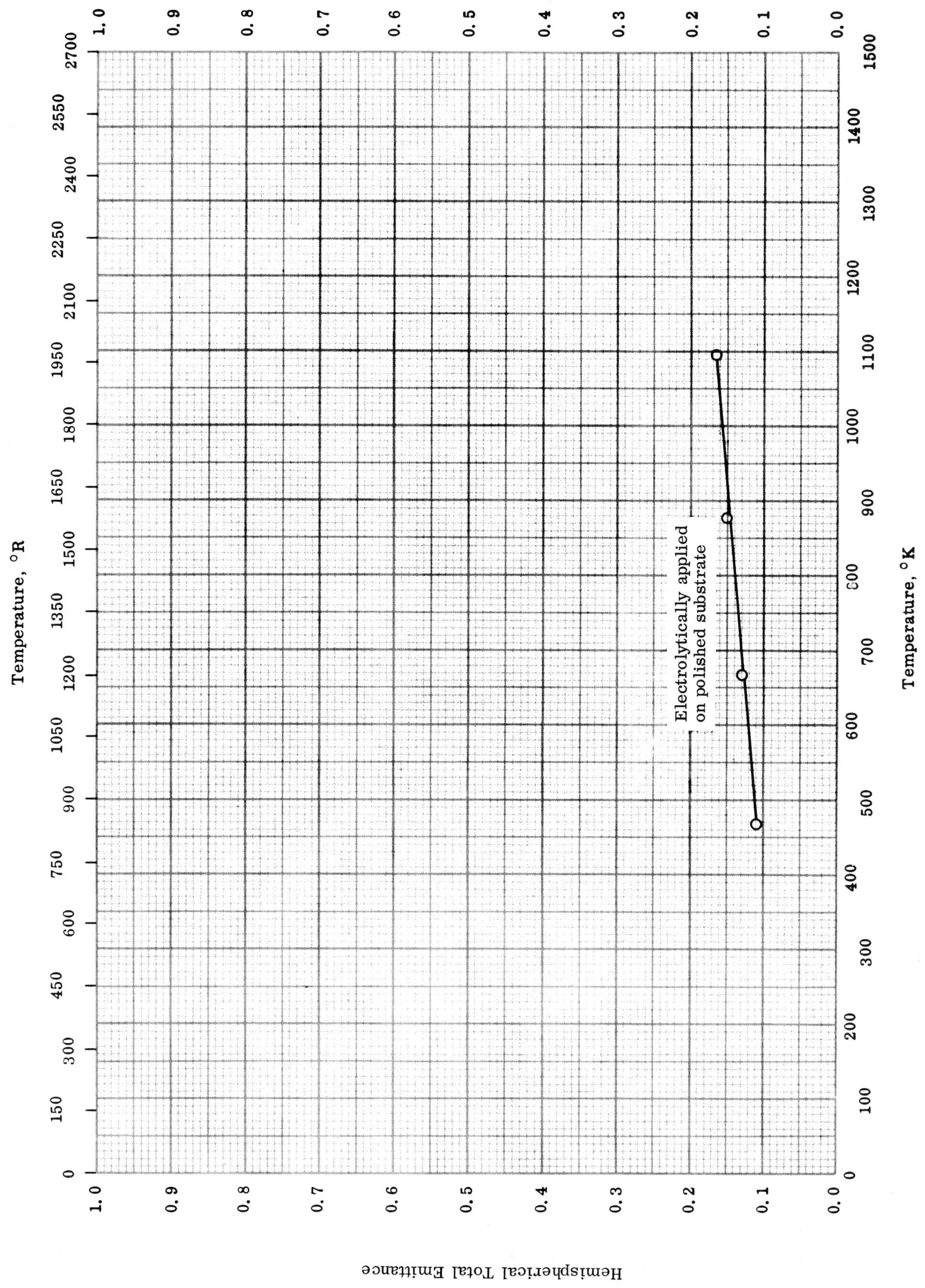

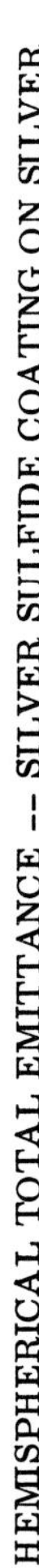

HEMISPHERICAL TOTAL EMITTANCE -- SILVER SULFIDE COATING ON SILVER

Electrolytically applied on polished substrate

Temperature, °R

Temperature, °K

Hemispherical Total Emittance

HEMISPHERICAL TOTAL EMITTANCE -- SILVER SULFIDE COATING ON SILVER

REFERENCE INFORMATION

Symbol	Ref.	Temp. Range °K	Rept. Error %	Sample Specifications	Remarks
○	61-24	468-1093	≤ 10	Silver sulfide coating on silver.	Substrate polished, applied electrolytically at a potential of 9 volts for 45 sec., dried, and buffed; measured in vacuum (10^{-5} mm Hg).

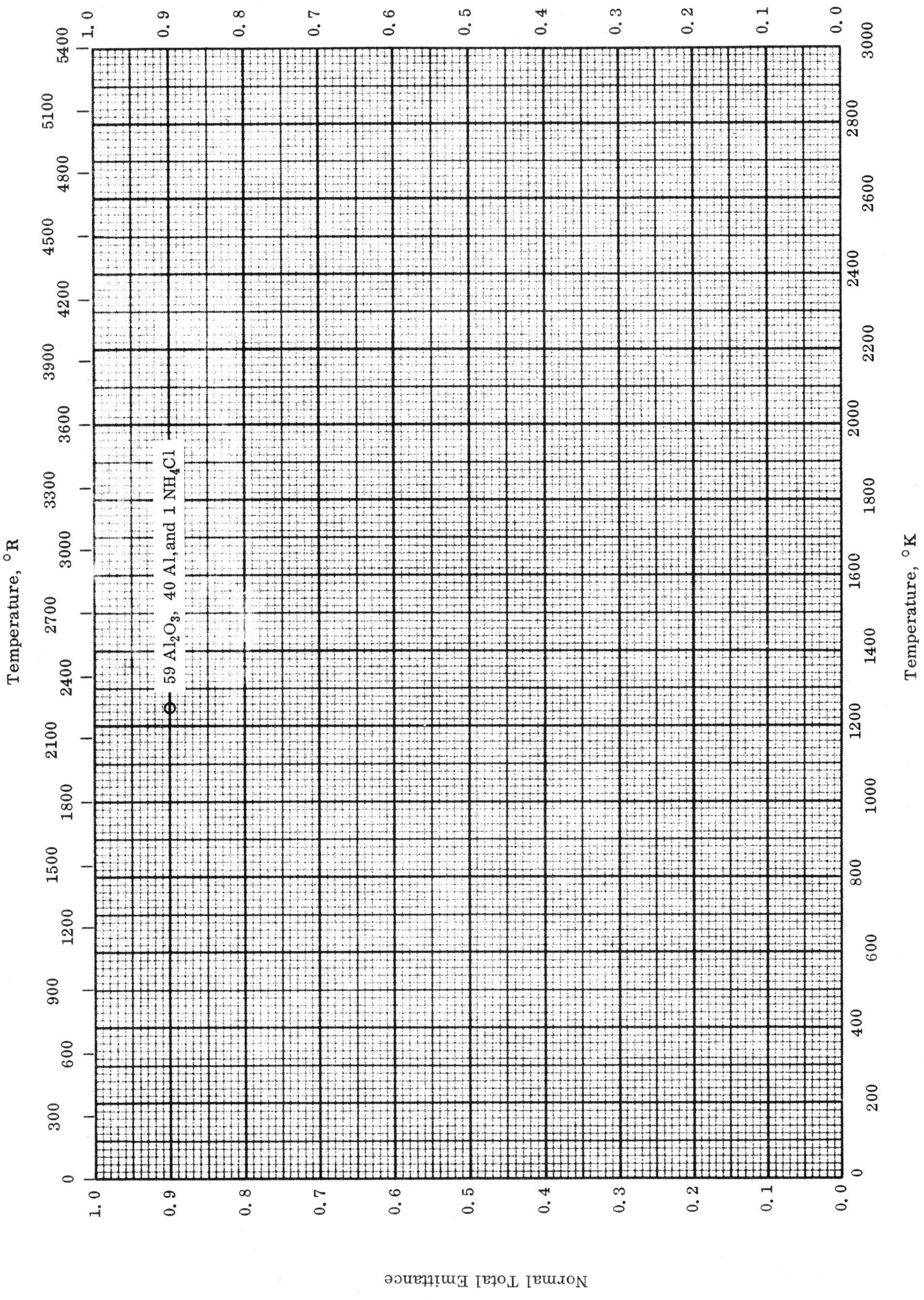

Temperature, °R

0 300 600 900 1200 1500 1800 2100 2400 2700 3000 3300 3600 3900 4200 4500 4800 5100 5400

Temperature, °K

0 200 400 600 800 1000 1200 1400 1600 1800 2000 2200 2400 2600 2800 3000

Normal Total Emittance

1.0 0.9 0.8 0.7 0.6 0.5 0.4 0.3 0.2 0.1 0.0

59 Al_2O_3, 40 Al, and 1 NH_4Cl

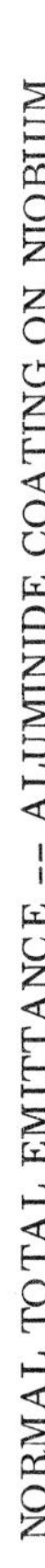

NORMAL TOTAL EMITTANCE -- ALUMINIDE COATING ON NIOBIUM

NORMAL TOTAL EMITTANCE -- ALUMINIDE COATING ON NIOBIUM

REFERENCE INFORMATION

Symbol	Ref.	Temp. Range °K	Rept. Error %	Sample Specifications	Remarks
○	63-16	1223	± 8	Highly pure Nb plate substrate; coating prepared by pack cementation with composition: 59 Al_2O_3, 40 Al, and 1 NH_4 Cl; coating thickness 0.001 in.	Measured in argon; calculated from spectral data.

Wavelength, microns
Normal Spectral Emittance
Pack cementation with
59 Al_2O_3, 40 Al, and 1 NH_4Cl
1.0 0.9 0.8 0.7 0.6 0.5 0.4 0.3 0.2 0.1 0.0
1 2 3 4 6 8 10 20 30 40 60 80 100

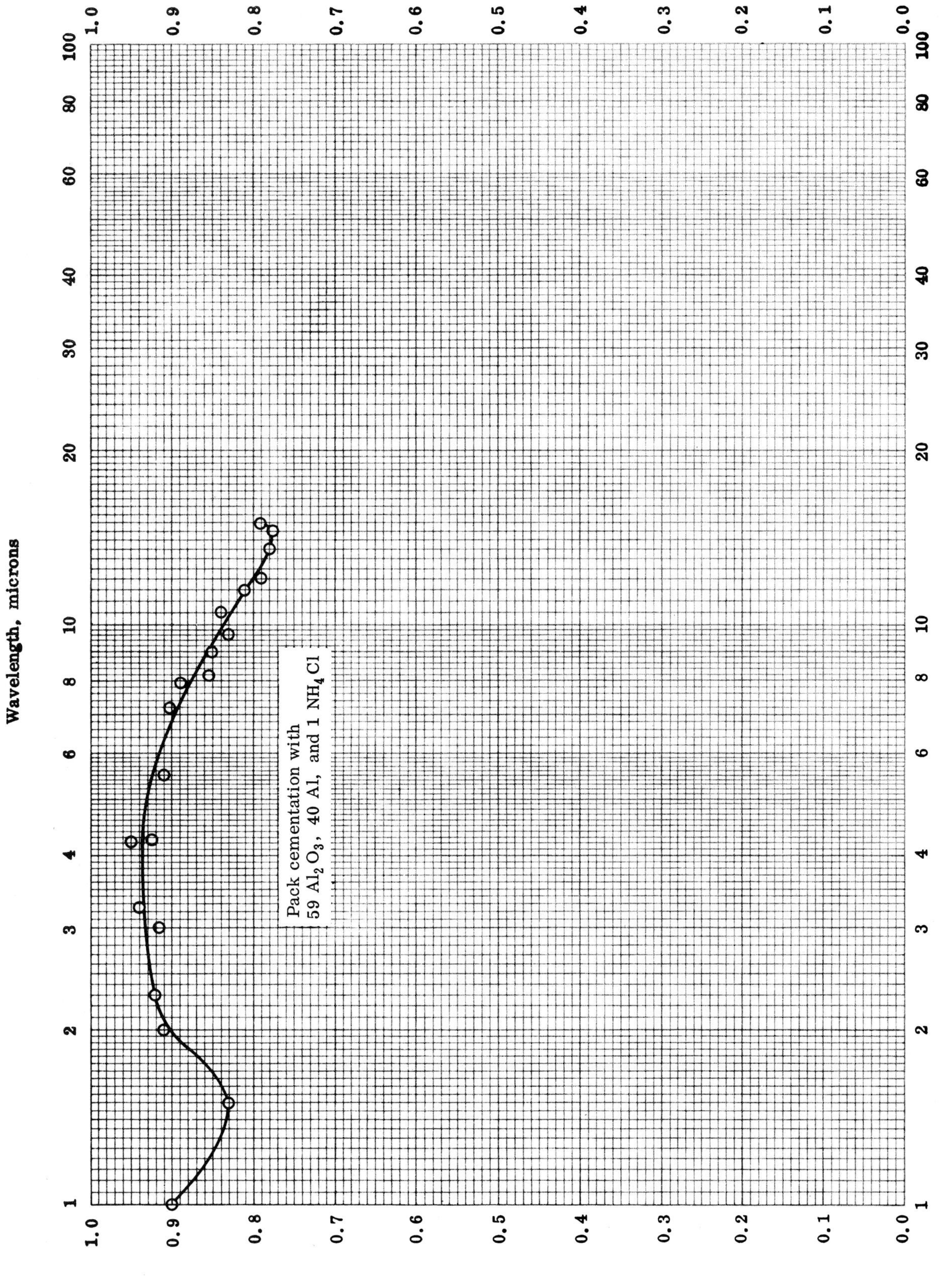

NORMAL SPECTRAL EMITTANCE -- ALUMINIDE COATING ON NIOBIUM

NORMAL SPECTRAL EMITTANCE -- ALUMINIDE COATING ON NIOBIUM

REFERENCE INFORMATION

Symbol	Ref.	Temp. ° K	Wavelength Range, μ	Rept. Error %	Sample Specifications	Remarks
○	63-16	1223	1-15		Highly pure Nb plate substrate; coating prepared by pack cementation with composition: 59 Al_2O_3, 40 Al, and 1 NH_4Cl; coating thickness 0.001 in.	Measured in argon; data taken from a curve.

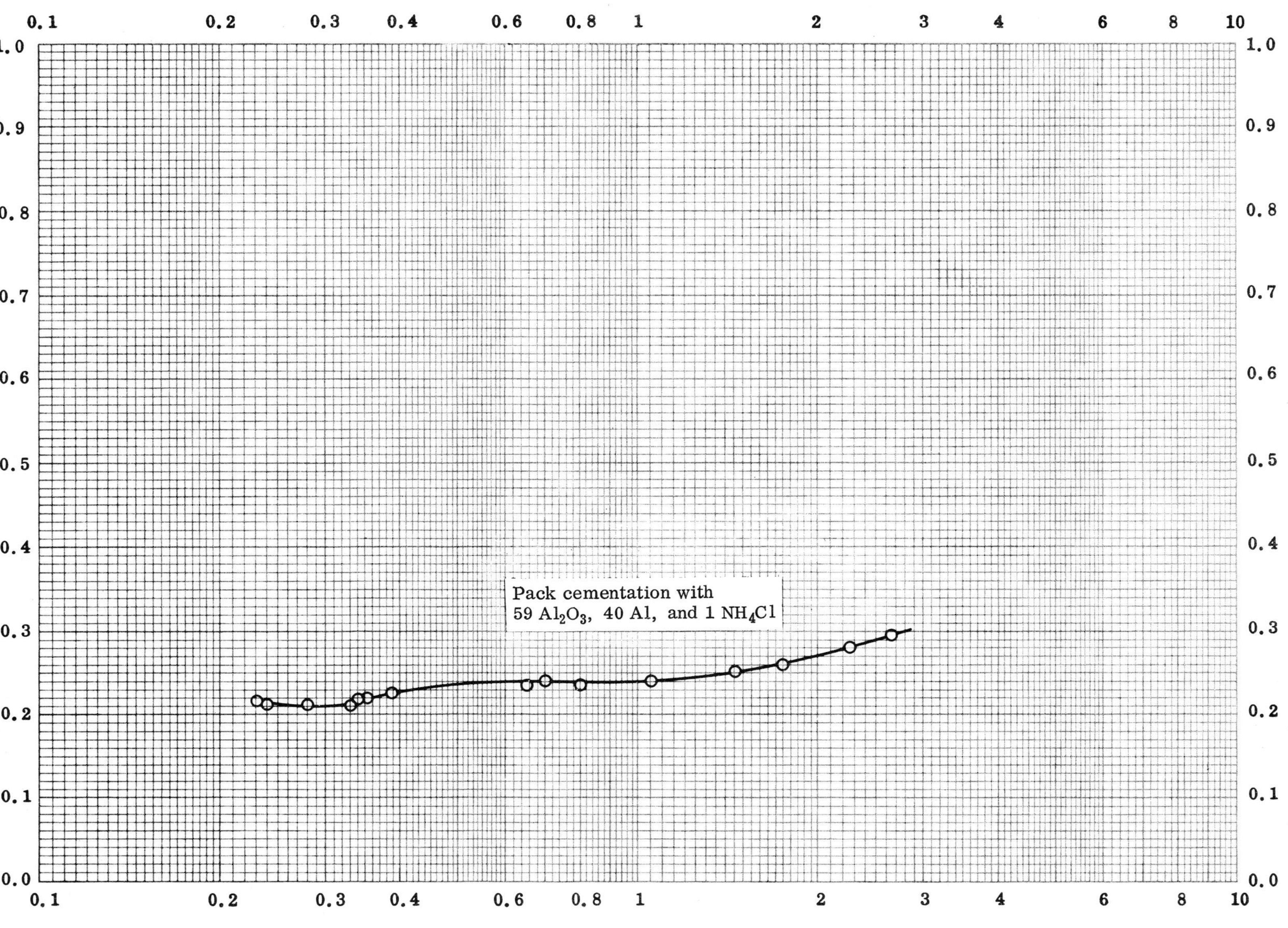

NORMAL SPECTRAL REFLECTANCE — ALUMINIDE COATING ON NIOBIUM

NORMAL SPECTRAL REFLECTANCE -- ALUMINIDE COATING ON NIOBIUM

REFERENCE INFORMATION

Symbol	Ref.	Temp. °K	Wavelength Range, μ	Rept. Error %	Sample Specifications	Remarks
○	63-16	298	0. 23-2. 65	5	Highly pure Nb plate substrate; coating prepared by pack cementation with composition: 59 Al_2O_3, 40 Al, and 1NH_4Cl; coating thickness 0. 001 in.	Data taken from a curve; MgO as reference standard; normal incidence, hemispherical viewing.

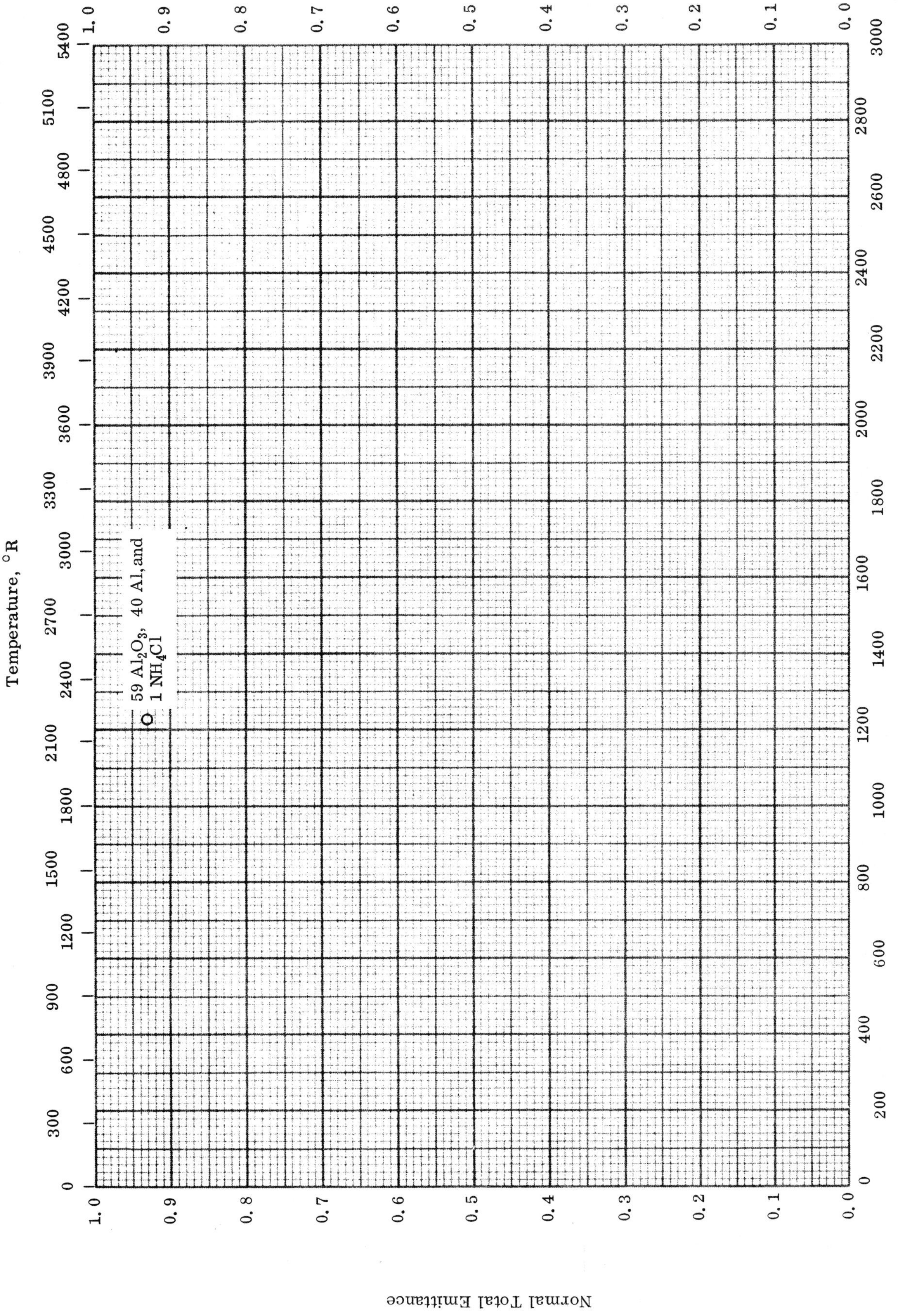

Temperature, °R

0 300 600 900 1200 1500 1800 2100 2400 2700 3000 3300 3600 3900 4200 4500 4800 5100 5400

O 59 Al_2O_3, 40 Al, and 1 NH_4Cl

Normal Total Emittance

1.0 0.9 0.8 0.7 0.6 0.5 0.4 0.3 0.2 0.1 0.0

0 200 400 600 800 1000 1200 1400 1600 1800 2000 2200 2400 2600 2800 3000

Temperature, °K

NORMAL TOTAL EMITTANCE -- ALUMINIDE COATING ON TANTALUM

NORMAL TOTAL EMITTANCE -- ALUMINIDE COATING ON TANTALUM

REFERENCE INFORMATION

Symbol	Ref.	Temp. Range °K	Rept. Error %	Sample Specifications	Remarks
○	63-16	1223	± 8	Highly pure Ta plate substrate; coating prepared by pack cementation with composition: 59 Al_2O_3, 40 Al, and 1 NH_4 Cl; coating thickness 0.001 in.	Measured in argon; calculated from spectral data.

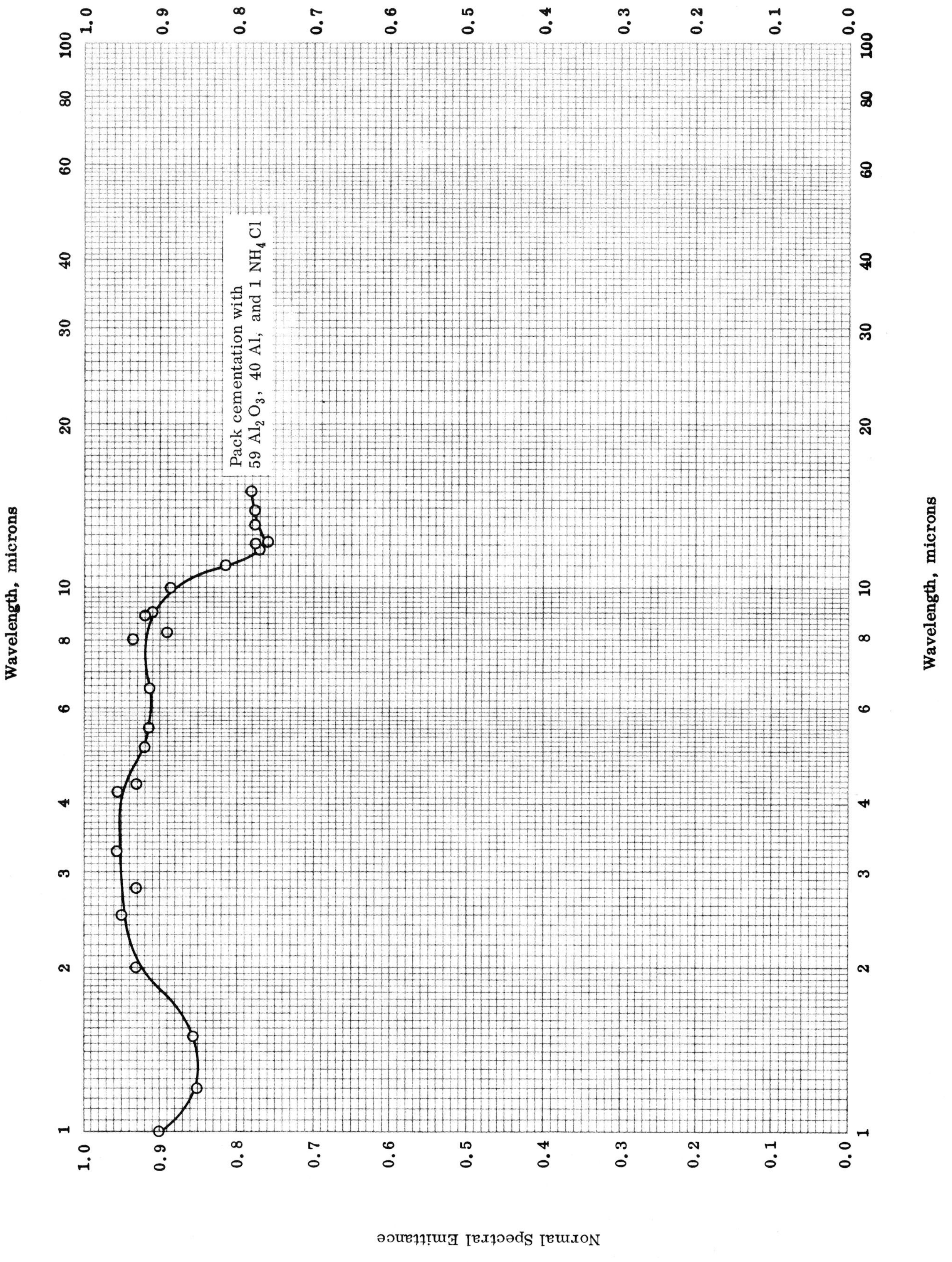

Wavelength, microns
1
2
3
4
6
8
10
20
30
40
60
80
100
Normal Spectral Emittance
1.0
0.9
0.8
0.7
0.6
0.5
0.4
0.3
0.2
0.1
0.0
Pack cementation with
59 Al_2O_3, 40 Al, and 1 NH_4Cl

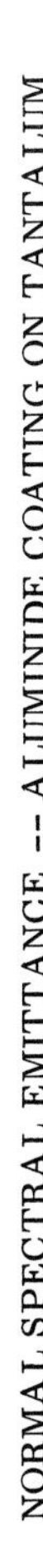

NORMAL SPECTRAL EMITTANCE -- ALUMINIDE COATING ON TANTALUM

NORMAL SPECTRAL EMITTANCE -- ALUMINIDE COATING ON TANTALUM

REFERENCE INFORMATION

Symbol	Ref.	Temp. °K	Wavelength Range, μ	Rept. Error %	Sample Specifications	Remarks
○	63-16	1223	1-15		Highly pure Ta plate substrate; coating prepared by pack cementation with composition: 59 Al_2O_3, 40 Al, and 1 NH_4Cl; coating thickness 0.001 in.	Measured in argon; data taken from a curve.

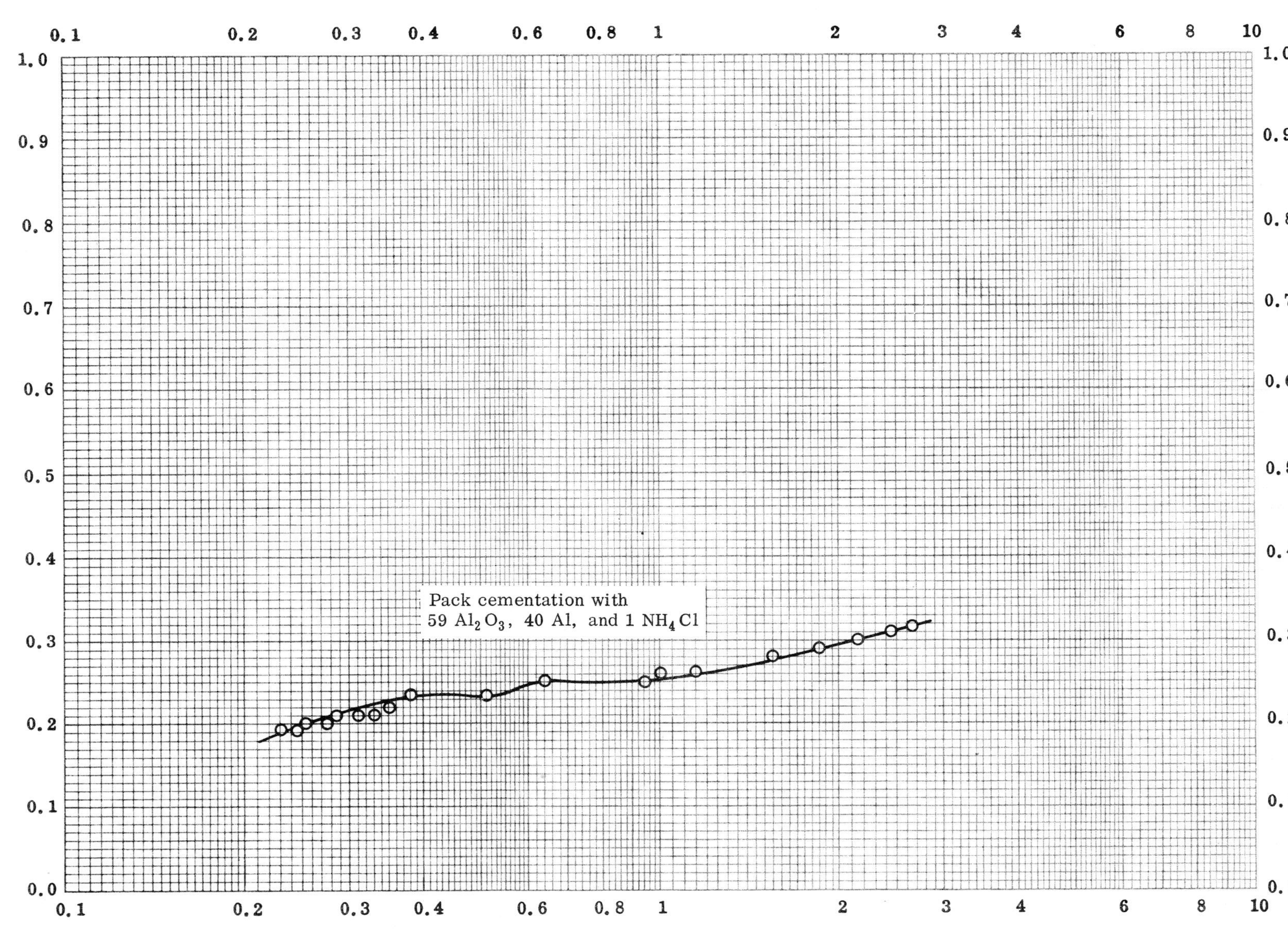

NORMAL SPECTRAL REFLECTANCE — ALUMINIDE COATING ON TANTALUM

NORMAL SPECTRAL REFLECTANCE -- ALUMINIDE COATING ON TANTALUM

REFERENCE INFORMATION

Symbol	Ref.	Temp. ° K	Wavelength Range, μ	Rept. Error %	Sample Specifications	Remarks
○	63-16	298	0.23-2.65	5	Highly pure Ta plate substrate; coating prepared by pack cementation with composition: 59 Al_2O_3, 40 Al, and NH_4Cl; coating thickness 0.001 in.	Data taken from a curve; MgO as reference standard; normal incidence, hemispherical viewing.

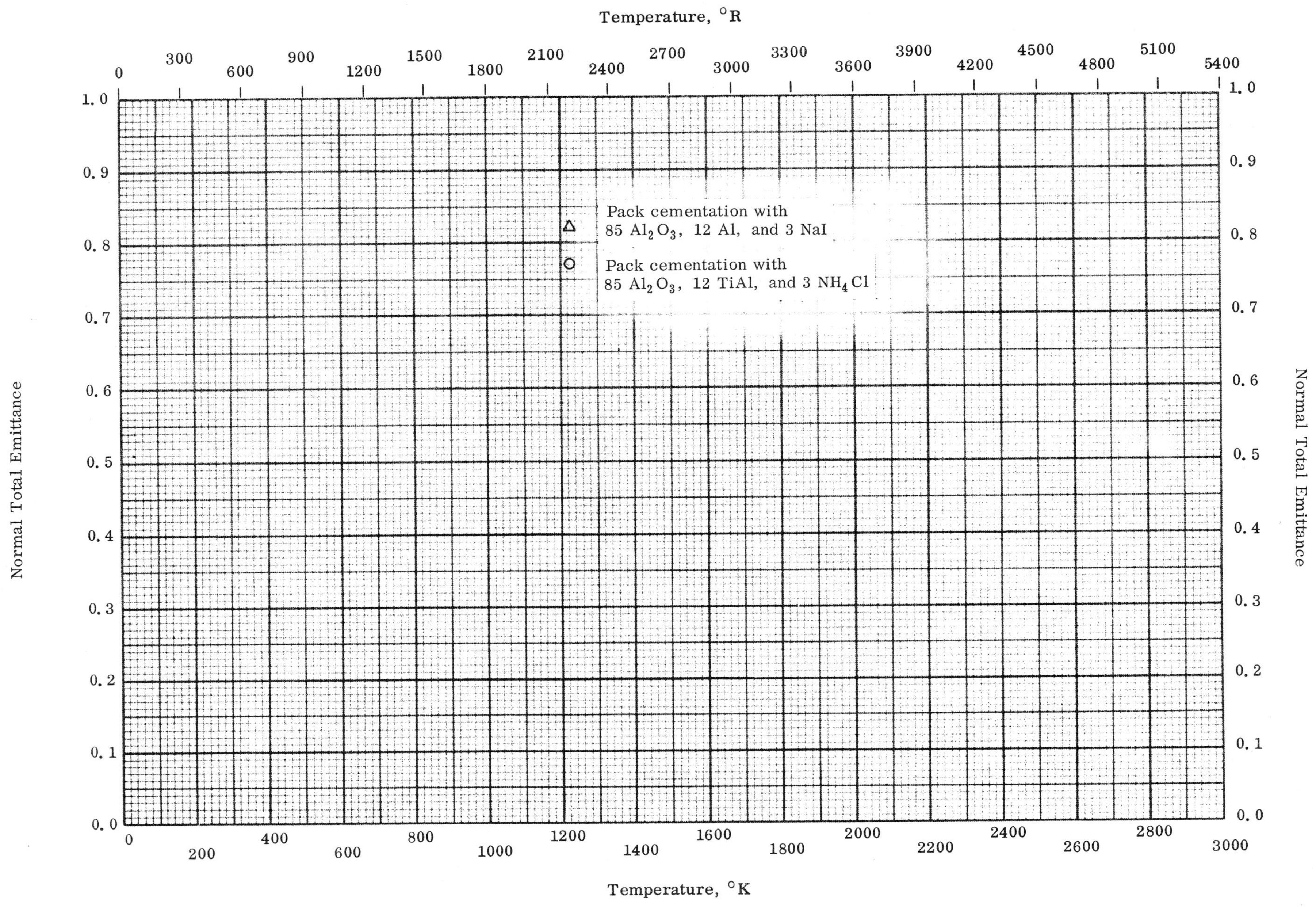

Normal Total Emittance

Temperature, °R

0 300 600 900 1200 1500 1800 2100 2400 2700 3000 3300 3600 3900 4200 4500 4800 5100 5400

Temperature, °K

0 200 400 600 800 1000 1200 1400 1600 1800 2000 2200 2400 2600 2800 3000

Normal Total Emittance

1.0 0.9 0.8 0.7 0.6 0.5 0.4 0.3 0.2 0.1 0.0

Δ Pack cementation with 85 Al_2O_3, 12 Al, and 3 NaI

O Pack cementation with 85 Al_2O_3, 12 TiAl, and 3 NH_4Cl

NORMAL TOTAL EMITTANCE -- ALUMINIDE COATING ON TITANIUM

NORMAL TOTAL EMITTANCE -- ALUMINIDE COATING ON TITANIUM

REFERENCE INFORMATION

Symbol	Ref.	Temp. Range °K	Rept. Error %	Sample Specifications	Remarks
○	63-16	1223	± 8	Highly pure Ti plate substrate; coating prepared by pack cementation with composition: 85 Al_2O_3, 12 Al, and 3 NaI; coating thickness 0.003 in.	Measured in argon; calculated from spectral data.
△	63-16	1223	± 8	Same as above except composition: 85 Al_2O_3, 12 TiAl, and 3 NH_4 Cl and coating thickness 0.004 in.	Same as above.

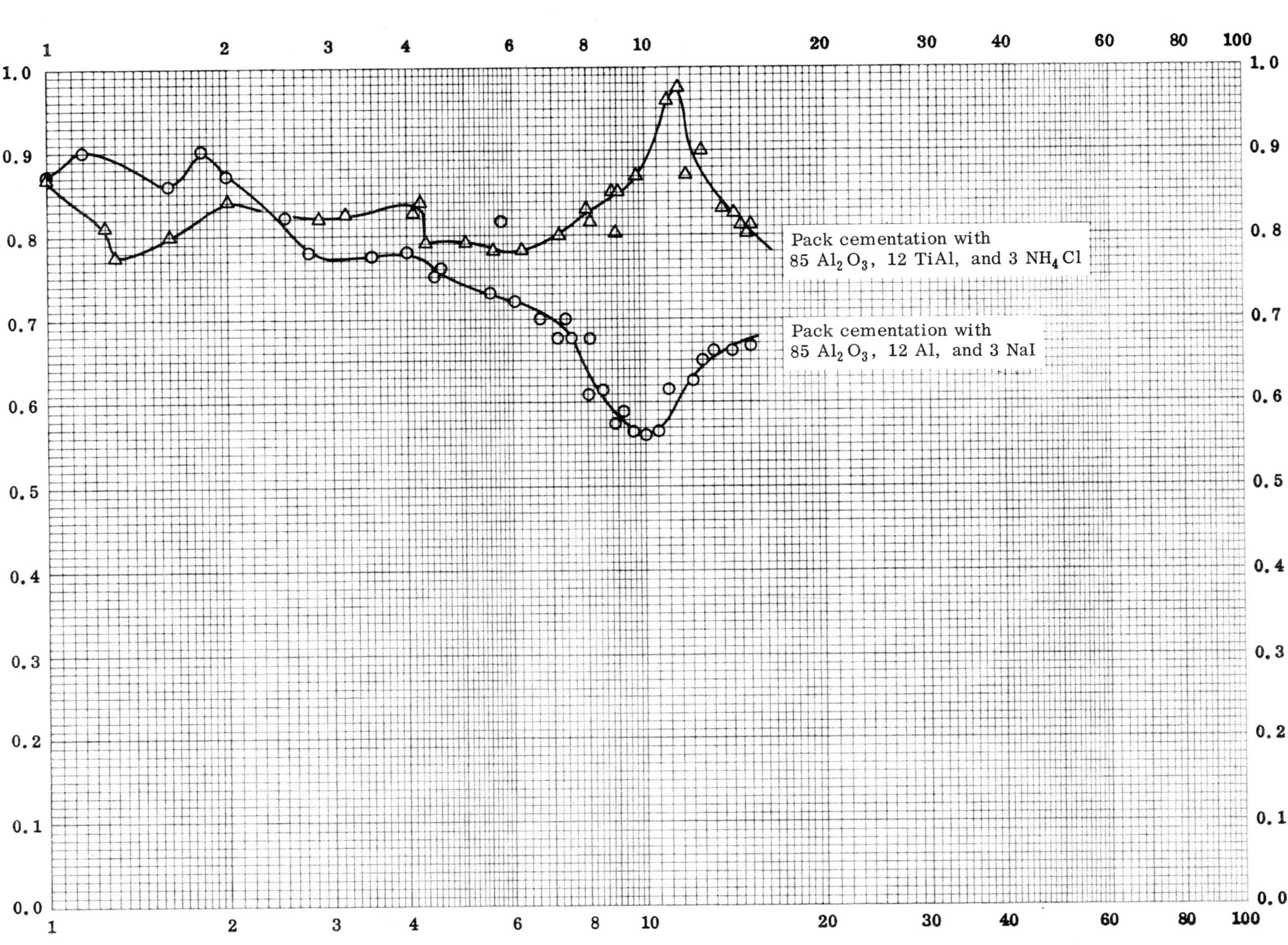

NORMAL SPECTRAL EMITTANCE -- ALUMINIDE COATING ON TITANIUM

NORMAL SPECTRAL EMITTANCE -- ALUMINIDE COATING ON TITANIUM

REFERENCE INFORMATION

Symbol	Ref.	Temp. °K	Wavelength Range, μ	Rept. Error %	Sample Specifications	Remarks
○	63-16	1223	1-15		Highly pure Ti plate substrate; coating prepared by pack cementation with composition: 85 Al_2O_3, 12 Al, and 3 NaI; coating thickness 0.003 in.	Measured in argon; data taken from a curve.
△	63-16	1223	1-15		Same as above except composition: 85 Al_2O_3, 12 TiAl, and 3 NH_4 Cl and coating thickness 0.004 in.	Same as above.

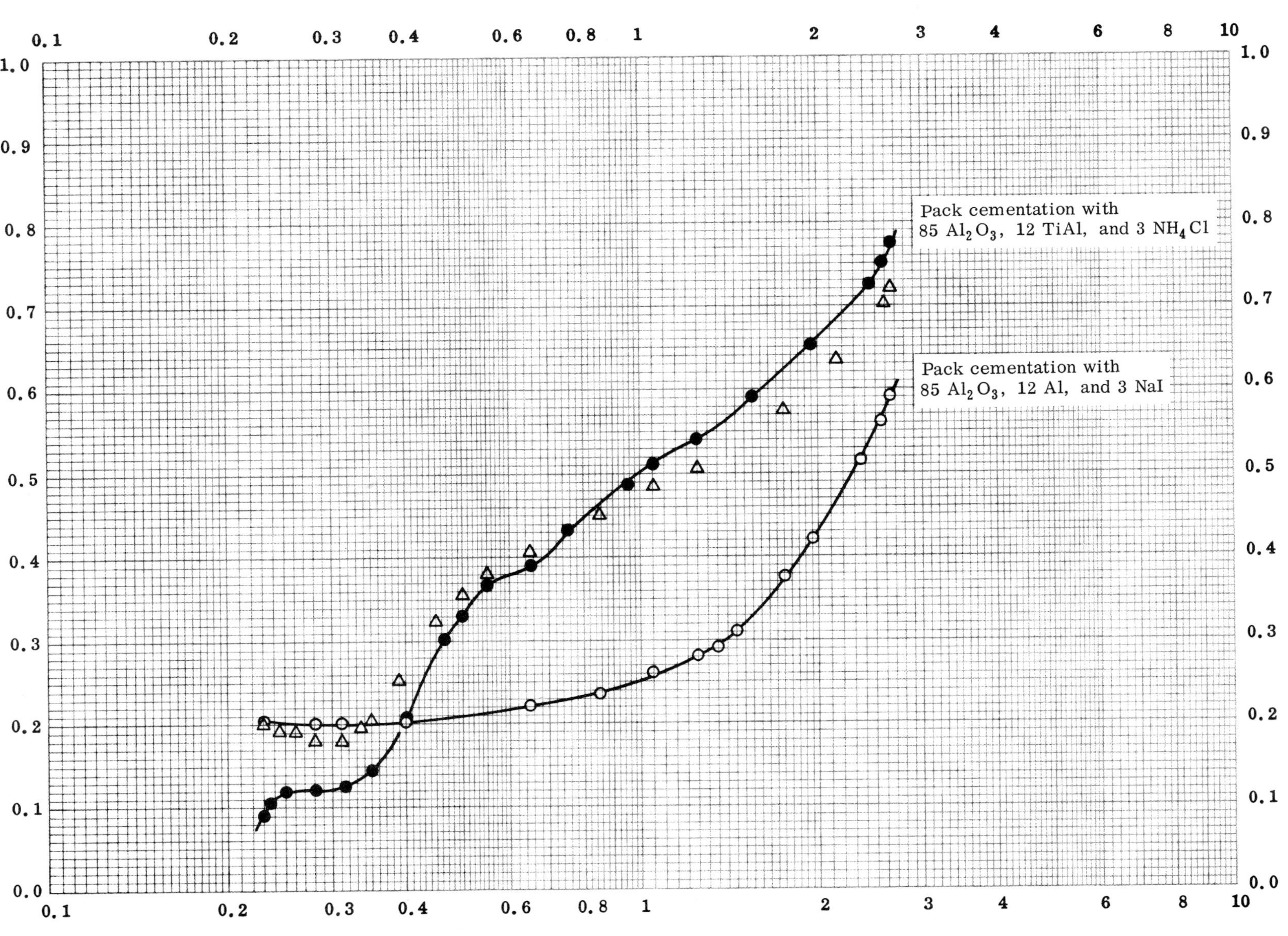

NORMAL SPECTRAL REFLECTANCE -- ALUMINIDE COATING ON TITANIUM

NORMAL SPECTRAL REFLECTANCE -- ALUMINIDE COATING ON TITANIUM

REFERENCE INFORMATION

Symbol	Ref.	Temp. °K	Wavelength Range, μ	Rept. Error %	Sample Specifications	Remarks
○	63-16	298	0.23-2.65	5	Highly pure Ti plate substrate; coating prepared by pack cementation with composition: 85 Al_2O_3, 12 Al, and 3 NaI; coating thickness 0.003 in.	Data taken from a curve; MgO as reference standard; normal incidence, hemispherical viewing.
●	63-16	298	0.23-2.65	5	Same as above except composition: 85 Al_2O_3, 12 Ti Al, and 3 NH_4 Cl and coating thickness 0.004 in.	Same as above.
△	63-16	298	0.23-2.65	5	Same as above except composition: 77 Al_2O_3, 7 Al, 13 Ti, and 3 NaI and coating thickness 0.003 in.	Same as above.

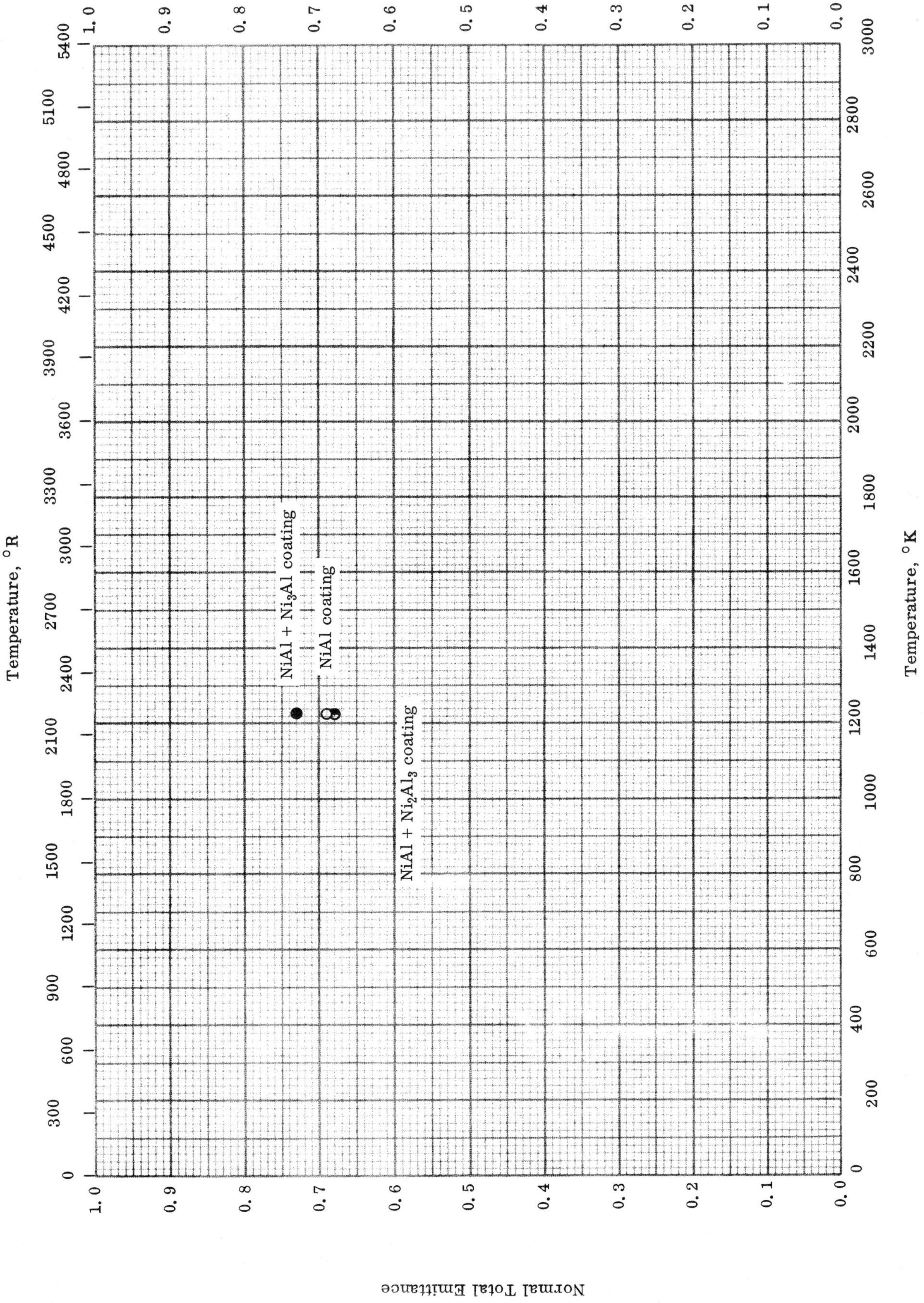

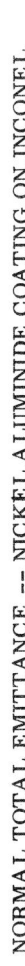

NORMAL TOTAL EMITTANCE -- NICKEL ALUMINIDE COATING ON INCONEL

NORMAL TOTAL EMITTANCE -- NICKEL ALUMINIDE COATING ON INCONEL

REFERENCE INFORMATION

Symbol	Ref.	Temp. Range °K	Rept. Error %	Sample Specifications	Remarks
○	63-16	1223	± 8	Highly pure Inconel plate substrate; NiAl coating thickness 0.0005 in.	Measured in argon; calculated from spectral data.
●	63-16	1223	± 8	Highly pure Inconel plate substrate; NiAl + Ni_3Al coating thickness 0.0015 in.	Measured in argon; calculated from spectral data.
◑	63-16	1223	± 8	Highly pure Inconel plate substrate; NiAl + Ni_2Al_3 coating thickness 0.002 in.	Measured in argon; calculated from spectral data.

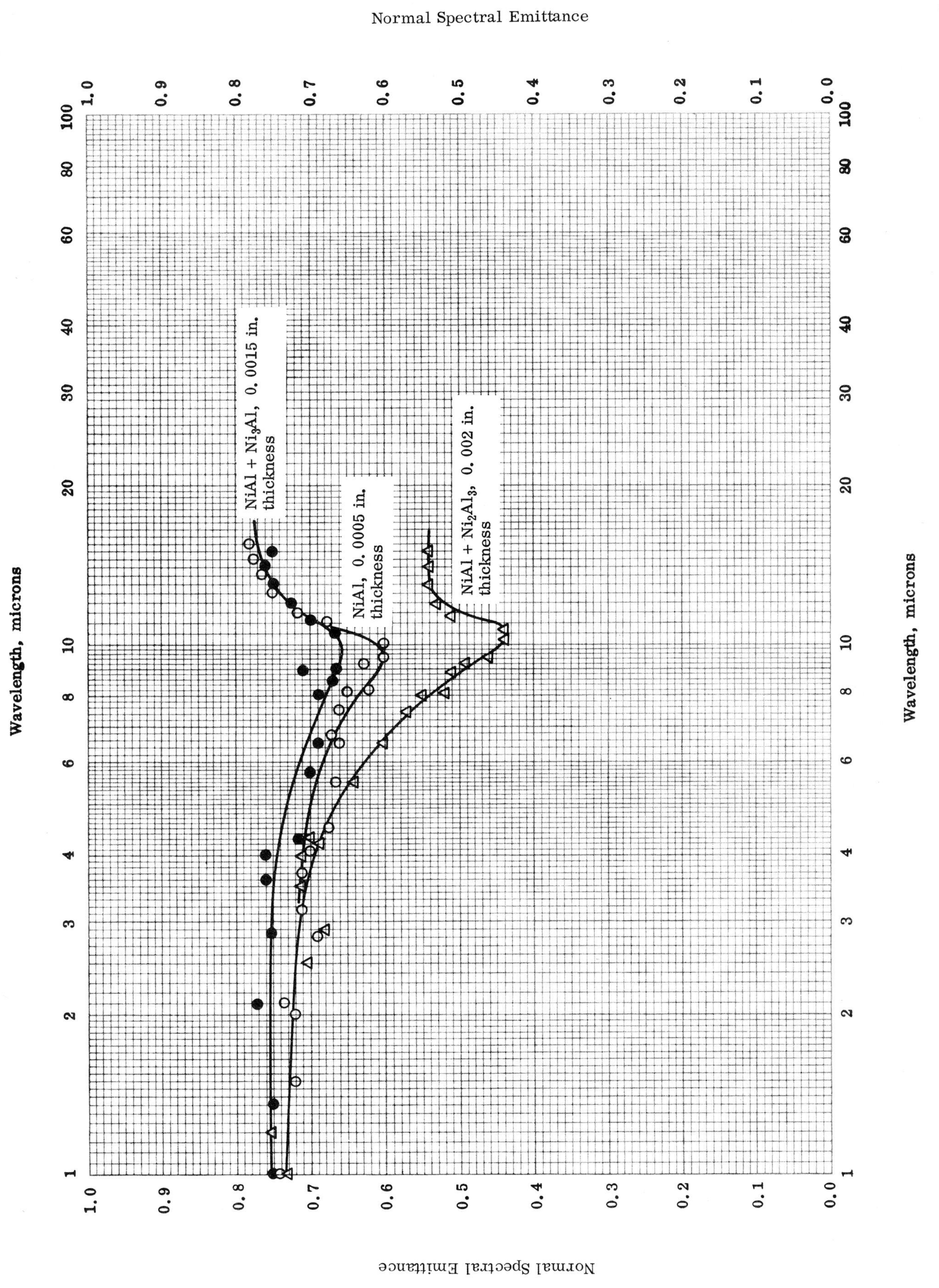

NORMAL SPECTRAL EMITTANCE -- NICKEL ALUMINIDE COATING ON INCONEL

NORMAL SPECTRAL EMITTANCE -- NICKEL ALUMINIDE COATING ON INCONEL

REFERENCE INFORMATION

Symbol	Ref.	Temp. °K	Wavelength Range, μ	Rept. Error %	Sample Specifications	Remarks
○	63-16	1223	1-15		Highly pure Inconel plate substrate; NiAl coating thickness 0.0005 in.	Measured in argon; data taken from a curve.
●	63-16	1223	1-15		Highly pure Inconel plate substrate; NiAl + Ni_3Al coating thickness 0.0015 in.	Measured in argon; data taken from a curve.
△	63-16	1223	1-15		Highly pure Inconel plate substrate NiAl + Ni_2Al_3 coating thickness 0.002 in.	Measured in argon; data taken from a curve.

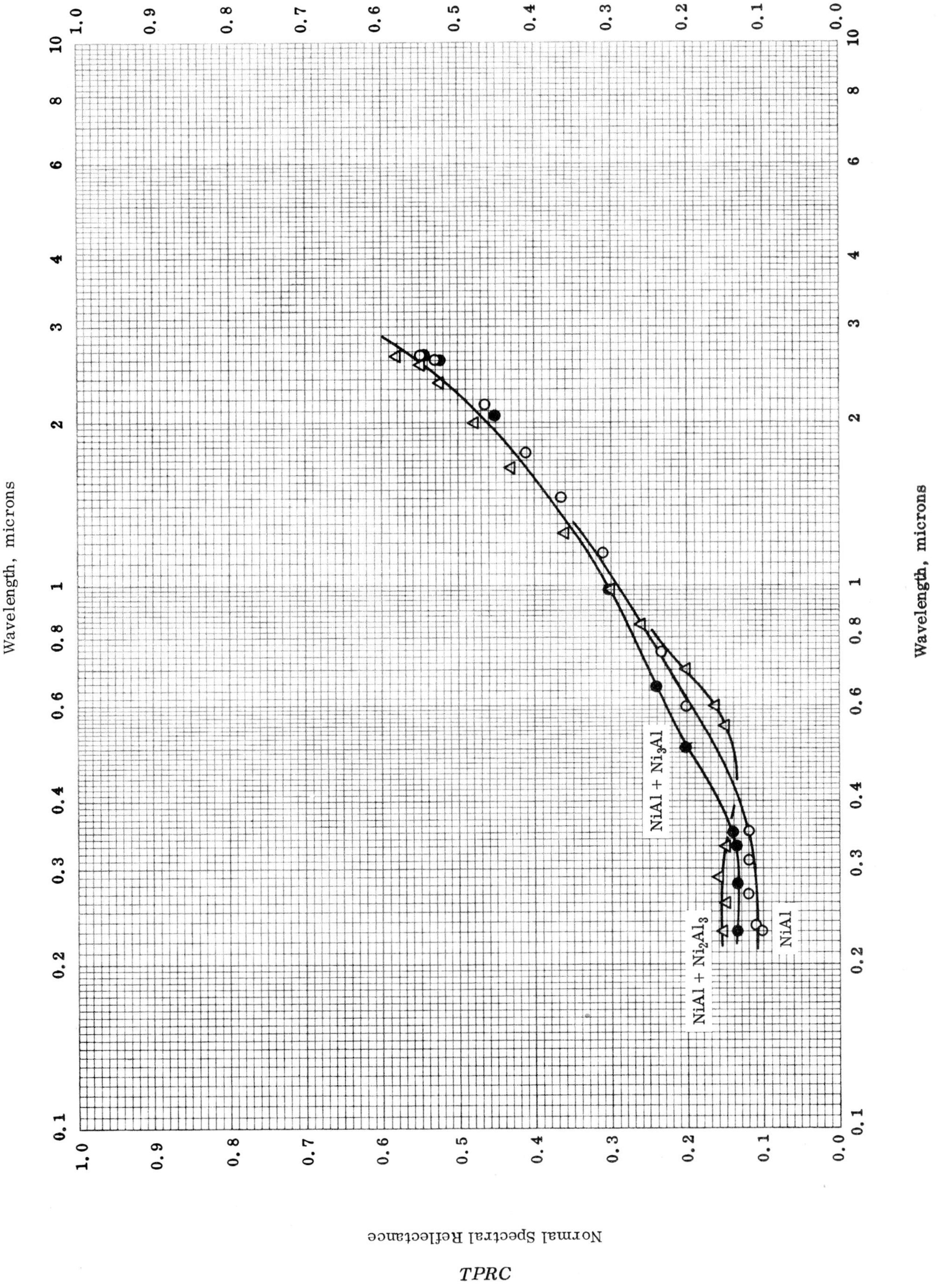

NORMAL SPECTRAL REFLECTANCE -- NICKEL ALUMINIDE COATING ON INCONEL

NORMAL SPECTRAL REFLECTANCE -- NICKEL ALUMINIDE COATING ON INCONEL

REFERENCE INFORMATION

Symbol	Ref.	Temp. °K	Wavelength Range, μ	Rept. Error %	Sample Specifications	Remarks
○	63-16	298	0.23-2.65	5	Highly pure Inconel plate substrate; NiAl coating thickness 0.0005 in.	Data taken from a curve; MgO as reference standard; normal incidence, hemispherical viewing.
●	63-16	298	0.23-2.65	5	Highly pure Inconel plate substrate; NiAl + Ni_3Al coating thickness 0.0015 in.	Data taken from a curve; MgO as reference standard; normal incidence, hemispherical viewing.
△	63-16	298	0.23-2.65	5	Highly pure Inconel plate substrate; NiAl + Ni_2Al_3 coating thickness 0.002 in.	Data taken from a curve; MgO as reference standard; normal incidence, hemispherical viewing.

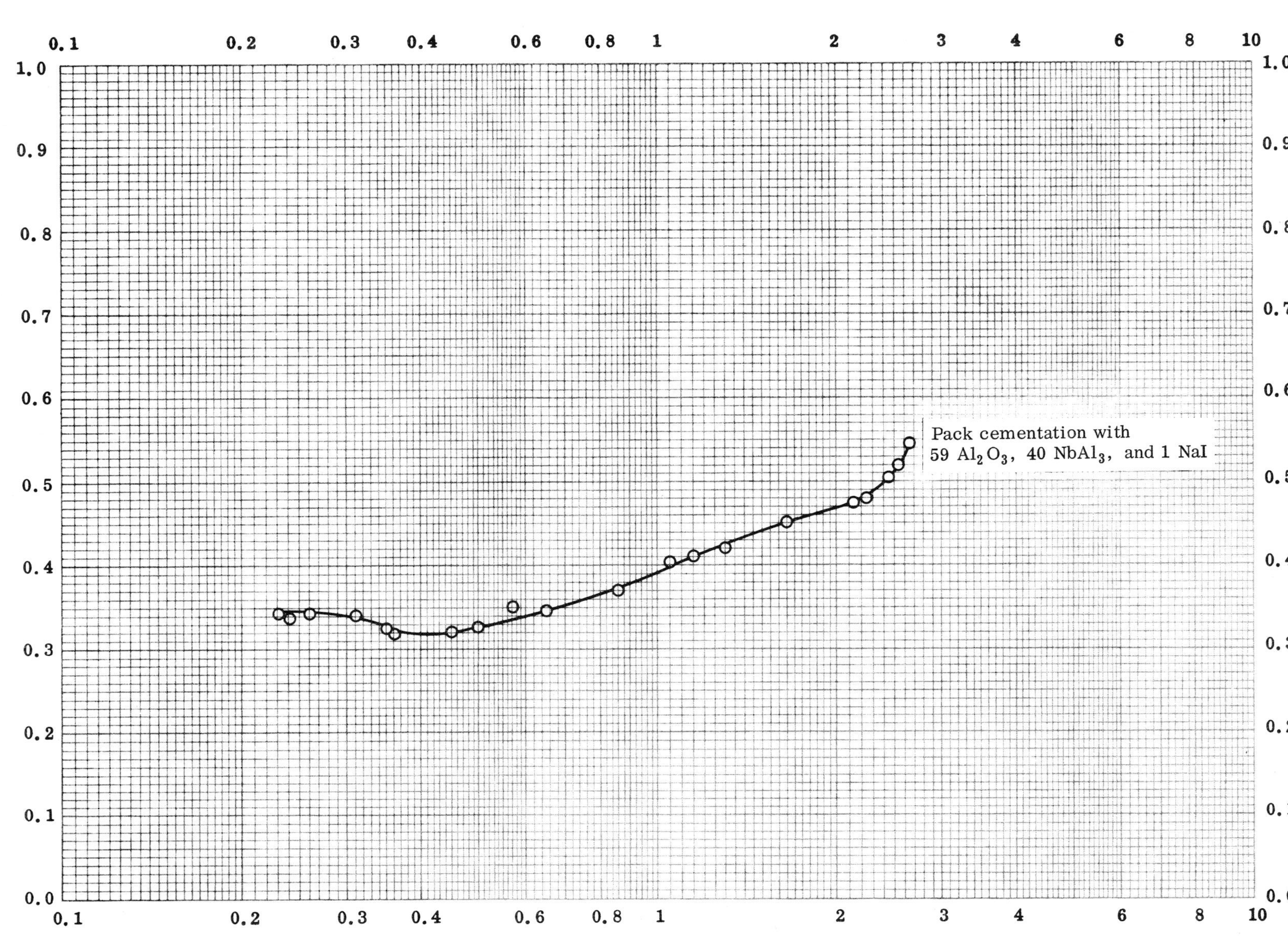

NORMAL SPECTRAL REFLECTANCE -- NIOBIUM ALUMINIDE COATING ON NIOBIUM

NORMAL SPECTRAL REFLECTANCE -- NIOBIUM ALUMINIDE COATING ON NIOBIUM

REFERENCE INFORMATION

Symbol	Ref.	Temp. °K	Wavelength Range, μ	Rept. Error %	Sample Specifications	Remarks
○	63-16	298	0.23-2.65	5	Highly pure Nb plate substrate; coating prepared by pack cementation with composition: 59 Al_2O_3, 40 Nb Al_3, and 1 NaI; coating thickness 0.001 in.	Data taken from a curve; MgO as reference standard; normal incidence, hemispherical viewing.

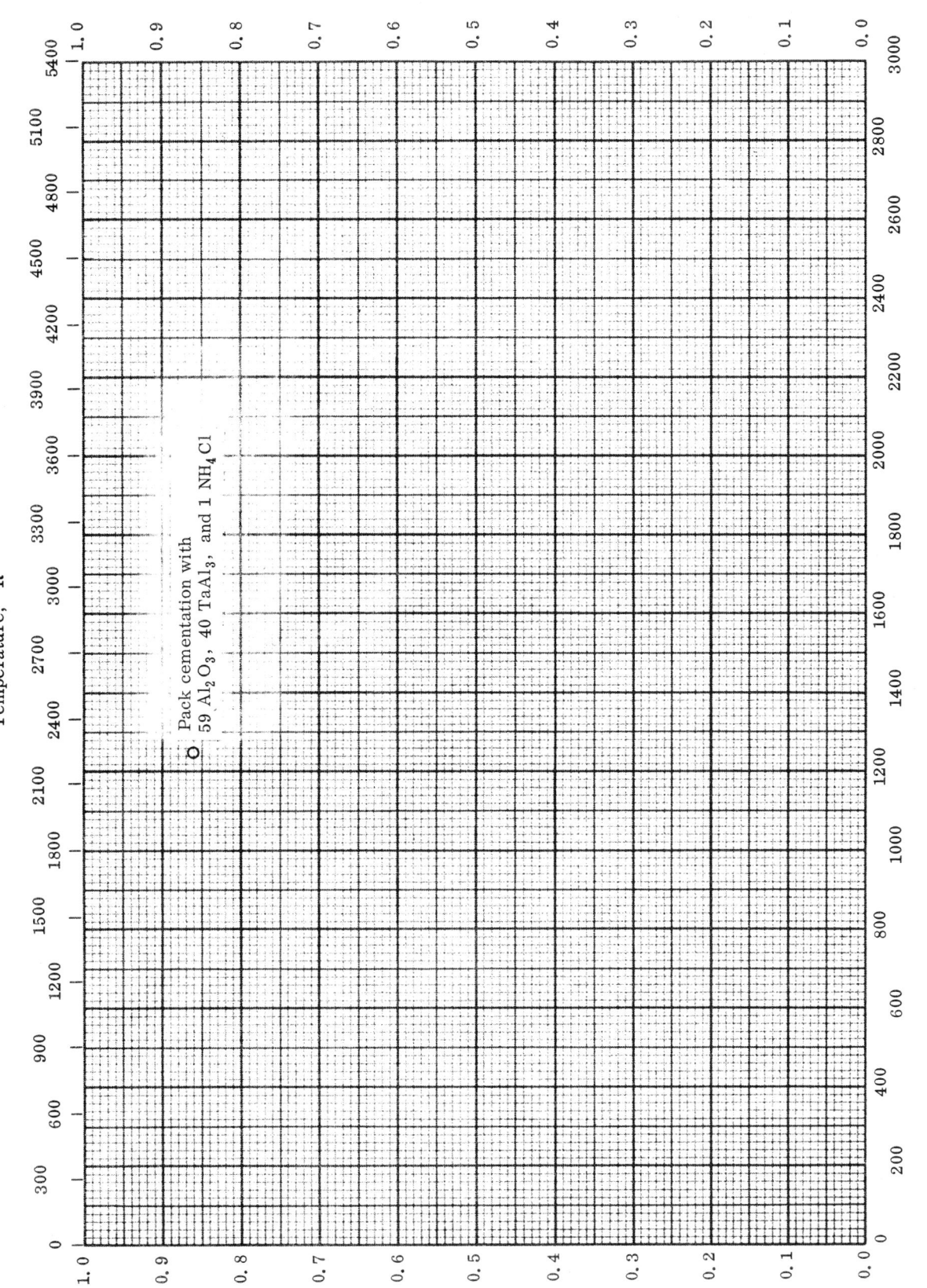

Temperature, °R

0 300 600 900 1200 1500 1800 2100 2400 2700 3000 3300 3600 3900 4200 4500 4800 5100 5400

Normal Total Emittance

1.0 0.9 0.8 0.7 0.6 0.5 0.4 0.3 0.2 0.1 0.0

○ Pack cementation with 59 Al_2O_3, 40 $TaAl_3$, and 1 NH_4Cl

0 200 400 600 800 1000 1200 1400 1600 1800 2000 2200 2400 2600 2800 3000

Temperature, °K

NORMAL TOTAL EMITTANCE -- TANTALUM ALUMINIDE COATING ON TANTALUM

NORMAL TOTAL EMITTANCE -- TANTALUM ALUMINIDE COATING ON TANTALUM

REFERENCE INFORMATION

Symbol	Ref.	Temp. Range °K	Rept. Error %	Sample Specifications	Remarks
○	63-16	1223	± 8	Highly pure Ta plate substrate; coating prepared by pack cementation with composition: 59 Al_2O_3, 40 $TaAl_3$, and 1 NH_4Cl; coating thickness 0.001 in.	Measured in argon; calculated from spectral data.

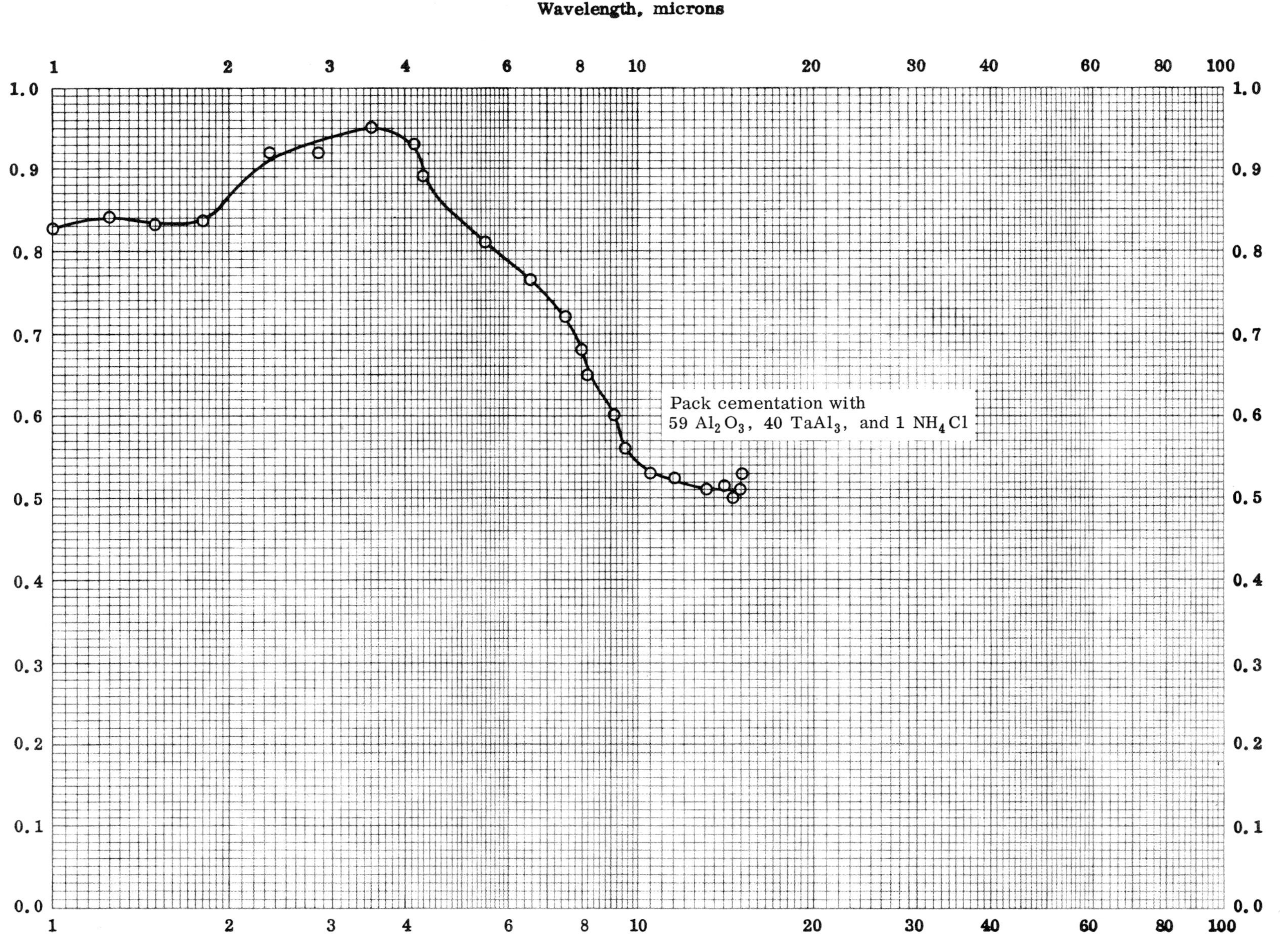

NORMAL SPECTRAL EMITTANCE — TANTALUM ALUMINIDE COATING ON TANTALUM

NORMAL SPECTRAL EMITTANCE — TANTALUM ALUMINIDE COATING ON TANTALUM

REFERENCE INFORMATION

Symbol	Ref.	Temp. ° K	Wavelength Range, μ	Rept. Error %	Sample Specifications	Remarks
○	63-16	1223	1-15		Highly pure Ta plate substrate; coating prepared by pack cementation with composition: 59 Al_2O_3, 40 $TaAl_3$, 1 NH_4Cl, coating thickness 0.001 in.	Measured in argon; data taken from a curve.

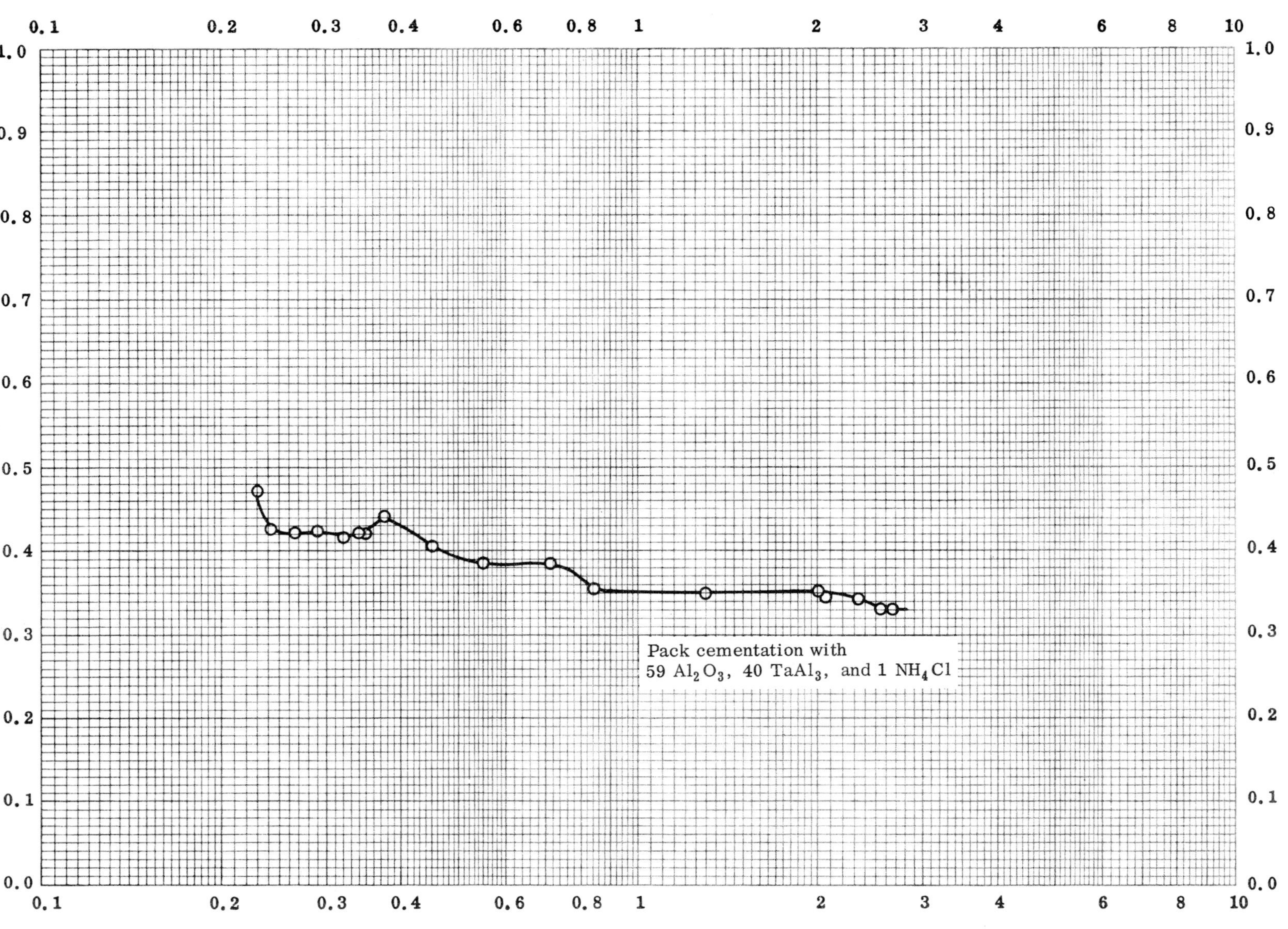

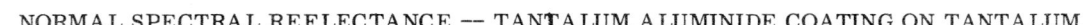

NORMAL SPECTRAL REFLECTANCE -- TANTALUM ALUMINIDE COATING ON TANTALUM

NORMAL SPECTRAL REFLECTANCE -- TANTALUM ALUMINIDE COATING ON TANTALUM

REFERENCE INFORMATION

Symbol	Ref.	Temp. °K	Wavelength Range, μ	Rept. Error %	Sample Specifications	Remarks
○	63-16	298	0.23-2.65	5	Highly pure Ta plate substrate; coating prepared by pack cementation with composition: 59 Al_2O_3, 40 $TaAl_3$, and 1 NH_4 Cl; coating thickness 0.001 in.	Data taken from a curve; MgO as reference standard; normal incidence, hemispherical viewing.

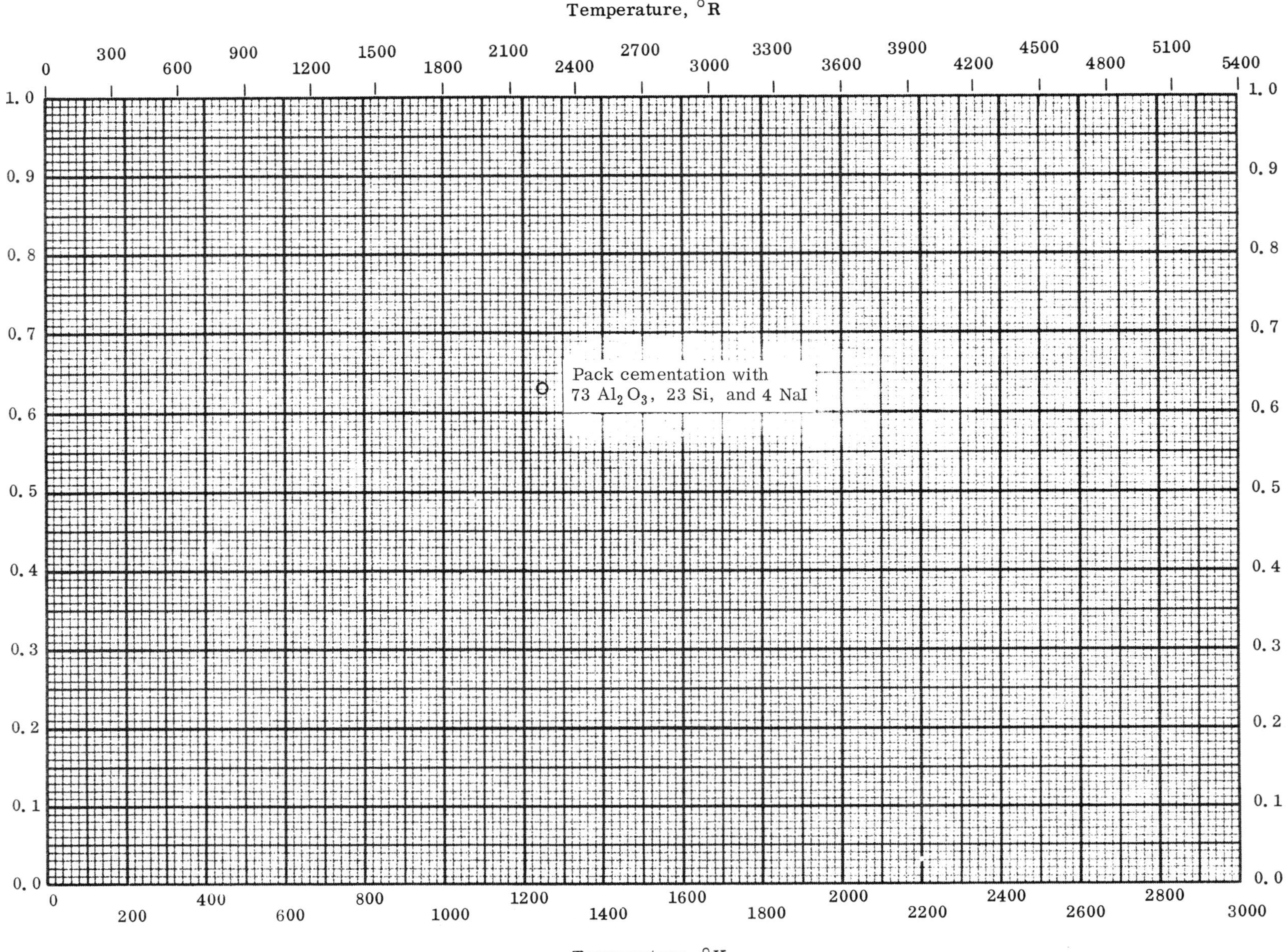

NORMAL TOTAL EMITTANCE -- SILICIDE COATING ON MOLYBDENUM

NORMAL TOTAL EMITTANCE -- SILICIDE COATING ON MOLYBDENUM

REFERENCE INFORMATION

Symbol	Ref.	Temp. Range °K	Rept. Error %	Sample Specifications	Remarks
○	63-16	1223	± 8	Highly pure Mo plate substrate; coating prepared by pack cementation with composition: 73 Al_2O_3, 23 Si, and 4 NaI; coating thickness 0.002 in.	Measured in argon; calculated from spectral data.

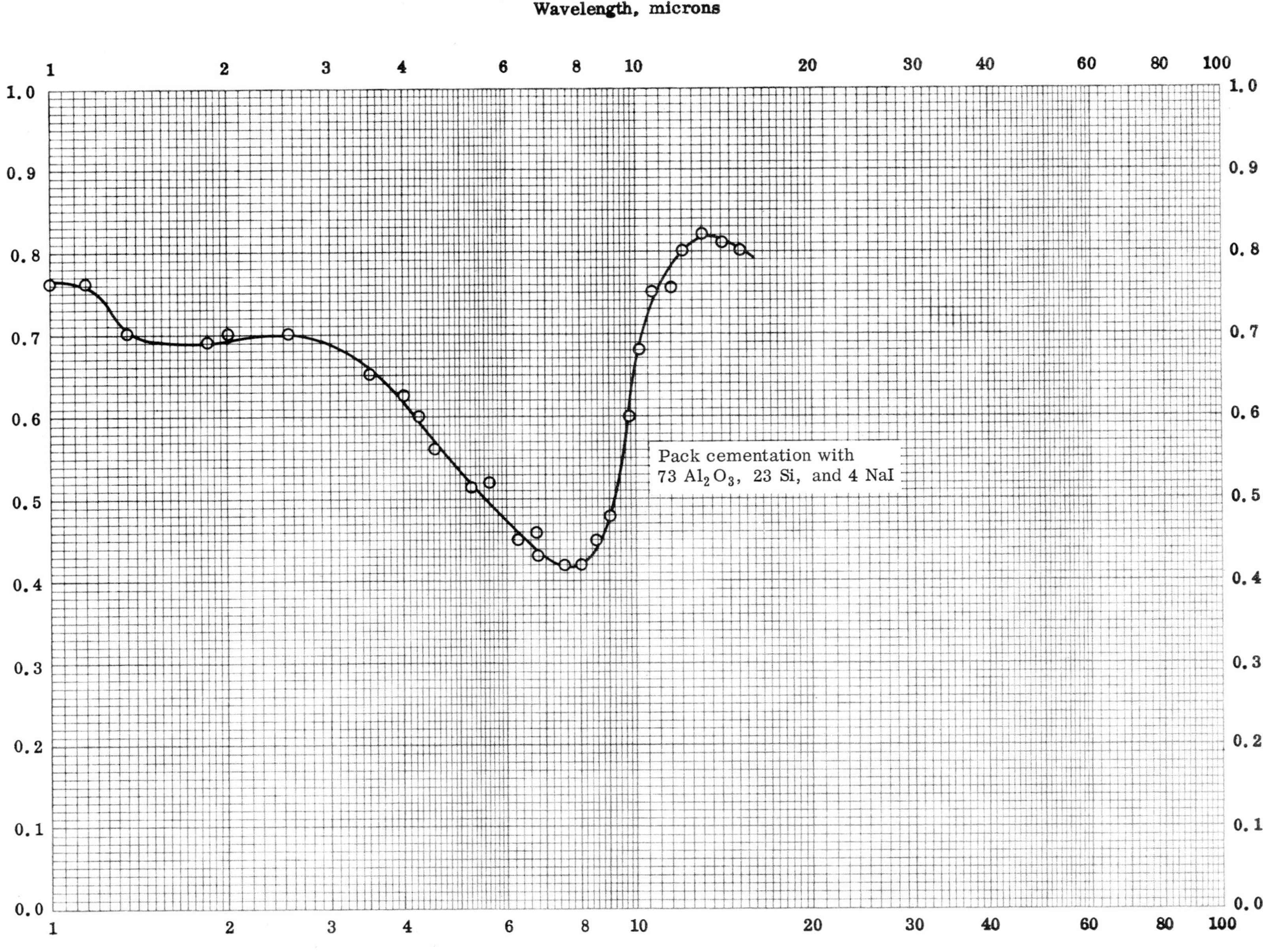

NORMAL SPECTRAL EMITTANCE -- SILICIDE COATING ON MOLYBDENUM

NORMAL SPECTRAL EMITTANCE -- SILICIDE COATING ON MOLYBDENUM

REFERENCE INFORMATION

Symbol	Ref.	Temp. °K	Wavelength Range, μ	Rept. Error%	Sample Specifications	Remarks
○	63-16	1223	1-15		Highly pure Mo plate substrate; coating prepared by pack cementation with composition: 73 Al_2O_3, 23 Si, and 4 NaI; coating thickness 0.002 in.	Measured in argon; data taken from a curve.

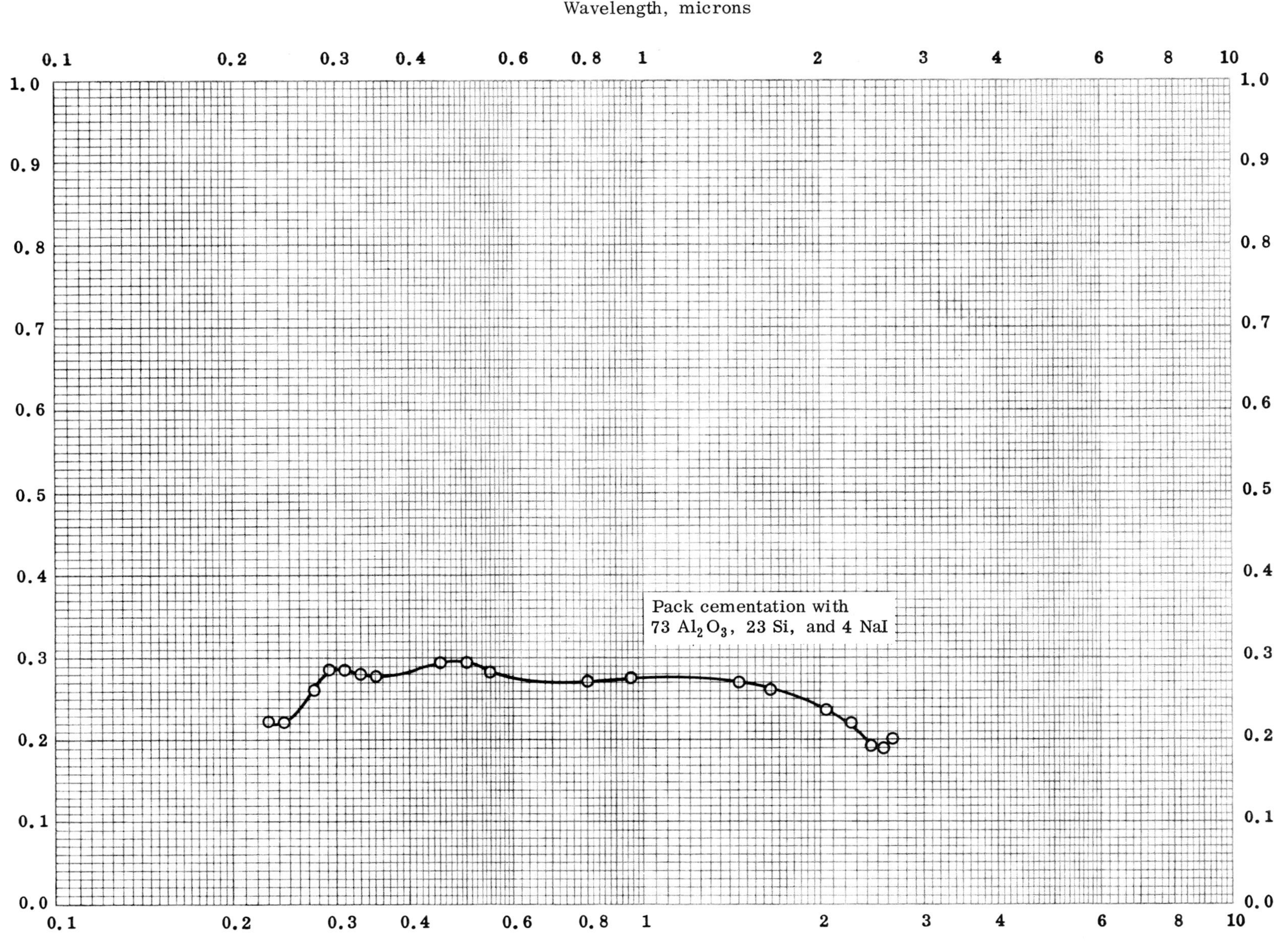

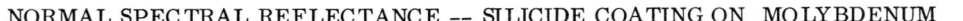

NORMAL SPECTRAL REFLECTANCE -- SILICIDE COATING ON MOLYBDENUM

NORMAL SPECTRAL REFLECTANCE -- SILICIDE COATING ON MOLYBDENUM

REFERENCE INFORMATION

Symbol	Ref.	Temp. °K	Wavelength Range, μ	Rept. Error%	Sample Specifications	Remarks
○	63-16	298	0.23-2.65	5	Highly pure Mo plate substrate; coating prepared by pack cementation with composition: 73 Al_2O_3, 23 Si, and 4 NaI; coating thickness 0.002 in.	Data taken from a curve; MgO as reference standard; normal incidence, hemispherical viewing.

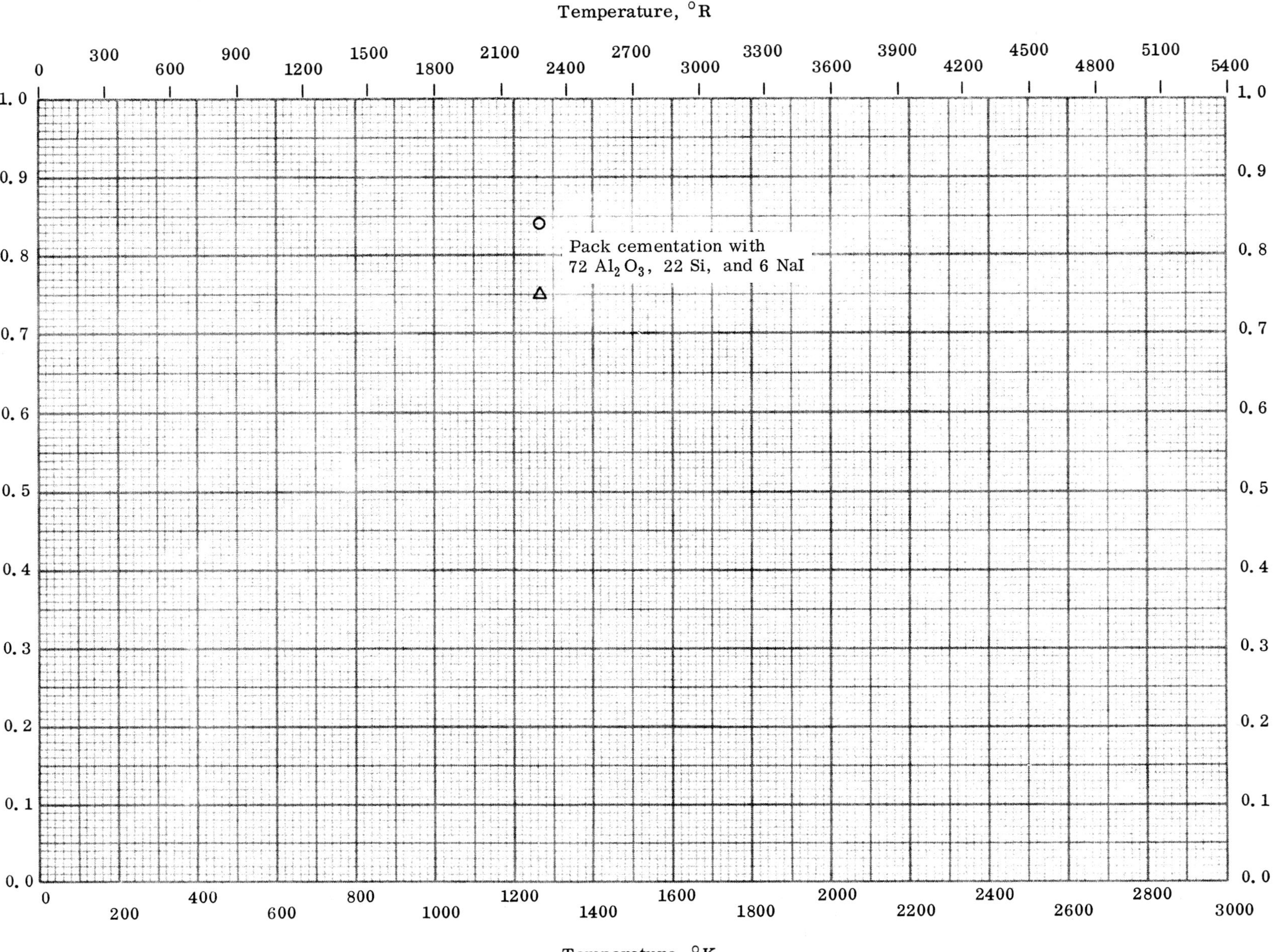

NORMAL TOTAL EMITTANCE -- SILICIDE COATING ON TANTALUM

NORMAL TOTAL EMITTANCE -- SILICIDE COATING ON TANTALUM

REFERENCE INFORMATION

Symbol	Ref.	Temp. Range °K	Rept. Error %	Sample Specifications	Remarks
○	63-16	1223	± 8	Highly pure Ta plate substrate; coating prepared by pack cementation with composition: 72 Al_2O_3, 22 Si, and 6 NaI; coating thickness 0.002 in.	Measured in argon; calculated from spectral data; first run.
△	63-16	1223	± 8	Same as above.	Same as above; second run.

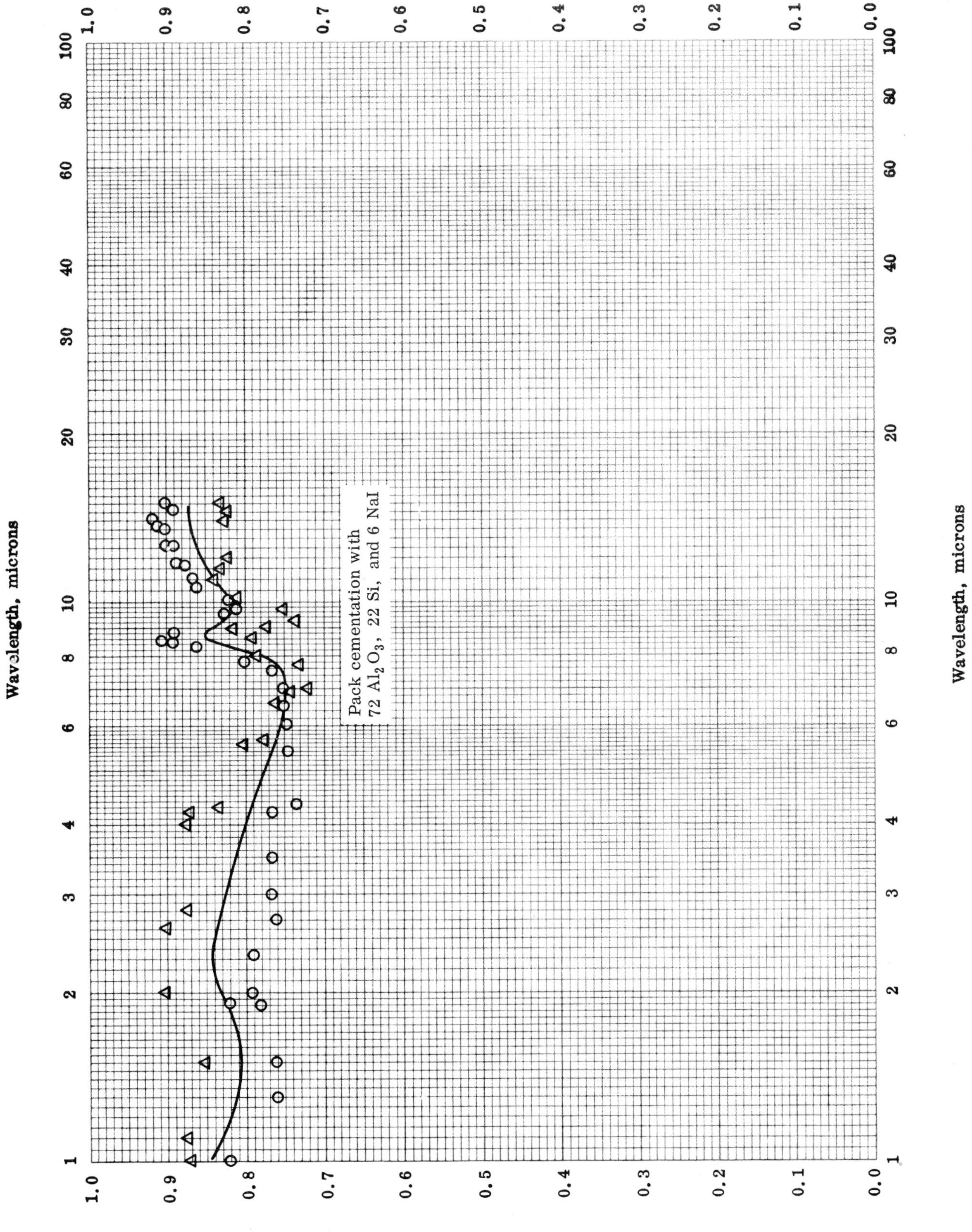

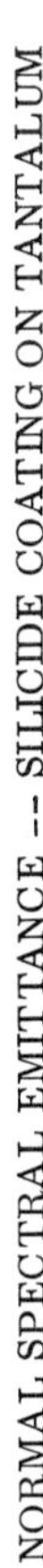

Wavelength, microns
Normal Spectral Emittance
Pack cementation with
72 Al_2O_3, 22 Si, and 6 NaI
1 2 3 4 6 8 10 20 30 40 60 80 100
0.0 0.1 0.2 0.3 0.4 0.5 0.6 0.7 0.8 0.9 1.0

NORMAL SPECTRAL EMITTANCE -- SILICIDE COATING ON TANTALUM

NORMAL SPECTRAL EMITTANCE -- SILICIDE COATING ON TANTALUM

REFERENCE INFORMATION

Symbol	Ref.	Temp. °K	Wavelength Range, μ	Rept. Error %	Sample Specifications	Remarks
○	63-16	1223	1-15		Highly pure Ta plate substrate; coating prepared by pack cementation with composition: 72 Al_2O_3, 22 Si, and 6 NaI; coating thickness 0.002 in.	Measured in argon; data taken from a curve; first run.
△	63-16	1223	1-15		Same as above.	Same as above; second run.

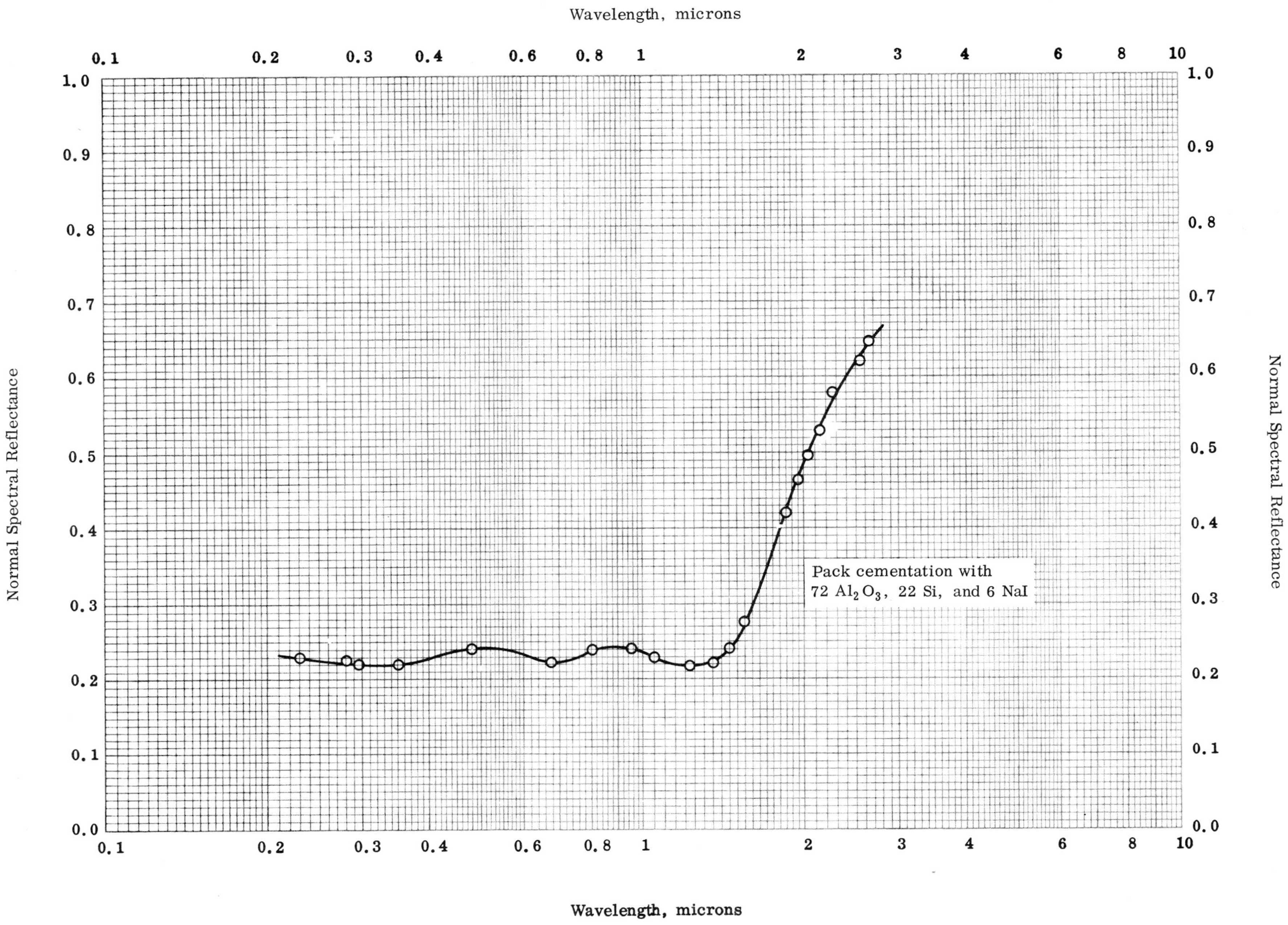

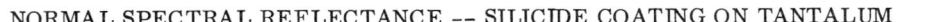

Wavelength, microns
0.1
0.2
0.3
0.4
0.6
0.8
1
2
3
4
6
8
10
Normal Spectral Reflectance
0.0
0.1
0.2
0.3
0.4
0.5
0.6
0.7
0.8
0.9
1.0
Pack cementation with
72 Al_2O_3, 22 Si, and 6 NaI

NORMAL SPECTRAL REFLECTANCE -- SILICIDE COATING ON TANTALUM

NORMAL SPECTRAL REFLECTANCE -- SILICIDE COATING ON TANTALUM

REFERENCE INFORMATION

Symbol	Ref.	Temp. °K	Wavelength Range, μ	Rept. Error%	Sample Specifications	Remarks
o	63-16	298	0.23-2.65	5	Highly pure Ta plate substrate; coating prepared by pack cementation with composition: 72 Al_2O_3, 22 Si, and 6 NaI; coating thickness 0.002 in.	Data taken from a curve; MgO as reference standard; normal incidence, hemispherical viewing.

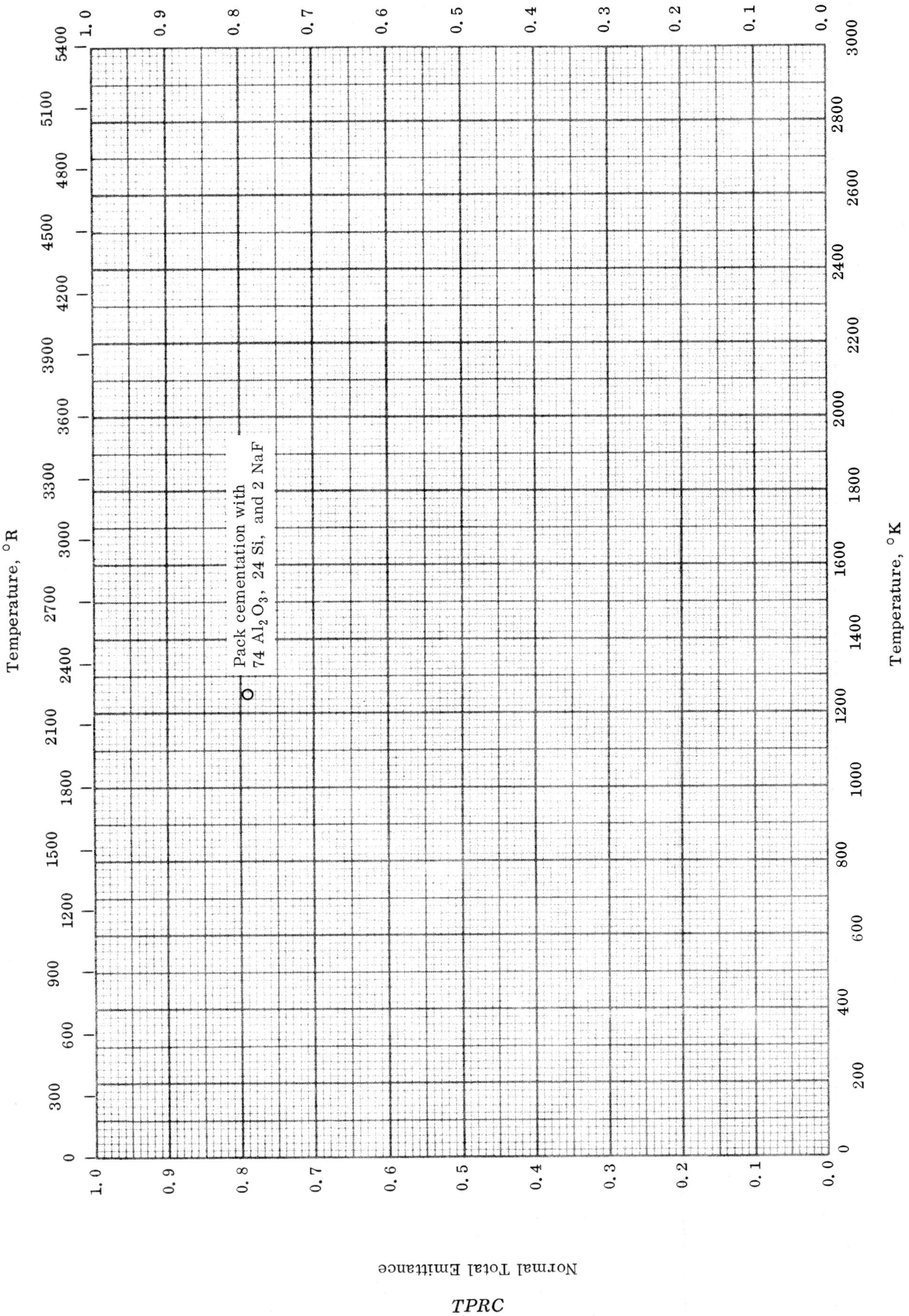

Pack cementation with 74 Al_2O_3, 24 Si, and 2 NaF

Temperature, °R

Temperature, °K

Normal Total Emittance

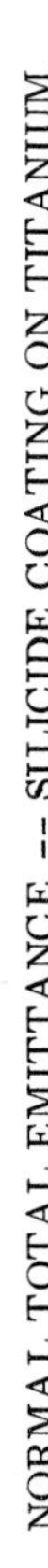

NORMAL TOTAL EMITTANCE -- SILICIDE COATING ON TITANIUM

NORMAL TOTAL EMITTANCE -- SILICIDE COATING ON TITANIUM

REFERENCE INFORMATION

Symbol	Ref.	Temp. Range °K	Rept. Error %	Sample Specifications	Remarks
○	63-16	1223	± 8	Highly pure Ti plate substrate; coating prepared by pack cementation with composition: 74 Al_2O_3, 24 Si and 2 NaF; coating thickness 0.002 in.	Measured in argon atmosphere; calculated from spectral data.

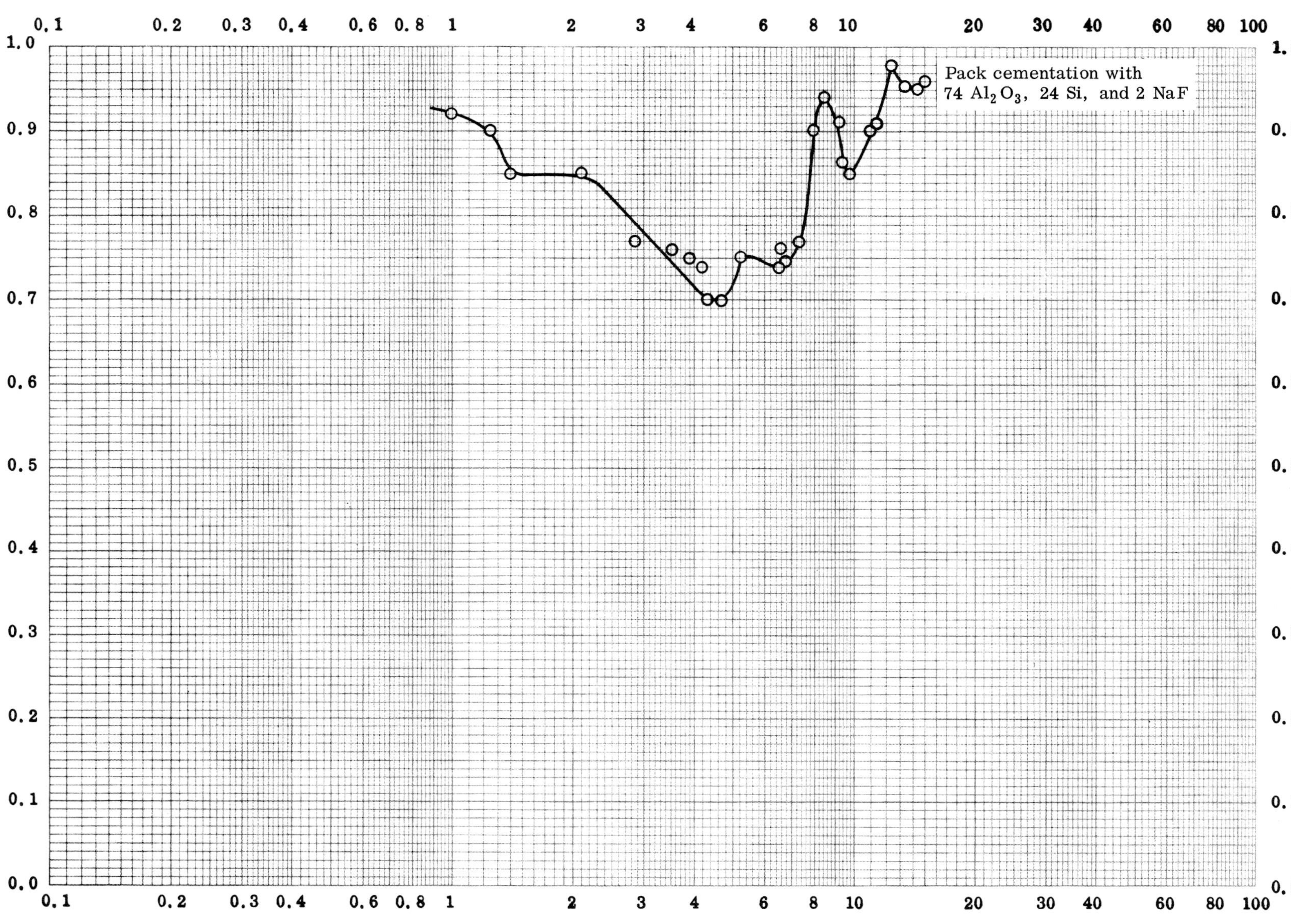

NORMAL SPECTRAL EMITTANCE -- SILICIDE COATING ON TITANIUM

NORMAL SPECTRAL EMITTANCE -- SILICIDE COATING ON TITANIUM

REFERENCE INFORMATION

Symbol	Ref.	Temp. °K	Wavelength Range, μ	Rept. Error %	Sample Specifications	Remarks
○	63-16	1223	1-15		Highly pure Ti plate substrate; coating prepared by pack cementation with composition: 74 Al_2O_3, 24 Si, and 2 NaF; coating thickness 0.002 in.	Measured in argon; data taken from a curve.

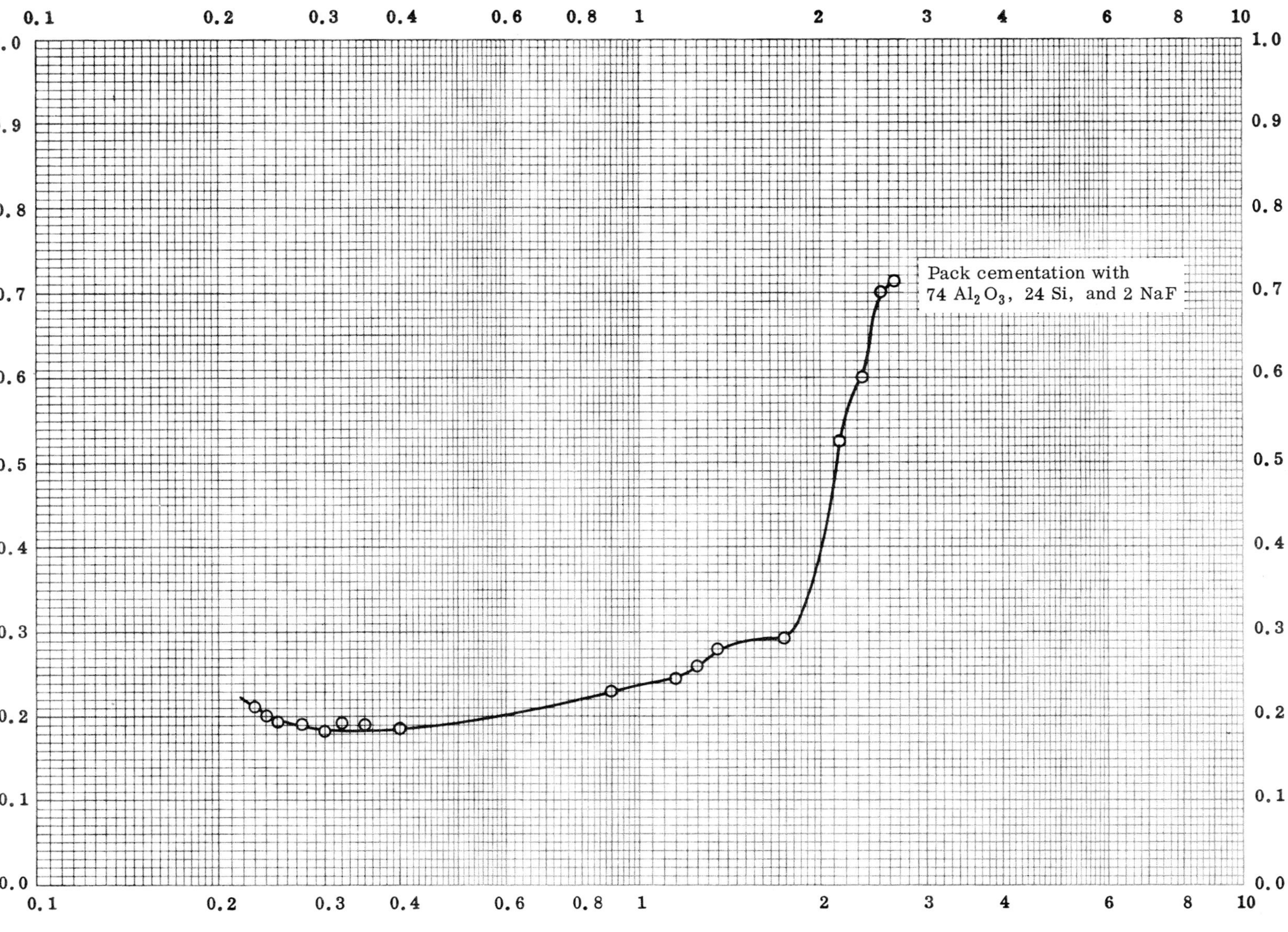

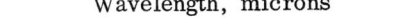

NORMAL SPECTRAL REFLECTANCE -- SILICIDE COATING ON TITANIUM

NORMAL SPECTRAL REFLECTANCE -- SILICIDE COATING ON TITANIUM

REFERENCE INFORMATION

Symbol	Ref.	Temp. °K	Wavelength Range, μ	Rept. Error%	Sample Specifications	Remarks
○	63-16	298	0.23-2.65	5	Highly pure Ti plate substrate; coating prepared by pack cementation with composition: 74 Al_2O_3, 24 Si, and 2 NaF; coating thickness 0.002 in.	Data taken from a curve; MgO as reference standard; normal incidence, hemispherical viewing.

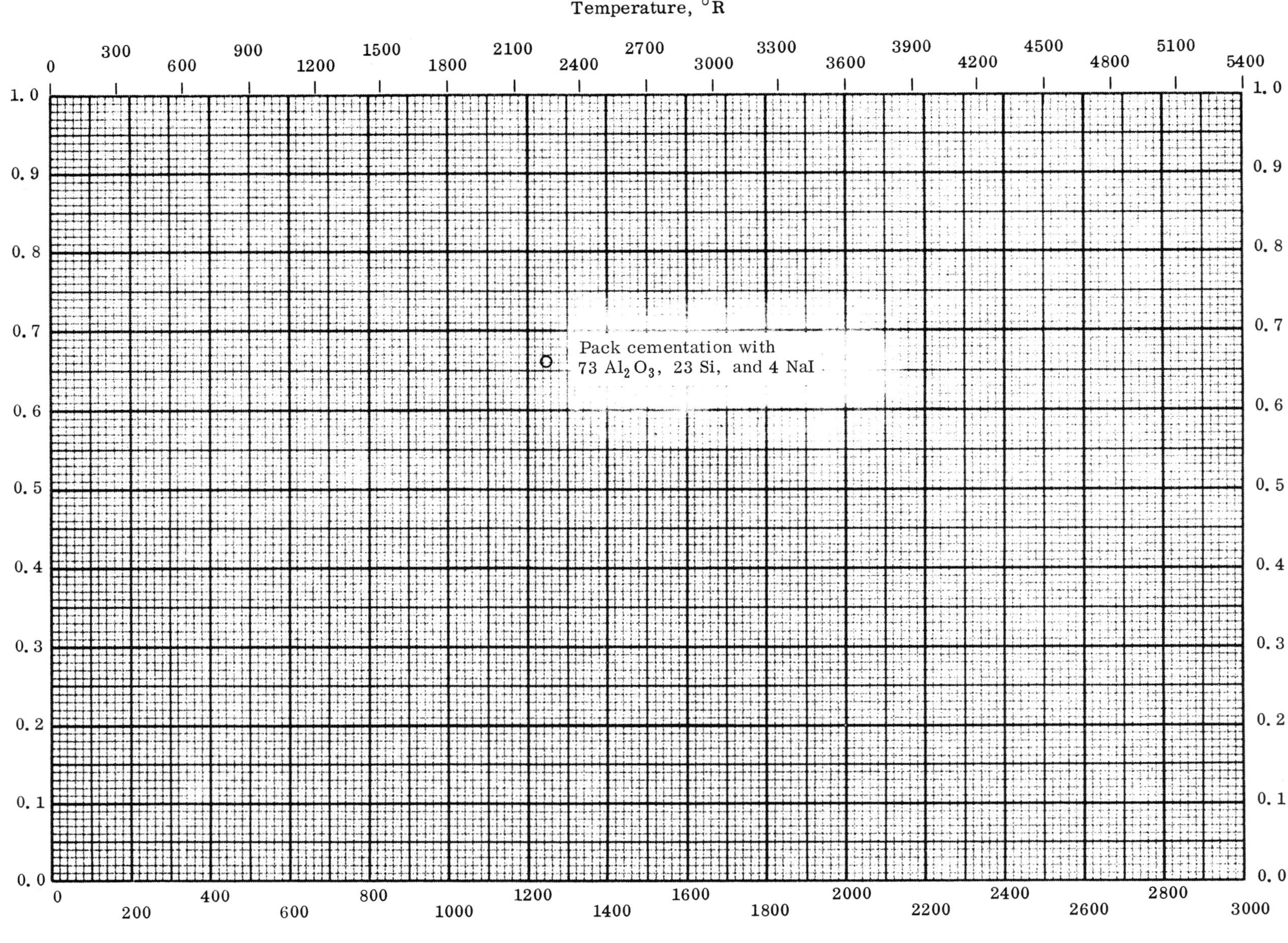

NORMAL TOTAL EMITTANCE -- SILICIDE COATING ON TUNGSTEN

NORMAL TOTAL EMITTANCE -- SILICIDE COATING ON TUNGSTEN

REFERENCE INFORMATION

Symbol	Ref.	Temp. Range °K	Rept. Error %	Sample Specifications	Remarks
○	63-16	1223	± 8	Highly pure W plate substrate; coating prepared by pack cementation with composition: 73 Al_2O_3, 23 Si, and 4 NaI; coating thickness 0.001 in.	Measured in argon; calculated from spectral data.

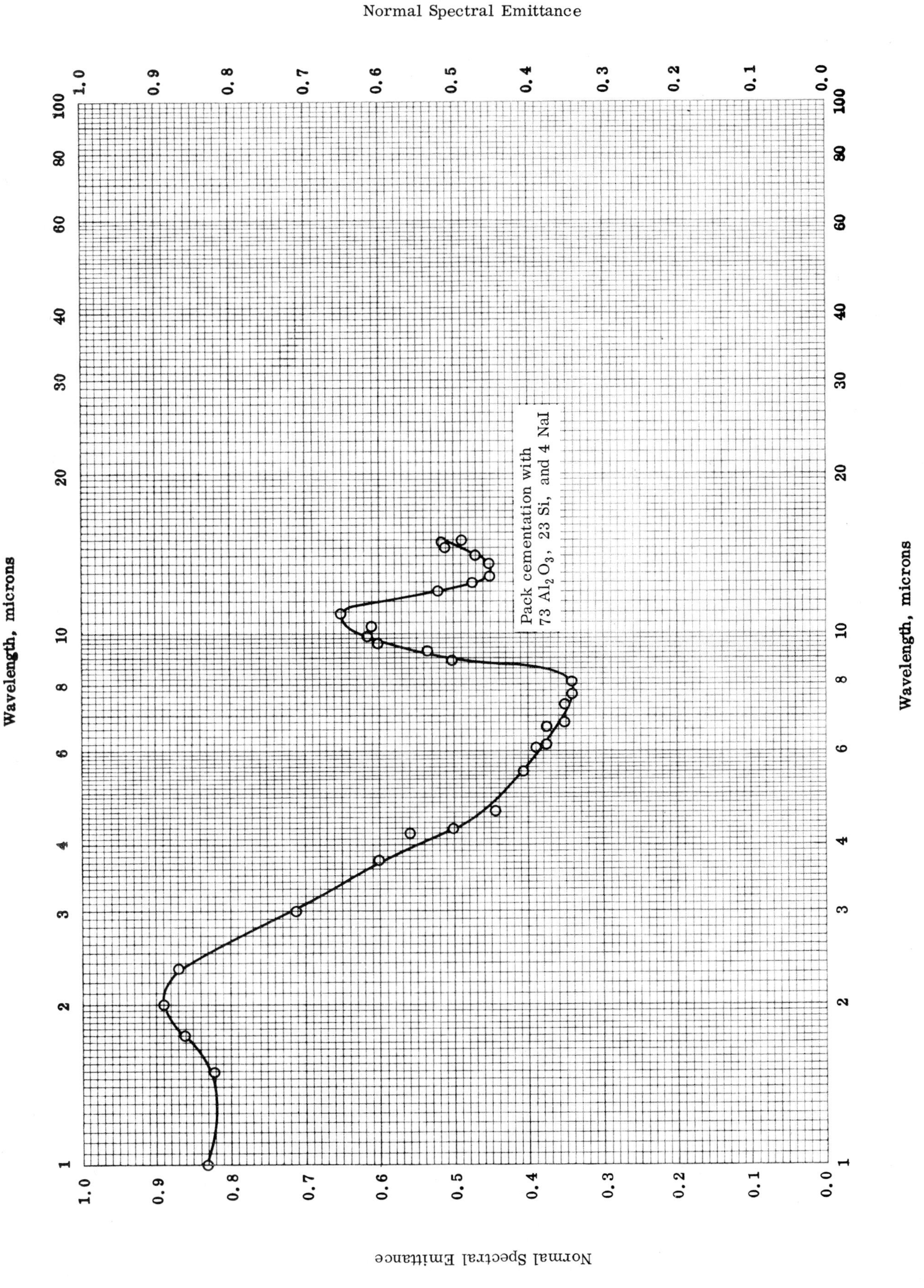

Wavelength, microns

Normal Spectral Emittance

Pack cementation with
73 Al_2O_3, 23 Si, and 4 NaI

Normal Spectral Emittance

Wavelength, microns

NORMAL SPECTRAL EMITTANCE -- SILICIDE COATING ON TUNGSTEN

NORMAL SPECTRAL EMITTANCE -- SILICIDE COATING ON TUNGSTEN

REFERENCE INFORMATION

Symbol	Ref.	Temp. °K	Wavelength Range, μ	Rept. Error %	Sample Specifications	Remarks
○	63-16	1223	1-15		Highly pure W plate substrate; coating prepared by pack cementation with composition: 73 Al_2O_3, 23 Si, and 4 NaI; coating thickness 0.001 in.	Measured in argon; data taken from a curve.

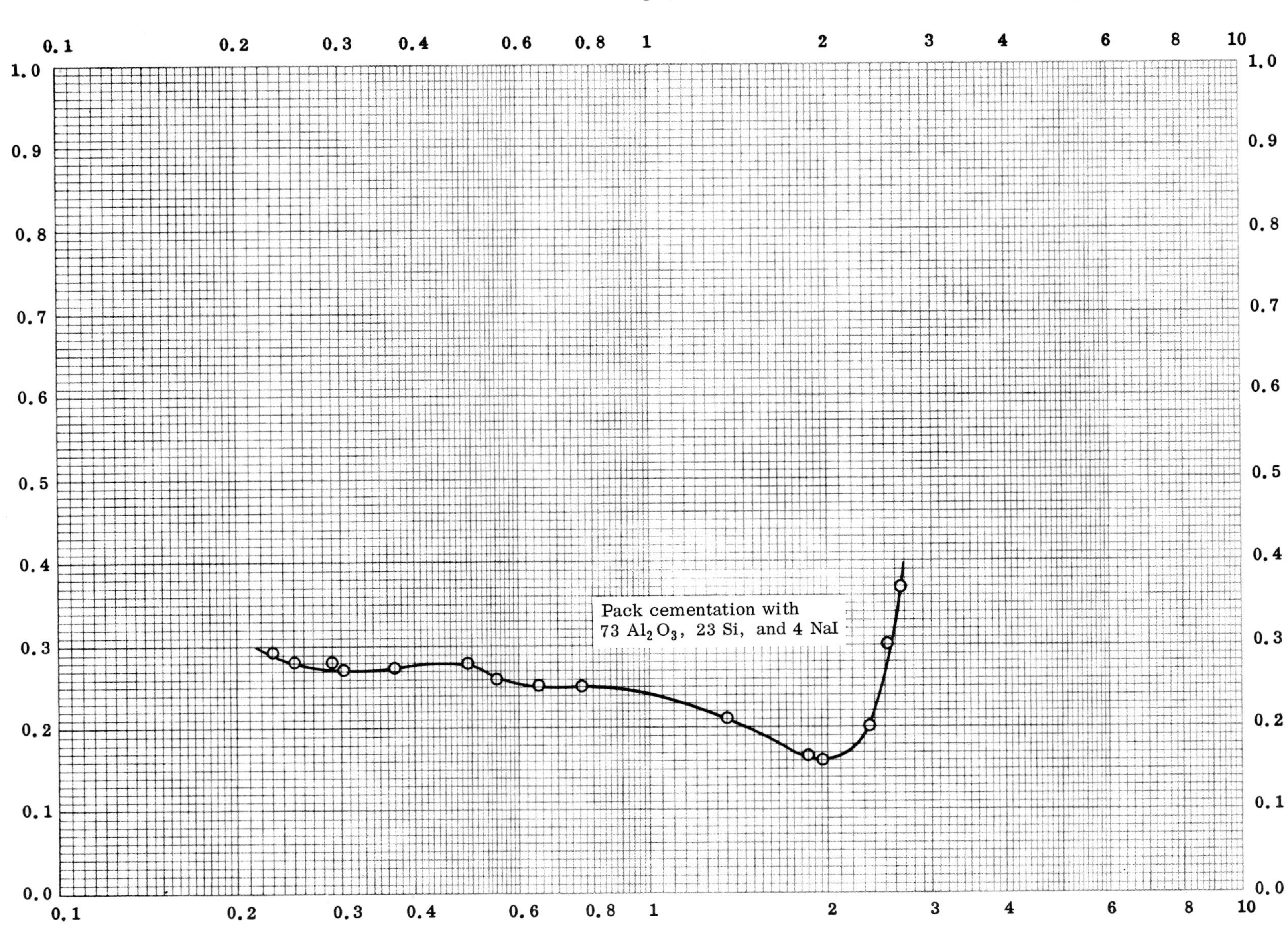

Wavelength, microns

NORMAL SPECTRAL REFLECTANCE -- SILICIDE COATING ON TUNGSTEN

NORMAL SPECTRAL REFLECTANCE -- SILICIDE COATING ON TUNGSTEN

REFERENCE INFORMATION

Symbol	Ref.	Temp. °K	Wavelength Range, μ	Rept. Error%	Sample Specifications	Remarks
○	63-16	298	0.23-2.65	5	Highly pure W plate substrate; coating prepared by pack cementation with composition: 72 Al_2O_3, 23 Si, and 4 NaI; coating thickness 0.001 in.	Data taken from a curve; MgO as reference standard; normal incidence, hemispherical viewing.

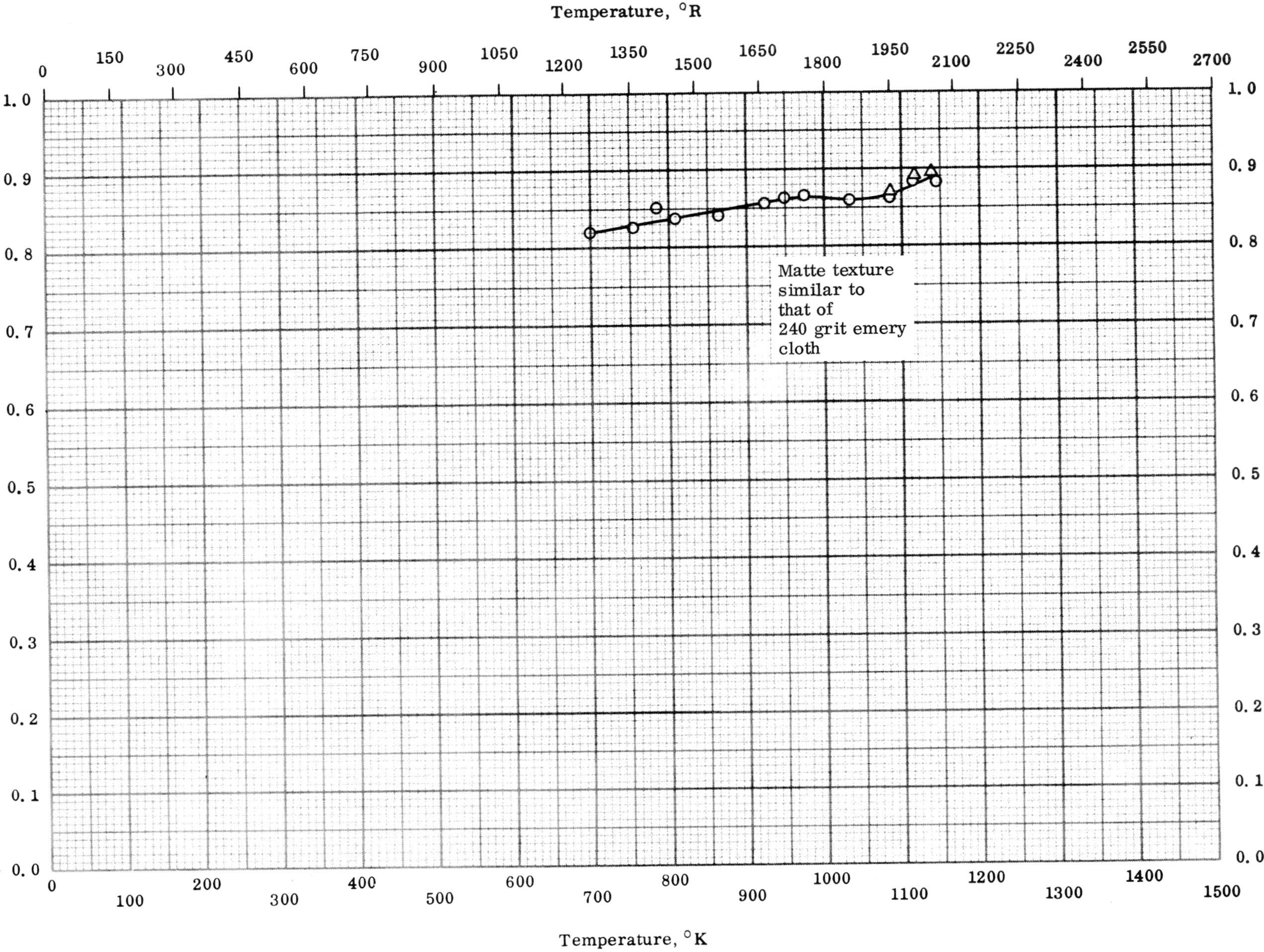

HEMISPHERICAL TOTAL EMITTANCE -- KENNAMETAL K-151A COATING ON STAINLESS STEEL

HEMISPHERICAL TOTAL EMITTANCE -- KENNAMETAL K-151A COATING ON STAINLESS STEEL

REFERENCE INFORMATION

Symbol	Ref.	Temp. Range °K	Rept. Error %	Sample Specifications	Remarks
○	63-23	699-1144		Oxidized Kennametal K-151A coating on AISI-310 stainless steel; coating thickness 0.004 in. with matte texture similar to that of 240 grit emery cloth.	Plasma-arc spray; measured in vacuum; using thermocouple.
△	63-23	1086-1139		Same as above.	Same as above; using optical pyrometer.

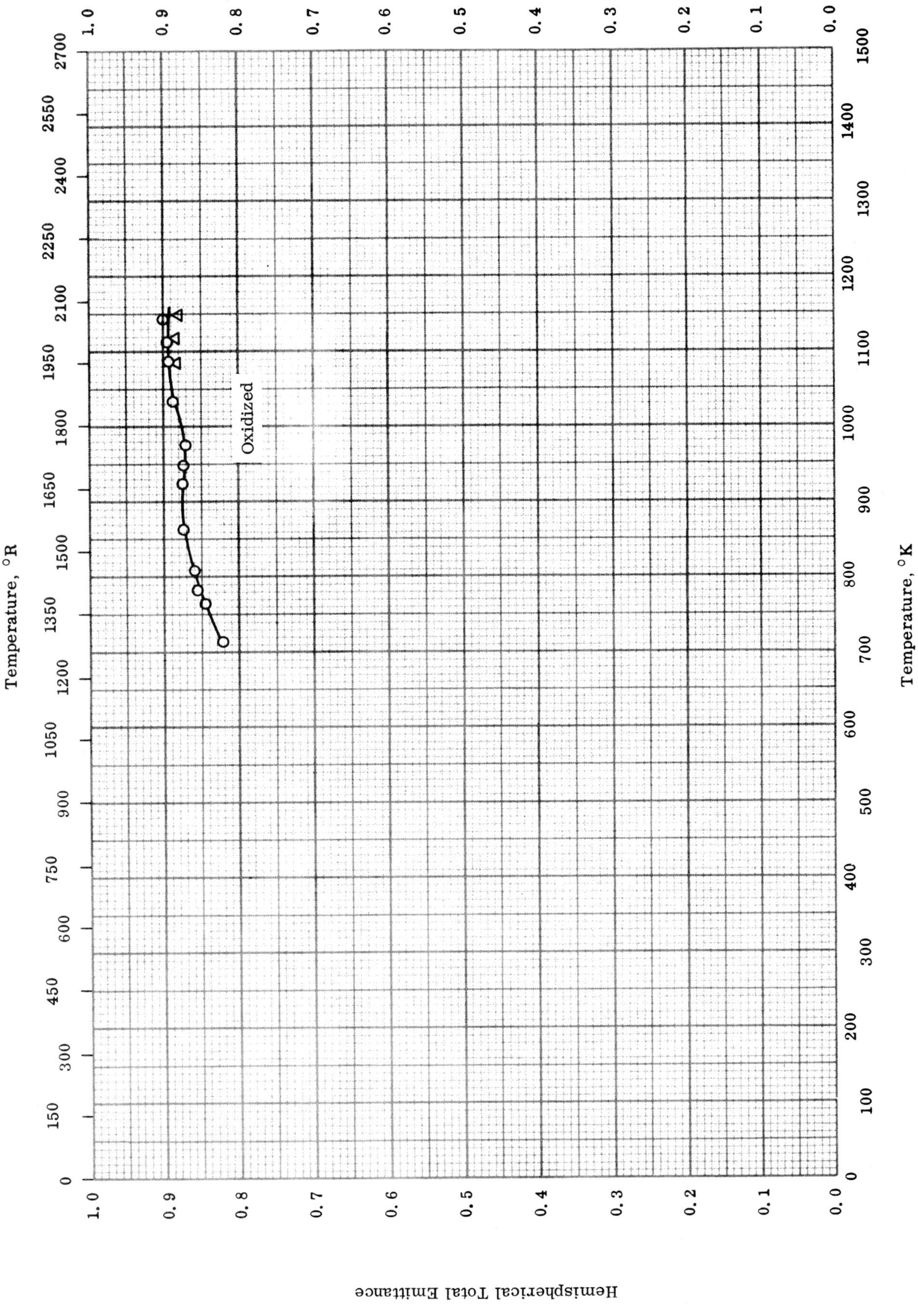

HEMISPHERICAL TOTAL EMITTANCE -- KENNAMETAL K-162B COATING ON STAINLESS STEEL

HEMISPHERICAL TOTAL EMITTANCE -- KENNAMETAL K-162B COATING ON STAINLESS STEEL

REFERENCE INFORMATION

Symbol	Ref.	Temp. Range °K	Rept. Error %	Sample Specifications	Remarks
○	63-23	717-1144		Oxidized Kennametal K-162B coating on AISI 310 stainless steel; coating thickness 0.005 in. with a texture of coating similar to that of 240 grit emery cloth.	Plasma-arc sprayed; measured in vacuum; using thermocouple.
△	63-23	1088-1150		Same as above.	Same as above; using optical pyrometer.

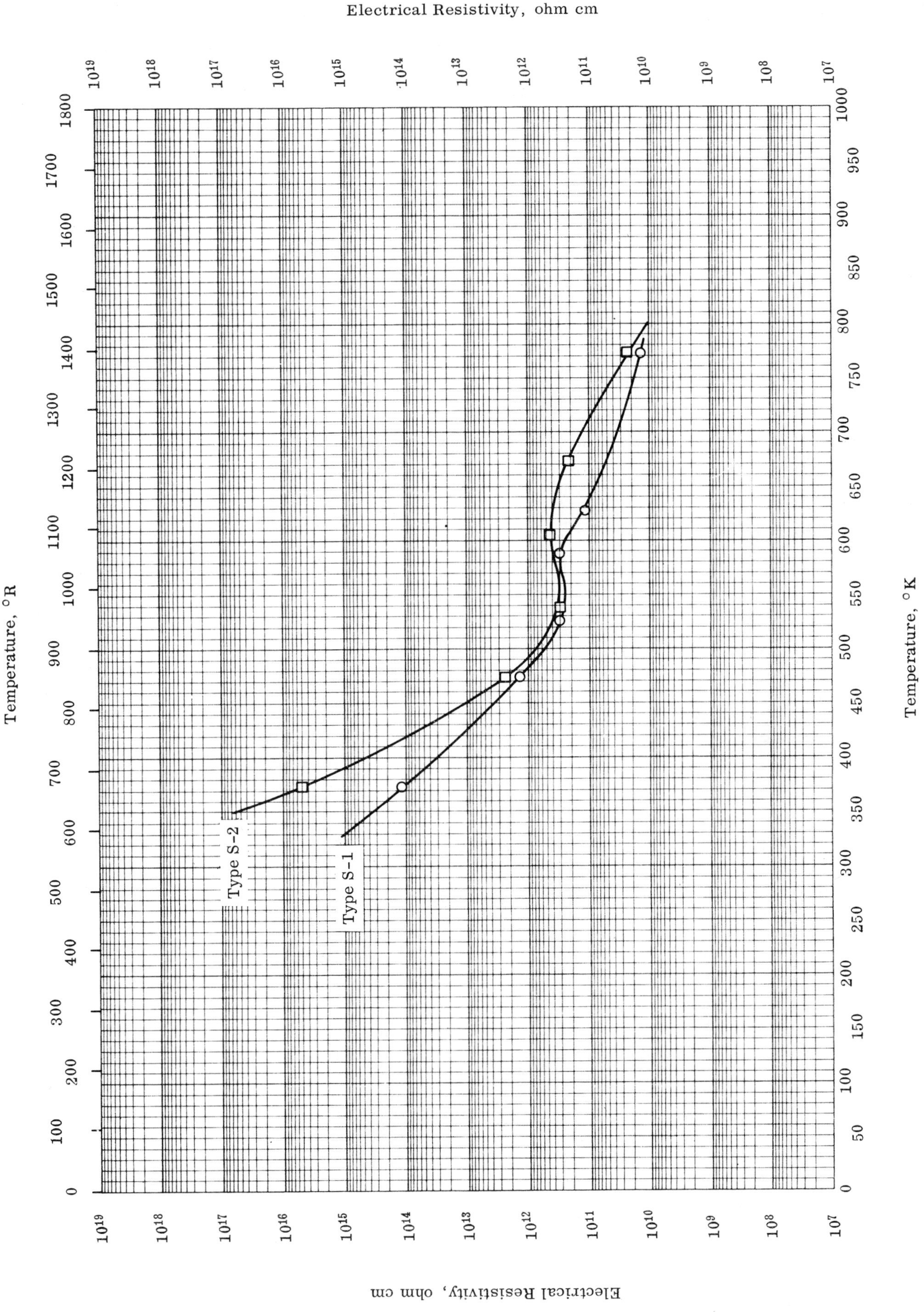

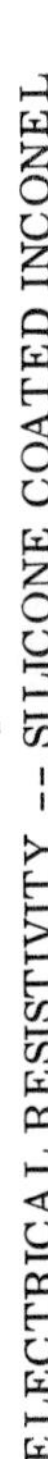

Electrical Resistivity, ohm cm

ELECTRICAL RESISTIVITY -- SILICONE COATED INCONEL

REFERENCE INFORMATION

Symbol	Ref.	Temp. Range °K	Rept. Error %	Sample Specifications	Remarks
○	53-10	373-673		Silicone type S-1 coating on inconel; type S-1: 50 solids, 50 clear varnish; thickness 0. 005-0. 025 in.	Applied to 0. 040 in. thick inconel, dipped, air dried, cured at 200 C for 2-24 hrs 10 C min^{-1} rise, polarity reversed every 2 min.
□	53-10	373-673		Silicone type S-2 coating on inconel; type S-2: 70 type S-1 varnish, 30 mica; thickness 0. 005-0. 025 in.	Same as above.

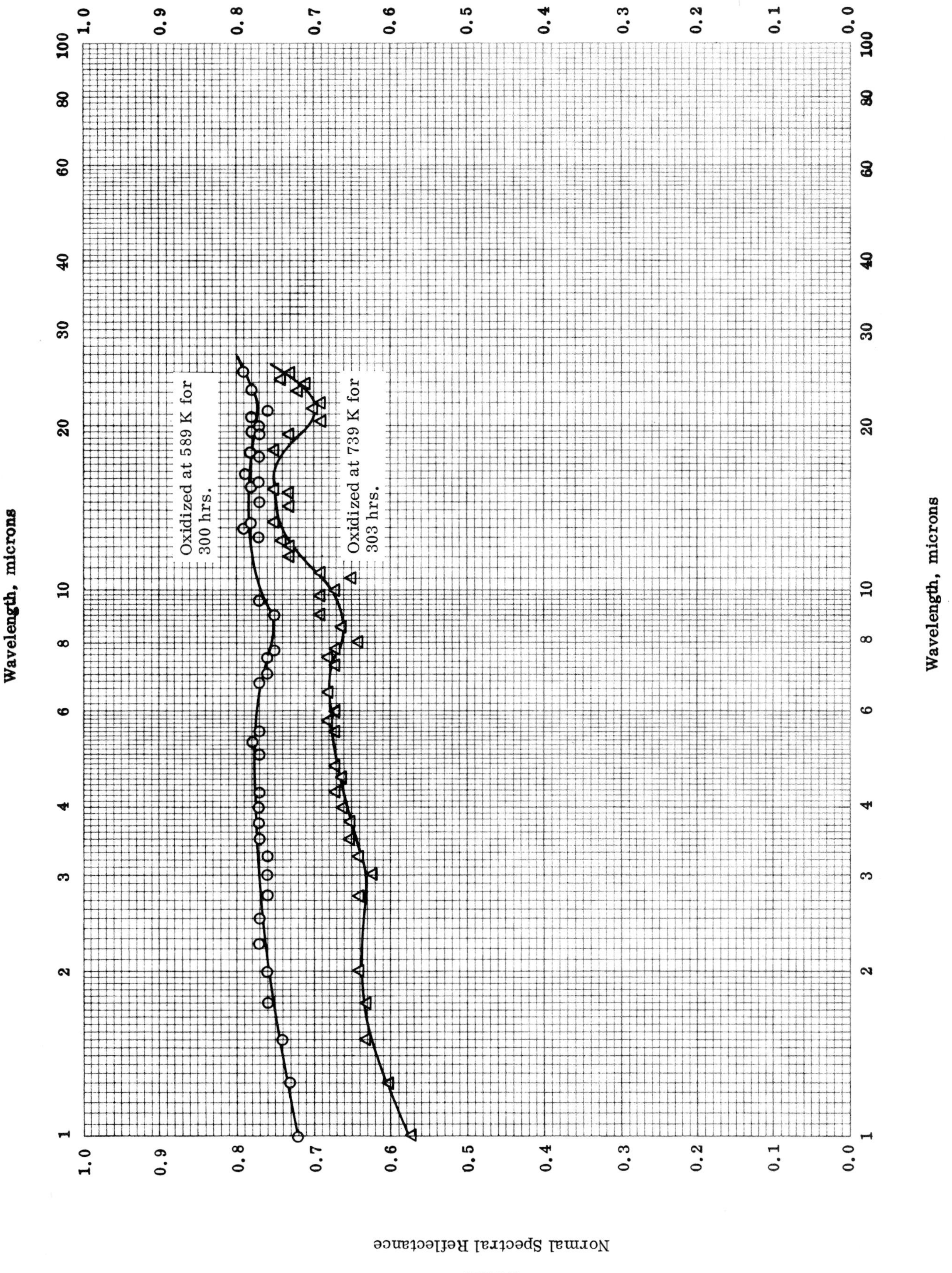

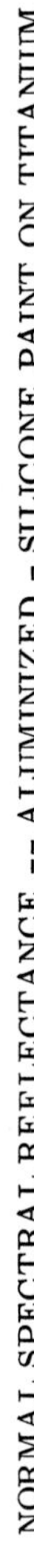

Wavelength, microns
Normal Spectral Reflectance
Oxidized at 589 K for 300 hrs.
Oxidized at 739 K for 303 hrs.
1
2
3
4
6
8
10
20
30
40
60
80
100
0.0
0.1
0.2
0.3
0.4
0.5
0.6
0.7
0.8
0.9
1.0

NORMAL SPECTRAL REFLECTANCE -- ALUMINIZED - SILICONE PAINT ON TITANIUM

NORMAL SPECTRAL REFLECTANCE -- ALUMINIZED - SILICONE PAINT ON TITANIUM

REFERENCE INFORMATION

Symbol	Ref.	Temp. °K	Wavelength Range, μ	Rept. Error %	Sample Specifications	Remarks
○	58-13	311	1-25	± 3	Dow-Corning XP-310 aluminized-silicone paint on Ti-75A, AMS 4901.	Oxidized 300 hrs at 589 K after painting; hemispherical illumination, normal viewing.
△	58-13	311	1-25	± 4	Same as above.	Oxidized 303 hrs at 739 K after painting; hemispherical illumination, normal viewing.

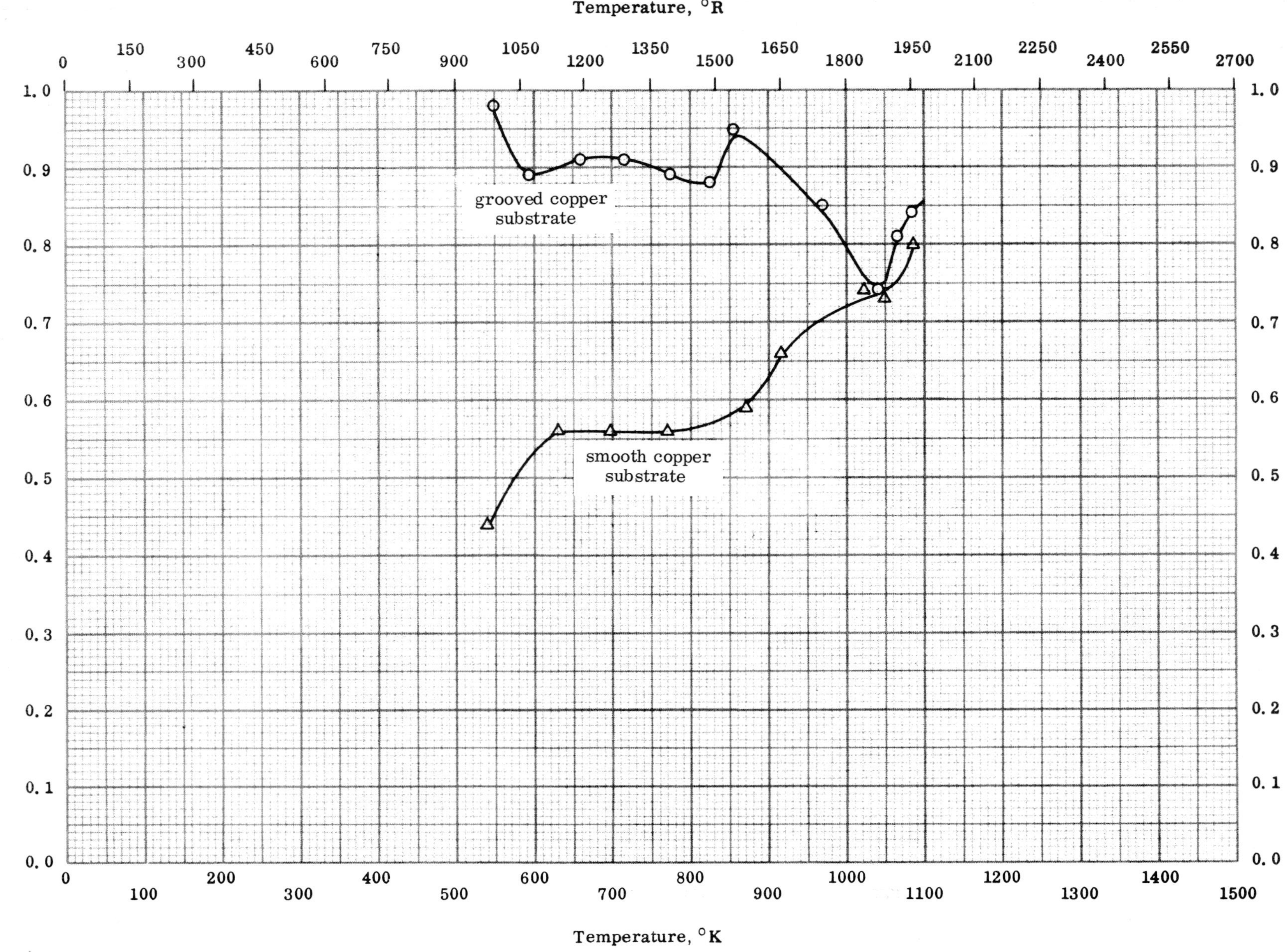

NORMAL TOTAL EMITTANCE -- CHRYCOTE COATING ON COPPER

NORMAL TOTAL EMITTANCE -- CHRYCOTE COATING ON COPPER

REFERENCE INFORMATION

Symbol	Ref.	Temp. Range °K	Rept. Error %	Sample Specifications	Remarks
○	63-25	549-1083	± 10	Grooved copper disc.	Measured in dry air.
△	63-25	539-1088	± 10	Smooth copper disc.	Same as above.

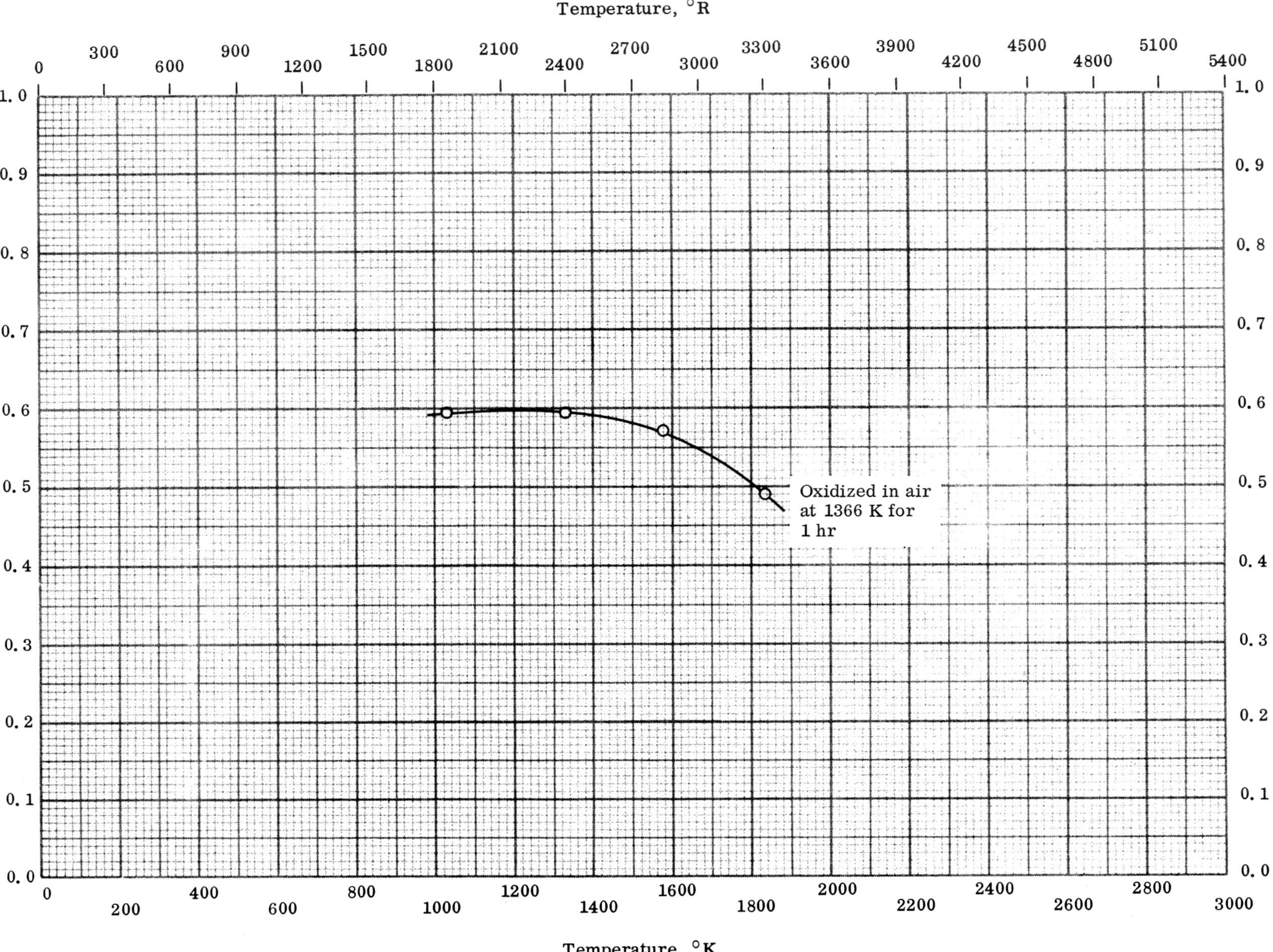

NORMAL TOTAL EMITTANCE -- DURAK - MG COATING ON Mo-Ti ALLOY

NORMAL TOTAL EMITTANCE -- DURAK - MG COATING ON Mo-Ti ALLOY

REFERENCE INFORMATION

Symbol	Ref.	Temp. Range °K	Rept. Error %	Sample Specifications	Remarks
○	60-26	1033-1833	± 5	Smooth and flat surface; 0.02 in. nominal pack deposited on Mo-Ti alloy.	Oxidized in air at 1366 K for 1 hr; measured in argon-hydrogen atm.; averaged over two cycles.

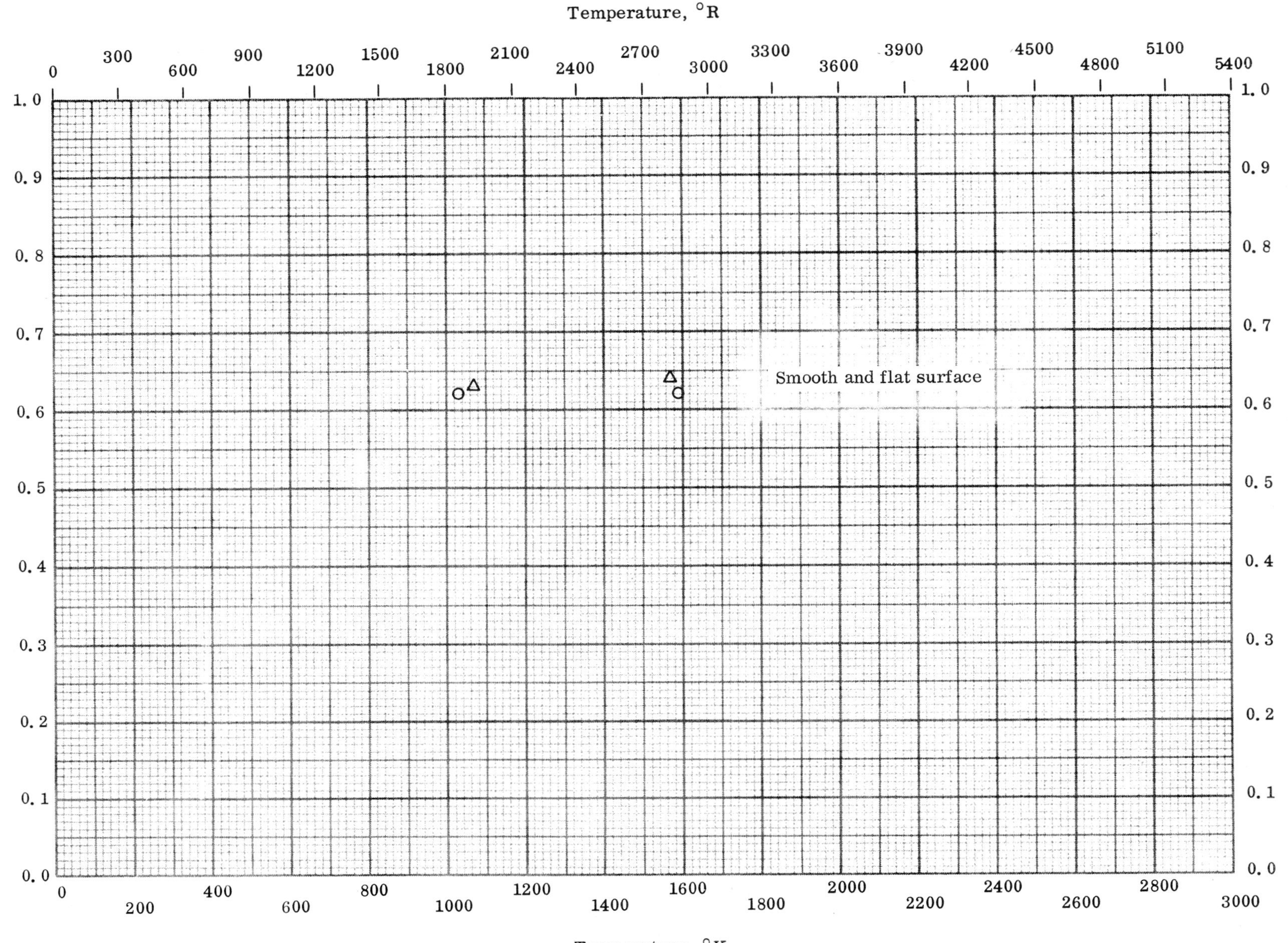

ANGULAR TOTAL EMITTANCE -- DURAK-MG COATING ON Mo-Ti ALLOY

ANGULAR TOTAL EMITTANCE -- DURAK-MG COATING ON Mo-Ti ALLOY

REFERENCE INFORMATION

Symbol	Ref.	Temp. Range °K	Rept. Error %	Sample Specifications	Remarks
○	60-26	1033-1589	± 5	Smooth and flat surface; 0.02 in. nominal pack deposited on Mo-Ti alloy.	Measured in argon-hydrogen atm.; 30 degree from normal.
△	60-26	1066-1572	± 5	Same as above.	Same as above; 45 degree from normal.

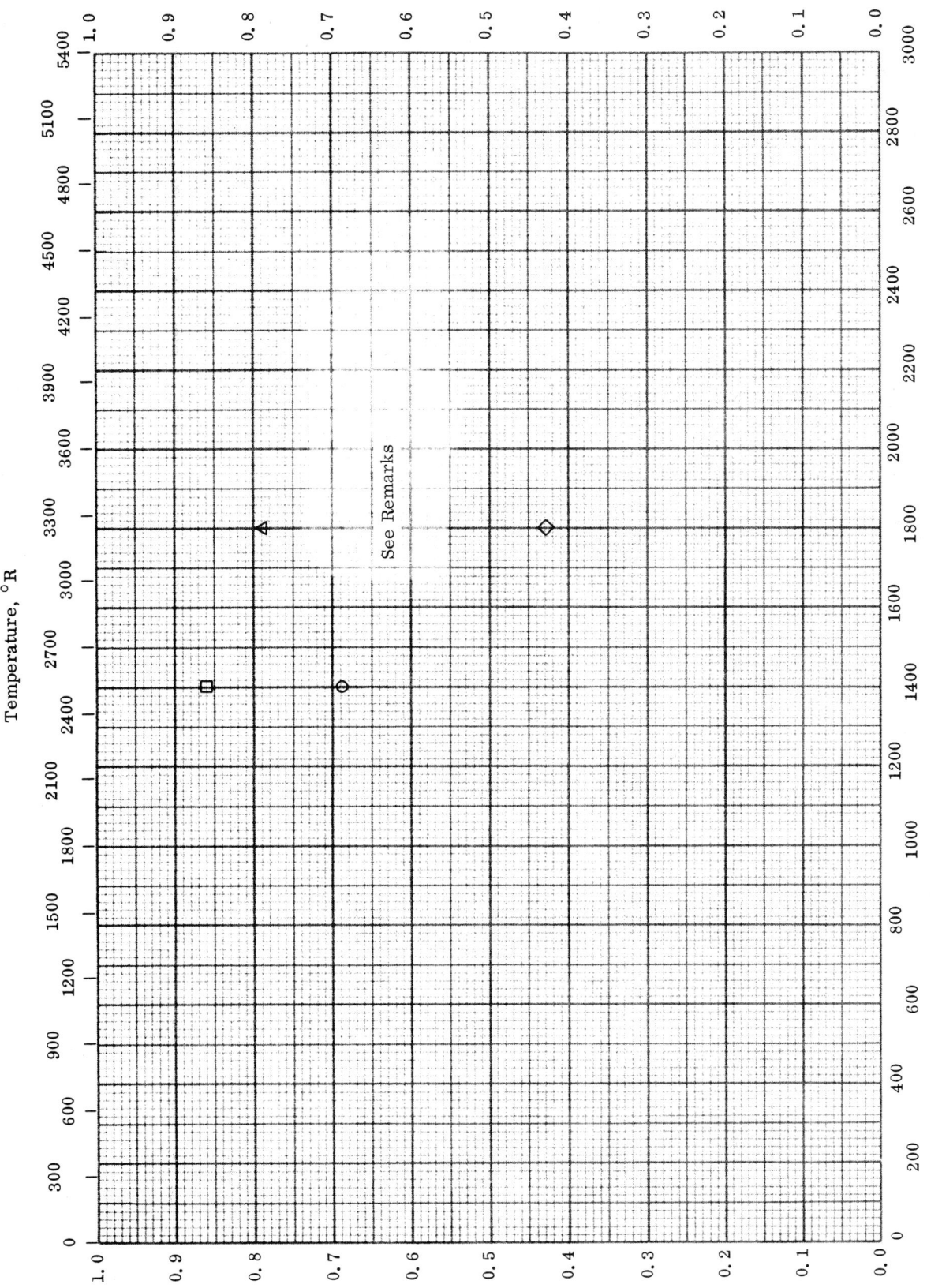

Temperature, °R

0 300 600 900 1200 1500 1800 2100 2400 2700 3000 3300 3600 3900 4200 4500 4800 5100 5400

Normal Total Emittance

1.0 0.9 0.8 0.7 0.6 0.5 0.4 0.3 0.2 0.1 0.0

See Remarks

0 200 400 600 800 1000 1200 1400 1600 1800 2000 2200 2400 2600 2800 3000

Temperature, °K

NORMAL TOTAL EMITTANCE -- CHROMALLOY W-2 COATING ON Mo-Ti ALLOY

NORMAL TOTAL EMITTANCE -- CHROMALLOY W-2 COATING ON Mo-Ti ALLOY

REFERENCE INFORMATION

Symbol	Ref.	Temp. Range °K	Rept. Error %	Sample Specifications	Remarks
○	60-24	1400		Molybdenum substrate (99.5 Mo and 0.5 Ti).	Calculated from spectral data.
□	60-24	1400		Same as above.	Measured after heating in air at 1800 K for 6 hrs; calculated from spectral data.
◇	60-24	1800		Same as above.	Calculated from spectral data.
△	60-24	1800		Same as above.	Measured after heating 2 hrs at 1400 K, 2 hrs at 1600 K, and 2 hrs at 1800 K in air; calculated from spectral data.

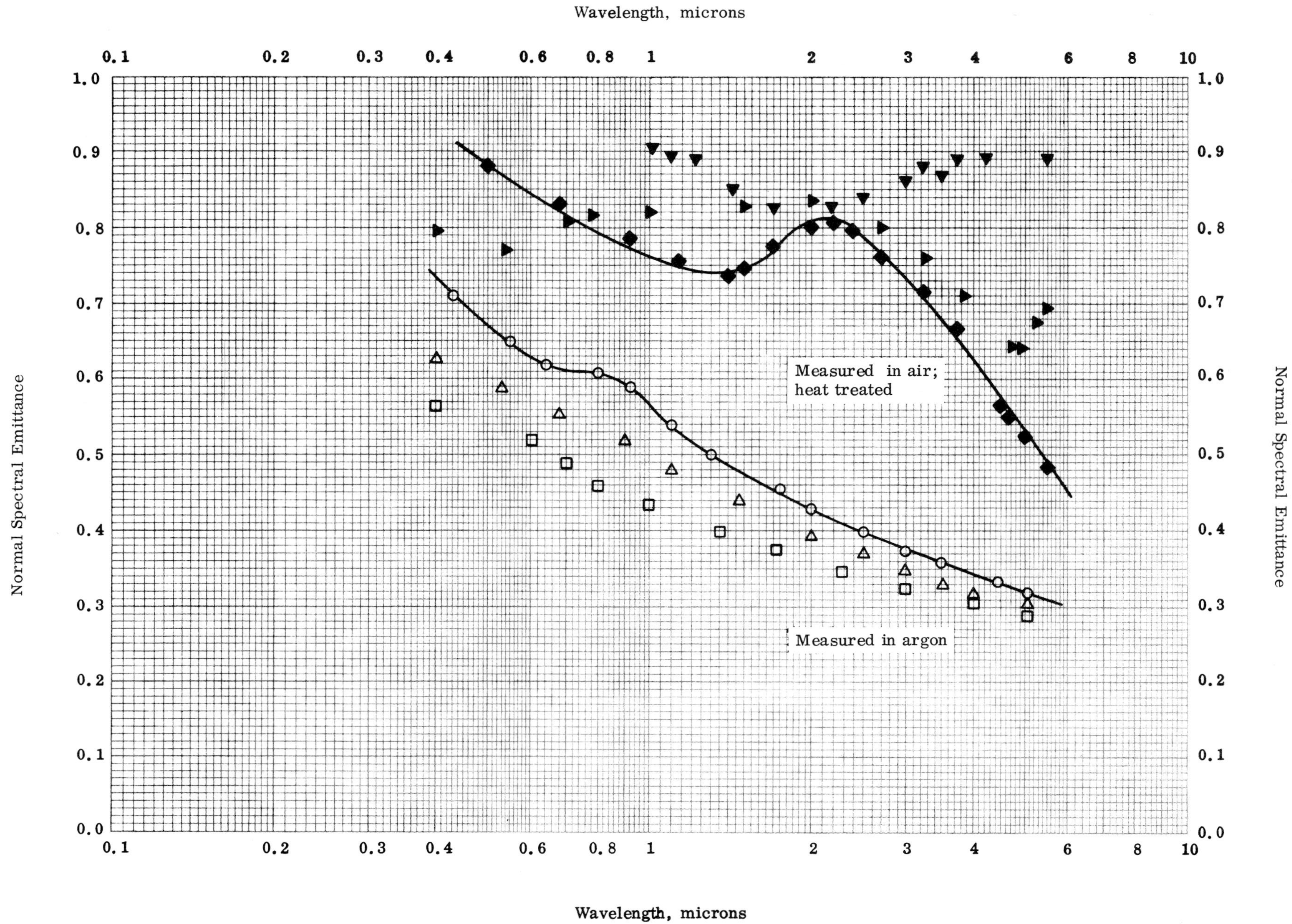

Wavelength, microns

Normal Spectral Emittance

Measured in air; heat treated

Measured in argon

Wavelength, microns

NORMAL SPECTRAL EMITTANCE -- CHROMALLOY W-2 COATING ON Mo-Ti ALLOY

NORMAL SPECTRAL EMITTANCE -- CHROMALLOY W-2 COATING ON Mo-Ti ALLOY

REFERENCE INFORMATION

Symbol	Ref.	Temp. °K	Wavelength Range, μ	Rept. Error %	Sample Specifications	Remarks
○	63-24	1603	0.43-5.05		Chromalloy W-2 coating on molybdenum alloy (99.5 Mo and 0.5 Ti).	Measured in argon at 1/3 atm.; data taken from smooth curve.
△	63-24	1775	0.40-5.05		Same as above.	Same as above.
□	63-24	1905	0.40-5.05		Same as above.	Same as above.
◆	63-24	1400	0.5-5.50		Same as above.	Measured in air; data taken from smooth curve.
▼	63-24	1400	1.02-5.50		Same as above.	After heating at 1400 K for 6 hrs.
▶	63-24	1800	0.40-5.50		Same as above.	After heating at 1400 K for 2 hrs and 1600 K for 2 hrs.

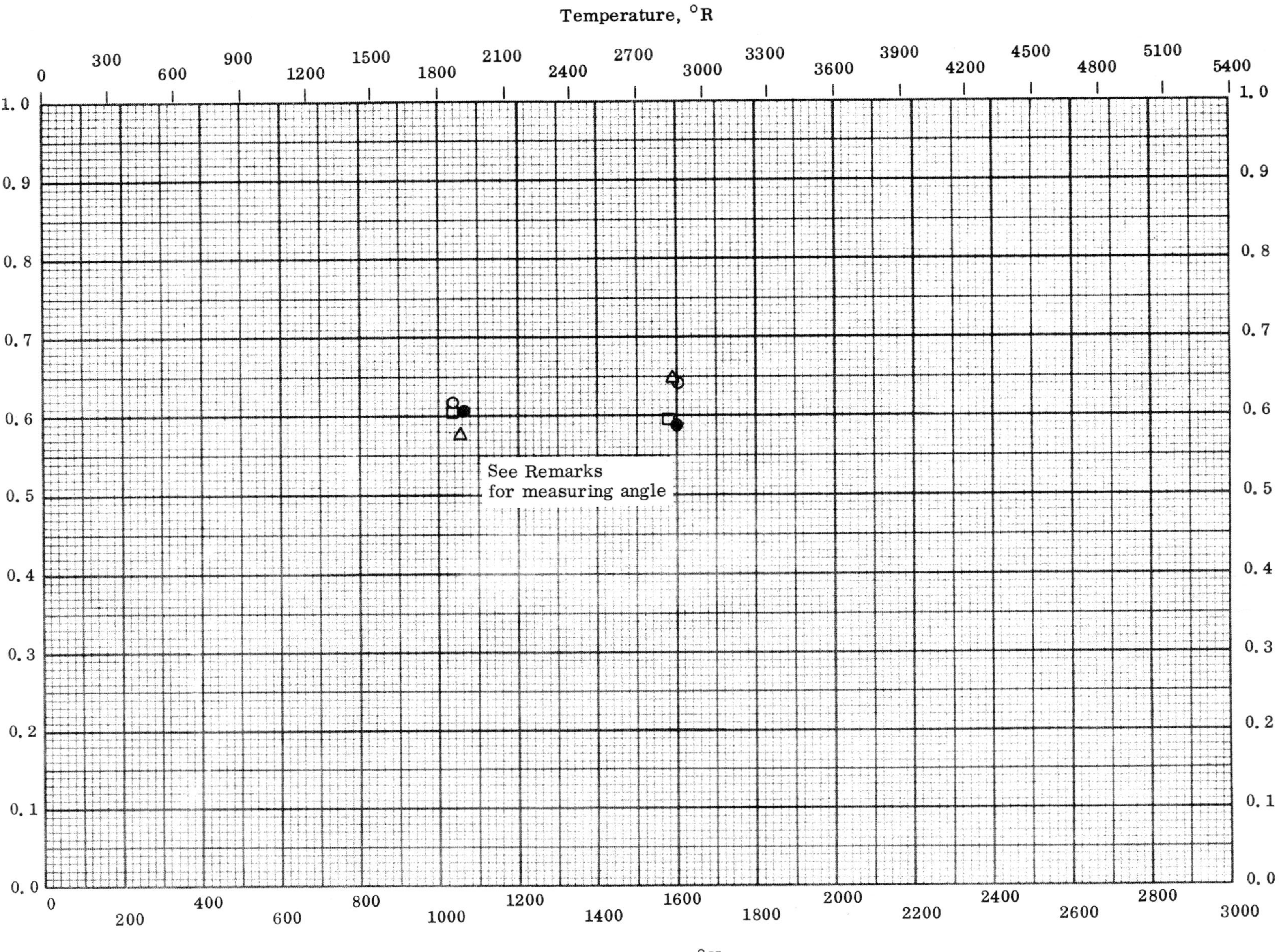

ANGULAR TOTAL EMITTANCE -- CHROMALLOY W-2 COATING ON Mo-Ti ALLOY

ANGULAR TOTAL EMITTANCE -- CHROMALLOY W-2 COATING ON Mo-Ti ALLOY

REFERENCE INFORMATION

Symbol	Ref.	Temp. Range °K	Rept. Error %	Sample Specifications	Remarks
○	60-26	1033-1600	± 5	Flat and relatively smooth; 0.004 in. nominal pack deposited on Mo-Ti alloy.	Measured in argon-hydrogen atm. 30 degree from normal.
△	60-26	1047-1589	± 5	Same as above.	Same as above; 45 degree from normal.
□	60-26	1033-1578	± 5	Same as above.	Same as above; oxidized in air at 1366 K for 1 hr.
●	60-26	1061-1600	± 5	Same as above.	Same as above; 60 degree from normal.

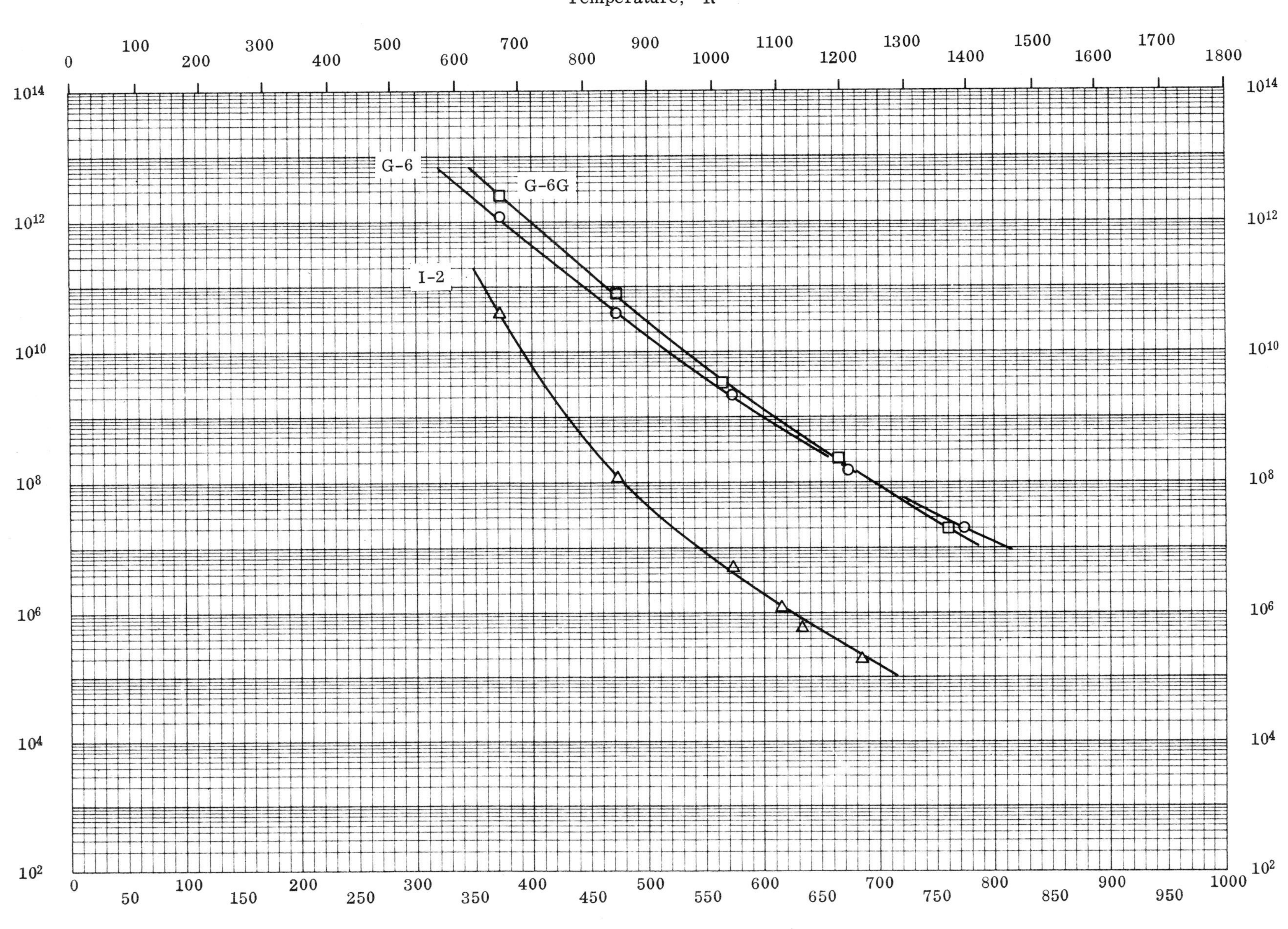

ELECTRICAL RESISTIVITY -- FIRED ENAMEL ON INCONEL

ELECTRICAL RESISTIVITY -- FIRED ENAMEL ON INCONEL

REFERENCE INFORMATION

Symbol	Ref.	Temp. Range °K	Rept. Error %	Sample Specifications	Remarks
○	53-10	373-773		Fired enamel G-6: 29.53 BaO, 28.76 Cr_2O_3, 27.73 SiO_2, 4.36 B_2O_3, 3.36 ZnO, 2.68 CaO, 1.90 Al_2O_3, and 1.68 BeO.	Enamel applied to 0.040 in. thick inconel; fired 4.5 min at 1010 C; 0.004-0.022 in. thick.
□	53-10	373-773		Fired enamel G-6G: 30.29 BaO, 28.76 Cr_2O_3, 28.40 SiO_2, 4.46 B_2O_3, 3.44 ZnO, 2.75 CaO, and 1.90 Al_2O_3.	Same as above; 0.005-0.020 in. thick.
△	53-10	373-773		Fired enamel I-2: 49.48 SiO_2, 15.24 B_2O_3, 13.75 Na_2O, 7.37 Al_2O_3, 5.21 CaO, 3.54 K_2O, 3.44 F_2, 0.76 MnO, 0.65 NiO, and 0.56 CoO.	Same as above; 0.012-0.016 in. thick.

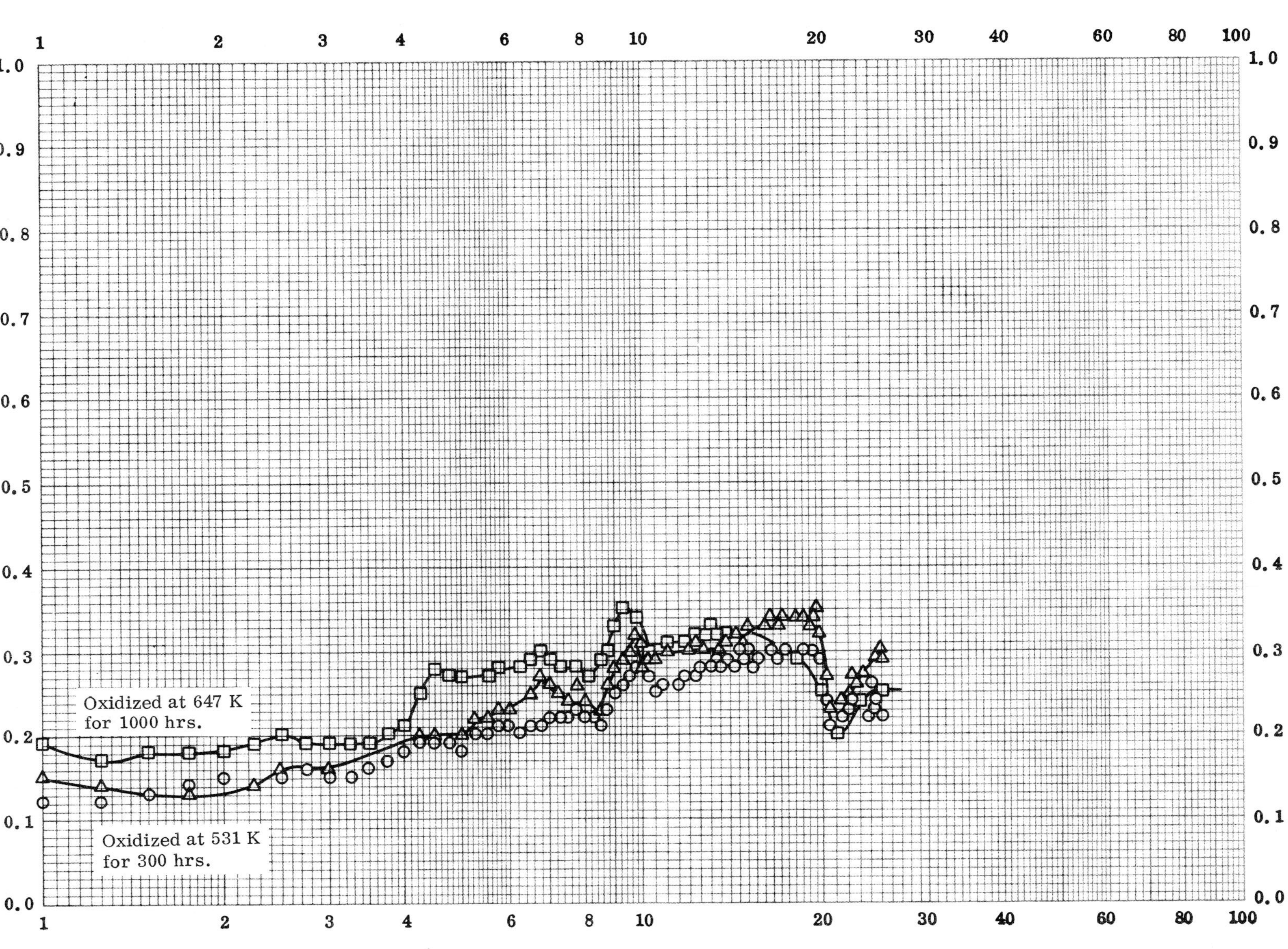

NORMAL SPECTRAL REFLECTANCE -- RINSED-MASON BLACK ENAMEL ON AISI 321 STEEL

NORMAL SPECTRAL REFLECTANCE -- RINSED-MASON BLACK ENAMEL ON AISI 321 STEEL

REFERENCE INFORMATION

Symbol	Ref.	Temp. °K	Wavelength Range, μ	Rept. Error %	Sample Specifications	Remarks
○	58-13	311	1-25	± 17	Rinsed-Mason black heat-resistant air-dry enamel H 12144 on tyne 321 corrosion-resistant steel, MIL-S-6721.	Hemispherical illumination, normal viewing.
△	58-13	311	1-25	± 13	Same as above.	Oxidized at 531 K for 300 hrs; hemispherical illumination, normal viewing.
□	58-13	311	1-25	± 11	Same as above.	Oxidized at 647 K for 1000 hrs; same as above.

Temperature, °R

Temperature, °K

Hemispherical Total Emittance

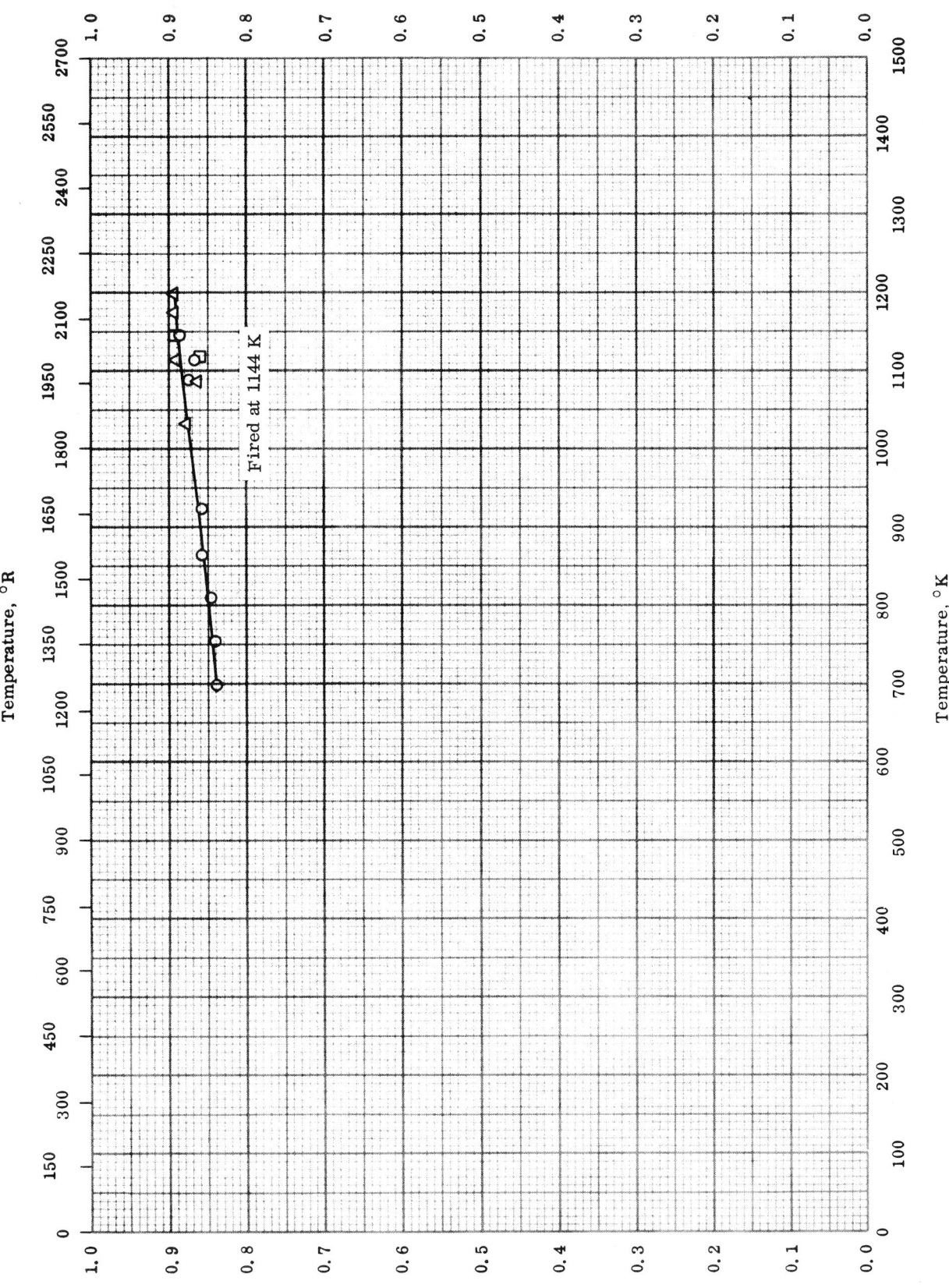

Fired at 1144 K

HEMISPHERICAL TOTAL EMITTANCE -- SPINEL ENAMEL COATING ON STAINLESS STEEL

HEMISPHERICAL TOTAL EMITTANCE -- SPINEL ENAMEL COATING ON STAINLESS STEEL

REFERENCE INFORMATION

Symbol	Ref.	Temp. Range °K	Rept. Error %	Sample Specifications	Remarks
○	63-23	699-1144		Coating contained a large percentage of iron spinel; AISI-310 stainless steel substrate coating thickness 0.002 in.	Coating fired at 1144 K; measured in vacuum; using thermocouple; first run.
△	63-23	1033-1199		Same as above.	Same as above; second run.
□	63-23	1118-1144		Same as above.	Same as above; using optical pyrometer; first run.

REFERENCES

1926

1. Wohler, L. and Schliphake, O., Z. Anorg. Chem., 11, 1951.

1931

1. Agte, C. and Moers, K., Z. Anorg. Chem., 198, 233.

1932

1. Andrieux, L. and Barbetti, A., Compt. rend., 194, 1573.

1933

1. Zintl and Huseman, Z. Phys. Chem., 21, 148.

1937

1. Hashimoto, U., Nippon Kinzoku Gakkai Shi., 1, 135.

1938

1. Koster and Mulfinger, Z. Metallkunde, 30(9), 348.
2. Vogel, R. and Ergang, R., Arch. Eisenhuttenw, 12(3), 155-6.

1939

1. Keeley, K.K., J. Am. Chem. Soc., 61, 203-7.

1940

1. Vieweg, R. and Gottwald, F., Kunststoffe, 30, 138-41.
2. Thompson, N., Proc. Phys. Soc. (London), 52, 217-28.

1943

1. Rolla, L., Z. Metallkunde, 35, 29-42.
2. Bommer, H. and Kross, E., Z. Anorg. Chem., 252 (1/2),62-4.

1945

1. Bitsianes, G., Cont. W-7405- eng-175, 1-32.
2. Axilrod, B.M. and Koenig, E., NBS NACA TN No. 991, 1-26.

1947

1. Rehner, J. Jr., J. Polymer Sci., 2, 263-74.
2. Reysen, W.H. and Vanstrum, P.R., USAEC Publ. AECD-2032, 1-8.

1948

1. Robertson, W.D. and Uhlig, H.H., Am. Inst. Min. Met. Eng. Inst. Metals Div. Metals, Technol. Tech. Publ. No. 2468, 15(7), 1-11.
2. Baenziger, N.C., USAEC Publ. AECD-3237, also ISC-99, 1-114.
3. Zachariasen, W.H., USAEC Publ. AECD-2092 (ANL-FWHZ 152)
4. Cohn, J., Kartz, J., and Giardini, A., Z. Krist., 111, 53.
5. Teitel, R., AECD-2251.

1949

1. Redmond, J.G. and Smith, E. N., Trans AIME, 185, 987-93.
2. Boltakes, B.I., Doklady Akad. Nauk SSSR, 64, 653-6.
3. Kurnakov, N. N. and Troneva, M. Ya., Doklady Akad Nauk, SSSR, 68, 73-6.
4. Deutsch, G. C., Repko, A. J., and Lidman, W. G., Natl. Advisory Comm. Aeronaut. Tech. Note 1915, 1-47.
5. Ehrlich, P., Z. Anorg. Chem., 259, 1-41.
6. Maxwell, W.A., NACA RM E9G01, 1-27.
7. Brewer, L., Edwards, R.K., and Templeton, D.H., USAEC Publ. AECD 2730, 1-15.
8. Rundle, R.E. and Wilson, A.S., Acta Cryst., 2, 148-50. (Same as USAEC Publ. AECD-2388)
9. Noeron, J.T., Blumenthal, H., and Sindeband, S.J., J. Metals, 1, 749-51.

1949 (Continued)

10. Kiessling, R., Acta Chem. Scand., 3, 595-603.
11. Zalkin, A. and Templeton, D.H., USAEC Publ. AECD-2762, 1-4.
12. Kiessling, R., Acta Chem. Scand., 3, 603-15.
13. Brewer, L., et al., USAEC Publ. AECU-607.
14. Wilhelm, H.A. and Carlson, O.N., USAEC Publ. AECD-2717, 1-20.

1950

1. Long, R.A., NACA RM E50F-22, 1-34.
2. Gulbransen, E.A. and Andraw, K. F., J. Electrochem. Soc., 97, 383-95.
3. Brauer, G. and Tiesler, J., Z. Anorg. Chem., 262, 319-27.
4. Brewer, L., Searcy, A.W., Templeton, D.H., and Danben, C.H., J. Am. Ceram. Soc., 33(10), 291-4.
5. Mass. Inst. of Tech., USAEC Publ. MIT-1052, I, 1-74.
6. Gordon, P. and Kaufmann, A.R., USAEC Publ. AECD-2683, 1-41.
7. Baenziger, N.C. et al., Acta Cryst., 3, 34-40.
8. Bowles, P.J. et al., USAEC Publ. AERE-M/R-581, 1-12.
9. Borie, B.S. Jr., USAEC Publ. ORNL-810, 1-14.
10. Chiotti, P., USAEC Publ. AECD-3204 and ISC-44.

1951

1. Evans, J.E. Jr., NACA-RM-E50L07, 1-15.
2. Blackburn, A.R. and Shevlin, T.S., J. Am. Ceram. Soc., 34, 327-31.
3. Crandall, W.B. and Lawrence, W.G., Periodic Status Rept. No. 25, NP 3044, 1-8.
4. Lemons, C. and Maisner, H., Douglas Aircraft Co., Inc., Rept. No. DEV-709, 1-48. [AD 75 127]
5. Robards, C.F. and Gangler, J.J., Natl. Advisory Comm. Aeronaut. RM E50G 21, 1-18.
6. Lucks, C.F., Thompson, H.B., Smith, A.R., Curry, F.P., Deem, H.W., and Bing, G.F., USAF Tech. Rept. 6145, I, 7-16. [AD 117 715]
7. Florio, J. V., Rundle, R.E., and Snow, A.I., USAEC Publ. AECD-3249, 1-35.
8. Lafferty, J., J. Appl. Phys., 22(3), 299.
9. Hansen, M., Kessler, H., and McPherson, D., Am. Soc. Metals, Preprint No. 4.
10. Dreeszen, W.E., Quarterly Summary Res. Rept., ISC-137.
11. Venturello, G. and Burdese, A., Alluminio, 20, 558.

1951 (Continued)

12. Russi, R. and Wilhelm, H., AECD-3610 and ISC-204.

1952

1. Glaser, F.W., Arbiter, W., Ivanick, W., et al, Progr. Rept Mar. 1 to Oct. 1, 1951, Task Order 1, NR 035-401, 1-83. [ATI 201 475]
2. Post, B. and Glaser, F.W., J. Metals Trans., 4, 631-2.
3. Searcy, A.W., Proc. WADC Ceramic Conf. on Cermets, WADC TR 52-327, 275-9. [AD 1183]
4. Lucks, C.F. and Bing, G.F., AF Tech. Rept. No. 6145, II, 1-32. [AD 95239]
5. Claiborns, S.J., ORNL Central files No. 52-11-72, 1-2.
6. Glaser, F.W., Arbiter, W., Ford, M. J., and others, Summary prog. Rept. USN Contr. No.-ONR-256, 1-146.
7. Maxwell, W.A., NACA RM E52A04, 1-17.
8. Furukawa, G.T., McCoskey, R.E., and King, G.J., J. Res. Natl. Bur. of Standards, 49, 273-8.
9. Freiling, J., Eckert, R.E., and Westwater, J.W., Ind. Eng. Chem., 44, 906-10.
10. Taylor, A. and Floyd, R.W., J. Inst. Metals (paper No. 1411), 81, 25-32.
11. American Electro Metal Corp., Progress Rept. No. 2-3, 1-5. [Contr. AF 33 (038) - 10716]. (Insufficient reference citation given in the orginal handbook).
12. Laquer, H.L., USAEC Publ. AECD-3706, 1-58.
13. Laquer, H.L. and Head, E.L., USAEC Publ. LADC-1230 rev., AECU-2116, 1-24. [AD 7185]
14. Abe, F., Kimura, K., and Saito, T., Tetsu-to-Hagane, 38, 214-9.
15. Gurland, J. and Norton, J.T., J. Metals, 4, 1050-6.
16. Burney, J.D., P.R. Mallory Co., WADC-TR-52-327, 1-350. [AD 1183]
17. Shevlin, T.S., WADC-TR-53-17, 1-52.
18. McCreight, L.R., USAEC Publ. KAPL-M-LRM-7, 1-10.
19. Knudsen, F.P., Progress Rept. No. 2, Natl. Bur. Standards 1503, 1-17. [ATI-140033]
20. Massengale, C.B., et al., NBS Rept. 2129, 1-24. [AD 137 413]
21. Hamjian, H.J. and Lidman, W.G., J. Am. Ceram. Soc., 35, 44-8.
22. Teitel, R.J., Trans. AIMME, 194, 397.
23. Ferro, R., Atti. Accad. Nazi. Lincei, Rend. Classe Sci. Fis. Mat. E Mat., 13, 401-5.
24. Shaler, A.J., WADC-TR-52-327, 20-9. [AD 1183]
25. Kieffer, R. Benesovsky, F., and Galistl, E., Z. Metallk, 43, 284.
26. Am. Electro Metal Corp., Progr. Rept. No. 1 under Contr. No. AF33 (616)-109.
27. Armour Research Foundation, Phase diagram of zirconium base Binary Alloys, COO-89.

1952 (Continued)

28. Searcy, A.W., Peavler, R.J., and Yearian, H.J., J. Am. Chem. Soc., 74, 566-7.

1953

1. Gilles, P.W. and Pollock, B.D., USAEC Publ. AECU-2894, 1-29. [AD 72 027]

2. Searcy, A.W. and McNees, R.A. Jr., 1-14 (Contract N 7 onr-39412). (Insufficient reference citation given by the original handbook). [AD 5753]

3. Hoch, M., Nakata, M., and Johnston, H.L., Cryogenic Lab., Ohio State U., Rept. no. TR 280-11. [AD 18364]

4. Marshall, T.A., Brit. J. Appl. Physics, 4 (4), 112-4.

5. Doolittle, J.S., N. Car. State College Raleigh, Quarterly Rept. No. 3, 1-4. [AD 122 141]

6. Ueberreiter, K. and Otto-Laupenmiihlen, E., Kolloid-Z., 133 (1), 26-32.

7. Ueberreiter, K. and Otto-Laupenmuhlen , E., Z. Naturforsch, II, 8 A, 664-73.

8. Smoke, E.J., Snyder, N.H., Wisely, H.R., Ruh, E., Illyn, A.V., and Eichbaum, B.R., N.J. Ceramic Res. Sta., Rutgers Univ., Third Quarterly Progr. Rept., Signal Corps, USAF, 1-25. [AD 19833-19838]

9. Busch, G. and Winkler,U., Helv. Phys. Acta, 26 (3/4), 395-9.

10. Strauss, S.W., Richards, L.E., and Moore, D.G., Natl. Bur. Standard, Special Tech. Publ. No. 153, 1-8. [AD 29 990]

11. Douglas, T.B. and Logan, W.M., Natl. Bur. Standard, WADC-TR-53-201, 1-13. [AD 24 019]

12. Marx, P. and Dole, M., Tech. Rept. No. 3, 1-4. [AD 98 078]

13. Arbiter, W., WADC-TR-53-190, 1-85. [AD 29396]

14. Greenspan, J., US AEC Rept. No. MIT-1113 (Del.), 159-212.

15. Alliegro, R.A., Coffin, L.B., and Tinklepaugh, J.R., N.Y. State College of Ceramics, Alfred Univ., Quarterly Progr. Rept. No. 5, 1-29. [AD 17 643]

16. Searcy, A.W. and Jacobson E.L., Tech Report No. 3 under Contr. N7onr-39412, 1-12. (Insufficient reference citation given by the original handbook.)

17. Elliott, R.P., Rostoker, W., and McPherson, D.J.,Armour Research Found., Quarterly Progr. Rept. No. 3, 1-14. [AD 28 937]

18. Ferro, R., Atti. Accad. Nazi. Lincei. Rend. Classe Sci. Fis. Mat. E Mat., 14, 89-94.

19. Howe, J.T. (ED.), USAEC Publ. ORNI-1301, 1-53.

20. Glaser, F., Moskovitz, D., and Post, B., J. Metals, 5(1), 1119.

21. Gilles, P. and Polock, B., J. Metals, 5, 1539.

22. Schwarzkopf, P. and Glaser, F., Z. Metallk, 44, 353.

23. Kieffer, R., Benesovsky, F., Nowatny, H., and Schachner, H., Z. Metallk., 44, 242.

1953 (Cont.)

24. Kenny, D.J., Wilhelm, H.A., and Carlson, O.N., ISC-353.

25. Kieffer, R., Benesovsky, F., and Schroth, H., Z. Metallkunde, 44, 437-42.

26. Rostoker, W. and Yamamoto, A., Trans. Am. Soc. Metals, Preprint No. 29.

27. Schwarzkopf, P. and Kieffer, R., Refractory Hard Metals, MacMillan Co., N. Y.

28. Searcy, A.W. and McNees, R.A. Jr., J. Am. Chem. Soc., 75(7), 1578.

29. Searcy, A.W. and Peavler, R.J., J. Am. Chem. Soc., 75, 5657-9.

30. USAEC, USAEC Publ. AECD-3647.

1954

1. Kingery, W.D. and Norton, F.H., USAEC Rept. NYO-6446, 1-7. [AD 53 808]

2. Ewing, C.T. and Baker, B.E., Naval Res. Lab., WADC TR-54-185, Pt 1, 1-27. [AD 50 565]

3. West, E.D., Ditmars, D.A., and Ginnings, D.C., Nat'l Bur Standard, WADC TR 53-201, pt. 5, 1-19. [AD 49 098]

4. Hoch, M. and Johnston, H.L., Cryogenic Lab., Ohio State U., Rept. no. TR-280-12, 1-10.

5. Kitzes, A.S. and Hullings, W.Q., USAEC Publ. AECD-3625, 25-40.

6. O'Brien, F.R., Covington, P.C., Harlan, W.J., and Oglesby, S. Jr., Southern Research Inst., Rept. No. 1864-523-IV, 1-40. [AD 65 211]

7. Rauch, W.G., Final Rept. AML-5268, 1-13.

8. Blunt, R.F. and Frederikse, H.P.R., et al, Phys. Rev., 96, 578-80.

9. Ewing, C.T. and Walker, B.E., NRL, WADC-TR-54-185, I, 1-27. [AD 50 565]

10. Kraig, R.S., Krier, C.A., Coffer, L.W., Bates, E.A., and Wallace, W.E., J. Am. Chem. Soc., 76, 238-40.

11. Lucks, C.F., Matolich, J., and Van Velzor, J. A., BMI, WADC, AF-TR-6145, 1-77. [AD 95 406]

12. McKinney, V.L. and Rockwell, T. III, USAEC Publ. AECD-3625, 3-24.

13. Mauer, F.A. and Bolz, L.H., Natl. Bur. of Standards, Progress Rept. No. 7, NBS Rept. No. 3324. 1-16.

14. Arbiter, W., Progress Rept. No. 6, 1-28. [Contr. AF 33 (616) 109]. (Insufficient reference citation given by the original handbook).

15. Rose, E.E., et al., Justi, H.D. and Son, Inc., USAF School of Aviation Medicine-Proj. No. 21 . 1603-0002 (Rept. 1), 1-9. [AD 57 939]

16. Kuchkuda, R.W., Picatinny Arsenal Proj. No. TB4-7211, Tech. Rept. No. 2025, 1-107. [AD 34 721]

17. Rudner, M.A., Graeff, R.F., and Bertolet, E.C., Jr., Final Rept. under Contr. Nobsr-63134, 1-39. [AD 45 199]

18. Shevlin, T.S. and Hauck, C.A., WADC-TR-54-173, I, 1-51. [AD49092]

1954 (Cont.)

19. Shevlin, T.S., J. Am. Ceram. Soc., 37, 140-5.

20. Knudsen, F.P., Moreland, R.E., and Geller, R.F., Natl. Bur. of Standards, WADC-TR-54-1, 1-70. [AD 39 070]

21. Post, B., Glaser, F.W., and Moskowitz, D., Acta Met., 2(1), 20-5.

22. Herz, W.H., Am. Electro Metal Corp., Progr. Rept. No. 6 under Contr. AF 33 (038) 10716, 1-8.

23. Carlson, O.N., Kenney, D.J., and Wilhelm, H.A., USAEC Publ. ISC-448, 1-28.

24. Frost, B.R.T. and Maskrey, J.T., J. Inst. Metals, 32, 171.

25. Blumenthal, H., Am. Electro Metal Corp., Final Rept. under Contr. AF 33 (616) - 89, 1-126.

26. Blumenthal, H., Progr. Rept. No. 14 under Contr. AF 33 (616) -89, 1-9. [AD 39 839]

27. Palty, A., Margolin, H., and Nielsen, J., Trans. Am. Soc. Met., 46, 312.

28. Hikido, T. and Nadler, M.R., TN-WERT-54-229.

29. Carlson, O.N., Armstrong, P.E., and Wilhelm, H.A., ISC-595.

30. Carlson, O.N., et al., Trans. Am. Soc. Metals, Preprint No. 1.

31. Matthias, B.T., et al., Phys. Rev., 95 (6), 1435.

32. McPherson, D.J. and Hansen, M., Trans. Am. Soc. Metals, 46, 354-71.

33. Miller, G.L., Zirconium, Academic Press.

34. Sully, A.H., Chromium, Academic Press, N.Y.

35. Vogel, R. and Klose, H., Z. Metallkunde, 45, 633-8.

36. Weber, B.C. and Hessinger, P.S., J. Am. Ceram. Soc., 37, 267.

1955

1. Krischer, O. and Esdon, H., VDI-Forschungsheft 450, 28-39.

2. Bostrom, W.A., Burkart, M.W., Halteman, E.K., Leggett, R.D., McGeary, R.K., and Padden, T.R., Westinghouse Electric Corp., Atomic Power Div., USAEC Rept. WAPD-127, 1-163.

3. O'Brien, F.R. and Oglesby, S.Jr., WADC Tech. Rept. No. 54-306, II, 1-69. [AD 91221]

4. Manowitz, R., USAEC Publ. MONT-164, 1-15.

5. O'Brien, F.R. and Oglesby, S.Jr., Southern Res. Inst., WADC TR 54-306, I, 1-133. [AD 81 159]

6. Pengelly, A.E., Brit. J. Appl. Phys., 6, 18-20.

7. Norton, F.H. and Kingery, W.D., USAEC, NYO-6449, 1-16.

8. Whitsett, C.R. and Danielson, G.C., USAEC Publ. ISC-714, 1-84.

9. Boltaks, B.I., Konorov, P.P., and Matveev, O.A., Zhur. Tekh. Fiz., 25, 2329-35.

10. Winkler, U., Helv. Phys. Acta, 28, 633-66.

1955 (Cont.)

11. Blunt, R.F., Frederikse, H.P.R., and Hosler, W.R., Phys. Rev., 100, 663-6.

12. Nasledov, D.N. and Khalilov, A. Yu., Trans. No. T215 R of Zhur. Tech. Fiz., 26: 6-14, 1955, 1-9. [AD 104 474]

13. Detwiler, D.P., Phys. Rev., 97(6), 1575-8.

14. Marx, P., Smith, C.W., et al., J. Phy. Chem., 59, 1015-9.

15. Mauer, F.A. and Bolz, L.H., Natl. Bur. Standards, WADC-TR-55-473, 1-63. [AD 95 329]

16. Harrison, N.J., Nopco Chem. Co., Rept. No. RADC TN-55-261, 1-21.

17. American Electro Metal Corp., Summary Progress Rept from Jan. 1, 1954 to July 31, 1955, 1-133. [AD 71 936]

18. Shippy, G. and Wyndham-Quin, E., B.S. Thesis, New York State College of Ceramics at Alfred Univ., 1-22.

19. Shevlin, T.S. and Hauck, C.A., J. Am. Ceram. Soc., 38 (12), 450-4.

20. Knudsen, F.P., Moreland, R.E., and Geller, R.F., J. Am. Ceram. Soc., 38, 312-23.

21. Binder, I. and Moskowitz, D., Am. Elec. Metal Corp., N.Y., Summary Progress Rept., 1-133. [AD 71 936]

22. Trostel, L.J. Jr., Univ. Microfilms, Ann Arbor, Mich., 1-106.

23. Markovskii, L.Y., et al., Zhur. Obshchei Khim., 25, 1045-52.

24. Vasenin, F.I., Zhur. Tekh. Fiz., 25, 1090-7.

25. Nopco Chem. Co., Rept. No. RADC-TN-55-261, under Contr. AF 30 (602) 1238, 1-21.

26. Konobeeyskii, S.T., Conf. Acad. Sci. USSR, Peaceful Uses Atomic Energy, Session Div. Chem. Sci., 207-14.

27. Willmore, T.A. and Bennett, D.G., WADC-TR-56-137, 1-19. [AD 99 655]

28. Geach, G.A. and Jones, F.O., Plansee Proc., 80-91.

29. Grinthal, R.D., Progr. Rept. No. 2 under Contr. No. AF 33 (616) 3198. [AD 89 650]

30. Raeuchle, R.F. and Batchelder, F.W. Acta Cryst., 8, 691-4.

31. Runnalls, O.J. C. and Boucher, R.R., Acta Cryst., 8 (9), 592.

32. Krikorian, O.H., USAEC Publ. UCRL-2888, 1-136. [AD 63120]

33. Smithells, C.J., Metals Reference Book, Interscience Publishers, N.Y.,

34. Am. Electro. Metal Corp., Progress Report No. 2-8.

35. Carlson, O.N., et al., Trans. Am. Soc., Metals, Preprint No. 48, No. 40.

36. Carpenter, J.H. and Searcy, A.W., Univ. Calif. Mineral Res. Lab. NP-5963.

37. Knapton, A.G., Nature, 175, 730.

38. Groeneveld Meijer, W.O.J., Am. Mineralogist, 40, 646-57.

39. Sully, A.H., Manganese, Academic Press, N.Y.

1955 (Continued)

40. Am. Soc. Metals, Metal Beryllium, Chap. XIA and X A.

41. Geller, S. et al., J. Am. Chem. Soc., 77, 210.

1956

1. Goldsmid, H. J., Proc. Phys. Soc., B69, 203-9.

2. Joffe , A.F., Canad. J. Phycics, 34 (12A), 1342-53.

3. White, D., Rept. No. MCC-TR-222, 1-8.

4. Mann, G. and Forsyth, F.G. E., Mod. Refrign., 59, 188-91.

5. Dietz, J. L. and Hangen, W.J., Tech. Memo. MT-M23, Mat'l lab. Dept., Redstone Chrysler Corp. Corp. Missile Operations, 1-38. [AD 289 592]

6. Loewen, E.G., Trans. Am. Soc. Mech. Engrs., 78, 667-70.

7. White, D. and Swift, R.M., Dept. of Chem., Univ. of Syracuse, 1-37. [AD 103 561]

8. Hashimoto, K. and Hirakawa, K., J. Phys. Soc. Japan, 11(6), 716-7.

9. Shigetomi, S. and Mori, S., J. Phys. Soc., 11(9), 915-9.

10. Kover, F., Compt. rend., 243, 648-50.

11. Yoshinaga, H. and Oetjen, R.A., Phys. Rev., 101, 526-31.

12. Walker, B.E., Grand, J.A., and Miller, R.R., J. Phys. Chem., 60, 231-3.

13. Rayne, J.A. and Kemp, W.R.G., Phil. Mag., 1, 918-22.

14. Beckman, G. and Kiessling, R., Nature, 178, 1341.

15. Loch, L.D., Engle, G.B., Snyder, M.J., and Duckworth, W.H., USAEC Rept. No. BMI-1124, 1-32.

16. Fisher, A. and Silver, I., NAVORD Rept. No. 4133, 1-18. [AD 103 722]

17. Barton, J.E. and Fulkerson, S.D., USAEC Publ. ORNL C.F. No. 56-11-59, 1-14.

18. Ferro, R., Acta Cryst., 9, 817-8.

19. Zhuralev, N.N. and Zhdanov, G.S., Kristallografiya, 1, 205-8.

20. Gronvold, F. and Jacobsen, E., Acta Chem. Scad., 10, 1440-54.

21. Dumitrescu, T., Nicolaid, M., and Iliescu, P., Rev. Met., Acad. Rep. Populaire Roumaine, 1, 33-53.

22. Samsonov, G.V., Izvest. Sektora. Fiz. Khim. Anal. Inst. Obshchei Neorg. Khim. Akad. Nauk. SSSR, 27, 97-125.

23. Teitel, R.J., J. Inst. Metals, 85(9), 409-12.

24. Grinthal, R.D., WADC-TR-53-190, V, 1-65. [AD 110 684]

25. Rieder, Z., USAEC Publ. NP-6166, 1-68.

26. Adams, C.H., Bourke, R., et al., WADC-TR-56-399, 1-118.

1956 (Cont.)

27. Pietrokowsky, P., Frink, E.P., and Duwez, P., Trans. Am. Inst. Min. Met. Eng., 206, 930-5.

28. Worner, H.W., J. Inst. Metals, 79, 173-88.

29. Dayton, R. and Tipton, C.R., USAEC Publ. BMI-1062 (Del.)

30. Cotter, P.G., Kohn, J.A., and Potter, R.A., J. Am. Ceram. Soc., 39, 11-2.

31. Carpenter, J.H. and Searcy, A.W., J. Am. Chem. Soc., 78 (10), 2079-81.

32. Samsonov, G.V. and Zorina, O.I., Zhur Neorg. Khim., 16/0, 2260-3.

33. Kieffer, R., Benesovsky, F., and Schmid, H., Z. Metallk, 47, 247.

34. Kieffer, R., Schmid, H., and Benesovsky, F., Plansee Proc., 1955, 154-65.

35. Page, J.P., CF-56-10-36.

36. Silverman, R., WADC-TR-53-190, IV.

37. Wolfson, M.R., Trans. Am. Soc., Metals, Preprint No. 44.

1957

1. Tramposch, H. and Gerard, G., Tech. Rept. No. SM 57-5, OSR TN-57-282, 1-26. [AD 132 253]

2. Smirous, K., Stourac, L., and Bednar, J., Czecheslov J. Phys., 7, 120-2.

3. Stuckes, A.D. and Chasmar, R.P., Rep. Meeting on Semi-Conductors (Phys. Soc.).

4. Satterhwaite, C.B. and Ure, R.W. Jr., Phys. Rev., 108, 1164-70.

5. Harman, T.C., Paris, B., Miller, S.E., and Goering, H.L., J. Phys. Chem. Solids, 2 (3), 181-90.

6. Deviatkova, E.D., Soviet Phys-Tech. Phys., 2 (3), 414-8.

7. Mark, M., Modern Plastics, 34 (9), 168, 247.

8. Covington, P.C. and Oglesby, S. Jr., SRI, WADC TR 57-10, 1-72. [AD 131 032]

9. Gast, Th., Hellwege, K. H., and Kohlhepp, E., Kolloid-Z., 152, 24-31.

10. McCreight, L.R., KAPL, USAEC Publ. TID-10062, 1-19.

11. Armour Res. Foundation, ANL, ARF Proj. G-025, 1-67.

12. Walker, B.E., Ewing, C.F., and Miller, R.R., J. Phys. Chem., 61, 1682-3.

13. Swift, R.M. and White, D., J. Am. Chem. Soc., 79, 3641-4.

14. Smith, J. H. and Street, R., Proc. Phys. Soc., B70., 1089-92.

15. Gast, Th. and Granberg, G., Gummi u. Asbest., 10, 618.

16. Suzuoka, T., J. Phys. Soc. Japan, 12, 1344-7.

17. Middleton, A.E., Herczog, A., et al., Scientific Rept. No. 5, 1-84. [AD 138 886]

18. McGlone, W.R., Dowell, A.M., and Wicklein, H.W., Tech. Memo. No. 479, 1-63. [AD 139 957]

19. Snyder, M.J. and Duckworth, W.H., BMI-1223, 1-35. [AD 145 106]

1957 (Cont.)

20. Llewellyn, J.P. and Smith, T., Proc. Phys. Soc., B70, 1113-22.

21. Ravdel, M.P. and Selisskii, Ya. P., Doklady Akad. Nauk., 115, 319-21.

22. Mauer, F.A., and Bolz, L.H., NBS Rept. No. 5837, suppl. 1 to WADC-TR-55-473 (AD 95 329), 1-47. [AD 155 555]

23. Isserow, S., Trans. Am. Inst. Min. Met. Eng., 209, 1236-9.

24. Schmidt, D.L., WADC-TR-57-580, 1-25. [AD 142 180]

25. Bodor, G., Faserforsch U. Textiltech, 8, 470-1.

26. Marcus, H. and Zaleski, F.V., WADC-TR-57-92, 1-26. [AD 130 920]

27. Kingery, W.D., J. Am. Ceram. Soc., 40, 351-2.

28. Grinthal, R.D., Bizzard, R., and Steinitz, R., Am. Electro. Metal Div., of firth Sterling, Inc., Progr. Rept. No. 2, 1-26. [AD 144 505].

29. Oak Ridge National Lab., USAEC Publ. ORNL-2413, 1-33.

30. Teitel, R.J., Trans. Am. Inst. Min. Met. Eng., 209, 131-6.

31. Grinthal, R.D., Bizzard, R., and Steinitz, R., Progr. Rept. No. 1, 1-16. [AD 135 860]

32. Markovskii, L. Ya., Vekshina, N.V., and Strikhman, R.A., Ogneupory, No. 1, 42.

33. Kieffer, R. and Schwarzkoff, P., Hard Alloys Metallurgizdat, Moscow.

34. Samsonov, G.V. and Unanskii, Ya. S., Hard Compounds of Refractory Metals, Metallurgizdat, Moscow.

35. Obrowski, W., Naturwissenschaften, 44, 581.

1958

1. Sirota, N.N. and Berger, L.I., Inzhener-Fiz-Thur., Akad. Nauk. SSR, 1 (11), 117-20.

2. Bowers, R., Ure, R.W. Jr., Beuerle, J.E., and Cornish, A.J., Westinghouse Res. Lab., Progr. Rept. No. 7. [AD 217 227]

3. Nii, R., J. Phys. Soc., Japan, 13(7), 769-70.

4. Bowley, A.E., Delves, R., and Goldsmid, H.J., Phys. Soc. Proc. (London), 72, 401-10.

5. Crespi, C., Materials, 47(1), 110-4.

6. Schultz, A.W. and Wong, A.K., WAL Rept. No. TR 397/10, 1-13. [AD 154 351]

7. Truesdale, R.S., Swica, J.J., and Tinklepaugh, J.R., WADC TR 58-452, 1-36. [AD 207 079]

8. Melonas, J.V., Covington, P.C., and Pears, C.D., WADC TR 58-179. [AD 204 795]

9. Fieldhouse, I.B., Hedge, J.C., Lang, J.I., and Waterman, T.E., WADC-TR-57-487, 1-79. [AD 150 954; PB 131 718]

10. Sibley, L.B., Allen, C.M., Zielenback, W.J., Peterson, C.L., and Goldthwaite, W.H., WADC-TR-58-299, 1-52. [AD 203 787]

1958 (Continued)

11. Westrum, E.F. Jr., Chou, C., Machol, R.E., and Gronvold, F., J. Chem. Phys., 28(3), 497-503.

12. Nachtrieb, N.H. and Clement, N., Univ. of Chicago, 1-134. [AD 202 338]

13. Bevans, J.I., Gier, J.T., and Dunkle, R.V., Trans. ASME, 80(7), 1405-16.

14. Stradley, J.G. and Shevlin, T.S., WADC-TR-54-173, V, 1-15. [AD 156 810]

15. Newkirk, H. and Sisler, H., J. Am. Ceram. Soc., 41(3), 93-103.

16. Cadoff, I.E., Miller, E., and Komarek, K., 1-4. (Insufficient reference citation given by the original handbook) [AD 158 418]

17. Batchelder, F. W., and Raeuchle, R.F., Acta Cryst., 11, 122.

18. Kudintseva, G.A., Pdyakova, M.D., Samsonov, G.V., and Tsarev, B.M., Fiz. Metall. i Metalloved, 6, 72.

19. Kieffer, R. and Benesovsky, F., Powder Metallurgy No. 1/2, 145.

20. Anon, Welding Engr. No. 4.

21. Hansen, M. and Anderko, K., Constitution of Binary Alloys, 2nd ed., McGraw-Hill Book Co., Inc., 1305.

22. Yerememko, V.N., Zudilova, G.V., and Gayevskaya, L.A., Metalloved i obrabotka Metal, No. 1, 11-6.

1959

1. Kanai, Y. and Nii, R., J. Phys. Chem. Solids, 8, 338-9; 361-2.

2. Tripler, A.B. Jr., Snyder, M.J., and Duckworth, W.H., BMI Rept. No. BMI-1310, 20-2.

3. Bowers, R., Bauerle, J.E., and Cornish, A.J., J. Appl. Phys., 30(7), 1050-4.

4. Lyden, H., Air Force Cambridge Res. Center, AFCRC-TN-60-125, 52-7. [AD 233 257]

5. Busch, G., Steigmeier, E., and Wettslein, E., Helvetica Physica Acta, 32, 463-5.

6. Paine, R.M., Stonehouse, A.J., and Beaver, W.W., WADC-TR-59-29, Pt. II, 1-119. [AD 244 758]

7. Cody, G.D., Dismukes, J.P., Hockings, E.F., and Richman, D., Quarterly Progr. Rept. no. 3, RCA Labs., 1-19. [AD 231 579]

8. Swann, R.T., NASA-TN-D-171, 1-24.

9. Martin Co., Nuclear Div., Baltimore, USAEC, MND-SR-1674, 1-72.

10. Kingery, W.D., J. Am. Ceram. Soc., 42(12), 617-27.

11. Dayton, R.W. and Tipton, C.R. Jr., USAEC Rept. BMI-1377, 1-108.

12. Krestovnikov, A.N. and Vendrikh, M.S., Izv. Vysshikh Uchebn. Zavedenii. Tsvet. Met., (2), 54-7.

13. Johnson, J.W., Stanford Res. Inst., Bi-monthly Progress Rept. No. 4, 1-8. [AD 228695]

14. Golutvin, Y.M., Russian J. Phys. Chem., 33(8), 164-8.

15. Gronvold, F. and Westrum, E.F. Jr., Acta Chemica Scand., 13, 241-8.

16. Gul'tyaev, P.V. and Petrov, A.V., Soviet Phys.-Solid State, 1, 330-4.

1959 (Continued)

17. Westrum, E.F. Jr., Chou, C., and Gronvold, F., J. Chem. Phys., 30(3), 761-4.
18. Richmond, J.C., and Stewart, J.E., NASA Memo. 4-9-59W, 1-30.
19. Olson, O.H. and Morris, J.C., ARF, WADC-TR-56-222, III, 1-96. [AD 239 302]
20. Giles, T.M., Shevlin, T.S., and Everhart, J.O., Ohio State Univ. Res. Foundation Rept. No. 806-7, 1-8. [AD 231 031]
21. Martin Co., Nuclear Div., Baltimore, USAEC Publ., MND-SR-1673, 1-85.
22. Lundin, C., Rare Earth Metal Phase Diagrams, Chicago.
23. Binder, I. and Steinitz, R., Planseeber Pubverment, 7, 18.
24. Nowotny, H., Benesovsky, F., and Kieffer, R., Z. Metallk, 50, 258.
25. Nowotny, H., Benesovsky, F., and Kieffer, R., Z. Metallk, 50, 417.
26. Neshpor, V.S. and Kislyi, P.S., Ognevpory, 23, 231.
27. Vol, A.E., Structure and Properties of Binary Metal Systems, 1, Fizmatgiz, Moscow.
28. Samsonov, G.V., Silicides and Their Application in Tech., Izd. AN. Ukr SSR, Kiev.
29. Knapton, A., Hochschmelzende Metalle, 3, Plansee-Seminar, DeReMetallica Wien, 1-412.

1960

1. Abeles, B., Cody, G.D., Dismukes, J.P., Hockings, E.F., Lindenblad, N.E., and Richman, D., RCA Labs., Quarterly Progr. Rept. no 7, 1-24. [AD 258 953]
2. Timberlake, A.B., Davis, P.W., and Shilliday, T.S., BMI, 14-21. [AD 260331]
3. Parker, W.J. and Jenkins, R.J., USNRDL-TR-462, 1-29. [AD 245557L; PB-159931]
4. Green, A. and Cowles, L.E.J., J. Sci. Instr., 37(9), 349-51.
5. Mihalow, F.A., Koubek, F.J., and Perry, H.A., Naval Ordnance Lab., White Oak, Md., USN NAVWEPS Rept 7314, 1-18. [AD 271112]
6. Sonnenschein, G. and Winn, R.A., WADC TR 59-273. [AD 236 600]
7. Zalar, S.M., Stone, L.P., and Cadoff, I., NYU, WADC, 1-5. [AD 234 080]
8. Morris, R.G., Hurst, J.G., McCarty, R.D., and Kalkbrenner, F.W., South Dakota School of Mines and Tech., ONR, 1-20. [AD 239 000]
9. Stuckes, A.D., Phil. Mag., 8, 5, 84-99.
10. Conn, J.B. and Taylor, R.C., J. Electrochem Soc., 107 (12), 977-82.
11. Westinghouse, Res. Lab., Pittsburgh, Quarterly Progr. Rept. no. 1, US Navy-Buships. [AD 244 959]
12. Tautz, H., Exp. Tech. der. physik, 8 (1), 34-7.
13. Francis, R.K. and Tinklepaugh, J.R., J. Am. Ceram. Soc., 43(11), 560-3.
14. Hager, N.E. Jr., Rev. Sci. Instr., 31 (2), 177-85.

1960 (Cont.)

15. Keller, D.L., Hodge, E.S., Boyer, C.B., Fox, J.B., Kizer, D.E., and Porembka, S.W., Battelle Memorial Inst., BMI-1475, 1-92.

16. Ho, J. and Wright, E.S., Lockheed Missiles and Space Div., Rept No. LMSD 288140, 2(2). [AD 241 410]

17. Pears, C.D. and Neel, D.S., Ceram. Age, 76(5), 30-5.

18. General Dynamics Corp., General Atomic Div., GA-1377, 1-28. [AD 245 051]

19. Boltakes, B.I. and Gutorov, Yu. A., Soviet Phys.-- Solid States, 1(7), 930-5.

20. Gronvold, F., Thurmann-Moe, T., Westrum, E.F. Jr., and Levitin, N.E., Acta. Chem. Scand., 64(3), 634-40.

21. Bolling, G.F., J. Chem. Phys., 33(1), 305-6. (Addendum, J. Chem. Phys., 36(4), 1085-6, 1962).

22. Kanazawa, E. and Packer, C.M., Lockheed Aircraft Corp., LMSD-288140, 2, 1-28. [AD 241 410]

23. Anthony, F.M. and Pearl, H.A., Bell Aircraft Corp., Buffalo, N.Y., WADC-TR-59-744, 3, 1-347. [AD 247 110L]

24. Coffman, J.A., Kibler, G.M., and Riethof, T.R., GE ARPA, 1-38. [AD 245 223]

25. Pratt and Whitney Aircraft, PWA-1877, 1-73.

26. Fieldhouse, I.B., Lang, J.I., and Blau, H.H., Armour Research Foundation, WADC-TR-59-744, 4, 1-78. [AD 249 166]

27. Krikorian, O.H., Univ. of Calif., Lawrence Radiation Lab., USAEC Rept. No. UCRL-6132, 1-7.

28. Booker, J., Paine, R.M., and Stonehouse, A.J., The Brush Beryllium Co., Tech. Rept. No. 176, USAF contract No. AF 33 (616)-6540, 1-23.

29. Booker, J., Paine, R.M., and Stonehouse, A.J., The Brush Beryllium Co., Tech. Rept. No. 183, USAF Contract No. AF 33 (616)-6540, 1-26.

30. Grisaffe, S.J., J. Am. Ceram. Soc., 43(9), 494.

31. Sibley, L.B., Mace, A.E., Grieser, D.R., and Allen, C.M., WADD-TR-60-54, 1-27. [AD 243 897]

32. Meerson, G.A., Kotelnikov, R.B., and Bashlikov, S.N., Atomniya Energiya, 9(5), 387-91.

33. Paprocki, S.J., Keller, D.L., Cunningham, G.W., and Kizer, D.E., USAEC Rept. No. BMI-1487, 1-64.

34. Samsonov, G.V., Doklady Akad Nauk SSSR, 133, 1344.

35. Samsonov, G.V., Paderno, Yu. B., and Fomenko, V.S., Izd. AN Ukr. SSR, Kiev, No. 8, 66.

36. Howlett, B., J. Inst. Metal, 88, 467.

37. Kolomytsev, P.T., Izvest. Akad. Nauk. SSSR, Otdel Khim. Nauk, Ser. Metallurgiya i Toplivo, No. 3, 83.

38. Binder, I., J. Am. Ceram. Soc., 43(6), 287-92.

39. Westbrook, D., Problemy Sovumennoi Metallurgii, No. 4, 1-111.

1961

1. Timberlake, A.B., Davis, P.W., and Shilliday, T.S., BMI, 12th Bimonthly Rept. under contract Nobs-77034, 23-30. [AD 258 988]

2. Pinnow, D.A., Li, C.Y., and Spencer, C.W., Rev. Sci. Instrum. (USA), 32(12), 1417-8.

3. Naval Ordnance Lab., White Oak, Md., 1-15. [AD 261 043]

4. Schmidt, D.L., WADD TR 60-862, 1-21. [AD-268 078]

5. Smith, W.K., NOTS, China Lake, Calif., NOTS TP 2624, 1-10.

6. Luft, L. (Editor), Gen. Elec. Co., Electronic Lab., Buships, 1-171. [AD 266 019]

7. Fieldhouse, I.B. and Lang, J.I., ARF, WADD TR 60-904, 1-119. [AD 268 304]

8. Movlanov, Sh., Abdulaev, G.B., Bashshaliev, A., Kuliev, A., and Kerimov, I., Doklady Akad. Nauk Azerbaid-zhan, 17(5), 375-9.

9. Booker, J., Paine, R.M., and Stonehouse, A.J., Brush Beryllium Co., WADD TR 60-889, 1-133. [AD 265 625]

10. Nowak, J.M., Ceram. Age, 77(10), 109-12, 114-5.

11. Chrysler Corp., Engr. Div., Res. Section, Bi-monthly Progr. Rept. no. 4, US Navy Bureau of Ships, 1-3. [AD 259 038]

12. Howse, P.T. Jr. and Pears, C.D., Modern Plastics, 39(1), 140, 146, 149, 153, 246, 248.

13. Howse, P.T., Pears, C.D., and Oglesby, S., WADD TR 60-567, 1-137. [AD 260 065]

14. Cunningham, G.W., Kizer, D.E., and Paprocki, S.J., Plansee Proc. 4th Seminar, Reutte Hyrol, 483-506.

15. Levinstein, M.A., Gen. Elec. Co. USAF, WADD-TR-60-654, 1-91. [AD 264 223]

16. Abeles, B., Cody, G.D., Dismukes, J.P., Hockings, E.F., Lindenblad, N.E., Richman, D., and Rosi, F.D., RCA Labs., Quarterly Progress Rept. No. 8, 1-92.

17. Chrysler , Corp., Engineering Div., Nav Buships, 1-19. [AD 265 949]

18. Woolley, J.C., and Pamplin, B.R., J. Electrochemical Soc., 108(9), 874-9.

19. Zhuze, V.P., Sergeeva, V.M., and Shelykh, A.I., Soviet Phys.-Solid State, 2(11), 2545-55.

20. Golutvin, Yu. M. and Liang, C.K., Russian J. Phys. Chem., 35(1), 62-7.

21. Gronvold, F., Thurmann-Moe, T., Westrum, E.F. Jr., and Chang, E., J. Chem. Phys., 35(5), 1665-9.

22. Westrum, E.F. Jr.,Carlson, H.G., Gronvold, F., and Kjekshus, A., J. Chem. Phys., 35(5), 1670-6.

23. Kochetkova, N.M. and Rezukhina, T.N., Semiconductor Minerials Conference, Moscow, 26-8.

24. Butler, C.P., Jenkins, R.L., Rudkin, R.L., and Laughridge, F.I., US Naval Radiological Defense Lab., USAF, WADD-TR-60-773, 229-52. [AD 267 310]

25. Nowotny, H., Vienna Univ., Austria, Final Tech. Rept., 1-49. [AD 261 390]

26. Taylor, K. M. and McMurtry, C.H., USAEC Rept. No. ORO-400, 1-90.

27. General Electric Co., Flight Propulsion Lab. Dept., USAEC Rept. No. GEMP-3A, 1-39.

1961 (Cont.)

28. General Electric Co., Flight Propulsion Lab. Dept., USAEC Rept. No. GEMP-5A, 1-57.

29. Markevich, G.S., Dissertation, Leningrad state Univ.

30. Sands, D., Cline, C., Zalkin, A., and Holnog, L., Acta Cryst., 14, 309.

31. Serebryankii, V.T., Epel'baum, V.A., and Zhdanov, G.S., Doklady Akad. Nauk SSSR, 141, 884.

32. Johnson, R. and Daane, A., J. Phys. Chem., 65, 909.

33. Hoenig, C.L., Cline, C.F., and Sands, D.E., J. Am. Ceram. Soc., 44(8), 385-9.

1962

1. Engholm, G., Lis, S.J., and Baschiere, R.J., Gen. Am. Transportation Corp., Niles, Ill., USAF ASD-TDR-62-810, 1-157. [AD 407 663]

2. Kosteleckey, R.J., South Dakota School of Mines and Tech. Dept. of Physics, Thesis, Tech. Rept. No 7, 1-62. [AD 288 825]

3. McHugh, J.P., Central Res. Lab., Westinghouse Electric Corp., Quarterly Progr. Rept. no. 2, 1-21. [AD 410 434]

4. Johnson, R.G.R., Central Res. Lab., Westinghouse Elec. Corp., Quarterly Progr. Rept. no. 2, 1-28. [AD 410 434]

5. Booker, J., Paine, R.M., and Stonehouse, A.J., Tech. Rept. WADD-TR-60-889, Pt, II , 1-82. [AD 284 945]

6. Pears, C.D., Southern Res. Inst., USAF ASD-TDR-62-765, 1-420. [AD 298 061]

7. Neel, D.S., Pears, C.D., and Oglesby, S. Jr., Southern Res. Inst., WADD-TR-60-924, 58-201. [AD 275 536 ; Nb2-12987]

8. Ewing, C.T., Walker, B.E. Jr., Spann, J.R., Steinkuller, E.W., and Miller, R.R., US Naval Res. Lab., J. Chem. and Engr. Data, 7(2), 251-6.

9. Brixner, L.H., J. Inorg. Nucl. Chem., 24, 257-63.

10. Truesdale, R.S., Lympany, B.B., Bielawski, C.A., Grala, E.W., and Beaver, W.W., Brush Beryllium Co., Cleveland, O., ASD-TDR-62-476, 1-251. [AD 278807]

11. Haskins, J.F., Jones, H., and Pearcy, J.L., MRG-323, 1-18. [AD 291 518]

12. Patten, G.A. and Skochelopole, R.E., Modern Plastics, 39(11), 149-52, 191.

13. Hirayama, C., Central Res. Lab., Westinghouse Elec. Corp., Materials Lab. Paper No. p-62136-3, Quarterly Rept. No. 2, 1-7. [AD 410 434]

14. Hirayama, C., Central Res. Lab., Westinghouse Elec. Corp., Materials Lab. Paper p-62136-2, Quarterly Rept. No. 2, 1-6. [AD 410 434]

15. Leitnaker, J.M., Bowman, M.G., and Gilles, P.W., J. Chem. Phys., 36(2), 350-8.

16. Baskin, Y. and Handwerk, J.H., USAEC Publ. ANL-6529, 1-29.

1962 (Cont.)

17. Cape, J.A. and Taylor, R.E., Atomics International, WADD-TR-60-581, II, 1-22. [AD 264 228]

18. McClaine, L.A., Arthur D. Little Inc., ASD-TDR-62-204, 1-83. [AD 277 500]

19. Barriault, R.J., Bender, S.L., Dreikorn, R.E., Einwohner, R.C., Feber, R.E., Gannon, P.L., Hanst, M.E., Ihnat, M.E., Phaneuf, J.P., Schick, H.L., and Ward, C.H., AVCO Corp., USAF ASD-TR-61-260, 1, I, 1-404. [AD 278 633]

20. Mezaki, R., Tilleux, E.W., Barnes, D.W., and Margrove, J.L., Proc. Intern. Symp. Thermodynamics Nuclear Materials, Paper S-M 26/48, Vienna, 775-88.

21. Savitskii, E.M., Terekhova, V.F., Burov, I.V., Markov, I.A., and Naumkin, O.P., Publishing House of The Acedamy of Science, USSR, Moscow. (Translated by the U.S. Joint Publication Res. Services, N.Y. AEC-tr-6151).

22. Abeles, B., Cody, G.D., Dismukes, J.P., Ekstron, L., Hookings, E.F., Lindenblad, N.E., Richman, D., Rosi. F.D., and Vohl, P., David Sarnoff Res. Center, Quarterly Progress Rept.no.4, 1-32. [AD 291 456]

23. Golutvin, Y.M. and Kozlovskaya, T.M., Russian J. Phys. Chem., 36(2), 183-4.

24. Harris, P.M., MacWood, G.E., and White, D., Ohio State Univ. Res. Foundation, USAF, WADD-TR-60-771, 1-80. [AD 275508]

25. Gronvold, F. and Westrum, E.F. Jr., Inorg. Chem., 1 (1), 36-48.

26. Baer, Y., Busch, G., Froehlich, C., and Steigmeier, E., Z. Naturforsch, 17a, 886-9.

27. Walker, B.E. Jr., Ewing, C.T., and Miller, R.R., J. Chem. Eng. Data, 7, 595-7.

28. Riethof, T.R. and DeSantis, V.J., Space Sci. Lab., Gen. Elect. Co., NASA, NBS, and USAF, NASA-SP-31, 565-84.

29. Chandler, H.H. and Hancock, E., General Dynamics/ Convair, USAF, FTDM-2435, 1-9. [AD 285 153]

30. Southern Research Inst., USAF, 5617-1399-IV, Progress Rept. No. 2, 1-19.

31. Wade, W.R. and Slamp, W.S., Langley Research Center, Langley Air Force Base, NASA, NASA TN-D-198, 1-35. [AD 272 614]

32. Scharz, E.A. and McCandless, L.C., Am. Machine and Founday Co., USAF, ASD-TR-62-443, 1-92. [AD 281 821]

33. Birkebak, R.C., Hartnett, J.P., and Eckert, R.G., ASME Second Symposium on Thermophysical Properties, Princeton, N.J., 563-74.

34. Adams, J.G., Northrop Corp., Norair Div., Hawthorne, Calif., NOR-61-189, 1-259. [AD 433 441 and 274 558]

35. Samsonov, G.V. and Portnoy, K. I., Air Force System Command Foreign Tech. Div. Translation No. FTD-TT-62-430, 1-387. [AD 283 859]

36. Zhuravlev, N.N. and Stepanova, A.A., Atomnaya Energiya (USSR), 13(2), 183-4.

37. Feigelson, R.S., Watertown Arsenal Lab., Tech. Rept. No. WAL-TR-853/1, 1-39. [AD 277 686]

38. DeMastry, J.A., Farkas, M.S., Bauer, A.A., and Dickerson, R.F., USAEC Rept. No. BMI-1565

1962 (Cont.)

(Del.), 32-5.

39. Logan, I. M. and Niesse, J. E., The Carborundum Co., USAF Rept. No. ASD-TDR-62-1055, 1-144. [AD 299 956]

40. Paprocki, S.J., Keller, D.L., and Kizer, D.E., USAEC Rept. No. BMI-1589 (Del.), D1-2.

41. Trulson, O.C. and Goldstein, H.W., Union Carbide Research Inst., Quarterly Progr. Report., III-18. [AD 277 432]

42. Goodman, E., Bargero, G.F., Huminik, J., Valve Eng. Co. Final Rept. [AD 273 853]

43. Matterson, K., Jones, H., and Moore, N., Pulvermetallurgie in der Atomkemtechnik, 4, Plansee Seminar, Springer-Verlog, 279.

44. Blum, A., Planseeberichte Fur pulvermetallurgie, 10(1-2), 72-7.

1963

1. Burdick, R.B. and Hoskyns, W.R., Materiadyne, Peaulder Permutit, Inc., ARL 63-170, 1-71. [AD 420 569]

2. Donaldson, W.E. and Castonguay, T.T., NOTS, China Lake, Calif., NAVMEPS-7918, NOTS-TP-2936, 1-16. [AD 403 360]

3. Sedillo, L., Castonguay, T.T., and Donaldson, W.E., Naval Ordnance Test Station, China Lake, Calif., NAVWEPS-7918, NOTS TP 2938, II, 1-28. [AD 407 515]

4. Brixner, L.H., J. Inorg. Nucl. Chem., 25, 257-60.

5. Wechsler, A.E. and Glaser, P.E., ASD-TDR-63-574, 1-171. [AD 420 193]

6. Ruh, R., J. Am. Ceram. Soc., 46(7), 301-7.

7. Kaufman, L. and Clougherty, E.V., Man Labs., Inc., USAF, RTD-TDR-63-4096, I, 1-375. [AD 428 006]

8. McClaine, L.A., Arthur D. Little, Inc., ASD-TDR-62-204, II, 1-125. [AD 412 353]

9. Westrum, E.F. Jr. and Clay, G.A., J. Phys. Chem., 67(11), 2385-7.

10. Hicks, W.T. and Valdsaar, H., E.I. Du Pont de Nemours and Co., Inc., NavBuShips, 1-37. [AD 404 023]

11. Pankratz, L.B. and Kelley, K.K., U.S. Bur. Mines, Rept. Invest. No. 6241, 1-5.

12. Golutvin, Yu. M., Kozlovskaya, T.M., and Maslennikova, E.G., Russian J. Phys. Chem., 37(6), 723-7.

13. Nadzhafov, Yu. B. and Sharifov, K.A., Tr. Inst. Fiz. Akad. Nauk. Azerb., SSR, 11, 31-5.

14. Piesbergen, U., Z. Naturforsch, A18(2), 141-7.

15. Lundin, C.E., Pool, M.J., and Sullivan, R.W., Air Force Cambridge Res. Lab., AFCRL-63-156, DRI-2115, 1-55 [AD 420 015]

1963 (Cont.)

16. Schatz, E.A., Goldberg, D.M., Pearson, E.G., and Burks, T.L., Aeronautical System Div., AF Materials Lab., Nonmetallic Materials Div., USAF, ASD-TDR-63-657, I, 1-181. [AD 423 743]

17. Engelke, W.T., Pears, C.D., and Ogelsby, S. Jr., Southern Research Inst., USAF, 5783-1399-IX, Progress Rept. No. 3, 1-40.

18. Southern Research Inst., USAF, 5919-1399-XII, Progress Rept. No. 4, 1-83.

19. Southern Research Inst., USAF, 6542-1399-XIX, Progress Rept. No. 6, 1-143.

20. Wulff, C.A. and Westrum, E.F. Jr., J. Phys. Chem., 67(11), 2376-8.

21. Moore, V.S., Stetson, A.R., and Metcalfe, A.G., NASA, NBS, and USAF, NASA-SP-31, 527-33.

22. Sklarew, S. and Rabensteine, A.S., Marquardt Corp., USAF, PR-281-3Q-1, 1-37. [AD 299 417]

23. Schwartz, H., NASA, Lewis Res. Center, Nuclear Tech. Branch, PWA-2309, NASA-CR-58054, 1-83. [N64-26808]

24. Coffman, J.A., Kibler, G.M., Lyon, T.F., and Acchione, B.D., Gen. Elec. Co., Cincinnati, O., USAF, WADD-TR-60-646, II, 1-183. [AD 297 946]

25. Southern Research Inst., Birmingham, Ala., NASA-CR-55073, 1-77. [N64-12156]

26. Houska, C.R. and Keplin, E., Union Carbide Res. Inst., Quarterly Progress Rept. from July 1, 1963 to Sept. 30, 1963, ARPA, Chapter III, 50-1. (Contract. No. DA-30-069-ORD-2787).

27. Keihn, F.G., Union Carbide Res. Inst., Quarterly Progress Rept. from Oct. 1 1963 to Dec. 31, 1963, Chapter III, 30. [AD 426 741]

28. Neshpor, V.S. and Reznichenko, M.I., Ogneupory, 3, 134-7. (English translation: Refractories, 28(3), 145-8, 1963)

29. Mandorf, V., Hartwig, J., and Seldin, E.J., AIME Proc. Conf. on High Temperature Material II, 1961, 455-67.

30. Harrington, L.C. and Rowe, G.H., Proc. Am. Soc. Testing Mat., 63, 620-32.

31. Harrington, L.C. and Rowe, G.H., Proc. Am. Soc. Test. Mat., 63, 633-45. (also USAEC Rept. No. CNLM-4479, 1-35, 1963).

32. Gerchikova, N.S., Kolobnev, N.I., Stepanova, M.G., and Fridlyander, I.N., JPRS: 17818, 1-15. [OTS 63-21205]

33. Neshpor, V.S. and Yupko, V.L., Zhur. Priklad. Khim., 36, 1139.

34. Baskin, Y. and Schell, D.C., J. Am. Ceram. Soc., 46(4), 174-7.

1964

1. Arias, A., Lewis Res. Center, Cleveland, O., NASA TN-D-2464, 1-72.

2. Feith, A.D., USAEC Rept. GEMP-296, 1-29.

3. Westrum, E.F. Jr., Arthur D. Little, Inc., ASD-TDR-62-204, III, 1-222. [AD 601 424]

4. Kirillin, V.A., Sheindlin, A.E., Chekhovskoi, V.Ya., and Tyukaev, V.I., High Temperature, 2(5), 640-4.

5. Valentine, R.H., Jambois, T.F., and Margrove, J.L., J. Chem. and Eng. Data, 9(2), 182-4.

6. Taylor, R.E. and Nakata, M.M., Atomics International, WADD-TR-60-581, IV, 1-109. [AD 428 669]

7. Dismukes, J.P., Ekstrom, L., Hockings, E., Kudman, I., Lindenlad, N.E., Miller, R.E., Rosi, F.D., and Steigmeier, E.F., RCA, BuShips, 1-100. [AD 441 794]

8. Kalishevich, G.I., Gel'd, P.V., and Krentsis, R.P., High Temperature, 2(1), 11-4.

9. Kibler, G.M., Lyon, T.F., Linevsky, M.J., and DeSantis, V.J., Gen Elec. Co., WADD-TR-60-646, III, vol. II, 1-167. [AD 438 050]

10. Southern Research Institute, AF System Command., 6868-1399-1-XII, 1-46.

11. Bogdan, L., Cornell Aeronaut. Lab., Inc., NASA-CR-27, 1-39.

12. Cox, J.T., Hass, G., and Ramsey, J.B., U.S. Army R and D Labs., Fort Belvoir, Va., Proc. 1964 Army Sci. Conf., U.S. Military Acad., West Point, N.Y., 1, 193-205. [AD 612 134]

13. Weast, R.C., Selby, S.M., and Hodgman, C.D., Handbook of Chemistry and Physics, 45th. ed., The Chemical Rubber Co., Cleveland, O., 1964-5.

14. Keihn, F.G., Union Carbide Res. Inst., Progress Rept from Jan. 1, 1964 to March 31, 1964, Chapter III, 54. [AD 434 588]

15. Ladd, L.S., Clark, R., and Roy, D., Eastman Kodak Co., Apparatus Optical Div., AF System Command Res and Tech. Div., Tech. Doc. Rept. No. RTD-TDR-64-9, 1-44. [AD 433 950]

16. Griesenauer, N.M., Parkas, M.S., and Rough, F.A., USAEC, BMI-1680, 1-35.

17. Keihn, F.G., Union Carbide Res. Inst., Quarterly Progress Rept. from Oct. 1, 1964 to Dec.31, 1964, APRA Contract No. DA-30-069-ORD-2787, Chapter III, 25-7.

18. Zhuravlev, N.N. and Stepanova, A.A., Poroshkovaya Met. Akad. Nauk. Ukr. SSR, (6), 83-4.

19. Dull, R.B., National Carbon Co., WADD-TR-61-72, XXVI, 1-448. [AD 602 607]

20. Kennmetal Inc., Form No. B-800A, 1-25.

21. Cherniack, G.B. and Elliot, A.G., J. Am. Ceram. Soc., 47(3), 136-41.

22. Bever, M.B., Howlett, S.M., Robinson, D.M., Beardmore, P., MIT, AFCRL 64 623, 1-44. [AD 606 470]

1965

1. Gerlich, D., Abeles, B., and Miller., R.E., J. Appl. Phys., 36 (1), 76-9.

2. Mezaki, R., Tilleux, E.W., Jambois, T.F., and Margrave, J.L., Third ASME Symp. on Thermophysical Properties, Purdue Univ., 138-45.

3. Campbell, N.D., Hertz, J., O'Barr, G.L., and Haskins, J.F., ML-TDR-64-33, II, 1-37. [AD 464 555; X65-16852]

No Date

1. Ellerbeck, E.J., Special Rept. No. D2-1471,1-103. [AD 138 376]

MATERIAL INDEX

MATERIAL INDEX

Material Name	Volume	Density	Melting Point	Heat of Fusion	Heat of Vaporization	Heat of Sublimation	Electrical Resistivity	Specific Heat	Thermal Conductivity	Thermal Diffusivity	Thermal Linear Expansion	Thermal Absorptance	Thermal Emittance	Thermal Reflectance	Thermal Transmittance	Vapor Pressure
A																
Acrylics	6-II	1020	1020	-	-	-	-	1022	1024	-	1026	-	-	-	-	-
Actinium (Ac)	1	3	3	3	3	-	-	-	-	-	-	-	-	-	-	5
Aggregates	5	-	-	-	-	-	-	1023	1025	-	-	-	-	-	-	-
AISI 201	3	-	-	-	-	-	-	-	-	-	114	-	-	-	-	-
AISI 202	3	-	-	-	-	-	-	-	-	92	-	-	-	-	-	-
AISI 301	3	145	140	-	-	-	-	159	172	182	203	-	243	274	-	-
AISI 302	3	-	140	-	-	-	-	-	166	186	227	-	236	-	-	-
AISI 302B	3	140	-	-	-	-	-	-	-	-	-	-	-	-	-	-
AISI 303	3	-	140	-	-	-	151	-	176	-	-	-	236, 245	-	-	-
AISI 304	3	145	140	-	-	-	151	161	-	189	211	-	257, 262	286	-	-
AISI 304L	3	145	-	-	-	-	-	-	-	-	-	-	-	-	-	-
AISI 305	3	-	140	-	-	-	-	-	-	-	-	-	-	-	-	-
AISI 308	3	-	140	-	-	-	-	-	-	-	-	-	-	-	-	-
AISI 309	3	-	140	-	-	-	-	-	-	193	-	-	-	286	-	-
AISI 310	3	140	141	-	-	-	153	164	180	-	213	-	233	286	-	-
AISI 310 coated with Hastelloy C	6-II	-	-	-	-	-	-	-	-	-	-	-	1337	-	-	-
AISI 310 coated with Hastelloy X	6-II	-	-	-	-	-	-	-	-	-	-	-	1339	-	-	-
AISI 310 coated with Kennametal K-151A	6-II	-	-	-	-	-	-	-	-	-	-	-	1491	-	-	-
AISI 310 coated with Kennametal K-162B	6-II	-	-	-	-	-	-	-	-	-	-	-	1493	-	-	-
AISI 310 coated with spinal enamel	6-II	-	-	-	-	-	-	-	-	-	-	-	1515	-	-	-
AISI 310 coated with strontium titanate	6-II	-	-	-	-	-	-	-	-	-	-	-	1393	-	-	-
AISI 314	3	-	-	-	-	-	-	-	-	-	223	-	-	-	-	-
AISI 316	3	140, 145	141	-	-	-	149	161	174	184	209	229	236, 247, 259, 264	276	-	-
AISI 317	3	-	141	-	-	-	-	-	-	-	-	-	-	-	-	-
AISI 321	3	140, 145	-	-	-	-	-	-	-	186	205	227	236, 249, 259, 266	278	-	-
AISI 321 coated with rinsed-Mason black enamel	6-II	-	-	-	-	-	-	-	-	-	-	-	-	1513	-	-
AISI 321 plated with silver . . .	6-II	-	-	-	-	-	-	-	-	-	-	-	-	1321	-	-
AISI 330	3	-	-	-	-	-	-	-	-	-	213, 407	-	-	-	-	-
AISI 347	3	-	141	-	-	-	149	161	176	186	208	-	251	-	-	-
AISI 403	3	-	53	-	-	-	-	-	79	87	110	-	-	-	-	-
AISI 405	3	-	53	-	-	-	-	-	-	-	-	-	-	-	-	-

Material Name	Volume	Density	Melting Point	Heat of Fusion	Heat of Vaporization	Heat of Sublimation	Electrical Resistivity	Specific Heat	Thermal Conductivity	Thermal Diffusivity	Thermal Linear Expansion	Thermal Absorptance	Thermal Emittance	Thermal Reflectance	Thermal Transmittance	Vapor Pressure
AISI 410	3	55	53	–	–	–	–	–	–	87	110	120	122	138	–	–
AISI 414	3	–	–	–	–	–	–	–	–	–	197	–	–	–	–	–
AISI 416	3	–	53	–	–	–	–	–	169	87	110	–	–	–	–	–
AISI 420	3	–	–	–	–	–	–	73	166	87	110, 195	–	–	138	–	–
AISI 422	3	–	–	–	–	–	–	–	–	–	104	–	–	–	–	–
AISI 430	3	–	53	–	–	–	–	73	79	90	–	–	–	138	–	–
AISI 430F	3	–	53	–	–	–	–	–	–	–	–	–	–	–	–	–
AISI 431	3	–	–	–	–	–	–	–	–	–	197	–	–	286	–	–
AISI 440A	3	–	53	–	–	–	–	–	–	–	112	–	–	–	–	–
AISI 440B	3	–	53	–	–	–	–	–	–	–	112	–	–	–	–	–
AISI 440C	3	–	53	–	–	–	–	–	81	–	112	–	–	–	–	–
AISI 446	3	55	53	–	–	–	59	67, 73	79	94	98	120	124, 131	138	–	–
AISI 446 coated with aluminum oxide coating	6-II	–	–	–	–	–	–	–	–	–	–	–	1349	–	–	–
AISI 446 coated with Rokide A coating	6-II	–	–	–	–	–	–	–	–	–	–	–	1351	–	–	–
AISI 611	3	–	–	–	–	–	–	–	–	–	452	–	–	–	–	–
AISI 612	3	–	–	–	–	–	–	–	–	–	353	–	–	–	–	–
AISI 613	3	–	–	–	–	–	–	–	–	–	353	–	–	–	–	–
AISI 650	3	–	–	–	–	–	–	–	–	–	401	–	–	–	–	–
AISI 660	3	–	–	–	–	–	–	–	–	–	401	–	–	–	–	–
AISI 661	3	–	–	–	–	–	–	–	–	–	219	–	–	–	–	–
AISI 662	3	–	–	–	–	–	–	–	–	–	401	–	–	–	–	–
AISI 663	3	–	–	–	–	–	–	–	–	–	401	–	–	–	–	–
AISI 664	2-II	–	–	–	–	–	–	–	–	–	1265	–	–	–	–	–
AISI 665	3	–	–	–	–	–	–	–	–	–	401	–	–	–	–	–
AISI 681	2-II	–	–	–	–	–	–	–	–	–	1267	–	–	–	–	–
AISI 682	2-II	–	–	–	–	–	–	–	–	–	1267	–	–	–	–	–
AISI 690	2-II	–	–	–	–	–	–	–	–	–	1227	–	–	–	–	–
AISI C1006	3	–	–	–	–	–	–	–	–	329	–	–	–	–	–	–
AISI C1010	3	–	310	–	–	–	312	316	325	329	335	–	–	–	–	–
AISI C1018	3	–	–	–	–	–	–	–	–	333	–	–	–	–	–	–
AISI C1020	3	–	–	–	–	–	–	–	–	329	–	345-347	–	–	–	–
AISI C1045	3	–	–	–	–	–	–	–	–	333	–	–	–	–	–	–
AISI 3140	3	–	–	–	–	–	–	–	–	365	–	–	–	–	–	–
AISI 4130	3	–	–	–	–	–	–	–	–	85	–	–	–	–	–	–
AISI 4340	3	–	–	–	–	–	–	–	387	395	–	–	–	–	–	–
AISI 8630	3	–	–	–	–	–	–	–	–	–	337	–	–	–	–	–
Akermanite	4-II	–	–	–	–	–	–	1239	–	–	–	–	–	–	–	–
Alathon-10	6-II	1030	–	–	–	–	–	–	–	–	–	–	–	–	–	–
Alberit 1005	6-II	–	–	–	–	–	1082	–	–	–	–	–	–	–	–	–

Material Name	Volume	Density	Melting Point	Heat of Fusion	Heat of Vaporization	Heat of Sublimation	Electrical Resistivity	Specific Heat	Thermal Conductivity	Thermal Diffusivity	Thermal Linear Expansion	Thermal Absorptance	Thermal Emittance	Thermal Reflectance	Thermal Transmittance	Vapor Pressure
Alberit 8391-SO	6-II	-	-	-	-	-	1082	-	-	-	-	-	-	-	-	-
Alcoa	1	-	-	-	-	-	-	-	-	-	-	-	19	-	-	-
Alkali and alkaline earth aluminum borosilicate glass	4-II	-	-	-	-	-	-	-	-	-	1715	-	-	-	-	-
Alkyd-isocyanate foam	6-II	952	-	-	-	-	-	954	956	-	958	-	-	-	-	-
Alumina	4-I	3	3	-	-	3	5	8	11-18	20	22-26	-	28-32	34	37	39
Alumina + Mullite	4-II	-	-	-	-	-	-	-	1534	-	-	-	-	-	-	-
Aluminide coating on niobium . .	6-II	-	-	-	-	-	-	-	-	-	-	-	1435-1437	1439	-	-
Aluminide coating on tantalum . .	6-II	-	-	-	-	-	-	-	-	-	-	-	1441-1443	1445	-	-
Aluminide coating on titanium . .	6-II	-	-	-	-	-	-	-	-	-	-	-	1447-1449	1451	-	-
Aluminized-silicone paint on titanium	6-II	-	-	-	-	-	-	-	-	-	-	-	-	1497	-	-
Aluminum (Al)	1	7	7	7	7	7	9	11	13	15	17	-	19-23	25	28	30
Aluminum clad boron carbide . .	5	979	-	-	-	-	-	981	-	-	-	-	-	-	-	-
Aluminum coated with silicon (di-)oxide	6-II	-	-	-	-	-	-	-	-	-	-	-	-	1391	-	-
Aluminum coated with silicon (mon-)oxide	6-II	-	-	-	-	-	-	-	-	-	-	-	-	1389	-	-
Aluminum coating on mylar . .	6-II	-	-	-	-	-	-	-	-	-	-	-	-	1287	-	-
Aluminum, Kaiser	1	-	-	-	-	-	-	-	-	-	-	-	19	-	-	-
Aluminum + ΣX_i	2-II	-	-	-	-	-	-	-	829	831	-	-	-	-	-	-
Aluminum + Beryllium	2-I	-	-	-	-	-	-	-	-	-	3	-	-	-	-	-
Aluminum + Beryllium + ΣX_i . .	2-II	-	-	-	-	-	-	-	-	-	729	-	-	-	-	-
Aluminum + Copper	2-I	-	-	-	-	-	5	7	9	-	11	-	-	-	-	-
Aluminum + Copper + ΣX_i . . .	2-II	731	731	731	-	-	733	735	737-739	741	743-752	-	754-757	759	-	-
Aluminum + Iron	2-I	-	-	-	-	-	-	-	13	-	-	-	-	-	-	-
Aluminum + Magnesium	2-I	-	-	-	-	-	15	-	17	-	-	-	-	-	-	-
Aluminum + Magnesium + ΣX_i .	2-II	763	763	-	-	-	765	-	767	-	769	-	771	773	-	-
Aluminum + Manganese	2-I	-	-	-	-	-	-	-	-	-	-	-	19-21	-	-	-
Aluminum + Nickel + ΣX_i . . .	2-II	-	-	-	-	-	775	-	778	-	781	-	-	-	-	-
Aluminum + Silicon	2-I	-	-	-	-	-	-	-	-	-	23	-	-	-	-	-
Aluminum + Silicon + ΣX_i . . .	2-II	-	-	-	-	-	783-785	-	788-794	-	796-804	-	-	-	-	-
Aluminum + Silver	2-I	25, 431	-	-	-	25	27	29	-	-	-	-	-	-	-	-
Aluminum + Uranium	2-I	-	-	-	-	-	-	-	31	-	34	-	-	-	-	-

Material Name	Volume	Density	Melting Point	Heat of Fusion	Heat of Vaporization	Heat of Sublimation	Electrical Resistivity	Specific Heat	Thermal Conductivity	Thermal Diffusivity	Thermal Linear Expansion	Thermal Absorptance	Thermal Emittance	Thermal Reflectance	Thermal Transmittance	Vapor Pressure
Aluminum + Zinc + ΣX_i	2-II	806	806	806	–	–	808	810	812	814	816	–	818-823	825	–	–
Aluminum alloys (Special designations)																
2S	2-II	–	–	–	–	–	–	–	829	831	–	–	–	–	–	–
14S	2-II	–	–	–	–	–	–	–	739	–	–	–	–	–	–	–
17S	2-II	–	–	–	–	–	–	–	–	–	743	–	–	–	–	–
24S	2-II	731	–	–	–	–	–	735	737	741	745	–	754-757	759	–	–
75S	2-II	806	–	–	–	–	–	810	812	814	816	–	818-823	825	–	–
1075	1	–	–	–	–	–	–	–	–	–	–	–	–	25	–	–
1100	2-II	–	–	–	–	–	–	–	–	831	–	–	–	–	–	–
2024	2-II	731	–	–	–	–	–	735	737	741	745	–	754-757	759	–	–
2219	2-II	–	–	–	–	–	–	–	–	–	–	–	–	759	–	–
3003	2-I	–	–	–	–	–	–	–	–	–	–	–	19-21	–	–	–
6061	2-II	–	–	–	–	–	–	–	–	–	–	–	771	773	–	–
7075	2-II	806	–	–	–	–	–	810	812	814	816	–	818-823	825	–	–
Alpax Gamma	2-II	–	–	–	–	–	785	–	794	–	802	–	–	–	–	–
C-46	2-II	731	731	731	–	–	–	–	–	–	747	–	–	–	–	–
Duralite	2-II	731	731	731	–	–	–	–	739	–	743	–	–	–	–	–
Gamma, γ	2-II	–	–	–	–	–	–	–	–	–	747	–	–	–	–	–
Hydronalium 5	2-I	–	–	–	–	–	15	–	17	–	–	–	–	–	–	–
Hydronalium 7	2-II	–	–	–	–	–	765	–	767	–	–	–	–	–	–	–
Hydronalium 51	2-II	–	–	–	–	–	765	–	767	–	–	–	–	–	–	–
L'A-Z5G	2-II	806	806	806	–	–	808	810	812	–	816	–	–	–	–	–
Lo-Ex	2-II	–	–	–	–	–	785	–	794	–	798	–	–	–	–	–
RAE 40C	2-II	–	–	–	–	–	775	–	778	–	781	–	–	–	–	–
RAE 47B	2-II	–	–	–	–	–	775	–	778	–	781	–	–	–	–	–
RAE 47D	2-II	–	–	–	–	–	775	–	778	–	–	–	–	–	–	–
RAE 55	2-II	–	–	–	–	–	775	–	778	–	781	–	–	–	–	–
RAE 470	2-II	–	–	–	–	–	–	–	–	–	781	–	–	–	–	–
RAE SA1	2-II	–	–	–	–	–	785	–	792	–	798	–	–	–	–	–
RAE SA44	2-II	–	–	–	–	–	785	–	792	–	798	–	–	–	–	–
RR50	2-II	–	–	–	–	–	783	–	–	–	796	–	–	–	–	–
RR50C	2-II	–	–	–	–	–	–	–	788	–	–	–	–	–	–	–
RR53C	2-II	–	–	–	–	–	783	–	788	–	796	–	–	–	–	–
RR59	2-II	–	–	–	–	–	733	–	739	–	745	–	–	–	–	–
RR77	2-II	–	–	–	–	–	808	–	812	–	816	–	–	–	–	–
RR131D	2-II	–	–	–	–	–	765	–	767	–	769	–	–	–	–	–
Thermafond C3-INA	2-II	731	731	731	–	–	–	–	739	–	743	–	–	–	–	–

Material Name	Volume	Density	Melting Point	Heat of Fusion	Heat of Vaporization	Heat of Sublimation	Electrical Resistivity	Specific Heat	Thermal Conductivity	Thermal Diffusivity	Thermal Linear Expansion	Thermal Absorptance	Thermal Emittance	Thermal Reflectance	Thermal Transmittance	Vapor Pressure
Aluminum alloys (Special designations) (cont.)																
Y	2-II	-	-	-	-	-	733	-	739	-	-	-	-	-	-	-
Aluminum antimonide (AlSb) . .	6-I	-	-	-	-	-	45	47	-	-	49	-	-	-	-	-
Aluminum borate ($2Al_2O_3 \cdot B_2O_3$)	4-II	-	-	-	-	-	-	-	-	-	-	-	-	-	-	1035
Aluminum borides																
AlB_{10}	6-I	-	160	-	-	-	-	-	-	-	-	-	-	-	-	-
AlB_{12}	6-I	-	160	-	-	-	162	-	-	-	-	-	-	-	-	-
Aluminum bubbles - graphite fibers composite system . . .	6-II	-	-	-	-	-	-	-	1279	-	-	-	-	-	-	-
Aluminum carbide (Al_4C_3) . . .	5	-	294	-	-	-	-	-	-	-	-	-	-	-	-	-
Aluminum carbide + Aluminum oxide	5	-	-	-	-	-	-	803	-	-	-	-	-	-	-	-
Aluminum-chromium-molybdenum cermets	6-II	930	-	-	-	-	-	-	-	-	-	-	-	-	-	-
Aluminum fluoride (AlF_3) . . .	5	407	407	-	-	407	-	-	-	-	-	-	-	-	-	-
Aluminum-nickel-titanium cermets	6-II	925	-	-	-	-	-	-	-	-	-	-	-	-	-	-
Aluminum niobate ($Al_2O_3 \cdot Nb_2O_5$)	4-II	-	1121	-	-	-	-	-	-	-	-	-	-	-	-	-
Aluminum nitride (AlN)	5	481	481	-	-	-	-	483	485	-	487	-	489-491	493	-	-
Aluminum oxides																
Aluminum oxide (Al_2O_3) . . .	4-I	3	3	-	-	3	5	8	11-18	20	22-26	-	28-32	34	37	39
38-900	4-I	-	-	-	-	-	-	-	11	-	-	-	-	-	-	-
AD-85	4-I	-	-	-	-	-	-	-	-	-	-	-	637	-	639	-
AD-94	4-I	-	-	-	-	-	-	-	-	-	-	-	637	-	639	-
AD-96	4-I	-	-	-	-	-	-	-	-	-	-	-	32	-	37	-
AD-99	4-I	-	-	-	-	-	-	-	-	-	-	-	32	-	37	-
AD-995	4-I	-	-	-	-	-	-	-	-	20	-	-	32	-	-	-
AP-30	4-I	-	-	-	-	-	-	-	11	-	-	-	-	-	-	-
AP-35	4-I	-	-	-	-	-	-	-	-	20	-	-	32	-	37	-
AV-30	4-I	-	-	-	-	-	-	-	-	-	-	-	32	-	37	-
FS-54	4-I	-	-	-	-	-	-	-	-	20	-	-	-	-	-	-
GD-10	4-I	-	-	-	-	-	-	-	-	20	-	-	-	-	-	-
Gulton HSB	4-I	-	-	-	-	-	-	-	11	-	-	-	-	-	-	-
LA-603	4-I	-	-	-	-	-	-	-	-	-	-	-	28-30	-	-	-
RA-4213	4-I	-	-	-	-	-	-	-	-	-	-	-	28-30	-	-	-
TWA 2, A402	4-I	-	-	-	-	-	-	-	-	-	-	-	32	-	-	-
Wesgo Al-300	4-I	-	-	-	-	-	-	-	14	-	-	-	-	-	-	-
Aluminum oxide foam	4-I	-	-	-	-	-	-	-	18	-	26	-	-	-	-	-
Aluminum oxide reinforced by molybdenum fibers	6-II	-	-	-	-	-	-	-	1261	-	1263	-	-	-	-	-

Material Name	Volume	Density	Melting Point	Heat of Fusion	Heat of Vaporization	Heat of Sublimation	Electrical Resistivity	Specific Heat	Thermal Conductivity	Thermal Diffusivity	Thermal Linear Expansion	Thermal Absorptance	Thermal Emittance	Thermal Reflectance	Thermal Transmittance	Vapor Pressure
Aluminum oxide coating on AISI 446	6-II	–	–	–	–	–	–	–	–	–	–	–	1349	–	–	–
Aluminum oxide + ΣX_i	4-I	–	–	–	–	–	–	–	–	–	635	–	637	–	639	–
Aluminum oxide + Aluminum cermet	6-II	–	–	–	–	–	–	–	–	–	729	–	–	–	–	–
Aluminum oxide + Aluminum silicate	4-II	–	–	–	–	–	–	–	1534	–	–	–	–	–	–	–
Aluminum oxide + Beryllium oxide + Magnesium oxide . . .	4-I	–	–	–	–	–	–	–	–	–	599	–	–	–	–	–
Aluminum oxide + Chromium cermet	6-II	731	–	–	–	–	–	–	911	–	733	–	735	–	–	–
Aluminum oxide + Chromium (sesqui-) oxide	4-I	–	–	–	–	–	601	–	–	–	603	–	605	–	–	–
Aluminum oxide + Chromium + + Molybdenum cermet	6-II	737	–	–	–	–	–	–	–	–	739	–	–	–	–	–
Aluminum oxide + Iron cermet .	6-II	–	–	–	–	–	–	–	–	–	741	–	–	–	–	–
Aluminum oxide + Magnesium oxide + Beryllium oxide . . .	4-I	–	–	–	–	–	–	–	–	–	607	–	–	–	–	–
Aluminum oxide + Nickel aluminide	5	–	–	–	–	–	–	–	–	–	–	–	747-749	751	–	–
Aluminum oxide + Nickel (mon-) oxide	4-I	–	–	–	–	–	–	–	–	–	–	–	609	–	–	–
Aluminum oxide + Niobium (pent-) oxide	4-I	–	611	–	–	–	–	–	–	–	–	–	–	–	–	–
Aluminum oxide + Silicon (di-) oxide	4-I	–	–	–	–	–	613	–	615	–	617	–	619	–	–	–
Aluminum oxide + Silicon (di-) oxide + Titanium (di-) oxide	4-I	–	–	–	–	–	–	–	621	–	–	–	–	–	–	–
Aluminum oxide + Thorium (di-) oxide	4-I	–	623	–	–	–	–	–	–	–	–	–	–	–	–	–
Aluminum oxide + Thorium (di-) oxide + Beryllium oxide .	4-I	–	625	–	–	–	–	–	–	–	627	–	–	–	–	–
Aluminum oxide + Titanium aluminide	5	–	–	–	–	–	–	–	–	–	–	–	753-755	757	–	–
Aluminum oxide + Titanium (di-) oxide + Chromium + + Molybdenum cermet	6-II	–	–	–	–	–	–	–	–	–	–	–	747	–	–	–
Aluminum oxide + Tungsten + + Chromium cermet	6-II	–	–	–	–	–	–	–	–	–	743	–	745	–	–	–
Aluminum oxide + Uranium (di-) oxide	4-I	629	–	–	–	–	–	–	–	–	–	–	–	–	–	–
Aluminum oxide + Zirconium (di-) oxide	4-I	–	–	–	–	–	–	–	631	–	–	–	–	–	–	–
Aluminum oxide + Zirconium (di-) oxide + Beryllium oxide .	4-I	–	633	–	–	–	–	–	–	–	–	–	–	–	–	–
Aluminum phosphate coating on nickel	6-II	–	–	–	–	–	–	–	–	–	–	–	1429	–	–	–
Aluminum phosphide (AlP) . . .	5	–	–	–	–	–	–	627	–	–	–	–	–	–	–	–

Material Name	Volume	Density	Melting Point	Heat of Fusion	Heat of Vaporization	Heat of Sublimation	Electrical Resistivity	Specific Heat	Thermal Conductivity	Thermal Diffusivity	Thermal Linear Expansion	Thermal Absorptance	Thermal Emittance	Thermal Reflectance	Thermal Transmittance	Vapor Pressure
Aluminum silicates	4-II	–	–	–	–	–	1187	1189	1191	1193	1195-1197	–	1199-1201	–	1203	–
$Al_2O_3 \cdot SiO_2$	4-II	–	–	–	–	–	–	1189	1191	–	1195	–		–	–	–
$3\ Al_2O_3 \cdot 2\ SiO_2$	4-II	–	–	–	–	–	–	1189	1191	1193	1197	–	1501	–	1203	–
Aluminum silicate + Aluminum oxide	4-II	–	–	–	–	–	–	–	1562	–	–	–	–	–	–	–
Aluminum silicate + Magnesium oxide	4-II	–	1564	–	–	–	–	–	–	–	–	–	–	–	–	–
Aluminum silicate glass	4-II	–	–	–	–	–	–	1675	–	1677	–	–	1679	1681	1683-1685	–
Aluminum titanate ($Al_2O_3 \cdot TiO_2$) .	4-II	1368	1368	–	–	–	–	1370	1372	–	1374	–	–	–	–	–
Aluminum titanate, vitreous bonded	5	–	–	–	–	–	949-953	–	–	–	955 977	–	–	–	–	–
Aluminum titanate body	4-II	–	–	–	–	–	–	–	–	–	1374	–	–	–	–	–
Aluminum-vanadium intermetal-ics (Al_3V)	6-I	–	683	–	–	–	–	–	–	–	–	–	–	–	–	–
Alundun	4-I	–	–	–	–	–	–	–	11	–	–	–	–	–	–	–
Americium (Am)	1	32	–	–	–	32	–	–	–	–	–	–	–	–	–	34
Americium fluoride (AmF_3) . .	5	343	–	–	343	343	–	–	–	–	–	–	–	–	–	345
Analcite	4-II	–	–	–	–	–	–	1324	–	–	–	–	–	–	–	–
Anatase	4-I	445	–	–	–	–	–	454	–	–	–	–	–	–	–	–
Andalusite	4-II	–	–	–	–	–	–	1189	–	–	1195	–	–	–	–	–
Anilin resin	6-II	–	–	–	–	–	–	1078	–	–	–	–	–	–	–	–
Anorthite	4-II	–	–	–	–	–	–	1233	–	–	–	–	–	–	–	–
Antimony (Sb)	1	38	36	36	–	–	40	42	44	–	–	–	–	46	–	–
Antimony bismuth telluride ($Sb_{2-x}Bi_xTe_3$)	6-I	–	–	–	–	–	549	–	551	–	–	–	–	–	–	–
Antimony sulfide (Sb_2S_3)	5	–	–	–	–	–	–	643	–	–	–	–	–	645	–	–
Antimony telluride (Sb_2Te_3) . .	6-I	543	543	–	–	–	545	–	547	–	–	–	–	–	–	–
Antimony telluride + Bismuth telluride	6-I	–	–	–	–	–	705	–	–	–	–	–	–	–	–	–
Antimony telluride + Indium telluride	6-I	–	–	–	–	–	–	–	707	–	709	–	–	–	–	–
Antimony-zirconium inter-metallics ($SbZr_2$)	6-I	–	683	–	–	–	–	–	–	–	–	–	–	–	–	–
Araldite casting resin 501 . . .	6-II	–	–	–	–	–	–	–	–	–	1012	–	–	–	–	–
Armalon 410L	6-II	–	–	–	–	–	–	–	1218	–	–	–	–	–	–	–
Armco iron	1	578	–	–	–	–	581	583	585	587	589	592	594, 598	602	–	–
Armofoam	6-II	962	–	–	–	–	–	–	–	–	966	–	–	–	–	–
Arsenic aluminides																
AsAl	6-I	–	43	–	–	–	–	–	–	–	–	–	–	–	–	–
As_2Al_3	6-I	–	43	–	–	–	–	–	–	–	–	–	–	–	–	–
Arsenic sulfide (As_2S_3).	5	–	–	–	–	–	–	647	–	–	–	–	–	–	–	–
Arsenic telluride (As_2Te_3) . . .	6-I	–	–	–	–	–	–	–	640	–	–	–	–	–	–	–

Material Name	Volume	Density	Melting Point	Heat of Fusion	Heat of Vaporization	Heat of Sublimation	Electrical Resistivity	Specific Heat	Thermal Conductivity	Thermal Diffusivity	Thermal Linear Expansion	Thermal Absorptance	Thermal Emittance	Thermal Reflectance	Thermal Transmittance	Vapor Pressure
B																
Baddeleyite	4-I	-	-	-	-	-	-	-	-	-	585	-	-	-	-	-
Bakelites																
BM-261	6-II	-	-	-	-	-	-	-	-	-	988	-	-	-	-	-
BM-704	6-II	-	-	-	-	-	-	-	-	-	998	-	-	-	-	-
BM-3510	6-II	-	-	-	-	-	-	-	-	-	996	-	-	-	-	-
BM-13014	6-II	-	-	-	-	-	-	-	-	-	992	-	-	-	-	-
BM-13080	6-II	-	-	-	-	-	-	-	-	-	994	-	-	-	-	-
BM-13335	6-II	-	-	-	-	-	-	-	-	-	988	-	-	-	-	-
BM-14316	6-II	-	-	-	-	-	-	-	-	-	998	-	-	-	-	-
BM-14726	6-II	-	-	-	-	-	-	-	-	-	994	-	-	-	-	-
BM-15140	6-II	-	-	-	-	-	-	-	-	-	992	-	-	-	-	-
BM-16468	6-II	-	-	-	-	-	-	-	-	-	992	-	-	-	-	-
BM-17711	6-II	-	-	-	-	-	-	-	-	-	994	-	-	-	-	-
BM-17849	6-II	-	-	-	-	-	-	-	-	-	1000	-	-	-	-	-
DYNH	6-II	-	-	-	-	-	-	-	-	-	1045	-	-	-	-	-
Barium + Strontium	2-I	-	36	36	-	-	-	-	-	-	-	-	-	-	-	-
Barium aluminates																
$BaO \cdot Al_2O_3$	4-II	-	-	-	-	-	-	-	-	-	977	-	-	-	-	-
$3\ BaO \cdot Al_2O_3$	4-II	-	-	-	-	-	-	-	-	-	977	-	-	-	-	-
Barium aluminum silicate ($BaO \cdot Al_2O_3 \cdot 2\ SiO_2$)	4-II	-	-	-	-	-	-	1205	-	-	1207	-	-	-	-	-
Barium beryllium titanate ($BaO \cdot BeO \cdot TiO_2$)	4-II	-	-	-	-	-	-	-	-	-	1390	-	-	-	-	-
Barium borate glass	4-II	-	-	-	-	-	-	-	-	-	1609	-	-	-	-	-
Barium (hexa-)boride (BaB_6). .	6-I	-	296	-	-	-	300	-	-	-	302	-	-	-	-	-
Barium calcium silicate	4-II	-	-	-	-	-	-	-	-	-	1211	-	-	-	-	-
Barium calcium titanate [$(Ca_xBa_{1-x})O \cdot TiO_2$].	4-II	-	-	-	-	-	-	-	1392	1394	-	-	-	-	-	-
Barium carbide (BaC_2).	5	-	294	-	-	-	-	-	-	-	-	-	-	-	-	-
Barium cerium lead titanate [$(Ba_{1-x-y}Pb_xCe_y)O \cdot TiO_2$] . .	4-II	-	-	-	-	-	1398	-	-	-	-	-	-	-	-	-
Barium cerium titanate [$(Ba_{1-x}Ce_x)O \cdot TiO_2$].	4-II	-	-	-	-	-	1396	-	-	-	-	-	-	-	-	-
Barium cerium titanate silicate [$(Ba_{1-x}Ce_x)O \cdot (Ti_{1-x}Si_x)O_2$] .	4-II	-	-	-	-	-	1209	-	-	-	-	-	-	-	-	-
Barium cerium titanate stannate [$(Ba_{1-x}Ce_x)O \cdot (Ti_{1-y}Sn_y)O_2$] .	4-II	-	-	-	-	-	1354	-	-	-	-	-	-	-	-	-
Barium cerium titanate zirconate [$(Ba_{1-x}Ce_x)O \cdot (Ti_{1-y}Zr_y)O_2$].	4-II	-	-	-	-	-	1500	-	-	-	-	-	-	-	-	-
Barium copper silicate ($BaO \cdot CuO \cdot 4\ SiO_2$).	4-II	-	-	-	-	-	-	-	-	-	1213	-	-	-	-	-
Barium crown glass	4-II	-	-	-	-	-	-	1827	-	-	-	-	-	-	-	-
Barium fluoborate glass	4-II	-	-	-	-	-	-	-	-	-	1611	-	-	-	-	-

Material Name	Volume	Density	Melting Point	Heat of Fusion	Heat of Vaporization	Heat of Sublimation	Electrical Resistivity	Specific Heat	Thermal Conductivity	Thermal Diffusivity	Thermal Linear Expansion	Thermal Absorptance	Thermal Emittance	Thermal Reflectance	Thermal Transmittance	Vapor Pressure
Barium fluoride (BaF_2)	5	-	-	-	-	-	-	-	347	-	-	-	-	349	-	-
Barium lanthanum titanate [$(La_xBa_{1-x})O \cdot TiO_2$)]	4-II	-	-	-	-	-	1400	-	1402	-	-	-	-	-	-	-
Barium-lead intermetallics (Ba_2Pb)	6-I	-	-	-	-	-	-	-	642	-	-	-	-	-	-	-
Barium lead silicate glass . . .	4-II	-	-	-	-	-	1689	-	-	-	-	-	-	-	-	-
Barium lead titanates	4-II	-	-	-	-	-	-	-	-	-	1404	-	-	-	-	-
Barium magnesium silicates																
$BaO \cdot 3\ MgO \cdot SiO_2$	4-II	-	-	-	-	-	-	-	-	-	1215	-	-	-	-	-
$BaO \cdot 4\ MgO \cdot 3.5\ SiO_2$	4-II	-	-	-	-	-	-	-	-	-	1215	-	-	-	-	-
Barium magnesium aluminum silicate ($3\ BaO \cdot 2\ MgO \cdot 8\ Al_2O_3 \cdot 26\ SiO_2$)	4-II	-	-	-	-	-	-	-	-	-	1217-1221	-	-	-	-	-
Barium nitride (Ba_3N_2).	5	-	621	-	-	-	-	-	-	-	-	-	-	-	-	-
Barium oxide (BaO)	4-I	-	-	-	-	-	49	51	53	-	-	-	-	-	-	-
Barium oxide + Strontium oxide .	4-I	-	-	-	-	-	-	-	641	-	-	-	-	-	-	-
Barium oxide + Strontium oxide + + Zirconium cermet	6-II	-	-	-	-	-	-	-	911	-	-	-	-	-	-	-
Barium oxide + Strontium oxide + + Zirconium (di-) oxide	4-I	-	-	-	-	-	-	-	643	-	-	-	-	-	-	-
Barium phosphide (Ba_3P_2) . . .	5	-	635	-	-	-	-	-	-	-	-	-	-	-	-	-
Barium selenide (BaSe)	6-I	-	365	-	-	-	-	-	-	-	-	-	-	-	-	-
Barium silicate glass	4-II	-	-	-	-	-	-	-	-	1687	-	-	-	-	-	-
Barium silicide ($BaSi_2$)	6-I	-	371	-	-	-	-	-	-	-	373	-	-	-	-	-
Barium stannide (Ba_2Sn)	6-I	-	-	-	-	-	-	-	531	-	-	-	-	-	-	-
Barium strontium ferrites [$(Ba_xSr_{1-x})O \cdot 6\ Fe_2O_3$] . . .	4-II	1067	-	-	-	-	-	-	-	-	-	-	-	-	-	-
Barium strontium titanates . . .	4-II	-	-	-	-	-	-	-	-	-	1406	-	-	-	-	-
Barium sulfide (BaS)	5	649	649	-	-	-	-	651	-	-	-	-	-	-	-	-
Barium telluride (BaTe)	6-I	-	636	-	-	-	-	-	-	-	-	-	-	-	-	-
Barium titanates																
$BaO \cdot TiO_2$	4-II	-	1376	-	-	-	1378-1380	1382	1384	1386	1388	-	-	-	-	-
$BaO \cdot 3\ TiO_2$	4-II	-	-	-	-	-	-	-	-	-	1388	-	-	-	-	-
$BaO \cdot 4\ TiO_2$	4-II	-	-	-	-	-	-	-	-	-	1388	-	-	-	-	-
$BaO \cdot 5\ TiO_2$	4-II	-	-	-	-	-	-	-	-	-	1388	-	-	-	-	-
$BaO \cdot 6\ TiO_2$	4-II	-	-	-	-	-	-	-	-	-	1388	-	-	-	-	-
$BaO \cdot 18\ TiO_2$	4-II	-	-	-	-	-	-	-	-	-	1388	-	-	-	-	-
$2\ BaO \cdot TiO_2$	4-II	-	1376	-	-	-	-	1382	-	-	-	-	-	-	-	-
Barium titanate coating on niobium-zirconium alloy . . .	6-II	-	-	-	-	-	-	-	-	-	-	-	1369	-	-	-
Barium titanate + Calcium titanate	4-II	-	1579	-	-	-	-	-	-	-	-	-	-	-	-	-
Barium titanate + Lead titanate .	4-II	-	-	-	-	-	-	1581	-	-	-	-	-	-	-	-
Barium titanate + Manganese niobate	4-II	-	-	-	-	-	-	-	1583	-	-	-	-	-	-	-

Material Name	Volume	Density	Melting Point	Heat of Fusion	Heat of Vaporization	Heat of Sublimation	Electrical Resistivity	Specific Heat	Thermal Conductivity	Thermal Diffusivity	Thermal Linear Expansion	Thermal Absorptance	Thermal Emittance	Thermal Reflectance	Thermal Transmittance	Vapor Pressure
Barium titanate + Strontium titanate	4–II	–	–	–	–	–	–	1585	–	–	–	–	–	–	–	–
Barium titanium germanium oxide ($BaO \cdot TiO_2 \cdot 3\ GeO_2$). . .	4–II	–	–	–	–	–	–	–	–	–	1127	–	–	–	–	–
Barium titanium silicate glass .	4–II	–	–	–	–	–	–	–	–	–	1691	–	–	–	–	–
Barium uranate ($BaO \cdot UO_3$). . .	4–II	–	1482	–	–	–	–	1484	–	–	–	–	–	–	–	–
Barium zirconate ($BaO \cdot ZrO_2$) .	4–II	–	–	–	–	–	–	1496	–	–	1498	–	–	–	–	–
Beetle	6–II	–	–	–	–	–	–	–	–	–	1002	–	–	–	–	–
Beryl	4–II	–	–	–	–	–	–	–	1225	–	1227	–	–	–	–	–
Beryllia	4–I	55	55	55	55	–	57	59	61	65	67	71	73–77	79–81	83	85
Beryllium (Be)	1	48	48	48	48	48	50	53	55	57	59	–	61	63	–	65
Beryllium QM-V	1	–	–	–	–	–	51	–	–	–	–	–	–	–	–	–
Beryllium + ΣX_i	2–II	841	–	–	–	–	–	843	845	–	847	–	–	–	–	–
Beryllium + Aluminum	2–I	38	–	–	–	–	–	–	40	42	–	–	44	–	–	–
Beryllium + Aluminum + ΣX_i . .	2–II	–	–	–	–	–	–	–	–	–	833	–	–	–	–	–
Beryllium + Beryllium oxide cermet	6–II	751	–	–	–	751	–	753	757	–	762	–	–	–	–	764–766
Beryllium + Magnesium + ΣX_i .	2–II	835	–	–	–	–	837	–	839	–	–	–	–	–	–	–
Beryllium aluminate ($BeO \cdot Al_2O_3$)	4–II	–	–	–	–	–	–	979	–	–	981	–	–	–	–	–
Beryllium aluminosilicate ($3\ BeO \cdot Al_2O_3 \cdot 6\ SiO_2$)	4–II	–	–	–	–	–	–	–	1225	–	1227	–	–	–	–	–
Beryllium borides																
BeB	6–I	295	–	–	–	–	–	–	–	–	–	–	–	–	–	–
BeB_2	6–I	–	296	–	–	–	–	–	–	–	–	–	–	–	–	–
BeB_4	6–I	–	296	–	–	–	–	–	–	–	–	–	–	–	–	–
BeB_6	6–I	295	296	–	–	–	–	–	–	–	–	–	–	–	–	–
BeB_9	6–I	–	296	–	–	–	–	–	–	–	–	–	–	–	–	–
Be_2B	6–I	295	296	–	–	–	–	–	–	–	–	–	–	–	–	–
Be_5B	6–I	–	296	–	–	–	–	–	–	–	–	–	–	–	–	–
Beryllium indium selenide ($InBeSe_3$)	6–I	–	–	–	–	–	–	–	329	–	–	–	–	–	–	–
Beryllium carbide (Be_2C) . . .	5	15	15	15	15	–	–	17	–	–	19	–	–	–	–	21
Beryllium carbide + ΣX_i	5	–	–	–	–	–	–	303	305	–	–	–	–	–	–	–
Beryllium cermet BM15	6–II	–	–	–	–	–	–	–	757	–	–	–	–	–	–	–
Beryllium cermet LYB 1102 . .	6–II	–	–	–	–	–	–		757	–	–	–	–	–	–	–
Beryllium cermet Y6825	6–II	–	–	–	–	–	–	–	757	–	–	–	–	–	–	–
Beryllium cermet Y6826	6–II	–	–	–	–	–	–	–	757	–	–	–	–	–	–	–
Beryllium cermet Y9384	6–II	–	–	–	–	–	–	–	757	–	–	–	–	–	–	–
Beryllium cermet YB1000 . . .	6–II	–	–	–	–	–	–	–	31	–	–	–	–	–	–	–
Beryllium cermet YB9052 . . .	6–II	–	–	–	–	–	–	753	757	–	762	–	–	–	–	–
Beryllium cermet YB9053 . . .	6–II	–	–	–	–	–	–	–	–	–	762	–	–	–	–	–
Beryllium cermet YB9054 . . .	6–II	–	–	–	–	–	–	753	–	–	762	–	–	–	–	–

Material Name	Volume	Density	Melting Point	Heat of Fusion	Heat of Vaporization	Heat of Sublimation	Electrical Resistivity	Specific Heat	Thermal Conductivity	Thermal Diffusivity	Thermal Linear Expansion	Thermal Absorptance	Thermal Emittance	Thermal Reflectance	Thermal Transmittance	Vapor Pressure
Beryllium chromite ($BeO \cdot Cr_2O_3$)	4-II	-	-	-	-	-	-	-	-	-	1049	-	-	-	-	-
Beryllium fluoride (BeF_2) . . .	5	351	351	351	351	351	-	-	-	-	-	-	-	-	-	353
Beryllium nitrides																
Be_3N_2	5	-	495	495	495	-	-	-	497	-	-	-	-	-	-	-
Be_3N_4	5	-	495	-	-	-	-	-	-	-	-	-	-	-	-	-
Beryllium oxides																
Beryllium oxide (BeO) . . .	4-I	55	55	55	55	-	57	59	61	65	67	71	73-77	79-81	83	85
BD-98	4-I	-	-	-	-	-	-	-	61	65	-	-	77	-	-	-
UOX grade	4-I	-	-	-	-	-	-	-	61	-	-	-	-	-	-	-
Beryllium oxide + Aluminum oxide + Magnesium oxide . . .	4-I	-	-	-	-	-	-	-	-	-	645	-	-	-	-	-
Beryllium oxide + Aluminum oxide + Thorium (di-) oxide . .	4-I	-	-	-	-	-	-	-	647	-	649	-	-	-	-	-
Beryllium oxide + Aluminum oxide + Thorium (di-) oxide + + Magnesium oxide	4-I	-	-	-	-	-	-	-	651	-	-	-	-	-	-	-
Beryllium oxide + Aluminum oxide + Zirconium (di-) oxide .	4-I	-	-	-	-	-	-	-	653	-	-	-	-	-	-	-
Beryllium oxide + Aluminum oxide + Zirconium (di-) oxide + + Magnesium oxide	4-I	-	-	-	-	-	-	-	655	-	-	-	-	-	-	-
Beryllium oxide + Beryllium cermet	6-II	-	-	-	-	751	-	755	760	-	762	-	-	-	-	-
Beryllium oxide + Beryllium + +Molybdenum cermet	6-II	-	-	-	-	-	-	768	770	-	772	-	-	-	-	-
Beryllium oxide + Beryllium + + Silicon cermet	6-II	-	-	-	-	-	-	-	774	-	776	-	-	-	-	-
Beryllium oxide + Magnesium oxide + Aluminum oxide . . .	4-I	-	-	-	-	-	-	-	657	-	-	-	-	-	-	-
Beryllium oxide + Magnesium oxide + Aluminum oxide + + Thorium (di-) oxide	4-I	-	-	-	-	-	-	-	659	-	-	-	-	-	-	-
Beryllium oxide + Magnesium oxide + Aluminum oxide + + Zirconium (di-) oxide	4-I	-	-	-	-	-	-	-	661	-	-	-	-	-	-	-
Beryllium oxide + Magnesium oxide + Zirconium (di-) oxide + + Aluminum oxide	4-I	-	-	-	-	-	-	-	663	-	-	-	-	-	-	-
Beryllium oxide + Molybdenum cermet	6-II	-	-	-	-	-	-	778	-	-	-	-	-	-	-	-
Beryllium oxide + Molybdenum beryllide	5	-	-	-	-	-	-	759	-	-	-	-	-	-	-	-
Beryllium oxide + Niobium cermet	6-II	780	-	-	-	-	-	-	-	-	782	-	-	-	-	-
Beryllium oxide + Niobium beryllide	5	-	-	-	-	-	-	761	-	-	-	-	-	-	-	-
Beryllium oxide + Tanatlum beryllide	5	-	-	-	-	-	-	763	-	-	-	-	-	-	-	-

Material Name	Volume	Density	Melting Point	Heat of Fusion	Heat of Vaporization	Heat of Sublimation	Electrical Resistivity	Specific Heat	Thermal Conductivity	Thermal Diffusivity	Thermal Linear Expansion	Thermal Absorptance	Thermal Emittance	Thermal Reflectance	Thermal Transmittance	Vapor Pressure
Beryllium oxide + Thorium (di-)oxide + Aluminum oxide .	4-I	-	-	-	-	-	-	-	-	-	665	-	-	-	-	-
Beryllium oxide + Titanium beryllide	5	-	-	-	-	-	-	765	-	-	-	-	-	-	-	-
Beryllium oxide + Uranium (di-)oxide	4-I	-	-	-	-	-	-	-	667	-	-	-	-	-	-	-
Beryllium oxide + Zirconium beryllide	5	-	-	-	-	-	-	767	-	-	-	-	-	-	-	-
Beryllium oxide + Zirconium (di-)oxide + Magnesium oxide + + Aluminum oxide	4-I	-	-	-	-	-	-	-	669	-	-	-	-	-	-	-
Beryllium oxide porcelain type 4811	5	1003	-	-	-	-	-	-	1017	-	-	-	-	-	-	-
Beryllium silicate (2 BeO · SiO_2).	4-II										1223					
Beryllium sulfide (BeS)	5	653	653	-	-	-	-	-	-	-	-	-	-	-	-	655
Beryllium titanates																
BeO · TiO_2	4-II	-	-	-	-	-	-	-	-	-	1408	-	-	-	-	-
2 BeO · TiO_2	4-II	-	-	-	-	-	-	-	-	-	1408	-	-	-	-	-
4 BeO · TiO_2	4-II	-	-	-	-	-	-	-	-	-	1408	-	-	-	-	-
6 BeO · TiO_2	4-II	-	-	-	-	-	-	-	-	-	1408	-	-	-	-	-
Bismuth-cerium intermetallics																
BiCe	6-I	-	683	-	-	-	-	-	-	-	-	-	-	-	-	-
$BiCe_3$	6-I	-	683	-	-	-	-	-	-	-	-	-	-	-	-	-
Bi_3Ce_4	6-I	-	683	-	-	-	-	-	-	-	-	-	-	-	-	-
Bismuth selenide tellurides ($Bi_2Te_{3-x}Se_x$)	6-I	-	-	-	-	-	564	-	566	-	-	-	-	-	-	-
Bismuth stannate (Bi_2O_3 · 3 SnO_2)	4-II								1357							
Bismuth telluride(Bi_2Te_3) . . .	6-I	553	553	-	-	-	555	557	559	561	-	-	-	-	-	-
Bismuth telluride + Bismuth selenide	6-I	-	-	-	-	-	711	-	713	-	-	-	-	-	-	-
Bismuth tellurium sulfide (Bi_2Te_2S)	5	-	-	-	-	-	657	-	659	-	-	-	-	-	-	-
Boral clad with boron carbide. .	5	979	-	-	-	-	-	981	-	-	-	-	-	-	-	-
Borate glasses	4-II	1605	-	-	-	-	1607	-	-	-	1609-1633	-	-	-	-	-
Borolites																
Borolite	6-II	842	-	-	-	-	-	-	-	-	-	-	-	-	-	-
Borolite I, grade F	6-II	-	-	-	-	-	-	846	-	-	-	-	-	-	-	-
Borolite I, grade G	6-II	-	-	-	-	-	844	-	-	-	850	-	-	-	-	-
Borolite I, grade S	6-II	-	-	-	-	-	844	846	-	-	-	-	-	-	-	-
Borolite IV	6-II	913	-	-	-	-	-	-	-	-	-	-	-	-	-	-
Boron (B)	1	67	67	-	67	67	69	71	-	-	-	-	-	-	-	73
Boron coating on molybdenum .	6-II	-	-	-	-	-	-	-	-	-	-	-	1289	-	-	-
Boron coating on niobium-zirconium alloys	6-II	-	-	-	-	-	-	-	-	-	-	-	1291	-	-	-
Boron + ΣX_i	2-II	849	-	-	-	-	-	-	-	-	-	-	-	-	-	-

Material Name	Volume	Density	Melting Point	Heat of Fusion	Heat of Vaporization	Heat of Sublimation	Electrical Resistivity	Specific Heat	Thermal Conductivity	Thermal Diffusivity	Thermal Linear Expansion	Thermal Absorptance	Thermal Emittance	Thermal Reflectance	Thermal Transmittance	Vapor Pressure
Boron + Iron	2-I	-	-	-	-	46	-	-	-	-	-	-	-	-	-	48
Boron + Silicon	2-I	-	-	-	-	-	50	-	-	-	-	-	-	-	-	-
Boron aluminate ($2B_2O_3 \cdot 9Al_2O_3$)	4-II	-	-	-	-	-	-	-	-	-	983	-	-	-	-	-
Boron carbide (B_4C)	5	25	23	-	-	-	-	27	29	31	33	-	35	-	-	37
Boron carbide clad with aluminum	5	979	-	-	-	-	-	981	-	-	-	-	-	-	-	-
Boron carbide coating on Inconel X	6-II	-	-	-	-	-	-	-	-	-	-	-	1403	1405	-	-
Boron carbide + Iron cermet . .	6-II	928	-	-	-	-	-	-	-	-	-	-	-	-	-	-
Boron oxide (B_2O_3)	4-I	-	-	-	-	-	-	87	-	-	-	-	-	-	-	89
Boron oxide glass	4-II	-	-	-	-	-	-	1635	-	-	-	-	-	-	-	-
Boron nitride (BN)	5	499	499	-	499	-	501	503	505	-	507	-	509-513	515	-	-
Boron nitride + Boron oxide . .	5	-	-	-	-	-	832	834	836	-	838	-	-	-	-	-
Boron nitride + Graphite	5	-	-	-	-	-	-	828	830	-	-	-	-	-	-	-
Boron phosphide (BP)	5	-	635	-	-	-	-	-	-	-	-	-	-	-	-	-
Boron silicides																
B_4Si	6-I	-	-	-	-	-	-	-	-	-	-	-	375-377	379	-	-
B_6Si	6-I	-	-	-	-	-	-	-	-	-	-	-	375-377	379	-	-
Borosilicate glass	4-II	1693	1693	-	-	-	1695	1697	1699	1701	1703	-	1705-1707	1709	1711-1713	-
Brass	2-I	-	-	-	-	-	170	172	-	174	-	-	178-180	182	-	-
	2-II								1000							
Brass, aluminum	2-II	-	-	-	-	-	-	-	-	-	1004	-	-	-	-	-
Brass, free cutting leaded . . .	2-I	168	-	-	-	-	-	-	-	-	-	-	-	-	-	-
Brass, red	2-II	-	-	-	-	-	-	-	-	-	1002	-	-	-	-	-
Brass, yellow	2-I	-	-	-	-	-	-	-	-	174	-	-	176	-	-	-
	2-II								1000							
Brazing alloy																
GE-62	2-II	-	-	-	-	-	-	-	-	-	1168	-	-	-	-	-
GEH62-V	2-II	-	-	-	-	-	-	1130	-	-	-	-	-	-	-	-
GE-76	2-II	-	-	-	-	-	-	-	-	-	1378	-	-	-	-	-
Bricks																
Bricks	5	-	-	-	-	-	1029	-	1031-1033	-	1035-1037	-	1039-1043	-	-	-
Chrome-magnesite	5	-	-	-	-	-	1029	-	-	-	-	-	1039	-	-	-
Chromomagnesite	4-I	-	-	-	-	-	-	-	741	-	-	-	-	-	-	-
Forsterite	5	-	-	-	-	-	1029	-	1033	-	-	-	-	-	-	-
K-30 insulating	5	-	-	-	-	-	-	-	-	-	1035	-	-	-	-	-
Magnesia	5	-	-	-	-	-	1029	-	-	-	-	-	-	-	-	-
Magnesite	4-I	-	-	-	-	-	-	-	743	733, 737	-	-	-	-	-	-

Material Name	Volume	Density	Melting Point	Heat of Fusion	Heat of Vaporization	Heat of Sublimation	Electrical Resistivity	Specific Heat	Thermal Conductivity	Thermal Diffusivity	Thermal Linear Expansion	Thermal Absorptance	Thermal Emittance	Thermal Reflectance	Thermal Transmittance	Vapor Pressure
Bricks (cont.)																
Magnesite-chrome	5	–	–	–	–	–	1029	–	–	–	–	–	–	–	–	–
Magnesite "hu"	5	–	–	–	–	–	–	–	1033	–	–	–	–	–	–	–
Mica	5	–	–	–	–	–	–	–	989	–	–	–	–	–	–	–
Mica, white	5	–	–	–	–	–	–	–	989	–	–	–	–	–	–	–
Silica	4-I	–	–	–	–	–	–	–	816	363, 796, 818	–	–	–	–	–	–
. . . . . .	5	–	–	–	–	–	–	–	–	–	1037	–	1041	–	–	–
Silicon carbide	5	–	–	–	–	–	–	–	125	–	–	–	–	–	–	–
Sillimanite	4-I	–	–	–	–	–	–	–	615	–	–	–	–	–	–	–
Vermiculite insulating. . . .	5	–	–	–	–	–	–	–	989	–	–	–	–	–	–	–
Bromyrite	5	–	–	–	–	–	–	–	–	9	–	–	–	–	–	–
Bronze	2-I	154	–	–	–	–	156	–	–	–	–	–	162	–	–	–
. . . . . .	2-II	–	–	–	–	–	–	–	–	–	998	–	–	–	–	–
Bronze, aluminum	2-II	–	–	–	–	–	–	–	–	–	950	952	954-958	960	–	–
Bronze, lead	2-II	–	–	–	–	–	–	–	–	–	976	–	–	–	–	–
Bronze, phosnic	2-II	–	–	–	–	–	–	–	–	–	988	–	–	–	–	–
Bronze, silicon	2-II	–	–	–	–	–	–	–	–	–	994	–	–	–	–	–
Bronze, tellurium-aluminum . .	2-II	–	–	–	–	–	–	–	–	–	950	–	–	–	–	–
Bronze, Tin-Zinc	2-II	–	–	–	–	–	–	–	–	–	998	–	–	–	–	–
Buna S	6-II	–	–	–	–	–	–	–	–	1066	–	–	–	–	–	–
Butadiene-acrylonitrile copolymer	6-II	–	–	–	–	–	–	1054	–	1060	–	–	–	–	–	–
Butyl GR-1	6-II	–	–	–	–	–	–	–	–	1062	–	–	–	–	–	–
C																
CA-2, carbide tool steel	6-II	–	–	–	–	–	–	–	889	–	–	–	–	–	–	–
CA-4, carbide tool steel	6-II	–	–	–	–	–	–	–	889	–	–	–	–	–	–	–
Cadmium (Cd)	1	–	–	–	–	–	–	–	–	–	–	–	75	–	–	–
Cadmium + Silver	2-I	–	52	52	–	–	–	–	–	–	–	–	–	54	–	–
Cadmium lead silicate glass . .	4-II	–	–	–	–	–	1731	–	–	–	–	–	–	–	–	–
Cadmium oxides																
CdO	4-I	91	91	–	–	91	–	93	–	–	–	–	–	–	–	97
Cd_2O_3	4-I	–	–	–	–	–	–	–	–	–	95	–	–	–	–	–
Cadmium sulfide (CdS).	5	–	–	–	–	–	661	663	–	–	–	–	665	–	–	–
Cadmium telluride (CdTe) . . .	6-I	–	–	–	–	–	568	570	–	–	–	–	–	–	–	–
Calcia	4-I	99	99	–	–	–	101	103	105	–	107	–	–	–	–	109
Calcium (Ca)	1	–	77	77	–	–	79	–	–	–	–	–	–	–	–	81
Calcium + Magnesium	2-I	–	56	–	–	–	58	–	–	–	–	–	–	–	–	–

Material Name	Volume	Density	Melting Point	Heat of Fusion	Heat of Vaporization	Heat of Sublimation	Electrical Resistivity	Specific Heat	Thermal Conductivity	Thermal Diffusivity	Thermal Linear Expansion	Thermal Absorptance	Thermal Emittance	Thermal Reflectance	Thermal Transmittance	Vapor Pressure
Calcium aluminates																
$CaO \cdot Al_2O_3$	4-II	-	-	-	-	-	-	987	-	-	-	-	-	-	-	-
$CaO \cdot 2\ Al_2O_3$	4-II	985	985	-	-	-	-	987	-	-	-	-	-	-	-	-
$CaO \cdot 6\ Al_2O_3$	4-II	-	-	-	-	-	-	-	-	-	991	-	-	-	-	-
$3\ CaO \cdot Al_2O_3$	4-II	-	-	-	-	-	-	987	-	-	-	-	-	-	-	-
$3\ CaO \cdot 5\ Al_2O_3$	4-II	-	-	-	-	-	-	-	-	-	989	-	-	-	-	-
$12\ CaO \cdot 7\ Al_2O_3$	4-II	-	-	-	-	-	-	987	-	-	-	-	-	-	-	-
Calcium aluminate + Molybdenum disilicide cermet	6-II	-	-	-	-	-	-	-	-	-	784	-	-	-	-	-
Calcium aluminum silicates																
$CaO \cdot Al_2O_3 \cdot 2\ SiO_2$	4-II	-	-	-	-	-	-	1233	-	-	1235	-	-	-	-	-
$2\ CaO \cdot Al_2O_3 \cdot SiO_2$	4-II	-	-	-	-	-	-	1233	-	-	1235	-	-	-	-	-
$2\ CaO \cdot 2\ Al_2O_3 \cdot 8\ SiO_2 \cdot 7\ H_2O$	4-II	-	-	-	-	-	-	1233	-	-	-	-	-	-	-	-
Calcium barium cerium titanate $[(Ba_{1-x-y}Ca_xCe_y)O \cdot TiO_2]$	4-II	-	-	-	-	-	1420	-	-	-	-	-	-	-	-	-
Calcium borates																
$CaO \cdot B_2O_3$	4-II	-	1037	1037	-	-	-	1039	-	-	-	-	-	-	-	-
$CaO \cdot 2\ B_2O_3$	4-II	-	1037	1037	-	-	-	1039	-	-	-	-	-	-	-	-
$2\ CaO \cdot B_2O_3$	4-II	-	1037	1037	-	-	-	1039	-	-	-	-	-	-	-	-
$3\ CaO \cdot B_2O_3$	4-II	-	1037	1037	-	-	-	1039	-	-	-	-	-	-	-	-
Calcium borate glass	4-II	-	-	-	-	-	-	-	-	-	1613	-	-	-	-	-
Calcium (hexa-)boride (CaB_6)	6-I	-	296	-	-	-	300	-	-	-	302	-	-	-	-	-
Calcium carbide + Calcium oxide	5	-	-	-	-	-	-	805	-	-	-	-	-	-	-	-
Calcium carbonate ($CaCO_3$)	4-II	-	-	-	-	-	-	-	-	-	-	-	-	1045	-	-
Calcium copper silicate ($CaO \cdot CuO \cdot 4\ SiO_2$)	4-II	-	-	-	-	-	-	-	-	-	1238	-	-	-	-	-
Calcium ferrites																
$CaO \cdot Fe_2O_3$	4-II	-	-	-	-	-	-	1069	-	-	-	-	-	-	-	-
$2\ CaO \cdot Fe_2O_3$	4-II	-	-	-	-	-	-	1069	-	-	-	-	-	-	-	-
Calcium fluoride (CaF_2)	5	355	355	-	-	-	-	-	357	-	359	-	-	361	-	-
Calcium hafnate ($CaO \cdot HfO_2$)	4-II	1107	1107	-	-	-	-	-	-	-	1109	-	-	-	-	-
Calcium lanthanum manganese oxide ($La_xCa_{1-x}MnO_3$)	4-II	-	-	-	-	-	1129	-	1131	-	-	-	-	-	-	-
Calcium-lead intermetallics (Ca_2Pb)	6-I	-	-	-	-	-	-	-	646	-	-	-	-	-	-	-
Calcium lead silicate glass	4-II	-	-	-	-	-	1733	-	-	-	-	-	-	-	-	-
Calcium magnesium silicates																
$CaO \cdot MgO \cdot 2\ SiO_2$	4-II	-	-	-	-	-	-	1239	-	-	-	-	-	-	-	-
$2\ CaO \cdot MgO \cdot 2\ SiO_2$	4-II	-	-	-	-	-	-	1239	-	-	-	-	-	-	-	-
$3\ CaO \cdot MgO \cdot 2\ SiO_2$	4-II	-	-	-	-	-	-	1239	-	-	-	-	-	-	-	-
$2\ CaO \cdot 5\ MgO \cdot 8\ SiO_2 \cdot 2\ H_2O$	4-II	-	-	-	-	-	-	1239	-	-	-	-	-	-	-	-
Calcium molybdate ($CaO \cdot MoO_3$)	4-II	-	-	-	-	-	-	1111	-	-	-	-	-	-	-	-
Calcium nitrides																
CaN	5	-	621	-	-	-	-	-	-	-	-	-	-	-	-	-
Ca_3N_2	5	-	621	-	-	-	-	-	-	-	-	-	-	-	-	-

Material Name	Volume	Density	Melting Point	Heat of Fusion	Heat of Vaporization	Heat of Sublimation	Electrical Resistivity	Specific Heat	Thermal Conductivity	Thermal Diffusivity	Thermal Linear Expansion	Thermal Absorptance	Thermal Emittance	Thermal Reflectance	Thermal Transmittance	Vapor Pressure
Calcium oxide (CaO).	4-I	99	99	-	-	-	101	103	105	-	107	-	-	-	-	109
Calcium oxide + Titanium (di-) oxide	4-I	-	-	-	-	-	-	-	-	-	671	-	-	-	-	-
Calcium selenides (CaSe) . . .	6-I	-	365	-	-	-	-	-	-	-	-	-	-	-	-	-
Calcium silicates																
$CaO \cdot SiO_2$	4-II	-	-	-	-	-	-	1229	-	-	1231	-	-	-	-	-
$2\ CaO \cdot SiO_2$	4-II	-	-	-	-	-	-	1229	-	-	1231	-	-	-	-	-
$3\ CaO \cdot SiO_2$	4-II	-	-	-	-	-	-	1229	-	-	-	-	-	-	-	-
Calcium silicate glass	4-II	-	-	-	-	-	-	-	-	-	-	-	-	-	1729	-
Calcium silicides																
CaSi	6-I	-	523	-	-	-	-	-	-	-	-	-	-	-	-	-
$CaSi_2$	6-I	-	523	-	-	-	-	-	-	-	-	-	-	-	-	-
Ca_2Si	6-I	-	523	-	-	-	-	-	-	-	-	-	-	-	-	-
Calcium stannate ($CaO \cdot SnO_2$). .	4-II	-	-	-	-	-	-	-	1359	-	-	-	-	-	-	-
Calcium strontium barium cerium titanate $[(Ba_{1-x-y-z}Ca_xSr_yCe_z)O \cdot TiO_2]$	4-II	-	-	-	-	-	1422	-	-	-	-	-	-	-	-	-
Calcium titanates																
$CaO \cdot TiO_2$	4-II	1410	1410	-	-	-	1412	1414	1416	-	1418	-	-	-	-	-
$3\ CaO \cdot 2\ TiO_2$	4-II	-	-	-	-	-	-	1414	-	-	1418	-	-	-	-	-
Calcium titanate coating on niobium-zirconium alloy . . .	6-II	-	-	-	-	-	-	-	-	-	-	-	1371	-	-	-
Calcium tungstate ($CaO \cdot WO_3$) .	4-II	-	-	-	-	-	-	1472	-	-	-	-	-	-	-	-
Calcium uranate ($CaO \cdot UO_3$) . .	4-II	-	1482	-	-	-	-	1486	-	-	-	-	-	-	-	-
Calcium vanadates																
$CaO \cdot V_2O_5$	4-II	-	-	-	-	-	-	1488	-	-	-	-	-	-	-	-
$2\ CaO \cdot V_2O_5$	4-II	-	-	-	-	-	-	1488	-	-	-	-	-	-	-	-
$3\ CaO \cdot V_2O_5$	4-II	-	-	-	-	-	-	1488	-	-	-	-	-	-	-	-
Calcium zirconate ($CaO \cdot ZrO_2$) .	4-II	1502	1502	-	-	-	-	1504	-	-	1506	-	-	-	-	-
Carbide tool steels	6-II	-	-	-	-	-	-	-	889	-	-	-	-	-	-	-
Carbofrax	5	-	-	-	-	-	-	-	307	-	-	-	309-311	-	-	-
Carboloy 44A	6-II	887	-	-	-	-	-	-	-	-	-	-	-	-	-	-
Carboloy 55A	6-II	887	-	-	-	-	-	-	-	-	-	-	-	-	-	-
Carbons																
Carbon (C)	1	83	-	-	-	83	85	-	87	-	-	-	91-93	95	-	-
Amorphous	1	-	-	-	-	-	83	-	87	-	-	-	-	-	-	-
GA grade	1	-	-	-	-	-	-	-	-	-	-	-	91	95	-	-
Pyrolytic	1	83	-	-	-	-	-	-	89	-	-	-	-	-	-	-
Carbon coating on molybdenum .	6-II	-	-	-	-	-	-	-	-	-	-	1293	1295	-	-	-
Carbon electrode	1	-	-	-	-	-	85	-	87	-	-	-	-	-	-	-
Carbon impregnated graphite . .	1	-	-	-	-	-	-	-	358	-	-	-	-	-	-	-
Carbon-phenolic laminate MX-4926	6-II	-	-	-	-	-	-	1134	-	-	-	-	-	-	-	-

Material Name	Volume	Density	Melting Point	Heat of Fusion	Heat of Vaporization	Heat of Sublimation	Electrical Resistivity	Specific Heat	Thermal Conductivity	Thermal Diffusivity	Thermal Linear Expansion	Thermal Absorptance	Thermal Emittance	Thermal Reflectance	Thermal Transmittance	Vapor Pressure
Carbon steels	3	–	–	–	–	3	5, 312	7-10	–	12-14	16-20	–	–	–	–	22
Carbonyl nickel	1	–	694	–	–	–	–	–	–	–	–	–	–	–	–	–
Cast iron	3	27	–	–	–	–	–	–	29-37, 437	–	39-41, 444	–	–	–	–	–
Cast iron, gray (see grey cast iron)																
Cast iron, nodular (see Nodular cast iron)																
Castolite	6-II	974	–	–	–	–	–	–	976	1082	978	–	–	–	–	–
Catalin	6-II	–	–	–	–	–	–	–	–	–	986	–	–	–	–	–
Cellulose acetates	6-II	–	–	–	–	–	–	–	–	–	941	–	–	–	–	–
Cellulose acetate, expanded . .	6-II	–	–	–	–	–	–	–	939	–	–	–	–	–	–	–
Cellulose acetate butyrate . . .	6-II	–	–	–	–	–	–	–	–	–	946	–	–	–	–	–
Cellulose propionate	6-II	–	–	–	–	–	–	–	–	–	944	–	–	–	–	–
Cement-barytes aggregate . . .	5	–	–	–	–	–	–	1023	1025	–	–	–	–	–	–	–
Ceramic laminate	6-II	–	–	–	–	–	–	–	–	–	1225	–	–	–	–	–
Cercor	4-II	–	–	–	–	–	–	–	–	1591	–	–	–	–	–	–
Ceria	4-I	111	111	–	–	–	113	115	119	–	121	–	124-128	–	–	–
Cerium (Ce)	1	402	402	402	402	402	404	406	–	–	–	–	–	–	–	408
Cerium + ΣX_i	2-II	–	853	–	–	–	–	–	–	–	–	–	–	–	–	–
Cerium + Neodymium	2-I	–	–	–	–	–	–	–	–	–	60	–	–	–	–	–
Cerium + Silicon + ΣX_i	2-II	–	851	–	–	–	–	–	–	–	–	–	–	–	–	–
Cerium aluminate ($2CeO \cdot 3Al_2O_3$)	4-II	–	–	–	–	–	–	–	–	–	993	–	–	–	–	–
Cerium aluminides																
$CeAl$	6-I	–	43	–	–	–	–	–	–	–	–	–	–	–	–	–
$CeAl_2$	6-I	–	43	–	–	–	–	–	–	–	–	–	–	–	–	–
$CeAl_4$	6-I	–	43	–	–	–	–	–	–	–	–	–	–	–	–	–
Ce_3Al_2	6-I	–	43	–	–	–	–	–	–	–	–	–	–	–	–	–
Cerium aluminum silicides ($Ce_2Al_3Si_2$)	6-I	523	–	–	–	–	–	–	–	–	–	–	–	–	–	–
Cerium-bismuth intermetallics ($CeBi$)	6-I	662	–	–	–	–	–	–	–	–	–	–	–	–	–	–
Cerium borides																
CeB_4	6-I	296	–	–	–	–	–	–	–	–	–	–	–	–	–	–
CeB_6	6-I	295, 296	296	–	–	–	300	–	–	–	302	–	–	–	–	–
Cerium (tri-)bromide ($CeB4_3$) .	5	11	–	–	–	–	–	–	–	–	–	–	–	–	–	–
Cerium-cadmium intermetallics																
$CeCd$	6-I	662	–	–	–	–	–	–	–	–	–	–	–	–	–	–
$CeCd_2$	6-I	662	–	–	–	–	–	–	–	–	–	–	–	–	–	–
$CeCd_3$	6-I	662	–	–	–	–	–	–	–	–	–	–	–	–	–	–
$CeCd_{11}$	6-I	662	–	–	–	–	–	–	–	–	–	–	–	–	–	–

Material Name	Volume	Density	Melting Point	Heat of Fusion	Heat of Vaporization	Heat of Sublimation	Electrical Resistivity	Specific Heat	Thermal Conductivity	Thermal Diffusivity	Thermal Linear Expansion	Thermal Absorptance	Thermal Emittance	Thermal Reflectance	Thermal Transmittance	Vapor Pressure
Cerium carbides																
CeC_2	5	294	–	–	–	–	–	–	–	–	–	–	–	–	–	–
Ce_2C_3	5	294	–	–	–	–	–	–	–	–	–	–	–	–	–	–
Cerium (tri-) chloride ($CeCl_3$) .	5	339	–	–	–	–	–	–	–	–	–	–	–	–	–	–
Cerium-cobalt intermetallics																
$CeCo_2$	6-I	662	–	–	–	–	–	–	–	–	–	–	–	–	–	–
$CeCo_5$	6-I	662	–	–	–	–	–	–	–	–	–	–	–	–	–	–
Cerium-copper intermetallics																
CeCu	6-I	–	663	–	–	–	–	–	–	–	–	–	–	–	–	–
$CeCu_2$	6-I	–	663	–	–	–	–	–	–	–	–	–	–	–	–	–
$CeCu_4$	6-I	–	663	–	–	–	–	–	–	–	–	–	–	–	–	–
$CeCu_6$	6-I	–	663	–	–	–	–	–	–	–	–	–	–	–	–	–
Cerium (tri-) fluoride (CeF_3). .	5	363	363	–	–	–	–	365	–	–	–	–	–	–	–	–
Cerium-gallium intermetallics ($CeGa_2$)	6-I	662	–	–	–	–	–	–	–	–	–	–	–	–	–	–
Cerium-gold intermetallics																
CeAu	6-I	–	662	–	–	–	–	–	–	–	–	–	–	–	–	–
$CeAu_2$	6-I	–	662	–	–	–	–	–	–	–	–	–	–	–	–	–
$CeAu_3$	6-I	–	662	–	–	–	–	–	–	–	–	–	–	–	–	–
Ce_2Au	6-I	–	662	–	–	–	–	–	–	–	–	–	–	–	–	–
Cerium hydride (CeH_2).	5	467	–	–	–	–	–	–	–	–	–	–	–	–	–	–
Cerium-indium intermetallics ($CeIn_3$)	6-I	662	–	–	–	–	–	–	–	–	–	–	–	–	–	–
Cerium (tri-) iodide (CeI_3) . . .	5	–	477	–	–	–	–	–	–	–	–	–	–	–	–	–
Cerium-lead intermetallics																
$CePb_3$	6-I	662	663	–	–	–	–	–	–	–	–	–	–	–	–	–
Ce_2Pb	6-I	–	663	–	–	–	–	–	–	–	–	–	–	–	–	–
Cerium-magnesium intermetallics																
CeMg	6-I	662	663	–	–	–	–	–	–	–	–	–	–	–	–	–
$CeMg_3$	6-I	–	663	–	–	–	–	–	–	–	–	–	–	–	–	–
$CeMg_9$	6-I	–	663	–	–	–	–	–	–	–	–	–	–	–	–	–
Ce_4Mg	6-I	–	663	–	–	–	–	–	–	–	–	–	–	–	–	–
Cerium-mercury intermetallics (CeHg)	6-I	662	–	–	–	–	–	–	–	–	–	–	–	–	–	–
Cerium-nickel intermetallics																
$CeNi_2$	6-I	662	–	–	–	–	–	–	–	–	–	–	–	–	–	–
$CeNi_3$	6-I	662	–	–	–	–	–	–	–	–	–	–	–	–	–	–
$CeNi_5$	6-I	662	–	–	–	–	–	–	–	–	–	–	–	–	–	–
Ce_2Ni_7	6-I	662	–	–	–	–	–	–	–	–	–	–	–	–	–	–
Cerium nitride (CeN)	5	621	–	–	–	–	–	–	–	–	–	–	–	–	–	–
Cerium-osmium intermetallics ($CeOs_2$)	6-I	662	–	–	–	–	–	–	–	–	–	–	–	–	–	–

Material Name	Volume	Density	Melting Point	Heat of Fusion	Heat of Vaporization	Heat of Sublimation	Electrical Resistivity	Specific Heat	Thermal Conductivity	Thermal Diffusivity	Thermal Linear Expansion	Thermal Absorptance	Thermal Emittance	Thermal Reflectance	Thermal Transmittance	Vapor Pressure
Cerium oxides																
CeO	4-I	111	–	–	–	–	–	–	–	–	–	–	–	–	–	–
CeO_2	4-I	111	111	–	–	–	113	115	119	–	121	–	124-128	–	–	–
Ce_2O_3	4-I	111	–	–	–	–	–	117	–	–	–	–	–	–	–	–
Cerium (di-) oxide + Magnesium oxide	4-I	–	–	–	–	–	–	–	673	–	–	–	–	–	–	–
Cerium (di-) oxide + Uranium oxides	4-I	675	–	–	–	–	–	–	677	–	–	–	–	–	–	–
Cerium phosphide (CeP)	5	635	–	–	–	–	–	–	–	–	–	–	–	–	–	–
Cerium-platinum intermetallics ($CePt_2$)	6-I	662	–	–	–	–	–	–	–	–	–	–	–	–	–	–
Cerium selenides																
CeSe	6-I	365	–	–	–	–	–	–	–	–	–	–	–	–	–	–
Ce_3Se_4	6-I	365	–	–	–	–	–	–	–	–	–	–	–	–	–	–
Cerium silicide ($CeSi_2$)	6-I	523	523-524	–	–	–	–	–	–	–	–	–	–	–	–	–
Cerium-silver intermetallics																
CeAg	6-I	662	662	–	–	–	–	–	–	–	–	–	–	–	–	–
$CeAg_2$	6-I	–	662	–	–	–	–	–	–	–	–	–	–	–	–	–
$CeAg_3$	6-I	–	662	–	–	–	–	–	–	–	–	–	–	–	–	–
Cerium stannides																
$CeSn_3$	6-I	–	541	–	–	–	–	–	–	–	–	–	–	–	–	–
Ce_2Sn	6-I	–	541	–	–	–	–	–	–	–	–	–	–	–	–	–
Ce_2Sn_3	6-I	–	541	–	–	–	–	–	–	–	–	–	–	–	–	–
Cerium sulfides																
CeS	5	667	667	–	–	–	670	672	674	–	676	–	–	–	–	678
CeS_2	5	667	667	–	–	–	–	–	–	–	–	–	–	–	–	–
Ce_2S_3	5	667	667	–	–	–	–	672	674	–	676	–	–	–	–	–
Ce_3S_4	5	667	667	–	–	–	–	–	–	–	–	–	–	–	–	678
Cerium tellurides																
$CeTe_2$	6-I	636	–	–	–	–	–	–	–	–	–	–	–	–	–	–
Ce_3Te_4	6-I	636	–	–	–	–	–	–	–	–	–	–	–	–	–	–
Cerium-thallium intermetallics																
CeTl	6-I	–	663	–	–	–	–	–	–	–	–	–	–	–	–	–
$CeTl_3$	6-I	–	663	–	–	–	–	–	–	–	–	–	–	–	–	–
Ce_2Tl	6-I	–	663	–	–	–	–	–	–	–	–	–	–	–	–	–
Cerium vanadate ($Ce_2O_3 \cdot V_2O_5$) .	4-II	–	–	–	–	–	–	–	–	–	1490	–	–	–	–	–
Cermets (also see individual cermets)																
Aluminum-chromium-molybdenum cermets	6-II	930	–	–	–	–	–	–	–	–	–	–	–	–	–	–
Aluminum-nickel-titanium cermets	6-II	925	–	–	–	–	–	–	–	–	–	–	–	–	–	–

Material Name	Volume	Density	Melting Point	Heat of Fusion	Heat of Vaporization	Heat of Sublimation	Electrical Resistivity	Specific Heat	Thermal Conductivity	Thermal Diffusivity	Thermal Linear Expansion	Thermal Absorptance	Thermal Emittance	Thermal Reflectance	Thermal Transmittance	Vapor Pressure
Cermets (also see individual cermets) (cont.)																
Aluminum oxide + Aluminum cermet	6-II	-	-	-	-	-	-	-	-	-	729	-	-	-	-	-
Aluminum oxide + Chromium cermet	6-II	731	-	-	-	-	-	-	911	-	733	-	735	-	-	-
Aluminum oxide + Chromium + + Molybdenum cermet . . .	6-II	737	-	-	-	-	-	-	-	-	739	-	-	-	-	-
Aluminum oxide + Iron cermet	6-II	-	-	-	-	-	-	-	-	-	741	-	-	-	-	-
Aluminum oxide + Titanium (di-)oxide + Chromium + + Molybdenum cermet . . .	6-II	-	-	-	-	-	-	-	-	-	-	-	747	-	-	-
Aluminum oxide + Tungsten + + Chromium cermet	6-II	-	-	-	-	-	-	-	-	-	743	-	745	-	-	-
Barium oxide + Strontium oxide + Zirconium cermet. .	6-II	-	-	-	-	-	-	-	911	-	-	-	-	-	-	-
Beryllium + Beryllium oxide cermet	6-II	751	-	-	-	751	-	753	757	-	762	-	-	-	-	764-766
Beryllium oxide + Beryllium cermet	6-II	-	-	-	-	751	-	755	760	-	762	-	-	-	-	-
Beryllium oxide + Beryllium + + Molybdenum cermet . . .	6-II	-	-	-	-	-	-	768	770	-	772	-	-	-	-	-
Beryllium oxide + Beryllium + + Silicon cermet	6-II	-	-	-	-	-	-	-	774	-	776	-	-	-	-	-
Beryllium oxide + Molybdenum cermet	6-II	-	-	-	-	-	-	778	-	-	-	-	-	-	-	-
Beryllium oxide + Niobium cermet	6-II	780	-	-	-	-	-	-	-	-	782	-	-	-	-	-
Boron carbide + Iron cermet .	6-II	928	-	-	-	-	-	-	-	-	-	-	-	-	-	-
Calcium aluminate + + Molybdenum (di-) silicide cermet	6-II	-	-	-	-	-	-	-	-	-	784	-	-	-	-	-
Chromium-molybdenum-silicon cermets	6-II	925	-	-	-	-	-	-	-	-	-	-	-	-	-	-
Chromium-silicon-titanium cermets	6-II	925	-	-	-	-	-	-	-	-	-	-	-	-	-	-
Chromium boride + Chromium-molybdenum intermetallic cermet	6-II	913	-	-	-	-	-	-	-	-	-	-	-	-	-	-
Chromium silicide cermets .	6-II	-	-	-	-	-	-	-	-	-	915	-	-	-	-	-
Chromium-titanium intermetallics + Copper cermets .	6-II	917	-	-	-	-	-	-	-	-	-	-	-	-	-	-
Chromium-titanium intermetallics + Molybdenum cermets	6-II	919	-	-	-	-	-	-	-	-	-	-	-	-	-	-
Cobalt-chromium alloys + + Titanium (di-) boride cermet	6-II	930	-	-	-	-	-	-	-	-	-	-	-	-	-	-

Material Name	Volume	Density	Melting Point	Heat of Fusion	Heat of Vaporization	Heat of Sublimation	Electrical Resistivity	Specific Heat	Thermal Conductivity	Thermal Diffusivity	Thermal Linear Expansion	Thermal Absorptance	Thermal Emittance	Thermal Reflectance	Thermal Transmittance	Vapor Pressure
Cermets (also see individual cermets) (cont.)																
Europium oxide + Iron-chromium alloy cermet . . .	6-II	-	-	-	-	-	-	-	-	-	786	-	-	-	-	-
Hafnium carbide + Zirconium cermet	6-II	-	-	-	-	-	-	-	-	-	852	-	-	-	-	-
Magnesium oxide + Tungsten cermet	6-II	-	-	-	-	-	-	-	-	-	788	-	-	-	-	-
Molybdenum (di-) silicide + + Copper cermets	6-II	923	-	-	-	-	-	-	-	-	-	-	-	-	-	-
Molybdenum-silicon-titanium cermet	6-II	930	-	-	-	-	-	-	-	-	-	-	-	-	-	-
Silicon carbide + Magnesium oxide + Nickel aluminide cermet	6-II	-	-	-	-	-	-	-	-	-	854	-	-	-	-	-
Silicon carbide + Silicon cermet	6-II	-	-	-	-	-	-	-	856	-	-	-	-	-	-	-
Silicon (di-) oxide + Aluminum cermet	6-II	-	-	-	-	-	-	-	-	-	790	-	-	-	-	-
Sodium fluoride + Beryllium ferride cermet	6-II	-	-	-	-	-	-	-	911	-	-	-	-	-	-	-
Strontium titanate + Cobalt cermet	6-II	-	-	-	-	-	-	-	792	-	-	-	-	-	-	-
Tantalum carbide + Iron cermet	6-II	858	-	-	-	-	-	-	-	-	-	-	-	-	-	-
Tantalum carbide + Tungsten cermet	6-II	-	-	-	-	-	-	-	-	-	860	-	-	-	-	-
Thorium (di-) oxide + Tungsten cermet.	6-II	-	-	-	-	-	-	-	-	-	-	-	-	-	-	794
Titanium carbide + Cobalt cermet	6-II	862	-	-	-	-	-	-	911	-	864	-	-	-	-	-
Titanium carbide + Molybdenum + Tungsten cermet. .	6-II	-	-	-	-	-	-	-	-	-	866	-	-	-	-	-
Titanium carbide + Nickel cermet	6-II	868	-	-	-	-	-	871	873	-	875-877	-	-	-	-	-
Titanium carbide + Niobium carbide + Nickel cermet . .	6-II	-	-	-	-	-	-	-	911	-	-	-	-	-	-	-
Titanium carbide + Tungsten cermet	6-II	-	-	-	-	-	-	-	-	-	879	-	-	-	-	-
Titanium nitride + Chromium + + Titanium cermet	6-II	-	-	-	-	-	-	-	-	-	909	-	-	-	-	-
Titanium (mon-) oxide + + Chromium-titanium alloys cermet	6-II	-	-	-	-	-	-	-	-	-	796	-	-	-	-	-
Titanium tungsten (di-)carbide + Cobalt cermet . . .	6-II	-	-	-	-	-	-	-	-	-	881	-	-	-	-	-
Titanium tungsten (di-) carbide + Tantalum cermet . .	6-II	-	-	-	-	-	-	-	-	-	883	-	-	-	-	-
Tungsten carbide + Chromium-cobalt alloys cermet	6-II	-	-	-	-	-	-	-	-	-	895	-	-	-	-	-

Material Name	Volume	Density	Melting Point	Heat of Fusion	Heat of Vaporization	Heat of Sublimation	Electrical Resistivity	Specific Heat	Thermal Conductivity	Thermal Diffusivity	Thermal Linear Expansion	Thermal Absorptance	Thermal Emittance	Thermal Reflectance	Thermal Transmittance	Vapor Pressure
Cermets (also see individual cermets) (cont.)																
Tungsten carbide + Cobalt cermet	6-II	–	–	–	–	–	–	–	889	–	897-905	–	–	–	–	–
Tungsten carbide + Nickel cermet	6-II	–	–	–	–	–	–	–	–	–	907	–	–	–	–	–
Uranium (mono-) carbide + + Molybdenum cermet . . .	6-II	–	–	–	–	–	–	–	–	–	891	–	–	–	–	–
Uranium (mono-) carbide + + Uranium cermet	6-II	–	–	–	–	–	–	–	–	–	893	–	–	–	–	–
Uranium (di-) oxide + + Chromium cermet	6-II	–	–	–	–	–	798	–	800	–	802	–	–	–	–	–
Uranium (di-) oxide + + Molybdenum cermet . . .	6-II	–	–	–	–	–	804	–	806	–	808	–	–	–	–	–
Uranium (di-) oxide + + Niobium cermet	6-II	–	–	–	–	–	810	–	812	–	–	–	–	–	–	–
Uranium (di-) oxide + Stainless steel cermet	6-II	–	–	–	–	–	814	–	816	–	818	–	–	–	–	–
Uranium (di-) oxide + + Zirconium cermets	6-II	820	–	–	–	–	–	–	822	–	824	–	–	–	–	–
Zirconium (di-) boride cermet	6-II	842	–	–	–	–	844	846	848	–	850	–	–	–	–	–
Zirconium (di-) oxide + + Titanium cermet	6-II	–	–	–	–	–	–	826	828	830	832	–	–	–	–	–
Zirconium (di-) oxide + + Yttrium oxide + Zirconium cermet	6-II	–	–	–	–	–	–	–	834	–	–	–	–	–	–	–
Zirconium (di-) oxide + + Zirconium cermet	6-II	–	–	–	–	–	–	–	–	836	838	–	–	–	–	840
Cesium chloride (CsCl)	5	–	–	–	–	–	–	315	–	–	–	–	–	–	–	–
Chemaco 342	6-II	–	–	–	–	–	–	–	–	–	948	–	–	–	–	–
Chemaco 343	6-II	–	–	–	–	–	–	–	–	–	948	–	–	–	–	–
Chemaco 344	6-II	–	–	–	–	–	–	–	–	–	948	–	–	–	–	–
Chemaco 345	6-II	–	–	–	–	–	–	–	–	–	948	–	–	–	–	–
Chemaco 346	6-II	–	–	–	–	–	–	–	–	–	948	–	–	–	–	–
Chemaco SPZ 325	6-II	–	–	–	–	–	–	–	–	–	941	–	–	–	–	–
Chemaco SPZ 326	6-II	–	–	–	–	–	–	–	–	–	941	–	–	–	–	–
Chemaco SPZ 327	6-II	–	–	–	–	–	–	–	–	–	941	–	–	–	–	–
Chemaco SPZ 327-MS	6-II	–	–	–	–	–	–	–	–	–	941	–	–	–	–	–
Chemaco SPZ 329	6-II	–	–	–	–	–	–	–	–	–	941	–	–	–	–	–
Chemaco SPZ 330	6-II	–	–	–	–	–	–	–	–	–	941	–	–	–	–	–
Chemaco SPZ 331	6-II	–	–	–	–	–	–	–	–	–	941	–	–	–	–	–
Chemaco SPZ 332	6-II	–	–	–	–	–	–	–	–	–	941	–	–	–	–	–
Chloromethyoxetane, 3, 3 bis- .	6-II	–	1076	–	–	–	–	–	–	–	–	–	–	–	–	–
Chromalloy W-2 coating on molybdenum-titanium alloys .	6-II	–	–	–	–	–	–	–	–	–	–	–	1505-1509	–	–	–

Material Name	Volume	Density	Melting Point	Heat of Fusion	Heat of Vaporization	Heat of Sublimation	Electrical Resistivity	Specific Heat	Thermal Conductivity	Thermal Diffusivity	Thermal Linear Expansion	Thermal Absorptance	Thermal Emittance	Thermal Reflectance	Thermal Transmittance	Vapor Pressure
Chromium (Cr)	1	410	410	–	–	410	412	414	416	418	420	–	422-426	428-432	–	434
Chromium, electrolytic	1	–	–	–	–	–	412	–	416	–	420	–	–	–	–	–
Chromium + ΣX_i	2-II	873	–	–	–	873	875	–	877	–	–	–	–	–	–	–
Chromium + Aluminum + ΣX_i . .	2-II	–	–	–	–	–	–	855	–	–	–	–	–	–	–	–
Chromium + Iron	2-I	–	62	–	–	–	64	66	–	–	–	–	–	–	–	–
Chromium + Iron + ΣX_i	2-II	857	–	–	–	–	–	859	–	–	861	–	–	–	–	–
Chromium + Molybdenum . . .	2-I	–	–	–	–	–	–	–	–	–	68	–	–	–	–	–
Chromium + Molybdenum + ΣX_i .	2-II	863	–	–	–	–	–	–	–	–	865	–	–	–	–	–
Chromium + Nickel	2-I	–	–	–	–	–	–	–	–	–	70	–	–	–	–	–
Chromium + Nickel + ΣX_i . . .	2-II	–	867	–	–	–	–	–	–	–	–	–	–	–	–	–
Chromium + Silicon	2-I	72	–	–	–	–	–	–	–	–	–	–	–	–	–	–
Chromium + Silicon + ΣX_i . . .	2-II	869	–	–	–	–	–	–	–	–	–	–	–	–	–	–
Chromium + Tungsten	2-I	74	–	–	–	–	–	–	–	–	76	–	–	–	–	–
Chromium + Tungsten + ΣX_i . .	2-II	871	–	–	–	–	–	–	–	–	–	–	–	–	–	–
Chromium alloys (special designations)																
Ferrochromium	2-II	–	–	–	–	–	–	859	–	–	–	–	–	–	–	–
Aluminothermic chromium .	2-II	–	–	–	–	–	–	859	–	–	–	–	–	–	–	–
Chromium aluminides																
CrAl	6-I	–	–	–	–	–	–	–	–	–	5	–	–	–	–	–
$CrAl_3$	6-I	–	–	–	–	–	–	–	–	–	5	–	–	–	–	–
Cr_3Al	6-I	–	3	–	–	–	–	–	–	–	5	–	–	–	–	–
Chromium beryllide ($CrBe_2$) . .	6-I	–	158	–	–	–	–	–	–	–	–	–	–	–	–	–
Chromium borides																
CrB	6-I	164	164	–	–	–	–	166	–	–	–	–	–	–	–	–
CrB_2	6-I	164	164	–	–	–	–	166	–	–	168	–	–	–	–	–
Cr_2B	6-I	–	164	–	–	–	–	–	–	–	–	–	–	–	–	–
Cr_3B_4	6-I	–	164	–	–	–	–	–	–	–	–	–	–	–	–	–
Cr_4B	6-I	–	164	–	–	–	–	–	–	–	–	–	–	–	–	–
Cr_5B_3	6-I	–	164	–	–	–	–	–	–	–	–	–	–	–	–	–
Chromium (di-)boride + + Chromium-molybdenum intermetallic cermet	6-II	913	–	–	–	–	–	–	–	–	–	–	–	–	–	–
Chromium (di-)boride + + Titanium (di-)boride	6-I	723	–	–	–	–	–	–	–	–	–	–	–	–	–	–
Chromium (di-)boride + + Vanadium (di-)boride . . .	6-I	723	–	–	–	–	–	–	–	–	–	–	–	–	–	–
Chromium carbides																
CrC	5	–	39	–	–	–	–	–	–	–	–	–	–	–	–	–
Cr_3C_2	5	39	39	–	–	–	–	41	–	–	45	–	–	–	–	–
Cr_4C	5	–	–	–	–	–	–	43	–	–	–	–	–	–	–	–
Cr_5C_2	5	–	–	–	–	–	–	43	–	–	–	–	–	–	–	–
Cr_7C_3	5	–	39	–	–	–	–	43	–	–	–	–	47	–	–	–

Material Name	Volume	Density	Melting Point	Heat of Fusion	Heat of Vaporization	Heat of Sublimation	Electrical Resistivity	Specific Heat	Thermal Conductivity	Thermal Diffusivity	Thermal Linear Expansion	Thermal Absorptance	Thermal Emittance	Thermal Reflectance	Thermal Transmittance	Vapor Pressure
Chromium carbides (cont.)																
$Cr_{23}C_6$	5	-	39	-	-	-	-	-	-	-	-	-	-	-	-	-
Chromium carbide-cobalt blend on iron	6-II	-	-	-	-	-	-	-	-	-	-	1407	1409	-	-	-
Chromium-molybdenum silicides																
$(Cr, Mo)Si_2$	6-I	523	-	-	-	-	-	-	-	-	-	-	-	-	-	-
$(Cr, Mo)_3Si$	6-I	523	-	-	-	-	-	-	-	-	-	-	-	-	-	-
Chromium-molybdenum-silicon cermets	6-II	925	-	-	-	-	-	-	-	-	-	-	-	-	-	-
Chromium-niobium intermetallics (Cr_2Nb)	6-I	-	683	-	-	-	-	-	-	-	-	-	-	-	-	-
Chromium nitrides																
CrN	5	-	621	-	-	-	-	-	-	-	-	-	-	-	-	-
Cr_2N	5		621													
Chromium (sesqui-) oxide (Cr_2O_3)	4-I	-	-	-	-	-	130	132	-	-	134	-	136-138	140	-	-
Chromium (sesqui-) oxide + + Aluminum oxide	4-I	-	-	-	-	-	679	-	-	-	681	-	683	-	-	-
Chromium (sesqui-) oxide + + Molybdenum (di-) silicide . .	5	-	-	-	-	-	-	-	-	-	-	-	769	-	-	-
Chromium (sesqui-) oxide + + Nickel (mon-) oxide	4-I	-	-	-	-	-	685	-	-	-	-	-	-	-	-	-
Chromium (sesqui-) oxide + + Niobium (pent-) oxide	4-I	-	-	-	-	-	687	-	-	-	-	-	-	-	-	-
Chromium (sesqui-) oxide + + Titanium-chromium intermetallics	5	-	-	-	-	-	-	-	-	-	-	-	771-773	775	-	-
Chromium (sesqui-) oxide + + Yttrium oxide	4-I	-	-	-	-	-	-	-	-	-	-	-	689	-	-	-
Chromium phosphides (CrP) . .	5	635	635	-	-	-	639	-	-	-	-	-	-	-	-	-
Chromium silicides																
CrSi	6-I	-	381	-	-	-	383	385	-	-	389	-	-	-	-	-
$CrSi_2$	6-I	-	381	-	-	-	383	385	387	-	389	-	-	-	-	-
Cr_3Si	6-I	-	381	-	-	-	-	385	-	-	389	-	391-393	395	-	-
Cr_3Si_2	6-I	-	-	-	-	-	-	-	-	-	389	-	-	-	-	-
Cr_5Si	6-I	-	381	-	-	-	-	-	-	-	-	-	-	-	-	-
Cr_5Si_3	6-I	-	-	-	-	-	-	385	-	-	-	-	-	-	-	-
Chromium silicide cermets . .	6-II	-	-	-	-	-	-	-	-	-	915	-	-	-	-	-
Chromium (di-) silicide + + Molybdenum (di-) silicide . .	6-I	723	-	-	-	-	-	-	-	-	-	-	-	-	-	-
Chromium-silicon-titanium cermets	6-II	925	-	-	-	-	-	-	-	-	-	-	-	-	-	-
Chromium-tantalum intermetallics (Cr_3Ta_2)	6-I	-	683	-	-	-	-	-	-	-	-	-	-	-	-	-

Material Name	Volume	Density	Melting Point	Heat of Fusion	Heat of Vaporization	Heat of Sublimation	Electrical Resistivity	Specific Heat	Thermal Conductivity	Thermal Diffusivity	Thermal Linear Expansion	Thermal Absorptance	Thermal Emittance	Thermal Reflectance	Thermal Transmittance	Vapor Pressure
Chromium-titanium intermetallics + Chromium (sesqui-)-oxide	5	-	-	-	-	-	-	-	-	-	926	-	928-930	932	-	-
Chromium-titanium intermetallics + Copper cermets	5	917	-	-	-	-	-	-	-	-	-	-	-	-	-	-
Chromium-titanium intermetallics + Molybdenum cermets . .	6-II	919	-	-	-	-	-	-	-	-	-	-	-	-	-	-
Chromium zirconate ($Cr_2O_3 \cdot ZrO_2$)	4-II	-	-	-	-	-	-	-	-	-	1508	-	-	-	-	-
Chromium-zirconium intermetallics (Cr_2Zr)	6-I	-	683	-	-	-	-	-	-	-	-	-	-	-	-	-
Chronin	2-I	-	-	-	-	-	-	-	-	-	70	-	-	-	-	-
Chrycote coating on copper . . .	6-II	-	-	-	-	-	-	-	-	-	-	-	1499	-	-	-
Clad steel	6-II	-	-	-	-	-	-	-	-	-	1267	-	-	-	-	-
Clinoenstatite	4-II	-	-	-	-	-	-	-	-	-	1295	-	-	-	-	-
Coatings																
Aluminide on niobium	6-II	-	-	-	-	-	-	-	-	-	-	-	1435-1437	1439	-	-
Aluminide on titanium	6-II	-	-	-	-	-	-	-	-	-	-	-	1447-1449	1451	-	-
Aluminized-silicone paint on titanium	6-II	-	-	-	-	-	-	-	-	-	-	-	-	1497	-	-
Aluminum on mylar	6-II	-	-	-	-	-	-	-	-	-	-	-	-	1287	-	-
Aluminum oxide on AISI 446 .	6-II	-	-	-	-	-	-	-	-	-	-	-	-	1349	-	-
Aluminum phosphate on nickel	6-II	-	-	-	-	-	-	-	-	-	-	-	1431	-	-	-
Barium titanate on niobium-zirconium alloys	6-II	-	-	-	-	-	-	-	-	-	-	-	1371	-	-	-
Boron on molybdenum	6-II	-	-	-	-	-	-	-	-	-	-	-	1289	-	-	-
Boron on niobium-zirconium alloys	6-II	-	-	-	-	-	-	-	-	-	-	-	1291	-	-	-
Boron carbide on Inconel X .	6-II	-	-	-	-	-	-	-	-	-	-	-	1403	1405	-	-
Calcium titanate on niobium-zirconium alloys	6-II	-	-	-	-	-	-	-	-	-	-	-	1371	-	-	-
Carbon on molybdenum . . .	6-II	-	-	-	-	-	-	-	-	-	-	1293	1295	-	-	-
Chromalloy W-2 on molybdenum-titanium alloys . . .	6-II	-	-	-	-	-	-	-	-	-	-	-	1505-1509	-	-	-
Chromium carbide-cobalt blend on iron	6-II	-	-	-	-	-	-	-	-	-	-	1407	1409	-	-	-
Chrycote on copper	6-II	-	-	-	-	-	-	-	-	-	-	-	1499	-	-	-
Cobalt oxide on tantalum . .	6-II	-	-	-	-	-	-	-	-	-	-	-	1373-1375	-	-	-
Copper on mylar	6-II	-	-	-	-	-	-	-	-	-	-	-	-	1301	-	-
Dow-Corning XP-310 on Ti-75A (AMS 4901)	6-II	-	-	-	-	-	-	-	-	-	-	-	-	1497	-	-

Material Name	Volume	Density	Melting Point	Heat of Fusion	Heat of Vaporization	Heat of Sublimation	Electrical Resistivity	Specific Heat	Thermal Conductivity	Thermal Diffusivity	Thermal Linear Expansion	Thermal Absorptance	Thermal Emittance	Thermal Reflectance	Thermal Transmittance	Vapor Pressure
Coatings (cont.)																
Durak MG on molybdenum-titanium alloy	6-II	–	–	–	–	–	–	–	–	–	–	–	1501-1503	–	–	–
Enamel on AISI 310	6-II	–	–	–	–	–	–	–	–	–	–	–	1515	–	–	–
Enamel on AISI 321	6-II	–	–	–	–	–	–	–	–	–	–	–	1513	–	–	–
Enamel on Inconel	6-II	–	–	–	–	–	1511	–	–	–	–	–	–	–	–	–
Gold on mylar	6-II	–	–	–	–	–	–	–	–	–	–	–	–	1307	–	–
Gold on titanium	6-II	–	–	–	–	–	–	–	–	–	–	–	1303	1305	–	–
Graphite, pyrolytic, on tantalum	6-II	–	–	–	–	–	–	–	–	–	–	–	1297-1299	–	–	–
Hafnium (di-) oxide on tungsten	6-II	–	–	–	–	–	–	–	–	–	–	–	1377-1379	–	–	–
Hastelloy C on AISI 310 . . .	6-II	–	–	–	–	–	–	–	–	–	–	–	1337	–	–	–
Hastelloy X on AISI 310 . . .	6-II	–	–	–	–	–	–	–	–	–	–	–	1339	–	–	–
Iron(ic) oxide on stellite no. 25 (L-605)	6-II	–	–	–	–	–	–	–	–	–	–	–	1381-1383	–	–	–
Iron titanate on niobium-zirconium alloys	6-II	–	–	–	–	–	–	–	–	–	–	–	1385	–	–	–
Kennametal K-151A on AISI 310	6-II	–	–	–	–	–	–	–	–	–	–	–	1491	–	–	–
Kennametal K-162B on AISI 310	6-II	–	–	–	–	–	–	–	–	–	–	–	1493	–	–	–
Magnesium fluoride on quartz	6-II	–	–	–	–	–	–	–	–	–	–	–	–	1425	1427	–
Molybdenum on iron	6-II	–	–	–	–	–	–	–	–	–	–	1309	1311	–	–	–
NBS coating A-418 on Inconel	6-II	–	–	–	–	–	–	–	–	–	–	–	1361-1363	–	–	–
NBS coating A-418 on stainless steel	6-II	–	–	–	–	–	–	–	–	–	–	–	1365-1367	–	–	–
NBS coating N-143 on Inconel	6-II	–	–	–	–	–	–	–	–	–	–	–	1353-1355	–	–	–
NBS coating N-143 on stainless steel	6-II	–	–	–	–	–	–	–	–	–	–	–	1357-1359	–	–	–
Nickel aluminide on Inconel .	6-II	–	–	–	–	–	–	–	–	–	–	–	1453-1455	1457	–	–
Nickel chromite on niobium-zirconium alloys	6-II	–	–	–	–	–	–	–	–	–	–	–	1387	–	–	–
Nickel-chromium alloys on Inconel X	6-II	–	–	–	–	–	–	–	–	–	–	–	1333	1335	–	–
Niobium aluminide on niobium	6-II	–	–	–	–	–	–	–	–	–	–	–	–	1459	–	–
Platinum on copper	6-II	–	–	–	–	–	–	–	–	–	–	–	1313	–	–	–
Platinum on quartz	6-II	–	–	–	–	–	–	–	–	–	–	–	–	1317	1319	–
Platinum on stainless steel .	6-II	–	–	–	–	–	–	–	–	–	–	–	1315	–	–	–

Material Name	Volume	Density	Melting Point	Heat of Fusion	Heat of Vaporization	Heat of Sublimation	Electrical Resistivity	Specific Heat	Thermal Conductivity	Thermal Diffusivity	Thermal Linear Expansion	Thermal Absorptance	Thermal Emittance	Thermal Reflectance	Thermal Transmittance	Vapor Pressure
Coatings (cont.)																
Rokide A on AISI 446	6-II	-	-	-	-	-	-	-	-	-	-	-	-	1351	-	-
Rokide C on titanium alloy Ti-6 Al-4 V	6-II	-	-	-	-	-	-	-	-	-	-	-	1345-1347	-	-	-
Silicide on molybdenum . . .	6-II	-	-	-	-	-	-	-	-	-	-	-	1467-1469	1471	-	-
Silicide on tantalum.	6-II	-	-	-	-	-	-	-	-	-	-	-	1473-1475	1477	-	-
Silicide on titanium	6-II	-	-	-	-	-	-	-	-	-	-	-	1479-1481	1483	-	-
Silicide on tungsten	6-II	-	-	-	-	-	-	-	-	-	-	-	1485-1487	1489	-	-
Silicon carbide on niobium-zirconium alloys.	6-II	-	-	-	-	-	-	-	-	-	-	-	1415	-	-	-
Silicon carbide on tantalum .	6-II	-	-	-	-	-	-	-	-	-	-	-	1411-1413	-	-	-
Silicon (mon-) oxide on aluminum	6-II	-	-	-	-	-	-	-	-	-	-	-	-	1389	-	-
Silicon (di-) oxide on aluminum	6-II	-	-	-	-	-	-	-	-	-	-	-	-	1391	-	-
Silicone on Inconel	6-II	-	-	-	-	-	1495	-	-	-	-	-	-	-	-	-
Silver on AISI 321.	6-II	-	-	-	-	-	-	-	-	-	-	-	-	1321	-	-
Silver on mylar	6-II	-	-	-	-	-	-	-	-	-	-	-	-	1323	-	-
Silver sulfide on silver . . .	6-II	-	-	-	-	-	-	-	-	-	-	1431	1433	-	-	-
Strontium titanate on AISI 310	6-II	-	-	-	-	-	-	-	-	-	-	-	1393	-	-	-
Tantalum aluminide on tantalum	6-II	-	-	-	-	-	-	-	-	-	-	-	1461-1463	1465	-	-
Tantalum carbide on Inconel X	6-II	-	-	-	-	-	-	-	-	-	-	-	1417	1419	-	-
Titanium (di-) oxide and aluminum on molybdenum. .	6-II	-	-	-	-	-	-	-	-	-	-	-	1395	-	-	-
Tungsten on Inconel X. . . .	6-II	-	-	-	-	-	-	-	-	-	-	-	1329	1331	-	-
Tungsten on iron	6-II	-	-	-	-	-	-	-	-	-	-	1325	1327	-	-	-
Tungsten-cobalt alloys on Inconel X	6-II	-	-	-	-	-	-	-	-	-	-	-	1341	1343	-	-
Tungsten carbide on iron . .	6-II	-	-	-	-	-	-	-	-	-	-	1421	1423	-	-	-
Zirconium (di-) oxide on Inconel	6-II	-	-	-	-	-	-	-	-	-	-	-	-	1397	-	-
Zirconium (di-) oxide on Inconel X	6-II	-	-	-	-	-	-	-	-	-	-	-	1399	1401	-	-
Cobalt (Co)	1	436	436	-	-	-	438	440	442	-	444	446	448-450	-	-	-
Cobalt + Chromium + ΣX_i . . .	2-II	879, 882	879	-	-	-	-	884	886-888	890	892-906	-	908-914	916	-	-
Cobalt + Copper + ΣX_i	2-II	-	918	-	-	-	920	-	-	-	-	-	-	-	-	-
Cobalt + Gold	2-I	-	-	-	-	-	78	-	-	-	-	-	-	-	-	-
Cobalt + Gold + ΣX_i	2-II	-	922	-	-	-	924	-	-	-	-	-	-	-	-	-

Material Name	Volume	Density	Melting Point	Heat of Fusion	Heat of Vaporization	Heat of Sublimation	Electrical Resistivity	Specific Heat	Thermal Conductivity	Thermal Diffusivity	Thermal Linear Expansion	Thermal Absorptance	Thermal Emittance	Thermal Reflectance	Thermal Transmittance	Vapor Pressure
Cobalt + Iron	2-I	-	-	-	-	80	82	84	-	-	-	-	86	-	-	88
Cobalt + Iron + ΣX_i	2-II	-	-	-	-	-	-	-	-	-	926-930	-	-	-	-	-
Cobalt + Manganese + ΣX_i . . .	2-II	-	-	-	-	-	-	-	-	-	932	-	-	-	-	-
Cobalt + Nickel	2-I	92	-	-	-	90	-	-	-	-	-	-	94	-	-	96
Cobalt + Nickel + ΣX_i	2-II	-	-	-	-	-	-	-	934	936	938	-	-	-	-	-
Cobalt + Palladium + ΣX_i . . .	2-II	-	940	-	-	-	942-944	-	-	-	-	-	-	-	-	-
Cobalt + Vanadium	2-I	-	-	-	-	-	-	-	-	-	98	-	-	-	-	-
Cobalt alloys (special designations)																
Hastelloy 25	2-II	-	-	-	-	-	-	-	-	-	898	-	-	-	-	-
Haynes 152	2-II	-	-	-	-	-	-	-	-	-	898	-	-	-	-	-
HE 1049	2-II	-	-	-	-	-	-	884	888	-	900	-	-	-	-	-
J-1570	2-II	-	-	-	-	-	-	-	934	-	938	-	-	-	-	-
Jessop G32	2-II	879	-	-	-	-	-	-	888	-	892	-	-	-	-	-
Lohm	2-I	-	-	-	-	-	-	-	138	-	-	-	-	-	-	-
MAR-M302	2-II	-	-	-	-	-	-	-	-	-	898	-	-	-	-	-
PWA-653-A	2-II	-	-	-	-	-	-	-	-	-	898	-	-	-	-	-
Rexalloy 33	2-II	-	-	-	-	-	-	-	-	-	906	-	-	-	-	-
S-816	2-II	-	-	-	-	-	-	-	888, 934	890, 936	896, 938	-	-	-	-	-
SM-302	2-II	-	-	-	-	-	-	-	-	-	898	-	-	-	-	-
Stellites (see Stellite)																
V-36	2-II	-	-	-	-	-	-	-	-	-	896	-	-	-	-	-
Vitallium	2-II	-	879	-	-	-	-	-	-	-	894	-	-	-	-	-
WI-52	2-II	-	-	-	-	-	-	-	888	-	-	-	-	-	-	-
X-40	2-II	-	-	-	-	-	-	-	888	-	-	-	-	-	-	-
X-63	2-II	-	-	-	-	-	-	-	888	-	-	-	-	-	-	-
Cobalt aluminates																
$CoO \cdot Al_2O_3$	4-II	-	-	-	-	-	-	-	-	-	995	-	-	-	-	-
$Co_2O_3 \cdot Al_2O_3$	4-II	-	-	-	-	-	-	-	-	-	995	-	-	-	-	-
Cobalt aluminide (CoAl)	6-I	-	-	-	-	-	-	-	-	-	7	-	-	-	-	-
Cobalt beryllide (CoBe)	6-I	-	158	-	-	-	-	-	-	-	-	-	-	-	-	-
Cobalt blue glass	4-II	-	-	-	-	-	-	-	-	-	-	-	1847	1849	1851	-
Cobalt (mono-)boride (CrB) . .	6-I	-	296	-	-	-	-	-	-	-	-	-	-	-	-	-
Cobalt carbide (Co_3C)	5	-	294	-	-	-	-	-	-	-	-	-	-	-	-	-
Cobalt-chromium alloys + Titanium (di-)boride cermet .	6-II	-	930	-	-	-	-	-	-	-	-	-	-	-	-	-
Cobalt-chromium intermetallics (CoCr)	6-I	-	683	-	-	-	-	-	-	-	-	-	-	-	-	-
Cobalt ferrite ($CoO \cdot Fe_2O_3$). . .	4-II	-	-	-	-	-	1071	1073	-	-	-	-	-	-	-	-
Cobalt-lead silicate glass . . .	4-II	-	-	-	-	-	1735	-	-	-	-	-	-	-	-	-

Material Name	Volume	Density	Melting Point	Heat of Fusion	Heat of Vaporization	Heat of Sublimation	Electrical Resistivity	Specific Heat	Thermal Conductivity	Thermal Diffusivity	Thermal Linear Expansion	Thermal Absorptance	Thermal Emittance	Thermal Reflectance	Thermal Transmittance	Vapor Pressure
Cobalt-molybdenum intermetallics (CoMo)	6-I	-	683	-	-	-	-	-	-	-	-	-	-	-	-	-
Cobalt-niobium intermetallics (Co_5Nb_2)	6-I	-	683	-	-	-	-	-	-	-	-	-	-	-	-	-
Cobalt oxides																
CoO	4-I	-	-	-	-	-	-	142	-	-	146	-	-	-	-	-
Co_3O_4	4-I	-	-	-	-	-	-	144	-	-	-	-	-	-	-	-
Cobalt oxide coated tantalum . .	6-II	-	-	-	-	-	-	-	-	-	-	-	1373-1375	-	-	-
Cobalt(ous) oxide + Copper(ic) oxide	4-I	-	-	-	-	-	-	691	-	-	-	-	-	-	-	-
Cobalt(ous) oxide + Nickel (mon-) oxide	4-I	-	-	-	-	-	-	693	-	-	-	-	-	-	-	-
Cobalt (ortho-) phosphate (3 CoO · P_2O_5)	4-II	-	-	-	-	-	-	-	-	-	1169	-	-	-	-	-
Cobalt phosphide (Co_2P)	5	-	635	-	-	-	-	-	-	-	-	-	-	-	-	-
Cobalt silicides																
CoSi	6-I	-	397	-	-	-	399	401	529	-	403	-	-	-	-	-
$CoSi_2$	6-I	-	397	-	-	-	-	-	-	-	-	-	-	-	-	-
$CoSi_3$	6-I	-	397	-	-	-	-	-	-	-	-	-	-	-	-	-
Co_2Si	6-I	-	397	-	-	-	-	-	-	-	-	-	-	-	-	-
Co_3Si	6-I	-	397	-	-	-	-	-	-	-	403	-	-	-	-	-
Cobalt-titanium intermetallics																
CoTi	6-I	-	683	-	-	-	-	-	-	-	-	-	-	-	-	-
$CoTi_2$	6-I	-	683	-	-	-	-	-	-	-	-	-	-	-	-	-
Cobalt-tungsten intermetallics (CoW)	6-I	-	683	-	-	-	-	-	-	-	-	-	-	-	-	-
Cobalt-zirconium intermetallics (Co_4Zr)	6-I	-	683	-	-	-	-	-	-	-	-	-	-	-	-	-
Coke	1	-	-	-	-	-	85	-	87	-	-	-	-	-	-	-
Coke, graphitized	1	105	-	-	-	-	-	-	-	-	-	-	-	-	-	-
Composite systems																
Alumina bubbles - graphite fibers system	6-II	-	-	-	-	-	-	-	1279	-	-	-	-	-	-	-
Dexiglas paper - aluminum foil - graphite fiber system .	6-II	-	-	-	-	-	-	-	1283	-	-	-	-	-	-	-
Fiberfrax paper - tantalum shield - graphite fibers system	6-II	-	-	-	-	-	-	-	1285	-	-	-	-	-	-	-
Graphite fibers - tantalum shield system	6-II	-	-	-	-	-	-	-	1281	-	-	-	-	-	-	-
Concrete	5	-	-	-	-	-	-	-	1027	-	-	-	-	-	-	-
Conolon N-1 laminate	6-II	-	-	-	-	-	-	-	-	-	1174	-	-	-	-	-
Container glasses	4-II	-	-	-	-	-	-	-	-	-	-	-	1833	1835	1837	-
Contracid	2-II	-	-	-	-	-	-	-	1261	-	-	-	-	-	-	-
Copolyvinyl chloride + Acetate .	6-II	-	-	-	-	-	-	-	-	-	950	-	-	-	-	-

Material Name	Volume	Density	Melting Point	Heat of Fusion	Heat of Vaporization	Heat of Sublimation	Electrical Resistivity	Specific Heat	Thermal Conductivity	Thermal Diffusivity	Thermal Linear Expansion	Thermal Absorptance	Thermal Emittance	Thermal Reflectance	Thermal Transmittance	Vapor Pressure
Copper (Cu)	1	452	452	452	452	452	454	456	458	460	462	464	466-470	472-477	-	479
Copper, commercial coalesced .	1	452	-	-	-	-	-	-	-	-	-	-	-	-	-	-
Copper DS (British aircraft material spec.)	1	-	-	-	-	-	-	-	-	-	-	-	-	472	-	-
Copper, electrolytic	1	452	452	-	-	-	-	456	-	-	462	-	466	472	-	-
Copper, electrolytic tough pitch (Fed. Spec. QQC-502)	1	452	-	-	-	-	-	456	458	-	462	464	468	474	-	-
Copper, electrolytic tough pitch (Fed. Spec. QQC-576)	1	-	-	-	-	-	-	456	458	-	462	464	468	474	-	-
Copper, OFHC	1	-	-	-	-	-	-	-	458	460	-	-	-	-	-	-
Copper, tellurium	2-I	-	-	-	-	-	-	-	-	-	152	-	-	-	-	-
Copper coated with chrycote . .	6-II	-	-	-	-	-	-	-	-	-	-	-	1499	-	-	-
Copper coated with platinum coating	6-II	-	-	-	-	-	-	-	-	-	-	-	1313	-	-	-
Copper coating on mylar	6-II	-	-	-	-	-	-	-	-	-	-	-	-	1301	-	-
Copper + Aluminum	2-I	100	-	-	-	-	102-104	106	108	-	110	-	-	-	-	-
Copper + Aluminum + ΣX_i . . .	2-II	-	-	-	-	-	946	-	948	-	950	952	954-958	960	-	-
Copper + Beryllium	2-I	-	-	-	-	-	-	112	-	-	-	-	-	-	-	-
Copper + Chromium	2-I	-	-	-	-	-	114	-	116	-	-	-	-	-	-	-
Copper + Chromium + ΣX_i . . .	2-II	-	-	-	-	-	962	-	964	-	-	-	-	-	-	-
Copper + Cobalt	2-I	-	-	-	-	-	-	-	118	-	-	-	-	-	-	-
Copper + Cobalt + ΣX_i	2-II	-	966	-	-	-	968	-	970-972	-	-	-	-	-	-	-
Copper + Gold																
$CuAu_3$	2-I	-	-	-	-	-	-	204	-	-	206	-	-	-	-	-
Cu_3Au	2-I	-	-	-	-	-	-	204	-	-	206	-	-	-	-	-
Copper + Iron	2-I	-	-	-	-	-	120	122	124	-	-	-	-	-	-	-
Copper + Iron + ΣX_i	2-II	-	-	-	-	-	-	-	-	-	-	-	974	-	-	-
Copper + Lead	2-I	126	-	-	-	-	-	-	-	-	128	-	-	-	-	-
Copper + Lead + ΣX_i	2-II	-	-	-	-	-	-	-	-	-	976	-	-	-	-	-
Copper + Manganese	2-I	-	-	-	-	-	130	132	-	-	-	-	-	-	-	-
Copper + Manganese + ΣX_i . . .	2-II	-	-	-	-	-	978	-	980	-	-	-	-	-	-	-
Copper + Nickel	2-I	-	-	-	-	-	134	136	138	-	-	-	-	-	-	-
Copper + Nickel + ΣX_i	2-II	-	-	-	-	-	982	-	984-986	-	988	-	-	-	-	-
Copper + Palladium	2-I	-	-	-	-	-	140	-	142	-	-	-	-	-	-	-
Copper + Palladium + ΣX_i . . .	2-II	-	990	-	-	-	992	-	-	-	-	-	-	-	-	-
Copper + Platinum	2-I	-	-	-	-	-	144	-	-	-	-	-	-	-	-	-
Copper + Silicon	2-I	-	-	-	-	-	146	-	-	-	-	-	-	-	-	-
Copper + Silicon + ΣX_i	2-II	-	-	-	-	-	-	-	-	-	994	-	-	-	-	-
Copper + Silver	2-I	-	-	-	-	-	-	-	-	-	148	-	-	-	-	-
Copper + Tellurium	2-I	150	-	-	-	-	-	-	-	-	152	-	-	-	-	-

Material Name	Volume	Density	Melting Point	Heat of Fusion	Heat of Vaporization	Heat of Sublimation	Electrical Resistivity	Specific Heat	Thermal Conductivity	Thermal Diffusivity	Thermal Linear Expansion	Thermal Absorptance	Thermal Emittance	Thermal Reflectance	Thermal Transmittance	Vapor Pressure
Copper + Tin	2-I	154	-	-	-	-	156	-	158	-	160	-	162	-	-	-
Copper + Tin + ΣX_i	2-II	-	-	-	-	-	-	-	996	-	998	-	-	-	-	-
Copper + Titanium	2-I	164	164	-	-	-	-	-	-	-	-	-	-	-	-	-
Copper + Uranium	2-I	166	166	-	-	-	-	-	-	-	-	-	-	-	-	-
Copper + Zinc	2-I	168	-	-	-	-	170	172	-	174	-	-	176-180	182	-	-
Copper + Zinc + ΣX_i	2-II	-	-	-	-	-	-	-	1000	-	1002-1004	-	-	-	-	-
Copper + Zirconium	2-I	184	-	-	-	-	186	-	188	-	-	-	-	-	-	-
Copper + Zirconium + ΣX_i	2-II	-	-	-	-	-	1006	-	1008	-	-	-	-	-	-	-
Copper alloys (special designations)																
Admiralty nickel	2-II	-	-	-	-	-	-	-	-	-	988	-	-	-	-	-
Aterite	2-II	-	-	-	-	-	-	-	-	-	1004	-	-	-	-	-
Manganin	2-II	-	-	-	-	-	978	-	-	-	-	-	-	-	-	-
Monels (see Monel)																
Ms-58	2-II	-	-	-	-	-	-	-	1000	-	-	-	-	-	-	-
Ms-77-22-2	2-II	-	-	-	-	-	-	-	1000	-	-	-	-	-	-	-
Navy "M"	2-II	-	-	-	-	-	-	-	996	-	-	-	-	-	-	-
Porosint	2-I	-	-	-	-	-	-	-	158	-	-	-	-	-	-	-
Tempaloy 836	2-II	-	-	-	-	-	-	-	-	-	988	-	-	-	-	-
Tempaloy 841	2-II	-	-	-	-	-	-	-	-	-	950	-	-	-	-	-
Copper ferrites																
$CuO \cdot Fe_2O_3$	4-II	-	-	-	-	-	1075	1077	-	-	-	-	-	-	-	-
$Cu_xFe_{3-x}O_4$	4-II	-	-	-	-	-	-	1077	-	-	-	-	-	-	-	-
Copper indium telluride ($CuInTe_2$)	6-I	-	-	-	-	-	-	-	572	-	-	-	-	-	-	-
Copper oxide (CuO)	4-I	-	-	-	-	-	148	150	-	-	-	-	-	-	-	152
Copper silver indium tellurides ($Ag_xCu_{1-x}InTe_2$)	6-I	-	-	-	-	-	-	-	640	-	-	-	-	-	-	-
Cordierite	4-II	-	-	-	-	-	1298	1300	1302	-	1304-1308	-	-	-	-	-
Cordierite 202	4-II	-	-	-	-	-	-	-	1302	-	-	-	-	-	-	-
Cordierite, barium-	4-II	-	-	-	-	-	-	-	-	-	1217-1221	-	-	-	-	-
Cordierite, lead-	4-II	-	-	-	-	-	-	-	-	-	1252-1254	-	-	-	-	-
Cordierite, lead-barium	4-II	-	-	-	-	-	-	-	-	-	1256-1258	-	-	-	-	-
Cordierite bodies	4-II	-	-	-	-	-	-	-	-	-	1310	-	-	-	-	-
Corning 0080 glass	4-II	-	-	-	-	-	-	-	1795	1793	-	-	-	-	-	-
Corning 1723 glass	4-II	-	-	-	-	-	-	1675	-	1677	-	-	1679	1681	1683-1685	-
Corning 7740 glass	4-II	-	-	-	-	-	-	1697	-	1701	-	-	1705	1709	1711-1713	-
Corning 7900 glass	4-II	-	-	-	-	-	-	1655	-	1661	-	-	1665	1669	1671-1673	-

Material Name	Volume	Density	Melting Point	Heat of Fusion	Heat of Vaporization	Heat of Sublimation	Electrical Resistivity	Specific Heat	Thermal Conductivity	Thermal Diffusivity	Thermal Linear Expansion	Thermal Absorptance	Thermal Emittance	Thermal Reflectance	Thermal Transmittance	Vapor Pressure
Corning 7940 glass	4-II	-	-	-	-	-	-	1655	-	-	-	-	1665	1669	1671-1673	-
Corning 8325 glass	4-II	-	-	-	-	-	-	-	-	1687	-	-	-	-	-	-
Corning 8362 glass	4-II	-	-	-	-	-	-	-	-	1749	-	-	-	-	-	-
Corning 9752 glass	4-II	-	-	-	-	-	-	-	-	-	-	-	1847	1849	1851	-
Corundum	4-I	-	-	-	-	-	-	8	-	-	22	-	-	-	-	-
Cresol resin	6-II	-	-	-	-	-	-	1004	-	-	-	-	-	-	-	-
Cristobalite	4-I	-	-	-	-	-	-	-	-	-	367	-	-	-	-	-
Crown glass	4-II	1693	1693	-	-	-	-	1697	-	-	1723	-	-	-	-	-
Crystolon-R	5	-	-	-	-	-	-	-	-	-	-	-	131, 135	-	-	-
Curium (Cm)	1	481	-	-	-	-	-	-	-	-	-	-	-	-	-	-
D																
Dexiglas paper - aluminum foil - graphite fibers composite system	6-II	-	-	-	-	-	-	-	1283	-	-	-	-	-	-	-
Diall 50-01 resin	6-II	-	-	-	-	-	1111	-	-	-	-	-	-	-	-	-
Diall 50-51 resin	6-II	-	-	-	-	-	1111	-	-	-	-	-	-	-	-	-
Diall 50-52 resin	6-II	-	-	-	-	-	1111	-	-	-	-	-	-	-	-	-
Diall 52-01 resin	6-II	-	-	-	-	-	1111	-	-	-	-	-	-	-	-	-
Diall 52-20-30 resin	6-II	-	-	-	-	-	1111	-	-	-	-	-	-	-	-	-
Diallylphthalate, reinforced . .	6-II	-	-	-	-	-	1111	-	-	-	-	-	-	-	-	-
Diamond	1	392	392	-	-	392	-	394	396	-	398	-	-	400	-	-
Dihydroperfluorobutyl acrylate, 1,1-	6-II	1051	-	-	-	-	-	-	-	-	-	-	-	-	-	-
Dow-Corning XP-310 on Ti-75A (AMS 4901)	6-II	-	-	-	-	-	-	-	-	-	-	-	-	1497	-	-
Durak MG coating on molybdenum-titanium alloys	6-II	-	-	-	-	-	-	-	-	-	-	-	1501-1503	-	-	-
Duranickel 301	2-II	-	-	-	-	-	-	-	-	-	1117	-	-	-	-	-
Durchy	5	-	-	-	-	-	-	-	-	-	-	-	821	-	-	-
Dures 16274	6-II	-	-	-	-	-	982	-	-	-	-	-	-	-	-	-
Dures 16694	6-II	-	-	-	-	-	1111	-	-	-	-	-	-	-	-	-
Duroid 5600	6-II	1097	-	-	-	-	-	-	1099	-	-	-	-	-	-	-
Dynakon rod F	6-II	-	-	-	-	-	-	-	-	-	1109	-	-	-	-	-
Dynakon sheet A3A	6-II	-	-	-	-	-	-	-	-	-	1109	-	-	-	-	-
Dysprosia	4-I	154	154	-	-	-	-	156	-	-	158	-	-	-	-	-
Dysprosium (Dy)	1	483	483	483	483	483	485	-	-	-	-	-	-	-	-	487
Dysprosium + Tantalum + ΣX_i .	2-II	-	-	-	-	-	-	-	-	-	1010	-	-	-	-	-
Dysprosium aluminate ($Dy_2O_3 \cdot 2\ Al_2O_3$)	4-II	-	-	-	-	-	-	-	-	-	997	-	-	-	-	-

Material Name	Volume	Density	Melting Point	Heat of Fusion	Heat of Vaporization	Heat of Sublimation	Electrical Resistivity	Specific Heat	Thermal Conductivity	Thermal Diffusivity	Thermal Linear Expansion	Thermal Absorptance	Thermal Emittance	Thermal Reflectance	Thermal Transmittance	Vapor Pressure
Dysprosium borides																
DyB_4	6-I	295	-	-	-	-	-	-	-	-	-	-	-	-	-	-
DyB_6	6-I	295	-	-	-	-	-	-	-	-	-	-	-	-	-	-
Dysprosium carbide (DyC_2) . .	5	294	-	-	-	-	-	-	-	-	-	-	-	-	-	-
Dysprosium-cobalt intermetallics		-	-	-	-	-	-	-	-	-	-	-	-	-	-	-
$CyCo_2$	6-I	680	-	-	-	-	-	-	-	-	-	-	-	-	-	-
$DyCo_5$	6-I	680	-	-	-	-	-	-	-	-	-	-	-	-	-	-
Dysprosium hydride (DyH_3) . .	5	467	-	-	-	-	-	-	-	-	-	-	-	-	-	-
Dysprosium niobate ($Dy_2O_3 \cdot Nb_2O_5$)	4-II	-	-	-	-	-	-	-	-	-	1123	-	-	-	-	-
Dysprosium oxide (Dy_2O_3) . . .	4-I	154	154	-	-	-	-	156	-	-	158	-	-	-	-	-
Dysprosium oxide + Cerium (di-) oxide	4-I	-	-	-	-	-	-	-	-	-	695	-	-	-	-	-
Dysprosium oxide + Uranium (di-) oxide	4-I	-	-	-	-	-	-	-	-	-	697	-	-	-	-	-
Dysprosium oxide + Zirconium (di-) oxide	4-I	-	-	-	-	-	-	-	-	-	699	-	-	-	-	-
Dysprosium silicide ($DySi_2$) . .	6-I	523	524	-	-	-	527	-	-	-	-	-	-	-	-	-
Dysprosium sulfides																
DyS_2	5	732	-	-	-	-	-	-	-	-	-	-	-	-	-	-
Dy_2S_3	5	732	732	-	-	-	-	-	-	-	-	-	-	-	-	-
Dy_5S_7	5	732	732	-	-	-	-	-	-	-	-	-	-	-	-	-
E																
Eastman Intran glasses	4-II	-	-	-	-	-	-	1853	-	-	-	-	-	-	-	-
Eccofoam	6-II	1084	-	-	-	-	-	-	1080	-	-	-	-	-	-	-
Elastomer, isocyanate polyester	6-II	960	-	-	-	-	-	-	-	-	-	-	-	-	-	-
Electroconducting glass	4-II	-	-	-	-	-	-	-	-	-	-	-	1839	1841	1843-1845	-
Electroconducting glass 547-26 .	4-II	-	-	-	-	-	-	-	-	-	-	-	1839	1841	1843-1845	-
Electroconducting glass LOF-81E-19778	4-II	-	-	-	-	-	-	-	-	-	-	-	1839	1841	1843-1845	-
Electroconducting glass LOF-PB-19195	4-II	-	-	-	-	-	-	-	-	-	-	-	1839	1841	1843-1845	-
Enamel on Inconel	6-II	-	-	-	-	-	1511	-	-	-	-	-	-	-	-	-
Enamel, rinsed-Mason black, on AISI 321	6-II	-	-	-	-	-	-	-	-	-	-	-	-	1513	-	-
Enamel, spinel, coating on AISI 310	6-II	-	-	-	-	-	-	-	-	-	-	-	1515	-	-	-
Enstatite	4-II	-	-	-	-	-	-	-	-	-	1295	-	-	-	-	-
Epoxide	6-II	1006	-	-	-	-	-	-	1010	-	1012	-	-	-	-	-
Epoxide, Hysol 6000-OP	6-II	1006	-	-	-	-	-	-	1010	1082	1012	-	-	-	-	-

Material Name	Volume	Density	Melting Point	Heat of Fusion	Heat of Vaporization	Heat of Sublimation	Electrical Resistivity	Specific Heat	Thermal Conductivity	Thermal Diffusivity	Thermal Linear Expansion	Thermal Absorptance	Thermal Emittance	Thermal Reflectance	Thermal Transmittance	Vapor Pressure
Epoxide, reinforced	6-II	-	-	-	-	-	-	1117	1120	1220	1122-1124	-	-	-	-	-
Epoxy, DER332	6-II	-	-	-	-	-	-	1008	-	-	-	-	-	-	-	-
Epoxy and plyophen copolymer resin, reinforced	6-II	-	-	-	-	-	-	-	1218	-	-	-	-	-	-	-
Epoxy resin	6-II	-	-	-	-	-	-	1008	-	-	-	-	-	-	-	-
Epoxy resin, reinforced	6-II	-	-	-	-	-	-	1115-1117	1120	1220	1122-1124	-	-	-	-	-
Erbia	4-I	160	-	-	-	-	-	162	-	-	164	-	166	-	-	-
Erbium (Er)	1	489	489	489	489	489	491	493	-	-	495	-	497	-	-	499
Erbium borides																
ErB_4	6-I	295	-	-	-	-	-	-	-	-	-	-	-	-	-	-
ErB_6	6-I	295	-	-	-	-	-	-	-	-	-	-	-	-	-	-
Erbium carbide (ErC_2)	5	294	-	-	-	-	-	-	-	-	-	-	-	-	-	-
Erbium-cobalt intermetallics ($ErCo_5$)	6-I	680	-	-	-	-	-	-	-	-	-	-	-	-	-	-
Erbium-gallium intermetallics ($ErGa_2$)	6-I	680	-	-	-	-	-	-	-	-	-	-	-	-	-	-
Erbium hydride (ErH_3)	5	467	-	-	-	-	-	-	-	-	-	-	-	-	-	-
Erbium-manganese intermetallics ($ErMn_2$)	6-I	680	-	-	-	-	-	-	-	-	-	-	-	-	-	-
Erbium-nickel intermetallics ($ErNi_5$)	6-I	680	-	-	-	-	-	-	-	-	-	-	-	-	-	-
Erbium oxide (Er_2O_3)	4-I	160	-	-	-	-	-	162	-	-	164	-	166	-	-	-
Erbium selenides																
ErSe	6-I	-	-	-	-	-	367	-	-	-	-	-	-	-	-	-
Er_2Se_3	6-I	-	-	-	-	-	367	-	-	-	-	-	-	-	-	-
Erbium-silver intermetallics (ErAg)	6-I	680	-	-	-	-	-	-	-	-	-	-	-	-	-	-
Erbium sulfides																
ErS	5	732	-	-	-	-	-	-	-	-	-	-	-	-	-	-
Er_2S_3	5	732	732	-	-	-	-	-	-	-	-	-	-	-	-	-
Er_5S_7	5	732	732	-	-	-	-	-	-	-	-	-	-	-	-	-
Erbium tellurides (Er_2Te_3) . . .	6-I	-	-	-	-	-	638	-	-	-	-	-	-	-	-	-
Ethyl cellulose	6-II	-	-	-	-	-	-	-	-	-	948	-	-	-	-	-
Etruria Marl	4-I	-	-	-	-	-	-	-	-	-	802-812	-	-	-	-	-
Eucryptite	4-II	-	-	-	-	-	-	-	-	-	1270	-	-	-	-	-
Europium (Eu)	1	501	501	501	501	501	503	505	-	-	-	-	-	-	-	507
Europium (hexa-)boride (EuB_6) .	6-I	296	-	-	-	-	300	-	-	-	-	-	-	-	-	-
Europium oxide (Eu_2O_3)	4-I	168	168	-	-	-	-	170	-	-	172	-	-	-	-	-
Europium oxide + Iron-chromium alloy cermet	6-II	-	-	-	-	-	-	-	-	-	786	-	-	-	-	-
Europium silicide ($EuSi_2$) . . .	6-I	523	524	-	-	-	-	-	-	-	-	-	-	-	-	-

Material Name	Volume	Density	Melting Point	Heat of Fusion	Heat of Vaporization	Heat of Sublimation	Electrical Resistivity	Specific Heat	Thermal Conductivity	Thermal Diffusivity	Thermal Linear Expansion	Thermal Absorptance	Thermal Emittance	Thermal Reflectance	Thermal Transmittance	Vapor Pressure
Europium sulfides																
EuS	5	732	–	–	–	–	–	–	–	–	–	–	–	–	–	–
EuS_2	5	732	–	–	–	–	–	–	–	–	–	–	–	–	–	–
Eu_3S_4	5	732	–	–	–	–	–	–	–	–	–	–	–	–	–	–
Evanohm	2-II	1119	–	–	–	–	1124	–	–	–	–	–	–	–	–	–
F																
Fabrics																
Fiber glass	6-II	–	–	–	–	–	–	–	–	1269	–	–	–	–	–	–
Graphite	6-II	–	–	–	–	–	–	–	–	1271	–	–	–	–	–	–
Nylon	6-II	–	–	–	–	–	–	–	–	1273	–	–	–	–	–	–
Organic fiber	6-II	–	–	–	–	–	–	–	–	1275	–	–	–	–	–	–
Silica	6-II	–	–	–	–	–	–	–	–	1277	–	–	–	–	–	–
Feldspars																
Barium	4-II	–	–	–	–	–	–	1205	–	–	1207	–	–	–	–	–
Calcium	4-II	–	–	–	–	–	–	–	–	–	1235	–	–	–	–	–
Lithium	4-II	–	–	–	–	–	–	–	1266	–	1270	–	–	–	–	–
Lithium-potassium	4-II	–	–	–	–	–	–	–	–	–	1283	–	–	–	–	–
Sodium	4-II	–	–	–	–	–	–	–	–	–	1326	–	–	–	–	–
Sodium-potassium	4-II	–	–	–	–	–	–	–	–	–	1330	–	–	–	–	–
Strontium	4-II	–	–	–	–	–	–	–	–	–	1334	–	–	–	–	–
Ferramic E	4-II	–	–	–	–	–	–	1093	–	–	–	–	–	–	–	–
Ferroferric oxide + Iron(ic) oxide	4-I	–	–	–	–	–	–	–	–	–	–	–	715	–	–	–
Fiber cermets	6-II	928	–	–	–	–	–	–	–	–	–	–	–	–	–	–
Fiber glass fabrics	6-II	–	–	–	–	–	–	–	–	1269	–	–	–	–	–	–
Fiberfrax paper-tantalum shield-graphite fibers composite system	6-II	–	–	–	–	–	–	–	1285	–	–	–	–	–	–	–
Fiberite 4030-190	6-II	–	–	–	–	–	1103	–	–	–	–	–	–	–	–	–
Firebricks																
Alumina	4-I	–	–	–	–	–	613	–	621	–	–	–	–	–	–	–
ASTM group no. 16 insulating	5	–	–	–	–	–	–	–	1031	–	–	–	–	–	–	–
ASTM group no. 20 insulating	5	–	–	–	–	–	–	–	1031	–	–	–	–	–	–	–
ASTM group no. 23 insulating	5	–	–	–	–	–	–	–	1031	–	–	–	–	–	–	–
ASTM group no. 26 insulating	5	–	–	–	–	–	–	–	1031	–	–	–	–	–	–	–
ASTM group no. 28 insulating	5	–	–	–	–	–	–	–	1031	–	–	–	–	–	–	–
ASTM group no. 30 insulating	5	–	–	–	–	–	–	–	1031	–	–	–	–	–	–	–
Egyptian	4-I	–	–	–	–	–	–	–	798	800	–	–	–	–	–	–
Firebricks	4-I	–	–	–	–	–	–	–	798	789, 800	–	–	–	–	–	–
K-28 insulating	5	–	–	–	–	–	–	–	1031	–	–	–	–	–	–	–
Siliceous	5	–	–	–	–	–	–	–	–	–	–	–	1043	–	–	–

Material Name	Volume	Density	Melting Point	Heat of Fusion	Heat of Vaporization	Heat of Sublimation	Electrical Resistivity	Specific Heat	Thermal Conductivity	Thermal Diffusivity	Thermal Linear Expansion	Thermal Absorptance	Thermal Emittance	Thermal Reflectance	Thermal Transmittance	Vapor Pressure
Flint container glass.	4-II	-	-	-	-	-	-	-	-	-	-	-	1799	1801	1729	-
Flint glass	4-II	-	-	-	-	-	-	1829	-	-	-	-	-	-	-	-
Fluorothene	6-II	1030	-	-	-	-	-	-	-	-	1045	-	-	-	-	-
FM-5064 graphite-phenolic laminates	6-II	-	-	-	-	-	-	1140	-	-	-	-	-	-	-	-
Forsterite	4-II	1285	1285	-	-	-	1287	-	1291	-	-	-	-	-	-	-
Forsterite 243	4-II	1285	1285	-	-	-	-	-	-	-	-	-	-	-	-	-
Forsterite-stainless steel laminates	6-II	-	-	-	-	-	-	-	1221	-	-	-	-	-	-	-
Fortical 28227	6-II	-	-	-	-	-	-	-	-	-	944	-	-	-	-	-
Fortical 28238	6-II	-	-	-	-	-	-	-	-	-	944	-	-	-	-	-
Fresco FR0020	6-II	-	-	-	-	-	-	1214	-	-	-	-	-	-	-	-
FRLG 2502-1	6-II	-	-	-	-	-	-	-	-	1277	-	-	-	-	-	-
Furfural formaldehyde, wood flour filled	6-II	-	-	-	-	-	-	-	-	-	1000	-	-	-	-	-
G																
Gadolinia	4-I	174	174	-	-	-	-	176	178	-	180	-	182	-	-	-
Gadolinum (Gd)	1	509	509	509	509	509	511	-	-	-	513	-	-	-	-	-
Gadolinium + Tantalum	2-I	-	-	-	-	-	-	-	-	-	190	-	-	-	-	-
Gadolinium borides																
GdB_4	6-I	295	-	-	-	-	-	-	-	-	-	-	-	-	-	-
GdB_6	6-I	295	296	-	-	-	300	-	-	-	-	-	-	-	-	-
Gadolinium carbides																
GdC_2	5	294	294	-	-	-	-	-	-	-	-	-	-	-	-	-
Gd_2C_3	5	294	-	-	-	-	-	-	-	-	-	-	-	-	-	-
Gadolinium-cobalt intermetallics																
GdCo	6-I	665	-	-	-	-	-	-	-	-	-	-	-	-	-	-
$GdCo_2$	6-I	665	-	-	-	-	-	-	-	-	-	-	-	-	-	-
$GdCo_3$	6-I	665	-	-	-	-	-	-	-	-	-	-	-	-	-	-
$GdCo_4$	6-I	665	-	-	-	-	-	-	-	-	-	-	-	-	-	-
$GdCo_5$	6-I	665	-	-	-	-	-	-	-	-	-	-	-	-	-	-
Gd_2Co_3	6-I	665	-	-	-	-	-	-	-	-	-	-	-	-	-	-
Gd_3Co	6-I	665	-	-	-	-	-	-	-	-	-	-	-	-	-	-
Gadolinium-copper intermetallics																
GdCu	6-I	665	-	-	-	-	-	-	-	-	-	-	-	-	-	-
$GdCu_4$	6-I	665	-	-	-	-	-	-	-	-	-	-	-	-	-	-
$GdCu_5$	6-I	665	-	-	-	-	-	-	-	-	-	-	-	-	-	-
Gadolinium ferrides																
$GdFe_3$	6-I	306	-	-	-	-	-	-	-	-	-	-	-	-	-	-
$GdFe_4$	6-I	306	-	-	-	-	-	-	-	-	-	-	-	-	-	-
$GeFe_5$	6-I	306	-	-	-	-	-	-	-	-	-	-	-	-	-	-
Gd_2Fe_3	6-I	306	-	-	-	-	-	-	-	-	-	-	-	-	-	-

Material Name	Volume	Density	Melting Point	Heat of Fusion	Heat of Vaporization	Heat of Sublimation	Electrical Resistivity	Specific Heat	Thermal Conductivity	Thermal Diffusivity	Thermal Linear Expansion	Thermal Absorptance	Thermal Emittance	Thermal Reflectance	Thermal Transmittance	Vapor Pressure
Gadolinium ferrides (cont.)																
Gd_2Fe_7	6-II	306	-	-	-	-	-	-	-	-	-	-	-	-	-	-
Gadolinium (tri-) fluoride (GdF_3)	5	-	407	-	-	-	-	-	-	-	-	-	-	-	-	-
Gadolinium-gallium intermetallics ($GdGa_2$)	6-I	665	-	-	-	-	-	-	-	-	-	-	-	-	-	-
Gadolinium hydrides																
GdH_2	5	467	-	-	-	-	-	-	-	-	-	-	-	-	-	-
GdH_3	5	467	-	-	-	-	-	-	-	-	-	-	-	-	-	-
Gadolinium-nickel intermetallics																
GdNi	6-I	665	-	-	-	-	-	-	-	-	-	-	-	-	-	-
$GdNi_2$	6-I	665	-	-	-	-	-	-	-	-	-	-	-	-	-	-
$GdNi_3$	6-I	665	-	-	-	-	-	-	-	-	-	-	-	-	-	-
$GdNi_4$	6-I	665	-	-	-	-	-	-	-	-	-	-	-	-	-	-
$GdNi_5$	6-I	665	-	-	-	-	-	-	-	-	-	-	-	-	-	-
Gd_2Ni_7	6-I	665	-	-	-	-	-	-	-	-	-	-	-	-	-	-
Gd_2Ni_{17}	6-I	665	-	-	-	-	-	-	-	-	-	-	-	-	-	-
Gd_3Ni	6-I	665	-	-	-	-	-	-	-	-	-	-	-	-	-	-
Gd_3Ni_2	6-I	665	-	-	-	-	-	-	-	-	-	-	-	-	-	-
Gadolinium-osmium intermetallics (Gd_2Os_3)	6-I	665	-	-	-	-	-	-	-	-	-	-	-	-	-	-
Gadolinium oxide (Gd_2O_3) . . .	4-I	174	174	-	-	-	-	176	178	-	180	-	182	-	-	-
Gadolinium selenides																
GdSe	6-I	365	-	-	-	-	-	-	-	-	-	-	-	-	-	-
Gd_2Se_3	6-I	365	-	-	-	-	-	-	-	-	-	-	-	-	-	-
Gd_3Se_4	6-I	365	-	-	-	-	-	-	-	-	-	-	-	-	-	-
Gadolinium silicides ($GdSi_2$) . .	6-I	523	-	-	-	-	527	-	-	-	-	-	-	-	-	-
Gadolinium-silver intermetallics (GdAg)	6-I	665	-	-	-	-	-	-	-	-	-	-	-	-	-	-
Gadolinium sulfides																
GdS_2	5	732	-	-	-	-	-	-	-	-	-	-	-	-	-	-
Gd_2S_3	5	732	732	-	-	-	-	-	-	-	-	-	-	-	-	-
Gadolinium tellurides																
Gd_2Te	6-I	-	-	-	-	-	638	-	-	-	-	-	-	-	-	-
Gd_2Te_3	6-I	-	-	-	-	-	638	-	-	-	-	-	-	-	-	-
Gadolinium-yttrium-cobalt intermetallics ($Gd_{1-X}Y_XCo_5$) .	6-I	665	-	-	-	-	-	-	-	-	-	-	-	-	-	-
Galena	5	-	-	-	-	-	-	-	-	-	-	-	-	688	-	-
Gallium antimonide (GaSb) . . .	6-I	-	-	-	-	-	51	53	-	-	-	-	-	-	-	-
Gallium arsenide (GaAs)	6-I	-	-	-	-	-	-	83	-	85	-	-	-	-	-	-
Gallium (sesqui-) oxide (Ga_2O_3) .	4-I	-	-	-	-	-	-	184	-	-	-	-	-	-	-	-
Gallium phosphide (GaP)	5	-	-	-	-	-	-	629	-	-	-	-	-	-	-	-
Gallium telluride (Ga_2Te_3) . . .	6-I	-	-	-	-	-	-	574	-	-	-	-	-	-	-	-
Gehlenite	4-II	-	-	-	-	-	-	1233	-	-	1235	-	-	-	-	-

Material Name	Volume	Density	Melting Point	Heat of Fusion	Heat of Vaporization	Heat of Sublimation	Electrical Resistivity	Specific Heat	Thermal Conductivity	Thermal Diffusivity	Thermal Linear Expansion	Thermal Absorptance	Thermal Emittance	Thermal Reflectance	Thermal Transmittance	Vapor Pressure
German Flake	1	-	-	-	-	-	50	-	-	-	-	-	-	-	-	-
. . . . . .	2-II	841	-	-	-	-	-	-	845	-	-	-	-	-	-	-
Germanium (Ge)	1	515	515	515	515	515	517	519	521	524	526	-	528-530	-	-	532
Germanium + Silicon	2-I	192	-	-	-	-	194	-	-	-	-	-	-	-	-	-
Germanium bismuth telluride ($Ge_{1-x}Bi_xTe$)	6-I	-	-	-	-	-	582	-	584	-	-	-	-	-	-	-
Germanium (di-) oxide (GeO_2) .	4-I	-	-	-	-	-	-	186	-	-	188	-	-	-	-	190
Germanium oxide glass	4-II	1637	-	-	-	-	-	1639	-	-	-	-	-	-	-	-
Germanium silicide (GeSi) . . .	6-I	-	-	-	-	-	-	405	-	-	-	-	-	-	-	-
Germanium telluride (GeTe) . .	6-I	-	-	-	-	-	576	-	578	-	-	-	-	-	-	580
Germanium telluride + Silver antimony telluride	6-I	-	-	-	-	-	715	-	-	-	-	-	-	-	-	-
Glasses (see individual glasses)																
Glass ceramics (see also pyroceram)	4-II	-	-	-	-	-	-	1587	1589	1591	-	-	1593-1599	1601	1603	-
Glucina	4-I	-	-	-	-	-	57	-	-	-	-	-	-	-	-	-
GMGA 5003 silicone	6-II	-	-	-	-	-	1070	-	-	-	-	-	-	-	-	-
Gold (Au)	1	534	534	-	-	534	536	538	540	-	542	544-546	548	550-552	-	554
Gold coating on titanium	6-II	-	-	-	-	-	-	-	-	-	-	-	1303	1305	-	-
Gold coating on mylar	6-II	-	-	-	-	-	-	-	-	-	-	-	-	1307	-	-
Gold + Cadmium	2-I	196	196	196	-	-	198	-	-	-	-	-	-	-	-	200
Gold + Cobalt	2-I	-	-	-	-	-	202	-	-	-	-	-	-	-	-	-
Gold + Cobalt + ΣX_i	2-II	-	1012	-	-	-	1014	-	-	-	-	-	-	-	-	-
Gold + Copper	2-I	-	-	-	-	-	-	204	-	-	206	-	-	-	-	-
Gold + Copper + ΣX_i	2-II	-	-	-	-	-	1016	-	-	-	-	-	-	-	-	-
Gold + Iron	2-I	208	-	-	-	-	-	-	-	-	-	-	-	-	-	-
Gold + Manganese	2-I	210	-	-	-	-	212	-	-	-	-	-	-	-	-	-
Gold + Nickel	2-I	214	-	-	-	-	-	216	-	-	-	-	-	-	-	-
Gold + Palladium	2-I	-	-	-	-	-	218	-	-	-	220	-	-	-	-	-
Gold + Palladium + ΣX_i	2-II	-	1018	-	-	-	1020	-	-	-	-	-	-	-	-	-
Gold + Platinum	2-I	-	-	-	-	-	222	-	-	-	-	-	-	-	-	-
Gold + Silver	2-I	-	-	-	-	-	-	-	-	-	224	-	226	-	-	228
Gold + Uranium	2-I	230	-	-	-	-	-	-	-	-	-	-	-	-	-	-
Gold + Zinc	2-I	-	232	232	-	-	-	-	-	-	-	-	-	234	-	-
Gold alloy (special designations)																
Palau	2-I	-	-	-	-	-	-	-	-	-	220	-	-	-	-	-
Gold-manganese intermetallics (Au_2Mn)	6-I	-	-	-	-	-	648	-	-	-	-	-	-	-	-	-
Gold-titanium intermetallics (Au_2Ti)	6-I	-	683	-	-	-	-	-	-	-	-	-	-	-	-	-
Gold-zirconium intermetallics (Au_3Zr)	6-I	-	683	-	-	-	-	-	-	-	-	-	-	-	-	-

Material Name	Volume	Density	Melting Point	Heat of Fusion	Heat of Vaporization	Heat of Sublimation	Electrical Resistivity	Specific Heat	Thermal Conductivity	Thermal Diffusivity	Thermal Linear Expansion	Thermal Absorptance	Thermal Emittance	Thermal Reflectance	Thermal Transmittance	Vapor Pressure
Goodyear foam-inplace.	6-II	962	–	–	–	–	–	–	–	–	966	–	–	–	–	–
Graphites (Special designations)																
Grade 580	1	–	–	–	–	–	–	–	–	–	–	–	110-112	–	–	–
Grade 896G	1	–	–	–	–	–	371	–	–	–	114	–	–	–	–	–
Grade 942S	1	–	–	–	–	–	371	–	–	–	116	–	–	–	–	–
Grade 3474D	1	–	–	–	–	–	371	118	120	–	122	124	126-128	130	–	–
Grade 3499	1	–	–	–	–	–	371	–	–	–	132	–	–	–	–	–
Grade 7087	1	105	–	–	–	–	–	134	136	138	140	142	144-146	148	–	–
Grade 7100	1	–	–	–	–	–	–	–	–	–	–	–	150-152	–	–	–
Grade AGHT	1	–	–	–	–	–	–	–	154	–	–	–	–	–	–	–
Grade AGKSP	1	–	–	–	–	–	–	–	–	–	–	–	156	158	–	–
Grade AGKT	1	–	–	–	–	–	371	–	–	–	–	–	–	–	–	–
Grade AGOT	1	–	–	–	–	–	160	–	162	–	165	–	–	–	–	–
Grade AGOT-CSF.	1	–	–	–	–	–	160	–	–	–	–	–	–	–	–	–
Grade AGOT-KC	1	–	–	–	–	–	160	–	–	–	–	–	–	–	–	–
Grade AGR	1	–	–	–	–	–	371	–	–	–	167	–	–	–	–	–
Grade AGX	1	–	–	–	–	–	–	–	–	–	169	–	171	–	–	–
Grade ATJ	1	103	–	–	–	–	371	175	177	–	179	–	182-188	190	–	–
Grade ATL-82	1	–	–	–	–	–	–	–	192	–	194	–	–	–	–	–
Grade AUC	1	–	–	–	–	–	–	–	–	–	–	–	196-198	200	–	–
Grade AWG	1	–	–	–	–	–	202	–	204	–	–	–	–	–	–	–
Grade CEP	1	–	–	–	–	–	–	–	–	–	206	–	–	–	–	–
Grade CFW	1	–	–	–	–	–	208	–	–	–	210	–	–	–	–	–
Grade CFZ	1	–	–	–	–	–	–	–	–	–	212	–	–	–	–	–
Grade CS	1	–	–	–	–	–	371	214	216	218	–	–	–	–	–	–
Grade CSF	1	–	–	–	–	–	–	–	220	–	222	–	–	–	–	–
Grade EH	1	–	–	–	–	–	371	–	–	–	224	–	–	–	–	–
Grade GBE	1	–	–	–	–	–	–	–	226	–	228	230	232-234	236	–	–
Grade GBH	1	105	–	–	–	–	–	238	240	–	242	244	246-248	250	–	–
Grade H1LM	1	–	–	–	–	–	–	–	–	–	–	–	252-254	–	–	–
Grade H3LM	1	–	–	–	–	–	371	–	–	–	256	–	258-260	–	–	–
Grade H4LM	1	–	–	–	–	–	–	–	262	–	264	–	–	–	–	–
Grade MH4LM	1	–	–	–	–	–	–	–	266	–	–	–	–	–	–	–
Grade NT-0005	1	–	–	–	–	–	371	–	–	–	349	–	–	–	–	–
Grade R-0008	1	–	–	–	–	–	268	–	270	–	–	–	–	–	–	–
Grade R-0025	1	–	–	–	–	–	–	–	272	–	–	–	–	–	–	–

Material Name	Volume	Density	Melting Point	Heat of Fusion	Heat of Vaporization	Heat of Sublimation	Electrical Resistivity	Specific Heat	Thermal Conductivity	Thermal Diffusivity	Thermal Linear Expansion	Thermal Absorptance	Thermal Emittance	Thermal Reflectance	Thermal Transmittance	Vapor Pressure
Graphites (special design.) (cont)																
Grade RT-0003	1	–	–	–	–	–	–	–	274	–	–	–	–	–	–	–
Grade RVA	1	–	–	–	–	–	–	–	–	–	276	–	–	–	–	–
Grade RVC	1	–	–	–	–	–	–	–	–	–	278	–	–	–	–	–
Grade RVD	1	–	–	–	–	–	–	–	–	–	280	–	–	–	–	–
Grade SA-25	1	–	–	–	–	–	–	–	282	–	–	–	–	–	–	–
Grade SPK	1	–	–	–	–	–	–	–	–	–	–	–	284	286	–	–
Grade TS	1	–	–	–	–	–	–	–	–	–	288	–	–	–	–	–
Nuclear grade TSP	1	–	–	–	–	–	–	–	290	–	–	–	–	–	–	–
Grade TSX	1	–	–	–	–	–	–	–	–	–	292	–	–	–	–	–
Grade W	1	–	–	–	–	–	–	–	294	–	296	–	–	–	–	–
Grade WSF	1	–	–	–	–	–	–	–	–	–	298	–	–	–	–	–
Grade ZT	1	–	–	–	–	–	300	–	302	–	–	–	–	–	–	–
Grade ZT-5001	1	–	–	–	–	–	–	–	302	–	–	–	–	–	–	–
Grade ZTA	1	–	–	–	–	–	–	–	–	–	305	–	–	–	–	–
Grade ZTB	1	–	–	–	–	–	–	–	–	–	307	–	–	–	–	–
Grade ZTC	1	–	–	–	–	–	–	–	–	–	309	–	–	–	–	–
Grade ZTD	1	–	–	–	–	–	–	–	–	–	311	–	–	–	–	–
Grade ZTE	1	–	–	–	–	–	–	–	–	–	313	–	–	–	–	–
Grade ZTF	1	–	–	–	–	–	–	–	–	–	315	–	–	–	–	–
Graphites, others																
Artificial grades	1	–	–	–	–	–	–	–	360	–	363	–	–	–	–	–
Carbon impregnated	1	–	–	–	–	–	–	–	358	–	–	–	–	–	–	–
Ceylon graphite	1	–	–	–	–	–	352	–	354	–	356	–	–	–	–	–
Coated with grade W graphite .	1	–	–	–	–	–	–	–	294	–	296	–	–	–	–	–
Coated with silicon carbide .	1	–	–	–	–	–	–	–	–	–	–	–	386	–	–	–
Cumberland graphite	1	–	–	–	–	–	352	–	354	–	–	–	–	–	–	–
Electrode	1	–	–	–	–	–	–	–	360	–	–	–	365	–	–	–
Experimental grades	1	–	–	–	–	–	337	–	339	343	349	–	–	–	–	–
Flake	1	–	–	–	–	–	–	–	–	–	369	–	–	–	–	–
Great Lakes base stock grades	1	–	–	–	–	–	–	–	–	–	381	–	–	–	–	–
Great Lakes end-cap grades	1	–	–	–	–	–	–	–	–	–	381	–	–	–	–	–
Great Lakes impervious grades	1	–	–	–	–	–	–	–	–	–	381	–	–	–	–	–
Hilger H. S. grade	1	–	–	–	–	–	352	–	354	–	–	–	–	–	–	–
Karbate	1	–	–	–	–	–	–	–	358	–	–	–	–	–	–	–
Lampblack-base	1	–	–	–	–	–	–	–	367	–	–	–	–	–	–	–
Natural graphite-base	1	–	–	–	–	–	352	–	354	–	–	–	–	–	–	–
Pyrolytic	1	–	–	–	–	–	–	–	317	–	319	–	325-331	333-335	–	–
Pyrolytic coating on tantalum .	6-II	–	–	–	–	–	–	–	–	–	–	–	573-575	–	–	–
Pyrolytic, nucleated and regenerative	1	–	–	–	–	–	–	–	–	–	319	–	–	–	–	–
Silicon carbide bonded . . .	1	–	–	–	–	–	–	–	–	–	–	–	386	–	–	–

Material Name	Volume	Density	Melting Point	Heat of Fusion	Heat of Vaporization	Heat of Sublimation	Electrical Resistivity	Specific Heat	Thermal Conductivity	Thermal Diffusivity	Thermal Linear Expansion	Thermal Absorptance	Thermal Emittance	Thermal Reflectance	Thermal Transmittance	Vapor Pressure
Graphites, others (cont.)		-	-	-	-	-	-	-	-	-	-	-	-	-	-	-
Unspecified grades	1	105	105	-	-	105	371	375	377	379	383	-	386-388	-	-	390
Graphite + Silicon carbide . . .	5	-	-	-	-	-	-	737	-	-	-	-	-	-	-	-
Graphite + Thorium (di-) oxide .	5	-	-	-	-	-	-	-	739	-	-	-	-	-	-	-
Graphite + Uranium (di-) carbide	5	-	-	-	-	-	-	-	743	-	-	-	-	-	-	-
Graphite + Uranium (di-) oxide .	5	-	-	-	-	-	-	-	741	-	-	-	-	-	-	-
Graphite + Zirconium (pyro-)-carbide	5	-	-	-	-	-	-	-	-	-	745	-	-	-	-	-
Graphite fabric	6-II	-	-	-	-	-	-	-	-	1271	-	-	-	-	-	-
Graphite cloth laminates																
PT-0110	6-II	-	-	-	-	-	-	-	-	-	1227	-	-	-	-	-
PT-0111	6-II	-	-	-	-	-	-	-	-	-	1227	-	-	-	-	-
PT-0113	6-II	-	-	-	-	-	-	-	-	-	1227	-	-	-	-	-
PT-0114	6-II	-	-	-	-	-	-	-	-	-	1227	-	-	-	-	-
PT-0154	6-II	-	-	-	-	-	-	-	-	-	1227	-	-	-	-	-
PT-0156	6-II	-	-	-	-	-	-	-	-	-	1227	-	-	-	-	-
Graphite fibers - tantalum shield composite system	6-II	-	-	-	-	-	-	-	1281	-	-	-	-	-	-	-
Graphite-phenolic laminate FM-5064	6-II	-	-	-	-	-	-	1140	-	-	-	-	-	-	-	-
Gray cast iron	3	-	-	-	-	-	-	-	29-33	-	39	-	-	-	-	-
Gray cast iron, ferritic base . .	3	-	-	-	-	-	-	-	33	-	-	-	-	-	-	-
Gray cast iron, pearlitic base .	3	-	-	-	-	-	-	-	31	-	-	-	-	-	-	-
H																
Hafnia	4-I	192	192	-	-	-	194	196	198	-	200	-	202	-	-	204
Hafnium (Hf)	1	556	556	-	-	-	558	560	-	-	562	-	-	-	-	-
Hafnium + Zirconium	2-I	236	236	-	-	-	238	240	242	-	244	-	-	-	-	246
Hafnium antimonide (HfSb) . . .	6-I	-	-	-	-	-	55	-	-	-	-	-	-	-	-	-
Hafnium beryllide (Hf_2Be_{21}) . .	6-I	-	-	-	-	-	-	98	-	-	100	-	-	-	-	-
Hafnium (di-) boride (HfB_2) . .	6-I	170	170	-	-	-	172	174	176	-	178	-	180	-	-	-
Hafnium carbide (HfC).	5	49	49	-	-	-	51	53	55	57	59	-	61	-	-	-
Hafnium carbide + Zirconium cermet	6-II	-	-	-	-	-	-	-	-	-	852	-	-	-	-	-
Hafnium-chromium intermetallics ($HfCr_2$)	6-I	-	683	-	-	-	-	-	-	-	-	-	-	-	-	-
Hafnium-cobalt intermetallics ($HfCo_2$)	6-I	-	683	-	-	-	-	-	-	-	-	-	-	-	-	-
Hafnium ferrides ($HfFe_2$). . . .	6-I	-	306	-	-	-	-	-	-	-	-	-	-	-	-	-
Hafnium fluoride (HfF_4)	5	-	-	-	-	-	-	367	-	-	-	-	-	-	-	-
Hafnium germanide (HfGe) . . .	6-I	-	-	-	-	-	325	-	-	-	-	-	-	-	-	-
Hafnium-manganese intermetallics ($HfMn_2$)	6-I	-	683	-	-	-	-	-	-	-	-	-	-	-	-	-

Material Name	Volume	Density	Melting Point	Heat of Fusion	Heat of Vaporization	Heat of Sublimation	Electrical Resistivity	Specific Heat	Thermal Conductivity	Thermal Diffusivity	Thermal Linear Expansion	Thermal Absorptance	Thermal Emittance	Thermal Reflectance	Thermal Transmittance	Vapor Pressure
Hafnium-molybdenum intermetallics ($HfMo_2$)	6-I	-	684	-	-	-	-	-	-	-	-	-	-	-	-	-
Hafnium-nickel intermetallics ($HfNi_2$)	6-I	-	684	-	-	-	-	-	-	-	-	-	-	-	-	-
Hafnium nitride (HfN)	5	517	517	-	-	-	519	521	523	-	525	-	527-529	-	-	531
Hafnium (di-) oxide (HfO_2) . . .	4-I	192	192	-	-	-	194	196	198	-	200	-	202	-	-	204
Hafnium (di-) oxide coating on tungsten	6-II	-	-	-	-	-	-	-	-	-	-	-	1377-1379	-	-	-
Hafnium (di-) oxide + ΣX_i . . .	4-I	-	-	-	-	-	-	-	-	-	711	-	-	-	-	-
Hafnium (di-) oxide + Calcium oxide	4-I	-	-	-	-	-	-	-	-	-	701	-	-	-	-	-
Hafnium (di-) oxide + Magnesium oxide	4-I	-	-	-	-	-	-	-	-	-	703	-	-	-	-	-
Hafnium (di-) oxide + Tantalum (pent-) oxide	4-I	-	-	-	-	-	-	-	-	-	705	-	-	-	-	-
Hafnium (di-) oxide + Titanium (di-) oxide	4-I	-	-	-	-	-	-	-	-	-	707	-	-	-	-	-
Hafnium (di-) oxide + Titanium (di-) oxide + Zirconium (di-) oxide	4-I	-	-	-	-	-	-	-	-	-	709	-	-	-	-	-
Hafnium selenide (HfSe)	6-I	-	-	-	-	-	331	-	-	-	-	-	-	-	-	-
Hafnium silicate ($HfO_2 \cdot SiO_2$) . .	4-II	-	-	-	-	-	-	-	-	-	1241	-	-	-	-	-
Hafnium silicides																
HfSi	6-I	-	524	-	-	-	-	-	-	-	-	-	-	-	-	-
$HfSi_2$	6-I	523	-	-	-	-	-	-	-	-	-	-	-	-	-	-
Hafnium tellurides (HfTe) . . .	6-I	-	-	-	-	-	638	-	-	-	-	-	-	-	-	-
Hafnium-vanadium intermetallics (HfV_2)	6-I	-	684	-	-	-	-	-	-	-	-	-	-	-	-	-
Hafnon	4-II	-	-	-	-	-	-	-	-	-	1241	-	-	-	-	-
Hamilton standard foam-inplace.	6-II	962	-	-	-	-	-	-	-	-	966	-	-	-	-	-
Hastelloy 25	2-II	-	-	-	-	-	-	-	-	-	898	-	-	-	-	-
Hastelloy 500	2-II	-	-	-	-	-	-	-	-	-	1154	-	-	-	-	-
Hastelloy A	2-II	-	-	-	-	-	-	-	1261	-	-	-	-	-	-	-
Hastelloy B	2-II	1277	1275	-	-	-	-	1279	1281	-	1287	1289	1293-1295	1297	-	-
Hastelloy C	2-II	1119	-	-	-	-	-	1130	1136	-	1166	-	-	-	-	-
Hastelloy C (AMS-5530)	2-II	1277	-	-	-	-	-	-	1281	-	1283	1289	1291-1295	1297	-	-
Hastelloy C (AMS-5530C) . . .	2-II	-	-	-	-	-	-	-	-	-	-	1289	1293	1297	-	-
Hastelloy C coating on AISI 310 .	6-II	-	-	-	-	-	-	-	-	-	-	-	1337	-	-	-
Hastelloy D	2-II	-	-	-	-	-	-	-	-	-	1301	-	-	-	-	-
Hastelloy F	2-II	-	-	-	-	-	-	-	-	-	1164	-	-	-	-	-
Hastelloy N	2-II	1277	-	-	-	-	-	-	1281	-	1283	-	-	-	-	-
Hastelloy R-235	2-II	1122	-	-	-	-	-	1128	1136-1138	-	1161	-	-	-	-	-

Material Name	Volume	Density	Melting Point	Heat of Fusion	Heat of Vaporization	Heat of Sublimation	Electrical Resistivity	Specific Heat	Thermal Conductivity	Thermal Diffusivity	Thermal Linear Expansion	Thermal Absorptance	Thermal Emittance	Thermal Reflectance	Thermal Transmittance	Vapor Pressure
Hastelloy X	2-II	1119, 1257	-	-	-	-	-	-	1134, 1261	-	1164	-	1172, 1189	1203	-	-
Hastelloy X coating on AISI 310 .	6-II	-	-	-	-	-	-	-	-	-	-	-	1339	-	-	-
Hematite	4-I	-	-	-	-	-	214	218	-	-	222	-	-	224	-	-
Hidurel 6	2-II	-	-	-	-	-	962	-	964	-	-	-	-	-	-	-
Holmia	4-I	-	-	-	-	-	-	206	-	-	208	-	-	-	-	-
Holmium (Ho)	1	564	564	564	564	564	566	-	-	-	-	-	-	-	-	-
Holmium borides																
HoB_4	6-I	295	-	-	-	-	-	-	-	-	-	-	-	-	-	-
HoB_6	6-I	295	-	-	-	-	-	-	-	-	-	-	-	-	-	-
Holmium carbides																
HoC_2	5	294	-	-	-	-	-	-	-	-	-	-	-	-	-	-
Ho_2C_3	5	294	-	-	-	-	-	-	-	-	-	-	-	-	-	-
Holmium-cobalt intermetallics																
$HoCo_2$	6-I	680	-	-	-	-	-	-	-	-	-	-	-	-	-	-
$HoCo_5$	6-I	680	-	-	-	-	-	-	-	-	-	-	-	-	-	-
Holmium ferrides																
$HoFe_2$	6-I	306	-	-	-	-	-	-	-	-	-	-	-	-	-	-
$HoFe_5$	6-I	306	-	-	-	-	-	-	-	-	-	-	-	-	-	-
Holmium-gallium intermetallics ($HoGa_2$)	6-I	680	-	-	-	-	-	-	-	-	-	-	-	-	-	-
Holmium-manganese intermetallics																
$HoMn_2$	6-I	680	-	-	-	-	-	-	-	-	-	-	-	-	-	-
$HoMn_5$	6-I	680	-	-	-	-	-	-	-	-	-	-	-	-	-	-
Holmium-nickel intermetallics																
$HoNi_2$	6-I	680	-	-	-	-	-	-	-	-	-	-	-	-	-	-
$HoNi_5$	6-I	680	-	-	-	-	-	-	-	-	-	-	-	-	-	-
Holmium oxide (Ho_2O_3)	4-I	-	-	-	-	-	-	206	-	-	208	-	-	-	-	-
Honeycombs																
17-7PH stainless steel skin and core	6-II	-	-	-	-	-	-	1236	1230	-	1234	-	-	-	-	-
2024 T-3 aluminum alloy skin and core	6-II	-	-	-	-	-	-	1236	1230	-	1232	-	-	-	-	-
2024 T-3 aluminum alloy skin and alkyd isocyanate foam core	6-II	-	-	-	-	-	-	1236	1239	-	1243	-	-	-	-	-
2024 T-3 aluminum alloy skin and phenolic core	6-II	-	-	-	-	-	-	1236	1239	-	1241	-	-	-	-	-
Metal skin and metal core . .	6-II	-	-	-	-	-	-	1236	1230	-	1232-1234	-	-	-	-	-
Plastic and metal composites	6-II	-	-	-	-	-	-	1236	1239	-	1241-1245	-	-	-	-	-
Plastic skin and plastic core .	6-II	-	-	-	-	-	-	-	1247-1253	-	-	-	-	-	-	-

Material Name	Volume	Density	Melting Point	Heat of Fusion	Heat of Vaporization	Heat of Sublimation	Electrical Resistivity	Specific Heat	Thermal Conductivity	Thermal Diffusivity	Thermal Linear Expansion	Thermal Absorptance	Thermal Emittance	Thermal Reflectance	Thermal Transmittance	Vapor Pressure
Honeycombs (cont.)																
Polyester P-43 resin skin and 2024 T-3 aluminum alloy core	6-II	–	–	–	–	–	–	1236	1239	–	1245	–	–	–	–	–
Polyester resin no. P-43 skin and polyester honeycomb core	6-II	–	–	–	–	–	–	1236	–	–	–	–	–	–	–	–
Polyester resin skin and epoxy resin core.	6-II	–	–	–	–	–	–	–	1247	–	–	–	–	–	–	–
Polyester resin skin and phenolic resin core	6-II	–	–	–	–	–	–	–	1247	–	–	–	–	–	–	–
Polyester Vibrin 135 and 181 fabric faces and phenolic core	6-II	–	–	–	–	–	–	1236	–	–	–	–	–	–	–	–
TAC polyester Vibrin 135 and 181 fabric skin and alkyd isocyanate foam core. . . .	6-II	–	–	–	–	–	–	–	–	–	1249	–	–	–	–	–
Reinforced polyester skin and polyester core	6-II	–	–	–	–	–	–	–	–	–	1253	–	–	–	–	–
Hysol 6000-CP epoxide	6-II	1006	–	–	–	–	–	–	1010	1082	1012	–	–	–	–	–
I																
Igelit-PCU	6-II	–	–	–	–	–	–	1078	1086	1082	–	–	–	–	–	–
Ilmenite	4-II	–	–	–	–	–	1427	1429	–	–	1431	–	–	–	–	–
Incoloy	3	–	–	–	–	–	–	383	–	–	–	–	–	–	–	–
Incoloy 713C	2-II	–	–	–	–	–	–	1126	1140	–	1152	–	–	–	–	–
Incoloy 800	3	–	–	–	–	–	–	–	–	–	405	–	–	–	–	–
Incoloy 801	3	–	–	–	–	–	–	–	–	–	405	–	–	–	–	–
Incoloy 804	2-II	–	–	–	–	–	–	–	–	–	1164	–	–	–	–	–
Incoloy 825	2-II	–	–	–	–	–	–	–	–	–	1267	–	–	–	–	–
Incoloy 901	2-II	–	–	–	–	–	–	1259	1261	–	–	–	–	–	–	–
Incoloy T	3	–	–	–	–	–	–	–	–	–	405	–	–	–	–	–
Inconel	2-II	1119	1119	–	–	–	1124	1128	1140, 1144, 1145	1148	1158, 1161	–	1172, 1177, 1191	–	–	–
Inconel coated with enamel . . .	6-II	–	–	–	–	–	1151	–	–	–	–	–	–	–	–	–
Inconel coated with NBS coating A-418	6-II	–	–	–	–	–	–	–	–	–	–	–	1361-1363	–	–	–
Inconel coated with NBS coating N-143	6-II	–	–	–	–	–	–	–	–	–	–	–	1353-1355	–	–	–
Inconel coated with nickel aluminides	6-II	–	–	–	–	–	–	–	–	–	–	–	1453-1455	1457	–	–
Inconel coated with silicone . .	6-II	–	–	–	–	–	1495	–	–	–	–	–	–	–	–	–
Inconel coated with zirconium (di-)oxide	6-II	–	–	–	–	–	–	–	–	–	–	–	–	1397	–	–

Material Name	Volume	Density	Melting Point	Heat of Fusion	Heat of Vaporization	Heat of Sublimation	Electrical Resistivity	Specific Heat	Thermal Conductivity	Thermal Diffusivity	Thermal Linear Expansion	Thermal Absorptance	Thermal Emittance	Thermal Reflectance	Thermal Transmittance	Vapor Pressure
Inconel 600	2-II	1219, 1307	-	-	-	-	-	-	1223, 1313	-	1158	-	-	-	-	-
Inconel 604	2-II	-	-	-	-	-	-	-	-	-	1158	-	-	-	-	-
Inconel 625	2-II	-	-	-	-	-	-	-	-	-	1166	-	-	-	-	-
Inconel 700	2-II	-	-	-	-	-	-	-	1223	-	1227	-	-	-	-	-
Inconel 702	2-II	-	1119	-	-	-	-	1128	1144	-	1152	-	1193	1205	-	-
Inconel 718	2-II	-	-	-	-	-	-	-	-	-	1164	-	-	-	-	-
Inconel 721	2-II	-	-	-	-	-	-	-	-	-	1158	-	-	-	-	-
Inconel 722	2-II	-	-	-	-	-	-	-	-	-	1158	-	-	-	-	-
Inconel B	2-II	-	-	-	-	-	-	-	-	-	-	-	1174	-	-	-
Inconel M	2-II	-	-	-	-	-	-	-	-	-	1158	-	-	-	-	-
Inconel W	2-II	-	-	-	-	-	-	-	-	-	1158	-	-	-	-	-
Inconel X	2-II	1119	1119	-	-	-	1124	1128	1140	1148	1158	-	1172, 1177, 1186, 1195	1207	-	-
Inconel X coated with boron carbide	6-II	-	-	-	-	-	-	-	-	-	-	-	1403	1405	-	-
Inconel X coated with nickel-chromium alloy	6-II	-	-	-	-	-	-	-	-	-	-	-	1333	1335	-	-
Inconel X coated with tantalum carbide	6-II	-	-	-	-	-	-	-	-	-	-	-	1417	1419	-	-
Inconel X coated with tungsten .	6-II	-	-	-	-	-	-	-	-	-	-	-	1329	1331	-	-
Inconel X coated with tungsten-cobalt alloy	6-II	-	-	-	-	-	-	-	-	-	-	-	1341	1343	-	-
Inconel X coated with zirconium (di-)oxide	6-II	-	-	-	-	-	-	-	-	-	-	-	1399	1401	-	-
Inconel X 750	2-II	1122	-	-	-	-	-	-	1140	-	1158	-	-	-	-	-
Index rod (gas baked coke) . . .	1	-	-	-	-	-	85	-	87	-	-	-	-	-	-	-
Indium antimonide (InSb). . . .	6-I	-	-	-	-	-	57	59	61	63	65	-	-	-	-	-
Indium arsenide (InAs)	6-I	-	-	-	-	-	87	89	91	-	-	-	-	-	-	-
Indium bismuth selenide ($InBiSe_3$)	6-I	-	-	-	-	-	333	-	-	-	-	-	-	-	-	-
Indium (sesqui-)oxide (In_2O_3). .	4-I	-	-	-	-	-	-	-	-	-	210	-	-	-	-	-
Indium phosphide (InP)	5	-	-	-	-	-	631	633	-	-	-	-	-	-	-	-
Indium telluride (In_2Te_3)	6-I	-	-	-	-	-	586	-	588	-	-	-	-	-	-	-
Inquartation silver	1	-	-	-	-	-	-	904	-	-	-	-	-	-	-	-
Insulating bricks (see bricks)																
Insulating firebricks (see firebricks)																
Insurok C-T-601	6-II	1128	-	-	-	-	-	1142	-	-	-	-	-	-	-	-
Insurok XXX-T-640	6-II	1128	-	-	-	-	-	1142	-	-	-	-	-	-	-	-
Intermetallics (see each individual intermetallics)																
Inverse spinel	4-I	-	-	-	-	-	-	691-693	-	-	-	-	-	-	-	-
Iodide titanium	1	-	993	-	-	-	996	999	1001	-	1005	-	-	-	-	1017

Material Name	Volume	Density	Melting Point	Heat of Fusion	Heat of Vaporization	Heat of Sublimation	Electrical Resistivity	Specific Heat	Thermal Conductivity	Thermal Diffusivity	Thermal Linear Expansion	Thermal Absorptance	Thermal Emittance	Thermal Reflectance	Thermal Transmittance	Vapor Pressure
Iodide zirconium	1	–	1099	–	–	–	1102	1104	1106	–	1111	–	–	–	–	–
Iridium (Ir)	1	568	568	–	–	568	570	572	574	–	–	–	576	–	–	–
Iridium + Rhodium	2-I	–	–	–	–	–	–	–	–	–	–	–	–	–	–	248
Iridium (tri-) silicide ($IrSi_3$) . .	6-I	–	–	–	–	–	407	–	–	–	–	–	–	–	–	–
Iron (Fe)	1	578	578	578	–	578	581	583	585	587	589	592	594-600	602	–	604
Iron, Armco	1	578	–	–	–	–	581	583	585	587	589	592	594, 598	602	–	–
Iron, electrolytic	1	–	578	–	–	578	581	583	–	–	589	–	–	–	–	604
Iron, Svea	1	–	–	–	–	–	–	–	585	–	–	–	–	–	–	–
Iron coated with chromium carbide - cobalt blend.	6-II	–	–	–	–	–	–	–	–	–	–	1407	1409	–	–	–
Iron coated with molybdenum . .	6-II	–	–	–	–	–	–	–	–	–	–	1309	1311	–	–	–
Iron coated with tungsten. . . .	6-II	–	–	–	–	–	–	–	–	–	–	1325	1327	–	–	–
Iron coated with tungsten carbide	6-II	–	–	–	–	–	–	–	–	–	–	1421	1423	–	–	–
Iron + ΣX_i	3	461	–	–	–	–	463	–	465	–	–	–	–	–	–	–
Iron + Aluminum + ΣX_i	3	45	–	–	–	–	47-51	–	–	–	–	–	–	–	–	–
Iron + Carbon + ΣX_i (C ≤2.00) .	3	–	–	–	–	3	5	7-10	–	12-14	16-20	–	–	–	–	22
Iron + Carbon + ΣX_i (C >2.00) .	3	27	–	–	–	–	–	–	29-37	–	39-41	–	–	–	–	–
Iron + Chromium + ΣX_i	3	55	53	–	–	–	57-63	65-77	79-83	85-94	96-118	120	122-134	136-138	–	–
Iron + Chromium + Nickel + + ΣX_i	3	140, 145	140-141	–	–	–	147-153	155-164	166-180	182-193	195-227	229-231	233-272	274-286	–	–
Iron + Cobalt + ΣX_i	3	–	–	–	–	–	288-290	292-294	296	298	300	–	–	302	–	–
Iron + Copper + ΣX_i	3	–	–	–	–	–	304	306	308	–	–	–	–	–	–	–
Iron + Manganese + ΣX_i	3	310	–	–	–	–	312-314	316-323	325-327	329-333	335-343	–	345-347	349	–	–
Iron + Molybdenum + ΣX_i . . .	3	–	–	–	–	–	–	–	351	–	353	–	–	–	–	–
Iron + Nickel + ΣX_i	3	–	–	–	–	–	355	357-359	361-363	365	367-377	–	–	–	–	–
Iron + Nickel + Chromium + + ΣX_i	3	379	–	–	–	–	381	383	385-393	395-397	399-407	–	409-411	413	–	–
Iron + Platinum + ΣX_i	3	–	–	–	–	–	–	–	–	–	415	–	–	–	–	–
Iron + Silicon + ΣX_i	3	–	–	–	–	–	417-419	421-425	427-437	–	439-442	–	–	–	–	–
Iron + Tellurium + ΣX_i	3	–	–	–	–	–	–	446	–	–	–	–	–	–	–	–
Iron + Titanium + ΣX_i	3	–	–	–	–	–	–	448	–	–	–	–	–	–	–	–
Iron + Tungsten + ΣX_i	3	–	–	–	–	–	–	–	450	–	452	–	454	–	–	–
Iron + Vanadium + ΣX_i.	3	–	–	–	–	–	456-458	–	–	–	–	–	–	–	–	–
Iron alloys (see cast irons and steels for special design.)																

Material Name	Volume	Density	Melting Point	Heat of Fusion	Heat of Vaporization	Heat of Sublimation	Electrical Resistivity	Specific Heat	Thermal Conductivity	Thermal Diffusivity	Thermal Linear Expansion	Thermal Absorptance	Thermal Emittance	Thermal Reflectance	Thermal Transmittance	Vapor Pressure
Iron aluminates																
$FeO \cdot Al_2O_3$	4-II	-	-	-	-	-	-	999	-	-	-	-	-	-	-	-
$Fe_2O_3 \cdot 2\ Al_2O_3$	4-II	-	-	-	-	-	-	-	-	-	1001	-	-	-	-	-
Iron beryllide ($FeBe_2$)	6-I	-	158	-	-	-	-	-	-	-	-	-	-	-	-	-
Iron borides																
FeB	6-I	-	296	-	-	-	-	-	-	-	-	-	-	-	-	-
Fe_2B	6-I	-	296	-	-	-	-	-	-	-	-	-	-	-	-	-
Iron carbide (Fe_3C)	5	63	63	-	-	-	-	65	-	-	-	-	-	-	-	-
Iron chromites																
$FeO \cdot Cr_2O_3$	4-II	-	-	-	-	-	-	1051	-	-	1053	-	-	-	-	-
$Fe_2O_3 \cdot 2\ Cr_2O_3$	4-II	-	-	-	-	-	-	-	-	-	1053	-	-	-	-	-
Iron cobaltite ($FeO \cdot Co_2O_3$). . .	4-II	-	-	-	-	-	-	1065	-	-	-	-	-	-	-	-
Iron lead silicate glass	4-II	-	-	-	-	-	1737	-	-	-	-	-	-	-	-	-
Iron-niobium intermetallics (Fe_5Nb_3)	6-I	-	684	-	-	-	-	-	-	-	-	-	-	-	-	-
Iron nitride (Fe_4N)	5	-	621	-	-	-	-	-	-	-	-	-	-	-	-	-
Iron oxides																
FeO	4-I	-	-	-	-	-	-	216	-	-	222	-	-	-	-	-
Fe_2O_3	4-I	-	-	-	-	-	214	218	-	-	222	-	-	224	-	-
Fe_3O_4	4-I	212	212	-	-	-	-	220	-	-	-	-	-	-	-	-
Iron(ic) oxide coating on Haynes alloy no. 25 (L-605)	6-II	-	-	-	-	-	-	-	-	-	-	-	1381-1383	-	-	-
Iron(ic) oxide + Aluminum oxide	4-I	-	-	-	-	-	-	-	-	-	713	-	-	-	-	-
Iron(ic) oxide + Magnesium oxide	4-I	-	-	-	-	-	-	-	-	-	717	-	-	-	-	-
Iron(ic) oxide + Silicon (di-) oxide	4-I	-	-	-	-	-	-	719	-	-	-	-	-	-	-	-
Iron(ous) oxide + ΣX_i	4-I	-	-	-	-	-	-	-	-	-	721	-	-	-	-	-
Iron(ous, ic) oxide + Iron(ic) oxide	4-I	-	-	-	-	-	-	-	-	-	-	-	715	-	-	-
Iron phosphites																
Fe_2P	5	-	635	-	-	-	-	-	-	-	-	-	-	-	-	-
Fe_3P	5	-	635	-	-	-	-	-	-	-	-	-	-	-	-	-
Iron selenides																
FeSe	6-I	-	-	-	-	-	-	335	-	-	-	-	-	-	-	-
$FeSe_2$	6-I	-	-	-	-	-	-	335	-	-	-	-	-	-	-	-
Fe_3Se_4	6-I	-	-	-	-	-	-	335	-	-	-	-	-	-	-	-
Fe_7Se_8	6-I	-	-	-	-	-	-	335	-	-	-	-	-	-	-	-
Iron (ortho-) silicate ($2\ FeO \cdot SiO_2$)	4-II	-	-	-	-	-	-	1243	-	-	1245	-	-	-	-	-
Iron silicides																
FeSi	6-I	-	409	-	-	-	411	-	-	-	413	-	-	-	-	-
$FeSi_2$	6-I	-	409	-	-	-	-	-	-	-	413	-	-	-	-	-

Material Name	Volume	Density	Melting Point	Heat of Fusion	Heat of Vaporization	Heat of Sublimation	Electrical Resistivity	Specific Heat	Thermal Conductivity	Thermal Diffusivity	Thermal Linear Expansion	Thermal Absorptance	Thermal Emittance	Thermal Reflectance	Thermal Transmittance	Vapor Pressure
Iron silicides (cont.)																
Fe_3Si	6-I	–	409	–	–	–	–	–	–	–	413	–	–	–	–	–
Fe_5Si_3	6-I	–	409	–	–	–	–	–	–	–	–	–	–	–	–	–
Iron sulfides																
FeS	5	–	–	–	–	–	–	680	–	–	–	–	–	–	–	–
FeS_2	5	–	–	–	–	–	–	680	–	–	–	–	–	682	–	–
Iron tellurides																
FeTe	6-I	–	–	–	–	–	–	590	–	–	–	–	–	–	–	–
$FeTe_2$	6-I	–	–	–	–	–	–	590	–	–	592	–	–	–	–	–
Iron titanate ($FeO \cdot TiO_2$)	4-II	–	1425	1425	–	–	1427	1429	–	–	1431	–	–	–	–	–
Iron titanate coating on niobium-zirconium alloys	6-II	–	–	–	–	–	–	–	–	–	–	–	1385	–	–	–
Iron-zirconium intermetallics																
Fe_2Zr	6-I	–	684	–	–	–	–	–	–	–	–	–	–	–	–	–
Fe_3Zr	6-I	–	684	–	–	–	–	–	–	–	–	–	–	–	–	–
Isobutylene and isoprene copolymer	6-II	–	–	–	–	–	–	–	–	1062	–	–	–	–	–	–
Isocyanate polyester elastomer .	6-II	960	–	–	–	–	–	–	–	–	–	–	–	–	–	–
Isofoam	6-II	962	–	–	–	–	–	–	–	–	966	–	–	–	–	–
K																
Kel-F	6-II	1030	–	–	–	–	–	–	1037	–	1045	–	–	–	–	–
Kennametals																
3047	6-II	–	–	–	–	–	–	–	–	–	934	–	–	–	–	–
3109	6-II	–	–	–	–	–	–	–	–	–	934	–	–	–	–	–
3406	6-II	–	–	–	–	–	–	–	–	–	934	–	–	–	–	–
3411	6-II	–	–	–	–	–	–	–	–	–	934	–	–	–	–	–
K 1	6-II	–	–	–	–	–	–	–	–	–	934	–	–	–	–	–
K2S	6-II	–	–	–	–	–	–	–	889	–	885	–	–	–	–	–
K3H	6-II	–	–	–	–	–	–	–	–	–	881	–	–	–	–	–
K4H	6-II	–	–	–	–	–	–	–	–	–	885	–	–	–	–	–
K5H	6-II	–	–	–	–	–	–	–	–	–	885	–	–	–	–	–
K6	6-II	–	–	–	–	–	–	–	889	–	934	–	–	–	–	–
K7H	6-II	–	–	–	–	–	–	–	–	–	885	–	–	–	–	–
K8	6-II	–	–	–	–	–	–	–	–	–	897	–	–	–	–	–
K9	6-II	–	–	–	–	–	–	–	–	–	934	–	–	–	–	–
K10	2-I	–	–	–	–	–	–	–	–	–	565	–	–	–	–	–
K11	6-II	–	–	–	–	–	–	–	–	–	897	–	–	–	–	–
K21	6-II	–	–	–	–	–	–	–	–	–	883	–	–	–	–	–
K45	6-II	–	–	–	–	–	–	–	–	–	885	–	–	–	–	–
K68	6-II	–	–	–	–	–	–	–	–	–	934	–	–	–	–	–
K81	6-II	–	–	–	–	–	–	–	–	–	881	–	–	–	–	–

Material Name	Volume	Density	Melting Point	Heat of Fusion	Heat of Vaporization	Heat of Sublimation	Electrical Resistivity	Specific Heat	Thermal Conductivity	Thermal Diffusivity	Thermal Linear Expansion	Thermal Absorptance	Thermal Emittance	Thermal Reflectance	Thermal Transmittance	Vapor Pressure
Kennametals (cont.)																
K82	6-II	-	-	-	-	-	-	-	-	-	881	-	-	-	-	-
K84	6-II	-	-	-	-	-	-	-	-	-	881	-	-	-	-	-
K86	6-II	-	-	-	-	-	-	-	-	-	881	-	-	-	-	-
K90	6-II	-	-	-	-	-	-	-	-	-	903	-	-	-	-	-
K91	6-II	-	-	-	-	-	-	-	-	-	903	-	-	-	-	-
K92	6-II	-	-	-	-	-	-	-	-	-	903	-	-	-	-	-
K94	6-II	-	-	-	-	-	-	-	-	-	901	-	-	-	-	-
K95	6-II	-	-	-	-	-	-	-	-	-	899	-	-	-	-	-
K96	6-II	-	-	-	-	-	-	-	-	-	899	-	-	-	-	-
K138	6-II	136	-	-	-	-	-	-	-	-	864	-	-	-	-	-
K138A	6-II	136	-	-	-	-	-	-	-	-	864	-	-	-	-	-
K150A	6-II	-	-	-	-	-	-	-	-	-	875	-	-	-	-	-
K151	6-II	-	-	-	-	-	-	-	-	-	875	-	-	-	-	-
K151A	6-II	-	-	-	-	-	-	-	-	-	875	-	-	-	-	-
K151B	6-II	-	-	-	-	-	-	-	-	-	877	-	-	-	-	-
K152B	6-II	142	-	-	-	-	-	-	-	-	877	-	-	-	-	-
K161B	6-II	-	-	-	-	-	-	871	873	-	875	-	-	-	-	-
K162B	6-II	-	-	-	-	-	-	-	-	-	877	-	-	-	-	-
K601	6-II	-	-	-	-	-	-	-	-	-	860	-	-	-	-	-
K701	6-II	-	-	-	-	-	-	-	-	-	895	-	-	-	-	-
K801	6-II	-	-	-	-	-	-	-	-	-	907	-	-	-	-	-
KM	6-II	-	-	-	-	-	-	-	-	-	883	-	-	-	-	-
Kennametal K-151A coating on AISI 310	6-II	-	-	-	-	-	-	-	-	-	-	-	1491	-	-	-
Kennametal K-162B coating on AISI 310	6-II	-	-	-	-	-	-	-	-	-	-	-	1493	-	-	-
Kennertium W-2	6-II	-	-	-	-	-	-	-	-	-	934	-	-	-	-	-
Kennertium W-10	6-II	-	-	-	-	-	-	-	-	-	934	-	-	-	-	-
Kimble N-51A glass	4-II	-	-	-	-	-	-	-	-	-	-	-	1707	1709	1713	-
Kyanite	4-II	-	-	-	-	-	-	1189	1191	-	1195	-		-	-	-
L																
Lamacoid 6045	6-II	-	-	-	-	-	-	-	-	1230	-	-	-	-	-	-
Lamicoid C-6030	6-II	1130	-	-	-	-	-	1144	-	-	-	-	-	-	-	-
Laminac 4129	6-II	-	-	-	-	-	-	-	-	-	968	-	-	-	-	-
Laminates																
Ceramic	6-II	-	-	-	-	-	-	-	-	-	1225	-	-	-	-	-
Forsterite-stainless steel . .	6-II	-	-	-	-	-	-	-	1223	-	-	-	-	-	-	-
Graphite cloth	6-II	-	-	-	-	-	-	-	-	-	1227	-	-	-	-	-
Reinforced epoxide	6-II	-	-	-	-	-	-	1117	1120	1220	1122-1124	-	-	-	-	-

Material Name	Volume	Density	Melting Point	Heat of Fusion	Heat of Vaporization	Heat of Sublimation	Electrical Resistivity	Specific Heat	Thermal Conductivity	Thermal Diffusivity	Thermal Linear Expansion	Thermal Absorptance	Thermal Emittance	Thermal Reflectance	Thermal Transmittance	Vapor Pressure
Laminates (cont.)																
Reinforced epoxy resin . . .	6-II	-	-	-	-	-	-	1115-1117	1120	1220	1122-1124	-	-	-	-	-
Reinforced epoxy and plyophen copolymer resin	6-II	-	-	-	-	-	-	-	-	1218	-	-	-	-	-	-
Reinforced copolymer of phenolic and epoxide resins .	6-II	-	-	-	-	-	-	-	-	-	1126	-	-	-	-	-
Reinforced melamine-formaldehyde resin.	6-II	-	-	-	-	-	-	-	-	1128	-	-	-	-	-	-
Reinforced phenolic resin . .	6-II	1130	-	-	-	-	-	1132-1146	1148-1156	1159-1170, 1220	1172-1179	-	-	-	-	-
Reinforced phenyl silane resin	6-II	-	-	-	-	-	-	1212	-	1220	-	-	-	-	-	-
Reinforced polyester resin. .	6-II	1180	-	-	-	-	-	1191	1195-1198	1220	1200	-	-	-	-	-
Reinforced TAC polyester resin	6-II	1180	-	-	-	-	-	1183	1185	1220	1187-1189	-	-	-	-	-
Reinforced polytetrafluoro-ethylene	6-II	-	-	-	-	-	-	1214	1218	1220	-	-	-	-	-	-
Reinforced silicone resin . .	6-II	1204	-	-	-	-	-	1206	1208, 1218	1220	1200	-	-	-	-	-
Reinforced teflon	6-II	-	-	-	-	-	-	1214	1218	1220	-	-	-	-	-	-
Lampblacks																
Lampblack	1	-	-	-	-	-	-	-	97	-	-	-	99-101	103	-	-
CEP National	1	-	-	-	-	-	-	-	-	-	-	-	-	103	-	-
L 113SP	1	-	-	-	-	-	-	-	-	-	-	-	101	103	-	-
RW Spektral II	1	-	-	-	-	-	-	-	-	-	-	-	-	103	-	-
Lanthana	4-I	226	226	-	-	-	-	228	-	-	230	-	-	-	-	232
Lanthanum (La)	1	606	606	606	606	606	608	610	-	-	612	-	-	-	-	614
Lanthanum + Calcium	2-I	-	250	-	-	-	-	-	-	-	-	-	-	-	-	-
Lanthanum + Magnesium	2-I	252	-	-	-	-	-	-	-	-	-	-	-	-	-	-
Lanthanum + Magnesium + ΣX_i .	2-II	1022	1022	-	-	-	-	-	-	-	-	-	-	-	-	-
Lanthanum aluminides																
LaAl	6-I	43	43	-	-	-	-	-	-	-	-	-	-	-	-	-
$LaAl_2$	6-I	43	43	-	-	-	-	-	-	-	-	-	-	-	-	-
$LaAl_4$	6-I	43	43	-	-	-	-	-	-	-	-	-	-	-	-	-
La_3Al_2	6-I	-	43	-	-	-	-	-	-	-	-	-	-	-	-	-
Lanthanum antimonide																
La_2Sb	6-I	-	81	-	-	-	-	-	-	-	-	-	-	-	-	-
La_3Sb_2	6-I	-	81	-	-	-	-	-	-	-	-	-	-	-	-	-
Lanthanum arsenide (LaAs) . .	6-I	94	-	-	-	-	-	-	-	-	-	-	-	-	-	-
Lanthanum-bismuth intermetallics (LaBi)	6-I	667	-	-	-	-	-	-	-	-	-	-	-	-	-	-

Material Name	Volume	Density	Melting Point	Heat of Fusion	Heat of Vaporization	Heat of Sublimation	Electrical Resistivity	Specific Heat	Thermal Conductivity	Thermal Diffusivity	Thermal Linear Expansion	Thermal Absorptance	Thermal Emittance	Thermal Reflectance	Thermal Transmittance	Vapor Pressure
Lanthanum borides																
LaB_4	6-I	295	296	–	–	–	–	–	–	–	–	–	–	–	–	–
LaB_6	6-I	295	296	–	–	–	300	–	–	–	302	–	–	–	–	–
Lanthanum bromide ($LaBr_3$) . .	5	11	–	–	–	–	–	–	–	–	–	–	–	–	–	–
Lanthanum-cadmium intermetallics																
LaCd	6-I	667	–	–	–	–	–	–	–	–	–	–	–	–	–	–
$LaCd_2$	6-I	667	–	–	–	–	–	–	–	–	–	–	–	–	–	–
$LaCd_{11}$	6-I	667	–	–	–	–	–	–	–	–	–	–	–	–	–	–
Lanthanum carbides																
LaC_2	5	294	–	–	–	–	–	–	–	–	–	–	–	–	–	–
La_2C_3	5	294	–	–	–	–	–	–	–	–	–	–	–	–	–	–
Lanthanum chloride ($LaCl_3$) . .	5	339	–	–	–	–	–	–	–	–	–	–	–	–	–	–
Lanthanum-copper intermetallics																
LaCu	6-I	667-668	668	–	–	–	–	–	–	–	–	–	–	–	–	–
$LaCu_2$	6-I	667-668	668	–	–	–	–	–	–	–	–	–	–	–	–	–
$LaCu_4$	6-I	–	668	–	–	–	–	–	–	–	–	–	–	–	–	–
$LaCu_5$	6-I	667	–	–	–	–	–	–	–	–	–	–	–	–	–	–
$LaCu_6$	6-I	–	668	–	–	–	–	–	–	–	–	–	–	–	–	–
Lanthanum fluoride (LaF_3) . . .	5	–	407	–	–	–	–	–	–	–	–	–	–	–	–	–
Lanthanum-gallium intermetallics ($LaGa_2$)	6-I	667	–	–	–	–	–	–	–	–	–	–	–	–	–	–
Lanthanum germanides ($LaGe_2$) .	6-I	323	–	–	–	–	–	–	–	–	–	–	–	–	–	–
Lanthanum-gold intermetallics																
LaAu	6-I	667-668	668	–	–	–	–	–	–	–	–	–	–	–	–	–
$LaAu_2$	6-I	–	668	–	–	–	–	–	–	–	–	–	–	–	–	–
$LaAu_3$	6-I	667	668	–	–	–	–	–	–	–	–	–	–	–	–	–
La_2Au	6-I	667	668	–	–	–	–	–	–	–	–	–	–	–	–	–
La_3Au	6-I	668	–	–	–	–	–	–	–	–	–	–	–	–	–	–
Lanthanum hydride (LaH_2) . . .	5	427	–	–	–	–	–	–	–	–	–	–	–	–	–	–
Lanthanum-indium intermetallics ($LaIn_3$)	6-I	667	–	–	–	–	–	–	–	–	–	–	–	–	–	–
Lanthanum-lead intermetallics																
LaPb	6-I	–	668	–	–	–	–	–	–	–	–	–	–	–	–	–
$LaPb_3$	6-I	667	668	–	–	–	–	–	–	–	–	–	–	–	–	–
La_2Pb	6-I	–	668	–	–	–	–	–	–	–	–	–	–	–	–	–
Lanthanum-magnesium intermetallics																
LaMg	6-I	667	668	–	–	–	–	–	–	–	–	–	–	–	–	–
$LaMg_3$	6-I	–	668	–	–	–	–	–	–	–	–	–	–	–	–	–
$LaMg_9$	6-I	–	668	–	–	–	–	–	–	–	–	–	–	–	–	–
La_4Mg	6-I	–	668	–	–	–	–	–	–	–	–	–	–	–	–	–

Material Name	Volume	Density	Melting Point	Heat of Fusion	Heat of Vaporization	Heat of Sublimation	Electrical Resistivity	Specific Heat	Thermal Conductivity	Thermal Diffusivity	Thermal Linear Expansion	Thermal Absorptance	Thermal Emittance	Thermal Reflectance	Thermal Transmittance	Vapor Pressure
Lanthanum-mercury intermetallics																
LaHg	6-I	667	–	–	–	–	–	–	–	–	–	–	–	–	–	–
$LaHg_2$	6-I	667	–	–	–	–	–	–	–	–	–	–	–	–	–	–
$LaHg_3$	6-I	667	–	–	–	–	–	–	–	–	–	–	–	–	–	–
Lanthanum-nickel intermetallics ($LaNi_5$)	6-I	667	–	–	–	–	–	–	–	–	–	–	–	–	–	–
Lanthanum nitride (LaN)	5	621	–	–	–	–	–	–	–	–	–	–	–	–	–	–
Lanthanum-osmium intermetallics ($LaOs_2$)	6-I	667	–	–	–	–	–	–	–	–	–	–	–	–	–	–
Lanthanum oxides																
LaO	4-I	226	–	–	–	–	–	–	–	–	–	–	–	–	–	–
La_2O_3	4-I	226	226	–	–	–	–	228	–	–	230	–	–	–	–	232
Lanthanum phosphide (LaP) . .	5	635	–	–	–	–	–	–	–	–	–	–	–	–	–	–
Lanthanum selenides																
LaSe	6-I	365	–	–	–	–	–	–	–	–	–	–	–	–	–	–
La_2Se_3	6-I	365	–	–	–	–	367	–	–	–	–	–	–	–	–	–
La_3Se_4	6-I	365	–	–	–	–	–	–	–	–	–	–	–	–	–	–
Lanthanum silicides ($LaSi_2$) . .	6-I	415	415	–	–	–	527	–	–	–	417	–	–	–	–	–
Lanthanum-silver intermetallics																
LaAg	6-I	667-668	668	–	–	–	–	–	–	–	–	–	–	–	–	–
$LaAg_2$	6-I	667-668	668	–	–	–	–	–	–	–	–	–	–	–	–	–
$LaAg_3$	6-I	667-668	668	–	–	–	–	–	–	–	–	–	–	–	–	–
Lanthanum stannides																
$LaSn_3$	6-I	541	541	–	–	–	–	–	–	–	–	–	–	–	–	–
La_2Sn	6-I	–	541	–	–	–	–	–	–	–	–	–	–	–	–	–
La_2Sn_3	6-I	–	541	–	–	–	–	–	–	–	–	–	–	–	–	–
Lanthanum sulfides																
LaS	5	684	684	–	–	–	–	–	–	–	686	–	–	–	–	–
LaS_2	5	684	–	–	–	–	–	–	–	–	–	–	–	–	–	–
La_2S_3	5	684	684	–	–	–	–	–	–	–	686	–	–	–	–	–
La_3S_4	5	684	684	–	–	–	–	–	–	–	–	–	–	–	–	–
Lanthanum telluride (La_2Te_3) .	6-I	–	–	–	–	–	638	–	–	–	–	–	–	–	–	–
Lanthanum-thallium intermetallics																
LaTl	6-I	–	669	–	–	–	–	–	–	–	–	–	–	–	–	–
$LaTl_3$	6-I	667	669	–	–	–	–	–	–	–	–	–	–	–	–	–
La_2Tl	6-I	–	669	–	–	–	–	–	–	–	–	–	–	–	–	–
Lanthanum-zinc intermetallics																
LaZn	6-I	667	–	–	–	–	–	–	–	–	–	–	–	–	–	–
$LaZn_5$	6-I	667	–	–	–	–	–	–	–	–	–	–	–	–	–	–

Material Name	Volume	Density	Melting Point	Heat of Fusion	Heat of Vaporization	Heat of Sublimation	Electrical Resistivity	Specific Heat	Thermal Conductivity	Thermal Diffusivity	Thermal Linear Expansion	Thermal Absorptance	Thermal Emittance	Thermal Reflectance	Thermal Transmittance	Vapor Pressure
Lanthanum-zinc intermetallics (cont.)																
$LaZn_{11}$	6-I	667	–	–	–	–	–	–	–	–	–	–	–	–	–	–
Lawsonite	4-II	–	–	–	–	–	–	1233	–	–	–	–	–	–	–	–
Lead + Copper	2-I	254	–	–	–	–	–	–	–	–	256	–	–	–	–	–
Lead aluminate ($PbO \cdot Al_2O_3$) . .	4-II	–	–	–	–	–	–	–	–	–	1003	–	–	–	–	–
Lead borate glass	4-II	–	–	–	–	–	–	–	–	–	1615	–	–	–	–	–
Lead borosilicate glass	4-II	–	–	–	–	–	–	–	–	–	1717	–	–	–	–	–
Lead-barium magnesium aluminum silicate	4-II	–	–	–	–	–	–	–	–	–	1256-1258	–	–	–	–	–
Lead boron silicate ($5\ PbO \cdot B_2O_3 \cdot SiO_2$)	4-II	–	–	–	–	–	–	–	–	–	1250	–	–	–	–	–
Lead germanium oxide ($2\ PbO \cdot GeO_2$)	4-II	–	–	–	–	–	–	–	–	–	1133	–	–	–	–	–
Lead germanium phosphate ($5\ PbO \cdot GeO_2 \cdot P_2O_5$)	4-II	–	–	–	–	–	–	–	–	–	1175	–	–	–	–	–
Lead magnesium aluminum silicate	4-II	–	–	–	–	–	–	–	–	–	1252-1254	–	–	–	–	–
Lead molybdate ($PbO_2 \cdot MoO_2$). .	4-II	–	–	–	–	–	–	1113	–	–	1115	–	–	–	–	–
Lead (mon-) oxide (PbO). . . .	4-I	–	–	–	–	–	–	234	–	–	–	–	–	–	–	–
Lead phosphates																
$PbO \cdot P_2O_5$	4-II	–	–	–	–	–	–	–	–	–	1171	–	–	–	–	–
$2\ PbO \cdot P_2O_5$	4-II	–	–	–	–	–	–	–	–	–	1171	–	–	–	–	–
$3\ PbO \cdot P_2O_5$	4-II	–	–	–	–	–	–	–	–	–	1171	–	–	–	–	–
$3\ PbO \cdot 2\ P_2O_5$	4-II	–	–	–	–	–	–	–	–	–	1171	–	–	–	–	–
$5\ PbO \cdot 2\ P_2O_5$	4-II	–	–	–	–	–	–	–	–	–	1171	–	–	–	–	–
$8\ PbO \cdot P_2O_5$	4-II	–	–	–	–	–	–	–	–	–	1171	–	–	–	–	–
Lead potassium silicate glass. .	4-II	–	–	–	–	–	–	–	–	1749	–	–	–	–	–	–
Lead silicates																
$PbO \cdot SiO_2$	4-II	–	–	–	–	–	–	–	–	–	1247	–	–	–	–	–
$2\ PbO \cdot SiO_2$	4-II	–	–	–	–	–	–	–	–	–	1247	–	–	–	–	–
$4\ PbO \cdot SiO_2$	4-II	–	–	–	–	–	–	–	–	–	1247	–	–	–	–	–
Lead silicate glass	4-II	–	–	–	–	–	1739	–	1741	–	–	–	1743	1745	1747	–
Lead silicon phosphate ($5\ PbO \cdot SiO_2 \cdot P_2O_5$)	4-II	–	–	–	–	–	–	–	–	–	1177	–	–	–	–	–
Lead strontium silicate glass . .	4-II	–	–	–	–	–	–	–	–	–	1751	–	–	–	–	–
Lead sulfide (PbS)	5	–	–	–	–	–	–	–	–	–	–	–	–	688	–	–
Lead telluride (PbTe)	6-I	–	–	–	–	–	594	–	596	–	–	–	–	–	–	–
Lead telluride + Tin telluride . .	6-I	–	–	–	–	–	717	–	–	–	–	–	–	–	–	–
Lead (meta-) titanate ($PbO \cdot TiO_2$)	4-II	–	–	–	–	–	–	–	1433	–	1435	–	–	–	–	–
Lead tungstate ($PbO \cdot WO_3$) . . .	4-II	–	–	–	–	–	–	1474	–	–	1476	–	–	–	–	–
Lead zirconate ($PbO \cdot ZrO_2$) . .	4-II	–	–	–	–	–	–	–	1510	–	–	–	–	–	–	–
Leonhardite	4-II	–	–	–	–	–	–	1233	–	–	–	–	–	–	–	–

Material Name	Volume	Density	Melting Point	Heat of Fusion	Heat of Vaporization	Heat of Sublimation	Electrical Resistivity	Specific Heat	Thermal Conductivity	Thermal Diffusivity	Thermal Linear Expansion	Thermal Absorptance	Thermal Emittance	Thermal Reflectance	Thermal Transmittance	Vapor Pressure
Libbey-Owens-Ford plate glass no. 9330	4-II	–	–	–	–	–	–	1791	–	–	–	–	–	–	–	–
Lime	4-I	99	99	–	–	–	101	103	105	–	107	–	–	–	–	109
Lime window glass	4-II	–	–	–	–	–	–	–	1831	–	–	–	–	–	–	–
Lithium + Sodium	2-I	–	–	–	–	–	–	–	–	258	–	–	–	–	–	–
Lithium aluminates																
$Li_2O \cdot Al_2O_3$	4-II	–	–	–	–	–	–	–	–	–	1005	–	–	–	–	–
$Li_2O \cdot 5\ Al_2O_3$	4-II	–	–	–	–	–	–	–	–	–	1005	–	–	–	–	–
Lithium aluminum borate glass .	4-II	–	–	–	–	–	–	–	–	–	1617	–	–	–	–	–
Lithium aluminum fluoride (Li_3AlF_6)	5	–	–	–	–	–	–	377	–	–	–	–	–	–	–	–
Lithium aluminum silicate																
$Li_2O \cdot Al_2O_3 \cdot 3\ SiO_2$	4-II	–	–	–	–	–	–	–	–	–	1275	–	–	–	–	–
$Li_2O \cdot Al_2O_3 \cdot 2\ SiO_2$	4-II	–	–	–	–	–	–	–	–	–	1268-1270	–	–	–	–	–
$Li_2O \cdot 1.08\ Al_2O_3 \cdot 3.5\ SiO_2$ . .	4-II	–	–	–	–	–	–	–	–	–	1268	–	–	–	–	–
$Li_2O \cdot Al_2O_3 \cdot 4\ SiO_2$	4-II	–	–	–	–	–	–	–	–	–	1268-1270	–	–	–	–	–
$Li_2O \cdot Al_2O_3 \cdot 6\ SiO_2$	4-II	–	–	–	–	–	–	–	–	–	1268-1270	–	–	–	–	–
$Li_2O \cdot Al_2O_3 \cdot 8\ SiO_2$	4-II	–	–	–	–	–	–	–	–	–	1268, 1275	–	–	–	–	–
$Li_2O \cdot Al_2O_3 \cdot 10\ SiO_2$	4-II	–	–	–	–	–	–	–	–	–	1275	–	–	–	–	–
Lithium aluminum silicate + + Lead bisilicate	4-II	–	–	–	–	–	–	–	–	–	1566	–	–	–	–	–
Lithium aluminum silicate + + Lead borate	4-II	–	–	–	–	–	–	–	–	–	1560	–	–	–	–	–
Lithium aluminum silicate + + Lithium aluminum germanium oxide	4-II	–	–	–	–	–	–	–	–	–	1568	–	–	–	–	–
Lithium aluminum silicate bodies, barium modified	4-II	–	–	–	–	–	–	–	–	–	1277-1281	–	–	–	–	–
Lithium aluminum silicate glass.	4-II	–	–	–	–	–	–	–	–	–	1757-1759	–	–	–	–	–
Lithium beryllium borate glass .	4-II	–	–	–	–	–	–	–	–	–	1619	–	–	–	–	–
Lithium beryllium fluoride (Li_2BeF_4)	5	–	–	–	–	–	–	379	–	–	–	–	–	–	–	–
Lithium (meta-)borate ($Li_2O \cdot B_2O_3$)	4-II	–	–	–	–	1041	–	–	–	–	–	–	–	–	–	1043
Lithium borate glass	4-II	–	–	–	–	–	1607	–	–	–	–	–	–	–	–	–
Lithium borosilicate glass . . .	4-II	–	–	–	–	–	–	–	–	–	1719	–	–	–	–	–
Lithium calcium silicate glass .	4-II	–	–	–	–	–	–	–	–	–	1761	–	–	–	–	–
Lithium carbide (Li_4C_2)	5	294	–	–	–	–	–	–	–	–	–	–	–	–	–	–
Lithium chloride (LiCl and Li_2Cl_2)	5	317	317	–	317	317	–	–	–	–	–	–	–	–	–	319
Lithium cobalt oxide ($Li_XCo_{1-X}O$)	4-II	–	–	–	–	–	1135	–	–	–	–	–	–	–	–	–

Material Name	Volume	Density	Melting Point	Heat of Fusion	Heat of Vaporization	Heat of Sublimation	Electrical Resistivity	Specific Heat	Thermal Conductivity	Thermal Diffusivity	Thermal Linear Expansion	Thermal Absorptance	Thermal Emittance	Thermal Reflectance	Thermal Transmittance	Vapor Pressure
Lithium cobalt nickel oxide $[Li_x(Co_yNi_{1-y})_{1-x}O]$	4-II	–	–	–	–	–	1137	–	1139	–	–	–	–	–	–	–
Lithium copper oxide ($Li_xCu_{1-x}O$)	4-II	–	–	–	–	–	1141	–	1143	–	–	–	–	–	–	–
Lithium fluoride (LiF and Li_2F_2)	5	369	369	369	369	369	–	–	371	–	–	–	–	373	–	375
Lithium fluoride + Potassium fluoride	5	–	–	–	–	–	–	409	–	–	–	–	–	–	–	–
Lithium germanium oxides																
$Li_2O \cdot GeO_2$	4-II	–	–	–	–	–	–	–	–	–	1145	–	–	–	–	–
$Li_2O \cdot 7\ GeO_2$	4-II	–	–	–	–	–	–	–	–	–	1145	–	–	–	–	–
$2\ Li_2O \cdot GeO_2$	4-II	–	–	–	–	–	–	–	–	–	1145	–	–	–	–	–
$3\ Li_2O \cdot 2\ GeO_2$	4-II	–	–	–	–	–	–	–	–	–	1145	–	–	–	–	–
$3\ Li_2O \cdot 8\ GeO_2$	4-II	–	–	–	–	–	–	–	–	–	1145	–	–	–	–	–
Lithium hydride (LiH)	5	431	431	431	431	–	–	433	435	–	437	–	–	–	–	–
Lithium lead silicate glass . . .	4-II	–	–	–	–	–	1763		–	–	–	–	–	–	–	–
Lithium-magnesium-barium silicate glass	4-II	–	–	–	–	–	1765		–	–	–	–	–	–	–	–
Lithium magnesium borate glass	4-II	–	–	–	–	–	–	–	–		1621	–	–	–	–	–
Lithium manganese oxide ($Li_xMn_{1-x}O$)	4-II	–	–	–	–	–	1147	–	–	–	–	–	–	–	–	–
Lithium manganese selenide ($Li_xMn_{1-x}Se$)	6-I	–	–	–	–	–	337	–	339	–	–	–	–	–	–	–
Lithium nickel oxide ($Li_xNi_{1-x}O$)	6-II	–	–	–	–	–	1149	–	1151	–	–	–	–	–	–	–
Lithium nitride (Li_3N)	5	621	–	621	621	–	–	–	–	–	–	–	–	–	–	–
Lithium oxide (Li_2O).	4-I	236	236	236	236	236	–	238	–	–	–	–	–	–	–	240
Lithium potassium aluminum silicate	4-II	–	–	–	–	–	–	–	–	–	1283	–	–	–	–	–
Lithium silicates																
$Li_2O \cdot 2\ SiO_2$	4-II	–	–	–	–	–	–	–	–	–	1260	–	–	–	–	–
$2\ Li_2O \cdot SiO_2$	4-II	–	–	–	–	–	–	–	–	–	1260	–	–	–	–	–
Lithium silicate glass	4-II	–	–	–	–	–	1753	–	–	–	1755	–	–	–	–	–
Lithium silicate - quartz body . .	4-II	–	–	–	–	–	–	–	–	–	1262-1264	–	–	–	–	–
Lithium sodium silicate glass .	4-II	–	–	–	–	–	1767	–	–	–	–	–	–	–	–	–
Lithium titanate ($Li_2O \cdot TiO_2$) . .	4-II	–	–	–	–	–	–	1437	–	–	–	–	–	–	–	–
Lithium uranate ($Li_2O \cdot UO_3$) . .	4-II	–	1482	–	–	–	–	–	–	–	–	–	–	–	–	–
Lithium zinc ferrite ($Li_xZn_{0.9}Fe_{2.1-x}O_4$)	4-II	–	–	–	–	–	–	1101	–	–	–	–	–	–	–	–
Lockfoam	6-II	962	–	–	–	–	–	–	–	–	966	–	–	–	–	–
Lohm	2-I	–	–	–	–	–	–	–	138	–	–	–	–	–	–	–
LT-1 Metamic cermet	6-II	731	–	–	–	–	–	–	–	–	–	–	735	–	–	–
LT-1B Haynes cermet	6-II	–	–	–	–	–	–	–	–	–	739	–	747	–	–	–
LT-2 Haynes cermet.	6-II	–	–	–	–	–	–	–	–	–	743	–	745	–	–	–
Lucalox	4-I	–	–	–	–	–	–	–	11	–	22	–	32	–	–	–
Lucite	6-II	1020	–	–	–	–	–	–	1024	–	–	–	–	–	–	–

Material Name	Volume	Density	Melting Point	Heat of Fusion	Heat of Vaporization	Heat of Sublimation	Electrical Resistivity	Specific Heat	Thermal Conductivity	Thermal Diffusivity	Thermal Linear Expansion	Thermal Absorptance	Thermal Emittance	Thermal Reflectance	Thermal Transmittance	Vapor Pressure
Lustrex L-2020	6-II	–	1076	–	–	–	–	–	–	–	–	–	–	–	–	–
Lutecium (Lu)	1	616	616	616	616	616	618	620	–	–	–	–	–	–	–	–
Lutecium borides																
LuB_4	6-I	295	–	–	–	–	–	–	–	–	–	–	–	–	–	–
LuB_6	6-I	295	–	–	–	–	–	–	–	–	–	–	–	–	–	–
Lutecium carbide (LuC_2)	5	294	–	–	–	–	–	–	–	–	–	–	–	–	–	–
Lutecium-osmium intermetallics ($LuOs_2$)	6-I	680	–	–	–	–	–	–	–	–	–	–	–	–	–	–
Lutecium oxide (Lu_2O_3).	4-I	–	–	–	–	–	–	242	–	–	244	–	246	–	–	–
M																
Magnesia-alumina spinel. . . .	4-II	–	–	–	–	–	–	–	–	1015	–	–	–	–	–	–
Magnesium (Mg)	1	622	622	622	–	622	624	626	628	630	632	–	634	636-638	–	640
Magnesium + ΣX_i	2-II	–	–	–	–	–	1071-1075	1077	1079	–	1081	–	–	–	–	–
Magnesium + Aluminum + ΣX_i .	2-II	1024	1024	1024	–	–	1026	1029	1031	1033	1035	–	–	1038-1042	–	–
Magnesium + Cerium	2-I	–	–	–	–	–	–	–	260	–	–	–	–	–	–	–
Magnesium + Cerium + ΣX_i. . .	2-II	–	–	–	–	–	–	–	1045	–	–	–	–	–	–	–
Magnesium + Thorium	2-I	264	262	262	–	–	–	–	–	–	–	–	–	–	–	–
Magnesium + Thorium + ΣX_i . .	2-II	–	1047	1047	–	–	1049-1053	1055	1057	–	1059	–	–	1061	–	–
Magnesium + Zinc	2-I	–	266	–	–	–	–	–	–	–	–	–	–	–	–	–
Magnesium + Zinc + ΣX_i	2-II	–	1063	1063	–	–	–	1065	1067	–	1069	–	–	–	–	–
Magnesium L120 (British aircraft material spec.).	1	–	–	–	–	–	–	–	–	–	–	–	–	636	–	–
Magnesium alloys (special designation)																
1959	2-I	–	–	–	–	–	–	–	260	–	–	–	–	–	–	–
1960	2-I	–	–	–	–	–	–	–	260	–	–	–	–	–	–	–
1961	2-I	–	–	–	–	–	–	–	260	–	–	–	–	–	–	–
1964	2-II	–	–	–	–	–	–	–	1045	–	–	–	–	–	–	–
1992	2-II	–	–	–	–	–	–	–	1045	–	–	–	–	–	–	–
AM-100A	2-II	–	–	–	–	–	1026	–	–	–	–	–	–	–	–	–
AN-M-29	2-II	1024	–	–	–	–	–	1029	1031	1033	1035	–	–	–	–	–
AX-81-X1	2-II	–	–	–	–	–	–	–	–	–	1035	–	–	–	–	–
AZ-31	2-II	–	–	–	–	–	–	–	–	–	–	–	–	1038	–	–
AZ-31A	2-II	–	1024	1024	–	–	1026	–	–	–	1035	–	–	1040	–	–
AZ-31B	2-II	–	1024	1024	–	–	1026	1029	–	–	1035	–	–	1040-1042	–	–
AZ-63A	2-II	–	–	–	–	–	1026	–	–	–	1035	–	–	–	–	–
AZ-80	2-II	–	–	–	–	–	–	1029	–	–	–	–	–	–	–	–
AZ-81	2-II	–	–	–	–	–	–	–	–	–	1035	–	–	–	–	–

Material Name	Volume	Density	Melting Point	Heat of Fusion	Heat of Vaporization	Heat of Sublimation	Electrical Resistivity	Specific Heat	Thermal Conductivity	Thermal Diffusivity	Thermal Linear Expansion	Thermal Absorptance	Thermal Emittance	Thermal Reflectance	Thermal Transmittance	Vapor Pressure
Magnesium alloys (special designation) (cont.)																
AZ-91C	2-II	–	–	–	–	–	1026	–	–	–	–	–	–	–	–	–
AZ-92A	2-II	–	–	–	–	–	1026	–	–	–	1035	–	–	–	–	–
DTD 350	2-II	–	–	–	–	–	–	–	1079	–	–	–	–	–	–	–
DTD 360	2-II	–	–	–	–	–	–	–	1079	–	–	–	–	–	–	–
EK-30	2-II	–	–	–	–	–	–	–	–	–	1081	–	–	–	–	–
EK-30A	2-II	–	–	–	–	–	1071	–	–	–	–	–	–	–	–	–
EK-32A	2-II	–	–	–	–	–	–	–	–	–	1081	–	–	–	–	–
EK-33A	2-II	–	–	–	–	–	–	–	–	–	1081	–	–	–	–	–
EK-41	2-II	–	–	–	–	–	–	–	–	–	1081	–	–	–	–	–
EK-41A	2-II	–	–	–	–	–	1073	–	–	–	–	–	–	–	–	–
EZ-33A	2-II	–	–	–	–	–	1075	–	–	–	1081	–	–	–	–	–
H-807	2-II	–	–	–	–	–	–	–	1067	–	–	–	–	–	–	–
H-809	2-II	–	–	–	–	–	–	–	1031	–	–	–	–	–	–	–
H-811	2-II	–	–	–	–	–	–	–	1045, 1067	–	–	–	–	–	–	–
H-812	2-II	–	–	–	–	–	–	–	1045	–	–	–	–	–	–	–
H-817	2-II	–	–	–	–	–	–	–	1067	–	–	–	–	–	–	–
HK-31	2-II	–	–	–	–	–	–	–	–	–	1059	–	–	–	–	–
HK-31A	2-II	–	1047	1047	–	–	1049	1055	–	–	–	–	–	1061	–	–
HK-31XA	2-II	–	–	–	–	–	1049	–	–	–	1059	–	–	–	–	–
HM-21XA	2-II	–	1047	1047	–	–	1051	1055	–	–	–	–	–	–	–	–
HM-31XA	2-I	–	262	262	–	–	–	–	–	–	–	–	–	–	–	–
. . . . . .	2-II	–	–	–	–	–	–	1077	–	–	–	–	–	–	–	–
Hydronalium 71	2-II	–	–	–	–	–	1026	–	1031	–	–	–	–	–	–	–
HZ-32A	2-II	–	–	–	–	–	1053	–	–	–	–	–	–	–	–	–
HZ-32XA	2-II	–	–	–	–	–	1053	–	–	–	1059	–	–	–	–	–
Magnox B	2-II	–	–	–	–	–	–	–	1079	–	–	–	–	–	–	–
MSR	2-II	–	–	–	–	–	–	–	1079	–	–	–	–	–	–	–
RZ5	2-II	–	–	–	–	–	–	–	1067	–	–	–	–	–	–	–
TZ6	2-II	–	–	–	–	–	–	–	1067	–	–	–	–	–	–	–
Z3Z	2-II	–	–	–	–	–	–	–	1067	–	–	–	–	–	–	–
ZK-60	2-II	–	1063	1063	–	–	–	–	–	–	–	–	–	–	–	–
ZK-60A	2-II	–	–	–	–	–	–	1065	–	–	1069	–	–	–	–	–
ZREO	2-II	–	–	–	–	–	–	–	1045	–	–	–	–	–	–	–
ZT1	2-II	–	–	–	–	–	–	–	1057	–	–	–	–	–	–	–
ZTY	2-II	–	–	–	–	–	–	–	1057	–	–	–	–	–	–	–
Magnesium aluminate ($MgO \cdot Al_2O_3$)	4-II	1007	1007	–	–	–	1009	1011	1013	1015	1017	–	–	–	–	–
Magnesium aluminate + + Magnesium oxide	4-II	–	–	–	–	–	–	–	1520	–	1522	–	–	–	–	–

Material Name	Volume	Density	Melting Point	Heat of Fusion	Heat of Vaporization	Heat of Sublimation	Electrical Resistivity	Specific Heat	Thermal Conductivity	Thermal Diffusivity	Thermal Linear Expansion	Thermal Absorptance	Thermal Emittance	Thermal Reflectance	Thermal Transmittance	Vapor Pressure
Magnesium aluminate + Silicon (di-) oxide	4-II	–	–	–	–	–	–	–	1532	–	–	–	–	–	–	–
Magnesium aluminate + Sodium (mon-) oxide	4-II	–	–	–	–	–	–	1524	1526	1528	1530	–	–	–	–	–
Magnesium aluminate spinal . .	4-II	1007	1007	–	–	–	1009	1011	1013	1015	1017	–	–	–	–	–
Magnesium aluminate spinel with sodium (mon-) oxide . . .	4-II	–	–	–	–	–	–	1524	1526	1528	1530	–	–	–	–	–
Magnesium aluminum borate glass	4-II	–	–	–	–	–	–	–	–	–	1623	–	–	–	–	–
Magnesium aluminum silicate ($2\ MgO \cdot 2\ Al_2O_3 \cdot 5\ SiO_2$) . . .	4-II	–	–	–	–	–	1298	1300	1302	–	1304-1308	–	–	–	–	–
Magnesium aluminum silicate bodies	4-II	–	–	–	–	–	–	–	–	–	1310	–	–	–	–	–
Magnesium aluminum silicate glass	4-II	–	–	–	–	–	–	–	–	–	1769	–	–	–	–	–
Magnesium antimonide (Mg_3Sb_2).	6-I	–	–	–	–	–	67	–	–	–	–	–	–	–	–	–
Magnesium barium cerium titanate [$(Ba_{1-x-y}Mg_xCe_y)O \cdot TiO_2$]	4-II	–	–	–	–	–	1447	–	–	–	–	–	–	–	–	–
Magnesium barium titanate . . .	4-II	–	–	–	–	–	–	–	–	–	1445	–	–	–	–	–
Magnesium beryllium borate glass	4-II	–	–	–	–	–	–	–	–	–	1625	–	–	–	–	–
Magnesium borides																
MgB_2	6-I	–	–	–	–	–	–	182	–	–	–	–	–	–	–	184
MgB_4	6-I	–	–	–	–	–	–	182	–	–	–	–	–	–	–	–
Magnesium-cadmium intermetallics																
MgCd	6-I	–	–	–	–	–	–	644	–	–	–	–	–	–	–	–
$MgCd_3$	6-I	–	–	–	–	–	–	644	–	–	–	–	–	–	–	–
Mg_3Cd	6-I	–	–	–	–	–	–	644	–	–	–	–	–	–	–	–
Magnesium carbonate ($MgCO_3$) .	4-II	–	–	–	–	–	–	–	–	–	–	–	–	1047	–	–
Magnesium chloride ($MgCl_2$) . .	5	–	321	–	–	323	–	–	–	–	–	–	–	–	–	325
Magnesium chromites																
$MgO \cdot Cr_2O_3$	4-II	–	–	–	–	–	1055	1057	–	–	1059	–	–	–	–	–
$MgO \cdot 4\ Cr_2O_3$	4-II	–	–	–	–	–	1055	–	–	–	–	–	–	–	–	–
$4\ MgO \cdot Cr_2O_3$	4-II	–	–	–	–	–	1055	–	–	–	–	–	–	–	–	–
Magnesium chromite spinal . .	4-II	–	–	–	–	–	–	–	–	–	1059	–	–	–	–	–
Magnesium ferrites																
$MgO \cdot Fe_2O_3$	4-II	–	–	–	–	–	1079	1081	–	–	1083	–	–	–	–	–
$MgO \cdot 2\ FeO$	4-II	–	–	–	–	–	–	–	–	–	1083	–	–	–	–	–
Magnesium fluoride (MgF_2). . .	5	–	381	–	–	383	–	–	–	–	385	–	–	–	–	387
Magnesium fluoride coating on quartz	6-II	–	–	–	–	–	–	–	–	–	–	–	–	1425	1427	–
Magnesium germanide (Mg_2Ge) .	6-I	309	309	–	–	–	311	–	–	–	–	–	–	–	–	–
Magnesium hydride (MgH_2). . .	5	467	–	–	–	–	–	–	–	–	–	–	–	–	–	–

Material Name	Volume	Density	Melting Point	Heat of Fusion	Heat of Vaporization	Heat of Sublimation	Electrical Resistivity	Specific Heat	Thermal Conductivity	Thermal Diffusivity	Thermal Linear Expansion	Thermal Absorptance	Thermal Emittance	Thermal Reflectance	Thermal Transmittance	Vapor Pressure
Magnesium-lead intermetallics (Mg_2Pb)	6-I	-	-	-	-	-	650	-	-	-	-	-	-	-	-	-
Magnesium lead silicate glass .	4-II	-	-	-	-	-	1771	-	-	-	-	-	-	-	-	-
Magnesium molybdate ($MgO \cdot MoO_3$)	4-II	-	-	-	-	-	-	1117	-	-	-	-	-	-	-	-
Magnesium niobates																
$MgO \cdot Nb_2O_5$	4-II	-	-	-	-	-	-	-	-	-	1125	-	-	-	-	-
2 $MgO \cdot Nb_2O_5$	4-II	-	-	-	-	-	-	-	-	-	1125	-	-	-	-	-
3 $MgO \cdot Nb_2O_5$	4-II	-	-	-	-	-	-	-	-	-	1125	-	-	-	-	-
4 $MgO \cdot Nb_2O_5$	4-II	-	-	-	-	-	-	-	-	-	1125	-	-	-	-	-
Magnesium nitride (Mg_3N_2) . . .	5	-	-	-	-	-	-	533	-	-	-	-	-	-	-	-
Magnesium oxides																
Magnesium oxide (MgO) . . .	4-I	248	248	-	-	-	250	252	254	257	259	263	265-267	269	-	271
M-300	4-I	-	-	-	-	-	-	-	-	-	259	-	-	-	-	-
PC-235	4-I	-	-	-	-	-	-	-	-	257	-	-	-	-	-	-
SR-2808	4-I	-	-	-	-	-	-	-	-	257	-	-	-	-	-	-
Magnesium oxide + Aluminum oxide	4-I	-	-	-	-	-	-	-	-	723	-	-	-	-	-	-
Magnesium oxide + Aluminum oxide + Beryllium oxide. . . .	4-I	-	-	-	-	-	-	-	-	-	725	-	-	-	-	-
Magnesium oxide + Aluminum oxide + Iron(ic) oxide + + Silicon (di-) oxide + Calcium oxide	4-I	-	-	-	-	-	-	-	727	-	-	-	-	-	-	-
Magnesium oxide + Beryllium oxide	4-I	-	-	-	-	-	-	-	729	-	731	-	-	-	-	-
Magnesium oxide + Calcium oxide	4-I	-	-	-	-	-	-	-	-	733	735	-	-	-	-	-
Magnesium oxide + Calcium oxide + Iron(ic) oxide	4-I	-	-	-	-	-	-	-	-	737	-	-	-	-	-	-
Magnesium oxide + Chromium (sesqui-) oxide + Aluminum oxide + Iron(ic) oxide + + Silicon (di-) oxide	4-I	-	-	-	-	-	-	-	739	-	-	-	-	-	-	-
Magnesium oxide + Chromium (sesqui-) oxide + Iron(ic) oxide + Aluminum oxide + + Silicon (di-) oxide + + Iron(ous) oxide	4-I	-	-	-	-	-	-	-	741	-	-	-	-	-	-	-
Magnesium oxide + Iron(ic) oxide + Calcium oxide	4-I	-	-	-	-	-	-	-	743	-	-	-	-	-	-	-
Magnesium oxide + Magnesium aluminate	4-II	-	-	-	-	-	-	-	1536	-	-	-	-	-	-	-
Magnesium oxide + Magnesium silicate	4-II	-	-	-	-	-	-	-	1538	-	-	-	-	-	-	-
Magnesium oxide + Nickel (mon-) oxide	4-I	-	-	-	-	-	745	-	747	-	-	-	-	-	-	-
Magnesium oxide + Silicon (di-) oxide	4-I	-	-	-	-	-	-	-	749	-	751	-	-	-	-	-

Material Name	Volume	Density	Melting Point	Heat of Fusion	Heat of Vaporization	Heat of Sublimation	Electrical Resistivity	Specific Heat	Thermal Conductivity	Thermal Diffusivity	Thermal Linear Expansion	Thermal Absorptance	Thermal Emittance	Thermal Reflectance	Thermal Transmittance	Vapor Pressure
Magnesium oxide + Talc	4-II	-	-	-	-	-	-	-	1538	-	-	-	-	-	-	-
Magnesium oxide + Tin(ic) oxide	4-I	-	-	-	-	-	-	-	753	-	-	-	-	-	-	-
Magnesium oxide + Titanium (di-) oxide	4-I	-	-	-	-	-	-	-	-	-	755	-	-	-	-	-
Magnesium oxide + Tungsten cermet	6-II	-	-	-	-	-	-	-	-	-	788	-	-	-	-	-
Magnesium oxide + Uranium (di-) oxide	4-I	-	-	-	-	-	-	-	757	-	-	-	-	-	-	-
Magnesium oxide + Yttrium oxide	4-I	-	-	-	-	-	-	-	-	-	759	-	-	-	-	-
Magnesium oxide + Zinc oxide	4-I	-	-	-	-	-	-	-	761	-	-	-	-	-	-	-
Magnesium silicates																
$MgO \cdot SiO_2$	4-II	1285	1285	-	-	-	1287	1289	1293	-	1295	-	-	-	-	-
$2\ MgO \cdot SiO_2$	4-II	-	-	-	-	-	-	1289	1291	-	1295	-	-	-	-	-
$3\ MgO \cdot 4\ SiO_2 \cdot H_2O$	4-II	-	-	-	-	-	-	1289	-	-	-	-	-	-	-	-
Magnesium (ortho-) silicate + + Zinc (ortho-) silicate	4-II	-	-	-	-	-	-	-	-	-	1571	-	-	-	-	-
Magnesium silicides (Mg_2Si)	6-I	-	419	-	-	-	421	-	-	-	-	-	-	-	-	-
Magnesium silicide stannide ($Mg_2Si_xSn_{1-x}$)	6-I	-	-	-	-	-	537	-	539	-	-	-	-	-	-	-
Magnesium stannate ($MgO \cdot SnO_2$)	4-II	-	-	-	-	-	-	-	1361	-	-	-	-	-	-	-
Magnesium stannide (Mg_2Sn)	6-I	533	533	-	-	-	535	-	-	-	-	-	-	-	-	-
Magnesium titanates																
$MgO \cdot TiO_2$	4-II	-	-	-	-	-	1439	1441	-	-	1443	-	-	-	-	-
$MgO \cdot 2\ TiO_2$	4-II	-	-	-	-	-	1439	1441	-	-	1443	-	-	-	-	-
$MgO \cdot 5\ TiO_2$	4-II	-	-	-	-	-	-	-	-	-	1443	-	-	-	-	-
$2\ MgO \cdot TiO_2$	4-II	-	-	-	-	-	1439	1441	-	-	1443	-	-	-	-	-
$2\ MgO \cdot 3\ TiO_2$	4-II	-	-	-	-	-	-	-	-	-	1443	-	-	-	-	-
Magnesium titanate porcelain	5	1003	-	-	-	-	-	-	1017	-	-	-	-	-	-	-
Magnesium tungstate ($MgO \cdot WO_3$)	4-II	-	-	-	-	-	-	1478	-	-	-	-	-	-	-	-
Magnesium tungsten lead oxide ($2\ PbO \cdot MgO \cdot WO_3$)	4-II	-	-	-	-	-	-	-	-	-	1153	-	-	-	-	-
Magnesium vanadates																
$MgO \cdot V_2O_5$	4-II	-	-	-	-	-	-	1492	-	-	-	-	-	-	-	-
$2\ MgO \cdot V_2O_5$	4-II	-	-	-	-	-	-	1492	-	-	-	-	-	-	-	-
Magnesium uranate ($MgO \cdot UO_3$)	4-II	-	1482	-	-	-	-	-	-	-	-	-	-	-	-	-
Magnesium zirconate ($MgO \cdot ZrO_2$)	4-II	-	-	-	-	-	-	-	-	-	1512	-	-	-	-	-
Magnetite	4-I	212	212	-	-	-	-	220	-	-	-	-	-	-	-	-
Manganese (Mn)	1	642	642	-	-	642	644	646	-	-	648	-	-	650	-	652
Manganese, electrolytic	1	-	-	-	-	-	-	646	-	-	648	-	-	-	-	-
Manganese + Aluminum	2-I	-	-	-	-	-	-	268	-	-	-	-	-	-	-	-
Manganese + Copper	2-I	-	-	-	-	-	271	273	-	-	275-277	-	-	-	-	-

Material Name	Volume	Density	Melting Point	Heat of Fusion	Heat of Vaporization	Heat of Sublimation	Electrical Resistivity	Specific Heat	Thermal Conductivity	Thermal Diffusivity	Thermal Linear Expansion	Thermal Absorptance	Thermal Emittance	Thermal Reflectance	Thermal Transmittance	Vapor Pressure
Manganese + Copper + ΣX_i . . .	2-II	-	-	-	-	-	-	-	-	-	1083-1089	-	-	-	-	-
Manganese + Nickel	2-I	-	-	-	-	-	279	-	-	-	281	-	-	-	-	-
Manganese + Nickel + ΣX_i . . .	2-II	-	-	-	-	-	-	-	-	-	1091-1097	-	-	-	-	-
Manganese + Titanium	2-I	283, 519	-	-	-	-	-	-	-	-	-	-	-	-	-	-
Manganese alloys (special designations)																
A-47	2-I	-	-	-	-	-	-	268	-	-	-	-	-	-	-	-
A-48	2-I	-	-	-	-	-	-	268	-	-	-	-	-	-	-	-
A-49	2-I	-	-	-	-	-	-	268	-	-	-	-	-	-	-	-
A-49.5	2-I	-	-	-	-	-	-	268	-	-	-	-	-	-	-	-
A-50	2-I	-	-	-	-	-	-	268	-	-	-	-	-	-	-	-
A-51	2-I	-	-	-	-	-	-	268	-	-	-	-	-	-	-	-
A-52	2-I	-	-	-	-	-	-	268	-	-	-	-	-	-	-	-
A-53	2-I	-	-	-	-	-	-	268	-	-	-	-	-	-	-	-
A-54	2-I	-	-	-	-	-	-	268	-	-	-	-	-	-	-	-
A-55	2-I	-	-	-	-	-	-	268	-	-	-	-	-	-	-	-
A-56	2-I	-	-	-	-	-	-	268	-	-	-	-	-	-	-	-
A-57	2-I	-	-	-	-	-	-	268	-	-	-	-	-	-	-	-
A-58	2-I	-	-	-	-	-	-	268	-	-	-	-	-	-	-	-
A-59	2-I	-	-	-	-	-	-	268	-	-	-	-	-	-	-	-
A-60	2-I	-	-	-	-	-	-	268	-	-	-	-	-	-	-	-
Manganese aluminate ($MnO \cdot Al_2O_3$)	4-II	-	-	-	-	-	-	-	-	-	1019	-	-	-	-	-
Manganese aluminum carbide (Mn_3AlC)	5	-	-	-	-	-	-	73	-	-	-	-	-	-	-	-
Manganese antimonide ($MnSb$) .	6-I	-	-	-	-	-	69	-	-	-	-	-	-	-	-	-
Manganese arsenide (Mn_7As) . .	6-I	-	94	-	-	-	-	-	-	-	-	-	-	-	-	-
Manganese arsenide telluride ($MnTe_{1-x}As_x$)	6-I	-	-	-	-	-	600	-	602	-	-	-	-	-	-	-
Manganese carbide (Mn_3C) . . .	5	67	67	-	-	-	-	69	-	-	-	-	-	-	-	71
Manganese chromite ($MnO \cdot Cr_2O_3$)	4-II	-	-	-	-	-	-	-	-	-	1061	-	-	-	-	-
Manganese ferrite ($MnO \cdot Fe_2O_3$).	4-II	1085	-	-	-	-	-	-	-	-	-	-	-	-	-	-
Manganese nickel	2-II	-	-	-	-	-	-	-	-	-	1273	-	-	-	-	-
Manganese nitride (Mn_4N) . . .	5	-	621	-	-	-	-	-	-	-	-	-	-	-	-	-
Manganese oxides																
MnO	4-I	-	-	-	-	-	-	273	-	-	281	-	-	-	-	-
MnO_2	4-I	-	-	-	-	-	-	275	-	-	281	-	-	-	-	-
Mn_2O_3	4-I	-	-	-	-	-	-	277	-	-	-	-	-	-	-	-
Mn_3O_4	4-I	-	-	-	-	-	-	-	279	-	-	-	-	-	-	-
Manganese (sesqui-) oxide + + Magnesium oxide	4-I	-	-	-	-	-	-	-	763	-	-	-	-	-	-	-

Material Name	Volume	Density	Melting Point	Heat of Fusion	Heat of Vaporization	Heat of Sublimation	Electrical Resistivity	Specific Heat	Thermal Conductivity	Thermal Diffusivity	Thermal Linear Expansion	Thermal Absorptance	Thermal Emittance	Thermal Reflectance	Thermal Transmittance	Vapor Pressure
Manganese-palladium intermetallics (MnPd)	6-I	-	684	-	-	-	-	-	-	-	-	-	-	-	-	-
Manganese phosphides																
MnP	5	635	635	-	-	-	639	-	-	-	-	-	-	-	-	-
Mn_2P	5	-	635	-	-	-	-	-	-	-	-	-	-	-	-	-
Mn_3P	5	-	635	-	-	-	-	-	-	-	-	-	-	-	-	-
Mn_3P_2	5	-	635	-	-	-	-	-	-	-	-	-	-	-	-	-
Manganese selenide (MnSe). . .	6-I	-	-	-	-	-	-	341	-	-	-	-	-	-	-	-
Manganese silicate ($MnO \cdot SiO_2$) .	4-II	-	-	-	-	-	-	1312	-	-	1314	-	-	-	-	-
Manganese silicides																
$MnSi_{0.3-0.5}$	6-I	-	-	-	-	-	-	427	-	-	-	-	-	-	-	-
MnSi	6-I	-	423	-	-	-	425	427	-	-	431	-	-	-	-	-
$MnSi_2$	6-I	-	-	-	-	-	425	427	429	-	-	-	-	-	-	-
Mn_3Si	6-I	-	423	-	-	-	-	-	-	-	-	-	-	-	-	-
Mn_5Si_3	6-I	-	423	-	-	-	-	-	-	-	-	-	-	-	-	-
Manganese telluride (MnTe) . .	6-I	-	-	-	-	-	-	598	-	-	-	-	-	-	-	-
Manganese zinc carbide (Mn_3ZnC)	5	-	-	-	-	-	-	75	-	-	-	-	-	-	-	-
Manganin	2-II	-	-	-	-	-	978	-	-	-	-	-	-	-	-	-
Marlex 20	6-II	-	-	-	-	-	-	-	-	-	1045	-	-	-	-	-
Marlex 50	6-II	-	-	-	-	-	-	-	-	-	1045	-	-	-	-	-
Massicot	4-I	-	-	-	-	-	-	234	-	-	-	-	-	-	-	-
Matte silver	1	-	-	-	-	-	-	-	-	-	-	910	-	-	-	-
Melamine formaldehyde	6-II	-	1014	-	-	-	-	-	-	-	-	-	-	-	-	-
Melamine formaldehyde, reinforced	6-II	-	-	-	-	-	-	-	-	-	1101	-	-	-	-	-
Melamine formaldehyde, alpha cellulose filled	6-II	-	-	-	-	-	-	-	-	-	1018	-	-	-	-	-
Melamine formaldehyde, mineral filled	6-II	-	-	-	-	-	1016	-	-	-	-	-	-	-	-	-
Melamine-formaldehyde resin, reinforced	6-II	-	-	-	-	-	-	-	-	1128	-	-	-	-	-	-
Melmac 592	6-II	-	-	-	-	-	1016	-	-	-	-	-	-	-	-	-
Melmac 1077	6-II	-	-	-	-	-	-	-	-	-	1018	-	-	-	-	-
Melmac 1079	6-II	-	-	-	-	-	-	-	-	-	1018	-	-	-	-	-
Melmac 1502	6-II	-	-	-	-	-	-	-	-	-	1018	-	-	-	-	-
Merwinite	4-II	-	-	-	-	-	-	1239	-	-	-	-	-	-	-	-
Mercuric selenide (HgSe) . . .	6-I	-	-	-	-	-	-	343	-	-	-	-	-	-	-	-
Metal cermets	6-II	925	-	-	-	-	-	-	-	-	-	-	-	-	-	-
Metco XP-1103	6-II	-	-	-	-	-	-	-	-	-	-	1309	1311	-	-	-
Metco XP-1106	6-II	-	-	-	-	-	-	-	-	-	-	1325	1327	-	-	-
Metco XP-1109	6-II	-	-	-	-	-	-	-	-	-	-	1407	1409	-	-	-
Metco XP-1110	6-II	-	-	-	-	-	-	-	-	-	-	1421	1423	-	-	-

Material Name	Volume	Density	Melting Point	Heat of Fusion	Heat of Vaporization	Heat of Sublimation	Electrical Resistivity	Specific Heat	Thermal Conductivity	Thermal Diffusivity	Thermal Linear Expansion	Thermal Absorptance	Thermal Emittance	Thermal Reflectance	Thermal Transmittance	Vapor Pressure
Mica																
Mica	5	983	–	–	–	–	985-987	–	989-991	–	993-1001	–	–	–	–	–
Biotite	5	–	–	–	–	–	–	–	–	–	997	–	–	–	–	–
Cericite	5	–	–	–	–	–	–	–	–	–	993	–	–	–	–	–
Glass bonded	5	–	–	–	–	–	987	–	–	–	–	–	–	–	–	–
Illite	5	–	–	–	–	–	–	–	–	–	993	–	–	–	–	–
Iron	5	–	–	–	–	–	–	–	–	–	997	–	–	–	–	–
Magnesium	5	–	–	–	–	–	–	–	–	–	999	–	–	–	–	–
Muscovite	5	–	–	–	–	–	985	–	–	–	1001	–	–	–	–	–
Phlogophite	5	–	–	–	–	–	–	–	–	–	999	–	–	–	–	–
Ripidolite	5	–	–	–	–	–	–	–	–	–	995	–	–	–	–	–
Synthetic	5	–	–	–	–	–	985	–	991	–	–	–	–	–	–	–
Synthetic, barium-	5	–	–	–	–	–	985	–	–	–	–	–	–	–	–	–
Zinn waldite	5	–	–	–	–	–	–	–	–	–	995	–	–	–	–	–
Micro-Quartz type II	6-II	–	–	–	–	–	–	1216	–	–	–	–	–	–	–	–
MIL-C-7350 type I and II	6-II	–	–	–	–	–	–	–	–	1275	–	–	–	–	–	–
MIL-C-8021 type I	6-II	–	–	–	–	–	–	–	–	1275	–	–	–	–	–	–
MIL-C-8087	6-II	–	–	–	–	–	–	954	956	–	958	–	–	–	–	–
Mineral aluminum silicates	4-II	–	–	–	–	–	1187	–	–	–	–	–	–	–	–	–
Mo-9-8 molybdenum	1	–	–	–	–	–	–	658	–	–	–	–	–	–	–	–
Molybdenite	5	690	690	–	–	–	–	–	–	–	–	–	–	692	–	–
Molybdenum (Mo)	1	654	654	–	–	654	656	658	660	663	665	667	669-675	677	–	679
Molybdenum coated with boron	6-II	–	–	–	–	–	–	–	–	–	–	–	1289	–	–	–
Molybdenum coated with carbon	6-II	–	–	–	–	–	–	–	–	–	–	1293	1295	–	–	–
Molybdenum coated with silicide	6-II	–	–	–	–	–	–	–	–	–	–	–	1467-1469	1471	–	–
Molybdenum coated with titanium (di-) oxide and aluminum	6-II	–	–	–	–	–	–	–	–	–	–	–	1395	–	–	–
Molybdenum coating on iron	6-II	–	–	–	–	–	–	–	–	–	–	1309	1311	–	–	–
Molybdenum + ΣX_i	2-II	1109	–	–	–	–	–	–	–	–	–	–	–	–	–	–
Molybdenum + Iron	2-I	285	–	–	–	–	–	287	289	–	–	–	–	–	–	–
Molybdenum + Nickel + ΣX_i	2-II	1099	–	–	–	–	–	–	–	–	–	–	–	–	–	–
Molybdenum + Niobium + ΣX_i	2-II	1101	–	–	–	–	–	–	–	–	–	–	–	–	–	–
Molybdenum + Silicon	2-I	–	–	–	–	–	–	–	–	–	–	–	291	–	–	–
Molybdenum + Titanium	2-I	–	–	–	–	–	293	295	297	299	301	–	303-307	309	–	–
Molybdenum + Titanium + ΣX_i	2-II	1103	–	–	–	–	–	1105	–	–	1107	–	–	–	–	–
Molybdenum + Tungsten	2-I	–	–	–	–	–	–	311	313	315	317	–	319	–	–	–
Molybdenum aluminides																
MoAl	6-I	–	9	–	–	–	–	–	–	–	11	–	–	–	–	–
$MoAl_2$	6-I	–	–	–	–	–	–	–	–	–	11	–	–	–	–	–
Mo_3Al	6-I	–	9	–	–	–	–	–	–	–	–	–	–	–	–	–

Material Name	Volume	Density	Melting Point	Heat of Fusion	Heat of Vaporization	Heat of Sublimation	Electrical Resistivity	Specific Heat	Thermal Conductivity	Thermal Diffusivity	Thermal Linear Expansion	Thermal Absorptance	Thermal Emittance	Thermal Reflectance	Thermal Transmittance	Vapor Pressure
Molybdenum beryllides																
$MoBe_2$	6-I	–	102	–	–	–	–	–	–	–	–	–	–	–	–	–
$MoBe_{12}$	6-I	102	–	–	–	–	–	104	106	–	–	–	–	–	–	–
Molybdenum borides																
MoB	6-I	–	186	–	–	–	–	188	–	–	–	–	–	–	–	192
MoB_2	6-I	–	186	186	–	–	–	188	–	–	190	–	–	–	–	–
Mo_2B	6-I	–	186	–	–	–	–	188	–	–	–	–	–	–	–	192
Mo_2B_5	6-I	–	186	–	–	–	–	–	–	–	–	–	–	–	–	–
Mo_3B_2	6-I	–	186	–	–	–	–	–	–	–	–	–	–	–	–	–
(Di-) molybdenum boride + + Molybdenum (di-) silicide . .	6-I	–	724	–	–	–	–	–	–	–	–	–	–	–	–	–
(Di-) molybdenum boride + + (Penta-) niobium (tri-) - silicide	6-I	–	724	–	–	–	–	–	–	–	–	–	–	–	–	–
(Di-) molybdenum boride + + Tantalum (di-) silicide . . .	6-I	–	724	–	–	–	–	–	–	–	–	–	–	–	–	–
(Di-) molybdenum boride + + (Penta-) tantalum (tri-) - silicide	6-I	–	724	–	–	–	–	–	–	–	–	–	–	–	–	–
Molybdenum carbides																
MoC	5	–	–	–	–	–	–	–	–	–	87	–	–	–	–	–
Mo_2C	5	77	77	–	–	–	79	81	83	–	85	–	89	–	–	–
Molybdenum chromium silicides																
(Mo, Cr, Si)	6-I	523	–	–	–	–	–	–	–	–	–	–	–	–	–	–
$(Mo, Cr) Si_2$	6-I	523	–	–	–	–	–	–	–	–	–	–	–	–	–	–
Molybdenum germanide (Mo_3Ge_2)	6-I	–	313	–	–	–	–	–	–	–	–	–	–	–	–	315
Molybdenum nitride (Mo_3N). . .	5	–	621	–	–	–	–	–	–	–	–	–	–	–	–	–
Molybdenum oxides																
MoO_2	4-I	–	–	–	–	–	–	285	–	–	–	–	–	–	–	–
MoO_3	4-I	283	283	283	–	–	–	287	–	–	–	–	–	289	–	291
Molybdenum phosphide (MoP). .	5	635	635	–	–	–	639	–	–	–	–	–	–	–	–	–
Molybdenum selenides ($MoSe_2$) .	6-I	–	–	–	–	–	367	–	369	–	–	–	–	–	–	–
Molybdenum silicides																
$MoSi_2$	6-I	433	433	–	–	–	435	437	439	–	441	–	445-447	449	–	–
Mo_3Si	6-I	–	–	–	–	–	–	–	–	–	443	–	–	–	–	451
Mo_5Si_3	6-I	433	433	–	–	–	–	–	–	–	443	–	–	–	–	–
Molybdenum (di-) silicide + + Calcium aluminate	5	–	–	–	–	–	–	–	–	–	904	–	–	–	–	–
Molybdenum (di-) silicide + + Chromium (sesqui-) oxide. .	5	–	–	–	–	–	–	–	–	–	–	–	906	–	–	–
Molybdenum (di-) silicide + + Chromium (di-) silicide. . .	6-I	723	–	–	–	–	–	–	–	–	–	–	–	–	–	–
Molybdenum (di-) silicide + + Copper cermets	6-II	923	–	–	–	–	–	–	–	–	–	–	–	–	–	–

Material Name	Volume	Density	Melting Point	Heat of Fusion	Heat of Vaporization	Heat of Sublimation	Electrical Resistivity	Specific Heat	Thermal Conductivity	Thermal Diffusivity	Thermal Linear Expansion	Thermal Absorptance	Thermal Emittance	Thermal Reflectance	Thermal Transmittance	Vapor Pressure
Molybdenum (di-) silicide + + Molybdenum (tri-) oxide. . .	5	-	-	-	-	-	-	-	-	-	-	-	908-910	912	-	-
Molybdenum (di-) silicide + + Molybdenum (tri-) oxide + + Silicon (di-) oxide	5	-	-	-	-	-	-	-	-	-	-	-	914-916	918	-	-
Molybdenum (di-) silicide + + Silicon (di-) oxide	5	-	-	-	-	-	-	-	-	-	-	-	920-922	924	-	-
Molybdenum (di-) silicide + + Zirconium (di-) boride . . .	6-I	-	689, 724	-	-	-	-	-	-	-	-	-	-	-	-	-
Molybdenum-silicon-titanium cermet	6-II	930	-	-	-	-	-	-	-	-	-	-	-	-	-	-
Molybdenum sulfide (MoS_2) . . .	5	690	690	-	-	-	-	-	-	-	-	-	-	692	-	-
Molybdenum tellurides ($MoTe_2$) .	6-I	-	-	-	-	-	638	-	640	-	-	-	-	-	-	-
Molybdenum-titanium alloys coated with Chromalloy W-2 .	6-II	-	-	-	-	-	-	-	-	-	-	-	1505-1509	-	-	-
Molybdenum-titanium alloy coated with Durak-MG	6-II	-	-	-	-	-	-	-	-	-	-	-	1501-1503	-	-	-
Molybdenum-zirconium intermetallics (Mo_2Zr)	6-I	-	684	-	-	-	-	-	-	-	-	-	-	-	-	-
Monel	2-I	-	-	-	-	-	-	-	-	-	343	-	-	-	-	-
. . . . . .	2-II	-	-	-	-	-	-	1239	1241	-	1247-1251	-	1253	-	-	-
Monel 400	2-II	-	-	-	-	-	-	1239	1241	-	1247-1249	-	1253	-	-	-
Monel 401	2-II	-	-	-	-	-	-	-	-	-	988	-	-	-	-	-
Monel 403	2-II	-	-	-	-	-	-	-	-	-	1249	-	-	-	-	-
Monel 404	2-II	-	-	-	-	-	-	-	-	-	1251	-	-	-	-	-
Monel 501	2-II	-	-	-	-	-	-	-	-	-	1245	-	-	-	-	-
Monel, H-	2-II	-	-	-	-	-	-	-	1241	-	-	-	-	-	-	-
Monel, K-	2-II	1237	-	-	-	-	-	1239	1241	1243	1245	-	-	-	-	-
Monel K-500	2-II	1237	-	-	-	-	-	1239	1241	1243	1245	-	-	-	-	-
Monel 5700, K-	2-II	-	-	-	-	-	-	-	-	-	-	-	1255	-	-	-
Monel, KR-	2-II	-	-	-	-	-	-	-	-	-	1245	-	-	-	-	-
Monel, R	2-II	-	-	-	-	-	-	-	1241	-	1247	-	-	-	-	-
Monel, R-405	2-II	-	-	-	-	-	-	-	1241	-	1247	-	-	-	-	-
Monel, S-	2-II	-	-	-	-	-	-	-	1241	-	-	-	-	-	-	-
Monel, Si-	2-II	-	-	-	-	-	-	-	1241	-	-	-	-	-	-	-
Moplen	6-II	1076	1076	-	-	-	-	1078	1080	-	1088	-	-	-	-	-
Mullite	4-II	-	-	-	-	-	-	1189	1191	1193	1197	-	1201	-	1203	-
Mullite MV-20	4-II	-	-	-	-	-	-	-	-	1193	-	-	1201	-	-	-
Mullite MV-30	4-I	-	-	-	-	-	-	-	-	-	617	-	-	-	-	-

Material Name	Volume	Density	Melting Point	Heat of Fusion	Heat of Vaporization	Heat of Sublimation	Electrical Resistivity	Specific Heat	Thermal Conductivity	Thermal Diffusivity	Thermal Linear Expansion	Thermal Absorptance	Thermal Emittance	Thermal Reflectance	Thermal Transmittance	Vapor Pressure
Mullite + Alumina	4–II	–	–	–	–	–	–	–	1562	–	–	–	–	–	–	–
Muscovite	4–II	–	–	–	–	–	–	1573	–	–	–	–	–	–	–	–
MX-4926 carbon-phenolic laminate	6–II	–	–	–	–	–	–	1134	–	–	–	–	–	–	–	–
Mylar coated with aluminum . .	6–II	–	–	–	–	–	–	–	–	–	–	–	–	1287	–	–
Mylar coated with copper. . . .	6–II	–	–	–	–	–	–	–	–	–	–	–	–	1301	–	–
Mylar coated with gold.	6–II	–	–	–	–	–	–	–	–	–	–	–	–	1307	–	–
Mylar coated with silver	6–II	–	–	–	–	–	–	–	–	–	–	–	–	1323	–	–
N																
NBS coating A-418 on Inconel. .	6–II	–	–	–	–	–	–	–	–	–	–	–	1361–1363	–	–	–
NBS coating A-418 on stainless steel	6–II	–	–	–	–	–	–	–	–	–	–	–	1365–1367	–	–	–
NBS coating N-143 on Inconel. .	6–II	–	–	–	–	–	–	–	–	–	–	–	1353–1355	–	–	–
NBS coating N-143 on stainless steel	6–II	–	–	–	–	–	–	–	–	–	–	–	1357–1359	–	–	–
Neodymia	4–I	293	293	–	–	–	–	295	–	–	297	–	–	–	–	–
Neodymium (Nd)	1	681	681	681	681	682	684	686	–	–	688	–	–	–	–	690
Neodymium + Magnesium . . .	2–I	323	–	–	–	–	–	–	–	–	–	–	–	–	–	–
Neodymium + Magnesium + ΣX_i .	2–II	1115	1115	–	–	–	–	–	–	–	–	–	–	–	–	–
Neodymium aluminide (NdAl) . .	6–I	43	–	–	–	–	–	–	–	–	–	–	–	–	–	–
Neodymium-bismuth intermetallics (NdBi)	6–I	680	–	–	–	–	–	–	–	–	–	–	–	–	–	–
Neodymium borides																
NdB_4	6–I	296	–	–	–	–	–	–	–	–	–	–	–	–	–	–
NdB_6	6–I	296	296	–	–	–	300	–	–	–	–	–	–	–	–	–
Neodymium-cadmium intermetallics																
NdCd	6–I	680	–	–	–	–	–	–	–	–	–	–	–	–	–	–
$NdCd_2$	6–I	680	–	–	–	–	–	–	–	–	–	–	–	–	–	–
$NdCd_3$	6–I	680	–	–	–	–	–	–	–	–	–	–	–	–	–	–
$NdCd_{11}$	6–I	680	–	–	–	–	–	–	–	–	–	–	–	–	–	–
Neodymium carbides																
NdC_2	5	294	294	–	–	–	–	–	–	–	–	–	–	–	–	–
Nd_2C_3	5	294	–	–	–	–	–	–	–	–	–	–	–	–	–	–
Neodymium chloride ($NdCl_3$) . .	5	339	–	–	–	–	–	–	–	–	–	–	–	–	–	–
Neodymium-cobalt intermetallics ($NdCo_5$)	6–I	680	–	–	–	–	–	–	–	–	–	–	–	–	–	–
Neodymium-copper intermetallics ($NdCu_5$)	6–I	680	–	–	–	–	–	–	–	–	–	–	–	–	–	–
Neodymium-gallium intermetallics ($NdGa_2$)	6–I	680	–	–	–	–	–	–	–	–	–	–	–	–	–	–

Material Name	Volume	Density	Melting Point	Heat of Fusion	Heat of Vaporization	Heat of Sublimation	Electrical Resistivity	Specific Heat	Thermal Conductivity	Thermal Diffusivity	Thermal Linear Expansion	Thermal Absorptance	Thermal Emittance	Thermal Reflectance	Thermal Transmittance	Vapor Pressure
Neodymium germanides ($NdGe_2$)	6-I	323	-	-	-	-	-	-	-	-	-	-	-	-	-	-
Neodymium hydride (NdH_2) . . .	5	467	-	-	-	-	-	-	-	-	-	-	-	-	-	-
Neodymium-lead intermetallics ($NdPb_3$)	6-I	680	-	-	-	-	-	-	-	-	-	-	-	-	-	-
Neodymium-mercury intermetallics (NdHg)	6-I	680	-	-	-	-	-	-	-	-	-	-	-	-	-	-
Neodymium-nickel intermetallics ($NdNi_5$)	6-I	680	-	-	-	-	-	-	-	-	-	-	-	-	-	-
Neodymium nitride (NdN) . . .	5	621	-	-	-	-	-	-	-	-	-	-	-	-	-	-
Neodymium-osmium intermetallics ($NdOs_2$)	6-I	680	-	-	-	-	-	-	-	-	-	-	-	-	-	-
Neodymium oxides																
NdO	4-I	293	-	-	-	-	-	-	-	-	-	-	-	-	-	-
Nd_2O_3	4-I	293	293	-	-	-	-	295	-	-	297	-	-	-	-	-
Neodymium phosphide (NdP) . .	5	635	-	-	-	-	-	-	-	-	-	-	-	-	-	-
Neodymium selenides																
NdSe	6-I	365	-	-	-	-	-	-	-	-	-	-	-	-	-	-
Nd_2Se_3	6-I	365	-	-	-	-	-	-	-	-	-	-	-	-	-	-
Nd_3Se_4	6-I	365	-	-	-	-	-	-	-	-	-	-	-	-	-	-
Neodymium silicide ($NdSi_2$) . .	6-I	523	524	-	-	-	527	-	-	-	-	-	-	-	-	-
Neodymium-silver intermetallics (NdAg)	6-I	680	-	-	-	-	-	-	-	-	-	-	-	-	-	-
Neodymium sulfides																
NdS	5	694	694	-	-	-	-	-	-	-	696	-	-	-	-	-
NdS_2	5	-	694	-	-	-	-	-	-	-	-	-	-	-	-	-
Nd_2S_3	5	694	694	-	-	-	-	-	-	-	696	-	-	-	-	-
Nd_3S_4	5	694	694	-	-	-	-	-	-	-	-	-	-	-	-	-
Neoprene GN	6-II	-	-	-	-	-	-	-	-	1066	-	-	-	-	-	-
Neoprene W	6-II	1051	-	-	-	-	-	-	-	-	-	-	-	-	-	-
Nepheline syenite	4-II	-	-	-	-	-	-	-	-	-	1320	-	-	-	-	-
Neptunium (Np)	1	692	692	-	-	-	-	-	-	-	-	-	-	-	-	-
Neptunium + Calcium + ΣX_i . .	2-II	1111	-	-	-	-	-	1113	-	-	-	-	-	-	-	-
Neptunium + Uranium	2-I	321	321	-	-	-	-	-	-	-	-	-	-	-	-	-
Neptunium bromide ($NpBr_3$) . .	5	11	-	-	-	-	-	-	-	-	-	-	-	-	-	-
Neptunium chlorides																
$NpCl_3$	5	339	-	-	-	-	-	-	-	-	-	-	-	-	-	-
$NpCl_4$	5	339	-	-	-	-	-	-	-	-	-	-	-	-	-	-
Neptonium (di-)oxide (NpO_2) . .	4-I	-	-	-	-	-	-	299	-	-	-	-	-	-	-	-
Nichrome	2-I	-	-	-	-	-	-	-	-	-	-	-	331	-	-	-
Nickel (Ni)	1	694	694	-	-	-	696	698	700	702	704	706	708-714	716-718	-	720
Nickel, carbonyl	1	-	694	-	-	-	-	-	-	-	-	-	-	-	-	-
Nickel, electrolytic	1	694	694	-	-	-	-	698	-	-	704	-	-	716	-	-

Material Name	Volume	Density	Melting Point	Heat of Fusion	Heat of Vaporization	Heat of Sublimation	Electrical Resistivity	Specific Heat	Thermal Conductivity	Thermal Diffusivity	Thermal Linear Expansion	Thermal Absorptance	Thermal Emittance	Thermal Reflectance	Thermal Transmittance	Vapor Pressure
Nickel coated with aluminum phosphate	6-II	-	-	-	-	-	-	-	-	-	-	-	1429	-	-	-
Nickel + ΣX_i	2-II	1307	-	-	-	-	1309	1311	1313	1315	-	-	-	-	-	-
Nickel + Aluminum	2-I	-	-	-	-	-	325	-	-	-	-	-	-	-	-	-
Nickel + Aluminum + ΣX_i . . .	2-II	-	-	-	-	-	-	-	-	-	1117	-	-	-	-	-
Nickel + Chromium	2-I	-	-	-	-	-	327	329	-	-	-	-	331-333	-	-	-
Nickel + Chromium + ΣX_i . . .	2-II	1119, 1122	1119	-	-	-	1124	1126-1132	1134-1145	1148-1150	1152-1170	-	1172-1201	1203-1215	-	-
Nickel + Cobalt	2-I	335	-	-	-	-	-	-	337	-	-	-	-	-	-	-
Nickel + Cobalt + ΣX_i	2-II	1219	1217	-	-	-	1221	-	1223	-	1225-1227	-	1229-1231	-	-	-
Nickel + Copper	2-I	-	-	-	-	-	339	341	-	-	343	-	-	-	-	-
Nickel + Copper + ΣX_i	2-II	1237	-	-	-	-	-	1239	1241	1243	1245-1251	-	1253-1255	-	-	-
Nickel + Iron	2-I	-	-	-	-	-	345	347	349	-	-	-	-	-	-	-
Nickel + Iron + ΣX_i	2-II	1257	-	-	-	-	-	1259	1261	-	1263-1267	-	1269	-	-	-
Nickel + Manganese	2-I	-	-	-	-	-	351	-	353	-	355	-	-	-	-	-
Nickel + Manganese + ΣX_i . . .	2-II	-	-	-	-	-	-	1271	-	-	1273	-	-	-	-	-
Nickel + Molybdenum + ΣX_i . .	2-II	1277	1275	-	-	-	-	1279	1281	-	1283-1287	1289	1291-1295	1297	-	-
Nickel + Palladium	2-I	-	-	-	-	-	357	-	-	-	-	-	-	-	-	-
Nickel + Palladium + ΣX_i . . .	2-II	-	-	-	-	-	-	-	-	-	1299	-	-	-	-	-
Nickel + Silicon	2-I	-	-	-	-	-	359	-	-	-	-	-	-	-	-	-
Nickel + Silicon + ΣX_i	2-II	-	-	-	-	-	-	-	-	-	1301	-	-	-	-	-
Nickel + Titanium + ΣX_i	2-II	-	-	-	-	-	-	-	-	-	1303	-	-	-	-	-
Nickel + Tungsten + ΣX_i	2-II	-	-	-	-	-	-	-	-	-	1305	-	-	-	-	-
Nickel 200	2-I	-	-	-	-	-	-	-	-	-	355	-	-	-	-	-
(also) . . .	2-II	1307	-	-	-	-	-	-	-	-	-	-	-	-	-	-
Nickel 204	2-II	-	-	-	-	-	-	-	-	-	1227	-	-	-	-	-
Nickel 211	2-I	-	-	-	-	-	-	-	-	-	355	-	-	-	-	-
Nickel 270	1	-	-	-	-	-	-	-	-	-	704	-	-	-	-	-
Nickel A	1	-	-	-	-	-	-	-	700	-	-	-	-	-	-	-
(also) . . .	2-I	-	-	-	-	-	-	-	-	-	355	-	-	-	-	-
(also) . . .	2-II	1307	-	-	-	-	-	-	1313	-	-	-	-	-	-	-
Nickel, admiralty	2-II	-	-	-	-	-	-	-	-	-	988	-	-	-	-	-
Nickel D	2-I	-	-	-	-	-	-	-	-	-	355	-	-	-	-	-
(also) . . .	2-II	-	-	-	-	-	-	-	1313	-	-	-	-	-	-	-
Nickel, grade A	1	694	-	-	-	-	-	-	700	-	704	706	710-712	718	-	-
(also) . . .	2-I	-	-	-	-	-	-	-	353	-	-	-	-	-	-	-
(also) . . .	2-II	-	-	-	-	-	-	-	1223	-	1263, 1301	-	-	-	-	-
Nickel L	1	-	-	-	-	-	-	-	700	-	-	-	-	-	-	-

Material Name	Volume	Density	Melting Point	Heat of Fusion	Heat of Vaporization	Heat of Sublimation	Electrical Resistivity	Specific Heat	Thermal Conductivity	Thermal Diffusivity	Thermal Linear Expansion	Thermal Absorptance	Thermal Emittance	Thermal Reflectance	Thermal Transmittance	Vapor Pressure
Nickel alloys (special designations)																
60 - 15 Cr (ASTM B83-46) . .	2-II	1257	-	-	-	-	-	1259	-	-	-	-	-	-	-	-
80 Ni - 20 Cr	2-II	-	-	-	-	-	-	1130	1144	-	-	-	-	-	-	-
90 Ni - 10 Cr	2-II	-	-	-	-	-	-	1126	-	-	-	-	-	-	-	-
AISI alloy (see AISI designations)																
Alumel	2-II	-	-	-	-	-	-	1271	-	-	-	-	-	-	-	-
Astroloy	2-II	-	-	-	-	-	-	-	-	-	-	-	1229	1231	-	-
Brazing alloys GE-62	2-II	-	-	-	-	-	-	-	-	-	1168	-	-	-	-	-
Brazing compound GEH 62-V.	2-II	-	-	-	-	-	-	1130	-	-	-	-	-	-	-	-
Chromel-P	2-I	-	-	-	-	-	-	329	-	-	-	-	-	-	-	-
Contracid	2-II	-	-	-	-	-	-	-	1261	-	-	-	-	-	-	-
D-979	2-II	-	-	-	-	-	-	-	1261	-	-	-	-	-	-	-
Duranickel 301	2-II	-	-	-	-	-	-	-	-	-	1117	-	-	-	-	-
DVL 32	2-II	1219	-	-	-	-	-	-	-	-	1225	-	-	-	-	-
DVL 321a	2-II	1219	-	-	-	-	-	-	-	-	1225	-	-	-	-	-
DVL 321i	2-II	1219	-	-	-	-	-	-	-	-	1225	-	-	-	-	-
DVL 325a	2-II	1219	-	-	-	-	-	-	-	-	1225	-	-	-	-	-
EI-435	2-II	-	-	-	-	-	-	1132	1144	1150	-	-	-	-	-	-
EI-437	2-II	-	-	-	-	-	-	-	1140	-	-	-	-	-	-	-
EI-607	2-II	-	-	-	-	-	-	-	1145	-	1158	-	-	-	-	-
EI-617	2-II	-	-	-	-	-	-	-	-	-	1170	-	-	-	-	-
GMR-235	2-II	-	-	-	-	-	-	-	-	-	1161	-	-	-	-	-
Haskins alloy 667.	2-II	-	-	-	-	-	-	-	-	-	1273	-	-	-	-	-
Haynes alloy no. R-41. . . .	2-II	-	-	-	-	-	-	-	-	-	1154	-	-	-	-	-
Haynes alloy X	2-II	-	-	-	-	-	-	-	-	-	-	-	1172	-	-	-
Hastelloys (see Hastelloy)																
HU	2-II	-	-	-	-	-	-	-	-	-	1265	-	-	-	-	-
HW	2-II	-	-	-	-	-	-	-	-	-	1267	-	-	-	-	-
Illium alloy	2-II	-	-	-	-	-	-	-	-	-	1156	-	-	-	-	-
Illium G	2-II	-	-	-	-	-	-	-	1136	-	-	-	-	-	-	-
Illium R	2-II	-	-	-	-	-	-	-	1138	-	-	-	-	-	-	-
Inco (see Inco)																
Incoloys (see Incoloy)																
Inconels (see Inconel)																
INOR-8	2-II	-	-	-	-	-	-	-	1281	-	1285	-	1293	-	-	-
J-1500	2-II	-	-	-	-	-	-	-	1136	-	1166	-	-	-	-	-
J-1610	2-II	-	-	-	-	-	-	-	1134	-	1156	-	-	-	-	-
M-252	2-II	-	-	-	-	-	-	1130	1136	-	1166	-	1180, 1197	1209, 1215	-	-
Monels (see Monel)																

Material Name	Volume	Density	Melting Point	Heat of Fusion	Heat of Vaporization	Heat of Sublimation	Electrical Resistivity	Specific Heat	Thermal Conductivity	Thermal Diffusivity	Thermal Linear Expansion	Thermal Absorptance	Thermal Emittance	Thermal Reflectance	Thermal Transmittance	Vapor Pressure
Nickel alloys (special designations) (cont.)																
Ni-O-Nel	2-II	–	–	–	–	–	–	–	–	–	1267	–	–	–	–	–
Nichrome	2-I	–	–	–	–	–	–	–	–	–	–	–	331	–	–	–
Nichrome V	2-II	–	–	–	–	–	–	1130	1144	–	–	–	–	–	–	–
Nimonics (see Nimonic)																
OKh 20N60B	2-II	–	–	–	–	–	–	1132	1136	1150	–	–	–	–	–	–
OKh 21N78T	2-II	–	–	–	–	–	–	1132	–	1150	–	–	–	–	–	–
Permanickel 300	2-II	1257	–	–	–	–	–	–	–	–	1303	–	–	–	–	–
RCA-N91	2-I	–	–	–	–	–	–	–	337	–	–	–	–	–	–	–
RCA-N97	2-I	–	–	–	–	–	–	–	337	–	–	–	–	–	–	–
Refractaloy 26	2-II	–	–	–	–	–	–	–	1223	–	–	–	–	–	–	–
Rene 41	2-II	1122	–	–	–	–	–	1130	1134	–	1156	–	1184, 1199	1211	–	–
SM-200	2-II	–	–	–	–	–	–	–	–	–	1305	–	–	–	–	–
Udimets (see Udimet)																
Unitemp Waspalloy	2-II	–	–	–	–	–	–	–	1138	–	–	–	–	–	–	–
Waspalloy	2-II	–	–	–	–	–	–	–	1136	–	1154	–	–	–	–	–
Nickel aluminate ($NiO \cdot Al_2O_3$). .	4-II	–	–	–	–	–	–	–	–	–	1021	–	1023	–	–	–
Nickel aluminides																
NiAl	6-I	–	–	–	–	–	–	–	–	–	13	–	15-17	19	–	–
Ni_3Al	6-I	–	–	–	–	–	–	–	–	–	13	–	15-17	19	–	–
Nickel aluminides coating on Inconel	6-II	–	–	–	–	–	–	–	–	–	–	–	1453-1455	1457	–	–
Nickel aluminide + Aluminum oxide	5	–	–	–	–	–	–	–	–	–	–	–	844-846	848	–	–
Nickel aluminide + Nickel (mon-) oxide	5	–	–	–	–	–	–	–	–	–	–	–	850-852	854	–	–
Nickel aluminide + Nickel (mon-) oxide + Aluminum oxide	5	–	–	–	–	–	–	–	–	–	–	–	856-858	860	–	–
Nickel borides																
Ni_2B	6-I	–	296	–	–	–	–	–	–	–	–	–	–	–	–	–
Ni_3B	6-I	–	296	–	–	–	–	–	–	–	–	–	–	–	–	–
Ni_3B_2	6-I	–	296	–	–	–	–	–	–	–	–	–	–	–	–	–
Nickel carbide (Ni_3C)	5	–	294	–	–	–	–	–	–	–	–	–	–	–	–	–
Nickel chrome spinel coating on niobium-zirconium alloys . . .	6-II	–	–	–	–	–	–	–	–	–	–	–	1387	–	–	–
Nickel chromite coating on niobium-zirconium alloy . . .	6-II	–	–	–	–	–	–	–	–	–	–	–	1387	–	–	–

Material Name	Volume	Density	Melting Point	Heat of Fusion	Heat of Vaporization	Heat of Sublimation	Electrical Resistivity	Specific Heat	Thermal Conductivity	Thermal Diffusivity	Thermal Linear Expansion	Thermal Absorptance	Thermal Emittance	Thermal Reflectance	Thermal Transmittance	Vapor Pressure
Nickel-chromium alloy coating on Inconel X	6-II	–	–	–	–	–	–	–	–	–	–	–	1333	1335	–	–
Nickel ferride (Ni_3Fe)	6-I	–	–	–	–	–	–	–	–	–	304	–	–	–	–	–
Nickel ferrite ($NiO \cdot Fe_2O_3$) . . .	4-II	–	–	–	–	–	1087	1089	–	–	1091	–	–	–	–	–
Nickel ferrite spinal	4-II	–	–	–	–	–	–	1089	–	–	–	–	–	–	–	–
Nickel-lead silicate glass . . .	4-II	–	–	–	–	–	1773	–	–	–	–	–	–	–	–	–
Nickel-manganese intermetallics (Ni_3Mn)	6-I	–	–	–	–	–	652	654	–	–	–	–	–	–	–	–
Nickel (mon-) oxide (NiO) . . .	4-I	–	–	–	–	–	–	301	303	–	305	–	307-309	311	–	–
Nickel (mon-) oxide + Magnesium oxide	4-I	–	–	–	–	–	–	–	765	–	–	–	–	–	–	–
Nickel (mon-) oxide + Nickel aluminide	5	–	–	–	–	–	–	–	–	–	–	–	777-779	781	–	–
Nickel phosphides																
Ni_2P	5	–	635	–	–	–	–	–	–	–	–	–	–	–	–	–
Ni_3P	5	–	635	–	–	–	–	–	–	–	–	–	–	–	–	–
$Ni_{12}P_5$	5	–	635	–	–	–	–	–	–	–	–	–	–	–	–	–
Nickel selenides																
$NiSe_{1.0-2.05}$	6-I	345	–	–	–	–	–	347	–	–	–	–	–	–	–	–
Nickel silicides																
NiSi	6-I	–	453	–	–	–	–	–	–	–	–	–	–	–	–	–
$NiSi_2$	6-I	–	453	–	–	–	–	–	–	–	–	–	–	–	–	–
Ni_2Si	6-I	–	453	–	–	–	–	–	–	–	455	–	–	–	–	–
Ni_3Si	6-I	–	453	–	–	–	–	–	–	–	455	–	–	–	–	–
Ni_3Si_2	6-I	–	453	–	–	–	–	–	–	–	–	–	–	–	–	–
Nickel-tantalum intermetallics (Ni_3Ta)	6-I	–	684	–	–	–	–	–	–	–	–	–	–	–	–	–
Nickel tellurides																
NiTe	6-I	–	–	–	–	–	–	604	–	–	–	–	–	–	–	–
$NiTe_{1.1-1.5}$	6-I	–	–	–	–	–	–	604	–	–	–	–	–	–	–	–
$NiTe_2$	6-I	–	–	–	–	–	–	604	–	–	–	–	–	–	–	–
Nickel titanate ($NiO \cdot TiO_2$) . . .	4-II	–	–	–	–	–	1452	–	–	–	–	–	–	–	–	–
Nickel zinc ferrite ($Ni_xZn_{1-x}O \cdot Fe_2O_3$).	4-II	–	–	–	–	–	–	1093	1095	–	–	–	–	–	–	–
Nickel-zircorium intermetallics																
NiZr	6-I	–	684	–	–	–	–	–	–	–	–	–	–	–	–	–
Ni_3Zr	6-I	–	684	–	–	–	–	–	–	–	–	–	–	–	–	–
Ni_4Zr	6-I	–	684	–	–	–	–	–	–	–	–	–	–	–	–	–
Nimonic 75	2-II	–	–	–	–	–	–	–	1144	–	–	–	1182	–	–	–
Nimonic 80	2-II	–	–	–	–	–	–	–	1140	–	–	–	–	–	–	–
Nimonic 80/80A	2-II	–	–	–	–	–	–	–	1140	–	–	–	–	–	–	–
Nimonic 90	2-II	–	–	–	–	–	–	–	1136	–	–	–	–	–	–	–
Nimonic 95	2-II	–	–	–	–	–	–	–	1136	–	–	–	–	–	–	–

Material Name	Volume	Density	Melting Point	Heat of Fusion	Heat of Vaporization	Heat of Sublimation	Electrical Resistivity	Specific Heat	Thermal Conductivity	Thermal Diffusivity	Thermal Linear Expansion	Thermal Absorptance	Thermal Emittance	Thermal Reflectance	Thermal Transmittance	Vapor Pressure
Nimonic 100	2-II	1219	1217	–	–	–	–	–	1223	–	1227	–	–	–	–	–
Nimonic 105	2-II	–	–	–	–	–	–	–	1223	–	–	–	–	–	–	–
Niobium (Nb)	1	722	722	–	–	–	724	726	728	730	732	–	734-438	740	–	742
Niobium coated with aluminide .	6-II	–	–	–	–	–	–	–	–	–	–	–	1435-1437	1439	–	–
Niobium coated with niobium aluminide	6-II	–	–	–	–	–	–	–	–	–	–	–	–	1459	–	–
Niobium + ΣX_i	2-II	–	–	–	–	–	–	1361	–	–	–	–	–	–	–	–
Niobium + Iron + ΣX_i	2-II	–	–	–	–	–	–	1317	–	–	–	–	–	–	–	–
Niobium + Molybdenum + ΣX_i . .	2-II	1319	–	–	–	–	–	1321	1323	1325	1327	–	–	–	–	–
Niobium + Tantalum	2-I	–	361	–	–	–	363	–	365	–	–	–	–	–	–	–
Niobium + Tantalum + ΣX_i . . .	2-II	–	–	–	–	–	–	1329	1331	1333	1335	–	–	–	–	–
Niobium + Titanium	2-I	–	–	–	–	–	367	–	–	–	–	–	–	–	–	–
Niobium + Titanium + ΣX_i . . .	2-II	1337	–	–	–	–	–	1339	1341	1343	1345	–	1347	–	–	–
Niobium + Tungsten	2-I	–	–	–	–	–	–	–	–	–	–	–	369-371	–	–	–
Niobium + Tungsten + ΣX_i . . .	2-II	–	–	–	–	–	–	1349	1351	1353	1355	–	–	–	–	–
Niobium + Uranium	2-I	–	–	–	–	–	–	–	373	–	375	–	–	–	–	–
Niobium + Vanadium.	2-I	–	–	–	–	–	377	–	–	–	–	–	–	–	–	–
Niobium + Vanadium + ΣX_i . . .	2-II	–	–	–	–	–	–	–	1357	–	1359	–	–	–	–	–
Niobium + Zirconium	2-I	–	–	–	–	–	379	381	383	–	385	–	387-389	–	–	–
Niobium alloys (special design.)																
5 Mo -.5 V - Zr	2-II	–	–	–	–	–	–	1321	–	1325	–	–	–	–	–	–
27 Ta - 12 W - 0.5 Zr	2-II	–	–	–	–	–	–	1329	–	1333	–	–	–	–	–	–
10 Ti - 5 Zr	2-II	–	–	–	–	–	–	1339	–	1348	–	–	–	–	–	–
10 W - 1 Zr - 0.1 C	2-II	–	–	–	–	–	–	1349	–	1353	–	–	–	–	–	–
10 W - 5 Zr	2-II	–	–	–	–	–	–	1349	–	1353	–	–	–	–	–	–
15 W - 5 Mo - 1 Zr	2-II	–	–	–	–	–	–	1349	–	–	–	–	–	–	–	–
15 W - 5 Mo - 1 Zr - 0.5 C . .	2-II	–	–	–	–	–	–	–	–	1353	–	–	–	–	–	–
B-66	2-II	–	–	–	–	–	–	–	–	–	1327, 1359	–	–	–	–	–
Cb-752	2-II	–	–	–	–	–	–	1349	–	–	1355	–	–	–	–	–
F-48	2-II	–	–	–	–	–	–	1349	–	–	1355	–	–	–	–	–
Ferroniobium	2-II	–	–	–	–	–	–	1317	–	–	–	–	–	–	–	–
FS-82	2-II	–	–	–	–	–	–	–	–	–	1335	–	–	–	–	–
FS-82B	2-II	–	–	–	–	–	–	1329	–	–	1335	–	–	–	–	–
FS-85	2-II	–	–	–	–	–	–	–	–	–	1335	–	–	–	–	–
MAR-M200	2-II	–	–	–	–	–	–	–	–	–	1305	–	–	–	–	–
Niobium aluminide ($NbAl_3$) . . .	6-I	–	21	–	–	–	–	–	–	–	–	–	–	23	–	–
Niobium aluminide coating on niobium	6-II	–	–	–	–	–	–	–	–	–	–	–	–	1459	–	–

Material Name	Volume	Density	Melting Point	Heat of Fusion	Heat of Vaporization	Heat of Sublimation	Electrical Resistivity	Specific Heat	Thermal Conductivity	Thermal Diffusivity	Thermal Linear Expansion	Thermal Absorptance	Thermal Emittance	Thermal Reflectance	Thermal Transmittance	Vapor Pressure
Niobium beryllides																
$NbBe_{11}$	6-I	-	108	-	-	-	-	-	-	-	-	-	-	-	-	-
$NbBe_{12}$	6-I	-	108	-	-	-	-	110	112	-	114	-	116	120	-	-
Nb_2Be_{17}	6-I	-	-	-	-	-	-	-	112	-	-	-	116-118	120	-	-
Niobium borides																
NbB	6-I	-	194	-	-	-	-	-	-	-	-	-	-	-	-	-
NbB_2	6-I	194	194	-	-	-	-	196	-	-	198	-	200-202	-	-	-
Nb_3B_2	6-I	-	194	-	-	-	-	-	-	-	-	-	-	-	-	-
Nb_3B_4	6-I	-	194	-	-	-	-	-	-	-	-	-	-	-	-	-
Niobium (di-)boride + Zirconium (di-)boride	6-I	723	-	-	-	-	-	-	-	-	-	-	-	-	-	-
Niobium carbide (NbC).	5	91	91	-	-	-	93	95-97	99	-	101	-	104-106	-	-	-
Niobium-chromium intermetallics ($NbCr_2$)	6-I	-	684	-	-	-	-	-	-	-	-	-	-	-	-	-
Niobium-cobalt intermetallics ($NbCo_2$)	6-I	-	684	-	-	-	-	-	-	-	-	-	-	-	-	-
Niobium ferride ($NbFe_2$)	6-I	-	306	-	-	-	-	-	-	-	-	-	-	-	-	-
Niobium germanides																
$NbGe_2$	6-I	323	323	-	-	-	-	-	327	-	-	-	-	-	-	-
Nb_2Ge	6-I	-	323	-	-	-	-	-	-	-	-	-	-	-	-	-
Nb_3Ge	6-I	323	323	-	-	-	-	-	-	-	-	-	-	-	-	-
Niobium germanide silicides ($NbGe_xSi_{1-x}$)	6-I	-	-	-	-	-	-	-	529	-	-	-	-	-	-	-
Niobium-manganese intermetallics ($NbMn_2$)	6-I	-	684	-	-	-	-	-	-	-	-	-	-	-	-	-
Niobium nitrides																
NbN	5	535	535	-	-	-	537	-	-	-	539	-	-	-	-	-
Nb_2N	5	-	535	-	-	-	-	-	-	-	-	-	-	-	-	-
Niobium oxides																
NbO	4-I	-	-	-	-	-	-	315	-	-	-	-	-	-	-	-
NbO_2	4-I	-	-	-	-	-	-	317	-	-	-	-	-	-	-	-
Nb_2O_5	4-I	313	-	313	-	-	-	319	-	-	321	-	-	-	-	-
Niobium (pent-)oxide + + Aluminum oxide	4-I	-	767	-	-	-	-	-	-	-	769	-	-	-	-	-
Niobium (pent-)oxide + + Beryllium oxide	4-I	-	771	-	-	-	-	-	-	-	-	-	-	-	-	-
Niobium (pent-)oxide + + Magnesium oxide.	4-I	-	773	-	-	-	-	-	-	-	-	-	-	-	-	-
Niobium (pent-)oxide + + Titanium (di-)oxide	4-I	-	775	-	-	-	-	-	-	-	777	-	-	-	-	-
Niobium (pent-)oxide + + Zirconium (di-)oxide. . . .	4-I	-	779	-	-	-	-	-	-	-	781	-	-	-	-	-
Niobium phosphide (NbP) . . .	5	635	635	-	-	-	639	-	-	-	-	-	-	-	-	-
Niobium selenide ($NbSe_2$) . . .	6-I	-	-	-	-	-	367	-	369	-	-	-	-	-	-	-

Material Name	Volume	Density	Melting Point	Heat of Fusion	Heat of Vaporization	Heat of Sublimation	Electrical Resistivity	Specific Heat	Thermal Conductivity	Thermal Diffusivity	Thermal Linear Expansion	Thermal Absorptance	Thermal Emittance	Thermal Reflectance	Thermal Transmittance	Vapor Pressure
Niobium silicides																
$NbSi_2$	6-I	–	–	–	–	–	527	–	529	–	–	–	–	–	–	–
Nb_4Si	6-I	–	457	–	–	–	–	–	–	–	–	–	–	–	–	–
Nb_5Si_3	6-I	–	457	–	–	–	–	–	–	–	459	–	–	–	–	–
(Penta-) niobium (tri-) silicide + + (Di-) molybdenum boride . .	6-I	–	724	–	–	–	–	–	–	–	–	–	–	–	–	–
Niobium silicide germanides																
NbSiGe	6-I	–	–	–	–	–	317	–	319	–	–	–	–	–	–	–
$NbSi_{1-X}Ge_X$	6-I	–	–	–	–	–	317	–	319	–	–	–	–	–	–	–
Niobium stannide (Nb_3Sn) . . .	6-I	–	541	–	–	–	–	–	–	–	–	–	–	–	–	–
Niobium telluride ($NbTe_2$) . . .	6-I	–	–	–	–	–	606	–	608	–	–	–	–	–	–	–
Niobium-zirconium alloy coated with barium titanate	6-II	–	–	–	–	–	–	–	–	–	–	–	1369	–	–	–
Niobium-zirconium alloy coated with boron	6-II	–	–	–	–	–	–	–	–	–	–	–	1291	–	–	–
Niobium-zirconium alloy coated with calcium titanate	6-II	–	–	–	–	–	–	–	–	–	–	–	1371	–	–	–
Niobium-zirconium alloy coated with iron titanate	6-II	–	–	–	–	–	–	–	–	–	–	–	1385	–	–	–
Niobium-zirconium alloy coated with nickel chromite	6-II	–	–	–	–	–	–	–	–	–	–	–	1387	–	–	–
Niobium-zirconium alloys coated with silicon carbide	6-II	–	–	–	–	–	–	–	–	–	–	–	1415	–	–	–
Nodular cast iron	3	–	–	–	–	–	–	–	35-37, 437	–	41, 444	–	–	–	–	–
Nodular cast iron, ferritic base .	3	–	–	–	–	–	–	–	37	–	–	–	–	–	–	–
Nodular cast iron, pearlitic base	3	–	–	–	–	–	–	–	35	–	41	–	–	–	–	–
Nycar PA-21	6-II	1051	–	–	–	–	–	–	–	–	–	–	–	–	–	–
Nylon	6-II	–	–	–	–	–	–	1047	–	–	1049	–	–	–	–	–
Nylon 1 N fabrics	6-II	–	–	–	–	–	–	–	–	1273	–	–	–	–	–	–
Nylon 6	6-II	–	–	–	–	–	–	1047	–	–	1049	–	–	–	–	–
Nylon 9	6-II	–	–	–	–	–	–	–	–	–	1049	–	–	–	–	–
Nylon 11	6-II	–	–	–	–	–	–	–	–	–	1049	–	–	–	–	–
Nylon 11 N fabric	6-II	–	–	–	–	–	–	–	–	1273	–	–	–	–	–	–
Nylon 66	6-II	–	–	–	–	–	–	–	–	–	1049	–	–	–	–	–
Nylon fabric	6-II	–	–	–	–	–	–	–	–	1273	–	–	–	–	–	–
Nylon FM-1	6-II	–	–	–	–	–	–	–	–	–	1049	–	–	–	–	–

Material Name	Volume	Density	Melting Point	Heat of Fusion	Heat of Vaporization	Heat of Sublimation	Electrical Resistivity	Specific Heat	Thermal Conductivity	Thermal Diffusivity	Thermal Linear Expansion	Thermal Absorptance	Thermal Emittance	Thermal Reflectance	Thermal Transmittance	Vapor Pressure
O																
OFHC copper	1	–	–	–	–	–	–	–	458	460	–	–	–	–	–	–
Opalon 300 FM	6-II	–	1076	–	–	–	–	–	–	–	–	–	–	–	–	–
Organic fiber cloth	6-II	–	–	–	–	–	–	–	–	–	1275	–	–	–	–	–
Osmium (Os)	1	744	744	–	–	–	746	–	748	–	–	–	750	–	–	–
P																
Palatinol AH	6-II	–	–	–	–	–	–	–	1086	–	–	–	–	–	–	–
Palladium (Pd)	1	752	752	–	–	–	754	756	758	–	–	760	762-764	766	–	–
Palladium + Cobalt + ΣX_i . . .	2-II	–	1363	–	–	–	1366-1368	–	–	–	–	–	–	–	–	–
Palladium + Copper + ΣX_i . . .	2-II	–	1370	–	–	–	–	1372	–	–	–	–	–	–	–	–
Palladium + Gold + ΣX_i	2-II	–	1374	–	–	–	1376	–	–	–	–	–	–	–	–	–
Palladium + Nickel	2-I	–	–	–	–	–	391	–	–	–	–	–	–	–	–	–
Palladium + Nickel + ΣX_i . . .	2-II	–	–	–	–	–	–	–	–	–	1378	–	–	–	–	–
Palladium + Uranium	2-I	–	393	–	–	–	–	–	–	–	–	–	–	–	–	–
Palladium aluminides																
PdAl	6-I	–	43	–	–	–	–	–	–	–	–	–	–	–	–	–
Pd_3Al	6-I	–	43	–	–	–	–	–	–	–	–	–	–	–	–	–
Palladium beryllides																
PdBe	6-I	–	158	–	–	–	–	–	–	–	–	–	–	–	–	–
$PdBe_{12}$	6-I	–	158	–	–	–	–	–	–	–	–	–	–	–	–	–
Palladium brazing alloy GE-76 .	2-II	–	–	–	–	–	–	–	–	–	1378	–	–	–	–	–
Palladium tellurides																
PdTe	6-I	–	–	–	–	–	–	610	–	–	–	–	–	–	–	–
$PdTe_2$	6-I	–	–	–	–	–	–	610	–	–	–	–	–	–	–	–
Panelyte, grade 942	6-II	–	–	–	–	–	–	–	–	–	1107	–	–	–	–	–
Paraplex P43	6-II	–	–	–	–	–	–	–	–	–	978	–	–	–	–	–
Penton 1215	6-II	–	1076	–	–	–	–	–	–	–	–	–	–	–	–	–
Perbunan 18	6-II	–	–	–	–	–	–	–	–	1060	–	–	–	–	–	–
Perbunan 26	6-II	–	–	–	–	–	–	–	–	1060	–	–	–	–	–	–
Perbunan 35	6-II	–	–	–	–	–	–	–	–	1060	–	–	–	–	–	–
Periclase	4-I	–	–	–	–	–	–	–	254	–	–	–	–	–	–	–
Periclase, synthetic	4-I	–	–	–	–	–	–	–	254	–	–	–	–	–	–	–
Permanickel 300	2-II	1257	–	–	–	–	–	–	–	–	1303	–	–	–	–	–
Phenacite, synthetic	4-II	–	–	–	–	–	–	–	–	–	1223	–	–	–	–	–
Phenol formaldehyde	6-II	–	–	–	–	–	–	–	–	–	986	–	–	–	–	–
Phenol formaldehyde, asbestos filled	6-II	–	–	–	–	–	–	–	–	–	988	–	–	–	–	–
Phenol formaldehyde, ceramic filled	6-II	–	–	–	–	–	–	–	–	–	990	–	–	–	–	–
Phenol formaldehyde, cord filled	6-II	–	–	–	–	–	–	–	–	–	992	–	–	–	–	–

Material Name	Volume	Density	Melting Point	Heat of Fusion	Heat of Vaporization	Heat of Sublimation	Electrical Resistivity	Specific Heat	Thermal Conductivity	Thermal Diffusivity	Thermal Linear Expansion	Thermal Absorptance	Thermal Emittance	Thermal Reflectance	Thermal Transmittance	Vapor Pressure
Phenol formaldehyde, cotton flock filled	6-II	-	-	-	-	-	-	-	-	-	994	-	-	-	-	-
Phenol formaldehyde, fabric filled	6-II	-	-	-	-	-	-	-	-	-	996	-	-	-	-	-
Phenol formaldehyde, stupalith A-2412	6-II	-	-	-	-	-	-	-	-	-	990	-	-	-	-	-
Phenol formaldehyde, wood flour filled	6-II	-	-	-	-	-	-	-	-	-	998	-	-	-	-	-
Phenolic, alpha cellulose paper reinforced	6-II	-	-	-	-	-	-	-	-	-	1105	-	-	-	-	-
Phenolic, cotton fabric reinforced	6-II	-	-	-	-	-	-	-	-	-	1107	-	-	-	-	-
Phenolic, LMI 304 nylon reinforced	6-II	-	-	-	-	-	1103	-	-	-	-	-	-	-	-	-
Phenolic, long glass fiber reinforced	6-II	-	-	-	-	-	1103	-	-	-	-	-	-	-	-	-
Phenolic and epoxide copolymer resin, reinforced	6-II	-	-	-	-	-	-	-	-	-	1126	-	-	-	-	-
Phenolic novolak	6-II	-	-	-	-	-	982	-	-	-	-	-	-	-	-	-
Phenolic, reinforced	6-II	-	-	-	-	-	1103	-	-	-	1105-1107	-	-	-	-	-
Phenolic resin	6-II	980	-	-	-	-	982	-	984	1082	-	-	-	-	-	-
Phenolic resin, reinforced . . .	6-II	1130	-	-	-	-	-	1132-1146	1148-1156	1159-1170	1172-1179	-	-	-	-	-
Phenolic resin, type S	6-II	980	-	-	-	-	-	-	984	1082	-	-	-	-	-	-
Phenolites																
Phenolite	6-II	-	-	-	-	-	-	-	-	-	1101, 1176	-	-	-	-	-
NEMA C	6-II	-	-	-	-	-	-	-	-	-	1107	-	-	-	-	-
NEMA L	6-II	-	-	-	-	-	-	-	-	-	1107	-	-	-	-	-
NEMA LE	6-II	-	-	-	-	-	-	-	-	-	1107	-	-	-	-	-
NEMA X	6-II	-	-	-	-	-	-	-	-	-	1107	-	-	-	-	-
NEMA XP	6-II	-	-	-	-	-	-	-	-	-	1105	-	-	-	-	-
NEMA XXX	6-II	-	-	-	-	-	-	-	-	-	1105	-	-	-	-	-
NEMA XXXP	6-II	-	-	-	-	-	-	-	-	-	1105	-	-	-	-	-
XXXP	6-II	-	-	-	-	-	-	-	-	-	1105	-	-	-	-	-
Phenyl silane resin	6-II	-	-	-	-	-	-	1074	-	-	-	-	-	-	-	-
Phenyl silane resin, reinforced.	6-II	-	-	-	-	-	-	1212	-	1220	-	-	-	-	-	-
Phenyl silane SC-1013 Monsanto	6-II	-	-	-	-	-	-	1074	-	-	-	-	-	-	-	-
Phosphate glass	4-II	1649	-	-	-	-	-	-	-	-	-	-	-	-	-	-
Phosphorus (pent-)oxide + + Zirconium (di-)oxide. . . .	4-I	-	-	-	-	-	-	-	-	-	787	-	-	-	-	-
Pittsburg no. 3235 glass	4-II	-	-	-	-	-	-	1697	-	-	-	-	1705	1709	1711-1713	-
Plate glass	4-II	1779	-	-	-	-	-	1791	1783	1793	1797	-	-	-	-	-
Plate glass no. 9330.	4-II	-	-	-	-	-	-	1791	-	-	-	-	-	-	-	-

Material Name	Volume	Density	Melting Point	Heat of Fusion	Heat of Vaporization	Heat of Sublimation	Electrical Resistivity	Specific Heat	Thermal Conductivity	Thermal Diffusivity	Thermal Linear Expansion	Thermal Absorptance	Thermal Emittance	Thermal Reflectance	Thermal Transmittance	Vapor Pressure
Platinum (Pt)	1	768	768	–	–	–	770	772	774	776	778	780	782-788	790	–	–
Platinum coating on copper . . .	6-II	–	–	–	–	–	–	–	–	–	–	–	1313	–	–	–
Platinum coating on quartz . . .	6-II	–	–	–	–	–	–	–	–	–	–	–	–	1317	1319	–
Platinum coating on stainless steel	6-II	–	–	–	–	–	–	–	–	–	–	–	1315	–	–	–
Platinum + Copper	2-I	–	–	–	–	–	395-397	–	–	–	–	–	–	–	–	–
Platinum + Iron	2-I	–	–	–	–	–	399	–	–	–	401	–	–	–	–	–
Platinum + Rhodium	2-I	–	–	–	–	–	–	–	403	–	–	–	405	407	–	–
Platinum arsenide (Pt_2As_3) . . .	6-I	–	94	–	–	–	–	–	–	–	–	–	–	–	–	–
Platinum beryllide ($PtBe_{12}$) . .	6-I	158	–	–	–	–	–	–	–	–	–	–	–	–	–	–
Platinum stannide (Pt_3Sn) . . .	6-I	–	541	–	–	–	–	–	–	–	–	–	–	–	–	–
Platinum sulfides																
PtS	5	–	–	–	–	–	–	698	–	–	–	–	–	–	–	–
PtS_2	5	–	–	–	–	–	–	698	–	–	–	–	–	–	–	–
Platinum tellurides																
PtTe	6-I	–	–	–	–	–	–	612	–	–	–	–	–	–	–	–
$PtTe_2$	6-I	–	–	–	–	–	–	612	–	–	–	–	–	–	–	–
Plexiglas 11	6-II	–	–	–	–	–	–	–	–	–	1026	–	–	–	–	–
Plexiglas AN-P-44A	6-II	1020	1020	–	–	–	–	1022	1024	–	1026	–	–	–	–	–
Plutonium (Pu)	1	794	792	–	792	–	796	799	–	–	801	–	–	–	–	–
Plutonium + Cerium + ΣX_i . . .	2-II	–	–	–	–	–	–	1380	–	–	–	–	–	–	–	–
Plutonium + Osmium	2-I	409	–	–	–	–	–	–	–	–	–	–	–	–	–	–
Plutonium + Thorium	2-I	411	–	–	–	–	–	–	–	–	–	–	–	–	–	–
Plutonium beryllide ($PuBe_{13}$) . .	6-I	158	158	–	–	–	–	–	–	–	–	–	–	–	–	–
Plutonium bromide ($PuBr_3$) . . .	5	3	3	3	3	3	–	–	–	–	–	–	–	–	–	5
Plutonium carbides																
PuC	5	–	–	–	–	–	110	112	–	–	114	–	–	–	–	–
Pu_2C_3	5	108	–	–	–	–	–	–	–	–	117	–	–	–	–	–
Plutonium chloride ($PuCl_3$) . . .	5	327	327	327	327	327	–	–	–	–	–	–	–	–	–	329
Plutonium ferrides																
$PuFe_2$	6-I	306	306	–	–	–	–	–	–	–	–	–	–	–	–	–
Pu_6Fe	6-I	306	–	–	–	–	–	–	–	–	–	–	–	–	–	–
Plutonium fluoride (PuF_3) . . .	5	389	389	389	389	389	–	–	–	–	–	–	–	–	–	391
Plutonium iodide (PuI_3)	5	471	471	471	471	471	–	–	–	–	–	–	–	–	–	473
Plutonium-lead intermetallics ($PuPb_3$)	6-I	–	671	–	–	–	–	–	–	–	–	–	–	–	–	–
Plutonium-manganese intermetallics ($PuMn_2$)	6-I	671	671	–	–	–	–	–	–	–	–	–	–	–	–	–
Plutonium-nickel intermetallics																
PuNi	6-I	–	671	–	–	–	–	–	–	–	–	–	–	–	–	–
$PuNi_2$	6-I	–	671	–	–	–	–	–	–	–	–	–	–	–	–	–
$PuNi_5$	6-I	–	671	–	–	–	–	–	–	–	–	–	–	–	–	–

Material Name	Volume	Density	Melting Point	Heat of Fusion	Heat of Vaporization	Heat of Sublimation	Electrical Resistivity	Specific Heat	Thermal Conductivity	Thermal Diffusivity	Thermal Linear Expansion	Thermal Absorptance	Thermal Emittance	Thermal Reflectance	Thermal Transmittance	Vapor Pressure
Plutonium nitride (PuN)	5	–	–	–	–	–	–	–	–	–	541	–	–	–	–	–
Plutonium–osmium intermetallics ($PuOs_2$)	6–I	671	671	–	–	–	–	–	–	–	–	–	–	–	–	–
Plutonium oxides																
PuO	4–I	–	–	–	–	323	–	–	–	–	–	–	–	–	–	329
PuO_2	4–I	323	323	–	–	–	–	325	–	–	327	–	–	–	–	329
Plutonium silicide ($PuSi_2$) . . .	6–I	523	–	–	–	–	–	–	–	–	–	–	–	–	–	–
Polonium (Po)	1	–	–	–	–	–	–	–	–	–	–	–	–	–	–	803
Polybutadiene	6–II	–	–	–	–	–	–	–	–	1066	–	–	–	–	–	–
Polychlorotrifluoroethylene . .	6–II	–	–	–	–	–	–	–	1037	–	1045	–	–	–	–	–
Polyester, glass fiber reinforced	6–II	–	–	–	–	–	–	–	–	–	1109	–	–	–	–	–
Polyester, unsaturated	6–II	–	–	–	–	–	–	–	–	–	968	–	–	–	–	–
Polyester resin, reinforced . .	6–II	1180	–	–	–	–	–	1191	1195–1198	1220	1200	–	–	–	–	–
Polyethylene	6–II	1030	–	–	–	–	–	–	1037	–	1045	–	–	–	–	–
Polyethylene, halogenated . . .	6–II	1030	–	–	–	–	–	–	–	–	1045	–	–	–	–	–
Polyethylene PE 575	6–II	–	1030	–	–	–	–	–	–	–	–	–	–	–	–	–
Polyfluorobutyl acrylate rubber .	6–II	1051	–	–	–	–	–	–	–	–	–	–	–	–	–	–
Polyisoprene	6–II	–	–	–	–	–	–	–	–	1066	–	–	–	–	–	–
Polymethyl methacrylate	6–II	–	–	–	–	–	–	–	–	–	1026	–	–	–	–	–
Polymethyl methacrylate, alumina filled	6–II	–	–	–	–	–	–	–	–	–	1028	–	–	–	–	–
Polymethyl methacrylate, boron phosphate filled	6–II	–	–	–	–	–	–	–	–	–	1028	–	–	–	–	–
Polymethyl methacrylate, calcium carbonate filled . . .	6–II	–	–	–	–	–	–	–	–	–	1028	–	–	–	–	–
Polymethyl methacrylate, silica filled	6–II	–	–	–	–	–	–	–	–	–	1028	–	–	–	–	–
Polymethyl methacrylate, zinc oxide filled	6–II	–	–	–	–	–	–	–	–	–	1028	–	–	–	–	–
Polypropylene	6–II	1076	1076	–	–	–	–	1078	1080	–	1088	–	–	–	–	–
Polystyrene	6–II	–	1076	–	–	–	–	–	1090	–	1092	–	–	–	–	–
Polystyrene, Grade 912A . . .	6–II	–	–	–	–	–	–	–	–	–	1092	–	–	–	–	–
Polystyrene foam	6–II	–	–	–	–	–	–	–	1090	–	–	–	–	–	–	–
Polytetrafluoroethylene	6–II	–	–	–	–	–	–	1035	1039	–	1045	–	–	–	–	–
Polytetrafluoroethylene laminate	6–II	–	–	–	–	–	–	1214	1218	1220	–	–	–	–	–	–
Polythene, germanium (di-) oxide filled	6–II	–	–	–	–	–	–	–	–	–	1041	–	–	–	–	–
Polythene, iron(ic) oxide filled .	6–II	–	–	–	–	–	–	–	–	–	1041	–	–	–	–	–
Polythene, scandium oxide filled	6–II	–	–	–	–	–	–	–	–	–	1041	–	–	–	–	–
Polythene PM-1	6–II	–	–	–	–	–	–	–	–	–	1045	–	–	–	–	–
Polyurethane foam	6–II	962	–	–	–	–	–	–	964	–	966	–	–	–	–	–
Polyvinyl carbazole	6–II	–	–	–	–	–	–	970	972	–	–	–	–	–	–	–
Polyvinyl chloride	6–II	–	1076	–	–	–	–	–	1086	–	–	–	–	–	–	–

Material Name	Volume	Density	Melting Point	Heat of Fusion	Heat of Vaporization	Heat of Sublimation	Electrical Resistivity	Specific Heat	Thermal Conductivity	Thermal Diffusivity	Thermal Linear Expansion	Thermal Absorptance	Thermal Emittance	Thermal Reflectance	Thermal Transmittance	Vapor Pressure
Polyvinyl chloride, cellular . .	6-II	-	-	-	-	-	-	-	1086	-	-	-	-	-	-	-
Porcelain	5	1003	-	-	-	-	1005-1013	1015	1017	-	1019-1021	-	-	-	-	-
Porcelain 7A2	5	-	-	-	-	-	-	-	1017	-	-	-	-	-	-	-
Porcelain 576	5	1003	-	-	-	-	-	-	1017	-	-	-	-	-	-	-
Porcelain, aluminum oxide . . .	5	1003	-	-	-	-	-	1015	1017	-	-	-	-	-	-	-
Porcelain, cone 14	5	-	-	-	-	-	1007	-	-	-	-	-	-	-	-	-
Porcelains, electrical																
K-3 body	5	-	-	-	-	-	1005	-	-	-	-	-	-	-	-	-
K-5 body	5	-	-	-	-	-	1005	-	-	-	-	-	-	-	-	-
K-6 body	5	-	-	-	-	-	1005	-	-	-	-	-	-	-	-	-
K-7 body	5	-	-	-	-	-	1005	-	-	-	-	-	-	-	-	-
K-8 body	5	-	-	-	-	-	1005	-	-	-	-	-	-	-	-	-
K-9 body	5	-	-	-	-	-	1005	-	-	-	-	-	-	-	-	-
Li-K-1 body	5	-	-	-	-	-	1011	-	-	-	-	-	-	-	-	-
Li-K-2a body	5	-	-	-	-	-	1011	-	-	-	-	-	-	-	-	-
Li-K-2b body	5	-	-	-	-	-	1011	-	-	-	-	-	-	-	-	-
Li-K-2c body	5	-	-	-	-	-	1011	-	-	-	-	-	-	-	-	-
Li-K-2d body	5	-	-	-	-	-	1011	-	-	-	-	-	-	-	-	-
Li-K-2e body	5	-	-	-	-	-	1011	-	-	-	-	-	-	-	-	-
Lithium modified	5	-	-	-	-	-	1011	-	-	-	-	-	-	-	-	-
Pelalite body	5	-	-	-	-	-	1011	-	-	-	-	-	-	-	-	-
Porcelain, feldspar, dinnerware cone 12-14	5	-	-	-	-	-	1007	-	-	-	-	-	-	-	-	-
Porcelain, zircon	5	1003	-	-	-	-	1013	-	1017	-	1021	-	-	-	-	-
Potassium aluminum silicates .	4-II	-	-	-	-	-	-	-	-	-	1316-1318	-	-	-	-	-
Potassium aluminum silicate + + Iron(ic) oxide	4-II	-	-	-	-	-	-	1573	-	-	-	-	-	-	-	-
Potassium borate glass	4-II	1605	-	-	-	-	1607	-	-	-	-	-	-	-	-	-
Potassium bromide (KBr) . . .	5	-	-	-	-	-	-	-	-	-	-	-	-	7	-	-
Potassium chloride (KCl) . . .	5	-	-	-	-	-	-	-	-	-	-	-	-	331	-	-
Potassium feldspar	4-II	-	-	-	-	-	-	-	-	-	1316-1318	-	-	-	-	-
Potassium fluoride + Lithium fluoride	5	-	-	-	-	-	-	409	-	-	-	-	-	-	-	-
Potassium mica	5	-	-	-	-	-	-	-	-	-	1001	-	-	-	-	-
Potassium sodium aluminum silicates	4-II	-	-	-	-	-	-	-	-	-	1320	-	-	-	-	-
Potassium uranate ($K_2O \cdot UO_3$) .	4-II	-	1482	-	-	-	-	-	-	-	-	-	-	-	-	-
Potassium lead silicate glass . .	4-II	-	-	-	-	-	1777	-	-	-	-	-	-	-	-	-
Potassium silicate glass	4-II	-	-	-	-	-	-	-	-	-	1775	-	-	-	-	-
Praseodymium (Pr)	1	805	805	805	805	-	807	809	-	-	-	-	-	-	-	811
Praseodymium + ΣX_i	2-II	-	1382	-	-	-	-	-	-	-	-	-	-	-	-	-

Material Name	Volume	Density	Melting Point	Heat of Fusion	Heat of Vaporization	Heat of Sublimation	Electrical Resistivity	Specific Heat	Thermal Conductivity	Thermal Diffusivity	Thermal Linear Expansion	Thermal Absorptance	Thermal Emittance	Thermal Reflectance	Thermal Transmittance	Vapor Pressure
Praseodymium + Magnesium . .	2-I	413	–	–	–	–	–	–	–	–	–	–	–	–	–	–
Praseodymium + Neodymium . .	2-I	–	–	–	–	–	–	–	–	–	415	–	–	–	–	–
Praseodymium + Silicon	2-I	–	–	–	–	–	–	417	–	–	–	–	–	–	–	–
Praseodymium aluminides																
PrAl	6-I	–	43	–	–	–	–	–	–	–	–	–	–	–	–	–
$PrAl_2$	6-I	–	43	–	–	–	–	–	–	–	–	–	–	–	–	–
$PrAl_4$	6-I	–	43	–	–	–	–	–	–	–	–	–	–	–	–	–
Pr_3Al_2	6-I	–	43	–	–	–	–	–	–	–	–	–	–	–	–	–
Praseodymium-bismuth intermetallics (PrBi)	6-I	673	–	–	–	–	–	–	–	–	–	–	–	–	–	–
Praseodymium borides																
PrB_4	6-I	296	–	–	–	–	–	–	–	–	–	–	–	–	–	–
PrB_6	6-I	295-296	–	–	–	–	300	–	–	–	–	–	–	–	–	–
Praseodymium bromide ($PrBr_3$)	5	11	–	–	–	–	–	–	–	–	–	–	–	–	–	–
Praseodymium-cadmium intermetallics																
PrCd	6-I	673	–	–	–	–	–	–	–	–	–	–	–	–	–	–
$PrCd_2$	6-I	673	–	–	–	–	–	–	–	–	–	–	–	–	–	–
$PrCd_3$	6-I	673	–	–	–	–	–	–	–	–	–	–	–	–	–	–
$PrCd_{11}$	6-I	673	–	–	–	–	–	–	–	–	–	–	–	–	–	–
Praseodymium carbides																
PrC_2	5	294	–	–	–	–	–	–	–	–	–	–	–	–	–	–
Pr_2C_3	5	294	–	–	–	–	–	–	–	–	–	–	–	–	–	–
Praseodymium chloride ($PrCl_3$).	5	339	–	–	–	–	–	–	–	–	–	–	–	–	–	–
Praseodymium-cobalt intermetallics																
$PrCo_2$	6-I	673	–	–	–	–	–	–	–	–	–	–	–	–	–	–
$PrCo_5$	6-I	673	–	–	–	–	–	–	–	–	–	–	–	–	–	–
Praseodymium-copper intermetallics																
PrCu	6-I	–	673	–	–	–	–	–	–	–	–	–	–	–	–	–
$PrCu_2$	6-I	–	673	–	–	–	–	–	–	–	–	–	–	–	–	–
$PrCu_4$	6-I	–	673	–	–	–	–	–	–	–	–	–	–	–	–	–
$PrCu_6$	6-I	–	673	–	–	–	–	–	–	–	–	–	–	–	–	–
Praseodymium-gallium intermetallics ($PrGa_2$)	6-I	673	–	–	–	–	–	–	–	–	–	–	–	–	–	–
Praseodymium germanides																
PrGe	6-I	323	–	–	–	–	–	–	–	–	–	–	–	–	–	–
$PrGe_2$	6-I	323	–	–	–	–	–	–	–	–	–	–	–	–	–	–
Praseodymium-gold intermetallics																
PrAu	6-I	–	673	–	–	–	–	–	–	–	–	–	–	–	–	–
$PrAu_2$	6-I	–	673	–	–	–	–	–	–	–	–	–	–	–	–	–

Material Name	Volume	Density	Melting Point	Heat of Fusion	Heat of Vaporization	Heat of Sublimation	Electrical Resistivity	Specific Heat	Thermal Conductivity	Thermal Diffusivity	Thermal Linear Expansion	Thermal Absorptance	Thermal Emittance	Thermal Reflectance	Thermal Transmittance	Vapor Pressure
Praseodymium-gold intermetallics (cont.)																
$PrAu_3$	6-I	-	673	-	-	-	-	-	-	-	-	-	-	-	-	-
Pr_2Au	6-I	-	673	-	-	-	-	-	-	-	-	-	-	-	-	-
Praseodymium hydride (PrH_2) .	5	467	-	-	-	-	-	-	-	-	-	-	-	-	-	-
Praseodymium-indium intermetallics																
$PrIn_3$	6-I	673	-	-	-	-	-	-	-	-	-	-	-	-	-	-
Pr_3In	6-I	673	-	-	-	-	-	-	-	-	-	-	-	-	-	-
Praseodymium-lead intermetallics																
PrPb	6-I	-	674	-	-	-	-	-	-	-	-	-	-	-	-	-
$PrPb_3$	6-I	673	674	-	-	-	-	-	-	-	-	-	-	-	-	-
Pr_2Pb	6-I	-	674	-	-	-	-	-	-	-	-	-	-	-	-	-
Praseodymium-magnesium intermetallics																
PrMg	6-I	673	674	-	-	-	-	-	-	-	-	-	-	-	-	-
$PrMg_3$	6-I	673	674	-	-	-	-	-	-	-	-	-	-	-	-	-
$PrMg_9$	6-I	-	674	-	-	-	-	-	-	-	-	-	-	-	-	-
Pr_4Mg	6-I	-	674	-	-	-	-	-	-	-	-	-	-	-	-	-
Praseodymium-mercury intermetallics (PrHg)	6-I	673	-	-	-	-	-	-	-	-	-	-	-	-	-	-
Praseodymium-nickel intermetallics ($PrNi_5$)	6-I	673	-	-	-	-	-	-	-	-	-	-	-	-	-	-
Praseodymium-osmium intermetallics ($PrOs_2$)	6-I	673	-	-	-	-	-	-	-	-	-	-	-	-	-	-
Praseodymium oxides																
$PrO_{1.70-1.83}$	4-I	-	-	-	-	-	-	-	-	-	-	-	-	-	-	335
Pr_6O_{11}	4-I	-	-	-	-	-	-	331	-	-	333	-	-	-	-	-
Praseodymium phosphide (PrP).	5	635	-	-	-	-	-	-	-	-	-	-	-	-	-	-
Praseodymium selenides																
PrSe	6-I	365	-	-	-	-	-	-	-	-	-	-	-	-	-	-
Pr_2Se_3	6-I	365	-	-	-	-	-	-	-	-	-	-	-	-	-	-
Pr_3Se_4	6-I	365	-	-	-	-	-	-	-	-	-	-	-	-	-	-
Praseodymium silicides ($PrSi_2$).	6-I	523	-	-	-	-	-	-	-	-	-	-	-	-	-	-
Praseodymium-silver intermetallics																
PrAg	6-I	673	673	-	-	-	-	-	-	-	-	-	-	-	-	-
$PrAg_2$	6-I	-	673	-	-	-	-	-	-	-	-	-	-	-	-	-
$PrAg_3$	6-I	-	673	-	-	-	-	-	-	-	-	-	-	-	-	-
Praseodymium stannides																
$PrSn_3$	6-I	-	541	-	-	-	-	-	-	-	-	-	-	-	-	-
Pr_2Sn	6-I	-	541	-	-	-	-	-	-	-	-	-	-	-	-	-
Pr_2Sn_3	6-I	-	541	-	-	-	-	-	-	-	-	-	-	-	-	-

Material Name	Volume	Density	Melting Point	Heat of Fusion	Heat of Vaporization	Heat of Sublimation	Electrical Resistivity	Specific Heat	Thermal Conductivity	Thermal Diffusivity	Thermal Linear Expansion	Thermal Absorptance	Thermal Emittance	Thermal Reflectance	Thermal Transmittance	Vapor Pressure
Praseodymium sulfides																
PrS	5	700	–	–	–	–	–	–	–	–	702	–	–	–	–	–
PrS_2	5	700	–	–	–	–	–	–	–	–	–	–	–	–	–	–
Pr_2S_3	5	700	–	–	–	–	–	–	–	–	702	–	–	–	–	–
Pr_3S_4	5	700	–	–	–	–	–	–	–	–	–	–	–	–	–	–
Praseodymium-thallium intermetallics																
$PrTl$	6-I	–	674	–	–	–	–	–	–	–	–	–	–	–	–	–
$PrTl_3$	6-I	–	674	–	–	–	–	–	–	–	–	–	–	–	–	–
Pr_2Tl	6-I	–	674	–	–	–	–	–	–	–	–	–	–	–	–	–
Promethium (Pm)	1	–	813	813	–	813	–	–	–	–	–	–	–	–	–	–
Protactinium (Pa)	1	815	815	–	–	–	–	–	–	–	–	–	–	–	–	–
Protactinium oxide (PaO) . . .	4-I	337	–	–	–	–	–	–	–	–	–	–	–	–	–	–
Protoenstatite	4-II	–	–	–	–	–	–	–	–	–	1295	–	–	–	–	–
Pu-Ce-Co eutectic alloy	2-II	–	–	–	–	–	–	1380	–	–	–	–	–	–	–	–
Pyrex 774	4-II	1693	–	–	–	–	–	–	1699	1701	1703	–	1707	1709	1713	–
Pyrex 7740	4-II	–	–	–	–	–	–	1697	–	1701	–	–	1705	1709	1711-1713	–
Pyrex glasses	4-II	1693	–	–	–	–	–	1697	1699	1701	1703	–	1705-1707	1709	1711-1713	–
Pyrocerams																
Pyroceram 9606	4-II	–	–	–	–	–	–	1587	1589	1591	–	–	1593-1599	1601	1603	–
Pyroceram 9608	4-II	–	–	–	–	–	–	1587	1589	1591	–	–	1593-1599	1601	1603	–
Pyroceram 9690	4-II	–	–	–	–	–	–	–	–	1591	–	–	–	–	–	–
Pyrolytic carbon	1	83	–	–	–	–	–	–	89	–	–	–	–	–	–	–
Pyrolytic carbon EYX-4	1	–	–	–	–	–	–	–	89	–	–	–	–	–	–	–
Pyrolytic graphite	1	–	–	–	–	–	–	–	317	–	319	–	325-331	333-335	–	–
Pyrolytic graphite coating on tantalum	6-II	–	–	–	–	–	–	–	–	–	–	–	1297-1299	–	–	–
Pyrolytic graphite + Zirconium (pyro-) carbide	5	–	–	–	–	–	–	–	–	–	745	–	–	–	–	–
Q																
Quartz	4-I	353	353	–	–	–	355	357	361	365	–	–	–	379	381	–
Quartz coated with magnesium fluoride	6-II	–	–	–	–	–	–	–	–	–	–	–	–	1425	1427	–
Quartz coated with platinum . .	6-II	–	–	–	–	–	–	–	–	–	–	–	–	1317	1319	–
Quartz glass	4-II	1651	–	–	–	–	1653	1655	1657	–	–	–	–	–	–	–

Material Name	Volume	Density	Melting Point	Heat of Fusion	Heat of Vaporization	Heat of Sublimation	Electrical Resistivity	Specific Heat	Thermal Conductivity	Thermal Diffusivity	Thermal Linear Expansion	Thermal Absorptance	Thermal Emittance	Thermal Reflectance	Thermal Transmittance	Vapor Pressure
R																
Rene 41	2-II	1122	-	-	-	-	-	1130	1134	-	1156	-	1184, 1199	1211	-	-
Resimene 814 resin	6-II	-	1014	-	-	-	-	-	-	-	-	-	-	-	-	-
Rhenium (Re)	1	817	817	-	-	817	820	822	824	-	826	-	828-832	-	-	834
Rhenium + Tungsten	2-I	-	419	-	-	-	-	-	-	-	-	-	-	-	-	-
Rhenium arsenide (Re_3As_7) . . .	6-I	-	-	-	-	-	96	-	-	-	-	-	-	-	-	-
Rhenium phosphide (ReP) . . .	5	-	635	-	-	-	-	-	-	-	-	-	-	-	-	-
Rhenium selenide ($ReSe_2$) . . .	6-I	-	-	-	-	-	349	-	351	-	-	-	-	-	-	-
Rhenium silicides																
ReSi	6-I	-	461	-	-	-	-	-	-	-	463	-	-	-	-	465
$ReSi_2$	6-I	-	461	-	-	-	-	-	-	-	463	-	-	-	-	465
Re_3Si	6-I	-	461	-	-	-	-	-	-	-	-	-	-	-	-	465
Rhodium (Rh)	1	836	836	-	-	-	838	840	842	-	-	-	844-848	850	-	-
Rhodium germanides																
RhGe	6-I	323	-	-	-	-	-	-	-	-	-	-	-	-	-	-
Rh_2Ge	6-I	323	-	-	-	-	-	-	-	-	-	-	-	-	-	-
Rh_3Ge_4	6-I	323	-	-	-	-	-	-	-	-	-	-	-	-	-	-
Rh_5Ge_3	6-I	323	-	-	-	-	-	-	-	-	-	-	-	-	-	-
Rokide A coating on AISI 446 . .	6-II	-	-	-	-	-	-	-	-	-	-	-	-	1351	-	-
Rokide C coating on titanium alloy 6 Al - 4 V	6-II	-	-	-	-	-	-	-	-	-	-	-	1345-1347	-	-	-
Rubbers																
Board no. 2266, cellular . .	6-II	-	-	-	-	-	-	-	1056	-	-	-	-	-	-	-
Buna	6-II	1051	-	-	-	-	-	1054	1056	1066	-	-	-	-	-	-
Dielectric mix	6-II	-	-	-	-	-	-	-	1056	-	-	-	-	-	-	-
Natural	6-II	1051	-	-	-	-	-	-	1056	1058	1068	-	-	-	-	-
Perbunan	6-II	1051	-	-	-	-	-	1054	1056	1060	-	-	-	-	-	-
Silicone	6-II	-	-	-	-	-	-	-	-	1064	1068	-	-	-	-	-
Synthetic	6-II	1051	-	-	-	-	-	1054	1056	1060-1066	1068	-	-	-	-	-
Rubidium fluoride (RbF)	5	-	-	-	-	-	-	393	-	-	-	-	-	-	-	395
Ruthenium (Ru)	1	852	852	-	-	852	854	856	858	-	-	-	-	-	-	860
Ruthenium-tungsten intermetallics (Ru_2W_3)	6-I	-	684	-	-	-	-	-	-	-	-	-	-	-	-	-
Rutile	4-I	445	-	-	-	-	450	454	460	-	462	-	-	-	-	-

Material Name	Volume	Density	Melting Point	Heat of Fusion	Heat of Vaporization	Heat of Sublimation	Electrical Resistivity	Specific Heat	Thermal Conductivity	Thermal Diffusivity	Thermal Linear Expansion	Thermal Absorptance	Thermal Emittance	Thermal Reflectance	Thermal Transmittance	Vapor Pressure
S																
SAE 1006	3	-	-	-	-	-	-	-	-	329	-	-	-	-	-	-
SAE 1010	3	310	-	-	-	-	312	316	325	329	335	-	-	-	-	-
SAE 1018	3	-	-	-	-	-	-	-	-	333	-	-	-	-	-	-
SAE 1020	3	-	-	-	-	-	-	-	-	329	-	-	345-347	-	-	-
SAE 1045	3	-	-	-	-	-	-	-	-	333	-	-	-	-	-	-
SAE 3140	3	-	-	-	-	-	-	-	-	365	-	-	-	-	-	-
SAE 4130	3	-	-	-	-	-	-	-	-	85	-	-	-	-	-	-
SAE 4340	3	-	-	-	-	-	-	-	387	395	-	-	-	-	-	-
SAE 8630	3	-	-	-	-	-	-	-	-	-	337	-	-	-	-	-
Samaria	4-I	339	339	-	-	-	-	341	-	-	343	-	345	-	-	-
Samarium (Sm)	1	862	862	862	862	862	864	866	-	-	-	-	-	-	-	-
Samarium-bismuth intermetallics (SmBi)	6-I	681	-	-	-	-	-	-	-	-	-	-	-	-	-	-
Samarium borides																
SmB_4	6-I	295	-	-	-	-	-	-	-	-	-	-	-	-	-	-
SmB_6	6-I	295	296	-	-	-	300	-	-	-	302	-	-	-	-	-
Samarium-cadmium intermetallics																
SmCd	6-I	681	-	-	-	-	-	-	-	-	-	-	-	-	-	-
$SmCd_2$	6-I	681	-	-	-	-	-	-	-	-	-	-	-	-	-	-
$SmCd_{11}$	6-I	681	-	-	-	-	-	-	-	-	-	-	-	-	-	-
Samarium carbides																
SmC_2	5	294	294	-	-	-	-	-	-	-	-	-	-	-	-	-
Sm_2C_3	5	294	-	-	-	-	-	-	-	-	-	-	-	-	-	-
Samarium-cobalt intermetallics																
$SmCo_2$	6-I	681	-	-	-	-	-	-	-	-	-	-	-	-	-	-
$SmCo_5$	6-I	681	-	-	-	-	-	-	-	-	-	-	-	-	-	-
Samarium ferrides																
$SmFe_2$	6-I	306	-	-	-	-	-	-	-	-	-	-	-	-	-	-
$SmFe_5$	6-I	306	-	-	-	-	-	-	-	-	-	-	-	-	-	-
Samarium-gallium intermetallics ($SmGa_2$)	6-I	681	-	-	-	-	-	-	-	-	-	-	-	-	-	-
Samarium germanide ($SmGe_2$) .	6-I	323	-	-	-	-	-	-	-	-	-	-	-	-	-	-
Samarium hydrides																
SmH_2	5	467	-	-	-	-	-	-	-	-	-	-	-	-	-	-
SmH_3	5	467	-	-	-	-	-	-	-	-	-	-	-	-	-	-
Samarium-indium intermetallics ($SmIn_3$)	6-I	681	-	-	-	-	-	-	-	-	-	-	-	-	-	-
Samarium-lead intermetallics ($SmPb_3$)	6-I	681	-	-	-	-	-	-	-	-	-	-	-	-	-	-
Samarium-mercury intermetallics (SmHg)	6-I	681	-	-	-	-	-	-	-	-	-	-	-	-	-	-

Material Name	Volume	Density	Melting Point	Heat of Fusion	Heat of Vaporization	Heat of Sublimation	Electrical Resistivity	Specific Heat	Thermal Conductivity	Thermal Diffusivity	Thermal Linear Expansion	Thermal Absorptance	Thermal Emittance	Thermal Reflectance	Thermal Transmittance	Vapor Pressure
Samarium-nickel intermetallics																
$SmNi_2$	6-I	681	-	-	-	-	-	-	-	-	-	-	-	-	-	-
$SmNi_5$	6-I	681	-	-	-	-	-	-	-	-	-	-	-	-	-	-
Samarium (sesqui-) oxide (Sm_2O_3)	4-I	339	339	-	-	-	-	341	-	-	343	-	345	-	-	-
Samarium (sesqui-) oxide + + Gadolinium oxide	4-I	-	-	-	-	-	-	-	783	-	-	-	-	-	-	-
Samarium (sesqui-) oxide + + Gadolinium oxide + + Dysprosium oxide + Yttrium oxide	4-I	785	-	-	-	-	-	-	-	-	-	-	-	-	-	-
Samarium phosphide (SmP) . .	5	635	-	-	-	-	-	-	-	-	-	-	-	-	-	-
Samarium selenides (SmSe) . .	6-I	365	-	-	-	-	-	-	-	-	-	-	-	-	-	-
Samarium silicides ($SmSi_2$) . .	6-I	523	-	-	-	-	-	-	-	-	-	-	-	-	-	-
Samarium sulfides																
$SmS_{0.75}$	5	-	-	-	-	-	706	-	-	-	-	-	-	-	-	-
SmS	5	704	704	-	-	-	-	-	708	-	-	-	-	-	-	-
SmS_2	5	-	704	-	-	-	-	-	-	-	-	-	-	-	-	-
Sm_2S_3	5	704	704	-	-	-	-	-	-	-	-	-	-	-	-	-
Sm_3S_4	5	704	704	-	-	-	-	-	-	-	-	-	-	-	-	-
Sandwich panels, TAC-polyester skin and alkyd isocyanate foam core	6-II	-	-	-	-	-	-	1257	1259	-	-	-	-	-	-	-
Sapphire	4-I	41	41	-	-	-	43	8	45	-	47	-	-	-	-	-
Sapphire, synthetic	4-I	41	-	-	-	-	-	8	45	-	47	-	-	-	-	-
Scandia	4-I	347	347	-	-	-	-	349	-	-	351	-	-	-	-	-
Scandium (Sc)	1	868	868	868	868	868	870	872	-	-	874	-	-	-	-	876
Scandium boride (ScB_2)	6-I	204	204	-	-	-	-	-	-	-	206	-	-	-	-	-
Scandium carbide (ScC)	5	294	-	-	-	-	-	-	-	-	-	-	-	-	-	-
Scandium nitride (ScN)	5	621	-	-	-	-	-	-	-	-	-	-	-	-	-	-
Scandium oxide (Sc_2O_3)	4-I	347	347	-	-	-	-	349	-	-	351	-	-	-	-	-
Scandium selenide (Sc_2Se_3) . . .	6-I	365	-	-	-	-	-	-	-	-	-	-	-	-	-	-
Scandium sulfide (Sc_2S_3)	5	732	-	-	-	-	-	-	-	-	-	-	-	-	-	-
Scandium telluride (Sc_2Te_3) . .	6-I	636	-	-	-	-	-	-	-	-	-	-	-	-	-	-
Selectron 400	6-II	1020	-	-	-	-	-	-	-	-	1026	-	-	-	-	-
Selectron 5026	6-II	-	-	-	-	-	-	-	-	-	968	-	-	-	-	-
Si 142 silicon	1	-	-	-	-	-	-	-	-	890	-	-	-	-	-	-
Silastic 160	6-II	-	-	-	-	-	-	-	-	1064	1068	-	-	-	-	-
Silastic 180	6-II	-	-	-	-	-	-	-	-	1064	-	-	-	-	-	-
Silica	4-I	353	353	-	-	-	355	357	359	363	367	-	373-375	377	-	-
Silica fabric	6-II	-	-	-	-	-	-	-	-	1277	-	-	-	-	-	-
Silica glass	4-II	1651	1651	-	-	-	1653	1655	1657	1659-1661	1663	-	1665-1667	1669	1671-1673	-
Silica rock	4-I	820, 826	-	-	-	-	-	-	-	-	-	-	-	-	-	-

Material Name	Volume	Density	Melting Point	Heat of Fusion	Heat of Vaporization	Heat of Sublimation	Electrical Resistivity	Specific Heat	Thermal Conductivity	Thermal Diffusivity	Thermal Linear Expansion	Thermal Absorptance	Thermal Emittance	Thermal Reflectance	Thermal Transmittance	Vapor Pressure
Silicide coating on molybdenum .	6-II	-	-	-	-	-	-	-	-	-	-	-	1467-1469	1471	-	-
Silicide coating on tantalum. . .	6-II	-	-	-	-	-	-	-	-	-	-	-	1473-1475	1477	-	-
Silicide coating on titanium. . .	6-II	-	-	-	-	-	-	-	-	-	-	-	1479-1481	1483	-	-
Silicide coating on tungsten. . .	6-II	-	-	-	-	-	-	-	-	-	-	-	1485-1487	1489	-	-
Silicon (Si)	1	878	878	878	-	878	880-884	886	888	890	892	-	894-896	898	-	-
Silicon + ΣX_i	2-II	-	-	-	-	-	1384	1386	-	-	-	-	-	-	-	-
Silicon + Germanium	2-I	421	-	-	-	-	-	-	-	-	-	-	-	-	-	-
Silicon + Iron	2-I	-	-	-	-	-	-	423	425	-	427	-	-	-	-	-
Silicon alloys (special designations)																
Leboite	2-I	-	-	-	-	-	-	-	-	-	427	-	-	-	-	-
Silicon borides																
SiB_4	6-I	-	-	-	-	-	-	-	-	-	210	-	-	-	-	-
SiB_6	6-I	-	208	-	-	-	-	-	-	-	210	-	-	-	-	-
Silicon carbides																
(SiC)	5	119	119	-	-	-	121	123	125-127	-	129	-	131-135	137-139	-	-
Norton RC-4237	5	-	-	-	-	-	-	-	-	-	-	-	311	-	-	-
Silicon carbide coating on niobium-zirconium alloys . . .	6-II	-	-	-	-	-	-	-	-	-	-	-	1415	-	-	-
Silicon carbide coating on tantalum	6-II	-	-	-	-	-	-	-	-	-	-	-	1411-1413	-	-	-
Silicon carbide + Boron carbide .	5	297	-	-	-	-	-	-	-	-	299	-	-	-	-	-
Silicon carbide + Carbon	5	-	-	-	-	-	-	807	-	-	809	-	811	-	-	-
Silicon carbide + Graphite . . .	5	-	-	-	-	-	-	813	-	-	-	-	-	-	-	-
Silicon carbide + Graphite + Silicon	5	-	-	-	-	-	-	815	817	-	-	-	-	-	-	-
Silicon carbide + Magnesium oxide + Nickel aluminide cermet	6-II	-	-	-	-	-	-	-	-	-	854	-	-	-	-	-
Silicon carbide + Silicon	5	-	-	-	-	-	-	819	-	-	-	-	821	-	-	-
Silicon carbide + Silicon cermet.	6-II	-	-	-	-	-	-	-	856	-	-	-	-	-	-	-
Silicon carbide + Silicon nitride .	5	-	-	-	-	-	-	-	-	-	823	-	-	-	-	-
Silicon carbide + (Tetr-) boron carbide	5	297	-	-	-	-	-	-	-	-	299	-	-	-	-	-
Silicon carbide + ΣX_i	5	-	-	-	-	-	-	-	307	-	-	-	309-311	-	-	-
Silicon carbide foam	5	-	-	-	-	-	-	-	127	-	129	-	-	-	-	-
Silicon germanide (SiGe)	6-I	-	-	-	-	-	-	405	-	-	-	-	-	-	-	-
Silicon oxides																
SiO	4-I	-	-	-	-	-	-	-	-	-	-	-	371	-	-	-

Material Name	Volume	Density	Melting Point	Heat of Fusion	Heat of Vaporization	Heat of Sublimation	Electrical Resistivity	Specific Heat	Thermal Conductivity	Thermal Diffusivity	Thermal Linear Expansion	Thermal Absorptance	Thermal Emittance	Thermal Reflectance	Thermal Transmittance	Vapor Pressure
Silicon oxides (cont.)																
SiO_2	4-I	353	353	-	-	-	355	357	359-361	363-365	367-369	-	373-375	377-379	381	-
Silicon (di-) oxide coating on aluminum	6-II	-	-	-	-	-	-	-	-	-	-	-	-	1391	-	-
Silicon (di-) oxide foam	4-I	-	-	-	-	-	-	-	-	-	369	-	-	-	-	-
Silicon (mon-) oxide coating on aluminum	6-II	-	-	-	-	-	-	-	-	-	-	-	-	1389	-	-
Silicon (di-) oxide + ΣX_i	4-I	826	-	-	-	-	-	-	-	-	-	-	-	-	-	-
Silicon (di-) oxide + Aluminum cermet	6-II	-	-	-	-	-	-	-	-	-	790	-	-	-	-	-
Silicon (di-) oxide + Aluminum oxide + Calcium oxide	4-I	-	-	-	-	-	-	-	-	796	-	-	-	-	-	-
Silicon (di-) oxide + Aluminum oxide	4-I	-	-	-	-	-	-	-	-	789	792	-	794	-	-	-
Silicon (di-) oxide + Aluminum oxide + Iron(ic) oxide	4-I	-	-	-	-	-	-	-	798	800	802-812	-	-	-	-	-
Silicon (di-) oxide + Aluminum oxide + Iron(ic) oxide + + Magnesium oxide + Potassium (mon-) oxide	4-I	-	-	-	-	-	-	-	814	-	-	-	-	-	-	-
Silicon (di-) oxide + Calcium oxide	4-I	-	-	-	-	-	-	-	816	818	-	-	-	-	-	-
Silicon (di-) oxide + Iron(ic) oxide	4-I	820	-	-	-	-	-	-	-	-	-	-	-	-	-	-
Silicon (di-) oxide + Molybdenum (di-) silicide	5	-	-	-	-	-	-	-	-	-	-	-	783-785	787	-	-
Silicon (di-) oxide + Titanium (di-) oxide	4-I	-	-	-	-	-	822	-	-	-	824	-	-	-	-	-
Silicon nitride (Si_3N_4)	5	543	543	-	-	-	-	545	547	-	549	-	551-553	555	-	-
Silicon nitride + Silicon carbide .	5	840	-	-	-	-	-	-	-	-	-	-	-	-	-	-
Silicon telluride (SiTe).	6-I	614	614	-	-	-	616	-	640	-	-	-	-	-	-	-
Silicone DC-301	6-II	-	-	-	-	-	1113	-	-	-	-	-	-	-	-	-
Silicone GMGA 5003	6-II	-	-	-	-	-	1070	-	-	-	-	-	-	-	-	-
Silicone coating on Inconel . . .	6-II	-	-	-	-	-	1495	-	-	-	-	-	-	-	-	-
Silicone, filled	6-II	-	-	-	-	-	1070	-	-	-	-	-	-	-	-	-
Silicone, reinforced.	6-II	-	-	-	-	-	1113	-	-	-	-	-	-	-	-	-
Silicone foams																
Silicone foam R-7001.	6-II	1084	-	-	-	-	-	-	1080	-	-	-	-	-	-	-
Silicone foam R-7002.	6-II	1084	-	-	-	-	-	1072	1080	-	-	-	-	-	-	-
Silicone foam R-7091.	6-II	1084	-	-	-	-	-	-	1080	-	-	-	-	-	-	-
Silicone resin	6-II	-	-	-	-	-	-	1072	-	-	-	-	-	-	-	-
Silicone resin, reinforced . . .	6-II	1204	-	-	-	-	-	1206	1208, 1218	1220	1210	-	-	-	-	-
Sillimanite	4-II	-	-	-	-	-	-	1189	-	-	1195	-	1199	-	-	-

Material Name	Volume	Density	Melting Point	Heat of Fusion	Heat of Vaporization	Heat of Sublimation	Electrical Resistivity	Specific Heat	Thermal Conductivity	Thermal Diffusivity	Thermal Linear Expansion	Thermal Absorptance	Thermal Emittance	Thermal Reflectance	Thermal Transmittance	Vapor Pressure
Silver (Ag)	1	900	900	900	900	900	902	904	906	–	908	910	912-914	916-920	–	922
Silver coated with silver sulfide.	6-II	–	–	–	–	–	–	–	–	–	–	1433	1435	–	–	–
Silver coating on mylar	6-II	–	–	–	–	–	–	–	–	–	–	–	–	1325	–	–
Silver lume	1	–	–	–	–	–	–	–	–	–	–	910	–	–	–	–
Silver + Aluminum	2-I	431	–	–	–	429	433	–	–	–	–	–	–	–	–	–
Silver + Cadmium	2-I	–	–	–	–	–	–	–	435	–	–	–	–	437	–	439
Silver + Copper	2-I	–	–	–	–	–	–	–	–	–	441	–	–	–	–	–
Silver + Gold	2-I	–	–	–	–	–	–	–	–	–	443	–	–	–	–	445
Silver + Lead	2-I	–	–	–	–	–	–	–	–	–	447	–	–	–	–	–
Silver + Magnesium	2-I	–	–	–	–	–	–	–	–	–	–	–	–	–	–	449
Silver + Manganese	2-I	–	–	–	–	–	451	–	–	–	–	–	–	–	–	–
Silver + Palladium	2-I	–	–	–	–	–	458	–	–	–	–	–	–	–	–	–
Silver + Platinum	2-I	–	–	–	–	–	455	–	–	–	–	–	–	–	–	–
Silver + Zinc	2-I	459	457	457	–	–	–	–	–	–	–	–	–	461	–	–
Silver antimony telluride ($AgSbTe_2$)	6-I	–	–	–	–	–	620	–	–	622	–	–	–	–	–	–
Silver antimony telluride + + Germanium telluride	6-I	–	–	–	–	–	719	–	–	–	–	–	–	–	–	–
Silver antimony telluride + + Tin telluride	6-I	–	–	–	–	–	–	–	721	–	–	–	–	–	–	–
Silver beryllide ($AgBe_{12}$). . . .	6-I	158	–	–	–	–	–	–	–	–	–	–	–	–	–	–
Silver bromide (AgBr).	5	–	–	–	–	–	–	–	–	9	–	–	–	–	–	–
Silver indium telluride ($AgInTe_2$)	6-I	–	–	–	–	–	624	–	640	–	–	–	–	–	–	–
Silver oxide (Ag_2O)	4-I	–	–	–	–	–	–	383	–	–	–	–	–	–	–	–
Silver plated AISI 321	6-II	–	–	–	–	–	–	–	–	–	–	–	–	1321	–	–
Silver selenide (Ag_2Se)	6-I	–	–	–	–	–	–	353	355	–	–	–	–	–	–	–
Silver sulfide (Ag_2S).	5	–	–	–	–	–	–	710	–	–	–	–	–	–	–	–
Silver sulfide coating on silver .	6-II	–	–	–	–	–	–	–	–	–	–	1431	1433	–	–	–
Silver tellurides (Ag_2Te). . . .	6-I	–	–	–	–	–	–	618	–	–	–	–	–	–	–	–
Soda lime glass	4-II	–	–	–	–	–	–	–	–	–	–	–	1809	1811	1813-1815	–
Soda lime aluminosilicate glass .	4-II	–	–	–	–	–	1817	–	–	–	–	–	–	–	–	–
Soda-lime silicate glass	4-II	–	–	–	–	–	–	1791	1795	1793	1797	–	1799	1801	–	–
Soda lime glass LOF.	4-II	–	–	–	–	–	–	–	–	–	–	–	1809	1811	1813-1815	–
Sodium aluminum borate glass .	4-II	–	–	–	–	–	–	–	–	–	1627	–	–	–	–	–
Sodium aluminum silicates ($Na_2O \cdot Al_2O_3 \cdot 4\ SiO_2$)	4-II	–	–	–	–	–	–	1324	–	–	1326	–	–	–	–	–
Sodium barium silicate glass . .	4-II	–	–	–	–	–	–	–	–	–	1789	–	–	–	–	–
Sodium beryllium borate glass .	4-II	–	–	–	–	–	–	–	–	–	1629	–	–	–	–	–
Sodium borate glass	4-II	–	–	–	–	–	1607	–	–	–	–	–	–	–	–	–
Sodium borosilicate glass . . .	4-II	–	–	–	–	–	–	–	–	–	1721	–	–	–	–	–

Material Name	Volume	Density	Melting Point	Heat of Fusion	Heat of Vaporization	Heat of Sublimation	Electrical Resistivity	Specific Heat	Thermal Conductivity	Thermal Diffusivity	Thermal Linear Expansion	Thermal Absorptance	Thermal Emittance	Thermal Reflectance	Thermal Transmittance	Vapor Pressure
Sodium calcium silicate ($Na_2O \cdot CaO \cdot SiO_2$)	4-II	-	-	-	-	-	-	1328	-	-	-	-	-	-	-	-
Sodium calcium silicate glass. .	4-II	-	-	-	-	-	-	1791	1795	1793	1797	-	1799	1801	-	-
Sodium ferrite ($Na_2O \cdot Fe_2O_3$) . .	4-II	-	-	-	-	-	-	1097	-	-	-	-	-	-	-	-
Sodium fluoride + Beryllium ferride cermet	6-II	-	-	-	-	-	-	-	911	-	-	-	-	-	-	-
Sodium fluoride + Zirconium fluoride + Uranium (tetra-) fluoride	5	-	-	-	-	-	-	411	-	-	-	-	-	-	-	-
Sodium lead silicate glass . . .	4-II	-	-	-	-	-	1819	-	-	-	1803	-	-	-	-	-
Sodium magnesium borate glass.	4-II	-	-	-	-	-	-	-	-	-	1631	-	-	-	-	-
Sodium magnesium silicate glass	4-II	-	-	-	-	-	-	-	-	-	1805	-	-	-	-	-
Sodium magnesium copper silicate glass	4-II	-	-	-	-	-	-	-	-	-	1807	-	-	-	-	-
Sodium manganese telluride ($Na_XMn_{1-X}Te$)	6-I	-	-	-	-	-	626	-	628	-	-	-	-	-	-	-
Sodium molybdates																
$Na_2O \cdot MoO_3$	4-II	-	-	-	-	-	-	1119	-	-	-	-	-	-	-	-
$Na_2O \cdot 2\ MoO_3$	4-II	-	-	-	-	-	-	1119	-	-	-	-	-	-	-	-
Sodium (mon-) oxide (Na_2O) . .	4-I	-	-	-	-	-	-	385	-	-	-	-	-	-	-	-
Sodium phosphorus uranate ($2\ NaO \cdot UO_3 \cdot P_2O_5$).	4-II	-	1482	-	-	-	-	-	-	-	-	-	-	-	-	-
Sodium potassium aluminum silicates	4-II	-	-	-	-	-	-	-	-	-	1330	-	-	-	-	-
Sodium potassium borosilicate glass	4-II	-	-	-	-	-	-	-	-	-	1723	-	-	-	-	-
Sodium silicates																
$Na_2O \cdot SiO_2$	4-II	-	-	-	-	-	-	1322	-	-	-	-	-	-	-	-
$Na_2O \cdot 2\ SiO_2$	4-II	-	-	-	-	-	-	1322	-	-	-	-	-	-	-	-
Sodium silicate glass	4-II	1779	-	-	-	-	1781	-	1783	-	1785-1787	-	-	-	-	-
Sodium silicate glass no. 23 . .	4-II	-	-	-	-	-	-	1791	-	-	-	-	-	-	-	-
Sodium strontium alumino-silicate glass	4-II	-	-	-	-	-	-	-	-	-	1821	-	-	-	-	-
Sodium tellurate ($Na_2O \cdot TeO_3$) .	4-II	-	-	-	-	-	-	1366	-	-	-	-	-	-	-	-
Sodium titanates																
$Na_2O \cdot TiO_2$	4-II	-	-	-	-	-	-	1454	-	-	-	-	-	-	-	-
$Na_2O \cdot 2\ TiO_2$	4-II	-	-	-	-	-	-	1454	-	-	-	-	-	-	-	-
$Na_2O \cdot 3\ TiO_2$	4-II	-	-	-	-	-	-	1454	-	-	-	-	-	-	-	-
Sodium tungstates																
$Na_2O \cdot WO_3$	4-II	-	-	-	-	-	-	1480	-	-	-	-	-	-	-	-
$Na_2O \cdot 2\ WO_3$	4-II	-	-	-	-	-	-	1480	-	-	-	-	-	-	-	-
Sodium tungsten oxide (Na_XWO_3).	4-II	-	-	-	-	-	-	-	-	-	1155	-	-	-	-	-
Sodium uranate ($Na_2O \cdot UO_3$) . .	4-II	-	1482	-	-	-	-	-	-	-	-	-	-	-	-	-

Material Name	Volume	Density	Melting Point	Heat of Fusion	Heat of Vaporization	Heat of Sublimation	Electrical Resistivity	Specific Heat	Thermal Conductivity	Thermal Diffusivity	Thermal Linear Expansion	Thermal Absorptance	Thermal Emittance	Thermal Reflectance	Thermal Transmittance	Vapor Pressure
Sodium vanadates																
$Na_2O \cdot V_2O_5$	4-II	-	-	-	-	-	-	1494	-	-	-	-	-	-	-	-
$2\ Na_2O \cdot V_2O_5$	4-II	-	-	-	-	-	-	1494	-	-	-	-	-	-	-	-
$3\ Na_2O \cdot V_2O_5$	4-II	-	-	-	-	-	-	1494	-	-	-	-	-	-	-	-
Sodium zinc borosilicate glass .	4-II	-	-	-	-	-	-	-	-	-	1725	-	-	-	-	-
Solex 2808 plate glass	4-II	1779	-	-	-	-	-	1791	1783	1793	1797	-	-	-	-	-
Solex "S" plate glass.	4-II	1779	-	-	-	-	-	1791	1783	1793	1797	-	-	-	-	-
Spektralkohle artificial graphite.	1	-	-	-	-	-	-	-	360	-	-	-	-	-	-	-
Spinal, magnesium aluminate . .	4-II	1007	1007	-	-	-	1009	1011	1013	1015	1017	-	-	-	-	-
Spinal, magnesium aluminate, with sodium (mon-)oxide . . .	4-II	-	-	-	-	-	-	1524	1526	1528	1530	-	-	-	-	-
Spinal, magnesium chromite . .	4-II	-	-	-	-	-	-	-	-	-	1059	-	-	-	-	-
Spinal, nickel ferrite	4-II	-	-	-	-	-	-	1089	-	-	-	-	-	-	-	-
Spinal, zinc chromate	4-II	-	-	-	-	-	-	-	-	-	1063	-	-	-	-	-
Spodumene	4-II	-	-	-	-	-	-	-	1266	-	1270	-	-	-	-	-
Sponge zirconium	1	-	-	-	-	-	1102	-	1106	-	-	-	-	-	-	-
. . . . . .	2-I	-	-	-	-	-	699	-	-	-	-	-	-	-	-	-
Stafoam 604	6-II	-	-	-	-	-	-	-	964	-	-	-	-	-	-	-
Stainless steel coated with NBS coating A-418	6-II	-	-	-	-	-	-	-	-	-	-	-	1365-1367	-	-	-
Stainless steel coated with NBS coating N-143	6-II	-	-	-	-	-	-	-	-	-	-	-	1357-1359	-	-	-
Stainless steel coated with platinum	6-II	-	-	-	-	-	-	-	-	-	-	-	1315	-	-	-
Steatite	4-II	1285	-	-	-	-	1287	-	1293	-	1295	-	-	-	-	-
Steatite, ultra-	4-II	-	-	-	-	-	1287	-	-	-	-	-	-	-	-	-
Steatite 10B-2	4-II	-	-	-	-	-	-	-	1293	-	-	-	-	-	-	-
Steatite 12C-2	4-II	-	-	-	-	-	-	-	1293	-	-	-	-	-	-	-
Steatite, grade L-4, AlSiMag 196	4-II	-	-	-	-	-	1287	-	-	-	-	-	-	-	-	-
Steatite, grade L-5, Pass and Seymour E-211-M	4-II	-	-	-	-	-	1287	-	-	-	-	-	-	-	-	-
Steels (special designations)																
1 Kh18N9T	3	-	-	-	-	-	-	161	-	-	215	-	-	-	-	-
1.1 C tool steel	3	-	-	-	-	-	-	-	-	14	-	-	-	-	-	-
4 Kh13	3	-	-	-	-	-	-	73	-	-	-	-	-	-	-	-
12 MoV	3	-	-	-	-	-	-	-	-	-	104	-	-	-	-	-
15 KhM	3	-	-	-	-	-	-	-	-	-	100	-	-	-	-	-
17 - 4 PH	3	145	-	-	-	-	-	157	170	-	199	-	-	-	-	-
17 - 5 MnV	3	-	-	-	-	-	-	-	-	-	116	-	-	-	-	-
17 - 7 PH	3	140	-	-	-	-	-	159	172	-	199, 203	231	255, 259, 270	282	-	-
17 - 10 P	3	-	-	-	-	-	-	-	-	-	227	-	-	-	-	-

Material Name	Volume	Density	Melting Point	Heat of Fusion	Heat of Vaporization	Heat of Sublimation	Electrical Resistivity	Specific Heat	Thermal Conductivity	Thermal Diffusivity	Thermal Linear Expansion	Thermal Absorptance	Thermal Emittance	Thermal Reflectance	Thermal Transmittance	Vapor Pressure
Steels (cont.)																
18 - 8	3	-	-	-	-	-	-	-	-	-	-	-	236, 241	-	-	-
18 - 8 Cr-Cu	3	-	-	-	-	-	-	-	-	-	-	-	-	138	-	-
18 - 20 Cr-Mn	3	-	-	-	-	-	-	-	-	-	-	-	-	348	-	-
18 - 21 Cr-Co	3	-	-	-	-	-	-	-	-	-	-	-	-	302	-	-
19 - 9 DL	3	-	-	-	-	-	-	-	-	189	211	-	-	-	-	-
19 - 9 DX	3	-	-	-	-	-	-	-	-	-	225	-	-	-	-	-
23 D 245	3	-	-	-	-	-	-	-	-	85	-	-	-	-	-	-
815	3	310	-	-	-	-	-	-	-	-	340	-	-	-	-	-
A-286	3	379	-	-	-	-	-	-	391	397	401	-	409-411	413	-	-
AISI steels (see AISI designations)																
Allegheny 18 - 8 M	3	-	-	-	-	-	149	-	-	-	-	-	-	-	-	-
Allegheny steels	3	-	-	-	-	-	-	-	-	-	-	-	257	-	-	-
AM350	3	-	-	-	-	-	-	-	170	-	199	231	236, 259, 268	280	-	-
AM355	3	-	-	-	-	-	-	157	170	-	199	-	-	-	-	-
AMS 2713	3	-	-	-	-	-	-	-	385	-	-	-	-	-	-	-
AMS 2714	3	-	-	-	-	-	-	-	387	-	-	-	-	-	-	-
ATS	3	140	-	-	-	-	-	-	-	-	221	-	-	-	-	-
B-759	3	-	-	-	-	-	-	-	-	-	106	-	-	-	-	-
Carbon steel ASTM A105 grade II	3	-	-	-	-	-	-	-	-	-	337	-	-	-	-	-
Cor-ten	3	-	-	-	-	-	-	-	-	85	-	-	-	-	-	-
DVL 4/V 869	3	-	-	-	-	-	-	-	-	-	403	-	-	-	-	-
DVL 30	3	140	-	-	-	-	-	-	-	-	225	-	-	-	-	-
DVL 31	3	-	-	-	-	-	-	-	-	-	403	-	-	-	-	-
DVL 46	3	140	-	-	-	-	-	-	-	-	217	-	-	-	-	-
DVL 47	3	140	-	-	-	-	-	-	-	-	217	-	-	-	-	-
DVL 48	3	-	-	-	-	-	-	-	-	-	217	-	-	-	-	-
DVL 49	3	140	-	-	-	-	-	-	-	-	217	-	-	-	-	-
DVL 50	3	140	-	-	-	-	-	-	-	-	217	-	-	-	-	-
DVL 51	3	140	-	-	-	-	-	-	-	-	227	-	-	-	-	-
DVL 52	3	140	-	-	-	-	-	-	-	-	225	-	-	-	-	-
EI-257	3	-	-	-	-	-	-	155	-	-	-	-	-	-	-	-
EI-572	3	-	-	-	-	-	-	-	178	-	215	-	-	-	-	-
EI-606	3	-	-	-	-	-	-	-	172	-	215	-	-	-	-	-
EI-783	3	-	-	-	-	-	-	-	-	-	215	-	-	-	-	-
EI-802	3	-	-	-	-	-	-	-	-	-	104	-	-	-	-	-
EI-855	3	-	-	-	-	-	-	383	394	397	-	-	-	-	-	-
EME	3	-	-	-	-	-	-	-	-	-	225	-	-	-	-	-

Material Name	Volume	Density	Melting Point	Heat of Fusion	Heat of Vaporization	Heat of Sublimation	Electrical Resistivity	Specific Heat	Thermal Conductivity	Thermal Diffusivity	Thermal Linear Expansion	Thermal Absorptance	Thermal Emittance	Thermal Reflectance	Thermal Transmittance	Vapor Pressure
Steels (cont.)																
En 8	3	–	–	–	–	–	312	–	325	–	–	–	–	–	–	–
En 19	3	–	–	–	–	–	61	–	83	–	–	–	–	–	–	–
En 31	3	–	–	–	–	–	61	–	83	–	–	–	–	–	–	–
FCM	3	311	–	–	–	–	–	–	–	–	341	–	–	–	–	–
Feni 36	3	–	–	–	–	–	–	–	–	–	369	–	–	–	–	–
G 17	3	–	–	–	–	–	–	–	391	–	–	–	–	–	–	–
GX 4881	3	–	–	–	–	–	–	–	–	85	–	–	–	–	–	–
Haynes alloy no. 90.	3	–	–	–	–	–	–	–	–	–	106	–	–	–	–	–
Haynes alloy no. 93.	3	–	–	–	–	–	–	–	–	–	106	–	–	–	–	–
HF grade	3	–	141	–	–	–	–	–	–	–	195	–	–	–	–	–
H. G. T. 3 (British design.). .	3	55	–	–	–	–	61	–	81	–	102	–	–	–	–	–
High speed steel M1	3	–	–	–	–	–	–	–	351	–	–	–	–	–	–	–
High speed steel M2.	3	–	–	–	–	–	–	–	450	–	–	–	–	–	–	–
High speed steel M10	3	–	–	–	–	–	–	–	351	–	–	–	–	–	–	–
High speed steel Ti	3	–	–	–	–	–	–	–	450	–	–	–	–	–	–	–
HNM crucible	3	–	–	–	–	–	–	161	176	–	227	–	–	–	–	–
HX 4249	3	–	–	–	–	–	–	–	–	85	–	–	–	–	–	–
Incoloys (see Incoloy)																
Invar H	3	–	–	–	–	–	–	–	–	–	369	–	–	–	–	–
Jessop no. 40	3	55	–	–	–	–	–	–	–	–	102	–	–	–	–	–
Jessop no. 46	3	55	–	–	–	–	–	–	–	–	104	–	–	–	–	–
Jessop G-18B	3	379	–	–	–	–	–	–	168	–	217	–	–	–	–	–
Jessop G-21	3	140	–	–	–	–	–	–	–	–	225	–	–	–	–	–
Jessop H-40	3	–	–	–	–	–	–	–	81	–	–	–	–	–	–	–
Jessop R-20	3	140	–	–	–	–	–	–	176	–	221	–	–	–	–	–
Kovar	3	–	–	–	–	–	–	–	363	–	–	–	–	–	–	–
Low carbon	3	–	–	–	–	–	–	319	–	–	–	–	–	–	–	–
Macloy G	3	–	–	–	–	–	–	–	393	–	–	–	–	–	–	–
Mark 12MX	3	–	–	–	–	–	–	323	–	–	–	–	–	–	–	–
Mark 1x18N9T	3	–	–	–	–	–	–	161	–	–	215	–	–	–	–	–
Mild steel	3	311	–	–	–	–	–	316	–	–	–	–	–	–	–	–
Multimet N-155	3	140	–	–	–	–	–	–	180	191	219	120	126-128, 253, 259	–	–	–
Multimet N-155, low carbon.	3	–	–	–	–	–	–	–	296	–	–	–	–	–	–	–
Multimet NR-21 (AMS-55326)	3	140	–	–	–	–	–	–	–	–	219	–	–	–	–	–
Multimet NR-21, low carbon (AMS-53762)	3	–	–	–	–	–	–	–	–	–	219	–	–	–	–	–
N-A-X AC 9115	3	–	–	–	–	–	–	–	–	–	444	–	–	–	–	–
Ni-Span-C alloy 902	3	–	–	–	–	–	–	–	–	–	407	–	–	–	–	–
Okh 16N 36V3T	3	–	–	–	–	–	–	383	–	397	–	–	–	–	–	–

Material Name	Volume	Density	Melting Point	Heat of Fusion	Heat of Vaporization	Heat of Sublimation	Electrical Resistivity	Specific Heat	Thermal Conductivity	Thermal Diffusivity	Thermal Linear Expansion	Thermal Absorptance	Thermal Emittance	Thermal Reflectance	Thermal Transmittance	Vapor Pressure
Steels (cont.)																
P-193	3	379	-	-	-	-	-	-	-	-	405	-	-	-	-	-
PH 15-7 Mo	3	145	-	-	-	-	-	-	-	-	201	231	255, 259, 272	284	-	-
Porous	3	461	-	-	-	-	463	-	-	-	-	-	-	-	-	-
Rex 78	3	-	-	-	-	-	-	-	389	-	-	-	-	-	-	-
Roneusil	3	-	-	-	-	-	-	-	-	-	-	-	-	349	-	-
S-590	3	-	-	-	-	-	-	-	-	191, 298, 397	221	-	-	-	-	-
SAE steels (see SAE designations)																
SAS-8	3	140	-	-	-	-	-	-	-	-	227	-	-	-	-	-
Steel 15	3	-	-	-	-	-	-	-	-	331	-	-	-	-	-	-
Steel 19	3	-	-	-	-	-	-	71	-	-	-	-	-	-	-	-
Steel 35	3	-	-	-	-	-	-	-	-	331	-	-	-	-	-	-
Steel 45	3	-	-	-	-	-	-	-	-	331	-	-	-	-	-	-
Tenelon	3	-	-	-	-	-	-	-	-	-	116	-	-	-	-	-
U-8	3	-	-	-	-	-	-	10	-	12	-	-	-	-	-	-
Unitemp 212	3	-	-	-	-	-	-	-	391	-	-	-	-	-	-	-
V-444D	3	-	-	-	-	-	-	-	-	-	223	-	-	-	-	-
Vacromin F	3	-	-	-	-	-	-	-	393	-	-	-	-	-	-	-
Vascojet 1000	3	-	-	-	-	-	-	-	81	-	-	-	132	136	-	-
Vickers F. D. P.	3	-	-	-	-	-	-	-	-	-	-	-	257	-	-	-
W	3	-	-	-	-	-	-	-	-	-	203	-	-	-	-	-
WF100D	3	140	-	-	-	-	-	-	-	-	225	-	-	-	-	-
Steel, clad	6-II	-	-	-	-	-	-	-	-	-	1267	-	-	-	-	-
Stellite no. 3	2-II	-	-	-	-	-	-	-	-	-	904	-	-	-	-	-
Stellite no. 4	2-II	-	-	-	-	-	-	-	-	-	904	-	-	-	-	-
Stellite no. 6	2-II	-	-	-	-	-	-	-	-	-	902	-	-	-	-	-
Stellite no. 6B	2-II	-	-	-	-	-	-	-	-	-	902	-	-	-	-	-
Stellite no. 6K	2-II	-	-	-	-	-	-	-	-	-	902	-	-	-	-	-
Stellite no. 12	2-II	-	-	-	-	-	-	-	-	-	902	-	-	-	-	-
Stellite no. 19	2-II	-	-	-	-	-	-	-	-	-	904	-	-	-	-	-
Stellite no. 21 (AMS-5385; NR-10)	2-II	879	-	-	-	-	-	884	886	-	894	-	-	-	-	-
Stellite no. 23 (AMS-5375; NDRC-61)	2-II	879	-	-	-	-	-	-	886	-	900	-	-	-	-	-
Stellite no. 25 (L-605).	2-II	879, 882	-	-	-	-	-	-	-	890	898	-	908-914	916	-	-
Stellite no. 25 (L-605) coated with iron (ic) oxide	6-II	-	-	-	-	-	-	-	-	-	-	-	1381-1383	-	-	-
Stellite no. 27 (AMS-5378; NR-60)	2-II	1219	-	-	-	-	-	-	1223	-	1225	-	-	-	-	-

Material Name	Volume	Density	Melting Point	Heat of Fusion	Heat of Vaporization	Heat of Sublimation	Electrical Resistivity	Specific Heat	Thermal Conductivity	Thermal Diffusivity	Thermal Linear Expansion	Thermal Absorptance	Thermal Emittance	Thermal Reflectance	Thermal Transmittance	Vapor Pressure
Stellite no. 30 (AMS-5380; NR-12)	2-II	879	–	–	–	–	–	–	–	–	896	–	–	–	–	–
Stellite no. 31 (AMS-5382; NR-71)	2-II	879	–	–	–	–	–	–	886	–	896	–	–	–	–	–
Stellite no. 36 (L-251).	2-II	879	–	–	–	–	–	–	–	–	–	–	–	–	–	–
Stellite 98M2	2-II	–	–	–	–	–	–	–	–	–	906	–	–	–	–	–
Stellite HE1049	2-II	–	–	–	–	–	–	884	888	–	900	–	–	–	–	–
Stellite Star J-metal.	2-II	–	–	–	–	–	–	–	–	–	906	–	–	–	–	–
Strontium (Sr)	1	924	924	–	–	–	926	–	–	–	928	–	–	–	–	–
Strontium aluminates																
$SrO \cdot Al_2O_3$	4-II	1025	–	–	–	–	–	–	–	–	–	–	–	–	–	–
$SrO \cdot 2\ Al_2O_3$	4-II	–	1025	–	–	–	–	–	–	–	1027	–	–	–	–	–
$3\ SrO \cdot Al_2O_3$	4-II	1025	–	–	–	–	–	–	–	–	–	–	–	–	–	–
Strontium aluminum silicate ($SrO \cdot Al_2O_3 \cdot 2\ SiO_2$)	4-II	–	–	–	–	–	–	–	–	–	1334	–	–	–	–	–
Strontium barium cerium titanate $[(Ba_{1-x-y}Sr_xCe_y)O \cdot TiO_2]$.	4-II	–	–	–	–	–	1466	–	–	–	–	–	–	–	–	–
Strontium barium cerium titanate stannate $[(Ba_{1-x}Sr_{x-y}Ce_y)O \cdot (Ti_{1-z}Sn_z)O_2]$	4-II	–	–	–	–	–	1363	–	–	–	–	–	–	–	–	–
Strontium borate glass.	4-II	–	–	–	–	–	–	–	–	–	1633	–	–	–	–	–
Strontium (hexa-)boride (SrB_6).	6-I	295	296	–	–	–	–	–	–	–	–	–	–	–	–	–
Strontium chloride ($SrCl_2$) . . .	5	–	–	–	–	–	–	333	–	–	–	–	–	–	–	–
Strontium copper silicate ($SrO \cdot CuO \cdot 4\ SiO_2$)	4-II	–	–	–	–	–	–	–	–	–	1336	–	–	–	–	–
Strontium fluoride (SrF_2). . . .	5	397	397	–	–	–	–	399	–	–	–	–	–	401	–	–
Strontium lead silicate glass . .	4-II	–	–	–	–	–	1823	–	–	–	–	–	–	–	–	–
Strontium oxide (SrO)	4-I	387	387	–	–	387	389	391	393	–	395	–	–	–	–	397
Strontium oxide + Lithium (meta-) aluminate + Aluminum oxide	4-II	–	–	–	–	–	–	–	1540	–	–	–	–	–	–	–
Strontium oxide + Lithium zirconium silicate + Aluminum oxide	4-II	–	–	–	–	–	–	–	1542	–	–	–	–	–	–	–
Strontium oxide + Lithium zirconium silicate + Zinc oxide	4-II	–	–	–	–	–	–	–	1544	–	–	–	–	–	–	–
Strontium oxide + Titanium (di-) oxide	4-I	–	828	–	–	–	–	–	–	–	–	–	–	–	–	–
Strontium oxide + Titanium (di-) oxide + Lithium zirconium silicate	4-II	–	–	–	–	–	–	–	1546	–	–	–	–	–	–	–
Strontium oxide + Zinc oxide + + Lithium zirconium silicate .	4-II	–	–	–	–	–	–	–	1548	–	–	–	–	–	–	–
Strontium silicates																
$SrO \cdot SiO_2$	4-II	1332	1332	–	–	–	–	–	–	–	–	–	–	–	–	–
$2\ SrO \cdot SiO_2$	4-II	1332	–	–	–	–	–	–	–	–	–	–	–	–	–	–

Material Name	Volume	Density	Melting Point	Heat of Fusion	Heat of Vaporization	Heat of Sublimation	Electrical Resistivity	Specific Heat	Thermal Conductivity	Thermal Diffusivity	Thermal Linear Expansion	Thermal Absorptance	Thermal Emittance	Thermal Reflectance	Thermal Transmittance	Vapor Pressure
Strontium sulfide (SrS).	5	-	-	-	-	-	-	712	-	-	-	-	-	-	-	-
Strontium titanates																
$SrO \cdot TiO_2$	4-II	1456	1456	-	-	-	1458	1460	1462	-	1464	-	-	-	-	-
$SrO \cdot 2\ TiO_2$	4-II	-	-	-	-	-	-	-	-	-	1464	-	-	-	-	-
$2\ SrO \cdot TiO_2$	4-II	-	-	-	-	-	-	1460	-	-	-	-	-	-	-	-
Strontium titanate coating on AISI 310	6-II	-	-	-	-	-	-	-	-	-	-	-	1393	-	-	-
Strontium titanate + Cobalt cermet	6-II	-	-	-	-	-	-	-	792	-	-	-	-	-	-	-
Strontium uranate ($SrO \cdot UO_3$). .	4-II	-	1482	-	-	-	-	-	-	-	-	-	-	-	-	-
Strontium zirconate ($SrO \cdot ZrO_2$).	4-II	1514	-	-	-	-	-	1516	-	-	1518	-	-	-	-	-
Styrene-butadiene copolymer . .	6-II	-	-	-	-	-	-	1054	-	-	-	-	-	-	-	-
Styrofoam Q-103	6-II	-	-	-	-	-	-	-	1090	-	-	-	-	-	-	-
Super Dylon	6-II	1030	-		-	-	-	-	-	-	-	-	-	-	-	-
Supramica 557	5	-	-	-	-	-	987	-	-	-	-	-	-	-	-	-
Svea Iron	1	-	-	-	-	-	-	-	585	-	-	-	-	-	-	-
T																
TAC polyester	6-II	974	-	-	-	-	-	-	976	-	978	-	-	-	-	-
TAC polyester resin, reinforced	6-II	1180	-	-	-	-	-	1183	1185	1220	1187-1189	-	-	-	-	-
Talc	4-II	-	-	-	-	-	-	1289	-	-	-	-	-	-	-	-
Tan 9-4 tantalum	1	-	-	-	-	-	-	934	-	-	-	-	-	-	-	-
Tantalum (Ta)	1	930	930	-	-	930	932	934	936	938	940	942	944-950	952	-	954
Tantalum coated with aluminide.	6-II	-	-	-	-	-	-	-	-	-	-	-	1441-1443	1445	-	-
Tantalum coated with cobalt oxide	6-II	-	-	-	-	-	-	-	-	-	-	-	1373-1375	-	-	-
Tantalum coated with pyrolytic graphite	6-II	-	-	-	-	-	-	-	-	-	-	-	1297-1299	-	-	-
Tantalum coated with silicide. .	6-II	-	-	-	-	-	-	-	-	-	-	-	1473-1475	1477	-	-
Tantalum coated with silicon carbide	6-II	-	-	-	-	-	-	-	-	-	-	-	1411-1413	-	-	-
Tantalum coated with tantalum aluminide	6-II	-	-	-	-	-	-	-	-	-	-	-	1461-1463	1465	-	-
Tantalum + Copper + ΣX_i . . .	2-II	1388	-	-	-	-	-	-	1390	-	1392	-	-	-	-	-
Tantalum + Niobium	2-I	-	-	-	-	-	463	-	465	-	-	-	-	-	-	-
Tantalum + Niobium + ΣX_i . . .	2-II	-	-	-	-	-	-	1394	1396	1398	1400	-	-	-	-	-
Tantalum + Titanium	2-I	467, 549	-	-	-	-	-	-	-	-	-	-	-	-	-	-
Tantalum + Tungsten	2-I	-	-	-	-	-	-	469	471	473	475	477-479	-	-	-	-

Material Name	Volume	Density	Melting Point	Heat of Fusion	Heat of Vaporization	Heat of Sublimation	Electrical Resistivity	Specific Heat	Thermal Conductivity	Thermal Diffusivity	Thermal Linear Expansion	Thermal Absorptance	Thermal Emittance	Thermal Reflectance	Thermal Transmittance	Vapor Pressure
Tantalum + Tungsten + ΣX_i . . .	2-II	–	1402	–	–	–	1404	1406	1408	1410	1412	–	–	–	–	–
Tantalum + Zirconium + ΣX_i . .	2-II	1414	–	–	–	–	–	1416	1418	–	1420	–	–	–	–	–
Tantalum alloys (special designations)																
30 Nb - 7.5 V	2-II	–	–	–	–	–	–	1394	–	1398	–	–	–	–	–	–
8 W - 2 Hf	2-II	–	1402	–	–	–	1404	1406	–	1410	–	–	–	–	–	–
Tantalum aluminide ($TaAl_3$) . .	6-I	–	–	–	–	–	–	–	–	–	–	–	–	25	–	–
Tantalum aluminides coating on tantalum	6-II	–	–	–	–	–	–	–	–	–	–	–	1461-1463	1465	–	–
Tantalum antimonide (TaSb) . .	6-I	–	–	–	–	–	71	–	73	–	–	–	–	–	–	–
Tantalum arsenide (Ta_2As_3) . .	6-I	–	–	–	–	–	96	–	–	–	–	–	–	–	–	–
Tantalum beryllides																
$TaBe_{12}$	6-I	–	122	–	–	–	–	124	126	–	128	–	130-132	134	–	–
Ta_2Be_{17}	6-I	–	122	–	–	–	–	124	126	–	128	–	130-132	134	–	–
Tantalum beryllide + Beryllium oxide	5	–	–	–	–	–	–	–	–	–	–	–	868-870	872	–	–
Tantalum beryllide + Beryllium oxide + Tantalum (pent-) oxide .	5	–	–	–	–	–	–	–	–	–	–	–	874-876	878	–	–
Tantalum beryllide + Tantalum (pent-) oxide	5	–	–	–	–	–	–	–	–	–	–	–	880-882	884	–	–
Tantalum borides																
TaB	6-I	212	212	–	–	–	–	214	216	–	218	–	–	–	–	–
TaB_2	6-I	212	212	–	–	–	–	214	–	–	220	–	–	–	–	–
Ta_3B_2	6-I	–	212	–	–	–	–	–	–	–	–	–	–	–	–	–
Ta_3B_4	6-I	212	212	–	–	–	–	–	–	–	–	–	–	–	–	–
Tantalum carbides																
TaC	5	141	141	–	–	–	143	145	147	149	151	–	154-158	–	–	160
Ta_2C	5	–	141	–	–	–	–	–	–	–	–	–	–	–	–	–
Tantalum carbide coating on Inconel X	6-II	–	–	–	–	–	–	–	–	–	–	–	1417	1419	–	–
Tantalum carbide + Iron cermet.	6-II	858	–	–	–	–	–	–	–	–	–	–	–	–	–	–
Tantalum carbide + Tungsten cermet	6-II	–	–	–	–	–	–	–	–	–	860	–	–	–	–	–
Tantalum-cobalt intermetallics ($TaCo_2$)	6-I	–	684	–	–	–	–	–	–	–	–	–	–	–	–	–
Tantalum-chromium intermetallics ($TaCr_2$)	6-I	–	684	–	–	–	–	–	–	–	–	–	–	–	–	–
Tantalum ferrides ($TaFe_2$) . . .	6-I	–	306	–	–	–	–	–	–	–	–	–	–	–	–	–
Tantalum germanides																
TaGe	6-I	–	–	–	–	–	325	–	–	–	–	–	–	–	–	–

Material Name	Volume	Density	Melting Point	Heat of Fusion	Heat of Vaporization	Heat of Sublimation	Electrical Resistivity	Specific Heat	Thermal Conductivity	Thermal Diffusivity	Thermal Linear Expansion	Thermal Absorptance	Thermal Emittance	Thermal Reflectance	Thermal Transmittance	Vapor Pressure
Tantalum germanides (cont.)																
$TaGe_2$	6-I	–	–	–	–	–	325	–	327	–	–	–	–	–	–	–
Ta_4Ge	6-I	–	–	–	–	–	–	–	–	–	–	–	–	–	–	321
Tantalum germanide silicides																
$TaGeSi_2$	6-I	–	–	–	–	–	–	–	529	–	–	–	–	–	–	–
$TaGe_xSi_{1-x}$	6-I	–	–	–	–	–	–	–	529	–	–	–	–	–	–	–
Tantalum iron lead oxide ($4\ PbO \cdot Fe_2O_3 \cdot Ta_2O_5$)	4-II	–	–	–	–	–	–	–	–	–	1157	–	–	–	–	–
Tantalum nitrides																
TaN	5	557	557	–	–	–	559	561	563	–	565	–	567-569	–	–	–
Ta_2N	5	–	557	–	–	–	–	–	–	–	–	–	–	–	–	–
Tantalum (pent-) oxide (Ta_2O_5) .	4-I	–	–	–	–	–	–	399	–	–	401	–	403-405	407	–	–
Tantalum (pent-) oxide + + Tantalum beryllide	5	–	–	–	–	–	–	–	–	–	–	–	–	789	–	–
Tantalum phosphide (TaP) . . .	5	635	636	–	–	–	639	–	–	–	–	–	–	–	–	–
Tantalum selenides ($TaSe_2$). . .	6-I	–	–	–	–	–	367	–	369	–	–	–	–	–	–	–
Tantalum silicides																
Ta_5Si_3	6-I	–	467	–	–	–	–	–	–	–	–	–	–	–	–	–
$TaSi_2$	6-I	–	467	–	–	–	527	469	529	–	471	–	473-475	477	–	–
Ta_2Si	6-I	–	467	–	–	–	–	–	–	–	–	–	–	–	–	–
Ta_3Si_2	6-I	–	467	–	–	–	–	–	–	–	–	–	–	–	–	–
$Ta_{4.5}Si$	6-I	–	467	–	–	–	–	–	–	–	–	–	–	–	–	–
(Penta-) tantalum (tri-) silicide + + (Di-) molybdenum boride . .	6-I	–	724	–	–	–	–	–	–	–	–	–	–	–	–	–
Tantalum silicide germanides																
$TaGe_{1-x}Si_x$	6-I	–	–	–	–	–	325	–	–	–	–	–	–	–	–	–
TaGeSi	6-I	–	–	–	–	–	325	–	–	–	–	–	–	–	–	–
Tantalum tellurides																
TaTe	6-I	–	–	–	–	–	–	–	640	–	–	–	–	–	–	–
$TaTe_2$	6-I	–	–	–	–	–	630	–	640	–	–	–	–	–	–	–
$Ta_{31}Te_3$	6-I	–	–	–	–	–	630	–	–	–	–	–	–	–	–	–
Tantalum tungsten selenide ($W_{1-x}Ta_xSe_2$)	6-I	–	–	–	–	–	357	–	–	–	–	–	–	–	–	–
Teflon	6-II	1030	–	–	–	–	–	1035	1039	–	1045	–	–	–	–	–
Teflon, type TF-1	6-II	1030	–	–	–	–	–	–	–	–	1045	–	–	–	–	–
Teflon, barium titanate filled. .	6-II	1032	–	–	–	–	–	–	–	–	1043	–	–	–	–	–
Teflon, boron carbide filled . .	6-II	1032	–	–	–	–	–	–	–	–	1043	–	–	–	–	–
Teflon, calcium boride filled . .	6-II	1032	–	–	–	–	–	–	–	–	1043	–	–	–	–	–
Teflon, carbonyl iron grade HP filled	6-II	1032	–	–	–	–	–	–	–	–	1043	–	–	–	–	–
Teflon, J-ferrite filled	6-II	1032	–	–	–	–	–	–	–	–	1043	–	–	–	–	–
Teflon, J-mica filled	6-II	1032	–	–	–	–	–	–	–	–	1043	–	–	–	–	–

Material Name	Volume	Density	Melting Point	Heat of Fusion	Heat of Vaporization	Heat of Sublimation	Electrical Resistivity	Specific Heat	Thermal Conductivity	Thermal Diffusivity	Thermal Linear Expansion	Thermal Absorptance	Thermal Emittance	Thermal Reflectance	Thermal Transmittance	Vapor Pressure
Teflon laminate	6-II	–	–	–	–	–	–	1214	1218	1220	–	–	–	–	–	–
Teflon, litharge filled	6-II	1032	–	–	–	–	–	–	–	–	1043	–	–	–	–	–
Teflon, powdered iron-9 filled .	6-II	1032	–	–	–	–	–	–	–	–	1043	–	–	–	–	–
Teflon, quartz no. 7900 filled .	6-II	1032	–	–	–	–	–	–	–	–	1043	–	–	–	–	–
Teflon, reinforced	6-II	1097	–	–	–	–	–	–	1099	–	–	–	–	–	–	–
Teflon, titanium dioxide filled .	6-II	1032	–	–	–	–	–	–	–	–	1043	–	–	–	–	–
Teflon, zero-plast type 6 filled .	6-II	1032	–	–	–	–	–	–	–	–	1043	–	–	–	–	–
Television tube glass	4-II	–	–	–	–	–	–	–	–	–	–	–	1743	1745	1747	–
Tellurite	4-I	409	409	–	–	409	–	411	–	–	–	–	413	–	415	417
Tellurium (Te)	1	–	–	–	–	–	–	–	964	–	–	–	–	–	–	–
Tellurium + Chromium	2-I	–	–	–	–	–	481	483	–	–	–	–	–	–	–	–
Tellurium copper	2-I	–	–	–	–	–	–	–	–	–	152	–	–	–	–	–
Brass, tellurium-nickel	2-II	–	–	–	–	–	–	–	–	–	1002	–	–	–	–	–
Tellurium (di-) oxide (TeO_2) . .	4-I	409	409	–	–	409	–	411	–	–	–	–	413	–	415	417
Tellurium oxide - molybdenum oxide glass	4-II	–	–	–	–	–	–	–	–	–	1641	–	–	–	–	–
Tellurium oxide - tungsten oxide glass	4-II	–	–	–	–	–	–	–	–	–	1643	–	–	–	–	–
Tenite I 0072-MS	6-II	–	–	–	–	–	–	–	–	–	941	–	–	–	–	–
Tenite I 204-MS	6-II	–	–	–	–	–	–	–	–	–	946	–	–	–	–	–
Tenite II 205A-MS	6-II	–	–	–	–	–	–	–	–	–	946	–	–	–	–	–
Tenite G 204-H2	6-II	–	–	–	–	–	–	–	–	–	946	–	–	–	–	–
Tenite Q 264-H2	6-II	–	–	–	–	–	–	–	–	–	946	–	–	–	–	–
Tenite S 264-MS	6-II	–	–	–	–	–	–	–	–	–	946	–	–	–	–	–
Terbium (Tb)	1	956	956	956	956	956	958	960	–	–	962	–	–	–	–	–
Terbium borides																
TbB_4	6-II	295	–	–	–	–	–	–	–	–	–	–	–	–	–	–
TbB_6	6-I	295	–	–	–	–	300	–	–	–	–	–	–	–	–	–
Terbium carbides																
TbC_2	5	294	–	–	–	–	–	–	–	–	–	–	–	–	–	–
Tb_2C_3	5	294	–	–	–	–	–	–	–	–	–	–	–	–	–	–
Terbium-cobalt intermetallics ($TbCo_5$)	6-I	681	–	–	–	–	–	–	–	–	–	–	–	–	–	–
Terbium-gallium intermetallics ($TbGa_2$)	6-I	681	–	–	–	–	–	–	–	–	–	–	–	–	–	–
Terbium hydride (TbH_3)	5	467	–	–	–	–	–	–	–	–	–	–	–	–	–	–
Terbium oxide ($TbO_{1.814}$) . . .	4-I	–	–	–	–	–	–	–	–	–	–	–	–	–	–	419
Thorianite	4-I	421	421	–	–	422	425	428	430	–	432	–	435	–	–	437
Thorite	4-II	–	–	–	–	–	–	–	–	–	1338	–	–	–	–	–
Thorium (Th)	1	966	966	967	–	–	971	973	975	977	979	–	981	–	–	983
Thorium + Plutonium	2-I	411, 485	–	–	–	–	–	–	–	–	–	–	–	–	–	–
Thorium + Titanium	2-I	–	–	–	–	–	–	–	–	–	487	–	–	–	–	–
Thorium + Uranium	2-I	–	–	–	–	–	489	–	–	–	–	–	–	–	–	–

Material Name	Volume	Density	Melting Point	Heat of Fusion	Heat of Vaporization	Heat of Sublimation	Electrical Resistivity	Specific Heat	Thermal Conductivity	Thermal Diffusivity	Thermal Linear Expansion	Thermal Absorptance	Thermal Emittance	Thermal Reflectance	Thermal Transmittance	Vapor Pressure
Thorium + Uranium + ΣX_i . . .	2-II	-	1422	-	-	-	-	-	-	-	-	-	-	-	-	-
Thorium + Zirconium	2-I	-	-	-	-	-	-	-	-	-	491	-	-	-	-	-
Thorium + Zirconium + ΣX_i . .	2-II	-	1424	-	-	-	-	-	-	-	-	-	-	-	-	-
Thorium aluminate ($2\ ThO_2 \cdot 3\ Al_2O_3$)	4-II	-	-	-	-	-	-	-	-	-	1029	-	-	-	-	-
Thorium antimonides																
ThSb	6-I	81	-	-	-	-	-	-	-	-	-	-	-	-	-	-
$ThSb_2$	6-I	81	-	-	-	-	-	-	-	-	-	-	-	-	-	-
Th_3Sb_4	6-I	81	-	-	-	-	-	-	-	-	-	-	-	-	-	-
Thorium borides																
ThB_4	6-I	222	222	-	-	-	224	226	228	-	230	-	232	-	-	-
ThB_6	6-I	-	222	-	-	-	224	-	-	-	-	-	-	-	-	-
Thorium carbides																
ThC	5	-	162	-	-	-	-	-	168	-	-	-	172	-	-	-
ThC_2	5	162	162	-	-	-	164	166	168	-	170	-	172	-	-	-
Thorium carbide + Uranium (di-) carbide	5	-	-	-	-	-	-	-	-	-	301	-	-	-	-	-
Thorium chloride ($ThCl_4$) . . .	5	339	-	-	-	-	-	-	-	-	-	-	-	-	-	-
Thorium fluoride (ThF_4)	5	403	403	403	403	403	-	-	-	-	-	-	-	-	-	405
Thorium hydrides																
ThH_2	5	439	-	-	-	-	-	-	-	-	-	-	-	-	-	-
ThH_3	5	-	-	-	-	-	-	-	-	-	-	-	-	-	-	441
Thorium-manganese intermetallics																
$ThMn_{12}$	6-I	683	-	-	-	-	-	-	-	-	-	-	-	-	-	-
Th_6Mn_{23}	6-I	683	-	-	-	-	-	-	-	-	-	-	-	-	-	-
Thorium nitrides																
ThN	5	-	621	-	-	-	-	-	-	-	-	-	-	-	-	-
Th_3N_4	5	-	621	-	-	-	-	-	-	-	-	-	-	-	-	-
Thorium (di-) oxide (ThO_2) . . .	4-I	421	421	-	-	422	425	428	430	-	432	-	435	-	-	437
Thorium (di-) oxide, molybdenum fibers reinforced	6-II	-	-	-	-	-	-	-	1265	-	-	-	-	-	-	-
Thorium (di-) oxide + Aluminum oxide	4-I	-	830	-	-	-	-	-	-	-	-	-	-	-	-	-
Thorium (di-) oxide + Aluminum oxide + Beryllium oxide. . . .	4-I	-	832	-	-	-	-	-	-	-	-	-	-	-	-	-
Thorium (di-) oxide + Graphite .	5	-	-	-	-	-	-	-	739	-	-	-	-	-	-	-
Thorium (di-) oxide + Tungsten cermet	6-II	-	-	-	-	-	-	-	-	-	-	-	-	-	-	794
Thorium (di-) oxide + Uranium (di-) oxide	4-I	-	-	-	-	-	834	-	-	-	-	-	-	-	-	-
Thorium (di-) oxide + Uranium (di-) oxide + Yttrium oxide . .	4-I	-	-	-	-	-	-	-	-	-	-	-	-	-	-	836
Thorium (di-) oxide + Zirconium (di-) oxide	4-I	-	-	-	-	-	-	-	-	-	838	-	-	-	-	-

Material Name	Volume	Density	Melting Point	Heat of Fusion	Heat of Vaporization	Heat of Sublimation	Electrical Resistivity	Specific Heat	Thermal Conductivity	Thermal Diffusivity	Thermal Linear Expansion	Thermal Absorptance	Thermal Emittance	Thermal Reflectance	Thermal Transmittance	Vapor Pressure
Thorium (ortho-) silicate ($ThO_2 \cdot SiO_2$)	4-II	–	–	–	–	–	–	–	–	–	1338	–	–	–	–	–
Thorium silicides																
ThSi	6-I	–	524	–	–	–	–	–	–	–	–	–	–	–	–	–
$ThSi_2$	6-I	–	523-524	–	–	–	–	–	–	–	–	–	–	–	–	–
Thorium sulfides																
ThS	5	714	714	–	–	–	–	–	–	–	718	–	–	–	–	–
ThS_2	5	714	714	–	–	–	–	716	–	–	–	–	–	–	–	–
Th_2S_3	5	–	714	–	–	–	–	–	–	–	–	–	–	–	–	–
Th_4S_7	5	714	714	–	–	–	–	–	–	–	–	–	–	–	–	–
Th_7S_{12}	5	–	714	–	–	–	–	–	–	–	–	–	–	–	–	–
Thorium uranium beryllide [$(Th_9U)Be_{13}$]	6-I	–	–	–	–	–	–	–	–	–	136	–	–	–	–	–
Thorium uranium boride [$(Th_9U)B_4$]	6-I	–	–	–	–	–	–	–	–	–	234	–	–	–	–	–
Thorium uranium carbides																
$(Th_9U)C$	5	–	–	–	–	–	–	–	–	–	174	–	–	–	–	–
$(Th_9U)C_2$	5	–	–	–	–	–	–	–	–	–	174	–	–	–	–	–
Thulia	4-I	–	–	–	–	–	–	–	–	–	439	–	–	–	–	–
Thulium (Tm)	1	985	985	985	985	985	987	989	–	–	–	–	–	–	–	991
Thulium (hexa-)boride (TmB_6)	6-I	295	–	–	–	–	–	–	–	–	–	–	–	–	–	–
Thulium carbide (TmC_2)	5	294	–	–	–	–	–	–	–	–	–	–	–	–	–	–
Thulium oxide (Tm_2O_3)	4-I	–	–	–	–	–	–	–	–	–	439	–	–	–	–	–
Tin + Magnesium	2-I	–	–	–	–	–	493	–	–	–	–	–	–	–	–	–
Tin(ic) aluminate ($2SnO_2 \cdot 3Al_2O_3$)	4-II	–	–	–	–	–	–	–	–	–	1031	–	–	–	–	–
Tin(ic) oxide (SnO_2)	4-I	–	–	–	–	–	–	–	441	–	443	–	–	–	–	–
Tin(ic) oxide + Magnesium oxide	4-I	–	–	–	–	–	–	–	840	–	–	–	–	–	–	–
Tin(ic) oxide + Magnesium oxide + Zinc oxide	4-I	–	–	–	–	–	–	–	842	–	–	–	–	–	–	–
Tin(ic) oxide + Vanadium (pent-) oxide	4-I	–	–	–	–	–	–	–	–	–	844	–	–	–	–	–
Tin(ic) oxide + Zinc oxide	4-I	–	–	–	–	–	–	–	846	–	–	–	–	–	–	–
Tin(ic) oxide + Zinc oxide + + Magnesium oxide	4-I	–	–	–	–	–	–	–	848	–	–	–	–	–	–	–
Tin(ous) (ortho-) phosphate ($3\,SnO \cdot P_2O_5$)	4-II	–	–	–	–	–	–	–	–	–	1179	–	–	–	–	–
Tin sulfide (SnS)	5	–	–	–	–	–	–	–	–	–	–	–	–	720	–	–
Tin telluride (SnTe)	6-I	–	–	–	–	–	632	–	–	–	–	–	–	–	–	–
Tin telluride + Silver antimony telluride	6-I	–	–	–	–	–	–	–	721	–	–	–	–	–	–	–
Tin-zirconium intermetallics																
$SnZr_2$	6-I	–	684	–	–	–	–	–	–	–	–	–	–	–	–	–
Sn_3Zr_5	6-I	–	684	–	–	–	–	–	–	–	–	–	–	–	–	–

Material Name	Volume	Density	Melting Point	Heat of Fusion	Heat of Vaporization	Heat of Sublimation	Electrical Resistivity	Specific Heat	Thermal Conductivity	Thermal Diffusivity	Thermal Linear Expansion	Thermal Absorptance	Thermal Emittance	Thermal Reflectance	Thermal Transmittance	Vapor Pressure
Titanium (Ti)	1	993	993	–	–	993	996	999	1001	1003	1005	–	1007-1013	1015	–	1017
Titanium coated with aluminide .	6-II	–	–	–	–	–	–	–	–	–	–	–	1447-1449	1451	–	–
Titanium coated with aluminized-silicone paint	6-II	–	–	–	–	–	–	–	–	–	–	–	–	1497	–	–
Titanium coated with gold . . .	6-II	–	–	–	–	–	–	–	–	–	–	–	1303	1305	–	–
Titanium coated with silicides .	6-II	–	–	–	–	–	–	–	–	–	–	–	1479-1481	1483	–	–
Titanium A-55	1	–	–	–	–	–	996	–	–	–	1005	–	–	–	–	–
Titanium A-70	1	–	–	–	–	–	–	–	–	–	1005	–	–	–	–	–
Titanium Ti-75A	1	–	–	–	–	–	996	999	1001	–	1005	–	1007-1009	1015	–	–
Titanium Ti-75A (AMS 4901) coated with Dow-Corning XP-310	6-II	–	–	–	–	–	–	–	–	–	–	–	–	1497	–	–
Titanium RC-55	1	–	–	–	–	–	996	–	–	–	–	–	–	–	–	–
Titanium VT-1	1	–	–	–	–	–	–	–	–	1003	–	–	–	–	–	–
Titanium + ΣX_i	2-II	1502	–	–	–	–	1504	1506	–	–	1508	–	–	–	–	–
Titanium + Aluminum	2-I	–	–	–	–	–	495-501	–	503	505	–	–	–	–	–	–
Titanium + Aluminum + ΣX_i . .	2-II	–	–	–	–	–	1426-1432	1434	1436-1442	1444-1446	1448-1454	–	1456-1459	1461	–	–
Titanium + Chromium	2-I	–	–	–	–	–	–	–	–	–	507	–	–	–	–	–
Titanium + Chromium + ΣX_i . .	2-II	–	–	–	–	–	–	1464	1466	–	1468	–	–	–	–	–
Titanium + Copper	2-I	–	–	–	–	–	509	–	–	–	511	–	–	–	–	–
Titanium + Germanium	2-I	–	–	–	–	–	513	–	–	–	515	–	–	–	–	–
Titanium + Iron	2-I	–	–	–	–	–	–	–	–	–	517	–	–	–	–	–
Titanium + Iron + ΣX_i	2-II	1470	–	–	–	–	1472	–	1474	–	1476	–	–	–	–	–
Titanium + Manganese	2-I	519	–	–	–	–	521	523	525	527	529	–	531-535	537	–	–
Titanium + Manganese + ΣX_i . .	2-II	–	–	–	–	–	1478	–	–	–	1480	–	–	–	–	–
Titanium + Molybdenum	2-I	–	–	–	–	–	–	–	–	–	539	–	–	–	–	–
Titanium + Molybdenum + ΣX_i .	2-II	–	–	–	–	–	1482	–	–	–	–	–	–	–	–	–
Titanium + Nickel	2-I	–	–	–	–	–	–	–	–	–	541	–	–	–	–	–
Titanium + Niobium	2-I	–	–	–	–	–	543	–	–	–	545	–	–	–	–	–
Titanium + Silicon	2-I	–	–	–	–	–	–	–	–	–	547	–	–	–	–	–
Titanium + Tantalum	2-I	549	–	–	–	–	–	–	–	–	–	–	–	–	–	–
Titanium + Tin	2-I	–	–	–	–	–	551	–	553	–	–	–	–	–	–	–
Titanium + Tin + ΣX_i	2-II	–	–	–	–	–	1484	–	1486	–	–	–	–	–	–	–
Titanium + Tungsten.	2-I	555	–	–	–	–	–	–	–	–	–	–	–	–	–	–
Titanium + Vanadium	2-I	557	–	–	–	–	–	–	–	–	559	–	–	–	–	–
Titanium + Vanadium + ΣX_i. . .	2-II	1488	–	–	–	–	–	1490	1492	–	1494	–	–	1496	–	–
Titanium + Zirconium	2-I	–	–	–	–	–	561	–	–	–	563	–	–	–	–	–
Titanium + Zirconium + ΣX_i . .	2-II	–	–	–	–	–	1498	–	1500	–	–	–	–	–	–	–

Material Name	Volume	Density	Melting Point	Heat of Fusion	Heat of Vaporization	Heat of Sublimation	Electrical Resistivity	Specific Heat	Thermal Conductivity	Thermal Diffusivity	Thermal Linear Expansion	Thermal Absorptance	Thermal Emittance	Thermal Reflectance	Thermal Transmittance	Vapor Pressure
Titanium alloys (special designations)																
2.5 Al - 16 V	2-II	-	-	-	-	-	-	1490	-	-	-	-	-	-	-	-
3 Al - 2.5 V	2-II	-	-	-	-	-	-	-	-	-	1454	-	-	-	-	-
4 Al - 3 Mo	2-II	-	-	-	-	-	-	-	-	-	1452	-	-	-	-	-
4 Al - 3 Mo - 1 V	2-II	-	-	-	-	-	-	1434	-	-	-	-	-	-	-	-
4 Al - 4 Mn	2-II	-	-	-	-	-	-	-	-	-	1450, 1481	-	-	-	-	-
6 Al - 4 V	2-II	-	-	-	-	-	1428	1434	1440	1444	1454	-	1456-1459	-	-	-
7 Al - 4 Mo	2-II	-	-	-	-	-	-	-	-	-	1452	-	-	-	-	-
7 Al - 2 Nb - 1 Ta	2-II	-	-	-	-	-	-	-	-	-	1448	-	-	-	-	-
13 V - 11 Cr - 3 Al	2-II	-	-	-	-	-	-	1490	-	-	-	-	-	-	-	-
48 - OT - 3	2-I	-	-	-	-	-	-	-	-	505	-	-	-	-	-	-
A - 110 AT	2-II	-	-	-	-	-	1432	-	1438	-	1448	-	1456-1459	1461	-	-
B120VCA (crucible heat no. R6759 sheet no. 9MB3)	2-II	-	-	-	-	-	-	-	1492	-	1494	-	-	1496	-	-
BT-5	2-I	-	-	-	-	-	-	-	-	505	-	-	-	-	-	-
C-110M	2-I	-	-	-	-	-	521	523	525	527	529	-	533-535	537	-	-
C-120AV	2-II	-	-	-	-	-	-	-	-	-	1454	-	-	-	-	-
C-130AM	2-II	-	-	-	-	-	1426, 1478	-	1442	-	-	-	-	-	-	-
Cr - Mo	2-II	-	-	-	-	-	-	-	1466	-	-	-	-	-	-	-
Heat no. 32167 and sheet no. 1777A-1	2-II	-	-	-	-	-	-	-	-	-	1454	-	-	-	-	-
Heat no. R6736 sheet no. B-32	2-II	-	-	-	-	-	-	-	1436	-	1452	-	-	-	-	-
Heat no. 23345 sheet no. 1149-3	2-II	-	-	-	-	-	-	-	1492	-	1494	-	-	-	-	-
Hylite 20	2-II	-	-	-	-	-	1432	-	1438	-	-	-	-	-	-	-
Hylite 30	2-II	-	-	-	-	-	1426, 1478	-	1442	-	-	-	-	-	-	-
Hylite 40	2-II	-	-	-	-	-	1426, 1478	-	1442	-	-	-	-	-	-	-
Hylite 50	2-II	-	-	-	-	-	1432, 1482	-	1436	-	-	-	-	-	-	-
Hylite 55	2-II	-	-	-	-	-	1484	-	1486	-	-	-	-	-	-	-
Hylite 60	2-II	-	-	-	-	-	1484	-	1486	-	-	-	-	-	-	-
MST-3Mn	2-II	-	-	-	-	-	-	-	-	-	1481	-	-	-	-	-
RC-130A	2-I	-	-	-	-	-	521	523	525	527	529	-	533-535	537	-	-
RC-130B	2-II	-	-	-	-	-	1426, 1478	-	-	-	1450	-	-	-	-	-
RMI-8Mn	2-II	-	-	-	-	-	-	-	-	-	1481	-	-	-	-	-
RMI-30	2-I	-	-	-	-	-	-	-	-	-	517	-	-	-	-	-
RMI-40	2-I	-	-	-	-	-	-	-	-	-	517	-	-	-	-	-

Material Name	Volume	Density	Melting Point	Heat of Fusion	Heat of Vaporization	Heat of Sublimation	Electrical Resistivity	Specific Heat	Thermal Conductivity	Thermal Diffusivity	Thermal Linear Expansion	Thermal Absorptance	Thermal Emittance	Thermal Reflectance	Thermal Transmittance	Vapor Pressure
Titanium alloys (special designations) (cont.)																
RMI-55	2-I	–	–	–	–	–	–	–	–	–	517	–	–	–	–	–
RMI-70	2-I	–	–	–	–	–	–	–	–	–	517	–	–	–	–	–
RS-120	2-I	–	–	–	–	–	–	–	–	–	–	–	531	–	–	–
Ti-140A	2-II	–	–	–	–	–	1472	–	1474	–	–	–	–	–	–	–
Ti-150A	2-II	–	–	–	–	–	–	–	1466	–	–	–	–	–	–	–
Ti-155A	2-II	–	–	–	–	–	1432	–	1442	–	–	–	–	–	–	–
Titanium alloy 6 Al - 4 V coated with Rokide C	6-II	–	–	–	–	–	–	–	–	–	–	–	1345-1347	–	–	–
Titanium aluminide (TiAl) . . .	6-I	27	27	–	–	–	–	–	–	–	–	–	29-31	33	–	–
Titanium aluminide + Aluminum oxide	5	–	–	–	–	–	–	–	–	–	–	–	862-864	866	–	–
Titanium beryllides																
TiBe	6-I	138	–	–	–	–	–	–	–	–	–	–	–	–	–	–
$TiBe_2$	6-I	138	–	–	–	–	–	–	–	–	–	–	–	–	–	–
$TiBe_{12}$	6-I	–	–	–	–	–	–	140	142	–	–	–	–	–	–	–
Titanium borides																
TiB	6-I	236	–	–	–	–	–	–	–	–	–	–	–	–	–	–
TiB_2	6-I	236	236	–	–	–	238	240	242	–	244	–	246-248	–	–	–
Ti_2B	6-I	–	236	–	–	–	–	–	–	–	–	–	–	–	–	–
Titanium (di-) boride + + Aluminum boride	6-I	723	–	–	–	–	–	–	–	–	–	–	–	–	–	–
Titanium (di-) boride + + Boracic acid	5	–	–	–	–	–	–	–	–	–	–	–	886-888	890	–	–
Titanium (di-) boride + + Chromium (di-) boride . . .	6-I	723	–	–	–	–	–	–	–	–	–	–	–	–	–	–
Titanium (di-) boride + + (Penta-) niobium (tri-) - silicide	6-I	–	724	–	–	–	–	–	–	–	–	–	–	–	–	–
Titanium (di-) boride + + Tantalum (di-) silicide . . .	6-I	–	724	–	–	–	–	–	–	–	–	–	–	–	–	–
Titanium (di-) boride + + Titanium (di-) oxide	5	–	–	–	–	–	–	–	–	–	–	–	892-894	896	–	–
Titanium (di-) boride + + Titanium (di-) oxide + + Boracic acid	5	–	–	–	–	–	–	–	–	–	–	–	898-900	902	–	–
Titanium (di-) boride + + Titanium nitride	5	–	–	–	–	–	–	–	–	–	801	–	–	–	–	–
Titanium (di-) boride + + Vanadium (di-) boride . . .	6-I	723	–	–	–	–	–	–	–	–	–	–	–	–	–	–
Titanium carbide (TiC)	5	176	176	–	–	–	178	180	182	185	187	–	189-193	–	–	–

Material Name	Volume	Density	Melting Point	Heat of Fusion	Heat of Vaporization	Heat of Sublimation	Electrical Resistivity	Specific Heat	Thermal Conductivity	Thermal Diffusivity	Thermal Linear Expansion	Thermal Absorptance	Thermal Emittance	Thermal Reflectance	Thermal Transmittance	Vapor Pressure
Titanium carbide + Cobalt cermet	6-II	862	-	-	-	-	-	-	911	-	864	-	-	-	-	-
Titanium carbide + Molybdenum + + Tungsten cermet	6-II	-	-	-	-	-	-	-	-	-	866	-	-	-	-	-
Titanium carbide + Nickel cermet	6-II	868	-	-	-	-	-	871	873	-	875-877	-	-	-	-	-
Titanium carbide + Niobium carbide + Nickel cermet . . .	6-II	-	-	-	-	-	-	-	911	-	-	-	-	-	-	-
Titanium carbide + Tungsten cermet	6-II	-	-	-	-	-	-	-	-	-	879	-	-	-	-	-
Titanium-chromium intermetallics ($TiCr_2$)	6-I	-	-	-	-	-	-	-	-	-	-	-	656-658	660	-	-
Titanium-chromium intermetallics + Chromium (sesqui-)-oxide	5	-	-	-	-	-	-	-	-	-	926	-	928-930	932	-	-
Titanium-chromium intermetallics + Chromium (sesqui-)-oxide + Titanium (di-)oxide . .	5	-	-	-	-	-	-	-	-	-	-	-	934-936	938	-	-
Titanium-chromium intermetallics + Titanium (di-)oxide . .	5	-	-	-	-	-	-	-	-	-	-	-	940-942	944	-	-
Titanium ferrides																
TiFe	6-I	-	306	-	-	-	-	-	-	-	-	-	-	-	-	-
$TiFe_2$	6-I	-	306	-	-	-	-	-	-	-	-	-	-	-	-	-
Titanium-gold intermetallics																
TiAu	6-I	-	684	-	-	-	-	-	-	-	-	-	-	-	-	-
$TiAu_2$	6-I	-	684	-	-	-	-	-	-	-	-	-	-	-	-	-
Ti_3Au	6-I	-	684	-	-	-	-	-	-	-	-	-	-	-	-	-
Titanium hydride (TiH)	5	-	-	-	-	-	443	445	-	-	-	-	-	-	-	-
Titanium iodide (TiI_2)	5	-	-	-	-	-	-	-	-	-	475	-	-	-	-	-
Titanium nitride (TiN)	5	571	571	-	-	-	573	575	577	579	581	-	584	-	-	-
Titanium nitride + Chromium + + Titanium cermet	6-II	-	-	-	-	-	-	-	-	-	909	-	-	-	-	-
Titanium nitride + Titanium (di-)boride	5	-	-	-	-	-	-	-	-	-	842	-	-	-	-	-
Titanium oxides																
TiO	4-I	-	-	-	-	446	-	452	-	-	462	-	-	-	-	479
TiO_2	4-I	445	445	-	-	446	450	454	460	-	462	465	467-471	473-475	477	479
Ti_2O_3	4-I	-	-	-	-	-	-	456	-	-	-	-	-	-	-	-
Ti_3O_5	4-I	-	-	-	-	-	-	458	-	-	-	-	-	-	-	479
Titanium (mon-)oxide + + Chromium-titanium alloys cermet	6-II	-	-	-	-	-	-	-	-	-	796	-	-	-	-	-

Material Name	Volume	Density	Melting Point	Heat of Fusion	Heat of Vaporization	Heat of Sublimation	Electrical Resistivity	Specific Heat	Thermal Conductivity	Thermal Diffusivity	Thermal Linear Expansion	Thermal Absorptance	Thermal Emittance	Thermal Reflectance	Thermal Transmittance	Vapor Pressure
Titanium (di-) oxide and aluminum oxide coating on molybdenum	6-II	–	–	–	–	–	–	–	–	–	–	–	1395	–	–	–
Titanium (di-) oxide + Antimony (tri-) oxide	4-I	–	–	–	–	–	–	–	–	–	850	–	–	–	–	–
Titanium (di-) oxide + Beryllium oxide + Calcium titanium silicate + Magnesium oxide . .	4-II	–	–	–	–	–	–	–	–	–	1550	–	–	–	–	–
Titanium (di-) oxide + Lithium carbonate	4-II	–	–	–	–	–	–	–	–	–	1552	–	–	–	–	–
Titanium (di-) oxide + Manganese (di-) oxide	4-I	–	–	–	–	–	–	–	–	–	852	–	–	–	–	–
Titanium (di-) oxide + Niobium (pent-) oxide	4-I	–	854	–	–	–	–	–	–	–	856	–	–	–	–	–
Titanium (di-) oxide + Silicon (di-) oxide	4-I	–	–	–	–	–	858	–	–	–	860	–	–	–	–	–
Titanium (di-) oxide + Strontium oxide	4-I	–	862	–	–	–	–	–	–	–	–	–	–	–	–	–
Titanium (di-) oxide + Tin(ic) oxide	4-I	–	–	–	–	–	–	–	–	–	864	–	–	–	–	–
Titanium (di-) oxide + Titanium (di-) boride	5	–	–	–	–	–	–	–	–	–	–	–	791-793	795	–	–
Titanium (di-) oxide + Tungsten (tri-) oxide	4-I	–	–	–	–	–	–	–	–	–	866	–	–	–	–	–
Titanium (di-) oxide + Vanadium (pent-) oxide	4-I	–	–	–	–	–	–	–	–	–	868-870	–	–	–	–	–
Titanium (di-) oxide + Zirconium (di-) oxide	4-I	–	–	–	–	–	–	–	–	–	872	–	–	–	–	–
Titanium phosphates																
$TiO_2 \cdot P_2O_5$	4-II	–	–	–	–	–	–	–	–	–	1181	–	–	–	–	–
$5\ TiO_2 \cdot 2\ P_2O_5$	4-II	–	–	–	–	–	–	–	–	–	1181	–	–	–	–	–
Titanium phosphide (TiP) . . .	5	635	636	–	–	–	639	–	–	–	–	–	–	–	–	–
Titanium silicides																
TiSi	6-I	–	479	–	–	–	–	481	–	–	483	–	–	–	–	–
$TiSi_2$	6-I	479	479	–	–	–	–	481	–	–	483	–	485-487	489	–	–
Ti_5Si_3	6-I	–	479	–	–	–	–	481	–	–	483	–	–	489	–	–
Titanium (di-) silicide + + (Penta-) titanium (tri-) - silicide	6-I	–	–	–	–	–	–	–	–	–	–	–	693-695	697	–	–
(Penta-) titanium (tri-) silicide + + Titanium (di-) silicide . . .	6-I	–	–	–	–	–	–	–	–	–	–	–	699-701	703	–	–
Titanium tungsten (di-) carbide + + Cobalt cermet	6-II	–	–	–	–	–	–	–	–	–	881	–	–	–	–	–
Titanium tungsten (di-) carbide + + Tantalum cermet.	6-II	–	–	–	–	–	–	–	–	–	883	–	–	–	–	–

Material Name	Volume	Density	Melting Point	Heat of Fusion	Heat of Vaporization	Heat of Sublimation	Electrical Resistivity	Specific Heat	Thermal Conductivity	Thermal Diffusivity	Thermal Linear Expansion	Thermal Absorptance	Thermal Emittance	Thermal Reflectance	Thermal Transmittance	Vapor Pressure
Titanox TG	4-I	-	-	-	-	-	-	-	-	-	462	-	-	-	-	-
Transite	6-II	-	-	-	-	-	-	1216	-	-	-	-	-	-	-	-
Tremolite	4-II	-	-	-	-	-	-	1239	-	-	-	-	-	-	-	-
Trolitul Luv-M150	6-II	-	-	-	-	-	-	970	972	1082	-	-	-	-	-	-
Tungsten (W)	1	1019	1019	-	-	-	1021	1023	1025	1027	1029	-	1031-1038	1040-1042	-	1044
Tungsten, lamp grade	1	-	-	-	-	-	-	-	-	-	-	-	1038	-	-	-
Tungsten coated with hafnium (di-) oxide	6-II	-	-	-	-	-	-	-	-	-	-	-	1377-1379	-	-	-
Tungsten coated with silicide . .	6-II	-	-	-	-	-	-	-	-	-	-	-	1485-1487	1489	-	-
Tungsten coating on Inconel X .	6-II	-	-	-	-	-	-	-	-	-	-	-	1329	1331	-	-
Tungsten coating on iron	6-II	-	-	-	-	-	-	-	-	-	-	1325	1327	-	-	-
Tungsten + ΣX_i	2-II	1516	-	-	-	-	-	-	-	-	-	-	-	-	-	-
Tungsten + Cobalt	2-I	-	-	-	-	-	-	-	-	-	565	-	-	-	-	-
Tungsten + Copper	2-I	-	-	-	-	-	-	-	-	-	567	-	-	-	-	-
Tungsten + Molybdenum	2-I	-	-	-	-	-	-	-	-	-	-	-	569-573	-	-	-
Tungsten + Nickel + ΣX_i	2-II	1510	-	-	-	-	-	-	1512	-	1514	-	-	-	-	-
Tungsten + Niobium	2-I	-	575	-	-	-	-	-	-	-	-	-	-	-	-	-
Tungsten + Rhenium	2-I	-	-	-	-	-	577	-	-	-	-	-	-	-	-	-
Tungsten alloys (special design.)		-	-	-	-	-	-	-	-	-	-	-	-	-	-	-
B50YA12B	2-II	-	-	-	-	-	-	-	-	-	1514	-	-	-	-	-
Heavy alloy	2-II	-	-	-	-	-	-	-	-	-	1514	-	-	-	-	-
Mallory 1000	2-II	-	-	-	-	-	-	-	-	-	1514	-	-	-	-	-
Tungsten aluminide (WAl) . . .	6-I	-	43	-	-	-	-	-	-	-	-	-	-	-	-	-
Tungsten arsenide (W_3As_7) . . .	6-I	-	-	-	-	-	96	-	-	-	-	-	-	-	-	-
Tungsten borides																
WB	6-I	-	250	-	-	-	252	254	258	260	262	-	264	-	-	-
WB_2	6-I	-	250	-	-	-	-	-	-	-	-	-	-	-	-	-
W_2B	6-I	-	250	-	-	-	-	256	-	-	-	-	-	-	-	-
W_2B_5	6-I	-	250	-	-	-	-	256	-	-	-	-	-	-	-	-
Tungsten carbides																
WC	5	195	195	-	-	-	197	199	201	-	203	-	205-209	-	-	215
W_2C	5	-	195	-	-	-	-	-	-	-	203	-	211-213	-	-	-
Tungsten carbide coating on iron	6-II	-	-	-	-	-	-	-	-	-	-	1421	1423	-	-	-
Tungsten carbide + Chromium-cobalt alloys cermet	6-II	-	-	-	-	-	-	-	-	-	895	-	-	-	-	-
Tungsten carbide + Cobalt cermet	6-II	-	-	-	-	-	-	-	889	-	897-905	-	-	-	-	-

Material Name	Volume	Density	Melting Point	Heat of Fusion	Heat of Vaporization	Heat of Sublimation	Electrical Resistivity	Specific Heat	Thermal Conductivity	Thermal Diffusivity	Thermal Linear Expansion	Thermal Absorptance	Thermal Emittance	Thermal Reflectance	Thermal Transmittance	Vapor Pressure
Tungsten carbide + Nickel cermet	6-II	-	-	-	-	-	-	-	-	-	907	-	-	-	-	-
Tungsten-cobalt alloy coating on Inconel X	6-II	-	-	-	-	-	-	-	-	-	-	-	1341	1343	-	-
Tungsten-cobalt intermetallics (WCo_2)	6-I	-	684	-	-	-	-	-	-	-	-	-	-	-	-	-
Tungsten iron lead oxide ($3\ PbO \cdot Fe_2O_3 \cdot WO_3$)	4-II	-	-	-	-	-	-	-	-	-	1159	-	-	-	-	-
Tungsten nitride (WN)	5	-	621	-	-	-	-	-	-	-	-	-	-	-	-	-
Tungsten oxides																
WO_2	4-I	-	-	-	-	-	-	-	-	-	485	-	-	-	-	-
WO_3	4-I	-	-	-	-	-	-	481	483	-	485	-	-	-	-	-
$W_{18}O_{49}$	4-I	-	-	-	-	-	-	-	-	-	485	-	-	-	-	-
$W_{20}O_{58}$	4-I	-	-	-	-	-	-	-	-	-	485	-	-	-	-	-
Tungsten (tri-) oxide + Zinc oxide	4-I	-	-	-	-	-	-	-	874	-	-	-	-	-	-	-
Tungsten phosphide (WP). . . .	5	635	636	-	-	-	639	-	-	-	-	-	-	-	-	-
Tungsten selenide (WSe_2). . . .	6-I	-	-	-	-	-	359	-	361	-	-	-	-	-	-	-
Tungsten selenide tellurides ($WSe_{2-x}Te_x$)	6-I	-	-	-	-	-	634	-	-	-	-	-	-	-	-	-
Tungsten silicides																
WSi	6-I	-	491	-	-	-	-	-	-	-	-	-	-	-	-	-
WSi_2	6-I	-	491	-	-	-	-	493	495	-	497	-	-	499	-	-
W_5Si_2	6-I	-	491	-	-	-	-	-	-	-	-	-	-	-	-	-
W_5Si_3	6-I	-	491	-	-	-	-	-	-	-	-	-	-	-	-	-
Tungsten tellurides (WTe_2). . .	6-I	-	-	-	-	-	638	-	640	-	-	-	-	-	-	-
Tungsten-zirconium intermetallics (W_2Zr)	6-I	-	684	-	-	-	-	-	-	-	-	-	-	-	-	-
U																
Udimet 500	2-II	-	-	-	-	-	-	-	1134	-	-	-	1201, 1233	1213, 1235	-	-
Udimet 600	2-II	-	-	-	-	-	-	-	1134	-	-	-	-	-	-	-
Uranium (U)	1	1046	1046	-	-	-	1049	1051	1053	1056	1058	-	1061-1063	-	-	-
Uranium + ΣX_i	2-II	-	-	1544	1544	1544	-	-	-	-	-	-	-	-	-	1546
Uranium + Chromium	2-I	579	579	-	-	-	581	583	585	-	587	-	-	-	-	-
Uranium + Iron	2-I	589	-	-	-	-	-	-	-	-	591	-	-	-	-	-
Uranium + Magnesium	2-I	-	-	-	-	-	-	-	593	-	595	-	-	-	-	-
Uranium + Molybdenum	2-I	599	597	-	-	-	601	603	605	-	607-613	-	-	-	-	-
Uranium + Molybdenum + ΣX_i. .	2-II	-	1518	-	-	-	-	-	1520	-	1522-1526	-	-	-	-	-
Uranium + Niobium	2-I	-	617	-	-	-	-	-	619	-	-	-	621-623	-	-	-
Uranium + Plutonium + ΣX_i . .	2-II	-	1528	-	-	-	-	-	-	-	1530	-	-	-	-	-

Material Name	Volume	Density	Melting Point	Heat of Fusion	Heat of Vaporization	Heat of Sublimation	Electrical Resistivity	Specific Heat	Thermal Conductivity	Thermal Diffusivity	Thermal Linear Expansion	Thermal Absorptance	Thermal Emittance	Thermal Reflectance	Thermal Transmittance	Vapor Pressure
Uranium + Thorium + ΣX_i . . .	2-II	–	1532	–	–	–	–	–	–	–	–	–	–	–	–	–
Uranium + Zirconium	2-I	625	–	–	–	–	627	–	629	–	631-641	–	–	–	–	–
Uranium + Zirconium + ΣX_i . .	2-II	–	1534	–	–	–	1536	–	1538	–	–	–	1540-1542	–	–	–
Uranium alloys (special design.)																
Fissium alloy	2-II	–	1518	–	–	–	–	–	1520	–	–	–	–	–	–	–
U-3% FS	2-II	–	–	–	–	–	–	–	1520	–	–	–	–	–	–	–
U-5% FS	2-II	–	–	–	–	–	–	–	1520	–	–	–	–	–	–	–
U-5% FS - 2.25 Zr	2-II	–	–	–	–	–	–	–	1538	–	–	–	–	–	–	–
U-8% FS	2-II	–	–	–	–	–	–	–	1520	–	–	–	–	–	–	–
U-10% FS	2-II	–	–	–	–	–	–	–	1520	–	–	–	–	–	–	–
Uranium aluminides																
UAl_2	6-I	35	35	–	–	–	–	–	–	–	37	–	–	–	–	–
UAl_3	6-I	35	35	–	–	–	–	–	–	–	–	–	–	–	–	–
UAl_4	6-I	35	–	–	–	–	–	–	–	–	–	–	–	–	–	–
Uranium beryllide (UBe_{13}) . .	6-I	144	–	–	–	–	–	–	146	–	–	–	–	–	–	–
Uranium-bismuth intermetallics																
UBi	6-I	676	676	–	–	–	–	–	–	–	–	–	–	–	–	–
UBi_2	6-I	676	676	–	–	–	–	–	–	–	–	–	–	–	–	–
U_3Bi_4	6-I	676	676	–	–	–	–	–	–	–	–	–	–	–	–	–
U_4Bi_5	6-I	676	–	–	–	–	–	–	–	–	–	–	–	–	–	–
Uranium borides																
UB_2	6-I	–	266	–	–	–	–	–	–	–	268	–	–	–	–	–
UB_4	6-I	266	266	–	–	–	–	–	–	–	–	–	–	–	–	–
UB_{12}	6-I	–	266	–	–	–	–	–	–	–	–	–	–	–	–	–
Uranium bromide (UBr_3). . . .	5	11	–	–	–	–	–	–	–	–	–	–	–	–	–	–
Uranium carbides																
UC	5	217	217	–	–	–	219	223	231	235	237	–	243, 245	–	–	–
UC_2	5	–	217	–	–	–	221	225-227	233	–	239	–	243-245	–	–	–
U_2C_3	5	217	217	–	–	–	–	229	–	–	241	–	–	–	–	–
Uranium (mono-) carbide + + Molybdenum cermet	6-II	–	–	–	–	–	–	–	–	–	891	–	–	–	–	–
Uranium (mono-) carbide + + Uranium cermet	6-II	–	–	–	–	–	–	–	–	–	893	–	–	–	–	–
Uranium (di-) carbide + Graphite	5	–	–	–	–	–	–	–	743	–	–	–	–	–	–	–
Uranium chlorides																
UCl_3	5	335	–	–	–	–	–	337	–	–	–	–	–	–	–	–
UCl_4	5	335	–	–	–	–	–	337	–	–	–	–	–	–	–	–
Uranium-cobalt intermetallics																
UCo	6-I	676	–	–	–	–	–	–	–	–	–	–	–	–	–	–
U_6Co	6-I	676	–	–	–	–	–	–	–	–	–	–	–	–	–	–

Material Name	Volume	Density	Melting Point	Heat of Fusion	Heat of Vaporization	Heat of Sublimation	Electrical Resistivity	Specific Heat	Thermal Conductivity	Thermal Diffusivity	Thermal Linear Expansion	Thermal Absorptance	Thermal Emittance	Thermal Reflectance	Thermal Transmittance	Vapor Pressure
Uranium ferrides																
UFe_2	6-I	306	306	–	–	–	–	–	–	–	–	–	–	–	–	–
U_6Fe	6-I	306	306	–	–	–	–	–	–	–	–	–	–	–	–	–
Uranium fluorides																
UF_3	5	–	407	–	–	–	–	–	–	–	–	–	–	–	–	–
UF_4	5	407	407	–	–	–	–	–	–	–	–	–	–	–	–	–
Uranium hydride (UH_3).	5	447	–	–	–	–	–	449	–	–	–	–	–	–	–	–
Uranium iodides																
UI_3	5	–	477	–	–	–	–	–	–	–	–	–	–	–	–	–
UI_4	5	–	477	–	–	–	–	–	–	–	–	–	–	–	–	–
Uranium-lead intermetallics																
UPb	6-I	676	676	–	–	–	–	–	–	–	–	–	–	–	–	–
UPb_3	6-I	676	676	–	–	–	–	–	–	–	–	–	–	–	–	–
Uranium-manganese intermetallics																
UMn_2	6-I	676	676	–	–	–	–	–	–	–	–	–	–	–	–	–
U_6Mn	6-I	676	676	–	–	–	–	–	–	–	–	–	–	–	–	–
Uranium-nickel intermetallics (U_6Ni)	6-I	676	–	–	–	–	–	–	–	–	–	–	–	–	–	–
Uranium nitrides																
UN	5	586	586	–	–	–	–	–	588	590	592	–	–	–	–	–
$UN_{1.56-1.65}$	5	–	–	–	–	–	–	–	–	–	–	–	–	–	–	594
UN_2	5	586	–	–	–	–	–	–	–	–	–	–	–	–	–	–
U_2N_3	5	586	–	–	–	–	–	–	–	–	–	–	–	–	–	–
Uranium oxides																
UO_2	4-I	488	489	–	–	–	493	495	503-511	515	517	–	520	–	–	522
$UO_{2.03-2.18}$	4-I	–	–	–	–	–	–	–	508	–	517	–	–	–	–	–
UO_3	4-I	488	489	–	–	–	–	497	–	–	–	–	–	–	–	–
U_2O_3	4-I	–	–	–	–	–	493	–	–	–	–	–	–	–	–	–
U_2O_5	4-I	488	–	–	–	–	–	–	–	–	–	–	–	–	–	–
U_3O_8	4-I	488	489	–	–	–	–	499	513	–	–	–	–	–	–	–
U_4O_9	4-I	–	–	–	–	–	–	501	–	–	–	–	–	–	–	–
Uranium (di-) oxide powder. . .	4-I	–	–	–	–	–	–	–	511	–	–	–	520	–	–	–
Uranium (di-) oxide + Beryllium oxide	4-I	–	–	–	–	–	–	–	876	–	878	–	–	–	–	–
Uranium (di-) oxide + Chromium cermet	6-II	–	–	–	–	–	798	–	800	–	802	–	–	–	–	–
Uranium (di-) oxide + + Dysprosium oxide	4-I	–	–	–	–	–	–	–	–	–	880	–	–	–	–	–
Uranium (di-) oxide + Graphite .	5	–	–	–	–	–	–	–	741	–	–	–	–	–	–	–
Uranium (di-) oxide + + Magnesium oxide.	4-I	–	–	–	–	–	–	–	–	–	882	–	–	–	–	–
Uranium (di-) oxide + + Molybdenum cermet	6-II	–	–	–	–	–	804	–	806	–	808	–	–	–	–	–

Material Name	Volume	Density	Melting Point	Heat of Fusion	Heat of Vaporization	Heat of Sublimation	Electrical Resistivity	Specific Heat	Thermal Conductivity	Thermal Diffusivity	Thermal Linear Expansion	Thermal Absorptance	Thermal Emittance	Thermal Reflectance	Thermal Transmittance	Vapor Pressure
Uranium (di-) oxide + Niobium cermet	6-II	-	-	-	-	-	810	-	812	-	-	-	-	-	-	-
Uranium (di-) oxide + Stainless steel cermet	6-II	-	-	-	-	-	814	-	816	-	818	-	-	-	-	-
Uranium (di-) oxide + Thorium (di-) oxide	4-I	-	-	-	-	-	884	-	-	-	-	-	-	-	-	-
Uranium (di-) oxide + Thorium (di-) oxide + Yttrium oxide . .	4-I	-	-	-	-	-	-	-	-	-	-	-	-	-	-	886
Uranium (di-) oxide + Yttrium oxide	4-I	-	-	-	-	-	-	-	-	-	-	-	-	-	-	888
Uranium (di-) oxide + + Zirconium cermet	6-II	820	-	-	-	-	-	-	822	-	824	-	-	-	-	-
Uranium (di-) oxide + + Zirconium (di-) oxide	4-I	-	890	-	-	-	-	-	-	-	892	-	-	-	-	-
Uranium phosphate ($UO_2 \cdot P_2O_5$) .	4-II	-	-	-	-	-	-	-	-	-	1183	-	-	-	-	-
Uranium plutonium carbide ($U_{1-x}Pu_xC$)	5	-	-	-	-	-	247	-	-	-	-	-	-	-	-	-
Uranium silicides																
USi	6-I	501	501	-	-	-	-	-	-	-	509	-	-	-	-	-
USi_2	6-I	501	501	-	-	-	-	505	-	-	509	-	-	-	-	-
USi_3	6-I	501	501	-	-	-	503	505	-	-	509	-	-	-	-	-
U_3Si	6-I	501	501	-	-	-	503	505	507	-	509	-	-	-	-	-
U_3Si_2	6-I	501	501	-	-	-	-	-	-	-	509	-	-	-	-	-
Uranium stannide (USn_3)	6-I	541	-	-	-	-	-	-	-	-	-	-	-	-	-	-
Uranium sulfides																
US	5	722	722	-	-	-	-	-	-	-	724	-	-	-	-	-
US_2	5	722	722	-	-	-	-	-	-	-	-	-	-	-	-	-
Uranium thorium oxide ($Th_{1-x}U_xO_2$)	4-II	-	-	-	-	-	-	-	1161	-	-	-	-	-	-	-
Uranium-titanium intermetallics (U_2Ti)	6-I	-	676	-	-	-	-	-	-	-	-	-	-	-	-	-
Uranium zirconium carbide ($U_{1-x}Zr_xC$)	5	-	-	-	-	-	-	-	-	-	-	-	249	-	-	-
Uranium zirconium hydride ($U_{1-x}Zr_xH$)	5	-	-	-	-	-	-	-	-	-	451	-	-	-	-	-
Uranyl oxide	4-I	488	489	-	-	-	-	497	-	-	-	-	-	-	-	-
Urea formaldehyde, alpha cellulose filled	6-II	-	-	-	-	-	-	-	-	-	1002	-	-	-	-	-
V																
Vanadate glass	4-II	-	-	-	-	-	1645	-	-	-	1647	-	-	-	-	-
Vanadium (V)	1	1065	1065	-	-	1065	1067	1069	1071	-	1073	-	1075	1077	-	1079
Vanadium + ΣX_i	2-I	-	-	-	-	-	643	-	-	-	-	-	-	-	-	-
Vanadium + Aluminum	2-I	-	-	-	-	-	643	-	-	-	-	-	-	-	-	-
Vanadium + Antimony	2-I	-	-	-	-	-	643	-	-	-	-	-	-	-	-	-
Vanadium + Chromium	2-I	-	-	-	-	-	643	-	-	-	-	-	-	-	-	-

Material Name	Volume	Density	Melting Point	Heat of Fusion	Heat of Vaporization	Heat of Sublimation	Electrical Resistivity	Specific Heat	Thermal Conductivity	Thermal Diffusivity	Thermal Linear Expansion	Thermal Absorptance	Thermal Emittance	Thermal Reflectance	Thermal Transmittance	Vapor Pressure
Vanadium + Copper	2-I	-	-	-	-	-	643	-	-	-	-	-	-	-	-	-
Vanadium + Iron	2-I	-	-	-	-	-	643	-	-	-	-	-	-	-	-	-
Vanadium + Manganese	2-I	-	-	-	-	-	643	-	-	-	-	-	-	-	-	-
Vanadium + Nickel	2-I	-	-	-	-	-	643	-	-	-	-	-	-	-	-	-
Vanadium + Palladium	2-I	-	-	-	-	-	643	-	-	-	-	-	-	-	-	-
Vanadium + Silicon	2-I	-	-	-	-	-	-	-	-	-	645	-	-	-	-	-
Vanadium + Silicon + ΣX_i . . .	2-II	-	-	-	-	-	-	-	1548	-	-	-	-	-	-	-
Vanadium + Tin	2-I	-	-	-	-	-	643	-	-	-	-	-	-	-	-	-
Vanadium + Titanium	2-I	647	-	-	-	-	643	-	649	-	651	-	-	-	-	-
Vanadium + Titanium + ΣX_i . .	2-II	-	-	-	-	-	-	-	1550	-	-	-	-	-	-	-
Vanadium + Zirconium	2-I	-	-	-	-	-	643	-	-	-	-	-	-	-	-	-
Vanadium aluminide (V_5Al_8) . .	6-I	-	43	-	-	-	-	-	-	-	-	-	-	-	-	-
Vanadium beryllide (VBe_{13}) . .	6-I	-	158	-	-	-	-	-	-	-	-	-	-	-	-	-
Vanadium borides																
VB	6-I	-	270	-	-	-	-	-	-	-	-	-	-	-	-	-
VB_2	6-I	270	270	-	-	-	-	-	-	-	272	-	-	-	-	-
V_3B_2	6-I	-	270	-	-	-	-	-	-	-	-	-	-	-	-	-
V_3B_4	6-I	-	270	-	-	-	-	-	-	-	-	-	-	-	-	-
Vanadium (di-)boride + + Chromium (di-)boride . . .	6-I	723	-	-	-	-	-	-	-	-	-	-	-	-	-	-
Vanadium (di-)boride + + Titanium (di-)boride	6-I	723	-	-	-	-	-	-	-	-	-	-	-	-	-	-
Vanadium carbides																
VC	5	251	251	-	-	-	253	255	257	-	259	-	261	-	-	-
V_2C	5	-	251	-	-	-	-	-	-	-	259	-	-	-	-	-
Vanadium germanium lead oxide ($5\ PbO \cdot GeO_2 \cdot V_2O_5$)	4-II	-	-	-	-	-	-	-	-	-	1163	-	-	-	-	-
Vanadium hydride (VH)	5	-	-	-	-	-	-	453	-	-	-	-	-	-	-	-
Vanadium-manganese inter-metallics (VMn_2)	6-I	-	685	-	-	-	-	-	-	-	-	-	-	-	-	-
Vanadium nitride (VN)	5	596	596	-	-	-	-	598	-	-	600	-	-	-	-	-
Vanadium oxides																
VO	4-I	-	-	-	-	524	-	528	-	-	-	-	-	-	-	536
V_2O_3	4-I	-	-	-	-	-	526	530	-	-	-	-	-	-	-	-
V_2O_4	4-I	-	-	-	-	-	-	532	-	-	-	-	-	-	-	-
V_2O_5	4-I	524	524	-	-	-	526	534	-	-	-	-	-	-	-	-
Vanadium (pent-)oxide + + Titanium (di-)oxide	4-I	-	-	-	-	-	-	-	-	-	894	-	-	-	-	-
Vanadium phosphide (VP) . . .	5	635	636	-	-	-	639	-	-	-	-	-	-	-	-	-
Vanadium silicides																
VSi	6-I	-	511	-	-	-	-	-	-	-	-	-	-	-	-	-
VSi_2	6-I	-	-	-	-	-	-	513	-	-	515	-	-	-	-	-
V_3Si	6-I	-	511	-	-	-	-	513	-	-	515	-	-	-	-	-
V_5Si_3	6-I	-	511	-	-	-	-	513	-	-	515	-	-	-	-	-

Material Name	Volume	Density	Melting Point	Heat of Fusion	Heat of Vaporization	Heat of Sublimation	Electrical Resistivity	Specific Heat	Thermal Conductivity	Thermal Diffusivity	Thermal Linear Expansion	Thermal Absorptance	Thermal Emittance	Thermal Reflectance	Thermal Transmittance	Vapor Pressure
Vanadium silicon lead oxide (5 $PbO \cdot SiO_2 \cdot V_2O_5$).	4-II	–	–	–	–	–	–	–	–	–	1165	–	–	–	–	–
Vanadium-zirconium intermetallics (V_2Zr)	6-I	–	685	–	–	–	–	–	–	–	–	–	–	–	–	–
Vermiculite, expanded.	4-I	–	–	–	–	–	–	–	814	–	–	–	–	–	–	–
Vinylite VMCH	6-II	–	–	–	–	–	–	–	–	–	950	–	–	–	–	–
Vinylite VYDR	6-II	–	–	–	–	–	–	–	–	–	950	–	–	–	–	–
Vitreous bonded aluminum titanate	5	–	–	–	–	–	949-953	–	–	–	955-977	–	–	–	–	–
Vulcollan	6-II	1051	–	–	–	–	–	–	–	–	–	–	–	–	–	–
Vycor no. 790	4-II	–	1651	–	–	–	1653	–	–	–	1663	–	–	–	–	–
Vycor 7900	4-II	–	–	–	–	–	–	1655	–	1661	–	–	1665	1669	1671-1673	–
Vycor glasses	4-II	1651	1651	–	–	–	1653	1655	1657, 1699	1659-1661	1663	–	1665-1667	1669	1671-1673	–
W																
Willemite	4-II	–	–	–	–	–	–	1340	–	–	–	–	–	–	–	–
Wollastonite	4-II	–	–	–	–	–	–	1229	–	–	–	–	–	–	–	–
Wustite	4-I	–	–	–	–	–	–	–	–	–	222	–	–	–	–	–
Y																
Ytterbia	4-I	538	–	–	–	–	–	540	–	–	542	–	–	–	544	–
Ytterbium (Yb)	1	1081	1081	1081	1081	1081	1083	1085	–	–	–	–	–	–	–	–
Ytterbium + Calcium	2-I	–	–	–	–	–	–	–	–	–	653	–	–	–	–	–
Ytterbium borides																
YbB_4	6-I	295	–	–	–	–	–	–	–	–	–	–	–	–	–	–
YbB_6	6-I	295	–	–	–	–	300	–	–	–	–	–	–	–	–	–
Ytterbium carbide (YbC_2) . . .	5	294	–	–	–	–	–	–	–	–	–	–	–	–	–	–
Ytterbium oxide (Yb_2O_3)	4-I	538	–	–	–	–	–	540	–	–	542	–	–	–	544	–
Ytterbium selenide (YbSe) . . .	6-I	365	–	–	–	–	–	–	–	–	–	–	–	–	–	–
Ytterbium sulfide (Yb_2S_3) . . .	5	732	–	–	–	–	–	–	–	–	–	–	–	–	–	–
Yttria	4-I	546	–	–	–	–	–	548	550	–	552	–	555-559	–	561	–
Yttrium (Y)	1	1087	1087	1087	1087	1087	1089	1091	1093	–	–	–	1095	–	–	1097
Yttrium + ΣX_i	2-II	–	–	–	–	–	–	1554	–	1556	–	–	–	–	–	–
Yttrium + Tantalum	2-I	–	–	–	–	–	–	655	–	–	–	–	–	–	–	–
Yttrium + Terbium	2-I	–	–	–	–	–	657	–	–	–	–	–	–	–	–	–
Yttrium + Terbium + ΣX_i. . . .	2-II	1552	–	–	–	–	–	–	–	–	–	–	–	–	–	–
Yttrium borides																
YB_2	6-I	295	297	–	–	–	–	–	–	–	–	–	–	–	–	–
YB_4	6-I	295	297	–	–	–	–	–	–	–	–	–	–	–	–	–

Material Name	Volume	Density	Melting Point	Heat of Fusion	Heat of Vaporization	Heat of Sublimation	Electrical Resistivity	Specific Heat	Thermal Conductivity	Thermal Diffusivity	Thermal Linear Expansion	Thermal Absorptance	Thermal Emittance	Thermal Reflectance	Thermal Transmittance	Vapor Pressure
Yttrium borides (cont.)																
YB_6	6-I	295	297	-	-	-	300	-	-	-	-	-	-	-	-	-
Yttrium carbides																
YC	5	-	295	-	-	-	-	-	-	-	-	-	-	-	-	-
YC_2	5	294	295	-	-	-	-	-	-	-	-	-	-	-	-	-
Y_2C_3	5	-	295	-	-	-	-	-	-	-	-	-	-	-	-	-
Y_3C	5	294	-	-	-	-	-	-	-	-	-	-	-	-	-	-
Yttrium-cobalt intermetallics																
YCo_2	6-I	681	-	-	-	-	-	-	-	-	-	-	-	-	-	-
YCo_5	6-I	681	-	-	-	-	-	-	-	-	-	-	-	-	-	-
Yttrium-copper intermetallics (YCu_5)	6-I	681	-	-	-	-	-	-	-	-	-	-	-	-	-	-
Yttrium ferride (YFe_5)	6-I	306	-	-	-	-	-	-	-	-	-	-	-	-	-	-
Yttrium fluoride (YF_3)	5	407	407	-	-	-	-	-	-	-	-	-	-	-	-	-
Yttrium-gallium intermetallics (YGa_2)	6-I	681	-	-	-	-	-	-	-	-	-	-	-	-	-	-
Yttrium germanides (Y_5Ge_3) . .	6-I	323	-	-	-	-	-	-	-	-	-	-	-	-	-	-
Yttrium hydrides																
YH_2	5	455	-	-	-	-	-	-	-	-	-	-	-	-	-	-
YH_3	5	455	-	-	-	-	-	457	-	-	-	-	-	-	-	-
Yttrium-manganese intermetallics																
YMn_2	6-I	681	-	-	-	-	-	-	-	-	-	-	-	-	-	-
YMn_5	6-I	681	-	-	-	-	-	-	-	-	-	-	-	-	-	-
Yttrium-nickel intermetallics (YNi_5)	6-I	681	-	-	-	-	-	-	-	-	-	-	-	-	-	-
Yttrium nitride (YN).	5	621	621	-	-	-	-	-	-	-	-	-	-	-	-	-
Yttrium-osmium intermetallics (YOs_2)	6-I	681	-	-	-	-	-	-	-	-	-	-	-	-	-	-
Yttrium oxide (Y_2O_3)	4-I	546	-	-	-	-	-	548	550	-	552	-	555-559	-	561	-
Yttrium oxide + Chromium (sesqui-) oxide	4-I	-	-	-	-	-	-	-	-	-	-	-	896	-	-	-
Yttrium oxide + Uranium (di-) oxide	4-I	-	-	-	-	-	-	-	898	-	-	-	-	-	-	-
Yttrium-rhodium intermetallics (YRh)	6-I	681	-	-	-	-	-	-	-	-	-	-	-	-	-	-
Yttrium silicides																
YSi	6-I	523	524	-	-	-	-	-	-	-	-	-	-	-	-	-
YSi_2	6-I	523	524	-	-	-	-	-	-	-	-	-	-	-	-	-
Y_3Si_5	6-I	-	524	-	-	-	-	-	-	-	-	-	-	-	-	-
Y_5Si_3	6-I	523	524	-	-	-	-	-	-	-	-	-	-	-	-	-
Yttrium-silver intermetallics (YAg)	6-I	681	-	-	-	-	-	-	-	-	-	-	-	-	-	-

Material Name	Volume	Density	Melting Point	Heat of Fusion	Heat of Vaporization	Heat of Sublimation	Electrical Resistivity	Specific Heat	Thermal Conductivity	Thermal Diffusivity	Thermal Linear Expansion	Thermal Absorptance	Thermal Emittance	Thermal Reflectance	Thermal Transmittance	Vapor Pressure
Yttrium sulfides																
YS	5	732	732	–	–	–	–	–	–	–	–	–	–	–	–	–
YS_2	5	732	732	–	–	–	–	–	–	–	–	–	–	–	–	–
Y_2S_3	5	732	732	–	–	–	–	–	–	–	–	–	–	–	–	–
Y_5S_7	5	732	732	–	–	–	–	–	–	–	–	–	–	–	–	–
Yttrium tellurides (Y_2Te_3) . . .	6-I	–	–	–	–	–	638	–	–	–	–	–	–	–	–	–
Z																
Zinc + Copper	2-I	–	–	–	–	–	659	–	–	–	–	–	–	–	–	–
Zinc + Silver	2-I	–	661	661	–	–	–	–	–	–	–	–	–	–	–	–
Zinc + Zirconium	2-I	–	–	–	–	–	–	–	–	–	–	–	–	–	–	663
Zinc aluminate ($ZnO \cdot Al_2O_3$) . .	4-II	–	–	–	–	–	–	–	–	–	1033	–	–	–	–	–
Zinc antimonide (ZnSb)	6-I	–	–	–	–	–	75	–	77	–	–	–	–	–	–	79
Zinc chromate ($ZnO \cdot Cr_2O_3$) . .	4-II	–	–	–	–	–	–	–	–	–	1063	–	–	–	–	–
Zinc chromate spinal	4-II	–	–	–	–	–	–	–	–	–	1063	–	–	–	–	–
Zinc ferrite ($ZnO \cdot Fe_2O_3$) . . .	4-II	–	–	–	–	–	1099	1101	1103	–	1105	–	–	–	–	–
Zinc fluoride (ZnF_2)	5	407	407	–	–	–	–	–	–	–	–	–	–	–	–	–
Zinc germanide oxide ($2\,ZnO \cdot GeO_2$)	4-II	–	–	–	–	–	–	–	–	–	1167	–	–	–	–	–
Zinc germanium oxide + + Magnesium germanium oxide.	4-II	–	–	–	–	–	–	–	–	–	1556	–	–	–	–	–
Zinc germanium oxide + Zinc (ortho-) silicate	4-II	–	–	–	–	–	–	–	–	–	1558	–	–	–	–	–
Zinc lead silicate glass	4-II	–	–	–	–	–	1825	–	–	–	–	–	–	–	–	–
Zinc magnesium aluminum borosilicate glass	4-II	–	–	–	–	–	–	–	–	–	1727	–	–	–	–	–
Zinc oxide (ZnO)	4-I	–	–	–	–	–	563	–	565	–	567	–	569	–	–	–
Zinc oxide + Magnesium oxide .	4-I	–	–	–	–	–	–	–	900	–	–	–	–	–	–	–
Zinc oxide + Strontium oxide + + Lithium zirconium silicate .	4-II	–	–	–	–	–	–	–	1554	–	–	–	–	–	–	–
Zinc oxide + Tin(ic) oxide . . .	4-I	–	–	–	–	–	–	–	902	–	–	–	–	–	–	–
Zinc oxide + Tin(ic) oxide + + Magnesium oxide	4-I	–	–	–	–	–	–	–	904	–	–	–	–	–	–	–
Zinc selenide (ZnSe)	6-I	–	–	–	–	–	–	–	–	–	363	–	–	–	–	–
Zinc (ortho-) silicate ($2\,ZnO \cdot SiO_2$)	4-II	–	–	–	–	–	–	1340	–	–	1342	–	–	–	–	–
Zinc (ortho-) silicate + + Magnesium (ortho-) silicate .	4-II	–	–	–	–	–	–	–	–	–	1575	–	–	–	–	–
Zinc sulfide (ZnS)	5	–	–	–	–	–	726	–	–	–	–	–	–	728-730	–	–
Zinc (ortho-) titanate ($2\,ZnO \cdot TiO_2$)	4-II	–	–	–	–	–	–	1468	–	–	–	–	–	–	–	–
Zircaloy 2	2-I	–	–	–	–	–	699	702	704	–	–	–	709-714	–	–	–
Zircaloy 2, low nickel	2-I	–	–	–	–	–	–	702	–	–	–	–	–	–	–	–

Material Name	Volume	Density	Melting Point	Heat of Fusion	Heat of Vaporization	Heat of Sublimation	Electrical Resistivity	Specific Heat	Thermal Conductivity	Thermal Diffusivity	Thermal Linear Expansion	Thermal Absorptance	Thermal Emittance	Thermal Reflectance	Thermal Transmittance	Vapor Pressure
Zircaloy 4	2-I	-	-	-	-	-	-	702	-	-	-	-	-	-	-	-
Zircon	4-II	1344	-	-	-	-	1346	1348	-	-	-	-	-	-	-	-
Zircon 475	4-II	1344	-	-	-	-	-	-	-	-	-	-	-	-	-	-
Zircon CZ-5, Taylor	4-II	-	-	-	-	-	-	1348	1350	-	1352	-	-	-	-	-
Zircon + Beryl	4-II	-	-	-	-	-	-	-	-	-	1577	-	-	-	-	-
Zirconia	4-I	571	571	-	-	571	574	576	578	580	582-587	-	589-593	595	-	597
Zirconium (Zr)	1	1099	1099	-	-	1099	1102	1104	1106	1109	1111	-	1113-1117	-	-	1119
Zirconium no. 715	1	-	-	-	-	-	-	-	1106	-	-	-	-	-	-	-
Zirconium + ΣX_i	2-II	1580	-	-	-	-	1582	-	1584	-	1586	-	-	-	-	-
Zirconium + Aluminum	2-I	-	-	-	-	-	665	-	667	-	-	-	-	-	-	-
Zirconium + Aluminum + ΣX_i	2-II	1558	-	-	-	-	1560	-	1562	-	-	-	-	-	-	-
Zirconium + Boron	2-I	669	-	-	-	-	-	-	-	-	-	-	-	-	-	-
Zirconium + Hafnium	2-I	671	-	-	-	671	673	675	-	-	677	-	-	-	-	-
Zirconium + Hafnium + ΣX_i	2-II	-	-	-	-	-	-	1566	-	-	-	-	-	-	-	-
Zirconium + Indium	2-I	-	-	-	-	-	-	679	-	-	-	-	-	-	-	-
Zirconium + Iron + ΣX_i	2-II	-	-	-	-	-	-	1568	-	-	-	-	-	-	-	-
Zirconium + Molybdenum	2-I	-	-	-	-	-	681	-	683	-	-	-	-	-	-	-
Zirconium + Niobium	2-I	-	-	-	-	-	685	687	689	-	-	-	-	-	-	-
Zirconium + Silver	2-I	-	-	-	-	-	-	691	-	-	-	-	-	-	-	-
Zirconium + Tantalum + ΣX_i	2-II	-	-	-	-	-	1570	-	-	-	-	-	-	-	-	-
Zirconium + Thorium	2-I	-	-	-	-	-	-	-	-	-	693-695	-	-	-	-	-
Zirconium + Tin	2-I	697	-	-	-	-	699	702	704	-	707	-	709-714	-	-	-
Zirconium + Tin + ΣX_i	2-II	-	-	-	-	-	1572	-	-	-	-	-	-	-	-	-
Zirconium + Titanium	2-I	-	-	-	-	-	-	715	-	-	-	-	-	-	-	-
Zirconium + Uranium	2-I	717	-	-	-	-	719	721	723	-	725	-	-	-	-	-
Zirconium + Uranium + ΣX_i	2-II	-	-	-	-	-	-	1574	-	-	-	-	1576-1578	-	-	-
Zirconium alloys (special designations)																
3ZI	2-II	1558	-	-	-	-	1560	-	1562	1564	-	-	-	-	-	-
Zircaloys (see Zircaloy)																
Zirconium aluminides																
$ZrAl_2$	6-I	-	39	-	-	-	-	-	-	-	41	-	-	-	-	-
$ZrAl_3$	6-I	-	39	-	-	-	-	-	-	-	-	-	-	-	-	-
Zr_2Al_3	6-I	-	39	-	-	-	-	-	-	-	-	-	-	-	-	-
Zr_3Al_2	6-I	-	39	-	-	-	-	-	-	-	-	-	-	-	-	-
Zr_3Al_4	6-I	-	39	-	-	-	-	-	-	-	-	-	-	-	-	-
Zirconium beryllides																
$ZrBe_6$	6-I	-	148	-	-	-	-	-	-	-	-	-	-	-	-	-
$ZrBe_9$	6-I	-	148	-	-	-	-	-	-	-	-	-	-	-	-	-

Material Name	Volume	Density	Melting Point	Heat of Fusion	Heat of Vaporization	Heat of Sublimation	Electrical Resistivity	Specific Heat	Thermal Conductivity	Thermal Diffusivity	Thermal Linear Expansion	Thermal Absorptance	Thermal Emittance	Thermal Reflectance	Thermal Transmittance	Vapor Pressure
Zirconium beryllides (cont.)																
$ZrBe_{13}$	6-I	–	148	–	–	–	–	150	152	–	154	–	–	156	–	–
$ZrBe_{16}$	6-I	–	148	–	–	–	–	–	–	–	–	–	–	–	–	–
Zr_2Be_{17}	6-I	–	–	–	–	–	–	–	–	–	–	–	–	156	–	–
Zirconium borides																
ZrB	6-I	–	–	–	–	–	–	–	281	–	–	–	–	–	–	–
ZrB_2	6-I	274	274	–	274	–	277	279	–	–	283	–	286-288	291	–	293
ZrB_{12}	6-I	274	274	–	–	–	277	–	281	–	–	–	–	–	–	–
Zirconium (di-) boride cermet .	6-II	842	–	–	–	–	844	846	848	–	850	–	–	–	–	–
Zirconium (di-) boride + + Molybdenum (di-) boride . .	6-I	723	–	–	–	–	–	–	–	–	–	–	–	–	–	–
Zirconium (di-) boride + + Molybdenum (di-) silicide . .	6-I	–	689	–	–	–	–	–	–	–	691	–	–	–	–	–
Zirconium (di-) boride + + Niobium (di-) boride	6-I	723	–	–	–	–	–	–	–	–	–	–	–	–	–	–
Zirconium (di-) boride + + Tantalum (di-) boride. . . .	6-I	723	–	–	–	–	–	–	–	–	–	–	–	–	–	–
Zirconium carbide (ZrC). . . .	5	263	263	–	–	–	265	267	269	271	273	–	277-283	–	–	285
Zirconium (pyro-) carbide . . .	5	–	–	–	–	–	–	–	–	–	273	–	–	–	–	–
Zirconium carbide + Graphite .	5	–	–	–	–	–	–	–	–	–	825	–	–	–	–	–
Zirconium-cobalt intermetallics ($ZrCo_2$)	6-I	–	685	–	–	–	–	–	–	–	–	–	–	–	–	–
Zirconium ferride ($ZrFe_2$) . . .	6-I	–	306	–	–	–	–	–	–	–	–	–	–	–	–	–
Zirconium fluoride (ZrF_4) . . .	5	407	407	–	–	407	–	–	–	–	–	–	–	–	–	–
Zirconium fluoride + Lithium fluoride	5	–	413	–	–	–	–	–	–	–	–	–	–	–	–	415
Zirconium fluoride + Rubidium fluoride	5	–	417	–	–	–	–	–	–	–	–	–	–	–	–	419
Zirconium fluoride + Sodium fluoride	5	–	421	–	–	–	–	–	–	–	–	–	–	–	–	423
Zirconium germanides																
ZrGe	6-I	–	323	–	–	–	–	–	–	–	–	–	–	–	–	–
$ZrGe_2$	6-I	–	323	–	–	–	–	–	–	–	–	–	–	–	–	–
Zr_3Ge	6-I	–	323	–	–	–	–	–	–	–	–	–	–	–	–	–
Zr_5Ge_3	6-I	–	323	–	–	–	–	–	–	–	–	–	–	–	–	–
Zirconium hydride (ZrH_2) . . .	5	459	–	–	–	–	–	461	463	–	465	–	–	–	–	–
Zirconium nitride (ZrN)	5	602	602	–	–	–	–	604	606	608	610	–	613-615	–	–	617-619
Zirconium (di-) oxide (ZrO_2) . .	4-I	571	571	–	–	571	574	576	578	580	582-587	–	589-593	595	–	597
Zirconium (di-) oxide foam . . .	4-I	–	–	–	–	–	–	–	–	–	587	–	–	–	–	–
Zirconium (di-) oxide mix 148 .	4-I	–	–	–	–	–	–	–	916	–	–	–	–	–	–	–
Zirconium (di-) oxide mix 187 .	4-I	–	–	–	–	–	–	–	916	–	–	–	–	–	–	–

Material Name	Volume	Density	Melting Point	Heat of Fusion	Heat of Vaporization	Heat of Sublimation	Electrical Resistivity	Specific Heat	Thermal Conductivity	Thermal Diffusivity	Thermal Linear Expansion	Thermal Absorptance	Thermal Emittance	Thermal Reflectance	Thermal Transmittance	Vapor Pressure
Zirconium (di-) oxide Norton mix 302	4-I	–	–	–	–	–	–	–	–	580	–	–	–	–	–	–
Zirconium (di-) oxide ZP-58 . .	5	–	–	–	–	–	–	799	–	–	–	–	–	–	–	–
Zirconium (di-) oxide ZP-74 . .	5	–	–	–	–	–	–	799	–	–	–	–	–	–	–	–
Zirconium (di-) oxide coating on Inconel	6-II	–	–	–	–	–	–	–	–	–	–	–	–	1397	–	–
Zirconium (di-) oxide coating on Inconel X	6-II	–	–	–	–	–	–	–	–	–	–	–	1399	1401	–	–
Zirconium (di-) oxide + ΣX_i . .	5	–	–	–	–	–	–	799	–	–	–	–	–	–	–	–
Zirconium (di-) oxide + Aluminum oxide	4-I	–	–	–	–	–	–	–	–	906	908	–	–	–	–	–
Zirconium (di-) oxide + + Beryllium oxide + Aluminum oxide	4-I	–	–	–	–	–	–	–	–	–	910	–	–	–	–	–
Zirconium (di-) oxide + Calcium oxide	4-I	–	–	–	–	–	912	914	916	918	920	–	923	–	–	–
Zirconium (di-) oxide + Calcium oxide + Cerium (di-) oxide . .	4-I	–	–	–	–	–	–	–	925	–	–	–	–	–	–	–
Zirconium (di-) oxide + Calcium oxide + Silicon (di-) oxide . .	4-I	–	–	–	–	–	–	–	–	–	927	–	–	–	–	–
Zirconium (di-) oxide + Cerium (di-) oxide	4-I	–	–	–	–	–	–	–	–	929	931	–	–	–	–	–
Zirconium (di-) oxide + + Dysprosium oxide	4-I	–	–	–	–	–	–	–	–	–	934	–	–	–	–	–
Zirconium (di-) oxide + Hafnium + + Magnesium	5	–	–	–	–	–	–	797	–	–	–	–	–	–	–	–
Zirconium (di-) oxide + Hafnium (di-) oxide	4-I	–	936	–	–	–	–	–	–	–	–	–	–	–	–	–
Zirconium (di-) oxide + + Magnesium oxide	4-I	–	–	–	–	–	938	–	940	942	944	–	–	–	–	–
Zirconium (di-) oxide + + Magnesium oxide + Beryllium oxide	4-I	–	947	–	–	–	–	–	–	–	–	–	–	–	–	–
Zirconium (di-) oxide + Niobium (pent-) oxide	4-I	–	949	–	–	–	–	–	–	–	951	–	–	–	–	–
Zirconium (di-) oxide + + Phosphorus (pent-) oxide . .	4-I	–	–	–	–	–	–	–	–	–	953	–	–	–	–	–
Zirconium (di-) oxide + Silicon (di-) oxide	4-I	–	–	–	–	–	–	–	–	–	955	–	–	–	–	–
Zirconium (di-) oxide + Thorium (di-) oxide	4-I	–	–	–	–	–	–	–	–	–	958	–	–	–	–	–
Zirconium (di-) oxide + Titanium cermet	6-II	–	–	–	–	–	–	826	828	830	832	–	–	–	–	–
Zirconium (di-) oxide + Titanium (di-) oxide	4-I	–	–	–	–	–	–	–	–	–	960	–	–	–	–	–
Zirconium (di-) oxide + Uranium (di-) oxide	4-I	962	964	–	–	–	–	–	–	–	966	–	–	–	–	–
Zirconium (di-) oxide + Yttrium oxide	4-I	–	–	–	–	–	–	–	968	–	970	–	–	–	–	–
Zirconium (di-) oxide + Yttrium oxide + Cerium (di-) oxide . .	4-I	–	–	–	–	–	–	–	972	–	–	–	–	–	–	–

Material Name	Volume	Density	Melting Point	Heat of Fusion	Heat of Vaporization	Heat of Sublimation	Electrical Resistivity	Specific Heat	Thermal Conductivity	Thermal Diffusivity	Thermal Linear Expansion	Thermal Absorptance	Thermal Emittance	Thermal Reflectance	Thermal Transmittance	Vapor Pressure
Zirconium (di-) oxide + Yttrium oxide + Zirconium cermet. . .	6-II	-	-	-	-	-	-	-	834	-	-	-	-	-	-	-
Zirconium (di-) oxide + + Zirconium cermet	6-II	-	-	-	-	-	-	-	-	836	838	-	-	-	-	840
Zirconium (di-) oxide ZT-15-M cermet	6-II	-	-	-	-	-	-	826	-	830	-	-	-	-	-	-
Zirconium phosphates																
$ZrO_2 \cdot P_2O_5$	4-II	-	-	-	-	-	-	-	-	-	1185	-	-	-	-	-
$2\ ZrO_2 \cdot P_2O_5$	4-II	-	-	-	-	-	-	-	-	-	1185	-	-	-	-	-
Zirconium (ortho-) silicate ($ZrO_2 \cdot SiO_2$)	4-II	1344	1344	-	-	-	1346	1348	1350	-	1352	-	-	-	-	-
Zirconium (ortho-) silicate + + Beryllium aluminum silicate	4-II	-	-	-	-	-	-	-	-	-	1577	-	-	-	-	-
Zirconium silicides																
ZrSi	6-I	517	-	-	-	-	-	-	-	-	-	-	-	-	-	-
$ZrSi_2$	6-I	517	517	-	-	-	-	-	-	-	519	-	-	521	-	-
Zr_2Si	6-I	517	-	-	-	-	-	-	-	-	-	-	-	-	-	-
Zr_3Si_2	6-I	517	-	-	-	-	-	-	-	-	-	-	-	-	-	-
Zr_4Si	6-I	517	-	-	-	-	-	-	-	-	-	-	-	-	-	-
Zr_4Si_3	6-I	517	-	-	-	-	-	-	-	-	-	-	-	-	-	-
Zr_5Si_3	6-I	517	-	-	-	-	-	-	-	-	-	-	-	-	-	-
Zr_5Si_6	6-I	517	-	-	-	-	-	-	-	-	-	-	-	-	-	-
Zirconium tantalum carbide ($Ta_xZr_yC_z$)	5	-	-	-	-	-	-	-	-	-	287	-	290	-	-	-
Zirconium titanate ($ZrO_2 \cdot TiO_2$).	4-II	-	-	-	-	-	-	-	-	-	1470	-	-	-	-	-
Zirconium uranium carbide ($Zr_xU_{1-x}C$)	5	-	-	-	-	-	292	-	-	-	-	-	-	-	-	-
Zirconium-vanadium inter-metallics (ZrV_2)	6-I	-	685	-	-	-	-	-	-	-	-	-	-	-	-	-
Zirox, grade A	4-I	-	-	-	-	-	-	-	-	-	582	-	-	-	-	-
ZT-15-M zirconium (di-) oxide cermet	6-II	-	-	-	-	-	-	826	-	830	-	-	-	-	-	-